Biology

Custom Edition

Tenth Edition

Eldra Solomon | Charles Martin
Diana W. Martin | Linda R. Berg

CENGAGE
Learning·

Australia • Brazil • Japan • Korea • Mexico • Singapore • Spain • United Kingdom • United States

CENGAGE
Learning

Biology, Custom Edition, Tenth Edition

Senior Manager, Student Engagement:

Linda deStefano

Janey Moeller

Manager, Student Engagement:

Julie Dierig

Marketing Manager:

Rachael Kloos

Manager, Production Editorial:

Kim Fry

Manager, Intellectual Property Project Manager:

Brian Methe

Senior Manager, Production and Manufacturing:

Donna M. Brown

Manager, Production:

Terri Daley

Printed in the United States of America

Biology, 10th Edition
Eldra Solomon, Charles Martin, Diana W. Martin, Linda R. Berg

> For product information and technology assistance, contact us at
> **Cengage Learning Customer & Sales Support, 1-800-354-9706**
> For permission to use material from this text or product,
> submit all requests online at **cengage.com/permissions**
> Further permissions questions can be emailed to
> **permissionrequest@cengage.com**

This book contains select works from existing Cengage Learning resources and was produced by Cengage Learning Custom Solutions for collegiate use. As such, those adopting and/or contributing to this work are responsible for editorial content accuracy, continuity and completeness.

Compilation © 2014 Cengage Learning

ISBN-13: 978-1-305-28898-0

ISBN-10: 1-305-28898-X

WCN: 01-100-101

Cengage Learning

5191 Natorp Boulevard
Mason, Ohio 45040
USA

Cengage Learning is a leading provider of customized learning solutions with office locations around the globe, including Singapore, the United Kingdom, Australia, Mexico, Brazil, and Japan. Locate your local office at: **international.cengage.com/region.**

Cengage Learning products are represented in Canada by Nelson Education, Ltd.
For your lifelong learning solutions, visit **www.cengage.com/custom.**
Visit our corporate website at **www.cengage.com.**

About the Authors

Eldra P. Solomon has written several leading college textbooks in biology and in human anatomy and physiology. Her books have been translated into more than ten languages. She earned an M.S. from the University of Florida and an M.A. and Ph.D. from the University of South Florida. Dr. Solomon taught biology and nursing students for more than 20 years.

In addition to being a biologist and science author, Dr. Solomon is a biopsychologist with a special interest in the neurophysiology of traumatic experience. Her research has focused on the neurological, endocrine, and psychological effects of trauma, including complex posttraumatic stress disorder and development of maladaptive coping strategies.

Dr. Solomon has presented her research at numerous national and international conferences, and her work has been published in leading professional journals. She has been profiled more than 30 times in leading publications, including *Who's Who in America, Who's Who in Science and Engineering, Who's Who in Medicine and Healthcare, Who's Who in American Education, Who's Who of American Women,* and *Who's Who in the World.*

Charles E. Martin is professor emeritus of cell biology and neuroscience at Rutgers University. He received his Ph.D. in genetics from Florida State University and engaged in postdoctoral research in genetics and membrane biology at the University of Texas at Austin. He has taught general biology as well as undergraduate and graduate level courses in genetics and molecular cell biology throughout his career at Rutgers. An award-winning teacher for more than 30 years, in 2011 Dr. Martin was named Professor of the Year by the Molecular Biosciences Graduate Student Association.

His research on gene regulation of membrane protein enzyme systems in yeast and other fungi illustrates the interdisciplinary nature of the life sciences. He is most proud of the many generations of undergraduate, graduate, and postdoctoral students who contributed to this research and have gone on to productive careers. He continues to be committed to teaching and is grateful for the opportunities to pursue a teaching and research career in what continues to be the most exciting era of the biological sciences.

Diana W. Martin is professor emeritus and former director of general biology in the Division of Life Sciences at Rutgers University. Dr. Martin received an M.S. from Florida State University, where she studied the chromosomes of related plant species to understand their evolutionary relationships. She earned a Ph.D. from the University of Texas at Austin, where she studied the genetics of the fruit fly, *Drosophila melanogaster,* and then conducted postdoctoral research at Princeton University.

Dr. Martin taught general biology and other courses at Rutgers for more than 30 years and has been involved in writing textbooks since 1988. She is immensely grateful that her decision to study biology in college has led to a career that allows her many ways to share her excitement about all aspects of biology.

Linda R. Berg is an award-winning teacher and textbook author. She received a B.S. in science education, an M.S. in botany, and a Ph.D. in plant physiology from the University of Maryland. Her research focused on the evolutionary implications of steroid biosynthetic pathways in various organisms.

Dr. Berg taught at the University of Maryland at College Park for 17 years and at St. Petersburg College in Florida for 8 years. During her career, she taught introductory courses in biology, botany, and environmental science to thousands of students. At the University of Maryland, she received numerous teaching and service awards. Dr. Berg is also the recipient of many national and regional awards, including the National Science Teachers Association Award for Innovations in College Science Teaching, the Nation's Capital Area Disabled Student Services Award, and the Washington Academy of Sciences Award in University Science Teaching.

During her career as a professional science writer, Dr. Berg has authored or coauthored several leading college science textbooks. Her writing reflects her teaching style and love of science.

Brief Contents

Preface

This tenth edition of Solomon, Martin, Martin, and Berg's *Biology* conveys our vision of the dynamic science of biology and how it affects every aspect of our lives, from our own health and behavior to the challenging global environmental issues that confront us. New discoveries in the biological sciences continue to increase our understanding of both the unity and diversity of life's processes and adaptations. With this understanding, we become ever more aware of our interdependence with the vast diversity of organisms with which we share planet Earth.

BIOLOGY: THE STUDENT-FRIENDLY BIOLOGY BOOK

We want beginning students to experience learning biology as an exciting journey of discovery. In the tenth edition of *Biology*, we explore Earth's diverse organisms, their remarkable adaptations to the environment, and their evolutionary and ecological relationships. We present the workings of science and the contributions of scientists whose discoveries not only expand our knowledge of biology but also help shape and protect the future of our planet. *Biology* provides insight into what science is, how scientists work, what scientists have contributed, and how scientific knowledge affects daily life.

Since the first edition of *Biology*, we have worked very hard to present the principles of biology in an integrated way that is accurate, interesting, and conceptually accessible to students. In this tenth edition of *Biology*, we continue this tradition. We also continue to present biology in an inquiry-based framework. Some professors interpret inquiry as a learning method that takes place in the laboratory as students perform experiments. Laboratory research is certainly an integral part of inquiry-based learning, but inquiry is also a way of learning in which the student actively pursues knowledge outside the laboratory. In *Biology* we have always presented the history of scientific advances, including scientific debates, to help students understand that science is a process—that is, a field of investigative inquiry—as well as a body of knowledge, the product of inquiry. In the tenth edition of *Biology*, we make a concerted effort to further integrate inquiry-based learning into the textbook with the introduction of new features and the expansion of several others (discussed in the following sections).

Throughout the text we stimulate interest by relating concepts to experiences within the student's frame of reference. By helping students make such connections, we facilitate their mastery of general concepts. We hope the combined effect of an engaging writing style and interesting features will motivate and excite students in their study of biology.

THE SOLOMON/MARTIN/MARTIN/BERG LEARNING SYSTEM

In the tenth edition, we have continued to refine our highly successful *Learning System*. This system provides the student with the learning strategies needed to integrate biological concepts and demonstrate mastery of these concepts. Learning biology is challenging because the subject of biology is filled with so many new terms and so many facts that must be integrated into the framework of general biological principles. To help students focus on important principles and concepts, we provide *Learning Outcomes* for the course and *Learning Objectives* for each major section of every chapter. At the end of each section, we provide *Checkpoint* questions based on the *Learning Objectives* so that students can assess their level of understanding of the material presented in the section. At the end of each chapter, we include a *Summary: Focus on Learning Objectives* that is organized around the *Learning Objectives* and emphasizes key terms in context. The *Summary* is followed by *Test Your Understanding*, a set of questions organized according to Bloom's taxonomy. Questions include *Know and Comprehend* multiple-choice exercises as well as a variety of questions that encourage the student to *Apply and Analyze* and *Evaluate and Synthesize* the topics in the chapter.

Students are directed to **www.cengagebrain.com,** a powerful online tool that offers access to course materials such as *Aplia for Biology* and other companion resources. See the Resources for Students section of the Preface for details.

Pedagogical Features

Our *Learning System* includes numerous learning strategies that help students increase their success:

- *NEW* An updated and expanded *art program* reinforces concepts discussed in the text and presents complex processes in clear steps. This edition expands the number of *Key Experiment* figures, which encourage students to evaluate investigative approaches that scientists have taken. *Key Experiment* figures emphasize the scientific process in both classic and modern research; Figure 4-12 is a new example. Also included in this edition are newly designed *Key Point* figures, in which important concepts are stated in process diagrams of complex topics; new examples include Figures 4-11 and 4-15. Many of the *Key Point* figures have numbered parts that show sequences of events in biological processes or life cycles.

- Numerous photographs, both alone and combined with line art, help students grasp concepts by connecting the "real" to the "ideal." The line art uses features such as *orientation icons* to help students put the detailed figures into the broader context. We use symbols and colors consistently throughout the book to help students connect concepts. For example, the same four colors and shapes are used throughout the book to identify guanine, cytosine, adenine, and thymine. Similarly, the same colors are used consistently in illustrations and tables to indicate specific clades of organisms. *Research Method* figures describe why biologists use a particular method and explain how the method is executed. New examples include Figures 4-7 and 15-7.

- *NEW* Many questions have been added, and several types of questions carry special designations: *Predict; Connect; Visualize; Evolution Link; Interpret Data;* or *Science, Technology, and Society.* These questions emphasize that learning is enhanced by many diverse approaches.

- *Inquiring About* boxes explore issues of special relevance to students, such as the effects of smoking, how traumatic experiences affect the body, and breast cancer. These boxes also provide a forum for discussing some interesting topics in more detail, such as the smallest ancient humans, ancient plants and coal formation, hydrothermal vent communities, declining amphibian populations, and stratospheric ozone depletion.

- A list of *Key Concepts* at the beginning of each chapter provides a chapter overview and helps the student focus on important principles discussed in the chapter.

- *Learning Objectives* at the beginning of each major section in the chapter indicate, in behavioral terms, what the student must do to demonstrate mastery of the material in that section.

- Each major section of the chapter is followed by a series of *Checkpoint* questions that assess comprehension by asking the student to describe, explain, compare, contrast, or illustrate important concepts. The *Checkpoint* questions are based on the section *Learning Objectives.*

- *Concept Statement Subheads* introduce sections, previewing and summarizing the key idea or ideas to be discussed in that section.

- *Sequence Summaries* within the text simplify and summarize information presented in paragraph form. For example, paragraphs describing blood circulation through the body or the steps by which cells take in certain materials

are followed by a *Sequence Summary* listing the sequence of structures or steps.

- Numerous *tables,* many illustrated, help the student organize and summarize material presented in the text. Many tables are color-coded.

- A *Summary: Focus on Learning Objectives* at the end of each chapter is organized around the chapter *Learning Objectives.* This summary provides a review of the material, and because selected key terms are boldfaced in the summary, students learn vocabulary words within the context of related concepts.

- *NEW Test Your Understanding* end-of-chapter questions are now organized according to Bloom's taxonomy, providing students with the opportunity to evaluate their understanding of the material in the chapter. *Know and Comprehend* multiple-choice questions reinforce important terms and concepts. *Apply and Analyze* questions challenge students to integrate their knowledge. Higher-level *Evaluate and Synthesize* questions encourage students to apply the concepts just learned to new situations or to make connections among important concepts. Each chapter has one or more *Evolution Link* questions, and many chapters contain one or more *Interpret Data* questions that require students to actively interpret experimental data presented in the chapter. Also included are *Predict, Connect, Visualize,* and *Science, Technology, and Society* questions. Answers to the *Test Your Understanding* questions are provided in Appendix E.

- The *Glossary* at the end of the book, the most comprehensive glossary found in any biology text, provides precise definitions of terms. The *Glossary* is especially useful because it is extensively cross-referenced and includes pronunciations for many terms. The vertical green bar along the margin facilitates rapid access to the *Glossary.* The companion website also includes glossary flash cards with pronunciations.

Course Learning Outcomes

At the end of a successful study of introductory biology, the student can demonstrate mastery of biological concepts by responding accurately to the following *Course Learning Outcomes:*

- Design an experiment to test a given hypothesis, using the procedure and terminology of the scientific method.

- Cite the cell theory and relate the structure of organelles to their functions in both prokaryotic and eukaryotic cells.

- Describe the mechanisms of evolution, explain why evolution is the principal unifying concept in biology, and discuss natural selection as the primary agent of evolutionary change.

- Explain the role of genetic information in all species and discuss applications of genetics that affect society.

- Describe several mechanisms by which cells and organisms transfer information, including the use of nucleic acids in genetic transmission of information, signal transduction, chemical signals (such as hormones and pheromones), electrical signals (such as neural transmission), sounds, and visual displays.

- Provide examples (at various levels of complexity) of interactions among biological systems that illustrate the interdependence of these systems.

- Explain how any given structure is related to its function.

- Argue for or against the classification of organisms in three domains and several kingdoms or supergroups, characterizing each of these clades; based on your knowledge of genetics and evolution, give specific examples of the unity and diversity of organisms in different domains and supergroups.

- Compare the structural adaptations, life processes, and life cycles of a prokaryote, protist, fungus, plant, and animal.

- Define *homeostasis* and give examples of regulatory mechanisms, including feedback systems.

- Trace the flow of matter and energy through a photosynthetic cell and a nonphotosynthetic cell and through the biosphere, comparing the roles of producers, consumers, and decomposers.

- Describe the study of ecology at the levels of an individual organism, a population, a community, and an ecosystem.

WHAT'S NEW: AN OVERVIEW OF *BIOLOGY*, TENTH EDITION

Five themes are interwoven throughout *Biology*: the evolution of life, the transmission of biological information, the flow of energy through living systems, interactions among biological systems, and the inter-relationship of structure and function. As we introduce the concepts of modern biology, we explain how these themes are connected and how life depends on them.

Educators present the major topics of an introductory biology course in a variety of orders. For this reason, we carefully designed the eight parts of this book so that they do not depend heavily on preceding chapters and parts. This flexible organization means that an instructor can present the 57 chapters in any number of sequences with pedagogical success. Chapter 1, which introduces the student to the major principles of biology, provides a comprehensive springboard for future discussions, whether the professor prefers a "top-down" or "bottom-up" approach.

In this edition as in previous editions, we examined every line of every chapter for accuracy and currency, and we made a careful attempt to update every topic and verify all new material. Our efforts have been enhanced by an updated art program with many new illustrations. The following brief summary provides a general overview of the organization of *Biology* and some changes made to the tenth edition.

Part 1 The Organization of Life

The six chapters that make up Part 1 provide basic principles of biology and the concepts of chemistry and cell biology that lay the foundation upon which the remaining parts of the book build. We begin Chapter 1 with a discussion of the promise and challenges of stem cell research. We then introduce the main themes of the book: evolution, information transfer, energy transfer, interactions in biological systems, and the inter-relationship of structure and function. Chapter 1 examines several fundamental concepts in biology and the nature of the scientific process, including a discussion of systems biology. Chapters 2 and 3, which focus on the molecular level of organization, establish the foundations in chemistry necessary for understanding biological processes. Chapters 4, 5, and 6 focus on the cellular level of organization, including cell structure and function, cell membranes, and cell signaling. We have revised these chapters to place greater emphasis on the inter-disciplinary nature of cell research and have expanded coverage of transport between the nucleus and cytoplasm as well as the routing of proteins through the endomembrane system.

Part 2 Energy Transfer Through Living Systems

Because all living cells need energy for life processes, the flow of energy through living systems—that is, capturing energy and converting it to usable forms—is a basic theme of *Biology*. Chapter 7 examines how cells capture, transfer, store, and use energy. Chapters 8 and 9 discuss the metabolic adaptations by which organisms obtain and use energy through cellular respiration and photosynthesis.

Part 3 The Continuity of Life: Genetics

We have updated and expanded the eight chapters of Part 3 for the tenth edition. We begin this unit by discussing mitosis and meiosis in Chapter 10. Chapter 11 builds on this foundation as it considers Mendelian genetics and related patterns of inheritance. We then turn our attention to the structure and replication of DNA in Chapter 12. The discussion of RNA and protein synthesis in Chapter 13 includes new insights into how the small percentage of DNA that codes for polypeptides relates to the much larger percentage of the genome that is expressed. We introduce new information derived from the ENCODE project establishing that much of the genome encodes different classes of non-protein-coding RNAs, including microRNAs and long noncoding RNAs. The newly discovered regulatory functions of these RNAs are further explored in Chapter 14, which also includes new information on eukaryotic promoters, enhancers, and silencers as well as on epigenetic inheritance. In Chapter 15 we focus on DNA technology and genomics, including an expanded discussion of rapid DNA sequencing, as well as the importance of gene databases as tools for understanding gene regulation, gene functions, and molecular evolution. These chapters build the necessary foundation for exploring human genetics and the human genome in Chapter 16, which includes new sections on genomic imprinting and on genome-wide association studies. In Chapter 17 we introduce the role of genes in development, emphasizing studies on specific model organisms that have led to spectacular advances in this field; changes include new material on induced pluripotent stem cells as well as a comprehensive view of cancer and its relationship to cell signaling that has developed through the application of genome-wide association studies and whole genome sequencing.

Part 4 The Continuity of Life: Evolution

Although we explore evolution as the cornerstone of biology throughout the book, Part 4 discusses evolutionary concepts in depth. We provide the history behind the discovery of the scientific theory of evolution, the mechanisms by which it occurs, and the methods by which it is studied and tested. Chapter 18 introduces the Darwinian concept of evolution and presents several kinds of evidence that support the scientific theory of evolution. In Chapter 19 we examine evolution at the population level. Chapter 20 describes the evolution of new species and discusses aspects of macroevolution. Chapter 21 summarizes the evolutionary history of life on Earth. In Chapter 22 we recount the evolution of primates, including humans. New molecular and fossil findings, including those relating to recently discovered human relatives such as the Denisovans (a sister species to the Neandertals) and *Australopithecus sediba*, are explored.

Part 5 The Diversity of Life

Emphasizing the cladistic approach, we use an evolutionary framework to discuss each group of organisms. We present current hypotheses of how groups of organisms are related. Chapter 23 has been updated to reflect the effect of recent research on systematics. In this chapter we discuss *why* organisms are classified and provide insight into the scientific process of deciding *how* they are classified. New advances have enabled us to further clarify the connection between evolutionary history and systematics in the tenth edition. Chapter 24 focuses entirely on viruses and subviral agents. Information has been updated and expanded on giant viruses, viral origins, evolutionary

importance of viruses, and recent research on viruses. Chapter 25 is devoted to the prokaryotes, both bacteria and archaea. Information about the evolution, structure, ecology, and phylogeny of archaea has been expanded. Implications of research on the human microbiome are discussed and discussion of antibiotic resistance has been expanded. Chapter 26 describes the protists in the context of five "supergroups" of eukaryotes. Chapters 27 and 28 present the members of the plant kingdom. Chapter 27 considers the evolution of land plants and the evolution of seedless vascular plants. Discussion of the origin and early evolution of angiosperms is included in Chapter 28. Chapter 29 describes the fungi. In Chapters 30 through 32, we discuss the diversity of animals. We have updated the discussions of phylogenetic relationships to reflect recent research.

Part 6 Structure and Life Processes in Plants

Part 6 introduces students to the fascinating plant world. Here we stress relationships between structure and function in plant cells, tissues, organs, and individual organisms. In Chapter 33 we consider plant structure, growth, and differentiation in the context of cell division, cell expansion, cell differentiation, tissue culture, morphogenesis, pattern formation, positional information, and *Arabidopsis* mutants. Chapters 34 through 36 discuss the structural and physiological adaptations of leaves, stems, and roots; these chapters include special consideration of plant transport systems. Chapter 37 describes reproduction in flowering plants, including asexual reproduction, flowers, fruits, and seeds. Chapter 38 focuses on growth responses and regulation of growth, including the latest findings generated by the continuing explosion of knowledge in plant biology, particularly at the molecular level.

Part 7 Structure and Life Processes in Animals

In Part 7 we provide a strong emphasis on comparative animal physiology, showing the structural, functional, and behavioral adaptations that help animals meet environmental challenges. We use a comparative approach to examine how various animal groups have solved both similar and diverse problems. In Chapter 39 we discuss the basic tissues and organ systems of the animal body, homeostasis, and the ways that animals regulate their body temperature. Chapter 40 focuses on different types of body coverings, skeletons, and muscles, and discusses how they function. In Chapters 41 through 43, we discuss neural signaling, neural regulation, and sensory reception. In Chapters 44 through 51, we compare how different animal groups carry on life processes, such as internal transport, internal defense, gas exchange, digestion, reproduction, and development. Each chapter in this part considers the human adaptations for the life processes being discussed. Part 7 ends with a discussion of behavioral adaptations in Chapter 52. Reflecting recent research findings, we have updated or added new material on many topics, including neurotransmitters, cardiovascular disease, evolution of immunity in invertebrates, chronic inflammation, HIV, nutrition, regulation of appetite and energy metabolism, endocrine function, ovarian stem cells, contraception, sexually transmitted infections, and social learning and transmission of culture in vertebrates. The art program has been updated and improved, and new photographs and photomicrographs have been added.

Part 8 The Interactions of Life: Ecology

Part 8 focuses on the dynamics of populations, communities, and ecosystems and on the application of ecological principles to disciplines such as conservation biology. Chapters 53 through 56 give the student an understanding of the ecology of populations, communities, ecosystems, and the biosphere, and Chapter 57 focuses on global environmental issues. Among the many new and updated topics discussed in this unit are Antarctic tundra; the role of archaea in the carbon cycle, nitrogen cycle, and climate change; the Cross River gorilla (*Gorilla gorilla diehli*) as an example of a critically endangered species; new research on global climate change; updated information on stratospheric ozone depletion; and the effect of humans on the biosphere.

A COMPREHENSIVE PACKAGE FOR LEARNING AND TEACHING

A carefully designed supplement package is available to further facilitate learning. In addition to the usual print resources, we are pleased to present student multimedia tools that have been developed in conjunction with the text.

Resources for Students

MindTap, a fully online, highly personalized learning experience built on Cengage Learning content. MindTap combines student learning tools—readings, multimedia, activities, and assessments—into a singular Learning Path that guides students through their course. Instructors personalize the experience by customizing authoritative Cengage Learning content and learning tools, including the ability to add their own content in the Learning Path via apps that integrate into the MindTap framework seamlessly with Learning Management Systems.

MindTap for Biology is easy to use and saves instructors time by allowing them to:

- Seamlessly deliver appropriate content and technology assets from a number of providers to students, as they need them.

- Break course content down into movable objects to promote personalization, encourage interactivity, and ensure student engagement.

- Customize the course—from tools to text—and make adjustments "on the fly," making it possible to intertwine breaking news into their lessons and incorporate today's teachable moments.

- Bring interactivity into learning through the integration of multimedia assets.

- Track students' use, activities, and comprehension in real time, which provides opportunities for early intervention to influence progress and outcomes. Grades are visible and archived so that students and instructors always have access to current standings in the class.

Aplia offers a way to stay on top of coursework with regularly scheduled homework assignments. Interactive tools and additional content are provided to further increase engagement and understanding. Students, ask your instructor about Aplia!

Study Guide to accompany *Biology,* Tenth Edition, by Jennifer Aline Metzler of Ball State University and Robert Yost of Indiana University and Purdue University, Indianapolis. Updated for this edition, the study guide provides the student with many opportunities to review chapter concepts. Multiple-choice study questions, coloring-book exercises, vocabulary-building exercises, and many other types of active-learning tools are provided to suit different cognitive learning styles.

A Problem-based Guide to Basic Genetics by Donald Cronkite of Hope College. This brief guide provides students with a systematic approach to solving genetics problems along with numerous solved problems and practice problems.

Spanish Glossary. This Spanish glossary of biology terms is available to Spanish-speaking students.

Audio Study Tools. This tenth edition of *Biology* is accompanied by useful study tools, which contain valuable information such as reviews of important concepts, key terms, questions, and study tips. Students can download the audio study tools.

Virtual Biology Laboratory 4.0. Now with an upgraded user interface, these 14 online laboratory experiments allow students to "do" science by acquiring data, performing simulated experiments, and using data to explain biological concepts. Assigned activities automatically flow to the instructor's grade book. Self-designed activities ask students to plan their procedures around an experimental question and write up their results.

Additional Resources for Instructors

The instructors' examination copy for this edition lists a comprehensive package of print and multimedia supplements, including online resources, available to qualified adopters. Please ask your local sales representative for details.

Instructor Companion Site. Everything you need for your course in one place! This collection of book-specific lecture and class tools is available online via **www.cengage.com/login**. Access and download PowerPoint presentations, images, instructor's manual, videos, and more.

Cengage Learning Testing Powered by Cognero. A flexible, online system that allows you to import, edit, and manipulate test bank content from the test bank or elsewhere, including your own favorite test questions; create multiple test versions in an instant; and deliver tests from your LMS, your classroom, or wherever you want.

Aplia is a Cengage Learning online homework system dedicated to improving learning by increasing student effort and engagement. Aplia makes it easy for instructors to assign frequent online homework assignments. Aplia provides students with prompt and detailed feedback to help them learn as they work through the questions, and features interactive tutorials to fully engage them in learning course concepts. Automatic grading and powerful assessment tools give instructors real-time reports of student progress, participation, and performance, while Aplia's easy-to-use course management features let instructors flexibly administer course announcements and materials online. With Aplia, students will show up to class fully engaged and prepared, and instructors will have more time to do what they do best . . . teach.

Brooks/Cole Video Library (Featuring BBC Motion Gallery Video Clips). The Brooks/Cole Video Library contains many high-quality videos that can be used alongside the text. A wide range of video topics offer professors a great tool to engage students and help them connect the material to their lives outside of the classroom. Available on the Instructor Companion Site.

ACKNOWLEDGMENTS

The development and production of the tenth edition of *Biology* required extensive interaction and cooperation among the authors and many individuals in our family, social, and professional environments. We thank our editors, colleagues, students, family, and friends for their help and support. Preparing a book of this complexity is challenging and requires a cohesive, talented, and hardworking professional team. We appreciate the contributions of everyone on the editorial and production staff at Brooks/Cole–Cengage Learning who worked on this tenth edition of *Biology*. We thank our senior product team manager, Yolanda Cossio, for her commitment to *Biology* and for working closely with us throughout the entire process of development and production. We greatly appreciate the help of Suzannah Alexander, our very talented content developer, who was a critical part of our team. Suzannah expertly coordinated many aspects of this challenging project, including the complex new art rendered for this edition. She made herself available to advise and help us whenever we needed her, including late at night and during weekends.

We thank Tom Ziolkowski, our market development manager, and Nicole Hamm, our brand manager, whose expertise ensured that you would know about our new edition.

We appreciate the help of content project manager Hal Humphrey, who expertly guided overall production of the project.

We are grateful to product assistant Victor Luu for quickly providing us with resources whenever we needed them.

We thank creative director Rob Hugel, senior art director and cover designer John Walker, and text designer Jeanne Calabrese.

We appreciate the work of Lauren Oliveira, media developer, who coordinated the many high-tech components of the computerized aspects of our *Learning System*. We thank content coordinator Kellie Petruzzelli for coordinating the print supplements.

We are grateful to our production editor, Whitney Thompson of Lachina Publishing Services, for coordinating the many editors involved in the preparation of this edition and bringing together the thousands of complex pieces of the project that together produced *Biology*, Tenth Edition. We value the careful work of our copy editor, Kathleen Lafferty of Roaring Mountain Editorial Services, who helped us maintain consistency and improve the manuscript. We thank the artists at Lachina Publishing Services, Precision Graphics, and Dragonfly Media Group for greatly improving the art program for this book. We appreciate the efforts of photo research manager Jill Reichenbach of Bill Smith Group in helping us find excellent images. We appreciate the help, patience, and hard work of our production team. Our schedule for this project was very demanding. At times, it seemed like the team worked around the clock. When we sent e-mails late at night or during weekends, we often received immediate responses.

These dedicated professionals and many others on the Brooks/Cole team provided the skill, attention, patience, and good humor needed to produce *Biology*, Tenth Edition. We thank them for their help and support throughout this project.

We appreciate the help of obstetrician/gynecologist Dr. Amy Solomon for her input regarding the most recent information on pregnancy, childbirth, contraception, and sexually transmitted infections. We are grateful to Mical Solomon for his computer help. We thank Dr. David Axelrod for insightful discussions on the genetics and biology of cancer.

We thank our families and friends for their understanding, support, and encouragement as we struggled through many revisions and intense deadlines. We especially thank Dr. Kathleen M. Heide, Freda Brod, Alan Berg, Jennifer and Pat Roath, and Margaret Martin for their support and input.

Our colleagues and students who have used our book have provided valuable input by sharing their responses to past editions of *Biology*. We thank them and ask again for their comments and suggestions as they use this new edition. We can be reached via our website at **www.cengagebrain.com** or through our editors at Brooks/Cole, a division of Cengage Learning.

We greatly appreciate and want to acknowledge the participation and help of our contributors:

Peter K. Ducey
Professor and Department Chair
Biological Sciences Department
SUNY Cortland

Lois A. Ball
Meteorologist, Biologist, and Science Educator
University of South Florida

We express our thanks to the many biologists who have read the manuscript during various stages of its development and provided us with valuable suggestions for improving it. Tenth edition reviewers include the following:

Frank K. Ammer, Frostburg State University

Adébiyi Banjoko, Maricopa Community Colleges

Melissa Bartlett, Mohawk Valley Community College

Richard W. Cheney Jr., Christopher Newport University

Kendra Spence Cheruvelil, Michigan State University

Peter Ducey, SUNY Cortland

Cori Fata-Hartley, Michigan State University

Eric Green, Salt Lake Community College

Chris Haynes, Shelton State Community College

Jay Y. S. Hodgson, Armstrong Atlantic State University, Savannah, Georgia

Andrew J. Kreuz, Stevenson University

Gustave K. N. Mbuy, West Chester University of Pennsylvania

Jennifer A. Metzler, Ball State University

Jacalyn Newman, University of Pittsburgh

Ed Perry, Faulkner State Community College

Lori Rose, Hill College

Bruce Stallsmith, University of Alabama in Huntsville

Matt Williford, Faulkner State Community College

Robert Yost, Indiana University and Purdue University Indianapolis

We would also like to thank the hundreds of reviewers of previous editions, both professors and students, who are too numerous to mention. They asked thoughtful questions, provided new perspectives, offered alternative wordings to clarify difficult passages, and informed us of possible errors. We are truly indebted to their excellent feedback. Their suggestions have helped us improve each edition of *Biology*.

To the Student

We have learned a great deal from tens of thousands of students who have taken on the challenge of learning biology. Although they have varied in their life goals and academic preparation, most have found that they needed to modify their approach to learning to be successful.

You already know that memorization and cramming are unsuccessful, and you probably also know that many students fall back on these methods as default strategies. So, what really works?

Use the Wealth of Learning Aids That Accompany *Biology*

The *Learning System* we use in this book is described in the Preface. Using the strategies of the *Learning System* will help you master the language and concepts of biology. You will also want to use the many online tools available to *Biology* students. These tools, described in the Resources for Students section of the Preface, include *Aplia for Biology* and *MindTap* available at **www.cengagebrain.com.** In addition to these learning strategies, you can make the task of learning biology easier by using approaches that have been successful for a broad range of our students over the years.

Be Open to Many Learning Styles

There is a popular belief that each person has an innate "learning style" that is most successful for them. In fact, there is very little scientific evidence to support this view. What works will depend on the nature of the material being learned, and in most cases a mix of activities and a variety of sensory inputs will be most effective. *Biology* includes many kinds of questions to encourage you to think and learn in different ways. Make learning a part of your life as you think, listen, draw, write, argue, describe, speak, observe, explain, and experiment.

Know Your Professor's Expectations

Determine what your professor wants you to know and how your learning will be assessed. Some professors test almost exclusively on material covered in lecture. Others rely on their students' learning most of, or even all, the content assigned in chapters. Find out what your professor's requirements are because the way you study will vary accordingly.

If lectures are the main source of examination questions, make your lecture notes as complete and organized as possible. Before going to class, skim over the chapter, identifying key terms and examining the main figures, so that you can take effective lecture notes. Spend no more than 1 hour on this. Within 24 hours after class, type (or rewrite) your notes. Before typing them, however, read the notes and make marginal notes about anything that is not clear. Then read the corresponding material in your text. Do not copy the information; instead, process it and write out an explanation in your own words. Read the entire chapter, including parts that are not covered in lecture. This extra information will give you breadth of understanding and will help you grasp key concepts. In addition, you should make an effort to employ as many of the techniques described in the next paragraphs as possible.

If the assigned readings in the text are going to be tested, you must use your text intensively. After reading the chapter introduction, read the list of *Learning Objectives* for the first section. These objectives are written in behavioral terms; that is, they ask you to "do" something to demonstrate mastery. The objectives give you a concrete set of goals for each section of the chapter. At the end of each section, you will find *Checkpoint* questions keyed to the *Learning Objectives*. Carefully examine each figure, making certain that you understand what it is illustrating. Answer the question at the end of each *Key Point* figure and at the end of each *Key Experiment*.

Read each chapter section actively. Highlighting and underlining are not always active learning techniques; sometimes they postpone learning. ("This part is important; I'll learn it later.") An active learner always has questions in mind and is constantly making connections. For example, there are many processes that must be understood in biology. Don't try to blindly memorize them; instead, think about causes and effects so that every process becomes a story. Eventually, you'll see that many processes are connected by common elements.

To master the material, you will probably have to read each chapter more than once. Each time will be much easier than the previous time because you'll be reinforcing concepts that you have already partially learned.

Write a chapter outline and flesh out your outline by adding important concepts and boldface terms with definitions in your own words (not copied from the book or cut and pasted). Use this outline when preparing for the exam.

Now it is time to test yourself. Answer the *Test Your Understanding* questions (*Know and Comprehend, Apply and Analyze,* and *Evaluate and Synthesize*) at the end of the chapter. You will sharpen your thinking if you take the time to type or write out your answers. The answers are in Appendix E, but do not be too quick to check them. Think about them and discuss them with your fellow students if possible. Consider each question as a kind of springboard that leads to other questions. Finally, review the *Learning Objectives* in the *Summary* and try to answer them before reading the summary provided.

Learn the Vocabulary

One stumbling block for many students is learning the many terms that make up the language of biology. In fact, it would be much more difficult to learn and communicate if we did not have this terminology because words are really tools for thinking. Learning terminology generally becomes easier if you realize that most biological terms are modular. They consist of mostly Latin and Greek roots; once you learn many of these roots, you will have a good idea of the meaning of a new word even before it is defined. For this reason, we have included Appendix C, Understanding Biological Terms. To be sure that you understand the precise definition of a term, use the Index and the Glossary. The more you use biological terms in speech and writing, the more comfortable you will be with the language of biology.

Develop a Framework for Your Learning

Always aim to get the big picture before adding details. When attempting to learn a complex process, a struggling student will typically begin with the first part, try to learn all the details, and then give up. Instead, begin by making sure that you have a basic understanding of what is happening in the overall process. To encourage you in this way of thinking, we have modeled this approach in *Biology*. As just one example out of many, glycolysis is a multistep process covered in Chapter 8. Before presenting all the details, we provide an overview figure that emphasizes what the process accomplishes.

Form a Study Group

Active learning is facilitated if you do some of your studying collaboratively in a small group. In a study group, the roles of teacher and learner can be interchanged: a good way to learn material is to teach, through a process that cognitive scientists describe as *elaborative rehearsal* (not to be confused with memorization). A study group has other advantages: it can make learning more fun, lets you meet challenges in a nonthreatening environment, and can provide some emotional support. When combined with individual study of text and lecture notes, study groups can be effective learning tools.

Eldra P. Solomon
Charles E. Martin
Diana W. Martin
Linda R. Berg

This is an exciting time to study **biology**, the science of life. Biologists are making remarkable new discoveries that affect every aspect of our lives, including our health, food, safety, relationships with humans and other organisms, and the environment of our planet. New knowledge provides new insights into the human species and the millions of other organisms with which we share planet Earth. Biology affects our personal, governmental, and societal decisions.

One of the most exciting areas of current research is stem cell biology. **Stem cells** are unspecialized cells that have the capacity to divide, giving rise to more stem cells *and* to one or more specialized types of cell. For example, stem cells in the bone marrow differentiate to produce the various types of blood cells. Stem cells also allow the body to repair injury as well as to recover from normal wear and tear. For example, stem cells in the skin continuously divide, and some differentiate to replace skin cells that are constantly worn off from the body's surface.

Basic research in stem cell biology has helped scientists understand how unspecialized cells differentiate to become specific types of cells such as skin cells, white blood cells, or cells lining the intestine. Combined with technological advances, stem cell biology has led to exciting new advances and possibilities in such diverse fields as clinical medicine and ecology. For example, patients with leukemia and certain other cancers are often treated with radiation that destroys blood-producing stem cells in the bone marrow. Thousands of lives are saved each year using procedures in which stem cells are transplanted into the patient's bone marrow.

Researchers are developing methods for using stem cells to treat infertility and to repair spinal cord injury. In the future, stem cells may be used to cure genetic diseases and to treat diseases such as arthritis, Alzheimer's disease, Parkinson's disease, multiple sclerosis, and macular degeneration. Tissue may someday be cultured from a patient to replace organs that are diseased. For example, a diabetic patient may be given a new pancreas.

Biologists continue to discover new types of stem cells within the bodies of plants, humans, and research animals. The most versatile stem cells, called **pluripotent** stem cells, can give rise to all the tissues of the body. Biologists have discovered how to

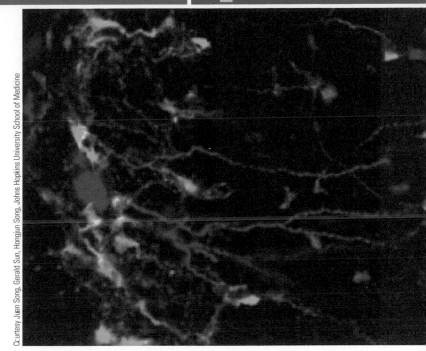

Courtesy Juan Song, Gerald Sun, Hongjun Song, Johns Hopkins University School of Medicine

Neural stem cells in the brain. Neural stem cells (*green*) in the hippocampus gather around a neuron (*purple*). Neural stem cells appear to receive and respond to signals transmitted from one neuron to another.

KEY CONCEPTS

1.1 Basic themes of biology include evolution, interactions of biological systems, inter-relationships of structure and function, information transfer, and energy transfer.

1.2 Characteristics of life include cellular structure, growth and development, self-regulated metabolism, response to stimuli, and reproduction.

1.3 Biological organization is hierarchical and includes chemical, cell, tissue, organ, organ system, and organism levels; ecological organization includes population, community, ecosystem, and biosphere levels.

1.4 Information transfer includes DNA transfer of information from one generation to the next, chemical and electrical signals within and among the cells of every organism, and sensory receptors and response systems that allow organisms to communicate with one another and interact with their environment.

1.5 Individual organisms and entire ecosystems depend on a continuous input of energy. Energy is transferred within cells and from one organism to another.

1.6 Evolution is the process by which populations of organisms change over time, adapting to changes in their environment; the tree of life includes three major branches, or domains.

1.7 Biologists ask questions, develop hypotheses, make predictions, and collect data by careful observation and experiment; based on their results, they come to conclusions and then share their work with other scientists and with the public.

induce pluripotent stem cells by reprogramming the genome of certain adult cells. These *induced pluripotent stem cells (iPSCs)* are similar in many ways to embryonic stem cells. An important advantage of iPSCs is that they give rise to tissues that are genetically identical to those of the patient.

Stem cells may also be used in the future to save endangered species. Researchers have already produced iPSCs from the tissues of an adult snow leopard, a jaguar, a Bengal tiger, and a serval (a medium-sized, slender cat, native to Africa). In the future they hope to clone the iPSCs and to produce eggs and sperm from them.

Recently, the journal *Nature* reported that researchers at the Johns Hopkins University School of Medicine have discovered that neural stem cells in the brain "listen in" on the chemical signals that neurons use to communicate with one another (see photograph). When necessary, the stem cells differentiate into neurons or glial cells, or signal the brain to produce new cells.

The 2012 Nobel Prize in Physiology or Medicine was awarded to John B. Gurdon and Shinya Yamanaka for their contributions to the development of stem cell research. In the 1960s, Gurdon transplanted differentiated cell nuclei taken from tadpoles into frog egg cells. He found that a few of these eggs developed into tadpoles (see Fig. 17-3). More than forty years later Yamanaka and his colleagues identified a combination of four genes from embryonic stem cells that could reprogram certain mature cells to become pluripotent stem cells.

Stem cell research is just one of hundreds of exciting areas of biological research that bring together science, technology, and society. Whatever your college major or career goals, knowledge of biological concepts is a vital tool for understanding our world and for meeting many of the personal, societal, and global challenges that confront us. Among these challenges are the expanding human population, decreasing biological diversity, diminishing natural resources, global climate change, and prevention and cure of diseases, such as heart disease, cancer, diabetes, and Alzheimer's disease. Meeting these challenges will require the combined efforts of biologists and other scientists, health professionals, educators, politicians, and biologically informed citizens.

This book is a starting point for your exploration of biology. It will provide you with the basic knowledge and the tools to become a part of this fascinating science as well as a more informed member of society.

1.1 MAJOR THEMES OF BIOLOGY

LEARNING OBJECTIVE

1 Describe five basic themes of biology.

In this first chapter we introduce five major themes of biology. These themes are interconnected with one another and with almost every concept that we discuss in this book.

1. **Biological systems interact.** Every organism is a biological system made up of millions of other biological systems. Each of its cells is a biological system, as is each organ (e.g., heart and liver) and body system (e.g., cardiovascular system and digestive system). Each of the multitude of microorganisms (e.g., bacteria) that inhabit an organism is also a biological system. Making this concept even more interesting, an organism cannot survive on its own. Every organism is a biological system that is interdependent with many other biological systems. Clearly, scientists can study biological systems and their interactions at many different levels.

2. **Structure and function are inter-related in all biological systems.** The structure of neurons that function to transmit information is very different from the structure of red blood cells, which function to transport oxygen. Similarly, on the level of organisms, the canine teeth of carnivorous mammals are adapted for stabbing their prey and ripping flesh. In contrast, horses and other herbivorous mammals have teeth adapted for cutting off bits of vegetation and grinding plant material. In each case, structure and function are inter-related.

3. **Information must be transmitted within organisms and among organisms.** Each organism must be able to receive information from the surrounding environment. The survival and function of every cell and every organism depend on the orderly transmission of information. As we will learn, evolution depends on the transmission of genetic information from one generation to another.

4. **Life depends on a continuous input of energy from the sun because every activity of a living cell or organism requires energy.** Energy from the sun flows through individual organisms and through ecosystems. Within living cells energy is continuously transferred from one chemical compound to another.

5. **Evolution is the process by which populations of organisms change over time.** Scientists have accumulated a wealth of evidence showing that the diverse life-forms on this planet are related and that populations have *evolved*— that is, have changed over time—from earlier forms of life. The process of *evolution* is the framework for the science of biology and is a major theme of this book.

The interaction of biological systems, the inter-relationship of structure and function, information transfer, energy transfer, and the process of evolution are forces that give life its unique characteristics. You will find reference to one or more of these unifying themes in every chapter of *Biology*. We begin our study of biology by developing a more precise understanding of the fundamental characteristics of living systems and of the levels of biological organization. We then take a closer look at some of the major themes of biology. We end Chapter 1 with a discussion of the process of science.

1.2 CHARACTERISTICS OF LIFE

LEARNING OBJECTIVE

2 Distinguish between living systems and nonliving things by describing the features that characterize living organisms.

We easily recognize that a pine tree, a butterfly, and a horse are living systems, whereas a rock is not. Despite their diversity, the organisms that inhabit our planet share a common set of characteristics that distinguish them from nonliving things. These features include a precise kind of organization, growth and development, self-regulated metabolism, the ability to respond to stimuli, reproduction, and adaptation to environmental change.

Organisms are composed of cells

Although they vary greatly in size and appearance, all organisms consist of basic units called **cells.** New cells are formed only by the division of previously existing cells. As will be discussed in Chapter 4, these concepts are expressed in the **cell theory**, another fundamental unifying concept of biology.

Some of the simplest life-forms, such as protozoa, are *unicellular* organisms, meaning that each consists of a single cell (FIG. 1-1a). In contrast, the body of a maple tree or a buffalo is made of billions of cells (FIG. 1-1b). In such complex *multicellular* organisms, life processes depend on the coordinated functions of component cells that are organized to form tissues, organs, and organ systems.

Every cell is enveloped by a protective **plasma membrane** that separates it from the surrounding external environment. The plasma membrane regulates passage of materials between the cell and its environment. Cells have specialized molecules that contain genetic instructions and transmit genetic information. In most cells, the genetic instructions are encoded in deoxyribonucleic acid, more simply known as **DNA.** Cells typically have internal structures called **organelles** that are specialized to perform specific functions.

There are two fundamentally different types of cells: prokaryotic and eukaryotic. *Prokaryotic cells* are exclusive to bacteria and to microscopic organisms called *archaea*. Prokaryotic cells do not have a nucleus or other membrane-enclosed organelles. All other organisms are characterized by their *eukaryotic cells*. These cells typically contain a variety of organelles enclosed by membranes, including a **nucleus,** which houses DNA.

Organisms grow and develop

Biological growth involves an increase in the size of individual cells of an organism, in the number of cells, or in both. Growth

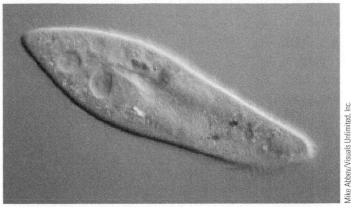

250 μm

Mike Abbey/Visuals Unlimited, Inc.

(a) Unicellular organisms consist of one cell that performs all the functions essential to life. Ciliates, such as this *Paramecium*, move about by beating their hairlike cilia.

McMurray Photography

(b) Multicellular organisms, such as this African buffalo (*Syncerus caffer*) and the plants on which it grazes, may consist of billions of cells specialized to perform specific functions.

Figure 1-1 Unicellular and multicellular life-forms

may be uniform in the various parts of an organism, or it may be greater in some parts than in others, causing the body proportions to change as growth occurs. Some organisms—most trees, for example—continue to grow throughout their lives. Many animals have a defined growth period that terminates when a characteristic adult size is reached. An intriguing aspect of the growth process is that each part of the organism typically continues to function as it grows.

Organisms develop as well as grow. **Development** includes all the changes that take place during an organism's life. The structures and body form that develop are exquisitely adapted to the functions the organism must perform. Like many other organisms, every human begins life as a fertilized egg that then grows and develops.

Organisms regulate their metabolic processes

Within all organisms, chemical reactions and energy transformations occur that are essential to nutrition, the growth and repair of cells, and the conversion of energy into usable forms. The sum of all the chemical activities of the organism is its **metabolism.**

Metabolic processes occur continuously in every organism, and they must be carefully regulated to maintain **homeostasis,** an appropriate, balanced internal environment. The term *homeostasis* also refers to the automatic tendency of the organism to maintain a steady state. When a particular substance is required, cell processes that produce it must be turned on. When enough of a cell product has been made, its manufacture must be decreased or turned off. These *homeostatic mechanisms* are self-regulating control systems that are remarkably sensitive and efficient.

The regulation of glucose (a simple sugar) concentration in the blood of complex animals is a good example of a homeostatic mechanism. Your cells require a constant supply of glucose molecules, which they break down to obtain energy. The circulatory system delivers glucose and other nutrients to all the cells. When the concentration of glucose in the blood rises above normal limits, glucose is stored in the liver and in muscle cells. When you have not eaten for a few hours, the glucose concentration begins to fall. Your body mobilizes stored glucose. If necessary, the body converts other stored nutrients to glucose, bringing the glucose concentration in the blood back to normal levels. When the glucose concentration decreases, you also feel hungry and can restore nutrients by eating.

Organisms respond to stimuli

All forms of life respond to **stimuli,** physical or chemical changes in their internal or external environment. Stimuli that evoke a response in most organisms are changes in the color, intensity, or direction of light; changes in temperature, pressure, or sound; and changes in the chemical composition of the surrounding soil, air, or water. Responding to stimuli involves movement, although not always locomotion (moving from one place to another).

In simple organisms, the entire individual may be sensitive to stimuli. Certain unicellular organisms, for example, respond to bright light by retreating. In some organisms, locomotion is achieved by the slow oozing of the cell, the process of *amoeboid movement.* Other organisms move by beating tiny, hairlike extensions of the cell called **cilia** or longer structures known as **flagella** (FIG. 1-2). Some bacteria move by rotating their flagella.

Most animals move very obviously. They wiggle, crawl, swim, run, or fly by contracting muscles. Sponges, corals, and oysters have free-swimming larval stages, but most are **sessile** as adults, meaning that they do not move from place to place. In fact, they may remain firmly attached to a surface, such as the sea bottom or a rock. Many sessile organisms have cilia or flagella that beat rhythmically, bringing them food and oxygen in

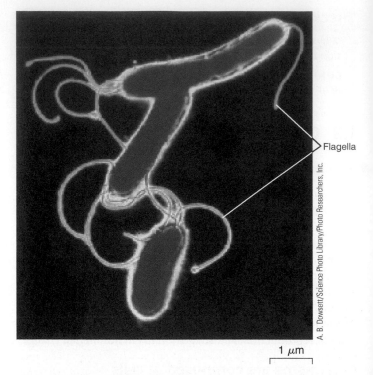

Flagella

1 μm

Figure 1-2 Biological movement

These bacteria (*Helicobacter pylori*), equipped with flagella for locomotion, have been linked to stomach ulcers. The photograph was taken using a scanning electron microscope. The bacteria are not really red and blue. Their color has been artificially enhanced.

the surrounding water. Complex animals, such as grasshoppers, lizards, and humans, have highly specialized cells that respond to specific types of stimuli. For example, cells in the retina of the vertebrate eye respond to light.

Although their responses may not be as obvious as those of animals, plants do respond to light, gravity, water, touch, and other stimuli. For example, plants orient their leaves to the sun and grow toward light. Many plant responses involve different growth rates of various parts of the plant body. A few plants, such as the Venus flytrap of the Carolina swamps, are very sensitive to touch and catch insects (FIG. 1-3). Their leaves are hinged along the midrib, and they have a scent that attracts insects. Trigger hairs on the leaf surface detect the arrival of an insect and stimulate the leaf to fold. When the edges come together, they interlock, preventing the insect's escape. The leaf then secretes enzymes that kill and digest the insect. The Venus flytrap usually grows in nitrogen-deficient soil. The plant obtains part of the nitrogen required for its growth from the insects it "eats."

Organisms reproduce

At one time, people thought worms arose spontaneously from horsehair in a water trough, maggots from decaying meat, and frogs from the mud of the Nile. Thanks to the work of a great many scientists, beginning with pioneering studies by Italian physician Francesco Redi in the 17th century and French chemist Louis Pasteur in the 19th century, we know that organisms arise only from previously existing organisms.

(a) When hairs on the leaf surface of the Venus flytrap (*Dionaea muscipula*) detect the touch of an insect, the leaf responds by folding.

(b) The edges of the leaf come together and interlock, preventing the fly's escape. The leaf then secretes enzymes that kill and digest the insect.

Figure 1-3 **Plants respond to stimuli**

Simple organisms, such as amoebas, perpetuate themselves by **asexual reproduction** (FIG. 1-4a). When an amoeba has grown to a certain size, it reproduces by splitting in half to form two new amoebas. Before an amoeba divides, its hereditary material (set of *genes*) is duplicated, and one complete set is distributed to each new cell. Except for size, each new amoeba is similar to the parent cell. The only way that variation occurs among asexually reproducing organisms is by genetic *mutation*, a permanent change in the genes.

In most plants and animals, **sexual reproduction** is carried out by the fusion of an egg and a sperm cell to form a fertilized egg (FIG. 1-4b). The new organism develops from the fertilized egg. Offspring produced by sexual reproduction are the product of the interaction of various genes contributed by the mother and the father. This genetic variation is important in the vital processes of evolution and adaptation.

Populations evolve and become adapted to the environment

The ability of a population to evolve over many generations and adapt to its environment equips it to survive in a changing world. **Adaptations** are inherited characteristics that enhance an organism's ability to survive in a particular environment. The long, flexible tongue of the frog is an adaptation for catching insects. The feathers and light-weight bones of birds are adaptations for flying, and their thick fur coats allow polar bears to survive in frigid temperatures. Adaptations may be structural, physiological, biochemical, behavioral, or a combination of all four (FIG. 1-5). Every biologically successful organism is a complex collection of coordinated adaptations produced through evolutionary processes.

CHECKPOINT 1.2

- *What characteristics distinguish a living organism from a rock?*
- PREDICT *What would be the consequences to an organism if its homeostatic mechanisms failed? Explain your answer.*

Figure 1-4 **Asexual and sexual reproduction**

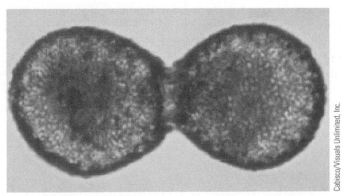

100 μm

(a) **Asexual reproduction.** One individual gives rise to two or more offspring that are similar to the parent. *Difflugia*, a unicellular amoeba, is shown dividing to form two amoebas.

(b) **Sexual reproduction.** Typically, each of two parents contributes a gamete (sperm or egg). Gametes fuse to produce the offspring, which has a combination of the traits of both parents. A pair of tropical flies is shown mating.

Figure 1-5 Adaptations

These Burchell's zebras (*Equus burchelli*), photographed in Tanzania, are behaviorally adapted to position themselves to watch for lions and other predators. Stripes are thought to be an adaptation for visual protection against predators. They serve as camouflage or to break up form when spotted from a distance. The zebra stomach is adapted for feeding on coarse grass passed over by other grazers, an adaptation that helps the animal survive when food is scarce.

1.3 LEVELS OF BIOLOGICAL ORGANIZATION

LEARNING OBJECTIVE

3 Construct a hierarchy of biological organization, including levels characteristic of individual organisms and levels characteristic of ecological systems.

Whether we study a single organism or the world of life as a whole, we can identify a hierarchy of biological organization (FIG. 1-6). At every level, structure and function are precisely coordinated. One way to study a particular level is by looking at its components. Biologists can gain insights about cells by studying atoms and molecules. Learning about a structure by studying its parts is called **reductionism.** However, the whole is more than the sum of its parts. Each level has **emergent properties,** characteristics not found at lower levels. For example, populations of organisms have emergent properties such as population density, age structure, and birth and death rates. The *individuals* that make up a population do not have these characteristics. Consider also the human brain. The brain is composed of billions of neurons (nerve cells). However, we could study every one of these individual neurons and have no clue about the functional capacities of the brain. Only when the neurons interact are the emergent properties, such as the capacity for thought, judgment, and motor coordination, evident.

Organisms have several levels of organization

The chemical level, the most basic level of organization, includes atoms and molecules. An **atom** is the smallest unit of a chemical element that retains the characteristic properties of that element.

For example, an atom of iron is the smallest possible amount of iron. Atoms combine chemically to form **molecules.** Two atoms of hydrogen combine with one atom of oxygen to form a single molecule of water. Although composed of two types of atoms that are gases under conditions found on Earth, water can exist as a gas, liquid, or solid. The properties of water are very different from those of its hydrogen and oxygen components, an example of emergent properties.

At the cellular level, many types of atoms and molecules associate with one another to form *cells*. However, a cell is much more than a heap of atoms and molecules. Its emergent properties make it the basic structural and functional unit of life, the simplest component of living matter that can carry on all the activities necessary for life.

During the evolution of multicellular organisms, cells associated to form **tissues.** For example, most animals have muscle tissue and nervous tissue. Plants have epidermis, a tissue that serves as a protective covering, and vascular tissues that move materials throughout the plant body. In most complex organisms, tissues organize into functional structures called **organs**, such as the heart and stomach in animals and roots and leaves in plants. In animals, each major group of biological functions is performed by a coordinated group of tissues and organs called an **organ system.** The circulatory and digestive systems are examples of organ systems. Functioning together with great precision, organ systems make up a complex, multicellular **organism.** Again, emergent properties are evident. An organism is much more than its component organ systems.

Several levels of ecological organization can be identified

Organisms interact to form still more complex levels of biological organization. All the members of one species living in the same geographic area at the same time make up a **population.** The populations of various types of organisms that inhabit a particular area and interact with one another form a **community.** A community can consist of hundreds of different types of organisms.

A community together with its nonliving environment is an **ecosystem.** An ecosystem can be as small as a pond (or even a puddle) or as vast as the Great Plains of North America or the Arctic tundra. All Earth's ecosystems together are known as the **biosphere.** The biosphere includes all systems of Earth that are inhabited by living organisms: the atmosphere, the hydrosphere (water in any form), and the lithosphere (Earth's crust). The study of how organisms relate to one another and to their physical environment is called **ecology** (derived from the Greek *oikos*, meaning "house").

CHECKPOINT 1.3

- *What are the levels of organization within an organism?*
- **PREDICT** *At which level do you think more biological systems would be interacting: organism, population, or ecosystem? Justify your answer.*

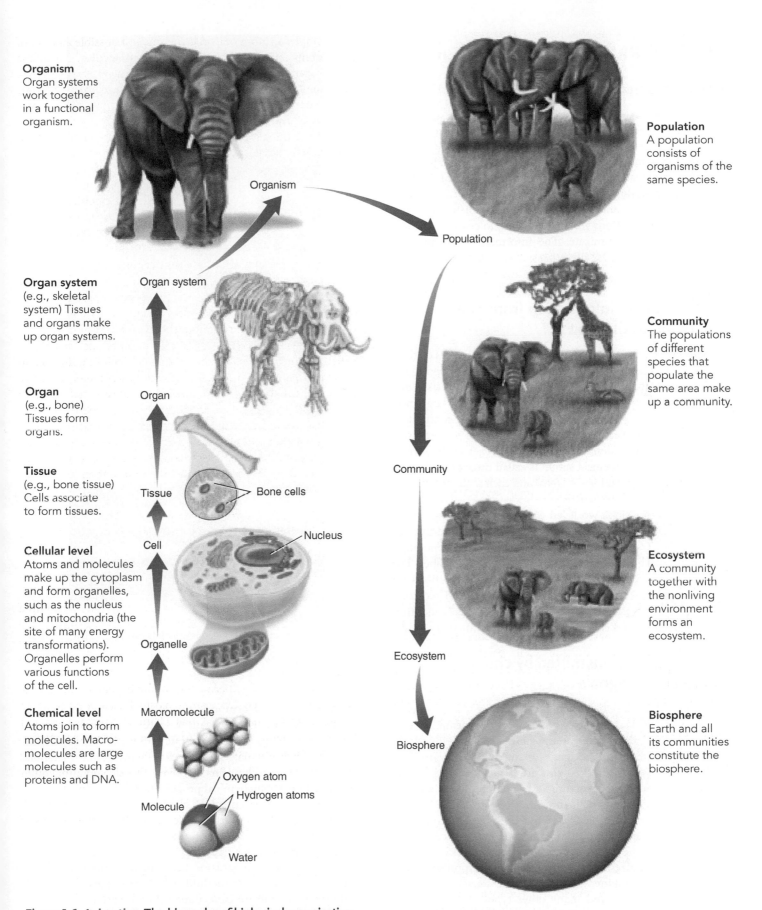

Organism
Organ systems work together in a functional organism.

Organism

Population
A population consists of organisms of the same species.

Population

Organ system
(e.g., skeletal system) Tissues and organs make up organ systems.

Organ system

Community
The populations of different species that populate the same area make up a community.

Organ
(e.g., bone) Tissues form organs.

Organ

Community

Tissue
(e.g., bone tissue) Cells associate to form tissues.

Tissue

Bone cells

Cellular level
Atoms and molecules make up the cytoplasm and form organelles, such as the nucleus and mitochondria (the site of many energy transformations). Organelles perform various functions of the cell.

Cell

Nucleus

Organelle

Ecosystem
A community together with the nonliving environment forms an ecosystem.

Ecosystem

Chemical level
Atoms join to form molecules. Macromolecules are large molecules such as proteins and DNA.

Macromolecule

Oxygen atom

Hydrogen atoms

Molecule

Water

Biosphere

Biosphere
Earth and all its communities constitute the biosphere.

Figure 1-6 *Animation* **The hierarchy of biological organization**

© Cengage Learning

1.4 INFORMATION TRANSFER

LEARNING OBJECTIVE

4   Summarize the importance of information transfer within and between living systems, giving specific examples.

Biological systems receive and respond to information. They also store information. An organism inherits the information it needs to grow, develop, carry on self-regulated metabolism, respond to stimuli, and reproduce. Each organism must also have precise instructions for making the molecules necessary for its cells to communicate. The information an organism requires to carry on these life processes is coded and transmitted in the form of chemical substances and electrical impulses.

DNA transmits information from one generation to the next

Humans give birth only to human babies, not to giraffes or rose-bushes. In organisms that reproduce sexually, each offspring is a combination of the traits of its parents. In 1953, James Watson and Francis Crick worked out the structure of DNA, the large molecule that makes up the **genes,** units of hereditary information (FIG. 1-7). A DNA molecule consists of two chains of atoms twisted into a helix. As will be described in Chapter 3, each chain is made up of a sequence of chemical subunits called **nucleotides.** There are four types of nucleotides in DNA, and each sequence of three nucleotides is part of the genetic code.

Watson and Crick's work led to the understanding of the genetic code. The information coded in sequences of nucleotides in DNA transmits genetic information from generation to generation. The code works somewhat like an alphabet. The nucleotides can "spell" an amazing variety of instructions for making organisms as diverse as bacteria, frogs, and redwood trees. The genetic code is universal—that is, virtually identical in all organisms—and is a dramatic example of the unity of life.

Information is transmitted by chemical and electrical signals

Genes control the development and functioning of every organism. As you will learn in later chapters, the information carried by the DNA that makes up the genes has many functions, including providing the "recipes" for making all the proteins required by the organism. **Proteins** are large molecules important in determining the structure and function of cells and tissues. For example, brain cells differ from muscle cells in large part because they have different types of proteins. Some proteins are important in communication within and among cells. Certain proteins on the surface of a cell serve as markers so that other cells "recognize" them. Other cell-surface proteins serve as receptors that combine with chemical messengers.

Cells use proteins and many other types of molecules to communicate with one another. In a multicellular organism, cells produce chemical compounds, such as **hormones,** that

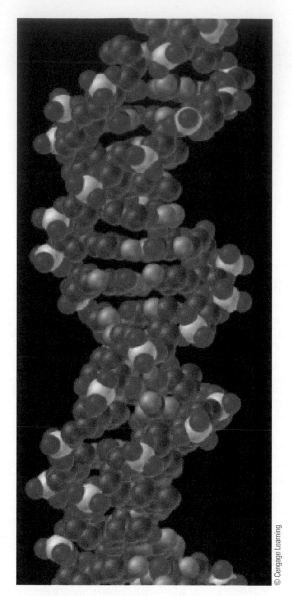

Figure 1-7 DNA

DNA is the hereditary material that transmits information from one generation to the next. As shown in this model, DNA is a macromolecule that consists of two chains of atoms twisted into a helix. Each chain consists of subunits called nucleotides. The sequence of nucleotides makes up the genetic code.

signal other cells. Hormones and other chemical messengers can signal cells in distant organs to secrete a particular required substance or change some metabolic activity. In this way chemical signals help regulate growth, development, and metabolic processes. The mechanisms involved in **cell signaling** often involve complex biochemical processes.

Cell signaling is currently an area of intense research. A major focus has been the transfer of information among cells of the immune system. A better understanding of how cells communicate promises new insights into how the body protects itself against disease organisms. Learning to manipulate cell signaling may lead to new methods of delivering drugs into cells and new treatments for cancer and other diseases.

Many organisms use electrical signals to transmit information. Most animals have nervous systems that transmit information by way of both electrical impulses and chemical compounds known as **neurotransmitters**. Information transmitted from one part of the body to another is important in regulating life processes. In complex animals, the nervous system gives the animal information about its outside environment by transmitting signals from sensory receptors such as the eyes and ears to the brain.

Organisms also communicate information to one another

Organisms communicate information to other organisms by releasing chemicals, sounds, and visual displays. Typically, organisms use a combination of several types of communication signals. A dog may signal aggression by growling, using a particular facial expression, and laying its ears back. Many animals perform complex courtship rituals in which they display parts of their bodies, often elaborately decorated, to attract a mate.

Seaweed algae compete with coral for light and space. Marine biologists studying endangered coral reefs have discovered that certain seaweed algae secrete chemical compounds that kill coral. Researchers have reported that some coral can fight back. When they come into contact with toxic seaweed, the coral release chemical compounds that signal certain species of goby fish. In response to this chemical signal, the fish eat the seaweed. This action helps preserve their coral reef habitat.

CHECKPOINT 1.4

- *What is the function of DNA?*
- *How does a nervous system transmit information?*

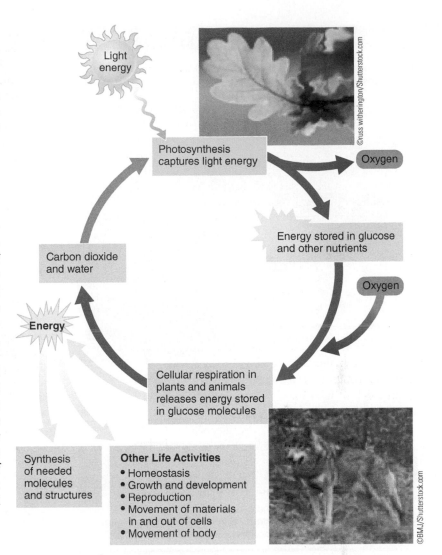

Figure 1-8 *Animation* **Energy flow within and among organisms**

Algae and certain plant cells carry on photosynthesis, a process that uses light energy to produce glucose from carbon dioxide and water. Energy is stored in the chemical bonds of glucose and other nutrients produced from glucose. Through the process of cellular respiration, cells of all organisms, including algae and plant cells, then break down glucose and other nutrients. The energy released can be used to produce needed molecules and to fuel other life activities.

© Cengage Learning

1.5 THE ENERGY OF LIFE

LEARNING OBJECTIVE

5 Summarize the flow of energy through ecosystems and contrast the roles of producers, consumers, and decomposers.

The sun provides most of the energy that powers life on Earth. All life processes, including thousands of chemical transactions that maintain life's organization, require a continuous input of energy. Organisms can neither create energy nor use it with complete efficiency. During every energy transaction, some energy is converted to heat and dispersed into the environment. Energy flows through individual organisms and through ecosystems.

A self-sufficient ecosystem consists of a physical environment inhabited by three types of organisms: producers, consumers, and decomposers. These organisms depend on one another and on the environment for nutrients, energy, oxygen, and carbon dioxide. Plants, algae, and certain bacteria are

producers, or **autotrophs**, organisms that produce their own food from simple raw materials. Most of these organisms carry on **photosynthesis**, the process during which autotrophs use carbon dioxide, water, and light energy to synthesize complex molecules such as glucose and other sugars (FIG. 1-8):

carbon dioxide + water + light energy ⟶
glucose + oxygen

The light energy is transformed into chemical energy, which is stored within the chemical bonds of the glucose and other food molecules produced. Oxygen, which is required by the cells of most organisms including plant cells, is produced as a byproduct of photosynthesis.

Recall that all the energy transformations and chemical processes that occur within an organism are referred to as its *metabolism*. Energy is necessary to carry on the metabolic

Energy flows from the sun to producers and then to consumers and decomposers.

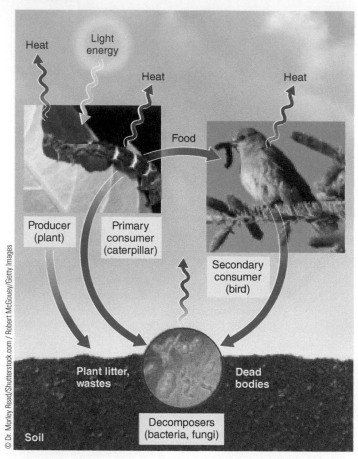

Figure 1-9 *Animation* **Energy flow through the biosphere**

Continuous energy input from the sun operates the biosphere. During photosynthesis, producers use the energy from sunlight to make complex molecules from carbon dioxide and water. Primary consumers, such as the caterpillar shown here, obtain energy, nutrients, and other required materials when they eat producers. Secondary consumers, such as the bird, obtain energy, nutrients, and other required materials when they eat primary consumers that have eaten producers. Decomposers obtain their energy and nutrients by breaking down wastes and dead organic material. During every energy transaction, some energy is lost to biological systems, dispersing into the environment as heat.

PREDICT How does air pollution caused by human activity affect the balance of energy flow through the biosphere?

activities essential for growth, repair, and maintenance. Each cell of an organism requires nutrients that contain energy. During **cellular respiration,** cells capture energy stored in glucose and other nutrient molecules through a series of carefully regulated chemical reactions. We can summarize these reactions as follows:

$$\text{glucose} + \text{oxygen} \longrightarrow \text{carbon dioxide} + \text{water} + \text{energy}$$

When chemical bonds are broken during cellular respiration, their stored energy is made available for life processes. Cells

use this energy to do work, including the synthesis of required materials, such as new cell components. Virtually all cells carry on cellular respiration.

Animals are **consumers,** or **heterotrophs**—that is, they are organisms that depend on producers for food, energy, and oxygen (FIG. 1-9). **Primary consumers** eat producers. **Secondary consumers** eat primary consumers. Consumers obtain energy by breaking down sugars and other nutrients originally produced during photosynthesis. Consumers also contribute to the balance of the ecosystem. For example, consumers produce carbon dioxide required by producers. (Note that producers also carry on cellular respiration.) The metabolism of consumers and producers helps maintain the life-sustaining mixture of gases in the atmosphere.

Most bacteria and fungi are **decomposers,** heterotrophs that obtain nutrients by breaking down nonliving organic material such as wastes, dead leaves and branches, and the bodies of dead organisms. In their process of obtaining energy, decomposers make the components of these materials available for reuse. If decomposers did not exist, nutrients would remain locked up in wastes and dead bodies, and the supply of elements required by living systems would soon be exhausted.

CHECKPOINT 1.5

- **PREDICT** *What components do you think a forest ecosystem might include?*

- **CONNECT** *In what ways do consumers depend on producers? on decomposers? Include energy considerations in your answer.*

1.6 EVOLUTION: THE BASIC UNIFYING CONCEPT OF BIOLOGY

LEARNING OBJECTIVES

6 Demonstrate the binomial system of nomenclature by using specific examples and classify an organism (such as a human) in its domain, kingdom, phylum, class, order, family, genus, and species.

7 Identify the three domains and the kingdoms of living organisms, and give examples of organisms assigned to each group.

8 Give a brief overview of the scientific theory of evolution and explain why it is the principal unifying concept in biology.

9 Apply the concept of natural selection to any given adaptation and suggest a logical explanation of how the adaptation may have evolved.

Evolution is the process by which populations of organisms change over time. The scientific theory of evolution has become the most important unifying concept of biology. As we will discuss, evolution involves passing genes for new traits from one generation to another, leading to differences in populations. The evolutionary perspective is important in every specialized field within biology. Biologists try to understand the structure, function, and behavior of organisms and their interactions with one another by considering them in light of the long, continuing process of evolution. Although we discuss evolution in depth in Chapters 18 through 22, we present a brief overview here to give you the background necessary to understand other aspects of biology. First, we examine how biologists organize the millions of organisms that have evolved, and then we summarize some of the mechanisms that drive evolution.

Biologists use a binomial system for naming organisms

Biologists have identified about 1.9 million kinds (species) of *extant* (currently living) organisms and estimate that several million more remain to be discovered. To study life, we need a system for organizing, naming, and classifying its myriad forms. **Systematics** is the field of biology that studies the diversity of organisms and their evolutionary relationships. **Taxonomy,** a subspecialty of systematics, is the science of naming and classifying organisms. In the 18th century, Carolus Linnaeus, a Swedish botanist, developed a hierarchical system of naming and classifying organisms. Biologists still use this system today, with some modification.

The **species** is a group of organisms with similar structure, function, and behavior. A species consists of one or more populations whose members are capable of breeding with one another; in nature, they do not breed with members of other species. Members of a population contribute to a common **gene pool** (all the genes present in the population) and share a common ancestry. Closely related species are grouped in the next broader category of classification, the **genus** (pl., *genera*).

The Linnaean system of naming species is known as the **binomial system of nomenclature** because each species is assigned a two-part name. The first part of the name is the genus, and the second part, the **specific epithet**, designates a particular species belonging to that genus. The specific epithet is often a descriptive word expressing some quality of the organism. It is always used together with the full or abbreviated generic name preceding it. The generic name is always capitalized; the specific epithet is generally not capitalized. Both names are always italicized or underlined. For example, the domestic dog, *Canis familiaris* (abbreviated *C. familiaris*), and the timber wolf, *Canis lupus* (*C. lupus*), belong to the same genus. The domestic cat, *Felis catus*, belongs to a different genus. The scientific name of the American white oak is *Quercus alba,* whereas the name of the European white oak is *Quercus robur*. Another tree, the white willow, *Salix alba,* belongs to a different genus. The scientific name for our own species is *Homo sapiens* ("wise man").

Taxonomic classification is hierarchical

Just as closely related species may be grouped in a common genus, related genera can be grouped in a more inclusive group, a **family.** Families are grouped into **orders,** orders into **classes,** and classes into **phyla** (sing., *phylum*). Phyla can be assigned to **kingdoms,** and kingdoms are grouped in **domains.** Each formal grouping at any given level is a **taxon** (pl., *taxa*). Note that each taxon is more inclusive than the taxon below it. Together they form a hierarchy ranging from species to domain TABLE 1-1 and FIG. 1-10.

Consider a specific example. The family Canidae, which includes all doglike carnivores (animals that eat mainly meat), consists of 12 genera and about 35 living species. Family Canidae, along with family Ursidae (bears), family Felidae (catlike animals), and several other families that eat mainly meat, are all placed in order Carnivora. Order Carnivora, order Primates (to which chimpanzees and humans belong), and several other orders belong to class Mammalia (mammals). Class Mammalia is grouped with several other classes that include fishes, amphibians, reptiles, and birds in subphylum Vertebrata. The vertebrates belong to phylum Chordata, which is part of kingdom Animalia. Animals are assigned to domain Eukarya.

Systematists classify organisms in three domains

Systematics itself has evolved as scientists have developed new techniques for inferring common ancestry among groups of organisms. Biologists seek to classify organisms based on evolutionary relationships. These relationships are based on shared characteristics that distinguish a particular group. A group of organisms with a common ancestor is a **clade.** Systematists have developed family trees showing proposed evolutionary relationships among organisms. These relationships are based on the patterns of traits shared by organisms and on fossil evidence. Shared characteristics include structural, developmental, behavioral, and molecular similarities. FIGURE 1-11 is a **cladogram,** a branching diagram, that depicts the three domains and several kingdoms of Domain Eukarya. As researchers report new findings, the classification of organisms changes and the branches of cladograms are redrawn.

Although the "tree of life" is a work in progress, most biologists now assign organisms to three domains and to several kingdoms or clades. The late microbiologist Carl Woese (pronounced "woes") was a pioneer in developing molecular approaches to systematics. Woese and his colleagues selected a molecule known as small subunit ribosomal RNA (rRNA) that functions in the process of manufacturing proteins in all organisms. Because its molecular structure differs somewhat

TABLE 1-1	Classification of the Cat, Human, and White Oak Tree		
CATEGORY	CAT	HUMAN	WHITE OAK
Domain	Eukarya	Eukarya	Eukarya
Kingdom	Animalia	Animalia	Plantae
Phylum	Chordata	Chordata	Anthophyta
Subphylum	Vertebrata	Vertebrata	None
Class	Mammalia	Mammalia	Eudicotyledones
Order	Carnivora	Primates	Fagales
Family	Felidae	Hominidae	Fagaceae
Genus	*Felis*	*Homo*	*Quercus*
Species	*Felis catus*	*Homo sapiens*	*Quercus alba*

© Cengage Learning

In the traditional system of classification, biologists classify organisms in a hierarchy of taxonomic categories from species to domain; each category is more general and more inclusive than the one below it.

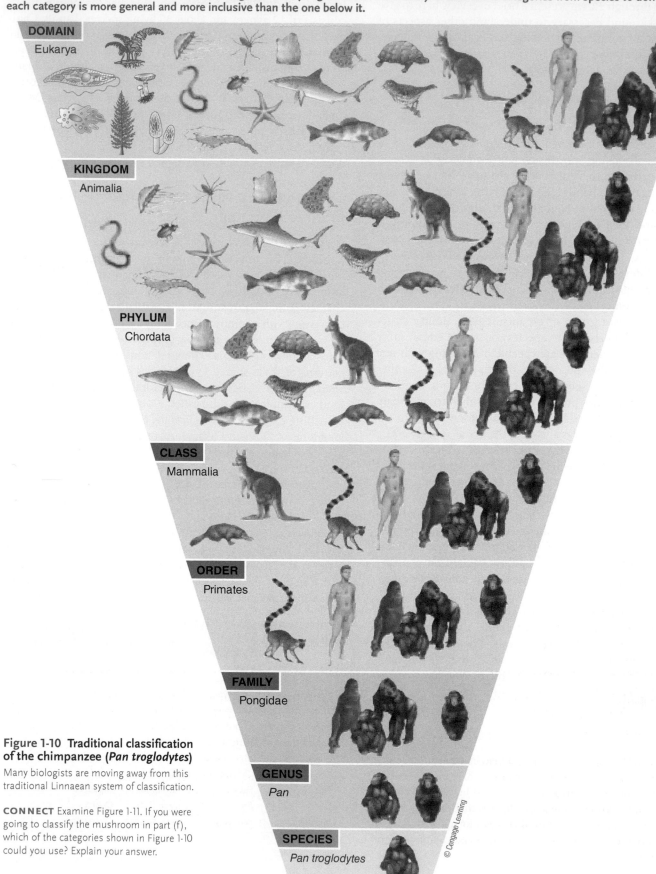

DOMAIN
Eukarya

KINGDOM
Animalia

PHYLUM
Chordata

CLASS
Mammalia

ORDER
Primates

FAMILY
Pongidae

GENUS
Pan

SPECIES
Pan troglodytes

© Cengage Learning

Figure 1-10 Traditional classification of the chimpanzee (*Pan troglodytes*)

Many biologists are moving away from this traditional Linnaean system of classification.

CONNECT Examine Figure 1-11. If you were going to classify the mushroom in part (f), which of the categories shown in Figure 1-10 could you use? Explain your answer.

This cladogram illustrates the evolutionary relationships among the three domains and among major groups of organisms that belong to these domains.

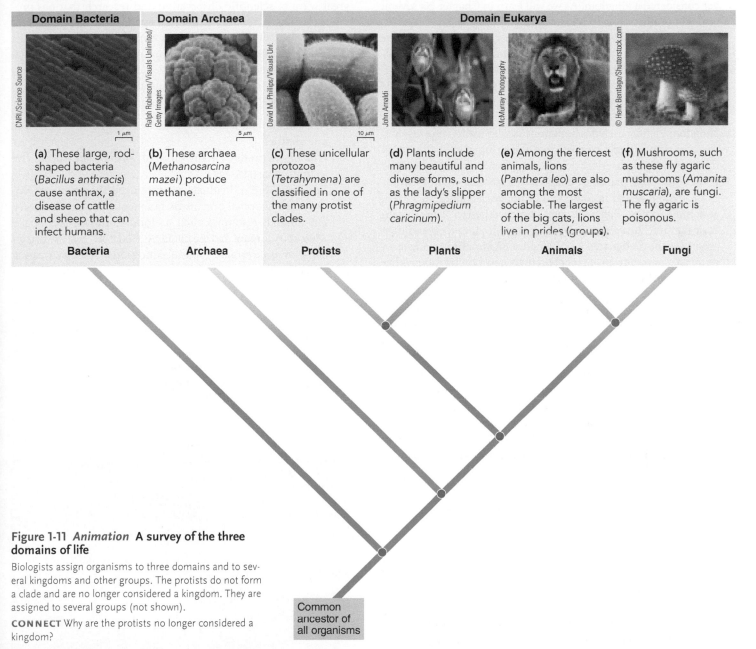

Domain Bacteria	Domain Archaea	Domain Eukarya			

(a) These large, rod-shaped bacteria (*Bacillus anthracis*) cause anthrax, a disease of cattle and sheep that can infect humans.

(b) These archaea (*Methanosarcina mazei*) produce methane.

(c) These unicellular protozoa (*Tetrahymena*) are classified in one of the many protist clades.

(d) Plants include many beautiful and diverse forms, such as the lady's slipper (*Phragmipedium caricinum*).

(e) Among the fiercest animals, lions (*Panthera leo*) are also among the most sociable. The largest of the big cats, lions live in prides (groups).

(f) Mushrooms, such as these fly agaric mushrooms (*Amanita muscaria*), are fungi. The fly agaric is poisonous.

Bacteria | Archaea | Protists | Plants | Animals | Fungi

Common ancestor of all organisms

Figure 1-11 *Animation* A survey of the three domains of life

Biologists assign organisms to three domains and to several kingdoms and other groups. The protists do not form a clade and are no longer considered a kingdom. They are assigned to several groups (not shown).

CONNECT Why are the protists no longer considered a kingdom?

in various organisms, Woese hypothesized that the molecular composition of rRNA in closely related organisms would be more similar than in distantly related organisms.

Bacteria have long been recognized as unicellular prokaryotic cells; they are referred to as **prokaryotes.** Woese's findings showed that there are two distinct groups of prokaryotes. He established the domain level of taxonomy and assigned the prokaryotes to two domains: **Bacteria** and **Archaea** (ar´-key-ah). The **eukaryotes,** organisms with eukaryotic cells, are classified in domain **Eukarya.** Woese's work became widely accepted in the mid-1990s.

In the classification system used in this book, each organism is assigned to a domain and to a kingdom or "supergroup." Two kingdoms correspond to the prokaryotic domains: kingdom Archaea corresponds to domain Archaea, and kingdom Bacteria corresponds to domain Bacteria. The remaining kingdoms and groups are assigned to domain Eukarya.

Protists (e.g., algae, slime molds, amoebas, and ciliates) are unicellular, colonial, or simple multicellular organisms that have a eukaryotic cell organization. The word *protist*, from the Greek for "the very first," reflects the idea that protists were the first eukaryotes to evolve. Protists are primarily aquatic organisms with diverse body forms, types of reproduction, modes of nutrition, and lifestyles. Some protists are adapted to carry out photosynthesis. Based mainly on molecular data that have clarified many evolutionary relationships among eukaryotes, the protists are no longer considered a kingdom. As we will learn in Chapter 26, several clades of protists have been identified.

Members of kingdom **Plantae** are complex multicellular organisms adapted to carry out photosynthesis. Among characteristic plant features are the *cuticle* (a waxy covering over aerial parts that reduces water loss) and *stomata* (tiny openings in stems and leaves for gas exchange); many plants have multicellular *gametangia* (organs that protect developing reproductive cells). Kingdom Plantae includes both nonvascular plants (mosses) and vascular plants (ferns, conifers, and flowering plants), those that have tissues specialized for transporting materials throughout the plant body. Most plants are adapted to terrestrial environments.

Kingdom **Fungi** is composed of the yeasts, mildews, molds, and mushrooms. Fungi do not photosynthesize. They obtain their nutrients by secreting digestive enzymes into food and then absorbing the predigested food. Kingdom **Animalia** is made up of multicellular organisms that obtain their nutrition by eating other organisms. Most animals exhibit considerable cell and tissue specialization and body organization. These characters have evolved along with complex sense organs, nervous systems, and muscular systems. Most animals reproduce sexually; they have large, nonmotile (do not move from place to place) eggs and small sperm with flagella that propel them in their journey to find the egg.

We have provided an introduction here to the groups of organisms that make up the tree of life. We will refer to them throughout this book as we consider the many kinds of challenges organisms face and the various adaptations that have evolved in response to them. We discuss the diversity of life in more detail in Chapters 23 through 32, and we summarize classification in Appendix B.

Species adapt in response to changes in their environment

Every organism is the product of numerous interactions between environmental conditions and the genes inherited from its ancestors. If all individuals of a species were exactly alike, any change in the environment might be disastrous to all, and the species would become extinct. Adaptations to changes in the environment occur as a result of evolutionary processes that take place over time and involve many generations.

Natural selection is an important mechanism by which evolution proceeds

Although philosophers and naturalists discussed the concept of evolution for centuries, Charles Darwin and Alfred Wallace first brought a scientific theory of evolution to general attention and suggested a plausible mechanism, **natural selection,** to explain it. In his book *On the Origin of Species by Natural Selection*, published in 1859, Darwin synthesized many new findings in geology and biology. He presented a wealth of evidence supporting

his hypothesis that present forms of life descended, with modifications, from previously existing forms.

Darwin's scientific theory of evolution has helped shape the biological sciences to the present day. His work generated a great wave of scientific observation and research that has provided much additional evidence that evolution is responsible for the great diversity of organisms on our planet. Even today, the details of evolutionary processes are a major focus of investigation and discussion.

Darwin based his concept of natural selection on the following four observations:

1. Individual members of a species show some variation from one another.
2. Organisms produce many more offspring than will survive to reproduce (FIG. 1-12).
3. Because more individuals are produced than the environment can support, organisms must compete for necessary, but limited, resources such as food, sunlight, and space. Also, some organisms are killed by predators, disease organisms, or unfavorable natural conditions, such as weather changes. Which organisms are more likely to survive?
4. Individuals with characteristics that enable them to obtain and use resources, escape predators, resist disease organisms, and withstand changes in the environment are more likely to survive to reproductive maturity than those without these characteristics. The survivors that reproduce pass their adaptations for survival on to their offspring. Thus, the best-adapted individuals of a population produce, on average, more offspring than do other individuals. Because of this *differential reproduction*, a greater proportion of the population

Figure 1-12 Egg masses of the wood frog (*Rana sylvatica*)
Many more eggs are produced than can develop into adult frogs. Random events are largely responsible for determining which of these developing frogs will hatch, reach adulthood, and reproduce. However, certain traits of each organism also contribute to the probability for success in its environment. Not all organisms are as prolific as the frog, but the generalization that more organisms are produced than survive is true throughout the living world.

Jack Jeffrey, Inc.

Sami Sarkis/Photographer's Choice/Getty Images

© Danita Delimont/Alamy

(a) The bill of this 'Akiapola'au male (*Hemignathus munroi*) is adapted for extracting insect larvae from bark. The lower mandible (jaw) is used to peck at and pull off bark, whereas the maxilla (upper jaw) and tongue remove the prey.

(b) 'I'iwi (*Vestiaria cocciniea*) in 'ohi'a blossoms. The bill is adapted for feeding on nectar in tubular flowers.

(c) Palila (*Loxiodes bailleui*) in mamane tree. This finch-billed honeycreeper feeds on immature seeds in pods of the mamane tree. It also eats insects, berries, and young leaves.

Figure 1-13 Adaptation and diversification in Hawaiian honeycreepers
All three species shown here are endangered, mainly because their habitats have been destroyed by humans or species introduced by humans.

becomes adapted to the prevailing environmental conditions and challenges. The environment *selects* the best-adapted organisms for survival. Note that *adaptation involves changes in populations rather than in individual organisms.*

Darwin did not know about DNA or understand the mechanisms of inheritance. Scientists now understand that most variations among individuals are a result of different varieties of genes that code for each characteristic. The ultimate source of these variations is random **mutations,** chemical or physical changes in DNA that persist and can be inherited. *Mutations modify genes and by this process provide the raw material for evolution.*

Populations evolve as a result of selective pressures from changes in their environment

All the genes present in a population make up its **gene pool**. By virtue of its gene pool, a population is a reservoir of variation. Natural selection acts on individuals within a population. Selection favors individuals with genes specifying traits that allow them to respond effectively to pressures exerted by the environment. These organisms are most likely to survive and produce offspring. As successful organisms pass on their genetic recipe for survival, their traits become more widely distributed in the population. Over time, as populations continue to change (and as the environment itself changes, bringing different selective pressures), the members of the population become better adapted to their environment and less like their ancestors.

As a population adapts to environmental pressures and exploits new opportunities for finding food, maintaining safety, and avoiding predators, the population diversifies and new species may evolve. The Hawaiian honeycreepers, a group of related birds, are a good example. When honeycreeper ancestors first reached Hawaii, few other birds were present, so there was little competition. Genetic variation among honeycreepers allowed some to move into different food zones, and over time, species with various types of bills evolved (FIG. 1-13; see also Chapter 20 and Fig. 20-18). Some honeycreepers now have long, curved

bills, adapted for feeding on nectar from tubular flowers. Others have short, thick bills for foraging for insects, and still others have adapted for eating seeds.

CHECKPOINT 1.6

- *The scientific name for the African rock python is* Python sebae. *Which name indicates its genus?*
- PREDICT *Why might biologists modify the tree showing the major forms of life?*
- CONNECT *How might you explain the sharp claws and teeth of tigers in terms of natural selection?*

1.7 THE PROCESS OF SCIENCE

LEARNING OBJECTIVES

10 Design a study to test a given hypothesis, using the procedure and terminology of the scientific method.
11 Compare the reductionist and systems approaches to biological research.

Biology is a science. The word *science* comes from a Latin word meaning "to know." Science is a way of thinking and a method of investigating the natural world in a systematic manner. We test ideas, and based on our findings, we modify or reject these ideas. The *process of science* is investigative, dynamic, and often controversial. The observations made, the range of questions asked, and the design of experiments depend on the creativity of the individual scientist. Science is influenced by cultural, social, historical, and technological contexts.

The **scientific method** involves a series of ordered steps. Using the scientific method, scientists make careful observations, ask critical questions, and develop *hypotheses*, which are tentative explanations. Using their hypotheses, scientists make predictions that can be tested by making further observations or by performing experiments. They gather *data,* information that they can analyze, often using computers and sophisticated statistical methods. They interpret the results of their experiments and draw conclusions from them. As we will discuss, scientists develop many hypotheses that cannot be tested by using all of the steps of the scientific method in a rigid way. Scientists use the scientific method as a generalized framework or guide.

Biologists explore every imaginable aspect of life from the structure of viruses and bacteria to the interactions of the communities of our biosphere. Some biologists work mainly in laboratories, and others do their work in the field (FIG. 1-14). Perhaps you will decide to become a research biologist and help unravel the complexities of the human brain, discover new hormones that stimulate plants to flower, identify new species of animals or bacteria, or develop new stem cell strategies to treat cancer, AIDS, or heart disease. Applications of basic biological research have provided the technology to transplant kidneys, livers, and hearts; manipulate genes; treat many diseases; and increase world food production. Biology has been a powerful force in providing the quality of life that most of us enjoy. You may choose to enter an applied field of biology, such as environmental science, dentistry, medicine, pharmacology, or veterinary medicine.

Science requires systematic thought processes

Science is systematic. Scientists organize and often quantify knowledge, making it readily accessible to all who wish to build on its foundation. In this way, science is both a personal and a social endeavor. Science is not mysterious. Anyone who understands its rules and procedures can take on its challenges. What distinguishes science is its insistence on rigorous methods to examine a problem. Science seeks to give precise knowledge about the natural world; the supernatural is not accessible to

Figure 1-14 Biologist at work
This biologist studying the rainforest canopy in Costa Rica is part of an international effort to study and preserve tropical rain forests. Researchers study the interactions of organisms and the effects of human activities on the rain forests.

scientific methods of inquiry. Science is not a replacement for philosophy, religion, or art. Being a scientist does not prevent one from participating in other fields of human endeavor, just as being an artist does not prevent one from practicing science.

Deductive reasoning begins with general principles
Scientists use two types of systematic thought processes: deduction and induction. With **deductive reasoning**, we begin with supplied information, called *premises*, and draw conclusions on the basis of that information. Deduction proceeds from general principles to specific conclusions. For example, if you accept the premise that all birds have wings and the second premise that sparrows are birds, you can conclude deductively that sparrows have wings. Deduction helps us discover relationships among known facts. A *fact* is information or knowledge based on evidence.

Inductive reasoning begins with specific observations
Inductive reasoning is the opposite of deduction. We begin with specific observations and draw a conclusion or discover a general principle. For example, you know that sparrows have wings, can fly, and are birds. You also know that robins, eagles, pigeons, and hawks have wings, can fly, and are birds. Considering these facts, you might *induce* that all birds have wings and fly. In this way, you can use the inductive method to organize raw data into manageable categories by answering this question: What do all these facts have in common?

A weakness of inductive reasoning is that conclusions generalize the facts to all possible examples. When we formulate the general principle, we go from many observed examples to all possible examples. This is known as an *inductive leap*. Without it, we could not arrive at generalizations. However, we must be sensitive to exceptions and to the possibility that the conclusion is not valid. For example, the kiwi bird of New Zealand does *not* have functional wings (FIG. 1-15). We can never conclusively prove a universal generalization. The generalizations in inductive conclusions come from the creative insight of the human mind, and creativity, however admirable, is not infallible.

Scientists make careful observations and ask critical questions

In 1928, British biologist Alexander Fleming observed that a blue mold had invaded one of his bacterial cultures. He almost discarded it, but then he noticed that the area contaminated by the mold was surrounded by a zone where bacterial colonies did not grow well. The bacteria were disease organisms of the genus *Staphylococcus*, which can cause boils and skin infections. Anything that could kill them was interesting! Fleming saved the mold, a variety of *Penicillium* (blue bread mold), and isolated the antibiotic penicillin from it. However, he had difficulty culturing it.

Even though Fleming recognized the potential practical benefit of penicillin, he did not develop the chemical techniques needed to purify it, and more than ten years passed before the drug was put to significant use. In 1939, Sir Howard Florey and Ernst Boris Chain developed chemical procedures to extract and produce the active agent penicillin from the mold. Florey took

Figure 1-15 Is this animal a bird?
The kiwi bird of New Zealand is about the size of a chicken. Its tiny 2-inch wings cannot be used for flight. The survivor of an ancient order of birds, the kiwi has bristly, hairlike feathers and other characteristics that qualify it as a bird.

the process to laboratories in the United States, and penicillin was first produced to treat wounded soldiers in World War II. In recognition of their work, Fleming, Florey, and Chain shared the 1945 Nobel Prize in Physiology or Medicine.

Chance often plays a role in scientific discovery

Fleming did not set out to discover penicillin. He benefited from the chance growth of a mold in one of his culture dishes. However, we may wonder how many times the same type of mold grew on the cultures of other biologists who failed to make the connection and simply threw away their contaminated cultures. Fleming benefited from chance, but his mind was prepared to make observations and formulate critical questions, and his pen was prepared to publish them. Significant discoveries are usually made by those who are in the habit of looking critically at nature and recognizing a phenomenon or problem. Of course, the technology necessary for investigating the problem must also be available.

A hypothesis is a testable statement

Scientists make careful observations, ask critical questions, and develop hypotheses. A **hypothesis** is a tentative explanation for observations or phenomena. A hypothesis is an abstract idea, but based on their hypotheses, scientists can make predictions that can be tested. For example, we might predict that biology students who study for ten hours will do better on an exam than students who study for one hour. As used here, a *prediction* is a deductive, logical consequence of a hypothesis. It does not have to be a future event. Hypotheses are typically stated in the form of predictions.

In the early stages of an investigation, a scientist typically thinks of many possible hypotheses. A good hypothesis exhibits the following characteristics. (1) It is reasonably consistent with well-established facts. (2) It generates predictions that can be tested (whether the results are positive or negative). (3) Test results should be repeatable by independent observers. (4) It is

falsifiable, which means that it can be proven false, as we will discuss in the next section.

After generating hypotheses, the scientist decides which, if any, could and should be subjected to experimental test. Why not test them all? Time and money are important considerations in conducting research. Scientists must establish priority among the hypotheses to decide which to test first.

A falsifiable hypothesis can be tested In science, a well-stated hypothesis can be tested. If no evidence is found to support it, the hypothesis is rejected. The hypothesis can be shown to be false. Even results that do not support the hypothesis may be valuable and may lead to new hypotheses. If the results do support a hypothesis, a scientist may use them to generate related hypotheses.

A hypothesis is not true just because some of its predictions (the ones people happen to have thought of or have thus far been able to test) have been shown to be true. After all, they could be true by coincidence. In fact, a hypothesis can be supported by data, but it cannot really be *proven* true.

An **unfalsifiable hypothesis** cannot be proven false; in fact, it cannot be scientifically investigated. Belief in an unfalsifiable hypothesis, such as the existence of invisible and undetectable elves, must be rationalized on grounds other than scientific ones.

Models are important in developing and testing hypotheses Hypotheses have many potential sources, including direct observations or even computer simulations. Increasingly in biology, hypotheses may be derived from *models* that scientists have developed to provide a comprehensive explanation for a large number of observations. Examples of such testable models include the model of the structure of DNA and the model of the structure of the plasma membrane (discussed in Chapter 5).

The best design for an experiment can sometimes be established by performing computer simulations. Virtual testing and evaluation are undertaken before the experiment is performed in the laboratory or field. Modeling and computer simulation save time and money.

Many hypotheses can be tested by experiment Many hypotheses can be tested by controlled experiments. Early biologists observed that the nucleus was the most prominent part of the cell, and they hypothesized that cells would be adversely affected if they lost their nuclei. Biologists predicted that if the nucleus were removed from the cell, the cell would die. They then experimented by surgically removing the nucleus of a unicellular amoeba. The amoeba continued to live and move, but it did not grow, and after a few days it died. These results suggested that the nucleus is necessary for the metabolic processes that provide for growth and cell reproduction.

But, the investigators asked, what if the operation itself, not the loss of the nucleus, caused the amoeba to die? They performed a controlled experiment, subjecting two groups of amoebas to the same operative trauma (**FIG. 1-16**). Ideally, an experimental group differs from a control group only with respect to the variable being studied. In the **control group,** the researcher inserted a microloop into each amoeba and pushed it around inside the cell to simulate removal of the nucleus; then the instrument was withdrawn, leaving the nucleus inside. In the **experimental group,** the nucleus was removed; in the control group, it was not.

Amoebas treated with such a sham operation recovered and subsequently grew and divided. This experiment showed that the removal of the nucleus, not simply the operation, caused the death of the amoebas. The conclusion is that amoebas cannot live without their nuclei. The results supported the hypothesis that if cells lose their nuclei, they are adversely affected. We can conclude that the nucleus is essential for the survival of the amoeba.

Researchers must avoid bias

In scientific studies, researchers must do their best to avoid bias or preconceived notions of what should happen. For example, to prevent bias, most medical experiments are carried out in a double-blind fashion. When a drug is tested, one group of patients receives the new medication, and a control group of matched patients receives a placebo (a harmless starch pill similar in size, shape, color, and taste to the pill being tested). This method is called a *double-blind study* because neither the patient nor the physician knows who is getting the experimental drug and who is getting the placebo. The pills or treatments are coded in some way, and the code is broken only after the experiment is over and the results are recorded. Not all experiments can be so neatly designed; for example, it is often difficult to establish appropriate controls.

Scientists interpret the results of experiments and make conclusions

Scientists gather data in an experiment, interpret their results, and then draw conclusions from them. In the amoeba experiment described earlier, investigators concluded that the data supported the hypothesis that the nucleus is essential for the survival of the cell. When the results do support a hypothesis, scientists may use them to generate related hypotheses. Even results that do not support the hypothesis may be valuable and may lead to new hypotheses.

Let us discuss another experiment. Research teams studying chimpanzee populations in Africa have reported that

chimpanzees appear to learn specific ways to use tools from one another. Behavior that is learned from others in a population and passed to future generations is what we call "culture." In the past, most biologists have thought that only humans had culture. It has been difficult to test this type of learning in the field, and the idea has been controversial.

Biologists have asked critical questions about whether chimpanzees learned how to use tools by observing one another. Investigators at Yerkes National Primate Research Center in Atlanta developed a hypothesis that chimpanzees can learn particular ways to use tools by observing other chimps. They

---

KEY EXPERIMENT

Is the nucleus essential for the well being of the cell?

DEVELOP HYPOTHESIS: Cells will be adversely affected if they lose their nuclei.

PERFORM EXPERIMENTS: Using a microloop, researchers removed the nucleus from each amoeba in the experimental group. Amoebas in the control group were subjected to the same surgical procedure, but their nuclei were not removed.

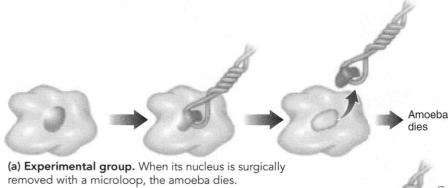

(a) Experimental group. When its nucleus is surgically removed with a microloop, the amoeba dies.

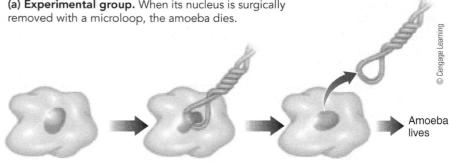

(b) Control group. A control amoeba subjected to similar surgical procedures (including insertion of a microloop), but without actual removal of the nucleus, does not die.

RESULTS: Amoebas without nuclei died. Amoebas in the control group lived.

CONCLUSION: Amoebas cannot live without their nuclei. The hypothesis is supported.

Figure 1-16 An experiment testing the importance of the nucleus

Scientists observed that the nucleus was the most prominent part of the cell. They asked critical questions about their observation and developed the hypothesis that cells would be adversely affected if they lost their nuclei. Based on their hypothesis, investigators performed experiments on amoebas. Their results supported the hypothesis.

PREDICT Could a cell without a nucleus survive if a nucleus of a different species is placed into the cell?

SOURCE: Classic enucleation studies are discussed in Brachet, J. (1961) Nucleocytoplasmic interactions in unicellular organisms. In *The Cell*, Vol. 2, (ed. J. Brachet and A.E. Mirksky), pp. 771–841. New York and London: Academic Press.

Can chimpanzees learn how to use tools by observing one another?

DEVELOP HYPOTHESIS: Chimpanzees can learn particular ways to use tools by observing other chimps.

PERFORM EXPERIMENTS: One female in each of two groups of 16 chimps was educated in a specific way to use a stick to obtain food. The two educated chimps were then returned to their respective groups. Chimpanzees in a control group were not taught how to use a stick.

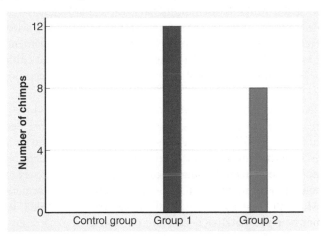

(a) Number of chimpanzees who successfully employed specific method of tool use.

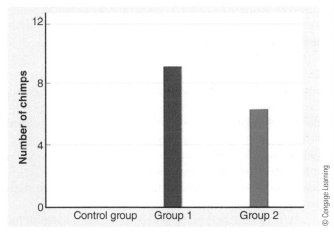

(b) Number of chimpanzees who successfully employed learned method of tool use two months later.

RESULTS: Chimpanzees in each experimental group observed the use of the stick by the educated chimp, and a majority began to use the stick in the same way. When tested two months later, many of the chimps in each group continued to use the stick. *The results presented here have been simplified and are based on the number of chimps observed to use the learned method at least ten times.* All but one chimp in each group learned the technology, but a few used it only a few times. Some chimps taught themselves the alternative method and used that alternative. However, most conformed to the group's use of the method that the investigator taught to the educated chimp.

CONCLUSION: Chimpanzees learn specific ways to use tools by observing other chimps. The hypothesis was supported.

SOURCE: Whiten, A., Horner, V., and de Waal, F.B.M. "Conformity to Cultural Norms of Tool Use in Chimpanzees," *Nature*, Vol. 437, Sept. 29, 2005.

Figure 1-17 An experiment testing learning in chimpanzee populations

In the photo, wild chimpanzees are shown observing a member of their group using a tool.

PREDICT If you repeated this experiment, how do you think your results would compare with those shown here?

predicted that if they taught one chimp to use a stick to obtain food from a dispenser, other chimps would learn the technique from the educated one (**FIG. 1-17**).

These researchers divided chimpanzees into two experimental groups with 16 in each group. Then they taught a high-ranking female in each group to use a stick to obtain food from an apparatus. The two chimps were taught different methods.

One chimp was taught to poke the stick inside the device to free the food. The other was taught to use the stick to lift a hook that removed a blockage, allowing the food to roll forward out of the device.

A third group served as a control group. The chimps in the control group were given access to the sticks and the apparatus with the food inside, but none were taught how to use the sticks.

All the control-group chimps manipulated the apparatus with the stick, but none succeeded in releasing food.

When the chimps were returned to their groups, other chimps observed how the educated chimps used the stick, and a large majority began to use sticks in the same way. The chimps in each experimental group (Group 1 and Group 2 in Fig. 1-17) learned the specific style of using the stick that their educated chimp had been taught. Most used the stick to obtain food at least ten times. Two months later, the apparatus was reintroduced to the chimps. Again, most of the chimps used the learned technique for obtaining food. The results of the experiment supported the hypothesis. The researchers concluded that chimpanzees are capable of culturally transmitting learned technology.

Sampling error can lead to inaccurate conclusions One reason for inaccurate conclusions is *sampling error*. Because not *all* cases of what is being studied can be observed or tested (scientists cannot study every amoeba or every chimpanzee population), scientists must be content with a sample. How can scientists know whether that sample is truly representative of whatever they are studying? If the sample is too small, it may not be representative because of random factors. A study with only two, or even nine, amoebas may not yield reliable data that can be generalized to other amoebas. If researchers test a large number of subjects, they are more likely to draw accurate scientific conclusions (**FIG. 1-18**). The scientist seeks to state with some level of confidence that any specific conclusion has a certain statistical probability of being correct.

Experiments must be repeatable After scientists conduct research and draw conclusions, they share their studies and conclusions with other scientists and with the public. Typically, they do this by sharing their work at conferences and by submitting articles describing their research to the editors of scientific journals. Reputable journals have a peer review process during which other scientists review and evaluate the study. If the article and the research described meet the criteria for a research study, the article is accepted for publication.

When researchers publish their findings in a scientific journal, they typically describe their methods and procedures in sufficient detail so that other scientists can repeat the experiments. When the findings are replicated, the conclusions are, of course, strengthened.

A scientific theory is supported by tested hypotheses

Nonscientists often use the word *theory* incorrectly to refer to a hypothesis or even to some untestable idea they wish to promote. A **scientific theory** is actually an integrated explanation of some aspect of the natural world that is based on a number of hypotheses, each supported by consistent results from many observations or experiments. A scientific theory relates data that previously appeared unrelated. A good scientific theory grows, building on additional facts as they become known. It predicts new facts and suggests new relationships among phenomena. It may even suggest practical applications.

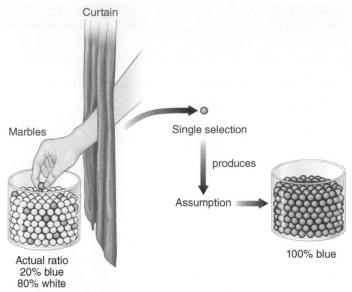

(a) Taking a single selection can result in sampling error. If the only marble selected is blue, we might assume all the marbles are blue.

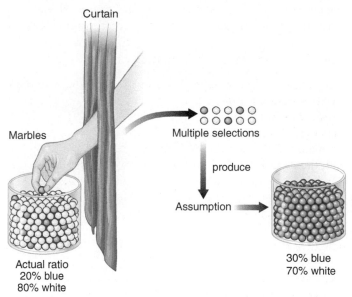

(b) The greater the number of selections we take of an unknown, the more likely we can make valid assumptions about it.

Figure 1-18 *Animation* **Statistical probability**
© Cengage Learning

A scientific theory, by showing the relationships among classes of facts, simplifies and clarifies our understanding of the natural world. As Albert Einstein wrote, "In the whole history of science from Greek philosophy to modern physics, there have been constant attempts to reduce the apparent complexity of natural phenomena to simple, fundamental ideas and relations." Developing scientific theories is indeed a major goal of science.

Many hypotheses cannot be tested by direct experiment

Some well-accepted scientific theories do not lend themselves to hypothesis testing by ordinary experiments. Often, these scientific theories describe events that occurred in the distant past. We cannot directly observe the origin of the universe from a very hot, dense state about 13.7 billion years ago (the Big Bang theory). However, physicists and cosmologists have been able to formulate many hypotheses related to the Big Bang and to test many of the predictions derived from these hypotheses.

Similarly, humans did not observe the evolution of major groups of organisms because that process took place over millions of years and occurred before humans had evolved. However, many hypotheses about evolution have been posed, and predictions based on them have been tested. For example, if complex organisms evolved from simple life-forms, we would find the fossils of the simplest organisms in the oldest strata (rock layers). As we explore more recent strata, we would expect to find increasingly complex organisms. Indeed, scientists have found this progression of simple to complex fossils.

In addition to fossils, evidence for evolution comes from many sources, including physical and molecular similarities between organisms. Evidence also comes from recent and current studies of evolution in action. Many aspects of ongoing evolution can, in fact, be studied in the laboratory or in the field. The evidence for evolution is so compelling that virtually all scientists today accept evolutionary theory as an integral part of biology.

Paradigm shifts accommodate new discoveries

A *paradigm* is a set of assumptions or concepts that constitute a way of thinking about reality. For example, from the time of Aristotle to the mid-19th century, biologists thought that organisms were either plants (kingdom Plantae) or animals (kingdom Animalia). This concept was deeply entrenched. However, with the development of microscopes, investigators discovered tiny life-forms—bacteria and protists—that were neither plant nor animal. Biologists had to make a *paradigm shift*—that is, they changed their view of reality—to accommodate this new knowledge. They assigned these newly discovered organisms to new kingdoms. In a more recent paradigm shift, biologists have revised their idea that we are born with all the brain cells we will ever have. We now understand that certain areas of the brain continue to produce new neurons throughout life.

Systems biology integrates different levels of information

In the *reductionist* approach to biology, researchers study the simplest components of biological processes. Their goal is to synthesize their knowledge of many small parts to understand the whole. Reductionism has been (and continues to be) important in biological research. However, as biologists and their tools have become increasingly sophisticated, huge amounts of data have been generated, bringing the science of biology to a different level.

Systems biology is a field of biology that builds on information provided by the reductionist approach and develops large data sets, typically analyzed by computers. Systems biology is also referred to as *integrative biology*. Reductionism and systems biology are complementary approaches. Using reductionism, biologists have discovered basic information about components, such as molecules, genes, cells, and organs. Systems biologists, who focus on systems as a whole rather than on individual components, need this basic knowledge to study, for example, the *interactions* among various parts and levels of an organism.

Systems biologists integrate data from various levels of complexity with the goal of understanding the big picture—how biological systems function. For example, systems biologists are developing models of different aspects of cell function. Normal cell function depends on the precise actions of hundreds of proteins that relay signals received from other cells. Proteins also relay signals from one part of the cell to another. Researchers are producing detailed maps of the molecular pathways that maintain cell function (FIG. 1-19).

One group of researchers has developed a model consisting of nearly 8000 chemical signals involved in a molecular network that leads to programmed cell death. By understanding cell communication, the interactions of genes and proteins in metabolic pathways, and physiological processes, systems biologists hope to eventually develop a model of the whole organism. Systems biology is increasingly used to study disease processes. For example, the interactions between the pathogen and the host cell can be mapped.

The development of systems biology was fueled by the huge amount of data generated by the Human Genome Project. Researchers working on this and related projects have identified the DNA sequences that make up the *human genome*, the complete set of human genetic material. Computer software developed for the Human Genome Project can analyze very

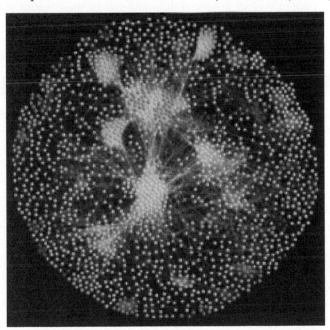

Figure 1-19 Map illustrating interactions among thousands of proteins in a cell of the fruit fly (*Drosophila melanogaster*)

Researchers gain insight into the cell as an integrated system by studying the interaction of its proteins. Because humans and many other animals share a common ancestor with fruit flies, similar cellular mechanisms operate in all of them. Understanding protein interactions and functions helps scientists understand cellular changes in health and disease. Each dot represents one protein.

Source: Guruharsha , KG, et al., 2011 Cell, Elsevier Limited; Image provided by Dr. Guruharsha, Artavanis-Tsakonas group, Harvard Medical School. Cell. 2011 Oct 28; 147(3):690–703.

large data sets. These programs are being used to integrate data about protein interactions and many other aspects of molecular biology. Systems biologists view biology in terms of information systems. Increasingly, they depend on mathematics, statistics, and engineering principles.

Science has ethical dimensions

Scientific investigation depends on a commitment to practical ideals, such as truthfulness and the obligation to communicate results. Honesty is particularly important in science. Consider the great (although temporary) damage done whenever an unprincipled or even desperate researcher, whose career may depend on the publication of a research study, knowingly disseminates false data. Until the deception is uncovered, other researchers may devote thousands of dollars and hours of precious professional labor to futile lines of research inspired by erroneous reports. Deception can also be dangerous, especially in medical research. Fortunately, science tends to correct itself through consistent use of the scientific process. Sooner or later, someone's experimental results are sure to cast doubt on false data.

Research in such areas as stem cells and the human genome brings with it many ethical concerns and responsibilities. For example, how do people safeguard the privacy of genetic information? Suppose that you have a family history of breast cancer and learn from genetic testing that you have one of the BRCA mutations. These mutations increase risk for developing breast cancer and certain other cancers. How can you be certain that knowledge of your individual genetic code would not be used against you when you seek employment or by insurance companies?

Scientists must be ethically responsible and must help educate people about their work, including its benefits relative to its risks. It is significant that at the very beginning of the Human Genome Project, part of its budget was allocated for research on the ethical, legal, and social implications of its findings.

Science, technology, and society interact

Science and technology continuously interact. As scientists doing basic research report new findings, engineers and other inventors develop new products. Many of those products contribute to our quality of life. New technology also provides scientists with more powerful tools for their research and increases the potential for new discoveries. For example, a few years ago determining the genome of any eukaryote required several rooms filled with machines that could sequence the genes. This endeavor also cost millions of dollars. New technologies have revolutionized gene sequencing, allowing complex genomes to be determined quickly, with less equipment, and at far less expense. Plans are under way to determine the genomes of about 10,000 vertebrate species.

Science and technology continue to change society, and these changes present new challenges. In addition to being ethical about their own work, scientists face many societal and political issues surrounding areas such as genetic research, stem cell research, cloning, climate change, and human and animal experimentation. Scientists, and the larger society, will need to determine whether the potential benefits of any research outweigh its ethical risks.

CHECKPOINT 1.7

- *What are the characteristics of a good hypothesis?*
- *Describe a "controlled" experiment.*
- **CONNECT** *In what ways does systems biology depend on reductionism?*

SUMMARY: FOCUS ON LEARNING OBJECTIVES

1.1 Major Themes of Biology *(page 2)*

1 Describe five basic themes of biology.
- (1) Every organism is a biological system made up of many other biological systems, and every organism is interdependent with many other biological systems. (2) Structure and function are inter-related in all biological systems. (3) Information must be transferred within organisms and among organisms, and organisms must be able to receive information from the nonliving environment. (4) All life processes require a continuous input of energy. (5) Evolution results in populations changing over time.

1.2 Characteristics of Life *(page 3)*

2 Distinguish between living and nonliving things by describing the features that characterize living organisms.
- Every living organism is composed of one or more **cells.** Living things grow by increasing the size and/or number of their cells.
- **Metabolism** includes all the chemical activities that take place in the organism, including the chemical reactions essential to nutrition, growth and repair, and conversion of energy to usable forms. **Homeostasis** refers to the appropriate, balanced internal environment, and the organized tendency of the organism to maintain such a steady state.

- Organisms respond to **stimuli,** physical or chemical changes in their external or internal environment. Responses typically involve movement.
- In **asexual reproduction,** offspring are typically identical to the single parent, except for size. In most plants and animals **sexual reproduction** involves the fusion of an egg and sperm. Genes are typically contributed by two parents, and there is variation in the offspring.
- As populations evolve, they become adapted to their environment. **Adaptations** are traits that increase an organism's ability to survive in its environment.

1.3 Levels of Biological Organization *(page 6)*

3 Construct a hierarchy of biological organization, including levels characteristic of individual organisms and levels characteristic of ecological systems.
- Biological organization is hierarchical. In a complex organism, cells associate to form **tissues** (e.g., muscle and connective tissues) that carry out specific functions. In most multicellular organisms tissues organize to form functional structures called **organs** (e.g., heart or brain). An organized group of tissues and organs form an **organ system** (e.g., the nervous system). Functioning together, organ systems make up a complex, multicellular **organism.**

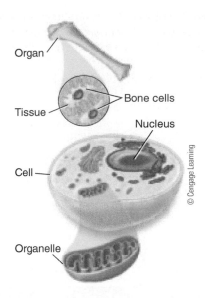

- The basic unit of ecological organization is the **population.** Various populations form **communities,** a community and its physical environment are an **ecosystem,** and all Earth's ecosystems together make up the **biosphere.**

1.4 Information Transfer *(page 8)*

4 Summarize the importance of information transfer within and between living systems, giving specific examples.

- Organisms transmit information chemically, electrically, and behaviorally.
- DNA, which makes up the **genes,** is the hereditary material. Information encoded in DNA is transmitted from one generation to the next. DNA contains the instructions for the development of an organism and for carrying out life processes. Among its many functions, DNA codes for **proteins,** which are important in determining the structure and function of cells and tissues.
- **Hormones,** chemical messengers that transmit messages from one part of an organism to another, are important in **cell signaling.**
- Many organisms use electrical signals to transmit information; most animals have nervous systems that transmit electrical impulses and release **neurotransmitters.**

1.5 The Energy of Life *(page 9)*

5 Summarize the flow of energy through ecosystems and contrast the roles of producers, consumers, and decomposers.

- Activities of living cells require energy. Life depends on continuous energy input from the sun. During **photosynthesis,** plants, algae, and certain bacteria use the energy of sunlight to synthesize complex molecules from carbon dioxide and water.
- Virtually all cells carry on **cellular respiration,** a biochemical process in which they capture the energy stored in nutrients by producers. Some of that energy is then used to synthesize required materials or to carry out other cell activities.
- A self-sufficient ecosystem includes **producers,** or **autotrophs,** which make their own food; **primary consumers,** which eat producers, and typically **secondary consumers** that eat primary consumers; and **decomposers,** which obtain energy by breaking down wastes and dead organisms. Consumers and decomposers are **heterotrophs,** organisms that depend on producers as an energy source and for food and oxygen.

1.6 Evolution: The Basic Unifying Concept of Biology *(page 10)*

6 Demonstrate the binomial system of nomenclature by using specific examples and classify an organism (such as a human) in its domain, kingdom, phylum, class, order, family, genus, and species.

- Millions of species have evolved. A **species** is a group of organisms with similar structure, function, and behavior that, in nature, breed only with one another. Members of a species contribute to a common **gene pool** and share a common ancestry.
- Biologists use a **binomial system of nomenclature** in which the name of each species includes a **genus** name and a **specific epithet.** Traditional taxonomic classification is hierarchical; it includes species, genus, **family, order, class, phylum, kingdom,** and **domain.** Each grouping is referred to as a **taxon.** A group of organisms with a common ancestor is a **clade.**

7 Identify the three domains and the kingdoms of living organisms, and give examples of organisms assigned to each group.

- Bacteria and archaea are **prokaryotes;** all other organisms are **eukaryotes.** Prokaryotes make up two of the three domains.
- Organisms are classified in three domains: **Archaea, Bacteria,** and **Eukarya** and several kingdoms or clades: **Archaea, Bacteria, Fungi** (e.g., molds and yeasts), **Plantae,** and **Animalia. Protists** (e.g., algae, water molds, slime molds, and amoebas) are now assigned to several clades.

8 Give a brief overview of the scientific theory of evolution and explain why it is the principal unifying concept in biology.

- **Evolution** is the process by which populations change over time in response to changes in the environment. The scientific theory of evolution explains how millions of species came to be and helps us understand the structure, function, behavior, and relationships of organisms.
- **Natural selection,** the major mechanism by which evolution proceeds, favors individuals with traits that enable them to cope with environmental changes. Charles Darwin based his theory of natural selection on his observations that individuals of a species vary, organisms produce more offspring than survive to reproduce, organisms must compete for limited resources, and individuals that are best adapted to their environment are more likely to survive and reproduce, thereby passing on their hereditary information. Their traits become more widely distributed in the population.
- The source of variation in a population is random **mutation.**

9 Apply the concept of natural selection to any given adaptation and suggest a logical explanation of how the adaptation may have evolved.

- When the ancestors of Hawaiian honeycreepers first reached Hawaii, few other birds were present, so there was little competition for food. Through many generations, honeycreepers with longer, more curved bills became adapted for feeding on nectar from tubular flowers. Perhaps those with the longest, most curved bills were best able to survive in this food zone and lived to transmit their genes to their offspring. Those with shorter, thicker bills were more successful foraging for insects and passed their genes to new generations of offspring. Eventually, different species evolved that were adapted to specific food zones.

1.7 The Process of Science *(page 15)*

10 Design a study to test a given hypothesis, using the procedure and terminology of the scientific method.

- The *process of science* is a dynamic approach to investigation. The **scientific method** is a general framework that scientists use in their work; it includes observing, recognizing a problem or stating a critical question, developing a hypothesis, making a prediction that can be tested, making further observations, performing experiments, interpreting results, and drawing conclusions that support or falsify the hypothesis.

- Deductive reasoning and inductive reasoning are two categories of systematic thought used in the scientific method. **Deductive reasoning** proceeds from general principles to specific conclusions and helps us discover relationships among known facts. **Inductive reasoning** begins with specific observations and draws conclusions from them. Inductive reasoning helps us discover general principles.

- A **hypothesis** is a tentative explanation for observations or phenomena. A hypothesis can be tested. If no evidence is found to support it, the hypothesis is rejected.

- A well-designed scientific experiment typically includes both a **control group** and an **experimental group,** and must be as free as possible from bias. The control group should be as closely matched to the experimental group as possible. Ideally, the experimental group differs from the control group only with respect to the variable being studied.

- A **scientific theory** is an integrated explanation of some aspect of the natural world that is based on a number of hypotheses, each supported by consistent results from many observations or experiments.

11 Compare the reductionist and systems approaches to biological research.

- Using reductionism, researchers study the simplest components of biological processes such as molecules or cells. **Systems biology** uses knowledge provided by reductionism. Systems biologists integrate data from various levels of complexity with the goal of understanding how biological systems function.

TEST YOUR UNDERSTANDING

Know and Comprehend

1. Cells (a) are not found among the bacteria (b) always have nuclei (c) are the building blocks of living organisms (d) are made up of tissues (e) a and b are true

2. DNA (a) is produced during cellular respiration (b) functions mainly to transmit information from one species to another (c) cannot be changed (d) is a good example of a biological system (e) makes up the genes

3. Cellular respiration (a) is a process whereby sunlight is used to synthesize cell components with the release of energy (b) occurs in heterotrophs only (c) is carried on by both autotrophs and heterotrophs (d) causes chemical changes in DNA (e) occurs in response to environmental changes

4. Fungi are assigned to domain (a) Protista (b) Archaea (c) Bacteria (d) Eukarya (e) Plantae

5. The scientific name for corn is *Zea mays*. *Zea* is the (a) specific epithet (b) genus (c) class (d) kingdom (e) phylum

6. Darwin suggested that evolution takes place by (a) mutation (b) changes in the individuals of a species (c) natural selection (d) interaction of hormones during competition for resources (e) homeostatic responses to each change in the environment

7. Ideally, an experimental group differs from a control group (a) only with respect to the hypothesis being tested (b) because its subjects are more reliable (c) in that it is less subject to bias (d) in that it is less vulnerable to sampling error (e) only with respect to the variable being studied

Apply and Analyze

8. Which of the following is a correct sequence of levels of biological organization? 1. organ system 2. chemical 3. tissue 4. organ 5. cell (a) 2, 3, 5, 4, 1 (b) 5, 3, 4, 1, 2 (c) 2, 5, 3, 1, 4 (d) 2, 5, 3, 4, 1 (e) 5, 2, 3, 4, 1

9. **VISUALIZE** Draw a simple cladogram illustrating the relationships among the following: Common ancestor of all organisms, Domain Eukarya, Domain Bacteria, Domain Archaea. To which domain do the organisms informally known as protists belong? To which domain do you belong? Refer to Figure 1-11 to check your answer.

10. **PREDICT** What would happen if a homeostatic mechanism failed? Give an example using a homeostatic mechanism at work in your body (other than the regulation of glucose cited in the chapter).

11. What are some characteristics of a good hypothesis? Give an example.

12. **PREDICT** Make a prediction and devise a suitably controlled experiment to test each of the following hypotheses: (a) A type of mold found in your garden produces an effective antibiotic. (b) The growth rate of a bean seedling is affected by temperature. (c) Estrogen alleviates symptoms of Alzheimer's disease in elderly women.

13. Contrast the reductionist approach with systems biology. How are the two approaches complementary? Which approach is more likely to consider emergent properties?

Evaluate and Synthesize

14. **INTERPRET DATA** Compare the two graphs in Figure 1-17. What information does the second graph illustrate? What possible explanation can you give for the differences shown in the two graphs?

15. **EVOLUTION LINK** In what ways does evolution depend on transfer of information? In what ways does transfer of information depend on evolution?

16. **EVOLUTION LINK** How might an understanding of evolutionary processes help a biologist doing research in (a) the development of a new antibiotic to replace one to which bacteria have become resistant? (b) conservation of a specific plant in a rain forest?

17. **SCIENCE, TECHNOLOGY, AND SOCIETY** In the future, gene technology may make it possible for parents to produce children with athletic ability, artistic talent, or high IQ. Do you have any ethical concerns about these possibilities? If so, where and how would you draw the line?

 To access course materials, such as Aplia and other companion resources, please visit **www.cengagebrain.com.**

Atoms and Molecules: The Chemical Basis of Life

2

NASA, ESA, and the Hubble Heritage (STScI/AURA)-ESA/Hubble Collaboration

The only elements formed at the beginning of our universe were hydrogen and helium. Since the "Big Bang," all the naturally occurring heavier elements have formed through processes occurring in stars, such as those depicted in the photograph. In this chapter we consider how the properties of the elements serve as the fundamental underpinnings for the ways structure and function work together in organisms and how these properties enable organisms to store and use both information and energy. Therefore, knowledge of chemistry is essential for understanding organisms and how they function. The chemical similarities among all organisms on Earth provide strong evidence for the evolution of all organisms from a common ancestor and explain why much of what biologists learn from studying bacteria or rats in laboratories can be applied to other organisms, including humans. Furthermore, the basic chemical and physical principles governing organisms are not unique to living things, for they apply to nonliving systems as well.

The success of the Human Genome Project and related studies has relied heavily on biochemistry and *molecular biology,* the chemistry and physics of the molecules that constitute living things. A biochemist may investigate the precise interactions among a cell's atoms and molecules that maintain the energy flow essential to life, and a molecular biologist may study how proteins interact with deoxyribonucleic acid (DNA) in ways that control the expression of certain genes. However, an understanding of chemistry is essential to *all* biologists. An evolutionary biologist may study evolutionary relationships by comparing the DNA of different types of organisms. An ecologist may study how energy is transferred among the organisms living in an estuary or may monitor the biological effects of changes in the salinity of the water. A botanist may study unique compounds produced by plants and may even be a "chemical prospector," seeking new sources of medicinal agents.

In this chapter we lay a foundation for understanding how the structure of atoms determines the way they form chemical bonds to produce complex compounds. Most of our discussion focuses on small, simple substances known as **inorganic compounds.** Among the biologically important groups of inorganic compounds are water, many simple acids and bases, and simple salts. We pay particular attention to water, the most abundant

Chemical elements forming in stars. These clusters of young stars photographed by the Hubble Space Telescope are about 20,000 light years away in a giant nebula (NGC 3603) in our Milky Way galaxy.

KEY CONCEPTS

2.1 Carbon, hydrogen, oxygen, and nitrogen are the most abundant elements in living things.

2.2 The chemical properties of an atom are determined by its highest-energy electrons, known as valence electrons.

2.3 A molecule consists of atoms joined by covalent bonds. Other important chemical bonds include ionic bonds. Hydrogen bonds and van der Waals interactions are weak attractions.

2.4 The energy of an electron is transferred in a redox reaction.

2.5 Water molecules are polar, having regions of partial positive charge and partial negative charge that permit them to form hydrogen bonds with one another and with other charged substances.

2.6 Acids are hydrogen ion donors; bases are hydrogen ion acceptors. The pH scale is a convenient measure of the hydrogen ion concentration of a solution.

substance in organisms and on Earth's surface, and we examine how its unique properties affect living things as well as their nonliving environment. In Chapter 3 we extend our discussion to **organic compounds,** carbon-containing compounds that are generally large and complex. In all but the simplest organic compounds, two or more carbon atoms are bonded to each other to form the backbone, or skeleton, of the molecule.

2.1 ELEMENTS AND ATOMS

LEARNING OBJECTIVES

1 Name the principal chemical elements in living things and provide an important function of each.

2 Compare the physical properties (mass and charge) and locations of electrons, protons, and neutrons. Distinguish between the atomic number and the mass number of an atom.

3 Define the terms *orbital* and *electron shell*. Relate electron shells to principal energy levels.

Elements are substances that cannot be broken down into simpler substances by ordinary chemical reactions. Each element has a **chemical symbol:** usually, it is the first letter or first and second letters of the English or Latin name of the element. For example, O is the symbol for oxygen, C for carbon, H for hydrogen, N for nitrogen, and Na for sodium (from the Latin word *natrium*). Just four elements—oxygen, carbon, hydrogen, and nitrogen—are responsible for more than 96% of the mass of most organisms. Others, such as calcium, phosphorus, potassium, and magnesium, are also consistently present but in smaller quantities. Some elements, such as iodine and copper, are known as *trace elements* because they are required only in minute amounts. **TABLE 2-1** lists the elements that make up organisms and briefly explains the importance of each in typical plants and animals.

An **atom** is defined as the smallest portion of an element that retains its chemical properties. Atoms are much too small to be visible under a light microscope, but by sophisticated techniques researchers have been able to photograph the positions of some large atoms in molecules.

The components of atoms are tiny particles of **matter** (anything that has mass and takes up space) known as *subatomic particles.* Physicists have discovered a number of subatomic particles, but for our purposes we need consider only three: electrons, protons, and neutrons. An **electron** is a particle that carries a unit of negative electric charge, a **proton** carries a unit of positive charge, and a **neutron** is an uncharged particle. In an electrically neutral atom, the number of electrons is equal to the number of protons.

Clustered together, protons and neutrons compose the atomic **nucleus.** Electrons, however, have no fixed locations and move rapidly through the mostly empty space surrounding the atomic nucleus.

An atom is uniquely identified by its number of protons

Every element has a fixed number of protons in the atomic nucleus, known as the **atomic number.** It is written as a subscript to the left of the chemical symbol. Thus, $_1H$ indicates that the hydrogen nucleus contains 1 proton, and $_8O$ means that the oxygen nucleus contains 8 protons. The atomic number determines an atom's identity and defines the element.

The **periodic table** is a chart of the elements arranged in order by atomic number (**FIG. 2-1** and Appendix A). The periodic table is useful because it lets us simultaneously correlate many of the relationships among the various elements.

Figure 2-1 includes representations of the **electron configurations** of several elements important in organisms. These *Bohr models*, which show the electrons arranged in a series of concentric circles around the nucleus, are convenient to use, but inaccurate. The space outside the nucleus is actually extremely large compared with the nucleus, and as you will see, electrons do not actually circle the nucleus in fixed concentric pathways.

Protons plus neutrons determine atomic mass

The mass of a subatomic particle is exceedingly small, much too small to be conveniently expressed in grams or even

TABLE 2-1	Functions of Elements in Organisms
ELEMENT* **(CHEMICAL SYMBOL)**	**FUNCTIONS**
Ⓞ OXYGEN	Required for cellular respiration; present in most organic compounds; component of water
Ⓒ CARBON	Forms backbone of organic molecules; each carbon atom can form four bonds with other atoms
Ⓗ HYDROGEN	Present in most organic compounds; component of water; hydrogen ion (H^+) is involved in some energy transfers
Ⓝ NITROGEN	Component of proteins and nucleic acids; component of chlorophyll in plants
Ⓒₐ CALCIUM	Structural component of bones and teeth; calcium ion (Ca^{2+}) is important in muscle contraction, conduction of nerve impulses, and blood clotting; associated with plant cell wall
Ⓟ PHOSPHORUS	Component of nucleic acids and of phospholipids in membranes; important in energy transfer reactions; structural component of bone
Ⓚ POTASSIUM	Potassium ion (K^+) is a principal positive ion (cation) in interstitial (tissue) fluid of animals; important in nerve function; affects muscle contraction; controls opening of stomata in plants
Ⓢ SULFUR	Component of most proteins
Ⓝₐ SODIUM	Sodium ion (Na^+) is a principal positive ion (cation) in interstitial (tissue) fluid of animals; important in fluid balance; essential for conduction of nerve impulses; important in photosynthesis in plants
Ⓜg MAGNESIUM	Needed in blood and other tissues of animals; activates many enzymes; component of chlorophyll in plants
Ⓒₗ CHLORINE	Chloride ion (Cl^-) is principal negative ion (anion) in interstitial (tissue) fluid of animals; important in water balance; essential for photosynthesis
Ⓕe IRON	Component of hemoglobin in animals; activates certain enzymes

*Other elements found in very small (trace) amounts in animals, plants, or both include iodine (I), manganese (Mn), copper (Cu), zinc (Zn), cobalt (Co), fluorine (F), molybdenum (Mo), selenium (Se), boron (B), silicon (Si), and a few others.

© Cengage Learning

The periodic table provides information about the elements: their compositions, structures, and chemical behavior.

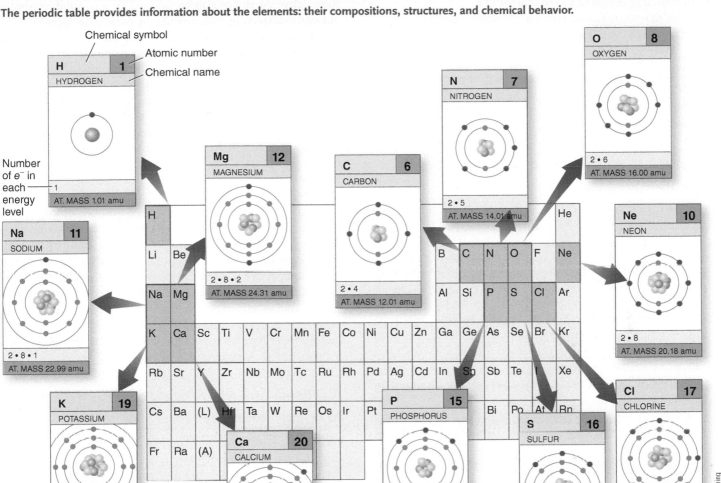

Figure 2-1 The periodic table
Note the Bohr models depicting the electron configuration of atoms of some biologically important elements, plus neon, which is unreactive because its valence shell is full (discussed later in this chapter). Although the Bohr model does not depict electron configurations accurately, it is commonly used because of its simplicity and convenience. A complete periodic table is given in Appendix A.

VISUALIZE Sketch a simple Bohr model for the element fluorine (F), which has an atomic number of 9.

micrograms.[1] Such masses are expressed in terms of the **atomic mass unit (amu),** also called the **dalton** in honor of John Dalton, the English chemist who formulated an atomic theory in the early 1800s. One amu is equal to the approximate mass of a single proton or a single neutron (1.7×10^{-24} g). Protons and neutrons make up almost all the mass of an atom. The mass of a single electron is only about 1/1800 the mass of a proton or neutron.

The **atomic mass** of an atom is a number that indicates approximately how much matter that atom contains compared with another atom. This value is determined by adding the number of protons to the number of neutrons and expressing the result in atomic mass units or daltons.[2] The mass of the electrons is ignored because it is so small. The atomic mass number is indicated by a superscript to the left of the chemical symbol.

[1] Tables of commonly used units of scientific measurement are printed inside the back cover of this text.

[2] Unlike weight, mass is independent of the force of gravity. For convenience, however, we consider mass and weight equivalent. Atomic weight has the same numerical value as atomic mass, but it has no units.

The common form of the oxygen atom, with 8 protons and 8 neutrons in its nucleus, has an atomic number of 8 and a mass of 16 amu. It is indicated by the symbol $^{16}_{8}O$.

The characteristics of protons, electrons, and neutrons are summarized in the following table:

Particle	Charge	Approximate Mass	Location
Proton	Positive	1 amu	Nucleus
Neutron	Neutral	1 amu	Nucleus
Electron	Negative	Approx. 1/1800 amu	Outside nucleus

Isotopes of an element differ in number of neutrons

Most elements consist of a mixture of atoms with different numbers of neutrons and thus different masses. Such atoms are called **isotopes.** Isotopes of the same element have the same number of protons and electrons; only the number of neutrons varies. The three isotopes of hydrogen, $^{1}_{1}H$ (ordinary hydrogen), $^{2}_{1}H$ (deuterium), and $^{3}_{1}H$ (tritium), contain 0, 1, and 2 neutrons, respectively. FIGURE 2-2 shows Bohr models of two isotopes of carbon, $^{12}_{6}C$ and $^{14}_{6}C$. The mass of an element is expressed as an average of the masses of its isotopes (weighted by their relative abundance in nature). For example, the atomic mass of hydrogen is not 1.0 amu, but 1.0079 amu, reflecting the natural occurrence of small amounts of deuterium and tritium in addition to the more abundant ordinary hydrogen.

Because they have the same number of electrons, all isotopes of a given element have essentially the same chemical characteristics. However, some isotopes are unstable and tend to break down, or decay, to a more stable isotope (usually becoming a different element); such **radioisotopes** emit radiation when they decay. For example, the radioactive decay of $^{14}_{6}C$ occurs as a neutron decomposes to form a proton and a fast-moving electron, which is emitted from the atom as a form of radiation known as a beta (β) particle. The resulting stable atom is the common form of nitrogen, $^{14}_{7}N$. Using sophisticated instruments, scientists can detect and measure β particles and other types of radiation. Radioactive decay can also be detected by a method known as **autoradiography**, in which radiation causes the appearance of dark silver grains in photographic film (FIG. 2-3).

Because the different isotopes of a given element have the same chemical characteristics, they are essentially interchangeable in molecules. Molecules containing radioisotopes are usually metabolized and/or localized in the organism in a similar way to their non-radioactive counterparts, and they can be substituted. For this reason, radioisotopes such as ^{3}H (tritium), ^{14}C, and ^{32}P are extremely valuable research tools used, for example, in dating fossils (see Fig. 18-10), tracing biochemical pathways, determining the sequence of genetic information in DNA (see Chapter 15), and understanding sugar transport in plants.

In medicine, radioisotopes are used for both diagnosis and treatment. The location and/or metabolism of a substance such as a hormone or drug can be followed in the body by labeling the substance with a radioisotope such as carbon-14 or tritium. Radioisotopes are used to test thyroid gland function, to provide images of blood flow in the arteries supplying the cardiac muscle, and to study many other aspects of body function and chemistry. Because radiation can interfere with cell division, radioisotopes have been used therapeutically in treating cancer, a disease often characterized by rapidly dividing cells.

Electrons move in orbitals corresponding to energy levels

Electrons move through characteristic regions of three-dimensional space, or **orbitals.** Each orbital contains a maximum of 2 electrons. Because it is impossible to know an electron's position at any given time, orbitals are most accurately

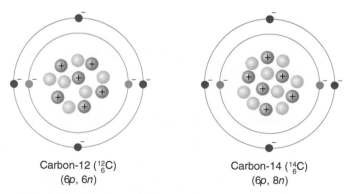

Figure 2-2 Isotopes

Carbon-12 ($^{12}_{6}C$) is the most common isotope of carbon. Its nucleus contains 6 protons and 6 neutrons, so its atomic mass is 12. Carbon-14 ($^{14}_{6}C$) is a rare radioactive carbon isotope. It contains 8 neutrons, so its atomic mass is 14.

© Cengage Learning

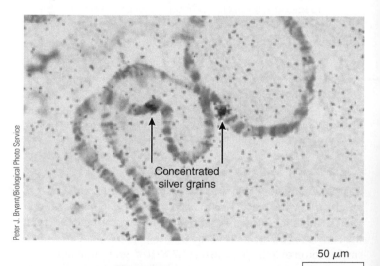

Figure 2-3 Autoradiography

The chromosomes of the fruit fly, *Drosophila melanogaster*, shown in this light micrograph have been covered with photographic film in which silver grains (*dark spots*) are produced when tritium (^{3}H) that has been incorporated into DNA undergoes radioactive decay. The concentrations of silver grains (*arrows*) mark the locations of specific DNA molecules.

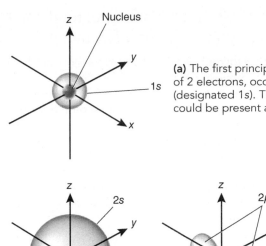

(a) The first principal energy level contains a maximum of 2 electrons, occupying a single spherical orbital (designated 1s). The electrons depicted in the diagram could be present anywhere in the blue area.

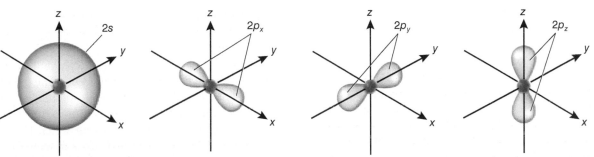

(b) The second principal energy level includes four orbitals, each with a maximum of 2 electrons: one spherical (2s) and three dumbbell-shaped (2p) orbitals at right angles to one another.

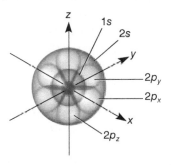

(c) Orbitals of the first and second principal energy levels of a neon atom are shown superimposed. Note that the single 2s orbital plus three 2p orbitals make up neon's full valence shell of 8 electrons. Compare this more realistic view of the atomic orbitals with the Bohr model of a neon atom at right.

(d) Neon atom (Bohr model)

Figure 2-4 *Animation* **Atomic orbitals**
Electrons occupy orbitals corresponding to energy levels. Each orbital is represented as an "electron cloud." The arrows labeled x, y, and z establish the imaginary axes of the atom.

© Cengage Learning

depicted as "electron clouds," shaded areas whose density is proportional to the probability that an electron is present there at any given instant. The energy of an electron depends on the orbital it occupies. Electrons in orbitals with similar energies, said to be at the same *principal energy level,* make up an **electron shell** (FIG. 2-4).

In general, electrons in a shell with a greater average distance from the nucleus have greater energy than those in a shell close to the nucleus. The reason is that energy is required to move a negatively charged electron farther away from the positively charged nucleus. The most energetic electrons, known as valence electrons, are said to occupy the *valence shell.* The valence shell is represented as the outermost concentric ring in a Bohr model. As you will see in the next sections, it is these valence electrons that play a key role in chemical reactions.

An electron can move to an orbital farther from the nucleus by receiving more energy, or it can give up energy and sink to a lower energy level in an orbital nearer the nucleus. Changes in electron energy levels are important in energy conversions in organisms. For example, during photosynthesis, light energy absorbed by chlorophyll molecules causes electrons to move to a higher energy level (see Fig. 9-3).

C**HECKPOINT 2.1**

- *Do all atoms of an element have the same atomic number? the same atomic mass?*
- *What is a radioisotope? What are some ways radioisotopes are used in biological research?*
- *How do electrons in different orbitals of the same electron shell compare with respect to their energy?*

2.2 CHEMICAL REACTIONS

LEARNING OBJECTIVES

4   Explain how the number of valence electrons of an atom is related to its chemical properties.

5   Distinguish among simplest, molecular, and structural chemical formulas.

6   Explain why the mole concept is so useful to chemists.

The chemical behavior of an atom is determined primarily by the number and arrangement of its **valence electrons.** The valence shell of hydrogen or helium is full (stable) when it contains 2 electrons. The valence shell of any other atom is full when it contains 8 electrons. When the valence shell is not full, the atom tends to lose, gain, or share electrons to achieve a full outer shell. The valence shells of all isotopes of an element are identical; for this reason, they have similar chemical properties and can substitute for one another in chemical reactions (e.g., tritium can substitute for ordinary hydrogen).

Elements in the same vertical column (belonging to the same *group*) of the periodic table have similar chemical properties because their valence shells have similar tendencies to lose, gain, or share electrons. For example, chlorine and bromine, included in a group commonly known as the *halogens,* are highly reactive. Because their valence shells have 7 electrons, they tend to gain an electron in chemical reactions. By contrast, hydrogen, sodium, and potassium each have a single valence electron, which they tend to give up or share with another atom. Helium (He) and neon (Ne) belong to a group referred to as the *noble gases.* They are quite unreactive because their valence shells are full. Note in Figure 2-1 the incomplete valence shells of some of the elements important in organisms, including carbon, hydrogen, oxygen, and nitrogen, and compare them with the full valence shell of neon in Figure 2-4d.

Atoms form compounds and molecules

Two or more atoms may combine chemically. When atoms of *different* elements combine, the result is a chemical compound. A **chemical compound** consists of atoms of two or more different elements combined in a fixed ratio. For example, water is a chemical compound composed of hydrogen and oxygen in a ratio of 2:1. Common table salt, sodium chloride, is a chemical compound made up of sodium and chlorine in a 1:1 ratio.

Two or more atoms may become joined very strongly to form a stable particle called a **molecule.** For example, when two atoms of oxygen combine chemically, a molecule of oxygen is formed. Water is a molecular compound, with each molecule consisting of two atoms of hydrogen and one of oxygen. However, as you will see, not all compounds are made up of molecules. Sodium chloride (common table salt) is an example of a compound that is not molecular.

Simplest, molecular, and structural chemical formulas give different information

A **chemical formula** is a shorthand expression that describes the chemical composition of a substance. Chemical symbols indicate the types of atoms present, and subscript numbers indicate the ratios among the atoms. There are several types of chemical formulas, each providing specific kinds of information.

In a **simplest formula** (also known as an *empirical formula*), the subscripts give the smallest whole-number ratios for the atoms present in a compound. For example, the simplest formula for hydrazine is NH_2, indicating a 1:2 ratio of nitrogen to hydrogen. (Note that when a single atom of a type is present, the subscript number 1 is never written.)

In a **molecular formula,** the subscripts indicate the actual numbers of each type of atom per molecule. The molecular formula for hydrazine is N_2H_4, which indicates that each molecule of hydrazine consists of two atoms of nitrogen and four atoms of hydrogen. The molecular formula for water, H_2O, indicates that each molecule consists of two atoms of hydrogen and one atom of oxygen.

A **structural formula** shows not only the types and numbers of atoms in a molecule but also their arrangement. For example, the structural formula for water is H—O—H. As you will learn in Chapter 3, it is common for complex organic molecules with different structural formulas to share the same molecular formula.

One mole of any substance contains the same number of units

The molecular mass of a compound is the sum of the atomic masses of the component atoms of a single molecule; thus, the molecular mass of water, H_2O, is (hydrogen: 2×1 amu) + (oxygen: 1×16 amu), or 18 amu. (Because of the presence of isotopes, atomic mass values are not whole numbers, but for easy calculation each atomic mass value has been rounded to a whole number.) Similarly, the molecular mass of glucose ($C_6H_{12}O_6$), a simple sugar that is a key compound in cell metabolism, is (carbon: 6×12 amu) + (hydrogen: 12×1 amu) + (oxygen: 6×16 amu), or 180 amu.

The amount of an element or compound whose mass in grams is equivalent to its atomic or molecular mass is 1 **mole (mol)**. Thus, 1 mol of water is 18 grams (g), and 1 mol of glucose has a mass of 180 g. The mole is an extremely useful concept because it lets us make meaningful comparisons between atoms and molecules of very different mass. The reason is that *1 mol of any substance always has exactly the same number of units*, whether those units are small atoms or large molecules. The very large number of units in a mole, 6.02×10^{23}, is known as **Avogadro's number,** named for the Italian scientist Amedeo Avogadro, whose pioneering work inspired later scientists to calculate it. Thus, 1 mol (180 g) of glucose contains 6.02×10^{23} molecules, as does 1 mol (2 g) of molecular hydrogen (H_2). Although it is impossible to count atoms and molecules individually, a scientist can calculate them simply by weighing a sample. Molecular biologists usually deal with smaller values, either millimoles (mmol, one-thousandth of a mole) or micromoles (μmol, one-millionth of a mole).

The mole concept also lets us make useful comparisons among solutions. A 1-molar solution, represented by 1 M, contains 1 mol of that substance dissolved in a total volume of 1 liter (L). For example, we can compare 1 L of a 1 M solution of glucose with 1 L of a 1 M solution of sucrose (table sugar, a larger molecule). They differ in the mass of the dissolved sugar (180 g and 340 g, respectively), but they each contain 6.02×10^{23} sugar molecules.

Chemical equations describe chemical reactions

During any moment in the life of an organism—a bacterial cell, a mushroom, or a butterfly—many complex chemical reactions are taking place. Chemical reactions, such as the reaction between glucose and oxygen, can be described by means of chemical equations:

$$C_6H_{12}O_6 + 6\,O_2 \longrightarrow 6\,CO_2 + 6\,H_2O + energy$$

Glucose   Oxygen   Carbon dioxide   Water

In a chemical equation, the **reactants**—the substances that participate in the reaction—are generally written on the left side, and the **products**—the substances formed by the reaction—are written on the right side. The arrow means "yields" and indicates the direction in which the reaction proceeds.

Chemical compounds react with one another in quantitatively precise ways. The numbers preceding the chemical symbols or formulas (known as *coefficients*) indicate the relative number of atoms or molecules reacting. For example, 1 mol of glucose burned in a fire or metabolized in a cell reacts with 6 mol of oxygen to form 6 mol of carbon dioxide and 6 mol of water.

Many reactions can proceed simultaneously in the reverse direction (to the left) and the forward direction (to the right). At **dynamic equilibrium,** the rates of the forward and reverse reactions are equal (see Chapter 7). Reversible reactions are indicated by double arrows:

$$CO_2 + H_2O \rightleftharpoons H_2CO_3$$

Carbon dioxide   Water   Carbonic acid

In this example the arrows are drawn in different lengths to indicate that when the reaction reaches equilibrium, there will be more reactants (CO_2 and H_2O) than product (H_2CO_3).

CHECKPOINT 2.2

- *What enables a radioisotope to substitute for an ordinary (nonradioactive) atom of the same element in a molecule?*
- *Which kind of chemical formula provides the most information?*
- PREDICT *How many particles would be included in 1 g of hydrogen atoms? in 2 g of hydrogen molecules?*

2.3 CHEMICAL BONDS

LEARNING OBJECTIVE

7 Distinguish among covalent bonds, ionic bonds, hydrogen bonds, and van der Waals interactions. Compare them in terms of the mechanisms by which they form and their relative strengths.

Atoms can be held together by forces of attraction called **chemical bonds.** Each bond represents a certain amount of chemical energy. **Bond energy** is the energy necessary to break a chemical bond. The valence electrons dictate how many bonds an atom can form. The two principal types of strong chemical bonds are covalent bonds and ionic bonds.

In covalent bonds electrons are shared

Covalent bonds involve the sharing of electrons between atoms in a way that results in each atom having a filled valence shell. A molecule consists of atoms joined by covalent bonds. A simple example of a covalent bond is the joining of two hydrogen atoms in a molecule of hydrogen gas, H_2. Each atom of hydrogen has 1 electron, but 2 electrons are required to complete its valence shell. The hydrogen atoms have equal capacities to attract electrons, so neither donates an electron to the other. Instead, the two hydrogen atoms share their single electrons so that the 2 electrons are attracted simultaneously to the 2 protons in the two hydrogen nuclei. The 2 electrons whirl around both atomic nuclei, thus forming the covalent bond that joins the two atoms. Similarly, unlike atoms can also be linked by covalent bonds to form molecules; the resulting compound is a **covalent compound.**

A simple way of representing the electrons in the valence shell of an atom is to use dots placed around the chemical symbol of the element. Such a representation is called the *Lewis structure* of the atom, named for G. N. Lewis, the American chemist who developed this type of notation. In a water molecule, two hydrogen atoms are covalently bonded to an oxygen atom:

$$H \cdot + H \cdot + \cdot \ddot{O} \cdot \longrightarrow H : \ddot{O} : H$$

Oxygen has 6 valence electrons; by sharing electrons with two hydrogen atoms, it completes its valence shell of 8. At the same time, each hydrogen atom obtains a complete valence shell of 2. (Note that in the structural formula H—O—H, each pair of shared electrons constitutes a covalent bond, represented by a solid line. Unshared electrons are usually omitted in a structural formula.)

The carbon atom has 4 electrons in its valence shell, all of which are available for covalent bonding:

$$\cdot \dot{C} \cdot$$

When one carbon and four hydrogen atoms share electrons, a molecule of the covalent compound methane, CH_4, is formed:

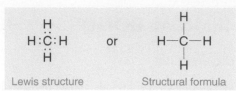

Lewis structure   Structural formula

The nitrogen atom has 5 electrons in its valence shell. Recall that each orbital can hold a maximum of 2 electrons. Usually, 2 electrons occupy one orbital, leaving 3 electrons available for sharing with other atoms:

When a nitrogen atom shares electrons with three hydrogen atoms, a molecule of the covalent compound ammonia, NH_3, is formed:

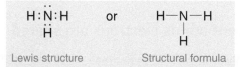

Lewis structure   Structural formula

When one pair of electrons is shared between two atoms, the covalent bond is called a **single covalent bond** (FIG. 2-5a). Two hydrogen atoms share a single pair of electrons. Two oxygen atoms may achieve stability by forming covalent bonds with each other. Each oxygen atom has 6 electrons in its outer shell. To become stable, the two atoms share two pairs of electrons,

forming molecular oxygen (FIG. 2-5b). When two pairs of electrons are shared in this way, the covalent bond is called a *double covalent bond*, which is represented by two parallel, solid lines. Similarly, a *triple covalent bond* is formed when three pairs of electrons are shared between two atoms (represented by three parallel, solid lines).

The number of covalent bonds usually formed by the atoms in biologically important molecules is summarized as follows:

ATOM	SYMBOL	COVALENT BONDS
Hydrogen	H	1
Oxygen	O	2
Carbon	C	4
Nitrogen	N	3
Phosphorus	P	5
Sulfur	S	2

The function of a molecule is related to its shape

In addition to being composed of atoms with certain properties, each kind of molecule has a characteristic size and a general overall shape. Although the shape of a molecule may change (within certain limits), the functions of molecules in living cells are dictated largely by their geometric shapes. A molecule

---

KEY POINT

Covalent bonds form when atoms share electrons.

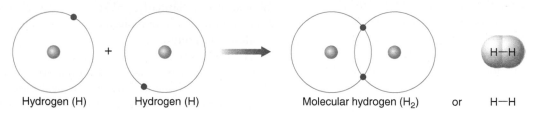

Hydrogen (H)   Hydrogen (H)   Molecular hydrogen (H_2)   or   H—H

(a) Single covalent bond formation. Two hydrogen atoms achieve stability by sharing a pair of electrons, thereby forming a molecule of hydrogen. In the structural formula on the right, the straight line between the hydrogen atoms represents a single covalent bond.

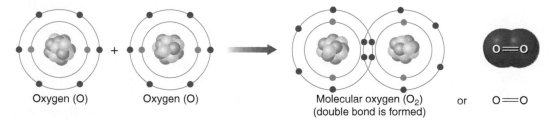

Oxygen (O)   Oxygen (O)   Molecular oxygen (O_2)   or   O=O
(double bond is formed)

(b) Double covalent bond formation. In molecular oxygen, two oxygen atoms share two pairs of electrons, forming a double covalent bond. The parallel straight lines in the structural formula represent a double covalent bond.

Figure 2-5 *Animation* **Electron sharing in covalent compounds**

VISUALIZE Molecular nitrogen (N_2) is formed when two nitrogen atoms are joined by a triple covalent bond. Use the information in Figure 2-1 to help you sketch a simple Bohr model of N_2.

© Cengage Learning

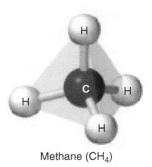

Methane (CH₄)

Figure 2-6 Orbital hybridization in methane
The four hydrogens are located at the corners of a tetrahedron because of
hybridization of the valence shell orbitals of carbon.
© Cengage Learning

that consists of two atoms is linear. Molecules composed of more than two atoms may have more complicated shapes. The geometric shape of a molecule provides the optimal distance between the atoms to counteract the repulsion of electron pairs.

When an atom forms covalent bonds with other atoms, the orbitals in the valence shell may become rearranged in a process known as **orbital hybridization,** thereby affecting the shape of the resulting molecule. For example, when four hydrogen atoms combine with one carbon atom to form a molecule of methane (CH₄), the hybridized valence shell orbitals of the carbon form a geometric structure known as a *tetrahedron*, with one hydrogen atom present at each of its four corners (FIG. 2-6; see also Fig. 3-2b).

We explore the importance of molecular shape in more detail in Chapter 3 and in our discussion of the properties of water in this chapter.

Covalent bonds can be nonpolar or polar

Atoms of different elements vary in their affinity for electrons. **Electronegativity** is a measure of an atom's attraction for shared electrons in chemical bonds. Very electronegative atoms such as oxygen, nitrogen, fluorine, and chlorine are sometimes called "electron greedy." When covalently bonded atoms have similar electronegativities, the electrons are shared equally and the bond is described as a **nonpolar covalent bond.** The covalent bond of the hydrogen molecule is nonpolar, as are the covalent bonds of molecular oxygen and methane.

In a covalent bond between two different elements, such as oxygen and hydrogen, the electronegativities of the atoms may be different. If so, electrons are pulled closer to the atomic nucleus of the element with the greater electron affinity (in this case, oxygen). A covalent bond between atoms that differ in electronegativity is called a **polar covalent bond.** Such a bond has two dissimilar ends (or poles), one with a partial positive charge and the other with a partial negative charge. Each of the two covalent bonds in water is polar because there is a partial positive charge at the hydrogen end of the bond and a partial negative charge at the oxygen end, where the "shared" electrons are more likely to be.

Covalent bonds differ in their degree of polarity, ranging from those in which the electrons are equally shared (as in the nonpolar hydrogen molecule) to those in which the electrons are much closer to one atom than to the other (as in water). Oxygen is quite electronegative and forms polar covalent bonds with carbon, hydrogen, and many other atoms. Nitrogen is also strongly electronegative, although less so than oxygen.

A molecule with one or more polar covalent bonds can be polar even though it is electrically neutral as a whole. The reason is that a **polar molecule** has one end with a partial positive charge and another end with a partial negative charge. One example is water (FIG. 2-7). The polar bonds between the hydrogens and the oxygen are arranged in a V shape, rather than linearly. The oxygen end constitutes the negative pole of the molecule, and the end with the two hydrogens is the positive pole.

Ionic bonds form between cations and anions

Some atoms or groups of atoms are not electrically neutral. A particle with 1 or more units of electric charge is called an ion. An atom becomes an ion if it gains or loses 1 or more electrons. An atom with 1, 2, or 3 electrons in its valence shell tends to lose electrons to other atoms. Such an atom then becomes positively charged because its nucleus contains more protons than the number of electrons orbiting around the nucleus. These positively charged ions are called **cations.** Atoms with 5, 6, or 7 valence electrons tend to gain electrons from other atoms and become negatively charged **anions.**

The properties of ions are quite different from those of the electrically neutral atoms from which they were derived. For example, although chlorine gas is a poison, chloride ions (Cl⁻)

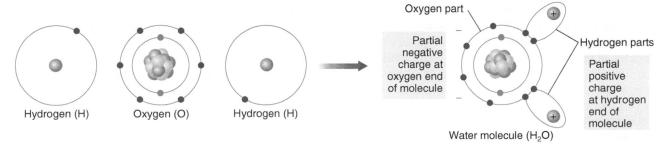

Hydrogen (H)   Oxygen (O)   Hydrogen (H)

Oxygen part
Partial negative charge at oxygen end of molecule
Hydrogen parts
Partial positive charge at hydrogen end of molecule
Water molecule (H₂O)

Figure 2-7 Animation Water, a polar molecule
Note that the electrons tend to stay closer to the nucleus of the oxygen atom than to the hydrogen nuclei. The result
is a partial negative charge on the oxygen portion of the molecule and a partial positive charge at the hydrogen end.
Although the water molecule as a whole is electrically neutral, it is a polar covalent compound.
© Cengage Learning

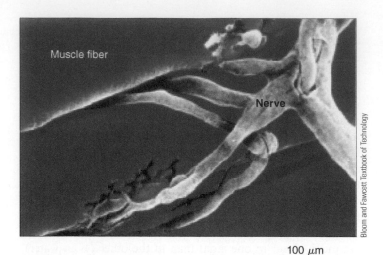

Muscle fiber

Nerve

Bloom and Fawcett Textbook of Technology

100 μm

Figure 2-8 Ions and biological processes
Sodium, potassium, and chloride ions are essential for this nerve cell to stimulate these muscle fibers, initiating a muscle contraction. Calcium ions in the muscle cell are required for muscle contraction.

are essential to life (see Table 2-1). Because their electric charges provide a basis for many interactions, cations and anions are involved in energy transformations within the cell, the transmission of nerve impulses, muscle contraction, and many other biological processes (FIG. 2-8).

A group of covalently bonded atoms can also become an ion (*polyatomic ion*). Unlike a single atom, a group of atoms can lose or gain protons (derived from hydrogen atoms) as well as electrons. Therefore, a group of atoms can become a cation if it loses 1 or more electrons or gains 1 or more protons. A group of atoms becomes an anion if it gains 1 or more electrons or loses 1 or more protons.

An **ionic bond** forms as a consequence of the attraction between the positive charge of a cation and the negative charge of an anion. An **ionic compound** is a substance consisting of anions and cations bonded by their opposite charges.

A good example of how ionic bonds are formed is the attraction between sodium ions and chloride ions. A sodium atom has 1 electron in its valence shell. It cannot fill its valence shell by obtaining 7 electrons from other atoms because it would then have a large unbalanced negative charge. Instead, it gives up its single valence electron to a very electronegative atom, such as chlorine, which acts as an electron acceptor (FIG. 2-9). Chlorine cannot give up the 7 electrons in its valence shell because it would then have a large positive charge. Instead, it strips an electron from an electron donor (sodium, in this example) to complete its valence shell.

When sodium reacts with chlorine, sodium's valence electron is transferred completely to chlorine. Sodium becomes a cation, with 1 unit of positive charge (Na^+). Chlorine becomes an anion, a chloride ion with 1 unit of negative charge (Cl^-). These ions attract each other as a result of their opposite charges. This electrical attraction in ionic bonds holds them together to form NaCl, sodium chloride, or common table salt.

The term *molecule* does not adequately explain the properties of ionic compounds such as NaCl. When NaCl is in its solid crystal state, each ion is actually surrounded by six ions

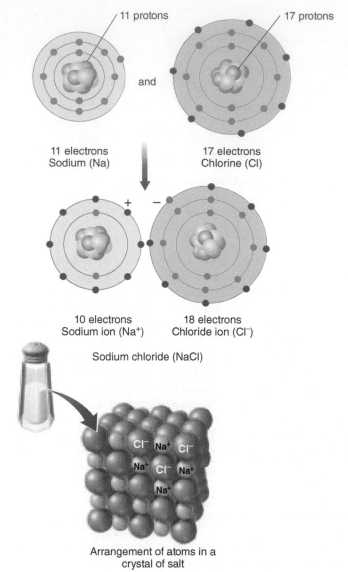

11 protons

17 protons

and

11 electrons
Sodium (Na)

17 electrons
Chlorine (Cl)

+   −

10 electrons
Sodium ion (Na^+)

18 electrons
Chloride ion (Cl^-)

Sodium chloride (NaCl)

Cl^- Na^+ Cl^-
Na^+ Cl^- Na^+
Na^+

Arrangement of atoms in a
crystal of salt

Figure 2-9 *Animation* Ionic bonding
Sodium becomes a positively charged ion when it donates its single valence electron to chlorine, which has 7 valence electrons. With this additional electron, chlorine completes its valence shell and becomes a negatively charged chloride ion. These sodium and chloride ions are attracted to one another by their unlike electric charges, forming the ionic compound sodium chloride.
© Cengage Learning

of opposite charge. The simplest formula, NaCl, indicates that sodium ions and chloride ions are present in a 1:1 ratio, but the actual crystal has no discrete molecules composed of 1 Na^+ ion and 1 Cl^- ion.

Compounds joined by ionic bonds, such as sodium chloride, have a tendency to *dissociate* (separate) into their individual ions when placed in water:

$$NaCl \xrightarrow{in\ H_2O} Na^+ + Cl^-$$

Sodium chloride   Sodium ion   Chloride ion

In the solid form of an ionic compound (that is in the absence of water), ionic bonds are very strong. Water, however, is an excellent **solvent;** as a liquid it is capable of dissolving many substances, particularly those that are polar or ionic, because of

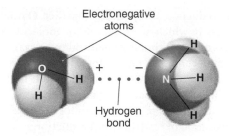

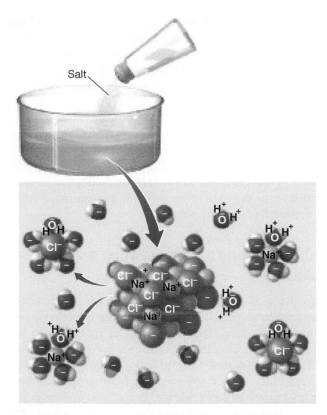

Figure 2-10 *Animation* **Hydration of an ionic compound**
When the crystal of NaCl is added to water, the sodium and chloride ions are pulled apart. When the NaCl is dissolved, each Na^+ and each Cl^- is surrounded by water molecules electrically attracted to it.
© Cengage Learning

the polarity of water molecules. The localized partial positive charge (on the hydrogen atoms) and partial negative charge (on the oxygen atom) on each water molecule attract and surround the anions and cations, respectively, on the surface of an ionic solid. As a result, the solid dissolves. A dissolved substance is referred to as a **solute.** In solution each cation and anion of the ionic compound is surrounded by oppositely charged ends of the water molecules. This process is known as **hydration** (FIG. 2-10). Hydrated ions still interact with one another to some extent, but the transient ionic bonds formed are much weaker than those in a solid crystal.

Hydrogen bonds are weak attractions

Another type of bond important in organisms is the **hydrogen bond.** When hydrogen combines with oxygen (or with another relatively electronegative atom such as nitrogen), it acquires a partial positive charge because its electron spends more time closer to the electronegative atom. Hydrogen bonds tend to form between an atom with a partial negative charge and a hydrogen atom that is covalently bonded to oxygen or nitrogen (FIG. 2-11). The atoms involved may be in two parts of the same large molecule or in two different molecules. Water molecules interact with one another extensively through hydrogen bond formation.

Hydrogen bonds are readily formed and broken. Although individually relatively weak, hydrogen bonds are collectively strong when present in large numbers. Furthermore, they have

a specific length and orientation. As you will see in Chapter 3, these features are very important in determining the 3-D structure of large molecules such as DNA and proteins.

van der Waals interactions are weak forces

Even electrically neutral, nonpolar molecules can develop transient regions of weak positive charge and weak negative charge. These slight charges develop as a consequence of the electrons always being in constant motion. A region with a temporary excess of electrons will have a weak negative charge, whereas one with an electron deficit will have a weak positive charge. Adjacent molecules may interact in regions of slight opposite charge. These attractive forces, called **van der Waals interactions,** operate over very short distances and are weaker and less specific than the other types of interactions we have considered. They are most important when they occur in large numbers and when the shapes of the molecules permit close contact between the atoms. Although a single interaction is very weak, the binding force of a large number of these interactions working together can be significant.

CHECKPOINT 2.3

- *Are all compounds composed of molecules? Explain.*
- *What are the ways an atom or a molecule can become an anion or a cation?*
- *How do ionic and covalent bonds differ?*
- CONNECT *Under what circumstances can weak forces such as hydrogen bonds and van der Waals interactions play significant roles in biological systems?*

2.4 REDOX REACTIONS

LEARNING OBJECTIVE

8 Distinguish between the terms *oxidation* and *reduction*, and relate these processes to the transfer of energy.

Many energy conversions that go on in a cell involve reactions in which an electron transfers from one substance to another. The reason is that the transfer of an electron also involves the transfer of the energy of that electron. Such an electron transfer is known as an oxidation–reduction reaction, or **redox reaction.**

Oxidation and reduction always occur together. **Oxidation** is a chemical process in which an atom, ion, or molecule *loses* one or more electrons. **Reduction** is a chemical process in which an atom, ion, or molecule *gains* one or more electrons. (The term refers to the fact that the gain of an electron results in the reduction of any positive charge that might be present.)

Rusting—the combining of iron (symbol Fe) with oxygen—is a simple illustration of oxidation and reduction:

$$4\ Fe + 3\ O_2 \longrightarrow 2\ Fe_2O_3$$
Iron (III) oxide

In rusting, each iron atom becomes oxidized as it loses 3 electrons.

$$4\ Fe \longrightarrow 4\ Fe^{3+} + 12e^-$$

The e^- represents an electron, and the $+$ superscript in Fe^{3+} represents an electron deficit. (When an atom loses an electron, it acquires 1 unit of positive charge from the excess of 1 proton. In this example each iron atom loses 3 electrons and acquires 3 units of positive charge.) Recall that the oxygen atom is very electronegative, able to remove electrons from other atoms. In this reaction, oxygen becomes reduced when it accepts electrons from the iron:

$$3\ O_2 + 12e^- \longrightarrow 6\ O^{2-}$$

Redox reactions occur simultaneously because one substance must accept the electrons that are removed from the other. In a redox reaction, one component, the *oxidizing agent*, accepts 1 or more electrons and becomes reduced. Oxidizing agents other than oxygen are known, but oxygen is such a common one that its name was given to the process. Another reaction component, the *reducing agent*, gives up 1 or more electrons and becomes oxidized. In our example, there was a complete transfer of electrons from iron (the reducing agent) to oxygen (the oxidizing agent). Similarly, Figure 2-9 shows that an electron was transferred from sodium (the reducing agent) to chlorine (the oxidizing agent).

Electrons are not easily removed from covalent compounds unless an entire atom is removed. In cells, oxidation often involves the removal of a hydrogen atom (an electron plus a proton that "goes along for the ride") from a covalent compound; reduction often involves the addition of the equivalent of a hydrogen atom (see Chapter 7).

CHECKPOINT 2.4

- *In what form is energy transferred in a redox reaction?*

2.5 WATER

LEARNING OBJECTIVE

9 Explain how hydrogen bonds between adjacent water molecules govern many of the properties of water.

A large part of the mass of most organisms is water. In human tissues the percentage of water ranges from 20% in bones to 85% in brain cells; about 70% of a human's total body weight is water.

As much as 95% of a jellyfish and certain plants is water. Water is the source, through photosynthesis, of the oxygen in the air we breathe, and its hydrogen atoms become incorporated into many organic compounds. Water is also the solvent for most biological reactions and a reactant or product in many chemical reactions.

Water is important not only as an internal constituent of organisms but also as one of the principal environmental factors affecting them (**FIG. 2-12**). Many organisms live in the ocean or in freshwater rivers, lakes, or puddles. Water's unique combination of physical and chemical properties is considered to have been essential to the origin of life as well as to the continued survival and evolution of life on Earth.

Hydrogen bonds form between water molecules

As discussed, water molecules are polar; that is, one end of each molecule bears a partial positive charge and the other a partial negative charge (see Fig. 2-7). The water molecules in liquid water and in ice associate by hydrogen bonds. The hydrogen atom of one water molecule, with its partial positive charge, is attracted to the oxygen atom of a neighboring water molecule, with its partial negative charge, forming a hydrogen bond. An oxygen atom in a water molecule has two regions of partial negative charge, and each of the two hydrogen atoms has a partial positive charge. Each water molecule can therefore form hydrogen bonds with a maximum of four neighboring water molecules (**FIG. 2-13**).

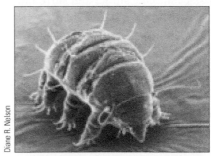

Diane R. Nelson

(a) Commonly known as "water bears," tardigrades, such as these members of the genus *Echiniscus*, are small animals (less than 1.2 mm long) that normally live in moist habitats, such as thin films of water on mosses.

100 μm

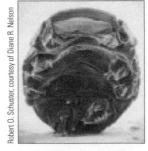

Robert O. Schuster, courtesy of Diane R. Nelson

(b) When subjected to desiccation (dried out), tardigrades assume a barrel-shaped form known as a *tun*, remaining in this state, motionless but alive, for as long as 100 years. When rehydrated, they assume their normal appearance and activities.

10 μm

Figure 2-12 The effects of water on an organism

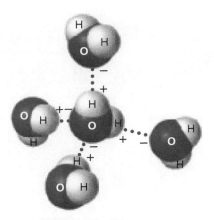

Figure 2-13 Hydrogen bonding of water molecules
Each water molecule can form hydrogen bonds (*dotted lines*) with as many as four neighboring water molecules.
© Cengage Learning

Water molecules have a strong tendency to stick to one another, a property known as **cohesion,** due to the hydrogen bonds among the molecules. Because of the cohesive nature of water molecules, any force exerted on part of a column of water is transmitted to the column as a whole. The major mechanism of water movement in plants (see Chapter 35) depends on the cohesive nature of water. Water molecules also display **adhesion,** the ability to stick to many other kinds of substances, most notably those with charged groups of atoms or molecules on their surfaces. These adhesive forces explain how water makes things wet.

A combination of adhesive and cohesive forces accounts for **capillary action,** which is the tendency of water to move in narrow tubes, even against the force of gravity (FIG. 2-14). For example, water moves through the microscopic spaces between soil particles to the roots of plants by capillary action.

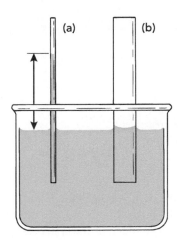

Figure 2-14 Capillary action
(a) In a narrow tube, there is adhesion between the water molecules and the glass wall of the tube. Other water molecules inside the tube are then "pulled along" because of cohesion, which is due to hydrogen bonds between the water molecules. **(b)** In the wider tube, a smaller percentage of the water molecules line the glass wall. As a result, the adhesion is not strong enough to overcome the cohesion of the water molecules beneath the surface level of the container, and water in the tube rises only slightly.
© Cengage Learning

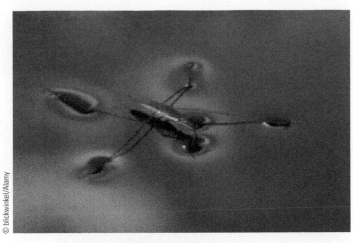
© blickwinkel/Alamy

Figure 2-15 Surface tension of water
Hydrogen bonding between water molecules is responsible for the surface tension of water, which causes a dimpled appearance of the surface as this water strider (genus, *Gerris*) walks across it. Fine hairs at the ends of the legs of these insects create highly water-repellent "cushions" of air.

Water has a high degree of **surface tension** because of the cohesion of its molecules, which have a much greater attraction for one another than for molecules in the air. Thus, water molecules at the surface crowd together, producing a strong layer as they are pulled downward by the attraction of other water molecules beneath them (FIG. 2-15).

Water molecules interact with hydrophilic substances by hydrogen bonding

Because its molecules are polar, water is an excellent solvent, a liquid capable of dissolving many kinds of substances, especially polar and ionic compounds. Earlier we discussed how polar water molecules pull the ions of ionic compounds apart so that they dissociate (see Fig. 2-10). Because of its solvent properties and the tendency of the atoms in certain compounds to form ions in solution, water plays an important role in facilitating chemical reactions.

Substances that interact readily with water are **hydrophilic** ("water-loving"). Examples include table sugar (sucrose, a polar compound) and table salt (NaCl, an ionic compound), which dissolve readily in water. Not all substances in organisms are hydrophilic, however. Many **hydrophobic** ("water-fearing") substances found in living things are especially important because of their ability to form associations or structures that are not disrupted. Hydrophobic interactions occur between groups of nonpolar molecules. Such molecules are insoluble in water and tend to cluster together. This tendency is not due to formation of bonds between the nonpolar molecules but rather to the hydrogen-bonded water molecules excluding them and in a sense "driving them together." **Hydrophobic interactions** explain why oil tends to form globules when added to water. Examples of hydrophobic substances include fatty acids and cholesterol, discussed in Chapter 3.

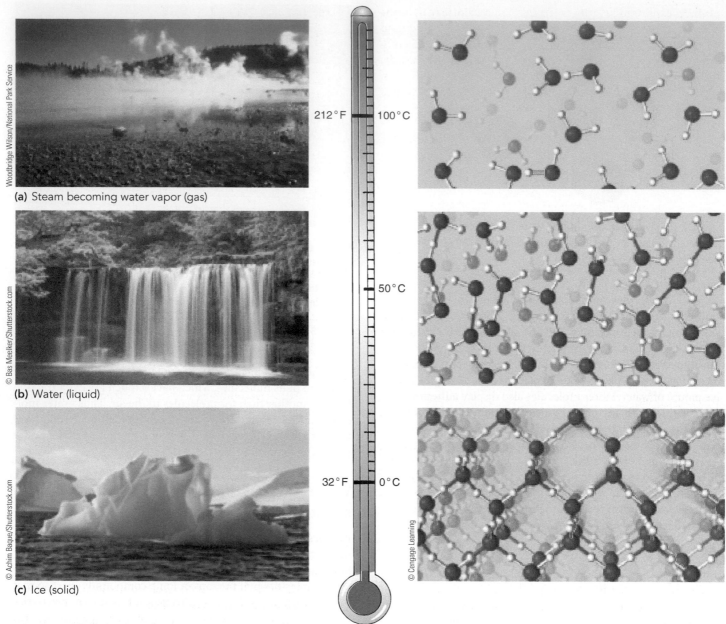

Figure 2-16 Three forms of water

(a) When water boils, as in this hot spring at Yellowstone National Park, many hydrogen bonds are broken, causing steam, which consists of minuscule water droplets, to form. If most of the remaining hydrogen bonds break, the molecules move more freely as water vapor (a gas). **(b)** Water molecules in a liquid state continually form, break, and re-form hydrogen bonds with one another. **(c)** In ice, each water molecule participates in four hydrogen bonds with adjacent molecules, resulting in a regular, evenly distanced crystalline lattice structure.

Water helps maintain a stable temperature

Hydrogen bonding explains the way water responds to changes in temperature. Water exists in three forms, which differ in their degree of hydrogen bonding: gas (vapor); liquid; and ice, a crystalline solid (**FIG. 2-16**). Hydrogen bonds are formed or broken as water changes from one state to another.

Raising the temperature of a substance involves adding heat energy to make its molecules move faster, that is, to increase the energy of motion—**kinetic energy**—of the molecules (see Chapter 7). The term **heat** refers to the *total* amount of kinetic energy in a sample of a substance; **temperature** is a measure of the *average*

kinetic energy of the particles. For the molecules to move more freely, some of the hydrogen bonds of water must be broken.

Much of the energy added to the system is used in breaking the hydrogen bonds, and only a portion of the heat energy is available to speed the movement of the water molecules, thereby increasing the temperature of the water. Conversely, when liquid water changes to ice, additional hydrogen bonds must be formed, making the molecules less free to move and liberating a great deal of heat into the environment.

Heat of vaporization, the amount of heat energy required to change 1 g of a substance from the liquid phase to the vapor phase, is expressed in units called *calories*. A **calorie (cal)** is the amount of heat energy (equivalent to 4.184 joules [J]) required to raise the temperature of 1 g of water 1 degree Celsius (C). Water has a high heat of vaporization—540 cal—because its molecules are held together by hydrogen bonds. The heat of vaporization of most other common liquid substances is much less. As a sample of water is heated, some molecules are moving much faster than others (they have more heat). These faster-moving molecules are more likely to escape the liquid phase and enter the vapor phase (see Fig. 2-16a). When they do, they take their heat with them, lowering the temperature of the sample in a process called *evaporative cooling*. For this reason, the human body can dissipate excess heat as sweat evaporates from the skin, and a leaf can keep cool in the bright sunlight as water evaporates from its surface.

Hydrogen bonding is also responsible for water's high **specific heat**; that is, the amount of energy required to raise the temperature of water is quite large. The specific heat of water is 1 cal/g of water per degree Celsius. Most other common substances, such as metals, glass, and ethyl alcohol, have much lower specific heat values. The specific heat of ethyl alcohol, for example, is 0.59 cal/g/1°C (2.46 J/g/1°C).

Because so much heat input is required to raise the temperature of water (and so much heat is lost when the temperature is lowered), the ocean and other large bodies of water have relatively constant temperatures. Thus, many organisms living in the ocean are provided with a relatively constant environmental temperature. The properties of water are crucial in stabilizing temperatures on Earth's surface. Although surface water is only a thin film relative to Earth's volume, the quantity is enormous compared to the exposed landmass. This relatively large mass of water resists both the warming effect of heat and the cooling effect of low temperatures.

Hydrogen bonding causes ice to have unique properties with important environmental consequences. Liquid water expands as it freezes because the hydrogen bonds joining the water molecules in the crystalline lattice keep the molecules far enough apart to give ice a density about 10% less than the density of liquid water (see Fig. 2-16c). When ice has been heated enough to raise its temperature above 0°C (32°F), the hydrogen bonds are broken, freeing the molecules to slip closer together. The density of water is greatest at 4°C. Above that temperature water begins to expand again as the speed of its molecules increases. As a result, ice floats on the denser cold water.

This unusual property of water has been important to the evolution of life. If ice had a greater density than water, the ice would sink; eventually, all ponds, lakes, and even the ocean would freeze solid from the bottom to the surface, making life impossible. When a deep body of water cools, it becomes covered with floating ice. The ice insulates the liquid water below it, retarding freezing and permitting organisms to survive below the icy surface.

The high water content of organisms helps them maintain relatively constant internal temperatures. Such minimizing of temperature fluctuations is important because biological reactions can take place only within a relatively narrow temperature range.

CHECKPOINT 2.5

- *What properties of a water molecule enable it to participate in the formation of hydrogen bonds?*
- **CONNECT** *What are some properties of water that result from hydrogen bonding? How do these properties contribute to the role of water as an essential component of organisms?*
- **CONNECT** *How can weak forces, such as hydrogen bonds, have significant effects in organisms?*

2.6 ACIDS, BASES, AND SALTS

LEARNING OBJECTIVES

10 Contrast acids and bases, and discuss their properties.
11 Convert the hydrogen ion concentration (moles per liter) of a solution to a pH value and describe how buffers help minimize changes in pH.
12 Describe the composition of a salt and explain the ways in which salts are important in organisms.

Water molecules have a slight tendency to ionize, that is, to dissociate into hydrogen ions (H^+) and hydroxide ions (OH^-). The H^+ immediately combines with a negatively charged region of a water molecule, forming a hydronium ion (H_3O^+). However, by convention, H^+, rather than the more accurate H_3O^+, is used. In pure water, a small number of water molecules ionize. This slight tendency of water to dissociate is reversible because hydrogen ions and hydroxide ions reunite to form water.

$$HOH \rightleftharpoons H^+ + OH^-$$

Because each water molecule splits into one hydrogen ion and one hydroxide ion, the concentrations of hydrogen ions and hydroxide ions in pure water are exactly equal (0.0000001 or 10^{-7} mol/L for each ion). Such a solution is said to be neutral, that is, neither acidic nor basic (alkaline).

An acid is a substance that dissociates in solution to yield hydrogen ions (H^+) and anions.

$$Acid \longrightarrow H^+ + anion$$

An **acid** is a proton *donor*. (Recall that a hydrogen ion, or H^+, is nothing more than a proton.) Hydrochloric acid (HCl) is a common inorganic acid.

A **base** is defined as a proton *acceptor*. Most bases are substances that dissociate to yield a hydroxide ion (OH^-) and a cation when dissolved in water.

$$NaOH \longrightarrow Na^+ + OH^-$$

A hydroxide ion can act as a base by accepting a proton (H^+) to form water.

$$OH^- + H^+ \longrightarrow H_2O$$

Sodium hydroxide (NaOH) is a common inorganic base. Some bases do not dissociate to yield hydroxide ions directly. For example, ammonia (NH_3) acts as a base by accepting a proton from water, producing an ammonium ion (NH_4^+) and releasing a hydroxide ion from water.

$$NH_3 + H_2O \longrightarrow NH_4^+ + OH^-$$

pH is a convenient measure of acidity

The degree of a solution's acidity is generally expressed in terms of **pH,** defined as the negative logarithm (base 10) of the hydrogen ion concentration (expressed in moles per liter):

$$pH = -\log_{10}[H^+]$$

The brackets refer to concentration; therefore, $[H^+]$ means "the concentration of hydrogen ions," which is expressed in moles per liter because we are interested in the *number* of hydrogen ions per liter. Because the range of possible pH values is broad, a logarithmic scale (with a 10-fold difference between successive units) is more convenient than a linear scale.

Hydrogen ion concentrations are nearly always less than 1 mol/L. One gram of hydrogen ions dissolved in 1 L of water (a 1 *M* solution) may not sound impressive, but such a solution would be extremely acidic. The logarithm of a number less than 1 is a negative number; thus, the *negative* logarithm corresponds to a *positive* pH value. (Solutions with pH values less than zero can be produced but do not occur under biological conditions.)

Whole-number pH values are easy to calculate. For instance, consider our example of pure water, which has a hydrogen ion concentration of 0.0000001 (10^{-7}) mol/L. The logarithm is –7. The negative logarithm is 7; therefore, the pH is 7. **TABLE 2-2** shows how to calculate pH values from hydrogen ion concentrations and how to do the reverse. For comparison, the table also includes the hydroxide ion concentrations, which can be calculated because the product of the hydrogen ion concentration and the hydroxide ion concentration is 1×10^{-14}:

$$[H^+][OH^-] = 1 \times 10^{-14}$$

Pure water is an example of a **neutral solution;** with a pH of 7, it has equal concentrations of hydrogen ions and hydroxide ions (the concentration of each is 10^{-7} mol/L). An **acidic solution** has a hydrogen ion concentration that is higher than its hydroxide ion concentration and has a pH value of less than 7. For example, the hydrogen ion concentration of a solution with pH 1 is ten times that of a solution with pH 2. A **basic solution** has a hydrogen ion concentration that is lower than its hydroxide ion concentration and has a pH greater than 7.

The pH values of some common substances are shown in **FIG. 2-17.** Although some very acidic compartments exist within cells (see Chapter 4), most of the interior of an animal or plant cell is neither strongly acidic nor strongly basic; rather, it is an

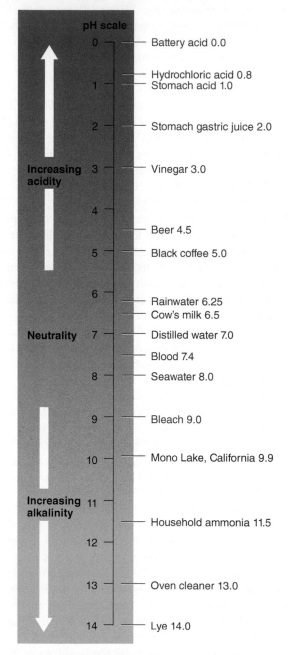

Figure 2-17 pH values of some common solutions
A neutral solution (pH 7) has equal concentrations of H^+ and OH^-. Acidic solutions, which have a higher concentration of H^+ than OH^-, have pH values less than 7; pH values greater than 7 characterize basic solutions, which have an excess of OH^-.

© Cengage Learning

TABLE 2-2	Calculating pH Values and Hydroxide Ion Concentrations from Hydrogen Ion Concentrations			
SUBSTANCE	$[H^+]$*	LOG $[H^+]$	pH	$[OH^-]$†
Gastric juice	0.01, 10^{-2}	–2	2	10^{-12}
Pure water, neutral solution	0.0000001, 10^{-7}	–7	7	10^{-7}
Household ammonia	0.00000000001, 10^{-11}	–11	11	10^{-3}

*$[H^+]$ = hydrogen ion concentration (mol/L)

†$[OH^-]$ = hydroxide ion concentration (mol/L)

© Cengage Learning

essentially neutral mixture of acidic and basic substances. Certain bacteria are adapted to life in extremely acidic environments (discussed in Chapter 25), but a substantial change in pH is incompatible with life for most cells. The pH of most types of plant and animal cells (and their environment) ordinarily ranges from around 7.2 to 7.4.

Buffers minimize pH change

Many mechanisms operate to maintain appropriate pH values in organisms. For example, the pH of human blood is about 7.4 and must be maintained within very narrow limits. If the blood becomes too acidic (e.g., as a result of respiratory disease), coma and death may result. Excessive alkalinity can result in overexcitability of the nervous system and even convulsions. Organisms contain many natural buffers. A **buffer** is a substance or combination of substances that resists changes in pH when an acid or base is added. A buffering system includes a weak acid or a weak base. A weak acid or weak base does not ionize completely. At any given instant, only a fraction of the molecules are ionized; most are not dissociated.

One of the most common buffering systems functions in the blood of vertebrates (see Chapter 46). Carbon dioxide, produced as a waste product of cell metabolism, enters the blood, the main constituent of which is water. The carbon dioxide reacts with the water to form carbonic acid, a weak acid that dissociates to yield a hydrogen ion and a bicarbonate ion. The following expression describes the buffering system:

$$CO_2 + H_2O \rightleftharpoons H_2CO_3 \rightleftharpoons H^+ + HCO_3^-$$

Carbon dioxide Water Carbonic acid Bicarbonate ion

As the double arrows indicate, all the reactions are reversible. Because carbonic acid is a weak acid, undissociated molecules are always present, as are all the other components of the system. The expression describes the system when it is at dynamic equilibrium, that is, when the rates of the forward and reverse reactions are equal and the relative concentrations of the components are not changing. A system at dynamic equilibrium tends to stay at equilibrium unless a stress is placed on it, which causes it to shift to reduce the stress until it attains a new dynamic equilibrium. A change in the concentration of any component is one such stress. Therefore, the system can be "shifted to the right" by adding reactants or removing products. Conversely, the system can be "shifted to the left" by adding products or removing reactants.

Hydrogen ions are the important products to consider in this system. The addition of excess hydrogen ions temporarily shifts the system to the left as they combine with the bicarbonate ions to form carbonic acid. Eventually, a new dynamic equilibrium is established. At this point the hydrogen ion concentration is similar to the original concentration, and the product of the hydrogen ion and hydroxide ion concentrations is restored to the equilibrium value of 1×10^{-14}.

If hydroxide ions are added, they combine with the hydrogen ions to form water, effectively removing a product and thus shifting the system to the right. As this process occurs, more carbonic acid ionizes, effectively replacing the hydrogen ions that were removed.

Organisms contain many weak acids and weak bases, which allows them to maintain an essential reserve of buffering capacity and helps them avoid pH extremes.

An acid and a base react to form a salt

When an acid and a base are mixed in water, the H^+ of the acid unites with the OH^- of the base to form a molecule of water. The remainder of the acid (an anion) combines with the remainder of the base (a cation) to form a salt. For example, hydrochloric acid reacts with sodium hydroxide to form water and sodium chloride:

$$HCl + NaOH \longrightarrow H_2O + NaCl$$

A **salt** is a compound in which the hydrogen ion of an acid is replaced by some other cation. Sodium chloride, NaCl, is a salt in which the hydrogen ion of HCl has been replaced by the cation Na^+.

When a salt, an acid, or a base is dissolved in water, its dissociated ions can conduct an electric current; these substances are called **electrolytes.** Sugars, alcohols, and many other substances do not form ions when dissolved in water; they do not conduct an electric current and are referred to as *non-electrolytes.*

Cells and extracellular fluids (such as blood) of animals and plants contain a variety of dissolved salts that are the source of the many important mineral ions essential for fluid balance and acid–base balance. Nitrate and ammonium ions from the soil are the important nitrogen sources for plants. In animals, nerve and muscle function, blood clotting, bone formation, and many other aspects of body function depend on ions. Sodium, potassium, calcium, and magnesium are the chief cations present; chloride, bicarbonate, phosphate, and sulfate are important anions. The concentrations and relative amounts of the various cations and anions are kept remarkably constant. Any marked change results in impaired cell functions and may lead to death.

CHECKPOINT 2.6

- *A solution has a hydrogen ion concentration of 0.01 mol/L. What is its pH? What is its hydroxide ion concentration? Is it acidic, basic, or neutral? How does the hydrogen ion concentration of this solution differ from one with a pH of 1?*

- **PREDICT** *Consider a reversible reaction that is at dynamic equilibrium. What would be the consequences of adding a reactant? adding a product? removing a reactant? removing a product?*

- **CONNECT** *What important role do buffers play in organisms? What prevents a strong acid or strong base from working as a buffer?*

- *What are the features of acids, bases, and salts that cause scientists to refer to them as electrolytes?*

2.1 Elements and Atoms (page 26)

1 Name the principal chemical elements in living things and provide an important function of each.

- An **element** is a substance that cannot be decomposed into simpler substances by normal chemical reactions. About 96% of an organism's mass consists of carbon, the backbone of organic molecules; hydrogen and oxygen, the components of water; and nitrogen, a component of proteins and nucleic acids.

2 Compare the physical properties (mass and charge) and locations of electrons, protons, and neutrons. Distinguish between the atomic number and the mass number of an atom.

- Each **atom** is composed of a nucleus containing positively charged **protons** and uncharged **neutrons.** Negatively charged **electrons** encircle the nucleus.

- An atom is identified as belonging to a particular element by its number of protons (**atomic number**). The **atomic mass** of an atom is equal to the sum of its protons and neutrons.

- A single proton or a single neutron each has a mass equivalent to one **atomic mass unit (amu).** The mass of a single electron is only about 1/1800 amu.

3 Define the terms *orbital* and *electron shell*. Relate electron shells to principal energy levels.

- In the space outside the nucleus, electrons move rapidly in electron **orbitals.** An **electron shell** consists of electrons in orbitals at the same *principal energy level*. Electrons in a shell distant from the nucleus have greater energy than those in a shell closer to the nucleus.

2.2 Chemical Reactions (page 30)

4 Explain how the number of valence electrons of an atom is related to its chemical properties.

- The chemical properties of an atom are determined chiefly by the number and arrangement of its most energetic electrons, known as **valence electrons.** The valence shell of most atoms is full when it contains 8 electrons; that of hydrogen or helium is full when it contains 2. An atom tends to lose, gain, or share electrons to fill its valence shell.

5 Distinguish among simplest, molecular, and structural chemical formulas.

- Different atoms are joined by chemical bonds to form **chemical compounds. A chemical formula** gives the types and relative numbers of atoms in a substance.

- A **simplest formula** gives the smallest whole-number ratio of the component atoms. A **molecular formula** gives the actual numbers of each type of atom in a molecule. A **structural formula** shows the arrangement of the atoms in a molecule.

6 Explain why the mole concept is so useful to chemists.

- One **mole** (the atomic or molecular mass in grams) of any substance contains 6.02×10^{23} atoms, molecules, or ions, enabling scientists to "count" particles by weighing a sample. This number is known as **Avogadro's number.**

2.3 Chemical Bonds (page 31)

7 Distinguish among covalent bonds, ionic bonds, hydrogen bonds, and van der Waals interactions. Compare them in terms of the mechanisms by which they form and their relative strengths.

- **Covalent bonds** are strong, stable bonds formed when atoms share valence electrons, forming molecules. When covalent bonds are formed, the orbitals of the valence electrons may

become rearranged in a process known as **orbital hybridization. Nonpolar covalent bonds** are formed if the electrons are shared equally between the two atoms. **Polar covalent bonds** are formed if one atom is more **electronegative** (has a greater affinity for electrons) than the other.

- An **ionic bond** is formed between a positively charged **cation** and a negatively charged **anion.** Ionic bonds are strong in the absence of water but relatively weak in aqueous solution.

- **Hydrogen bonds** are relatively weak bonds formed when a hydrogen atom with a partial positive charge is attracted to an atom (usually oxygen or nitrogen) with a partial negative charge already bonded to another molecule or in another part of the same molecule.

- **van der Waals interactions** are weak forces based on fluctuating electric charges.

2.4 Redox Reactions (page 35)

8 Distinguish between the terms *oxidation* and *reduction*, and relate these processes to the transfer of energy.

- **Oxidation** and **reduction** reactions (**redox reactions**) are chemical processes in which electrons (and their energy) are transferred from a reducing agent to an oxidizing agent. In oxidation, an atom, ion, or molecule loses electrons (and their energy). In reduction, an atom, ion, or molecule gains electrons (and their energy).

2.5 Water (page 36)

9 Explain how hydrogen bonds between adjacent water molecules govern many of the properties of water.

- Water is a **polar molecule** because one end has a partial positive charge and the other has a partial negative charge. Because its molecules are polar, water is an excellent **solvent** for ionic or polar **solutes.**

- Water molecules exhibit the property of **cohesion** because they form hydrogen bonds with one another; they also exhibit **adhesion** through hydrogen bonding to substances with ionic or polar regions.

- Water has a high **heat of vaporization.** Hydrogen bonds must be broken for molecules to enter the vapor phase. These molecules carry a great deal of heat, which accounts for *evaporative cooling.*

- Because hydrogen bonds must be broken to raise its temperature, water has a high **specific heat,** which helps organisms maintain a relatively constant internal temperature; this property also helps keep the ocean and other large bodies of water at a constant temperature.

- The hydrogen bonds between water molecules in ice cause it to be less dense than liquid water. Because ice floats, the aquatic environment is less extreme than it would be if ice sank to the bottom.

2.6 Acids, Bases, and Salts (page 39)

10 Contrast acids and bases, and discuss their properties.

- **Acids** are proton (hydrogen ion, H^+) donors; **bases** are proton acceptors. An acid dissociates in solution to yield H^+ and an anion. Many bases dissociate in solution to yield hydroxide ions (OH^-), which then accept protons to form water.

11 Convert the hydrogen ion concentration (moles per liter) of a solution to a pH value and describe how buffers help minimize changes in pH.

- **pH** is the negative log of the hydrogen ion concentration of a solution (expressed in moles per liter). A **neutral solution** with equal concentrations of H⁺ and OH⁻ (10^{-7} mol/L) has a pH of 7, an **acidic solution** has a pH less than 7, and a **basic solution** has a pH greater than 7.
- A buffering system is based on a weak acid or a weak base. A **buffer** resists changes in the pH of a solution when acids or bases are added.

12 Describe the composition of a salt and explain the ways in which salts are important in organisms.
- A **salt** is a compound in which the hydrogen atom of an acid is replaced by some other cation. Salts provide the many mineral ions essential for life functions.

TEST YOUR UNDERSTANDING

Know and Comprehend

1. Which of the following elements is *mismatched* with its properties or function? (a) carbon—forms the backbone of organic compounds (b) nitrogen—component of proteins (c) hydrogen—very electronegative (d) oxygen—can participate in hydrogen bonding (e) all of the above are correctly matched

2. $^{32}_{15}$P, a radioactive form of phosphorus, has (a) an atomic number of 32 (b) an atomic mass of 15 (c) an atomic mass of 47 (d) 32 electrons (e) 17 neutrons

3. Which of the following facts allows you to determine that atom A and atom B are isotopes of the same element? (a) they each have 6 protons (b) they each have 4 neutrons (c) the sum of the electrons and neutrons in each is 14 (d) they each have 4 valence electrons (e) they each have an atomic mass of 14

4. $^1_1$H and $^3_1$H have (a) different chemical properties because they have different atomic numbers (b) the same chemical properties because they have the same number of valence electrons (c) different chemical properties because they differ in their number of protons and electrons (d) the same chemical properties because they have the same atomic mass (e) the same chemical properties because they have the same number of protons, electrons, and neutrons

5. The orbitals composing an atom's valence electron shell (a) are arranged as concentric spheres (b) contain the atom's least energetic electrons (c) may change shape when covalent bonds are formed (d) never contain more than 1 electron each (e) more than one of the preceding is correct

6. Which of the following bonds and properties are correctly matched? (a) ionic bonds; are strong only if the participating ions are hydrated (b) hydrogen bonds; are responsible for bonding oxygen and hydrogen to form a single water molecule (c) polar covalent bonds; can occur between two atoms of the same element (d) covalent bonds; may be single, double, or triple (e) hydrogen bonds; are stronger than covalent bonds

7. In a redox reaction, (a) energy is transferred from a reducing agent to an oxidizing agent (b) a reducing agent becomes oxidized as it accepts an electron (c) an oxidizing agent accepts a proton (d) a reducing agent donates a proton (e) the electrons in an atom move from its valence shell to a shell closer to its nucleus

8. Water has a high specific heat because (a) hydrogen bonds must be broken to raise its temperature (b) hydrogen bonds must be formed to raise its temperature (c) it is a poor insulator (d) it has low density considering the size of the molecule (e) it can ionize

9. A solution at pH 7 is considered neutral because (a) its hydrogen ion concentration is 0 mol/L (b) its hydroxide ion concentration is 0 mol/L (c) the product of its hydrogen ion concentration and its hydroxide ion concentration is 0 mol/L (d) its hydrogen ion concentration is equal to its hydroxide ion concentration (e) it is nonpolar

10. A solution with a pH of 2 has a hydrogen ion concentration that is ___ the hydrogen ion concentration of a solution with a pH of 4. (a) 1/2 (b) 1/100 (c) 2 times (d) 10 times (e) 100 times

11. Which of the following cannot function as a buffer? (a) phosphoric acid, a weak acid (b) sodium hydroxide, a strong base (c) sodium chloride, a salt that ionizes completely (d) a and c (e) b and c

12. Which of the following statements is true? (a) the number of individual particles (atoms, ions, or molecules) contained in one mole varies depending on the substance (b) Avogadro's number is the number of particles contained in one mole of a substance (c) Avogadro's number is 10^{23} particles (d) one mole of ^{12}C has a mass of 12 g (e) b and d

Apply and Analyze

13. **VISUALIZE** Sketch simple Bohr diagrams for Elements A, B, and C. Element A has 2 electrons in its valence shell (which is complete when it contains 8 electrons). Would you expect element A to share, donate, or accept electrons? What would you expect of element B, which has 4 valence electrons, and element C, which has 7?

14. Consider the following reaction (in water):

$$HCl \longrightarrow H^+ + Cl^-$$

Name the reactant(s) and product(s). Does the expression indicate that the reaction is reversible? Could HCl be used as a buffer?

15. **INTERPRET DATA** Could you safely immerse your hand in water that contains 0.000,000,000,001 g of H⁺ per liter?

Evaluate and Synthesize

16. **PREDICT** A hydrogen bond formed between two water molecules is only about 1/20 as strong as a covalent bond between hydrogen and oxygen. In what ways would the physical properties of water be different if these hydrogen bonds were stronger (e.g., 1/10 the strength of covalent bonds)? What if hydrogen bonds were weaker (e.g., 1/100 the strength of covalent bonds)?

17. **EVOLUTION LINK** Scientists have proposed various initiatives to detect water vapor, as well as oxygen and carbon dioxide, in the atmospheres of distant planets. Which of these *biosignatures* (chemical markers that are evidence for life) would you consider the most fundamental indicator that life could have evolved on these planets? Explain your reasoning.

 To access course materials, such as Aplia and other companion resources, please visit **www.cengagebrain.com**.

The Chemistry of Life: Organic Compounds

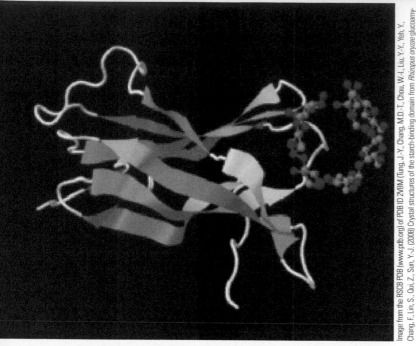

A computer-generated model of the starch-binding domain (*yellow* and *white*) of glycamylase, a fungal protein enzyme. The *red* and *gray* ring-shaped structure is β-cyclodextran, a polymer of glucose made by the partial digestion of starch.

KEY CONCEPTS

3.1 Carbon atoms join with one another or other atoms to form large molecules with a wide variety of shapes. Hydrocarbons are non-polar, hydrophobic molecules; their properties can be altered by adding functional groups.

3.2 Carbohydrates are composed of sugar subunits (monosaccharides), which can be joined to form disaccharides, storage polysaccharides, and structural polysaccharides.

3.3 Lipids store energy (triacylglycerols) and are the main structural components of cell membranes (phospholipids).

3.4 Proteins have multiple levels of structure and are composed of amino acid subunits joined by peptide bonds. The amino acid sequences of these large molecules produce diverse structures with many different types of functions.

3.5 Nucleic acids (DNA and RNA) are informational molecules composed of long chains of nucleotide subunits. ATP and some other nucleotides have a central role in energy metabolism.

3.6 Biological molecules have recognizable attributes that aid in their identification.

oth inorganic and organic forms of carbon occur widely in nature. Organic compounds are those in which carbon atoms are covalently bonded to one another to form the backbone of the molecule. Some very simple carbon compounds are considered inorganic if the carbon is not bonded to another carbon or to hydrogen. The carbon dioxide we exhale as a waste product from the breakdown of organic molecules to obtain energy is an example of an inorganic carbon compound. Organic compounds are so named because at one time it was thought that they could be produced only by living (organic) organisms. In 1828, German chemist Friedrich Wühler synthesized urea, a metabolic waste product. Since that time, scientists have learned to synthesize many organic molecules and have discovered organic compounds not found in any organism.

Organic compounds are extraordinarily diverse, and millions have been identified. There are many reasons for this diversity. Organic compounds can be produced in a wide variety of three-dimensional (3-D) shapes. Furthermore, the carbon atom forms bonds with a greater number of different elements than does any other type of atom. The addition of chemical groups containing atoms of other elements—especially oxygen, nitrogen, phosphorus, and sulfur—can profoundly change the properties of an organic molecule. Extremely large *macromolecules*, which cells construct from simpler modular subunits, are an important source of diversity. For example, protein molecules are built from smaller compounds called *amino acids*. Proteins have many different types of 3-D structures that depend on the composition and arrangements of their amino acid subunits. The function of an individual protein is determined by its structure.

As you study this chapter, you will develop an understanding of the major groups of organic compounds found in organisms, including carbohydrates, lipids, proteins, and nucleic acids (DNA and RNA). Why are these compounds of central importance to all living things? The answer to this question will become more obvious as you study subsequent chapters, in which we explore the evidence that all living things evolved from a common ancestor. Evolution provides a powerful explanation for the similarities of the molecules that make up the structures of cells and tissues, participate in and regulate metabolic reactions, transmit information, and provide energy for life processes.

3.1 CARBON ATOMS AND ORGANIC MOLECULES

LEARNING OBJECTIVES

1 Describe the properties of carbon that make it the central component of organic compounds.
2 Define the term *isomer* and distinguish among the three principal isomer types.
3 Identify the major functional groups present in organic compounds and describe their properties.
4 Explain the relationship between polymers and macromolecules.

Carbon has unique properties that allow the formation of the carbon backbones of the large, complex molecules essential to life (FIG. 3-1). Because a carbon atom has 4 valence electrons, it can complete its valence shell by forming a total of 4 covalent bonds (see Fig. 2-2). Each bond can link it to another carbon atom or to an atom of a different element. Carbon is particularly well suited to serve as the backbone of a large molecule because carbon-to-carbon bonds are strong and not easily broken. However, they are not so strong that it would be impossible for cells to break them. Carbon-to-carbon bonds are not limited to single bonds (based on sharing one electron pair).

Two carbon atoms can share two electron pairs with each other, forming double bonds:

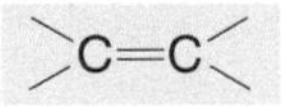

$$>C=C<$$

In some compounds, triple carbon-to-carbon bonds are formed:

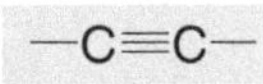

$$-C\equiv C-$$

As shown in Figure 3-1, **hydrocarbons,** organic compounds consisting only of carbon and hydrogen, can exist as unbranched or branched chains, or as rings. Rings and chains are joined in some compounds.

The molecules in the cell are analogous to the components of a machine. Each component has a shape that allows it to fill certain roles and to interact with other components (often with a complementary shape). Similarly, the shape of a molecule is important in determining its biological properties and function. Carbon atoms can link to one another and to other atoms to produce a wide variety of 3-D molecular shapes because the four covalent bonds of carbon do not form in a single plane. Instead, as discussed in Chapter 2, the valence electron orbitals become elongated and project from the carbon atom toward the corners of a tetrahedron (FIG. 3-2). The structure is highly symmetrical, with an angle of about 109.5 degrees between any two of these bonds. Keep in mind that for simplicity, many of the figures in this book are drawn as two-dimensional (2-D) graphic representations of 3-D molecules. Even the simplest hydrocarbon

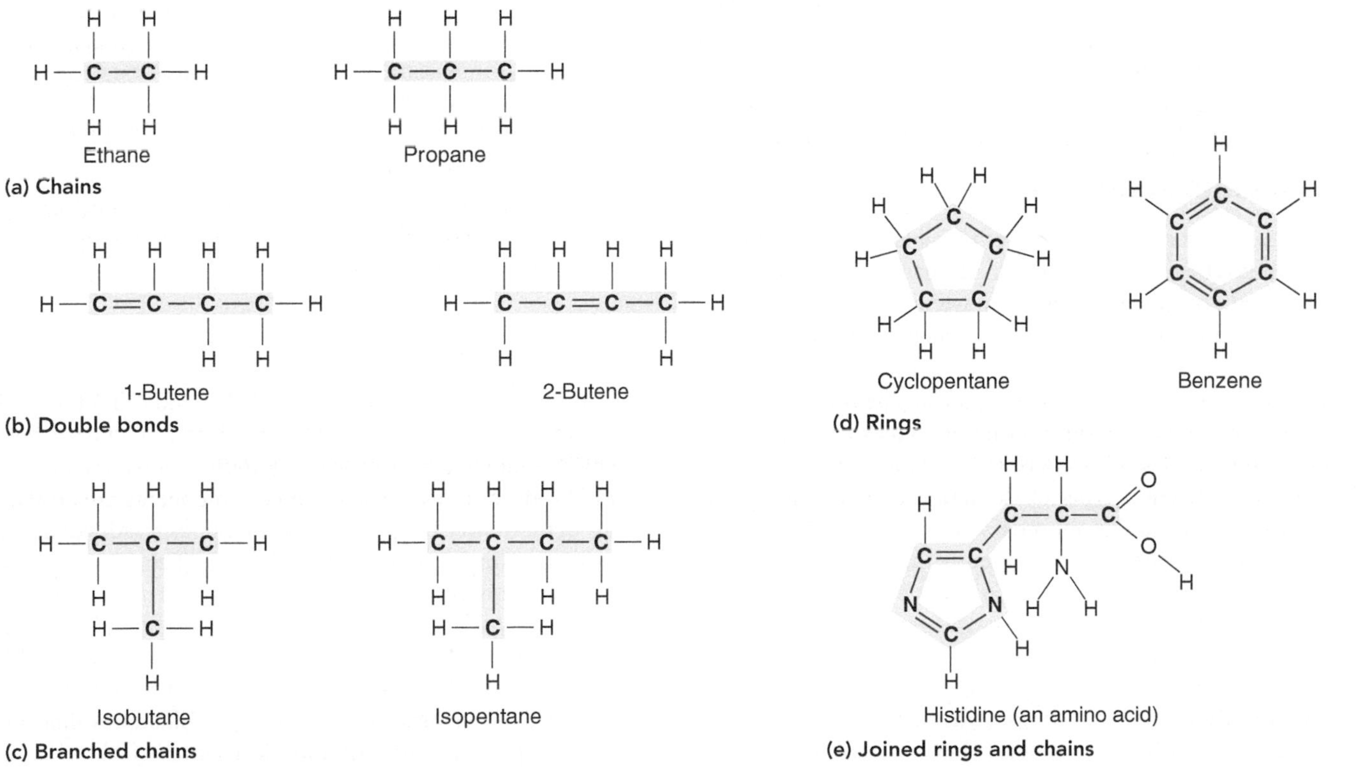

Figure 3-1 Diversity of organic molecules
Note that each carbon atom forms four covalent bonds, producing a wide variety of molecular shapes and sizes.
© Cengage Learning

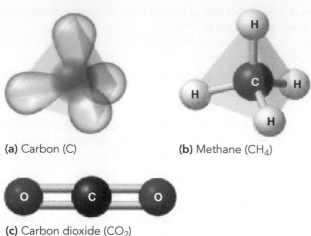

(a) Carbon (C)　　　　**(b)** Methane (CH₄)

(c) Carbon dioxide (CO₂)

Figure 3-2　Carbon bonding

(a) The 3-D arrangement of the electron orbitals of a carbon atom is responsible for **(b)** the tetrahedral architecture of methane. **(c)** In carbon dioxide, oxygen atoms are joined linearly to a central carbon by polar double bonds.

© Cengage Learning

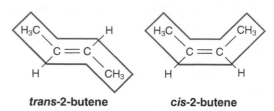

Ethanol (C_2H_6O)　　　Dimethyl ether (C_2H_6O)

(a) Structural isomers. Structural isomers differ in the covalent arrangement of their atoms.

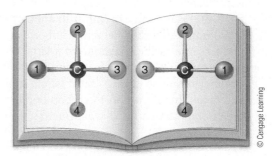

trans-2-butene　　　*cis*-2-butene

(b) Geometric isomers. Geometric, or *cis–trans*, isomers have identical covalent bonds but differ in the order in which groups are arranged in space.

© Cengage Learning

(c) Enantiomers. Enantiomers are isomers that are mirror images of each other. The central carbon is asymmetrical because it is bonded to four different groups. Because of their 3-D structure, the two figures cannot be superimposed no matter how they are rotated.

Figure 3-3　Isomers

Isomers have the same molecular formula, but their atoms are arranged differently.

chains, such as those in Figure 3-1, are not actually straight but have a 3-D zigzag structure.

Generally, there is freedom of rotation around each carbon-to-carbon single bond. This property permits organic molecules to be flexible and to assume a variety of shapes, depending on the extent to which each single bond is rotated. Double and triple bonds do not allow rotation, so regions of a molecule with such bonds tend to be inflexible.

Isomers have the same molecular formula but different structures

One reason for the great number of possible carbon-containing compounds is that the same components usually can link in more than one pattern, generating an even wider variety of molecular shapes. Compounds with the same molecular formulas but different structures and thus different properties are called **isomers.** Isomers do not have identical physical or chemical properties and may have different common names. Cells can distinguish between isomers. Usually, one isomer is biologically active and the other is not. Three types of isomers are structural isomers, geometric isomers, and enantiomers.

Structural isomers are compounds that differ in the covalent arrangements of their atoms. For example, **FIGURE 3-3a** illustrates two structural isomers with the molecular formula C_2H_6O. Large compounds have more possible structural isomers. There can be up to 366,319 isomers of $C_{20}H_{42}$.

Geometric isomers are compounds that are identical in the arrangement of their covalent bonds but different in the spatial arrangement of atoms or groups of atoms. Geometric isomers are present in some compounds with carbon-to-carbon double bonds. Because double bonds are not flexible, as single bonds are,

atoms joined to the carbons of a double bond cannot rotate freely about the axis of the bonds. These *cis–trans* isomers may be represented as shown in **FIGURE 3-3b**. The designation *cis* (Latin, "on this side") indicates that the two larger components are on the same side of the double bond. If they are on opposite sides of the double bond, the compound is designated a *trans* (Latin, "across") isomer.

Enantiomers are isomers that are mirror images of each other (**FIG. 3-3c**). Recall that the four groups bonded to a single carbon atom are arranged at the vertices of a tetrahedron. If the four bonded groups are all different, the central carbon is described as asymmetrical. Figure 3-3c illustrates that the four groups can be arranged around the asymmetrical carbon in two different ways that are mirror images of each other. The two molecules are enantiomers if they cannot be superimposed on each other no matter how they are rotated in space. Although enantiomers have similar chemical properties and most of their physical properties are identical, cells recognize the difference in shape, and usually only one form is found in organisms.

Functional groups change the properties of organic molecules

The existence of isomers is not the only source of variety among organic molecules. The addition of various combinations of atoms generates a vast array of molecules with different properties. Because covalent bonds between hydrogen and carbon are nonpolar, **hydrocarbons** lack distinct charged regions. For this reason, hydrocarbons are insoluble in water and tend to cluster together through **hydrophobic interactions.** "Water fearing," the literal meaning of the term *hydrophobic*, is somewhat misleading. Hydrocarbons interact with water, but much more weakly than the water molecules cohere to one another through hydrogen bonding. Hydrocarbons interact weakly with one another, but the main reason for hydrophobic interactions is that they are driven together in a sense, having been excluded by the hydrogen-bonded water molecules.

However, the characteristics of an organic molecule can be changed dramatically by replacing one or more of the hydrogens with a **functional group,** a group of atoms that help determine the types of chemical reactions and associations in which the compound participates. Most functional groups readily form associations, such as ionic and hydrogen bonds, with other molecules. Polar and ionic functional groups are **hydrophilic** because they associate strongly with polar water molecules.

The properties of the major classes of biologically important organic compounds—carbohydrates, lipids, proteins, and nucleic acids—are largely a consequence of the types and arrangement of functional groups they contain. When we know what kinds of functional groups are present in an organic compound, we can predict its chemical behavior. Note that the symbol *R* is used to represent the *remainder* of the molecule of which each functional group is a part. For example, the **methyl group,** a common nonpolar hydrocarbon group, is abbreviated $R—CH_3$. As you read the rest of this section, refer to TABLE 3-1 for the structural formulas of other important functional groups, as well as for additional information.

The **hydroxyl group** (abbreviated $R—OH$) is polar because of the presence of a strongly electronegative oxygen atom. Do not confuse it with the hydroxide ion, OH^-, discussed in Chapter 2. If a hydroxyl group replaces one hydrogen of a hydrocarbon, the resulting molecule can have significantly altered properties. For example, ethane (see Fig. 3-1a) is a hydrocarbon that is a gas at room temperature. If a hydroxyl group replaces a hydrogen atom, the resulting molecule is ethyl alcohol, or ethanol, which is found in alcoholic beverages (see Fig. 3-3a). Ethanol is somewhat cohesive because the polar hydroxyl groups of adjacent molecules interact; it is therefore liquid at room temperature. Unlike ethane, ethyl alcohol dissolves in water because the polar hydroxyl groups interact with the polar water molecules.

The **carbonyl group** consists of a carbon atom that has a double covalent bond with an oxygen atom. This double bond is polar because of the electronegativity of the oxygen; thus, the carbonyl group is hydrophilic. The position of the carbonyl group in the molecule determines the class to which the molecule belongs. An **aldehyde** has a carbonyl group positioned at the end of the carbon skeleton (abbreviated $R—CHO$); a **ketone** has an internal carbonyl group (abbreviated $R—CO—R$).

The **carboxyl group** (abbreviated $R—COOH$) in its non-ionized form consists of a carbon atom joined by a double covalent bond to an oxygen atom as well as by a single covalent bond to another oxygen, which is in turn bonded to a hydrogen atom. Two electronegative oxygen atoms in such close proximity establish an extremely polarized condition, which can cause the hydrogen atom to be stripped of its electron and released as a hydrogen ion (H^+). The resulting ionized carboxyl group has 1 unit of negative charge ($R—COO^-$):

$$R—C\!\!\!\begin{array}{c} O \\ \\ O—H \end{array} \longrightarrow R—C\!\!\!\begin{array}{c} O \\ \\ O^- \end{array} + H^+$$

Carboxyl groups are weakly acidic; only a fraction of the molecules ionize in this way. This group therefore exists in one of two hydrophilic states: ionic or polar. Carboxyl groups are essential constituents of amino acids.

An **amino group** (abbreviated $R—NH_2$) in its non-ionized form includes a nitrogen atom covalently bonded to two hydrogen atoms. Amino groups are weakly basic because they are able to accept a hydrogen ion (proton). The resulting ionized amino group has 1 unit of positive charge ($R—NH_3^+$). Amino groups are components of amino acids and of nucleic acids.

A **phosphate group** (abbreviated $R—PO_4H_2$) is weakly acidic. The attraction of electrons by the oxygen atoms can result in the release of one or two hydrogen ions, producing ionized forms with 1 or 2 units of negative charge. Phosphates are constituents of nucleic acids and certain lipids.

The **sulfhydryl group** (abbreviated $R—SH$), consisting of an atom of sulfur covalently bonded to a hydrogen atom, is found in molecules called *thiols*. As you will see, amino acids that contain a sulfhydryl group can make important contributions to the structure of proteins.

Many biological molecules are polymers

Many biological molecules such as proteins and nucleic acids are very large, consisting of thousands of atoms. Such giant molecules are known as **macromolecules.** Most macromolecules are **polymers,** produced by linking small organic compounds called **monomers** (FIG. 3-4). Just as all the words in this book have been written by arranging the 26 letters of the alphabet in various combinations, monomers can be grouped to form an almost infinite variety of larger molecules. The thousands of different complex organic compounds present in organisms are constructed from about 40 small, simple monomers. For example, the 20 monomers called *amino acids* can be linked end to end in countless ways to form the polymers known as *proteins*.

TABLE 3-1 | Some Biologically Important Functional Groups

FUNCTIONAL GROUP AND DESCRIPTION	STRUCTURAL FORMULA	CLASS OF COMPOUND CHARACTERIZED BY GROUP
HYDROXYL Polar because electronegative oxygen attracts covalent electrons	R—**OH**	Alcohols $\begin{array}{c} H\;\;\;H \\ \mid\;\;\;\mid \\ H-C-C-OH \\ \mid\;\;\;\mid \\ H\;\;\;H \end{array}$ Example, ethanol
CARBONYL **Aldehydes:** Carbonyl group carbon is bonded to at least one H atom; polar because electronegative oxygen attracts covalent electrons	$R-\overset{\displaystyle O}{\underset{}{C}}-H$	Aldehydes $H-\overset{\displaystyle O}{\underset{}{C}}-H$ Example, formaldehyde
Ketones: Carbonyl group carbon is bonded to two other carbons; polar because electronegative oxygen attracts covalent electrons	$R-\overset{\displaystyle O}{\underset{}{C}}-R$	Ketones $\begin{array}{c} H\;\;\;O\;\;\;H \\ \mid\;\;\;\parallel\;\;\;\mid \\ H-C-C-C-H \\ \mid\;\;\;\;\;\;\;\;\mid \\ H\;\;\;\;\;\;\;\;H \end{array}$ Example, acetone
CARBOXYL Weakly acidic; can release an H^+	$R-\overset{\displaystyle O}{\underset{}{C}}-OH$ Non-ionized $\qquad$ $R-\overset{\displaystyle O}{\underset{}{C}}-O^- + H^+$ Ionized	Carboxylic acids (organic acids) $R-\overset{\displaystyle O}{\underset{}{C}}-OH$ Example, amino acid
AMINO Weakly basic; can accept an H^+	$R-\overset{H}{\underset{H}{N}}$ Non-ionized $\qquad$ $R-\overset{H}{\underset{H}{N^+}}-H$ Ionized	Amines $R-\overset{\mathbf{NH_2}}{\underset{H}{C}}-\overset{O}{\underset{}{C}}-OH$ Example, amino acid
PHOSPHATE Weakly acidic; one or two H^+ can be released	$R-O-\overset{\displaystyle O}{\underset{OH}{P}}-OH$ Non-ionized $\qquad$ $R-O-\overset{\displaystyle O}{\underset{O^-}{P}}-O^-$ Ionized	Organic phosphates $HO-\overset{\displaystyle O}{\underset{OH}{P}}-O-R$ Example, phosphate ester (as found in ATP)
SULFHYDRYL Helps stabilize internal structure of proteins	R—**SH**	Thiols $\begin{array}{c} H\;\;\;H\;\;\;O \\ \mid\;\;\;\mid\;\;\;\parallel \\ H-C-C-C-OH \\ \mid\;\;\;\mid \\ SH\;\;NH_2 \end{array}$ Example, cysteine

© Cengage Learning

Polymers can be degraded to their component monomers by **hydrolysis reactions** ("to break with water"). In a reaction regulated by a specific enzyme (biological catalyst), a hydrogen from a water molecule attaches to one monomer, and a hydroxyl from water attaches to the adjacent monomer (**FIG. 3-5**).

Monomers become covalently linked by **condensation reactions.** Because the *equivalent* of a molecule of water is removed during the reactions that combine monomers, the term *dehydration synthesis* is sometimes used to describe condensation (see Fig. 3-5). However, in biological systems the synthesis

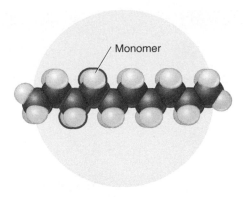

Figure 3-4 A simple polymer
This small polymer of polyethylene is formed by linking two-carbon ethylene (C_2H_4) monomers. One such monomer is outlined in *red*. The structure is represented by a space-filling model, which accurately depicts the 3-D shape of the molecule.
© Cengage Learning

of a polymer is not simply the reverse of hydrolysis, even though the net effect is the opposite of hydrolysis. Synthetic processes such as condensation require energy and are regulated by different enzymes.

In the following sections we examine carbohydrates, lipids, proteins, and nucleic acids. Our discussion begins with the smaller, simpler forms of these compounds and extends to the linking of these monomers to form macromolecules.

CHECKPOINT 3.1

- *What are some of the ways that the features of carbon-to-carbon bonds influence the stability and 3-D structure of organic molecules?*

- VISUALIZE *Draw pairs of simple sketches comparing two (1) structural isomers, (2) geometric isomers, and (3) enantiomers. Why are these differences biologically important?*

- VISUALIZE *Sketch the following functional groups: methyl, amino, carbonyl, hydroxyl, carboxyl, and phosphate. Include both non-ionized and ionized forms for acidic and basic groups.*

- CONNECT *How is the designation that a group is nonpolar, polar, acidic, or basic related to its hydrophilic or hydrophobic properties?*

- VISUALIZE *Draw simple sketches illustrating how the equivalent of a water molecule participates in the reactions of monomers in condensation and hydrolysis.*

3.2 CARBOHYDRATES

LEARNING OBJECTIVE

5 Distinguish among monosaccharides, disaccharides, and polysaccharides; compare storage polysaccharides with structural polysaccharides.

Sugars, starches, and cellulose are **carbohydrates.** Sugars and starches serve as energy sources for cells; cellulose is the main structural component of the walls that surround plant cells. Carbohydrates contain carbon, hydrogen, and oxygen atoms in a ratio of approximately one carbon to two hydrogens to one oxygen ($CH_2O)_n$. The term *carbohydrate*, meaning "hydrate (water) of carbon," reflects the 2:1 ratio of hydrogen to oxygen, the same ratio found in water (H_2O). Carbohydrates contain one sugar unit (monosaccharides), two sugar units (disaccharides), or many sugar units (polysaccharides).

Monosaccharides are simple sugars

Monosaccharides typically contain from three to seven carbon atoms. In a monosaccharide a hydroxyl group is bonded to each carbon except one; that carbon is double-bonded to an oxygen atom, forming a carbonyl group. If the carbonyl group is at the end of the chain, the monosaccharide is an aldehyde; if the carbonyl group is at any other position, the monosaccharide is a ketone. (By convention, the numbering of the carbon skeleton of a sugar begins with the carbon at or nearest the carbonyl end of the open chain.) The large number of polar hydroxyl groups, plus the carbonyl group, gives a monosaccharide hydrophilic properties. FIGURE 3-6 shows simplified, 2-D representations of some common monosaccharides. The simplest carbohydrates are the three-carbon sugars (trioses): glyceraldehyde and dihydroxyacetone. Ribose and deoxyribose are common pentoses, sugars that contain five carbons; they are components of nucleic acids (DNA, RNA, and related compounds). Glucose, fructose, galactose, and other six-carbon sugars are called hexoses. (Note that the names of carbohydrates typically end in *-ose*.)

Glucose ($C_6H_{12}O_6$), the most abundant monosaccharide, is used as an energy source in most organisms. During cellular respiration (see Chapter 8), cells oxidize glucose molecules, converting the stored energy to a form that can be readily used for cell work. Glucose is also used in the synthesis of other types of compounds such as amino acids and fatty acids. Glucose is

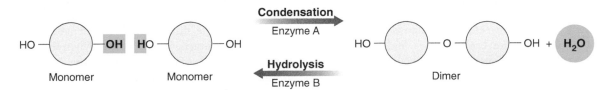

Figure 3-5 Condensation and hydrolysis reactions
Joining two monomers yields a dimer; incorporating additional monomers produces a polymer. Note that condensation and hydrolysis reactions are catalyzed by different enzymes.
© Cengage Learning

(a) Triose sugars (3-carbon sugars)

Glyceraldehyde ($C_3H_6O_3$)
(an aldehyde)

Dihydroxyacetone ($C_3H_6O_3$)
(a ketone)

(b) Pentose sugars (5-carbon sugars)

Ribose ($C_5H_{10}O_5$)
(the sugar component of RNA)

Deoxyribose ($C_5H_{10}O_4$)
(the sugar component of DNA)

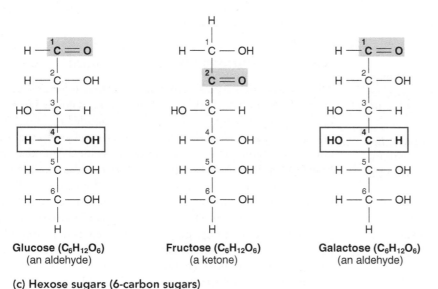

Glucose ($C_6H_{12}O_6$)
(an aldehyde)

Fructose ($C_6H_{12}O_6$)
(a ketone)

Galactose ($C_6H_{12}O_6$)
(an aldehyde)

(c) Hexose sugars (6-carbon sugars)

Figure 3-6 Monosaccharides

Shown are 2-D chain structures of **(a)** three-carbon trioses, **(b)** five-carbon pentoses, and **(c)** six-carbon hexoses. Although it is convenient to show monosaccharides in this form, the pentoses and hexoses are more accurately depicted as ring structures, as in Figure 3-7. The carbonyl group (*gray screen*) is terminal in aldehyde sugars and located in an internal position in ketones. Deoxyribose differs from ribose because deoxyribose has one less oxygen; a hydrogen (*yellow screen*) instead of a hydroxyl group (*blue screen*) is attached to carbon 2. Glucose and galactose differ in the arrangement of the hydroxyl group and hydrogen attached to carbon 4 (*red box*).

© Cengage Learning

so important in metabolism that mechanisms have evolved to maintain its concentration at relatively constant levels in the blood of humans and other complex animals (see Chapter 49).

Glucose and fructose are structural isomers: they have identical molecular formulas, but their atoms are arranged differently. In fructose (a ketone) the double-bonded oxygen is linked to a carbon within the chain rather than to a terminal carbon as in glucose (an aldehyde). Because of these differences, the two sugars have different properties. For example, fructose, found in honey and some fruits, tastes sweeter than glucose.

Glucose and galactose are both hexoses and aldehydes. However, they differ in the arrangement of the atoms attached to asymmetrical carbon atom 4.

The linear formulas in Figure 3-6 give a clear but somewhat unrealistic picture of the structures of some common monosaccharides. As we have mentioned, molecules are not 2-D; in fact, the properties of each compound depend largely on its 3-D structure. Thus, 3-D formulas are helpful in understanding the relationship between molecular structure and biological function.

Molecules of glucose and other pentoses and hexoses in solution are actually rings rather than extended straight carbon chains. Glucose in solution (as in the cell) typically exists as a ring of five carbons and one oxygen. It assumes this configuration when its atoms undergo a rearrangement, permitting a covalent bond to connect carbon 1 to the oxygen attached to carbon 5 (FIG. 3-7). When glucose forms a ring, two isomeric forms are possible, differing only in orientation of the hydroxyl (—OH) group attached to carbon 1. When this hydroxyl group is on the same side of the plane of the ring as the —CH_2OH side group, the glucose is designated beta glucose (β-glucose). When it is on the side (with respect to the plane of the ring) opposite the —CH_2OH side group, the compound is designated alpha glucose (α-glucose). Although the differences between these isomers may seem small, they have important consequences when the rings join to form polymers.

Disaccharides consist of two monosaccharide units

A **disaccharide** (two sugars) contains two monosaccharide rings joined by a glycosidic linkage, consisting of a central oxygen covalently bonded to two carbons, one in each ring (FIG. 3-8). The **glycosidic linkage** of a disaccharide generally forms between carbon 1 of one molecule and carbon 4 of the other molecule. The disaccharide maltose (malt sugar) consists of two covalently linked α-glucose units. Sucrose, common table sugar, consists of a glucose unit combined with a fructose unit. Lactose (the sugar present in milk) consists of one molecule of glucose and one of galactose.

As shown in Figure 3-8, a disaccharide can be hydrolyzed, that is, split by the addition of water, into two monosaccharide units. During digestion, maltose is hydrolyzed to form two molecules of glucose:

maltose + water ⟶ glucose + glucose

Similarly, sucrose is hydrolyzed to form glucose and fructose:

sucrose + water ⟶ glucose + fructose

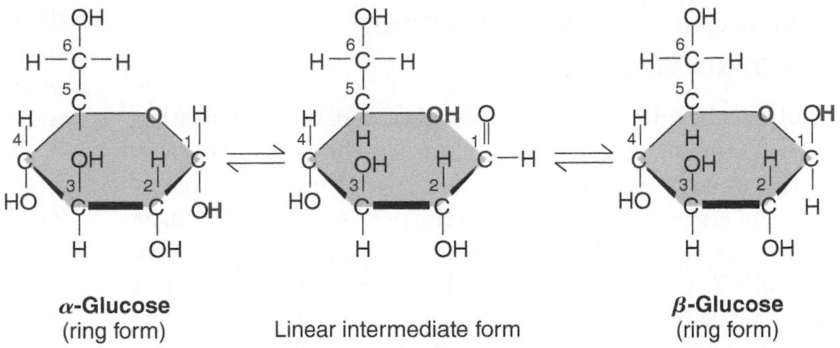

α-Glucose (ring form) Linear intermediate form **β-Glucose** (ring form)

(a) When dissolved in water, glucose undergoes a rearrangement of its atoms, forming one of two possible ring structures: α-glucose or β-glucose. Although the drawing does not show the complete 3-D structure, the thick, tapered bonds in the lower portion of each ring represent the part of the molecule that would project out of the page toward you.

α-Glucose **β-Glucose**

(b) The essential differences between α-glucose and β-glucose are more readily apparent in these simplified structures. By convention, a carbon atom is assumed to be present at each angle in the ring unless another atom is shown. Most hydrogen atoms have been omitted.

Figure 3-7 α and β forms of glucose
© Cengage Learning

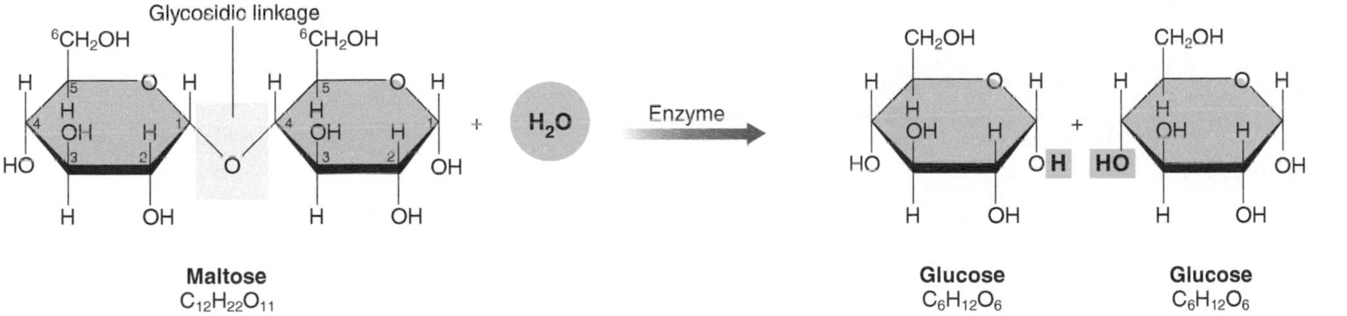

Maltose
$C_{12}H_{22}O_{11}$

Glucose
$C_6H_{12}O_6$

Glucose
$C_6H_{12}O_6$

(a) Maltose may be broken down (as during digestion) to form two molecules of glucose. The glycosidic linkage is broken in a hydrolysis reaction, which requires the addition of water.

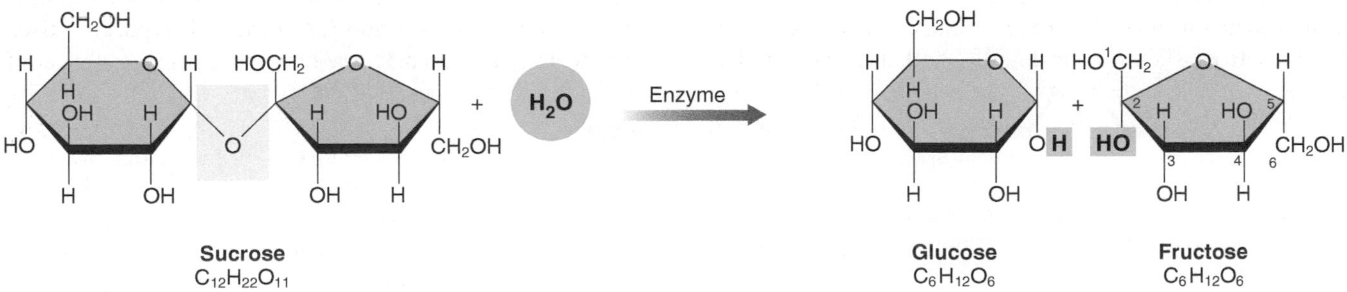

Sucrose
$C_{12}H_{22}O_{11}$

Glucose
$C_6H_{12}O_6$

Fructose
$C_6H_{12}O_6$

(b) Sucrose can be hydrolyzed to yield a molecule of glucose and a molecule of fructose.

Figure 3-8 Hydrolysis of disaccharides
Note that an enzyme is needed to promote these reactions.
© Cengage Learning

Polysaccharides can store energy or provide structure

A **polysaccharide** is a macromolecule consisting of repeating units of simple sugars, usually glucose. The polysaccharides are the most abundant carbohydrates and include starches, glycogen, and cellulose. Although the precise number of sugar units varies, thousands of units are typically present in a single molecule. A polysaccharide may be a single long chain or a branched chain.

Because they are composed of different isomers and because the units may be arranged differently, polysaccharides vary in their properties. Those that can be easily broken down to their subunits are well suited for energy storage, whereas the macromolecular 3-D architecture of others makes them particularly well suited to form stable structures.

Starch, the typical form of carbohydrate used for energy storage in plants, is a polymer consisting of α-glucose subunits. These monomers are joined by α 1—4 linkages, which means that carbon 1 of one glucose is linked to carbon 4 of the next glucose in the chain (**FIG. 3-9**). Starch occurs in two forms: amylose and amylopectin. Amylose, the simpler form, is unbranched. Amylopectin, the more common form, usually consists of about 1000 glucose units in a branched chain.

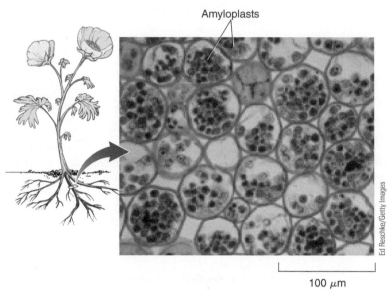

100 μm

(a) Starch (stained *purple*) is stored in specialized organelles, called *amyloplasts*, in these cells of a buttercup root.

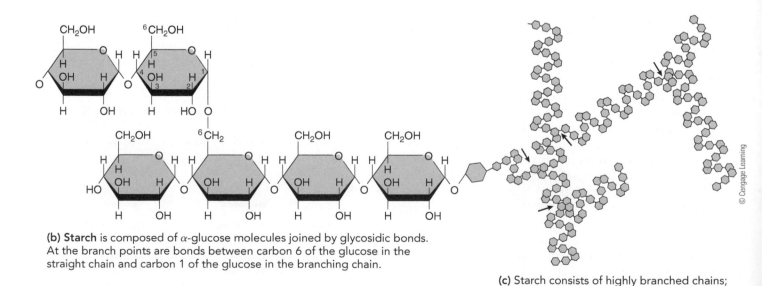

(b) Starch is composed of α-glucose molecules joined by glycosidic bonds. At the branch points are bonds between carbon 6 of the glucose in the straight chain and carbon 1 of the glucose in the branching chain.

(c) Starch consists of highly branched chains; the arrows indicate the branch points. Each chain is actually a coil or helix, stabilized by hydrogen bonds between the hydroxyl groups of the glucose subunits.

Figure 3-9 **Starch, a storage polysaccharide**

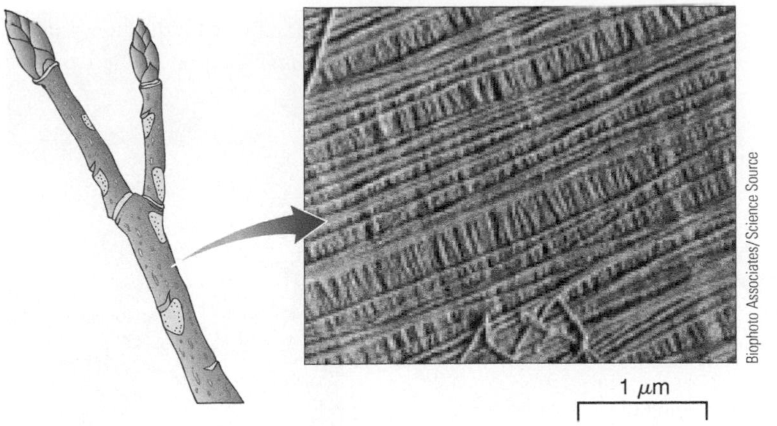

Biophoto Associates/Science Source

Figure 3-10 *Animation* Cellulose, a structural polysaccharide

1 μm

(a) Cellulose fibers from a cell wall. The fibers shown in this electron micrograph consist of bundles of cellulose molecules that interact through hydrogen bonds.

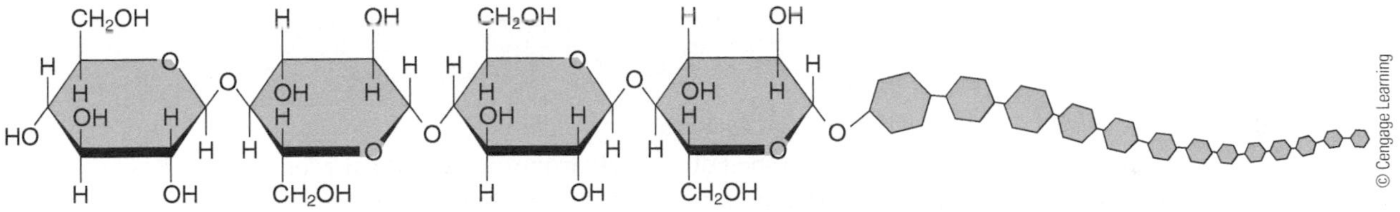

© Cengage Learning

(b) The cellulose molecule is an unbranched polysaccharide. It consists of about 10,000 β-glucose units joined by glycosidic bonds.

Plant cells store starch mainly as granules within specialized organelles called **amyloplasts** (see Fig. 3-9a); some cells, such as those of potatoes, are very rich in amyloplasts. When energy is needed for cell work, the plant hydrolyzes the starch, releasing the glucose subunits. Virtually all organisms, including humans and other animals, have enzymes that can break α 1—4 linkages.

Glycogen (sometimes referred to as *animal starch*) is the form in which glucose subunits, joined by α 1—4 linkages, are stored as an energy source in animal tissues. Glycogen is similar in structure to plant starch but more extensively branched and more water soluble. In vertebrates, glycogen is stored mainly in liver and muscle cells.

Carbohydrates are the most abundant group of organic compounds on Earth, and cellulose is the most abundant carbohydrate; it accounts for 50% or more of all the carbon in plants (FIG. 3-10). Cellulose is a structural carbohydrate. Wood is about half cellulose, and cotton is at least 90% cellulose. Plant cells are surrounded by strong supporting cell walls consisting mainly of cellulose.

Cellulose is an insoluble polysaccharide composed of many joined glucose molecules. The bonds joining these sugar units are different from those in starch. Recall that starch is composed of α-glucose subunits joined by α 1—4 glycosidic linkages. Cellulose contains β-glucose monomers joined by β 1—4 linkages. These bonds cannot be split by the enzymes that hydrolyze the α linkages in starch. Because humans, like other animals, lack enzymes that digest cellulose, we cannot use it as a nutrient. The

cellulose found in whole grains and vegetables remains fibrous and provides bulk that helps keep our digestive tract functioning properly.

Some microorganisms digest cellulose to glucose. In fact, cellulose-digesting bacteria live in the digestive systems of cows and sheep, enabling these grass-eating animals to obtain nourishment from cellulose. Similarly, the digestive systems of termites contain microorganisms that digest cellulose (see Fig. 26-4b).

Cellulose molecules are well suited for a structural role. The β-glucose subunits are joined in a way that allows extensive hydrogen bonding among different cellulose molecules, and they aggregate in long bundles of fibers (see Fig. 3-10a).

Some modified and complex carbohydrates have special roles

Many derivatives of monosaccharides are important biological molecules. Some form important structural components. The amino sugars galactosamine and glucosamine are compounds in which a hydroxyl group (—OH) is replaced by an amino group (—NH$_2$). Galactosamine is present in cartilage, a constituent of the skeletal system of vertebrates.

N-acetyl glucosamine (NAG) subunits, joined by glycosidic bonds, compose **chitin,** a main component of the cell walls of fungi and of the external skeletons of insects, crayfish, and other arthropods (FIG. 3-11). Chitin forms very tough structures because, as in cellulose, its molecules interact through multiple

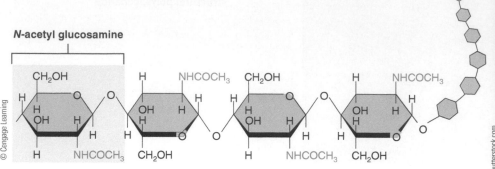

(a) **Chitin** is a polymer composed of *N*-acetyl glucosamine subunits.

(b) Chitin is an important component of the exoskeleton (outer covering) this cicada is shedding.

Figure 3-11 Chitin, a structural polysaccharide

hydrogen bonds. Some chitinous structures, such as the shell of a lobster, are further hardened by the addition of calcium carbonate ($CaCO_3$), an inorganic form of carbon.

Carbohydrates may also combine with proteins to form **glycoproteins,** compounds present on the outer surface of cells other than bacteria. Some of these carbohydrate chains allow cells to adhere to one another, whereas others provide protection. Most proteins secreted by cells are glycoproteins. They include the major components of mucus, a protective material secreted by the mucous membranes of the respiratory and digestive systems. Carbohydrates combine with lipids to form **glycolipids,** compounds on the surfaces of animal cells that allow cells to recognize and interact with one another.

CHECKPOINT 3.2

- **VISUALIZE** *Draw simple sketches comparing hydrogen bonding in storage polysaccharides, such as starch and glycogen, with structural polysaccharides, such as cellulose and chitin.*

3.3 LIPIDS

LEARNING OBJECTIVE

6 Distinguish among fats, phospholipids, and steroids, and describe the composition, characteristics, and biological functions of each.

Unlike carbohydrates, which are defined by their structure, **lipids** are a heterogeneous group of compounds that are categorized by being soluble in nonpolar solvents (such as ether and chloroform) and relatively insoluble in water. Lipid molecules have these properties because they consist mainly of carbon and hydrogen, with few oxygen-containing functional groups.

Hydrophilic functional groups typically contain oxygen atoms; therefore, lipids, which have little oxygen, tend to be hydrophobic. Among the biologically important groups of lipids are fats, phospholipids, carotenoids (orange and yellow plant pigments), steroids, and waxes. Some lipids are used for energy storage, others serve as structural components of cell membranes, and some are important hormones.

Triacylglycerol is formed from glycerol and three fatty acids

The most abundant lipids in living organisms are **triacylglycerols.** These compounds, commonly known as *fats*, are an economical form of reserve fuel storage because, when metabolized, they yield more than twice as much energy per gram as do carbohydrates. Carbohydrates and proteins can be transformed by enzymes into fats and stored within the cells of adipose (fat) tissue of animals and in some seeds and fruits of plants.

A triacylglycerol molecule (also known as a *triglyceride*) consists of glycerol joined to three fatty acids (**FIG. 3-12**). **Glycerol** is a three-carbon alcohol that contains three hydroxyl (—OH) groups, and a **fatty acid** is a long, unbranched hydrocarbon chain with a carboxyl group (—COOH) at one end. A triacylglycerol molecule is formed by a series of three condensation reactions. In each reaction, the equivalent of a water molecule is removed as one of the glycerol's hydroxyl groups reacts with the carboxyl group of a fatty acid, resulting in the formation of a covalent linkage known as an **ester linkage** (see Fig. 3-12b). The first reaction yields a **monoacylglycerol** (*monoglyceride*); the second, a **diacylglycerol** (*diglyceride*); and the third, a triacylglycerol. During digestion, triacylglycerols are hydrolyzed to produce fatty acids and glycerol (see Chapter 47). Diacylglycerol is an important molecule for sending signals within the cell (see Chapters 6 and 49).

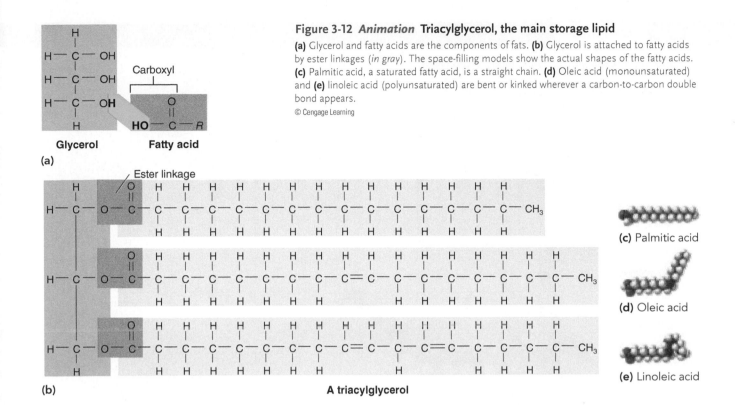

Figure 3-12 *Animation* **Triacylglycerol, the main storage lipid**

(a) Glycerol and fatty acids are the components of fats. **(b)** Glycerol is attached to fatty acids by ester linkages (*in gray*). The space-filling models show the actual shapes of the fatty acids. **(c)** Palmitic acid, a saturated fatty acid, is a straight chain. **(d)** Oleic acid (monounsaturated) and **(e)** linoleic acid (polyunsaturated) are bent or kinked wherever a carbon-to-carbon double bond appears.

© Cengage Learning

Glycerol

Fatty acid

Carboxyl

(a)

Ester linkage

(b)

A triacylglycerol

(c) Palmitic acid

(d) Oleic acid

(e) Linoleic acid

Saturated and unsaturated fatty acids differ in physical properties

About 30 different fatty acids are commonly found in lipids, and they typically have an even number of carbon atoms. For example, butyric acid, present in rancid butter, has four carbon atoms. Oleic acid, with 18 carbons, is the most widely distributed fatty acid in nature and is found in most animal and plant fats.

Saturated fatty acids contain the maximum possible number of hydrogen atoms. Palmitic acid, a 16-carbon fatty acid, is a common saturated fatty acid (see Fig. 3-12c). Fats high in saturated fatty acids, such as animal fat and solid vegetable shortening, tend to be solid at room temperature. The reason is that even electrically neutral, nonpolar fatty acyl chains can develop transient regions of weak positive charge and weak negative charge. This situation occurs because the constant motion of their electrons causes some regions to have a temporary excess of electrons, whereas others have a temporary electron deficit. These slight opposite charges result in van der Waals interactions between adjacent molecules (see Chapter 2). Although van der Waals interactions are weakly attractive, they are strong when many occur along hydrocarbon chains that can closely align together. These van der Waals interactions tend to make a substance more solid by limiting the motion of its molecules.

Unsaturated fatty acids include one or more adjacent pairs of carbon atoms joined by a double bond. Therefore, they are not fully saturated with hydrogen. Fatty acids with one double bond are **monounsaturated fatty acids,** whereas those with more than one double bond are **polyunsaturated fatty acids.** Oleic acid is a monounsaturated fatty acid, and linoleic acid is a common polyunsaturated fatty acid (see Figs. 3-12d and e). Fats containing a high proportion of monounsaturated or polyunsaturated fatty acids tend to be liquid at room temperature. The reason is that each double bond produces a bend in the hydrocarbon chain that prevents it from aligning closely with an adjacent chain. This limits the number of van der Waals interactions between chains, permitting freer molecular motion.

Food manufacturers commonly hydrogenate or partially hydrogenate cooking oils to make margarine and other foodstuffs, converting unsaturated fatty acids to saturated fatty acids and making the fat more solid at room temperature. This process makes the fat less healthful because saturated fatty acids in the diet are known to increase the risk of cardiovascular disease (see Chapter 44). The hydrogenation process has yet another effect. Note that in the naturally occurring unsaturated fatty acids oleic acid and linoleic acid shown in Figure 3-12, the two hydrogens flanking each double bond are on the same side of the hydrocarbon chain (the *cis* configuration). When fatty acids are artificially hydrogenated, the double bonds can become rearranged, resulting in a *trans* configuration, analogous to the arrangement shown in Figure 3-3b. *Trans* fatty acids are technically unsaturated, but they mimic many of the properties of saturated fatty acids. Because the *trans* configuration does not produce a bend at the site of the double bond, *trans* fatty acids are more solid at room temperature than *cis* fatty acids; like saturated fatty acids, they increase the risk of cardiovascular disease.

At least two unsaturated fatty acids (linoleic acid and arachidonic acid) are essential nutrients that must be obtained from food because the human body cannot synthesize them. However,

A lipid bilayer forms when phospholipids interact with water.

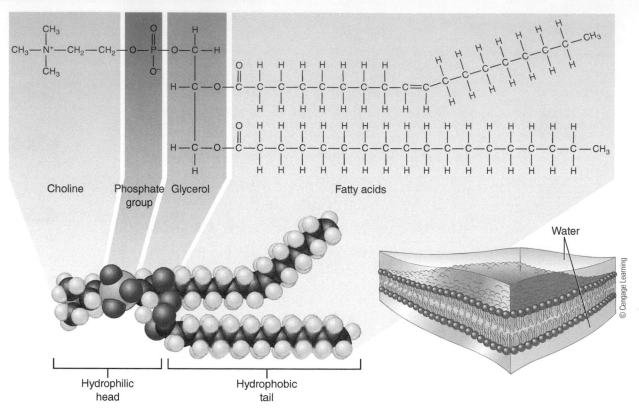

Choline | Phosphate group | Glycerol | Fatty acids

Hydrophilic head | Hydrophobic tail

Water

© Cengage Learning

(a) Phospholipid (lecithin). A phospholipid consists of a hydrophobic tail, made up of two fatty acids, and a hydrophilic head, which includes a glycerol bonded to a phosphate group, which is in turn bonded to an organic group that can vary. Choline is the organic group in lecithin (or phosphatidylcholine), the molecule shown. The fatty acid at the top of the figure is monounsaturated; it contains one double bond that produces a characteristic bend in the chain.

(b) Phospholipid bilayer. Phospholipids form lipid bilayers in which the hydrophilic heads interact with water and the hydrophobic tails are in the bilayer interior.

Figure 3-13 *Animation* **A phospholipid and a phospholipid bilayer**

PREDICT Examine Figure 3-12. Would you expect the structure of triacylglycerols to enable them to interact with water to form a bilayer? Support your answer.

the amounts required are small, and deficiencies are rarely seen. There is no dietary requirement for saturated fatty acids.

Phospholipids are components of cell membranes

Phospholipids belong to a group of lipids called **amphipathic lipids,** in which one end of each molecule is hydrophilic and the other end is hydrophobic (**FIG. 3-13**). The two ends of a phospholipid differ both physically and chemically. A **phospholipid** consists of a glycerol molecule attached at one end to two fatty acids and at the other end to a phosphate group linked to an organic compound such as choline. The organic compound usually contains nitrogen. (Note that phosphorus and nitrogen are absent in triacylglycerols, as shown in Fig. 3-12b.) The fatty acid portion of the molecule (containing the two hydrocarbon "tails") is hydrophobic and not soluble in water. However, the

portion composed of glycerol, phosphate, and the organic base (the "head" of the molecule) is ionized and readily water soluble. The amphipathic properties of phospholipids cause them to form lipid bilayers in aqueous (watery) solution (see Fig. 3-13b). Thus, they are uniquely suited as the fundamental components of cell membranes (discussed in Chapter 5).

Carotenoids and many other pigments are derived from isoprene units

The orange and yellow plant pigments called **carotenoids** are classified with the lipids because they are insoluble in water and have an oily consistency. These pigments, found in the cells of plants, play a role in photosynthesis. Carotenoid molecules, such as β-carotene, and many other important pigments consist of five-carbon hydrocarbon monomers known as *isoprene units* (**FIG. 3-14**).

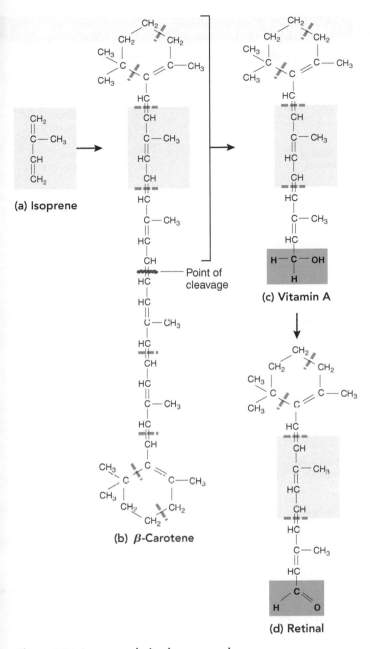

(a) Isoprene

Point of cleavage

(b) β-Carotene

(c) Vitamin A

(d) Retinal

Figure 3-14 Isoprene-derived compounds

(a) An isoprene subunit. **(b)** β-carotene, with dashed lines indicating the boundaries of the individual isoprene units within. The wavy line is the point at which most animals cleave the molecule to yield two molecules of **(c)** vitamin A. Vitamin A is converted to the visual pigment **(d)** retinal.
© Cengage Learning

Most animals convert carotenoids to vitamin A, which can then be converted to the visual pigment **retinal.** Three groups of animals—the mollusks, insects, and vertebrates—have eyes that use retinal in the process of light reception.

Notice that carotenoids, vitamin A, and retinal all have a pattern of double bonds alternating with single bonds. The electrons that make up these bonds can move about relatively easily when light strikes the molecule. Such molecules are *pigments;* they tend to be highly colored because the mobile electrons cause them to strongly absorb light of certain wavelengths and reflect light of other wavelengths.

(a) Cholesterol is an essential component of animal cell membranes.

Indicates double bond

(b) Cortisol is a steroid hormone secreted by the adrenal glands.

Figure 3-15 Steroids

Four attached rings—three six-carbon rings and one with five carbons—make up the fundamental structure of a steroid. Note that some carbons are shared by two rings. In these simplified structures, a carbon atom is present at each angle of a ring; the hydrogen atoms attached directly to the carbon atoms have not been drawn. Steroids are mainly distinguished by their attached functional groups.
© Cengage Learning

Steroids contain four rings of carbon atoms

A **steroid** consists of carbon atoms arranged in four attached rings; three of the rings contain six carbon atoms, and the fourth contains five (FIG. 3-15). The length and structure of the side chains that extend from these rings distinguish one steroid from another. Like carotenoids, steroids are synthesized from isoprene units.

Among the steroids of biological importance are cholesterol, bile salts, reproductive hormones, and cortisol as well as other hormones secreted by the adrenal cortex. Cholesterol is an essential structural component of animal cell membranes, but when excess cholesterol in blood forms plaques on artery walls, the risk of cardiovascular disease increases (see Chapter 44).

Plant cell membranes contain molecules similar to cholesterol. Interestingly, some of these plant steroids block the intestine's absorption of cholesterol. Bile salts emulsify fats in the intestine so that they can be enzymatically hydrolyzed. Steroid hormones regulate certain aspects of metabolism in a variety of animals and plants.

Some chemical mediators are lipids

Animal cells secrete chemicals to communicate with one another or to regulate their own activities. Some chemical mediators are produced by the modification of fatty acids that have been removed from membrane phospholipids. These mediators include *prostaglandins*, which have varied roles, including promoting inflammation and smooth muscle contraction. Certain hormones, such as the juvenile hormone of insects, are also fatty acid derivatives (discussed in Chapter 49).

CHECKPOINT 3.3

- *How do the shapes of saturated, unsaturated, and* trans *fatty acids cause them to differ in their properties?*
- *Explain why the structure of phospholipids enables them to form lipid bilayers in aqueous conditions, whereas triacylglycerols and diacylglycerols do not.*

3.4 PROTEINS

LEARNING OBJECTIVES

7 Give an overall description of the structure and functions of proteins.
8 Describe the features that are shared by all amino acids and explain how amino acids are grouped into classes based on the characteristics of their side chains.
9 Distinguish among the four levels of organization of protein molecules.

Proteins, macromolecules composed of amino acids, are the most versatile cell components. Each type of protein consists of a unique set of amino acids linked in a chain that can be from several amino acids to hundreds of amino acids in length. Each cell type contains a characteristic set of thousands of different types of proteins that largely determine what the cell looks like and how it functions. Muscle cells, for example, contain large amounts of the proteins myosin and actin, which are responsible for their ability to contract. The most abundant protein in red blood cells is hemoglobin, which is responsible for the specialized function of oxygen transport.

In this section we will see that the sequence of the amino acids in a protein chain determines its shape, which in turn determines its function. As will be discussed in Chapter 16, scientists have succeeded in sequencing all the genetic information in a human cell as well as in many other organisms. Some of this information is used to specify the amino acid sequences of cellular proteins, and biologists are now using this information to understand the structures, interactions, and functions of these multifaceted macromolecules that are of central importance in the chemistry of life.

TABLE 3-2 shows many of the different types of functions performed by proteins. Proteins are involved in virtually all aspects of metabolism because most **enzymes**, molecules that accelerate the thousands of different chemical reactions that take place in an organism, are proteins. Proteins are assembled

TABLE 3-2	Major Classes of Proteins and Their Functions	
PROTEIN CLASS	**FUNCTIONS**	**EXAMPLES**
Enzymes	Catalyze specific chemical reactions	Enzymes, thousand of different proteins that speed chemical reactions (e.g., enzymes that hydrolyze the bonds in starch and other food molecules)
Structural proteins	Strengthen and protect cells and tissues	Collagen in ligaments and tendons; keratin in hair and skin tissue
Storage proteins	Store nutrients	Ovalbumin: egg white protein; zein: corn seed protein
Transport proteins	Move substances between cells and across cell membranes	Hemoglobin: O_2 transport in blood. Proteins in cell membranes: transport of glucose, ions, and amino acids
Regulatory proteins	Control the activities of proteins, genes, cells and tissues	Protein kinases: control activities of other proteins; hormones (e.g., insulin): control activities of cells and tissues; transcription factors: control the activities of genes
Motile proteins	Generate movement in cells and tissues	Actin/myosin: muscle contraction and movement of intracellular structures
Protective proteins	Defend against foreign invaders	Antibodies: bind to specific foreign proteins; defensins: inhibit growth of microbial invaders

© Cengage Learning

into a variety of shapes, allowing them to serve as major structural components of cells and tissues. For this reason, growth and repair as well as maintenance of the organism depend of proteins.

Amino acids are the subunits of proteins

Amino acids, the constituents of proteins, have an amino group ($-NH_2$) and a carboxyl group ($-COOH$) bonded to the same asymmetrical carbon atom, known as the **alpha carbon**. Amino acids in solution at neutral pH are mainly *dipolar ions;* that is, they possess a positive charge at one end and a negative charge at the opposite end. This is generally how amino acids exist at cell pH. Each carboxyl group ($-COOH$) donates a proton and becomes ionized ($-COO^-$), whereas each amino group ($-NH_2$) becomes ionized as it accepts a proton and becomes $-NH_3^+$ (FIG. 3-16). Because of the ability of their amino and carboxyl groups to accept and release protons, amino acids in solution resist changes in acidity and alkalinity and are therefore important biological buffers.

Twenty amino acids are commonly found in proteins, each identified by the variable side chain (R group) bonded to the α carbon (FIG. 3-17). Glycine, the simplest amino acid, has a hydrogen atom as its R group; alanine has a methyl ($-CH_3$) group. The amino acids are grouped in Figure 3-17 by the properties of their

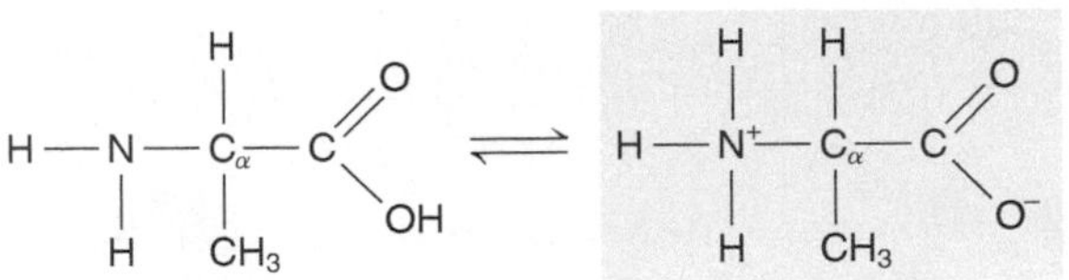

Figure 3-16 An amino acid at pH 7

In living cells, amino acids exist mainly in their ionized form, as dipolar ions.

© Cengage Learning

side chains. These broad groupings actually include amino acids with a fairly wide range of properties. Amino acids classified as having *nonpolar* side chains tend to have hydrophobic properties, whereas those classified as *polar* are more hydrophilic. An acidic amino acid has a side chain that contains a carboxyl group. At cell pH the carboxyl group is dissociated, giving the R group a negative charge. A basic amino acid becomes positively charged when an amino group in its side chain accepts a hydrogen ion. Acidic and basic side chains are ionic at cell pH and therefore hydrophilic.

Some proteins have unusual amino acids in addition to the 20 common ones. These rare amino acids are produced by the modification of common amino acids after they have become part of a protein. For example, after they have been incorporated into collagen, lysine and proline may be converted to hydroxylysine and hydroxyproline. These amino acids can form cross links between the peptide chains that make up collagen. Such cross links produce the firmness and great strength of the collagen molecule, which is a major component of cartilage, bone, and other connective tissues.

With some exceptions, prokaryotes and plants synthesize all their needed amino acids from simpler substances. If the proper raw materials are available, the cells of animals can manufacture some, but not all, of the biologically significant amino acids. **Essential amino acids** are those an animal cannot synthesize in amounts sufficient to meet its needs and must obtain from the diet. Animals differ in their biosynthetic capacities; what is an essential amino acid for one species may not be for another.

The essential amino acids for humans are isoleucine, leucine, lysine, methionine, phenylalanine, threonine, tryptophan, valine, and histidine. Arginine is added to the list for children because they do not synthesize enough to support growth.

Peptide bonds join amino acids

Amino acids combine chemically with one another by a condensation reaction that bonds the carboxyl carbon of one molecule to the amino nitrogen of another (FIG. 3-18). The covalent carbon-to-nitrogen bond linking two amino acids is a **peptide bond.** When two amino acids combine, a **dipeptide** is formed; a longer chain of amino acids is a **polypeptide.** A protein consists of one or more polypeptide chains. Each polypeptide has a free amino group at one end and a free carboxyl group (belonging to the last amino acid added to the chain) at the opposite end. The other amino and carboxyl groups of the amino acid monomers (except those in side chains) are part of the peptide bonds. The process by which polypeptides are synthesized is discussed in Chapter 13.

A polypeptide may contain hundreds of amino acids joined in a specific linear order. The flexible backbone of the polypeptide chain includes the repeating sequence

These backbones consist of the covalently linked amino nitrogen, α-carbon, and carboxyl group carbon atoms and all other atoms *except those in the R groups.* The two bonds that link the α carbon atoms to the amino and carboxyl groups along with the peptide bonds (shown in blue) form the backbone, whereas the R groups of the amino acids extend from the α-carbon atoms.

An almost infinite variety of protein molecules is possible, differing from one another in the number, types, and sequences of amino acids they contain. The 20 types of amino acids found in proteins may be thought of as letters of a protein alphabet; each protein is a very long sentence made up of amino acid letters.

Proteins have four levels of organization

The polypeptide chains making up a protein are twisted or folded to form a macromolecule with a specific *conformation*, or 3-D shape. Some polypeptide chains form long fibers, whereas *globular proteins* are tightly folded into compact, roughly spherical shapes. There is a close relationship between a protein's conformation and its function. For example, a typical enzyme is a globular protein with a unique shape that allows it to catalyze a specific chemical reaction. Similarly, the shape of a protein hormone enables it to combine with receptors on its target cell (the cell on which the hormone acts). Scientists recognize four main levels of protein organization: primary, secondary, tertiary, and quaternary.

Primary structure is the amino acid sequence The sequence of amino acids, joined by peptide bonds, is the **primary structure** of a polypeptide chain. As discussed in Chapter 13, this sequence is specified by the instructions in a gene. The primary structures of thousands of proteins are known. For example, glucagon, a hormone secreted by the pancreas, is a small polypeptide, consisting of only 29 amino acid units (FIG. 3-19).

Primary structure is always represented in a simple, linear, "beads-on-a-string" form. However, the overall conformation of a protein is far more complex, involving interactions among the various amino acids that make up the primary structure of the molecule. Therefore, the higher orders of structure—secondary, tertiary, and quaternary—that produce the 3-D shape of the molecule ultimately derive from the specific amino acid sequence (the primary structure).

Secondary structure results from hydrogen bonding involving the backbone Some regions of a polypeptide exhibit **secondary structure,** which is highly regular. The two most common types of secondary structure are the α-helix and the β-pleated sheet; the designations α and β refer simply to the order in which these two types of secondary structure were discovered. An **α-helix** is a region where a polypeptide chain forms a uniform helical coil (FIG. 3-20a). The helical structure

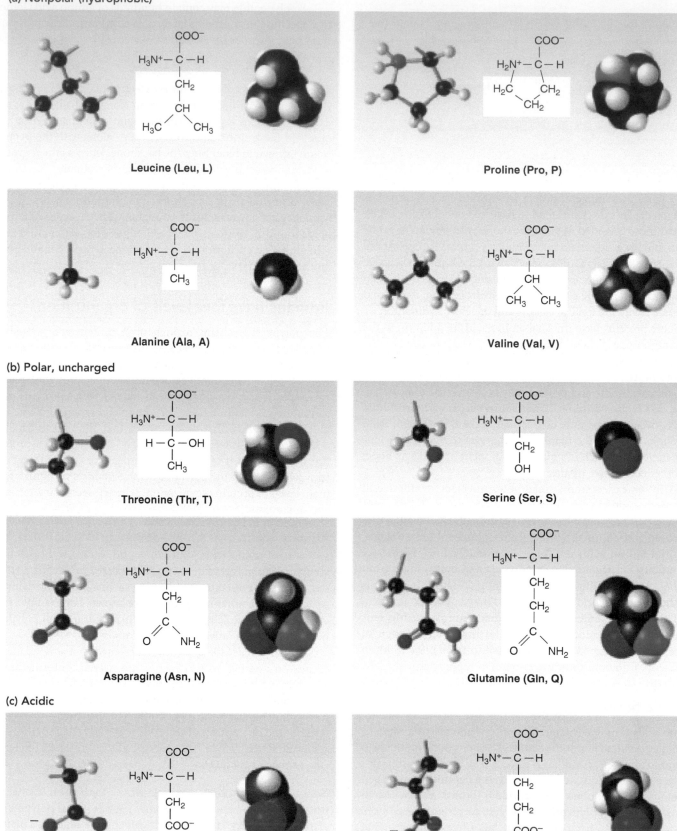

(a) Nonpolar (hydrophobic)

Leucine (Leu, L)

Proline (Pro, P)

Alanine (Ala, A)

Valine (Val, V)

(b) Polar, uncharged

Threonine (Thr, T)

Serine (Ser, S)

Asparagine (Asn, N)

Glutamine (Gln, Q)

(c) Acidic

Aspartic acid (Asp, D)

Glutamic acid (Glu, E)

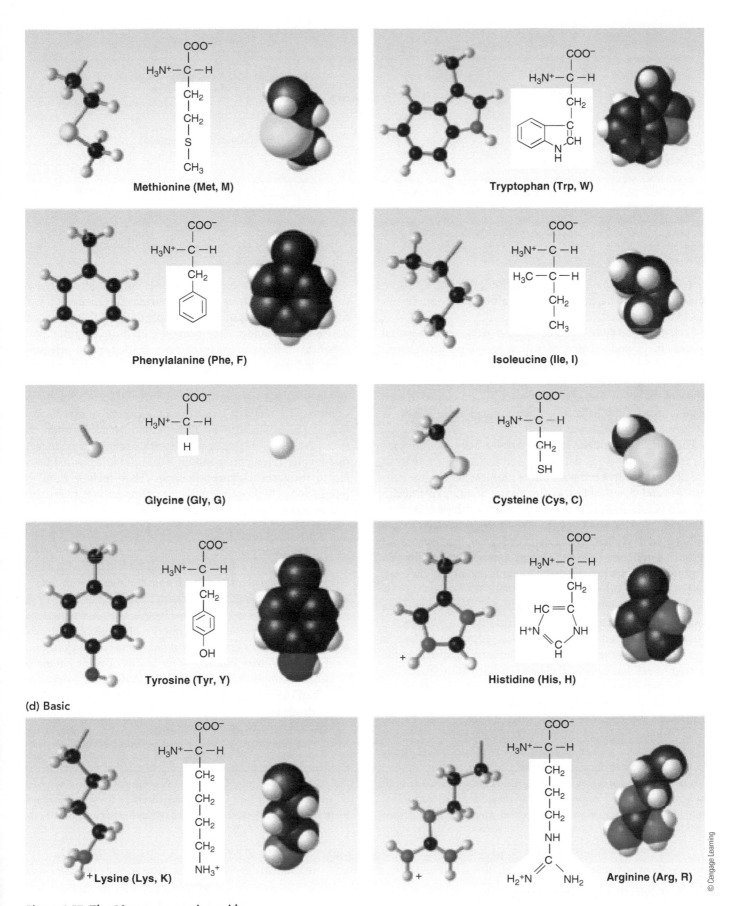

Figure 3-17 The 20 common amino acids

(a) Nonpolar amino acids (*yellow background*) have side chains that are relatively hydrophobic, whereas (b) polar amino acids (*green background*) have relatively hydrophilic side chains. Carboxyl groups and amino groups are electrically charged at cell pH; therefore, (c) acidic (*red background*) and (d) basic (*blue background*) amino acids are hydrophilic. The standard three-letter and one-letter abbreviations appear beside the amino acid names.

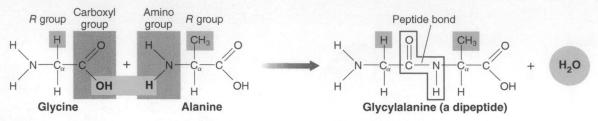

Figure 3-18 *Animation* **Peptide bonds**

A dipeptide is formed by a condensation reaction, that is, by the removal of the equivalent of a water molecule from the carboxyl group of one amino acid and the amino group of another amino acid. The resulting peptide bond is a covalent, carbon-to-nitrogen bond. Note that the carbon is also part of a carbonyl group and that the nitrogen is also covalently bonded to a hydrogen. Additional amino acids can be added to form a long polypeptide chain with a free amino group at one end and a free carboxyl group at the other.

© Cengage Learning

is determined and maintained by the formation of hydrogen bonds between the backbones of the amino acids in successive turns of the spiral coil.

Each hydrogen bond forms between an oxygen with a partial negative charge and a hydrogen with a partial positive charge. The oxygen is part of the carboxyl group of one amino acid; the hydrogen is part of the amino group of the fourth amino acid down the chain. Thus, 3.6 amino acids are included in each complete turn of the helix. Every amino acid in an α-helix is hydrogen bonded in this way.

The α-helix is the basic structural unit of some fibrous proteins that make up wool, hair, skin, and nails. The elasticity of these fibers is due to a combination of physical factors (the helical shape) and chemical factors (hydrogen bonding). Although hydrogen bonds maintain the helical structure, these bonds can be broken, allowing the fibers to stretch under tension (like a telephone cord). When the tension is released, the fibers recoil and hydrogen bonds re-form. This property explains why you can stretch the hairs on your head to some extent and they will snap back to their original length.

The hydrogen bonding in a **β-pleated sheet** takes place between the backbones of different regions of a polypeptide chain that has turned back on itself (**FIG. 3-20b**). Each chain is fully extended; however, because each has a zigzag structure, the resulting "sheet" has an overall pleated conformation (much like a sheet of paper that has been folded to make a fan). Although the pleated sheet is strong and flexible, it is not elastic because the distance between the pleats is fixed, determined by the strong covalent bonds of the polypeptide backbones. Fibroin, the protein of silk, is characterized by a β-pleated sheet structure, as are the cores of many globular proteins.

It is common for a single polypeptide chain to include both α-helical regions and regions with β-pleated sheet conformations. The properties of some biological materials result from

such combinations. A spider's web is composed of a material that is extremely strong, flexible, and elastic. Once again we see function and structure working together, as these properties derive from a spider silk's being a composite of proteins with α-helical conformations (providing elasticity) and others with β-pleated sheet conformations (providing strength).

Tertiary structure depends on interactions among side chains The **tertiary structure** of a protein molecule is the overall shape assumed by each individual polypeptide chain (**FIG. 3-21**). This 3-D structure is determined by four main factors that involve interactions among R groups (side chains) belonging to the same polypeptide chain. They include both weak interactions (hydrogen bonds, ionic bonds, and hydrophobic interactions) and strong covalent bonds.

1. Hydrogen bonds form between R groups of certain amino acid subunits.
2. An ionic bond can occur between an R group with a unit of positive charge and one with a unit of negative charge.
3. Hydrophobic interactions result from the tendency of nonpolar R groups to be excluded by the surrounding water and therefore to associate in the interior of the globular structure.
4. Covalent bonds known as *disulfide bonds* or *disulfide bridges* (—S—S—) may link the sulfur atoms of two cysteine subunits belonging to the same chain. A disulfide bridge forms when the sulfhydryl groups of two cysteines react; the two hydrogens are removed, and the two sulfur atoms that remain become covalently linked.

Quaternary structure results from interactions among polypeptides Many functional proteins are composed of two or more polypeptide chains that interact in specific ways to form a biologically active molecule. **Quaternary structure** is the

Figure 3-19 Primary structure of a polypeptide

Glucagon is a very small polypeptide made up of 29 amino acids. The linear sequence of amino acids is indicated by ovals containing their abbreviated names (see Fig. 3-17).

© Cengage Learning

Secondary structure is highly regular.

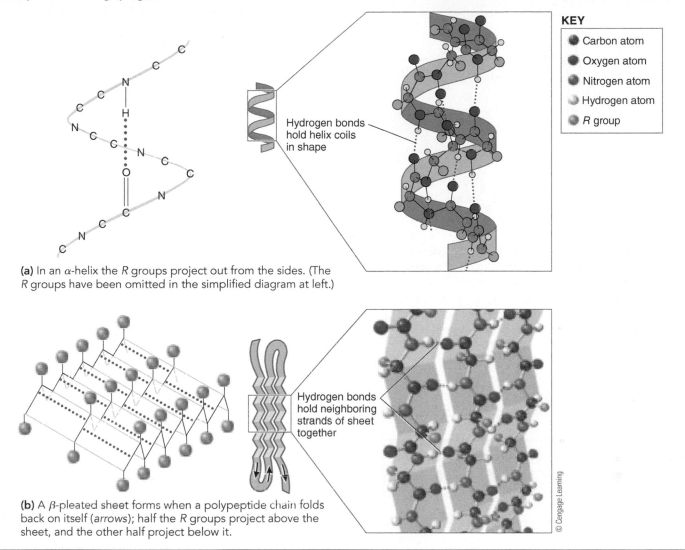

(a) In an α-helix the *R* groups project out from the sides. (The *R* groups have been omitted in the simplified diagram at left.)

(b) A β-pleated sheet forms when a polypeptide chain folds back on itself (*arrows*); half the *R* groups project above the sheet, and the other half project below it.

KEY
- ● Carbon atom
- ● Oxygen atom
- ● Nitrogen atom
- ○ Hydrogen atom
- ● *R* group

© Cengage Learning

Figure 3-20 Secondary structure of a protein

Hydrogen bonding of the backbone can produce two types of secondary structure: the α-helix and the β-pleated sheet.

PREDICT How might secondary structure be affected if some amino acids in the polypeptide chain were to include an additional carbon inserted between the α carbon and the peptide bond carbon?

resulting 3-D structure. The same types of interactions that produce secondary and tertiary structure can also occur between the polypeptide chains to contribute to quaternary structure; they include hydrogen bonding, ionic bonding, hydrophobic interactions, and disulfide bridges.

A functional antibody molecule, for example, consists of four polypeptide chains joined by disulfide bridges (**FIG. 3-22**). Disulfide bridges are a common feature of antibodies and other proteins secreted from cells. These strong bonds can link regions of the same polypeptide chain as well as form links between different polypeptide chains in proteins with quaternary structure.

Hemoglobin, the protein in red blood cells responsible for oxygen transport, is an example of a globular protein with a quaternary structure (**FIG. 3-23a**). Hemoglobin consists of 574

amino acids arranged in four polypeptide chains: two identical chains called *alpha chains* and two identical chains called *beta chains*.

Collagen, mentioned previously, has a fibrous type of quaternary structure that allows it to function as the major strengthener of animal tissues. It consists of three polypeptide chains wound about one another and bound by cross links between their amino acids (**FIG. 3-23b**).

The amino acid sequence of a protein determines its conformation

In 1972, U.S. researcher Christian B. Anfinsen was awarded the Nobel Prize in Chemistry for his studies on protein folding,

Tertiary structure depends on side chain interactions.

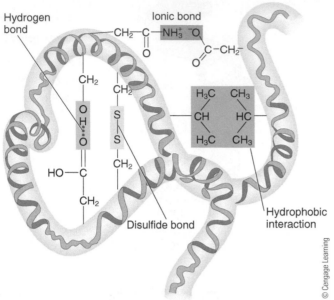

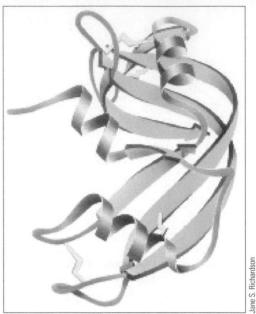

(a) Hydrogen bonds, ionic bonds, hydrophobic interactions, and disulfide bridges between *R* groups hold the parts of the molecule in the designated shape.

© Cengage Learning

(b) In this drawing, α-helical regions are represented by *purple coils,* β-pleated sheets by *broad green ribbons,* and connecting regions by *narrow tan ribbons.* The interactions among *R* groups that stabilize the bends and foldbacks that give the molecule its overall conformation (tertiary structure) are represented in *yellow.* This protein is bovine ribonuclease a.

Jane S. Richardson

Figure 3-21 *Animation* **Tertiary structure of a protein**

PREDICT Examine Figure 3-17. Would you expect the *R* groups of the following pairs of amino acids to interact? If so, by what mechanism: leucine and valine, alanine and serine, lysine and arginine, or glutamic acid and lysine?

which demonstrated that, at least under defined experimental conditions in vitro (outside a living cell), a polypeptide can spontaneously undergo folding processes that yield its normal, functional conformation. Since Anfinsen's pioneering work, many researchers studying various proteins and using a variety of highly sophisticated approaches have amassed evidence supporting the widely held conclusion that amino acid sequence is the ultimate determinant of protein conformation.

However, because conditions in vivo (in the cell) are quite different from defined laboratory conditions, proteins do not always fold spontaneously into their correct shape. On the contrary, scientists have learned that intracellular proteins known as **molecular chaperones** assist the folding of other protein molecules. Molecular chaperones are thought to make the folding process more orderly and efficient, and to prevent partially folded proteins from becoming inappropriately aggregated. However, there is no evidence that molecular chaperones actually dictate the folding pattern. For this reason, the existence of

chaperones is not an argument against the idea that amino acid sequence determines conformation.

Protein conformation determines function The overall structure of a protein helps determine its biological activity. A single protein may have more than one distinct structural region, called a **domain.** Each domain is a part of the amino acid sequence that can be independently folded and function free from the other parts of the protein. Many proteins are modular, consisting of two or more domains that are connected by less compact regions of the polypeptide chain.

Each domain may have a different function. Because a domain is a stable structure that has a specific function, one type of domain might be found in a number of different proteins that are generated through the process of molecular evolution. Researchers are now able to use genetic engineering methods to make recombinant proteins with new functions by linking together domains from different proteins.

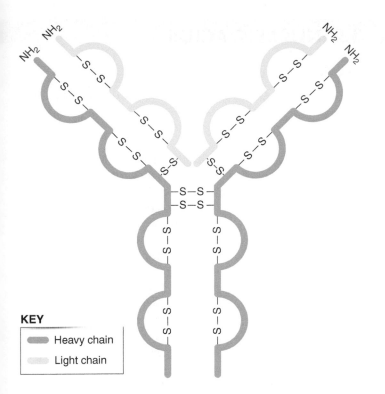

Figure 3-22 Disulfide bonds contribute to the structure of an antibody molecule

Antibody molecules consist of two light-chain and two heavy-chain polypeptides linked together by disulfide bonds. Each of the four chains also contains internal disulfide linkages that contribute to multiple structural and functional domains within each polypeptide.
© Cengage Learning

KEY

- ⬤ Heavy chain
- ⬤ Light chain

example, the genetic disease known as *sickle cell anemia* is due to a mutation that causes the substitution of the amino acid valine for glutamic acid at position 6 (the sixth amino acid from the amino end) in the beta chain of hemoglobin. The substitution of valine (which has a nonpolar side chain) for glutamic acid (which has a charged side chain) makes the hemoglobin less soluble and more likely to form crystal-like structures. This alteration of the hemoglobin affects the red blood cells, changing them to the crescent or sickle shapes that characterize this disease (see Fig. 16-9).

The biological activity of a protein may also be affected by agents or conditions that change its 3-D structure. When a protein is heated, subjected to significant pH changes, or treated with certain chemicals, its structure becomes disordered and the coiled peptide chains unfold, yielding a more random conformation. This unfolding, which is mainly due to the disruption of hydrogen bonds and ionic bonds, is typically accompanied by a loss of

Small changes in the primary structure of a protein can alter its shape and affect its function The biological activity of a protein can be disrupted by a change in amino acid sequence that results in a change in conformation. For

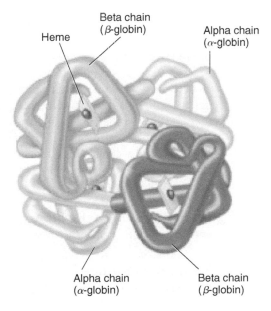

Heme

Beta chain
(β-globin)

Alpha chain
(α-globin)

Alpha chain
(α-globin)

Beta chain
(β-globin)

(a) Hemoglobin, a globular protein, consists of four polypeptide chains, each joined to an iron-containing molecule, a heme.

(b) Collagen, a fibrous protein, is a triple helix consisting of three long polypeptide chains.

Figure 3-23 Quaternary structure of a protein

Proteins with two or more polypeptide chains have quaternary structure.
© Cengage Learning

normal function. Such changes in shape and the accompanying loss of biological activity are termed *denaturation* of the protein.

For example, a denatured enzyme would lose its ability to catalyze a chemical reaction. An everyday example of denaturation occurs when we fry an egg. The consistency of the egg white protein, known as *albumin*, changes to a solid. Denaturation generally cannot be reversed (you cannot "unfry" an egg). Under certain conditions, however, some proteins have been denatured and have returned to their original shape and biological activity when normal environmental conditions were restored.

Protein conformation is studied through a variety of methods The architecture of a protein can be ascertained directly through various types of analysis, such as the X-ray diffraction studies discussed in Chapter 12 or nuclear magnetic resonance (NMR) methods. These methods provide the precise mathematical coordinates of individual atoms within the protein molecule that can be visualized by computer graphics as 3-D structures (see Fig. 3-23). Researchers can now use these computer-based models to simulate how molecules such as drugs (or another protein) might specifically bind to a protein to alter its function.

Today a protein's primary structure can be determined rapidly through the application of genetic engineering techniques (discussed in Chapter 15) or by the use of sophisticated technology such as mass spectrometry. Researchers use these amino acid sequence data to predict a protein's higher levels of structure. As we have seen, side chains interact in relatively predictable ways, such as through ionic and hydrogen bonds. In addition, regions with certain types of side chains are more likely to form α-helices or β-pleated sheets. Computer programs make such predictions that can be verified by X-ray diffraction or NMR methods.

Researchers also use computers to search databases to find polypeptides with similar sequences. If the conformations of any of those polypeptides or portions have already been determined directly by X-ray diffraction or other techniques, this information can be extrapolated to make similar correlations between amino acid sequence and 3-D structure for the protein under investigation.

Misfolded proteins are implicated in human diseases Studies on the mechanisms of protein folding, and on the relationship between the activity of a protein and its conformation, are increasingly of medical importance. For example, as discussed in Chapter 24, mad cow disease and related diseases in humans and other animals are caused by misfolded proteins called *prions*. Other serious diseases in which misfolded proteins appear to play an important role include Alzheimer's disease (see Chapter 41) and Huntington's disease (see Chapter 16).

CHECKPOINT 3.4

- **VISUALIZE** *Draw the structural formula of a simple amino acid. What is the importance of the carboxyl group, amino group, and R group?*
- *Explain how the primary structure of a polypeptide influences its secondary and tertiary structures.*

3.5 NUCLEIC ACIDS

LEARNING OBJECTIVE

10 Describe the components of a nucleotide. Name some nucleic acids and nucleotides, and discuss the importance of these compounds in living organisms.

Nucleic acids are macromolecules that transmit hereditary information and determine what proteins a cell manufactures. Two classes of nucleic acids are found in cells: deoxyribonucleic acid and ribonucleic acid. **Deoxyribonucleic acid (DNA)** makes up the genes, the hereditary material of the cell, and contains instructions for making all the proteins as well as all the RNA the organism needs. **Ribonucleic acid (RNA)** participates in the process in which amino acids are linked to form polypeptides. Some types of RNA, known as **ribozymes** (see Chapter 13 and Fig. 21-5) can even act as specific biological catalysts. Like proteins, nucleic acids are large, complex molecules. The name *nucleic acid* reflects that they are acidic and were first identified, by Swiss biochemist Friedrich Miescher in 1870, in the nuclei of pus cells.

Nucleic acids are polymers of **nucleotides,** molecular units that consist of (1) a five-carbon sugar, either **deoxyribose** (in DNA) or **ribose** (in RNA); (2) one or more phosphate groups, which make the molecule acidic; and (3) a nitrogenous base, a ring compound that contains nitrogen. The nitrogenous base may be either a double-ring **purine** or a single-ring **pyrimidine** (FIG. 3-24). DNA commonly contains the purines **adenine (A)** and **guanine (G),** the pyrimidines **cytosine (C)** and **thymine (T),** the sugar deoxyribose, and phosphate. RNA contains the purines adenine and guanine, and the pyrimidines cytosine and **uracil (U),** together with the sugar ribose, and phosphate.

The molecules of nucleic acids are made of linear chains of nucleotides, which are joined by **phosphodiester linkages**. Each linkage consists of a phosphate group and the covalent bonds that attach it to the sugars of adjacent nucleotides (FIG. 3-25). Note that each nucleotide is defined by its particular base and that nucleotides can be joined in any sequence. A nucleic acid molecule is uniquely defined by its specific sequence of nucleotides, which constitutes a code (see Chapter 13). Whereas RNA is usually composed of one nucleotide chain, DNA consists of two nucleotide chains held together by hydrogen bonds and entwined around each other in a double helix (see Fig. 1-7).

Some nucleotides are important in energy transfers and other cell functions

In addition to their importance as subunits of DNA and RNA, nucleotides perform other vital functions in living cells. **Adenosine triphosphate (ATP),** composed of adenine, ribose, and three phosphates (see Fig. 7-5), is of major importance as the primary energy currency of all cells (see Chapter 7). The two terminal phosphate groups are joined to the nucleotide by covalent bonds. These bonds are traditionally indicated by wavy lines, which indicate that ATP can transfer a phosphate group to

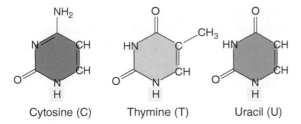

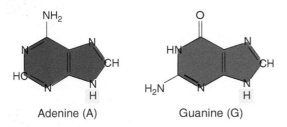

(a) Pyrimidines. The three major pyrimidine bases found in nucleotides are cytosine, thymine (in DNA only), and uracil (in RNA only).

Adenine (A) Guanine (G)

(b) Purines. The two major purine bases found in nucleotides are adenine and guanine.

Figure 3-24 *Animation* **Components of nucleotides**

The hydrogens indicated by the *yellow screens* are removed when the base is attached to a sugar.
© Cengage Learning

another molecule, making that molecule more reactive. In this way ATP is able to donate some of its chemical energy. Most of the readily available chemical energy of the cell is associated with the phosphate groups of ATP. Like ATP, **guanosine triphosphate (GTP)**, a nucleotide that contains the base guanine, can transfer energy by transferring a phosphate group and also has a role in cell signaling (see Chapter 6).

A nucleotide may be converted to an alternative form with specific cell functions. ATP, for example, is converted to **cyclic adenosine monophosphate (cyclic AMP, or cAMP)** by the enzyme adenylyl cyclase (FIG. 3-26). Cyclic AMP regulates certain cell functions, such as cell signaling, and is important in the mechanism by which some hormones act. A related molecule, **cyclic guanosine monophosphate (cGMP)**, also plays a role in certain cell signaling processes.

Cells contain several dinucleotides, which are of great importance in metabolic processes. For example, as discussed in Chapter 7, **nicotinamide adenine dinucleotide** has a primary role in oxidation and reduction reactions in cells. It can exist in an oxidized form (NAD^+) that is converted to a reduced form (**NADH**) when it accepts electrons (in association with hydrogen; see Fig. 7-7). These electrons, along with their energy, are transferred to other molecules.

CHECKPOINT 3.5

• **VISUALIZE** *Sketch a pyrimidine nucleotide subunit that would be found only in RNA. Circle and label the three components that make up this type of nucleotide. Explain what changes in the functional groups of this subunit would have to occur for it to be found in a DNA molecule.*

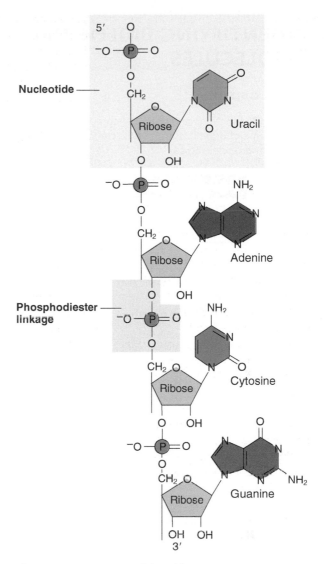

Figure 3-25 RNA, a nucleic acid

Nucleotides, each with a specific base, are joined by phosphodiester linkages.
© Cengage Learning

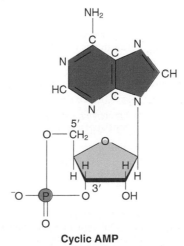

Cyclic AMP

Figure 3-26 Cyclic adenosine monophosphate (cAMP)

The single phosphate is part of a ring connecting two regions of the ribose.
© Cengage Learning

3.6 IDENTIFYING BIOLOGICAL MOLECULES

LEARNING OBJECTIVE

11 Compare the functions and chemical compositions of the major groups of organic compounds: carbohydrates, lipids, proteins, and nucleic acids.

Although the classes of biological molecules may seem overwhelming at first, you will learn to distinguish them readily by understanding their chief attributes. They are summarized in TABLE 3-3.

CHECKPOINT 3.6

- *How can you distinguish a pentose sugar from a hexose sugar? a disaccharide from a sterol? an amino acid from a monosaccharide? a phospholipid from a triacylglycerol? a protein from a polysaccharide? a nucleic acid from a protein?*

TABLE 3-3	Classes of Biologically Important Organic Compounds		
CLASS AND COMPONENT ELEMENTS	**DESCRIPTION**	**HOW TO RECOGNIZE**	**PRINCIPAL FUNCTION IN LIVING SYSTEMS**
CARBOHYDRATES C, H, O	Contain approximately 1 C:2 H:1 O (but make allowance for loss of oxygen when sugar units as nucleic acids and glycoproteins are linked)	Count the carbons, hydrogens, and oxygens.	Cell fuel; energy storage; structural component of plant cell walls; component of other compounds such as nucleic acids and glycoproteins
	1. *Monosaccharides* (simple sugars). Mainly five-carbon (pentose) molecules such as ribose or six-carbon (hexose) molecules such as glucose and fructose	Look for the ring shapes:	Cell fuel; components of other compounds
	2. *Disaccharides.* Two sugar units linked by a glycosidic bond, e.g., maltose, sucrose	Count sugar units.	Components of other compounds; form of sugar transported in plants
	3. *Polysaccharides.* Many sugar units linked by glycosidic bonds, e.g., glycogen, cellulose	Count sugar units.	Energy storage; structural components of plant cell walls
LIPIDS C, H, O (sometimes N, P)	Contain much less oxygen relative to carbon and hydrogen than do carbohydrates		Energy storage; cellular fuel, components of cells; thermal insulation
	1. *Fats.* Combination of glycerol with one to three fatty acids. Monoacylglycerol contains one fatty acid; diacylglycerol contains two fatty acids; triacylglycerol contains three fatty acids. If fatty acids contain double carbon-to-carbon linkages (C=C), they are unsaturated; otherwise, they are saturated.	Look for glycerol at one end of molecule:	Cell fuel; energy storage
	2. *Phospholipids.* Composed of glycerol attached to one or two fatty acids and to an organic base containing phosphorus	Look for glycerol and side chain containing phosphorus and nitrogen.	Components of cell membranes
	3. *Steroids.* Complex molecules containing carbon atoms arranged in four attached rings (Three rings contain six carbon atoms each, and the fourth ring contains five.)	Look for four attached rings:	Some are hormones; others include cholesterol, bile salts, vitamin D; components of cell membranes
	4. *Carotenoids.* Orange and yellow pigments; consist of isoprene units	Look for isoprene units.	Converted to retinal (important in photoreception) and vitamin A
PROTEINS C, H, O, N (usually S)	One or more polypeptides (chains of amino acids) coiled or folded in characteristic shapes	Look for amino acid units joined by C—N bonds.	Serve as enzymes; structural components; muscle proteins; hemoglobin
NUCLEIC ACIDS C, H, O, N, P	Backbone composed of alternating pentose and phosphate groups, from which nitrogenous bases project. DNA contains the sugar deoxyribose and the bases guanine, cytosine, adenine, and thymine. RNA contains the sugar ribose and the bases guanine, cytosine, adenine, and uracil. Each molecular subunit, called a nucleotide, consists of a pentose, a phosphate, and a nitrogenous base.	Look for a pentose–phosphate backbone. DNA forms a double helix.	Storage, transmission, and expression of genetic information; some important in energy transfers, cell signaling, and other aspects of metabolism.

3.1 Carbon Atoms and Organic Molecules *(page 45)*

1 Describe the properties of carbon that make it the central component of organic compounds.

- Each carbon atom forms four covalent bonds with up to four other atoms; these bonds are single, double, or triple bonds. Carbon atoms form straight or branched chains, or join into rings. Carbon forms covalent bonds with a greater number of different elements than does any other type of atom.

2 Define the term *isomer* and distinguish among the three principal isomer types.

- **Isomers** are compounds with the same molecular formula but different structures.
- **Structural isomers** differ in the covalent arrangements of their atoms. **Geometric isomers,** or *cis–trans isomers,* differ in the spatial arrangements of their atoms. **Enantiomers** are isomers that are mirror images of each other. Cells can distinguish between these configurations.

3 Identify the major functional groups present in organic compounds and describe their properties.

- **Hydrocarbons,** organic compounds consisting of only carbon and hydrogen, are nonpolar and **hydrophobic.** The **methyl group** is a hydrocarbon group.
- Polar and ionic functional groups interact with one another and are **hydrophilic.** Partial charges on atoms at opposite ends of a bond are responsible for the polar property of a functional group. **Hydroxyl** and **carbonyl groups** are polar.
- **Carboxyl** and **phosphate groups** are acidic, becoming negatively charged when they release hydrogen ions. The **amino group** is basic, becoming positively charged when it accepts a hydrogen ion.

4 Explain the relationship between polymers and macromolecules.

- Long chains of **monomers** (similar organic compounds) linked through **condensation reactions** are called **polymers.** Large polymers such as polysaccharides, proteins, and DNA are referred to as **macromolecules.** They can be broken down by **hydrolysis reactions.**

3.2 Carbohydrates *(page 49)*

5 Distinguish among monosaccharides, disaccharides, and polysaccharides; compare storage polysaccharides with structural polysaccharides.

- **Carbohydrates** contain carbon, hydrogen, and oxygen in a ratio of approximately one carbon to two hydrogens to one oxygen. **Monosaccharides** are simple sugars such as glucose, fructose, and ribose. Two monosaccharides join by a **glycosidic linkage** to form a **disaccharide** such as maltose or sucrose.

- Most carbohydrates are **polysaccharides,** long chains of repeating units of a simple sugar. Carbohydrates are typically stored in plants as the polysaccharide **starch** and in animals as the polysaccharide **glycogen.** The cell walls of plants are composed mainly of the structural polysaccharide **cellulose.**

3.3 Lipids *(page 54)*

6 Distinguish among fats, phospholipids, and steroids, and describe the composition, characteristics, and biological functions of each.

- **Lipids** are composed mainly of hydrocarbon-containing regions, with few oxygen-containing (polar or ionic) functional groups. Lipids have a greasy or oily consistency and are relatively insoluble in water.
- **Triacylglycerol,** the main storage form of fat in organisms, consists of a molecule of **glycerol** combined with three **fatty acids. Monoacylglycerols** and **diacylglycerols** contain one and two fatty acids, respectively. A fatty acid can be either **saturated** with hydrogen or **unsaturated.**

- **Phospholipids** are structural components of cell membranes. A phospholipid consists of a glycerol molecule attached at one end to two fatty acids and at the other end to a phosphate group linked to an organic compound such as choline.
- **Steroid** molecules contain carbon atoms arranged in four attached rings. Cholesterol, bile salts, and certain hormones are important steroids.

3.4 Proteins *(page 58)*

7 Give an overall description of the structure and functions of proteins.

- **Proteins** are complex macromolecules made of simpler subunits, called **amino acids,** joined by **peptide bonds.** Two amino acids combine to form a **dipeptide.** A longer chain of amino acids is a **polypeptide.** Proteins are the most versatile class of biological molecules, serving a variety of functions, such as **enzymes,** structural components, and cell regulators.
- Proteins are composed of various linear sequences of 20 different amino acids.

8 Describe the features that are shared by all amino acids and explain how amino acids are grouped into classes based on the characteristics of their side chains.

$$H_3N^+ - \overset{\displaystyle COO^-}{\underset{\displaystyle CH_3}{\overset{|}{\underset{|}{C}}} - H}$$

- All amino acids contain an amino group and a carboxyl group. Amino acids vary in their side chains, which dictate their chemical properties: nonpolar, polar, acidic, or basic. Amino acids generally exist as dipolar ions at cell pH and serve as important biological buffers.

9 Distinguish among the four levels of organization of protein molecules.

- **Primary structure** is the linear sequence of amino acids in the polypeptide chain.
- **Secondary structure** is a regular conformation, such as an α-helix or a β-pleated sheet; it is due to hydrogen bonding between elements of the backbones of the amino acids.
- **Tertiary structure** is the overall shape of the polypeptide chains, as dictated by chemical properties and interactions of the side chains of specific amino acids. Hydrogen bonds, ionic bonds, hydrophobic interactions, and disulfide bridges contribute to tertiary structure.
- **Quaternary structure** is determined by the association of two or more polypeptide chains.

3.5 Nucleic Acids *(page 66)*

10 Describe the components of a nucleotide. Name some nucleic acids and nucleotides, and discuss the importance of these compounds in living organisms.

- The nucleic acids **DNA** and **RNA,** composed of long chains of nucleotide subunits, store and transfer information that specifies the sequence of amino acids in proteins and ultimately the structure and function of the organism.

- **Nucleotides** are composed of a two-ring **purine** or one-ring **pyrimidine** nitrogenous base, a five-carbon sugar (**ribose** or **deoxyribose**), and one or more phosphate groups.

- **ATP (adenosine triphosphate)** is a nucleotide of special significance in energy metabolism. NAD$^+$ is also involved in energy metabolism through its role as an electron (hydrogen) acceptor in biological oxidation and reduction reactions.

3.6 Identifying Biological Molecules *(page 68)*

11 Compare the functions and chemical compositions of the major groups of organic compounds: carbohydrates, lipids, proteins, and nucleic acids.

- Review Table 3-3.

TEST YOUR UNDERSTANDING

Know and Comprehend

1. Carbon is particularly well suited to be the backbone of organic molecules because (a) it can form both covalent bonds and ionic bonds (b) its covalent bonds are very irregularly arranged in three-dimensional space (c) its covalent bonds are the strongest chemical bonds known (d) it can bond to atoms of a large number of other elements (e) all the bonds it forms are polar

2. **VISUALIZE** The structures depicted are (a) enantiomers (b) different views of the same molecule (c) geometric (*cis–trans*) isomers (d) both geometric isomers and enantiomers (e) structural isomers

3. Which of the following is a nonpolar molecule? (a) water, H_2O (b) ammonia, NH_3 (c) methane, CH_4 (d) ethane, C_2H_6 (e) more than one of the preceding is/are correct.

4. The synthetic process by which monomers are covalently linked is (a) hydrolysis (b) isomerization (c) condensation (d) glycosidic linkage (e) ester linkage

5. A monosaccharide designated as an aldehyde sugar contains (a) a terminal carboxyl group (b) an internal carboxyl group (c) a terminal carbonyl group (d) an internal carbonyl group (e) a terminal carboxyl group and an internal carbonyl group

6. Structural polysaccharides typically (a) have extensive hydrogen bonding between adjacent molecules (b) are much more hydrophilic than storage polysaccharides (c) have much stronger covalent bonds than do storage polysaccharides (d) consist of alternating α-glucose and β-glucose subunits (e) form helical structures in the cell

7. Saturated fatty acids are so named because they are saturated with (a) hydrogen (b) water (c) hydroxyl groups (d) glycerol (e) double bonds

8. Fatty acids in phospholipids and triacylglycerols interact with one another by (a) disulfide bridges (b) van der Waals interactions (c) covalent bonds (d) hydrogen bonds (e) fatty acids do not interact with one another

9. Which of the following levels of protein structure may be affected by hydrogen bonding? (a) primary and secondary (b) primary and tertiary (c) secondary, tertiary, and quaternary (d) primary, secondary, and tertiary (e) primary, secondary, tertiary, and quaternary

10. Which of the following associations between *R* groups are the strongest? (a) hydrophobic interactions (b) hydrogen bonds (c) ionic bonds (d) peptide bonds (e) disulfide bridges

11. Each phosphodiester linkage in DNA or RNA includes a phosphate joined by covalent bonds to (a) two bases (b) two sugars (c) two additional phosphates (d) a sugar, a base, and a phosphate (e) a sugar and a base

Apply and Analyze

12. **PREDICT** Do any of the amino acid side groups shown below have the potential to form an ionic bond with any of the other side groups shown? If so, which pair(s) could form such an association?
    (a) —CH_3
    (b) —CH_2—COO^-
    (c) —CH_2—CH_2—NH_3^+
    (d) —CH_2—CH_2—COO^-
    (e) —CH_2—OH

Evaluate and Synthesize

13. **PREDICT** Like oxygen, sulfur forms two covalent bonds. However, sulfur is far less electronegative. In fact, it is approximately as electronegative as carbon. How would the properties of the various classes of biological molecules be altered if you were to replace all the oxygen atoms with sulfur atoms?

14. Hydrogen bonds and van der Waals interactions are much weaker than covalent bonds, yet they are vital to organisms. Explain, providing some specific examples.

15 **EVOLUTION LINK** In what ways are all species alike biochemically? Identify some ways in which species may differ from one another biochemically. What do these similarities and differences suggest about the history of life on Earth?

16. **EVOLUTION LINK** The total number of possible amino acid sequences in a polypeptide chain is staggering. Given that there are 20 amino acids, potentially there could be 20^{100} different amino acid sequences just for polypeptides only 100 amino acids in length. However, the actual number of different polypeptides occurring in organisms is only a tiny fraction of this potential. What insight does this finding provide into the evolutionary process?

17. **EVOLUTION LINK** Each amino acid could potentially exist as one of two possible enantiomers, known as the D-form and the L-form (based on the arrangement of the groups attached to the asymmetric α carbon). However, in all organisms, only L-amino acids are found in proteins. What does this suggest about the evolution of proteins?

aplia To access course materials, such as Aplia and other companion resources, please visit **www.cengagebrain.com.**

Organization of the Cell | 4

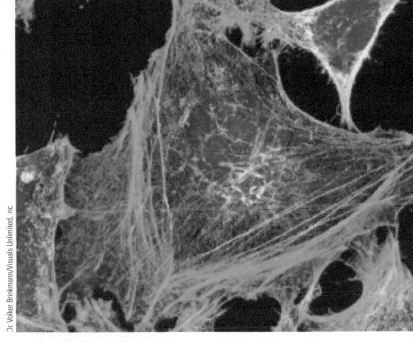

Dr. Volker Brinkmann/Visuals Unlimited, Inc.

The cell is the smallest unit that can carry out all activities we associate with life. When provided with essential nutrients and an appropriate environment, some cells can be kept alive and growing in the laboratory for many years. By contrast, no isolated part of a cell is capable of sustained survival. As you read this chapter, recall the discussion of systems biology in Chapter 1. Even as we describe individual components of cells, each of which is a system in itself, we discuss how these structures work together to generate ever more complex interacting biological systems within the cell. The cell itself is a highly intricate biological system, and groups of cells make up tissues, organs, and organisms that are biological systems of ever increasing complexity.

Most prokaryotes and many protists and fungi consist of a single cell. In contrast, most plants and animals are composed of millions of cells. Cells are the building blocks of complex multicellular organisms. Although they are basically similar, cells are also extraordinarily diverse and versatile. They are modified in a variety of ways to carry out specialized functions.

Cell biology is an interdisciplinary science. It draws on increasingly sophisticated tools from a wide array of scientific fields in the quest to better understand cellular structure and function. For example, investigation of the cytoskeleton (cell skeleton), currently an active and exciting area of research, has been greatly enhanced by advances in microscopy, biochemistry, molecular biology, genetics, and computational biology. The photomicrograph illustrates the extensive distribution of cytoskeletal fibers known as microfilaments (composed of the protein actin) and intermediate filaments (composed of the protein keratin) in cells. Biochemical studies of microfilaments, combined with computer-generated 3-D images of their protein subunits, have led to deep insights into how cells rapidly assemble and disassemble these dynamic and complex structures. Further understanding of microfilament functions comes from molecular genetic studies of cells that contain mutations in genes that regulate microfilament assembly. Through this combination of approaches, scientists are developing a comprehensive picture of how the cytoskeletal system maintains cell shape and functions in cell movement.

The cytoskeleton. The cell shown here was stained with fluorescent molecules that bind to DNA (*blue*), microfilaments (*green*), and intermediate filaments (*red*). This type of microscopy, known as confocal fluorescence microscopy, shows the extensive distribution of microfilaments in this cell.

KEY CONCEPTS

4.1 The cell is the basic unit of life, its organization is critical to its ability to carry out all life activities, and its size and shape are adapted for its functions.

4.2 Biologists connect cellular structures to their functions with an interdisciplinary approach that includes microscopy, biochemistry, genetics, and computational methods.

4.3 Unlike prokaryotic cells, eukaryotic cells have internal membranes that divide the cell into compartments, allowing cells to conduct specialized activities within separate, small spaces.

4.4 In eukaryotic cells, genetic information coded in DNA is located in the nucleus, which is typically the most prominent organelle in the cell.

4.5 Among the many organelles in the cytoplasm are ribosomes, which synthesize proteins; endoplasmic reticulum and Golgi complexes, which process proteins; and mitochondria and chloroplasts, which convert energy from one form to another.

4.6 The cytoskeleton is a dynamic internal framework that functions in various types of cell movement.

4.7 Most eukaryotic cells are surrounded by a cell coat; in addition, many animal cells are surrounded by an extracellular matrix; cells of most bacteria, archaea, fungi, and plants are surrounded by a cell wall.

4.1 THE CELL: BASIC UNIT OF LIFE

1　Connect the cell theory to the evolution of life.
2　Relate the organizational similarities of all cells to the need to conduct essential life functions.
3　Explain the functional significance of cell size and cell shape.

Cells, the building blocks of organisms, are dramatic examples of the underlying unity of all living things.

The cell theory is a unifying concept in biology

From their own microscopic observations and those of other scientists, botanist Matthias Schleiden in 1838 and zoologist Theodor Schwann in 1839, reasoned that all plants and animals consist of cells. Later, Rudolf Virchow, another German scientist, observed cells dividing and giving rise to daughter cells. In 1855, Virchow proposed that new cells form only by the division of previously existing cells. The work of Schleiden, Schwann, and Virchow contributed greatly to the development of the **cell theory**, the unifying concept that (1) cells are the basic living units of organization and function in all organisms and (2) all cells come from other cells.

Around 1880, another German biologist, August Weismann, added an important corollary to Virchow's concept by pointing out that the ancestry of all the cells alive today can be traced back to ancient times. Evidence that all living cells have a common origin is provided by the basic similarities in their structures and in the molecules of which they are made. When we examine a variety of diverse organisms, ranging from simple bacteria to the most complex plants and animals, we find striking similarities at the cellular level. Careful studies of shared cell characteristics help us trace the evolutionary history of various organisms and furnish powerful evidence that all organisms alive today had a common origin.

The organization and basic functions of all cells are similar

The organization of cells and their small size are critical properties that allow them to maintain an appropriate internal environment necessary for their biochemical systems to function. For the cell to maintain its interior composition, its contents must be separated from the external environment. The **plasma membrane** is a structurally distinctive surface membrane that surrounds all cells. By making the interior of the cell an enclosed compartment, the plasma membrane allows the chemical composition of the cell to be different from that outside the cell. The plasma membrane has unique properties that enable it to serve as a selective barrier between the cell contents and the exterior, permitting the cell to exchange materials with the environment and accumulate substances needed to drive its biochemical reactions.

Cells have internal structures, called **organelles**, that are specialized to carry out cell activities. Most of the organelles of eukaryotic cells (cells that possess a nucleus) consist of one or more membrane-enclosed compartments capable of regulating their own internal environments for specialized functions such as converting energy to usable forms, processing nutrients, and recycling damaged or unneeded structures. Genetic information stored in DNA molecules of all cells, for example, is contained, duplicated, and transcribed in the nuclear compartment of eukaryotic cells (see Chapter 15).

Cell membranes also serve as organizing surfaces for interacting proteins that function in certain types of biochemical reactions. These stepwise reactions are more efficient and more rapid when their components are arranged to minimize the distance reactants must travel. As you will see in this chapter and in Chapter 8, the inner membrane of the eukaryotic mitochondrial compartment (as well as the plasma membrane of prokaryotes) contains tightly packed protein complexes that rapidly exchange electrons and protons, converting energy from food stores into energy-rich ATP that is used in hundreds of different biochemical reactions that occur every moment in a living cell. These chemical reactions that convert energy from one form to another are essentially the same in all cells, from the reactions in bacteria to those of large, multicellular plants and animals. Such fundamental similarities are strong evidence of their evolutionary relationships.

Cell size is limited

Although their sizes vary over a wide range (FIG. 4-1), most cells are microscopic and must be measured by very small units. The basic unit of linear measurement in the metric system (see inside back cover) is the meter (m), which is just a little longer than 1 yard. One millimeter (mm) is 1/1000 of 1 meter and is about as long as the bar enclosed in parentheses (-). The micrometer (μm) is the most convenient unit for measuring cells. A bar 1 μm long is 1/1,000,000 (1 millionth) of a meter, or 1/1000 of a millimeter, which is far too short to be seen with the unaided eye. Most of us have difficulty thinking about units that are too small to see, but it is helpful to remember that a micrometer has the same relationship to a millimeter that a millimeter has to a meter (1/1000).

As small as it is, the micrometer is actually too large to measure most cell components. For this purpose biologists use the nanometer (nm), which is 1/1,000,000,000 (1 billionth) of a meter, or 1/1000 of a micrometer. To mentally move down to the world of the nanometer, recall that a millimeter is 1/1000 of a meter, a micrometer is 1/1000 of a millimeter, and a nanometer is 1/1000 of a micrometer.

A few specialized algae and animal cells are large enough to be seen with the naked eye. A human egg cell, for example, is about 130 μm in diameter, or approximately the size of the period at the end of this sentence. The largest cells are birds' eggs, but they are not typical cells because they include large amounts of food reserves: the yolk and the egg white. The functioning part of the cell is a small mass on the surface of the yolk.

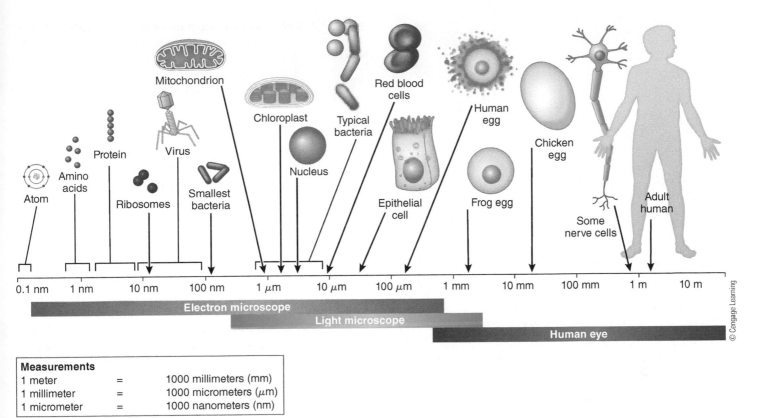

Measurements		
1 meter	=	1000 millimeters (mm)
1 millimeter	=	1000 micrometers (μm)
1 micrometer	=	1000 nanometers (nm)

Figure 4-1 Biological size and cell diversity

We can compare relative size from the chemical level to the level of an entire organism by using a logarithmic scale (multiples of 10). The prokaryotic cells of most bacteria range in size from 1 to 10 μm long. Most eukaryotic cells are between 10 and 30 μm in diameter. Mitochondria are about the size of small bacteria, whereas chloroplasts are usually larger, about 5 μm long. Ova (egg cells) are among the largest cells. Although microscopic, some nerve cells are very long. The cells shown here are not drawn to scale.

Why are most cells so small? If you consider what a cell must do to maintain its functions and to grow, it may be easier to understand the reasons for its small size. A cell must take in food and other materials and must rid itself of waste products generated by metabolic reactions. Everything that enters or leaves a cell must pass through its plasma membrane. The plasma membrane contains specialized "pumps" and channels with "gates" that selectively regulate the passage of materials into and out of the cell. The plasma membrane must be large enough relative to the cell volume to keep up with the demands of regulating the passage of materials. Thus, a critical factor in determining cell size is the ratio of its surface area (the plasma membrane) to its volume (FIG. 4-2).

As a cell becomes larger, its volume increases at a greater rate than its surface area (its plasma membrane), which effectively places an upper limit on cell size. Above some critical size, the number of molecules required by the cell could not be transported into the cell fast enough to sustain its needs. In addition, the cell would not be able to regulate its concentration of various ions or efficiently export its wastes.

Of course, not all cells are spherical or cuboid. Because of their shapes, some very large cells have relatively favorable ratios of surface area to volume. In fact, some variations in cell shape represent a strategy for increasing the ratio of surface area to

volume. For example, many large plant cells are long and thin, which increases their surface area–to–volume ratio. Some cells, such as epithelial cells lining the small intestine, have fingerlike projections of the plasma membrane, called **microvilli**, that significantly increase the surface area for absorbing nutrients and other materials (see Fig. 47-10).

Another reason for the small size of cells is that, once inside, molecules must be transported to the locations where they are converted into other forms. Because cells are small, the distances molecules travel within them are relatively short. Thus, molecules are rapidly available for cell activities.

Cell size and shape are adapted to function

The sizes and shapes of cells are adapted to the particular functions they perform. Some cells, such as amoebas and white blood cells, change their shape as they move about. Sperm cells have long, whiplike tails, called *flagella*, for locomotion. Nerve cells have long, thin extensions that enable them to transmit messages over great distances. The extensions of some nerve cells in the human body may be as long as 1 meter! Certain epithelial cells are almost rectangular and are stacked much like building blocks to form sheetlike tissues. (Epithelial tissue covers the body and lines body cavities.)

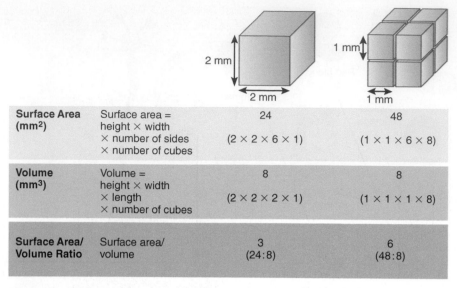

		2 mm cube	1 mm cubes
Surface Area (mm²)	Surface area = height × width × number of sides × number of cubes	24 (2 × 2 × 6 × 1)	48 (1 × 1 × 6 × 8)
Volume (mm³)	Volume = height × width × length × number of cubes	8 (2 × 2 × 2 × 1)	8 (1 × 1 × 1 × 8)
Surface Area/ Volume Ratio	Surface area/ volume	3 (24:8)	6 (48:8)

Figure 4-2 Surface area–to-volume ratio

The surface area of a cell must be large enough relative to its volume to allow adequate exchange of materials with the environment. Although their volumes are the same, eight small cells have a much greater surface area (plasma membrane) in relation to their total volume than one large cell does. In the example shown, the ratio of the total surface area to total volume of eight 1 mm cubes is double the surface area–to-volume ratio of the single large cube.

© Cengage Learning

CHECKPOINT 4.1

- **CONNECT** *How does the cell theory contribute to our understanding of the evolution of life?*

- **PREDICT** *Could a cell function if it were not enclosed by a selective barrier (i.e., a plasma membrane)?*

- *What molecule is used for information storage in all cells?*

- *What convenient form of chemical energy is used by all cells?*

- *Why is the relationship between surface area and volume of a cell important in determining cell size limits?*

4.2 METHODS FOR STUDYING CELLS

LEARNING OBJECTIVE

4 Compare methods that biologists use to study cells and point out the ways in which many of these approaches are complementary.

One of the most important tools biologists use for studying cell structures is the microscope. Using a microscope he had made, Robert Hooke, an English scientist, first described cells in 1665 in his book *Micrographia*. Hooke examined a piece of cork and then drew and described what he saw. Hooke chose the term *cell* because the tissue reminded him of the small rooms monks lived in. Interestingly, what Hooke saw were not actually living

cells but the walls of dead cork cells (FIG. 4-3a). Much later, scientists recognized that the interior enclosed by the walls is the important part of living cells.

A few years after Hooke's discovery and inspired by Hooke's work, Dutch naturalist Antonie van Leeuwenhoek viewed living cells with small lenses that he made. Leeuwenhoek was highly skilled at fabricating lenses and was able to magnify images more than 200 times. Among his important discoveries were bacteria, protists, blood cells, and sperm cells. Leeuwenhoek was among the first scientists to report cells in animals. He was a merchant and was not formally trained as a scientist, but his skill, curiosity, and diligence in sharing his discoveries with scientists at the Royal Society of London brought an awareness of microscopic life to the scientific world. Unfortunately, Leeuwenhoek did not share his techniques. Not until more than 170 years later, in the late 19th century, were microscopes sufficiently developed for biologists to seriously focus their attention on the study of cells.

Light microscopes are used to study stained or living cells

The **light microscope (LM),** the type used by most students, consists of a tube with glass lenses at each end. Because it contains several lenses, the modern light microscope is referred to as a *compound microscope*. Visible light passes through the specimen being observed and through the lenses. Light is refracted (bent) by the lenses, magnifying the image. Images obtained with light microscopes are referred to as light micrographs, or LMs.

Two features of a microscope determine how clearly a small object can be viewed: magnification and resolving power. **Magnification** is the ratio of the size of the image seen with the microscope to the actual size of the object. The best light microscopes usually magnify an object no more than 2000 times. **Resolution**, or **resolving power**, is the capacity to distinguish fine detail in an image; it is defined as the minimum distance between two points at which they can both be seen separately rather than as a single, blurred point. Resolving power depends on the quality of the lenses and the wavelength of the illuminating light. As the wavelength decreases, the resolution increases.

The visible light used by light microscopes has wavelengths ranging from about 400 nm (violet) to 700 nm (red); this limits the resolution of the light microscope to details no smaller than the diameter of a small bacterial cell (about 0.2 μm or 200 nm). By the early 20th century, refined versions of the light microscope became available.

The interior of many cells is transparent, and it is difficult to discern specific structures. Organic chemists contributed greatly

WHY IS IT USED? Cells are too small to be studied with the naked eye. Biologists use microscopes to view cells and structures inside cells. Many types of microscopes have been developed. Panels b–f are photomicrographs of *Paramecium*, a ciliated protist, made using several kinds of light microscopes.

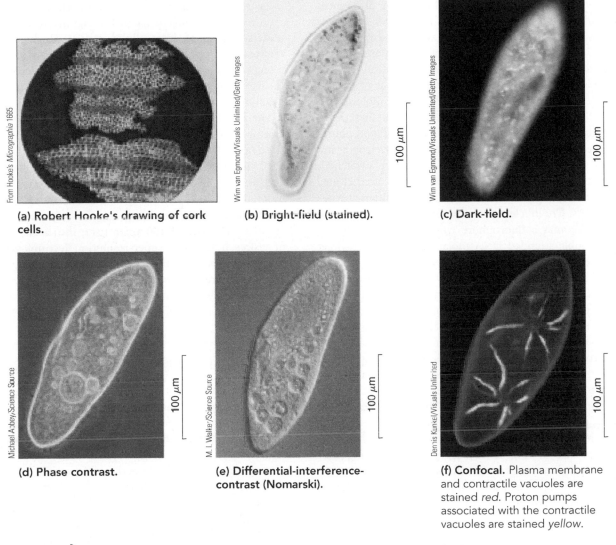

(a) Robert Hooke's drawing of cork cells.

From Hooke's *Micrographia* 1665

(b) Bright-field (stained).

Wim van Egmond/Visuals Unlimited/Getty Images

100 μm

(c) Dark-field.

Wim van Egmond/Visuals Unlimited/Getty Images

100 μm

(d) Phase contrast.

Michael Abbey/Science Source

100 μm

(e) Differential-interference-contrast (Nomarski).

M. I. Walker/Science Source

100 μm

(f) Confocal. Plasma membrane and contractile vacuoles are stained *red*. Proton pumps associated with the contractile vacuoles are stained *yellow*.

Dennis Kunkel/Visuals Unlimited

100 μm

HOW IS IT DONE? Using a microscope that he constructed, Robert Hooke looked at a thin slice of cork and drew what he saw. Biologists now view cells in more detail using the more sophisticated microscopes and techniques that have been developed. In the light microscope, a beam of light passes through the specimen being observed and through the lenses. The lenses refract the light, which magnifies the image. Bright-field microscopy can be enhanced by staining. The phase contrast and differential-interference-contrast microscopes enhance detail by increasing the differences in optical density in different regions of the cells. Confocal microscopes use a laser to illuminate a thin slice of the cell within the focal plane.

Figure 4-3 *Animation* Using light microscopy

to light microscopy by developing biological stains that enhance contrast in the microscopic image. Staining has enabled biologists to discover the many different internal cell structures, the organelles. Unfortunately, most methods used to prepare and stain cells for observation also kill them in the process.

Light microscopes with special optical systems now permit biologists to study living cells. In *bright-field microscopy*, an image is formed by transmitting light through a cell (or other specimen) (FIG. 4-3b). Because there is little contrast, the details of cell structure are not visible. In *dark-field microscopy*, rays of light are directed from the side, and only light scattered by the specimen enters the lenses. The cell is seen as a bright image against a dark background (FIG. 4-3c). The specimen does not need to be stained.

Phase contrast microscopy and *Nomarski differential-interference-contrast microscopy* take advantage of variations in density within the cell (FIG. 4-3d and e). These differences in density affect how various regions of the cytoplasm refract (bend) light. Using these microscopes, scientists can observe living cells in action and can view numerous internal structures that are constantly changing shape and location.

Cell biologists today widely use different types of *fluorescence microscopes* to detect the locations of specific molecules in cells. In the fluorescence microscope, filters transmit light that is emitted by fluorescent molecules, or *fluorophores*. Fluorophores are molecules that absorb light energy of one wavelength and then release some of that energy as light of a longer wavelength (like paints that glow under black light, see Fig. 9-3). Look closely at the chapter-opening photo, which shows three different types of fluorophores. The nucleus is stained with an organic compound that becomes a fluorophore when it binds within the grooves of double-stranded DNA molecules. When ultraviolet light is passed through the specimen, each fluorophore molecule absorbs the energy from an ultraviolet light photon and then releases part of that energy in the form of another photon that has the longer wavelength of visible blue light. The red color comes from a fluorophore that is chemically bonded to an antibody that specifically binds to the protein keratin, and the green color is derived from a fluorophore that is chemically bonded to phalloidin, a molecule isolated from a mushroom that specifically binds to microfilaments. **Antibodies** are proteins derived from the immune system (discussed in Chapter 45). Each type of antibody molecule can bind to only one specific region of another molecule (such as a small patch of amino acids on the surface of a protein; see Fig. 45-10). The green fluorescing molecule in the photo binds only to a small region of a microfilament subunit protein, and the red fluorescing antibody binds only to a specific region of keratin, an intermediate filament protein. Note that there are also yellow colors in the photograph. They are caused by the mixing of the green and red light from the microfilament and intermediate filament proteins that are very close to one another. This method (using highly sensitive microscopy) is commonly used to study the corresponding localizations (and possible interactions) of different proteins in cells.

Fluorescence microscopy using antibody labels must be done with nonliving cells that have been "fixed" by chemicals that form cross links between cellular proteins and other macromolecules to preserve them in their normal locations. Biologists today also employ types of fluorescent molecules to study the internal dynamics of living cells (in vivo). Certain types of fluorophores have been developed that will naturally diffuse into cells without killing them. Available today are wide arrays of compounds used to detect changes in intracellular pH, ion concentrations within intracellular compartments, and electrical charge differences across membranes. This is done by measuring shifts in the wavelength or the intensity of the emitted fluorescence. Biologists also use genetic engineering methods (see Chapter 15) to link the gene coding for a protein under study to part of another gene that encodes a *green fluorescent protein* (GFP) derived from a species of jellyfish. When the protein encoded by the modified gene is synthesized by the cell, it contains the GFP amino acid sequence as a "tag." The GFP tag functions as a fluorophore, allowing the intracellular movement of these "tagged" proteins to be tracked and measured in live cells by sensitive photodetectors.

Confocal microscopy has led to significant advances in our understanding of intracellular structural dynamics. These microscopes produce a sharper image than standard fluorescence microscopy (FIG. 4-3f). A confocal microscope uses a laser to excite fluorophores in just a thin "slice" through a cell, enabling an investigator to visualize objects in a single plane of sharp focus. In the chapter-opening photo, a computer has assembled a series of stacked images of a series of optical sections taken from the bottom to the top of the cell to construct a 3-D image. The use of powerful computer-imaging methods and ultrasensitive photodetectors has greatly improved the resolution of structures labeled by fluorescent dyes. Recent developments in fluorescence imaging have led to breakthroughs in the "resolution barrier" of 200 nm by using the shortest wavelengths of visible light. New super-resolution technologies can now resolve images of less than 70 nm derived from single molecules of fluorophores in living cells. For example, these advanced technologies have enabled researchers to monitor the intracellular movement within cells of brain tissue (FIG 4-4).

Electron microscopes provide a high-resolution image that can be greatly magnified

Even with improved microscopes and techniques for staining cells, ordinary light microscopes can distinguish only the gross details of many cell parts (FIG. 4-5a). With the development of the **electron microscope (EM),** which came into wide use in the 1950s, researchers could begin to study the fine details, or **ultrastructure,** of cells at the dimensions that could define the structure of cellular compartments and structures associated with cell membranes.

Because electrons have very short wavelengths on the order of about 0.1–0.2 nm, electron microscopes have resolving powers of just less than 1 nm. This high degree of resolution permits magnifications of more than 1 million times, compared with typical magnifications of no more than 1500 to 2000 times in light microscopy.

The image formed by the electron microscope is not directly visible. The electron beam itself consists of energized electrons, which, because of their negative charge, can be focused by electromagnets just as images are focused by glass lenses in a light microscope (FIG. 4-5b). Two main types of electron microscopes are the **transmission electron microscope (TEM)** and the **scanning electron microscope (SEM).** The acronyms TEM and SEM also identify that a micrograph was prepared using a transmission or scanning EM. Electron micrographs are black and white. They are often artificially colorized to highlight various structures.

In transmission electron microscopy, the specimen is embedded in plastic and then cut into extraordinarily thin sections

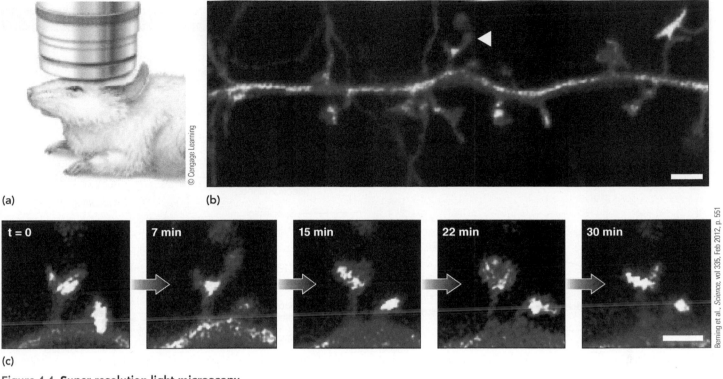

(a)

(b)

Berning et al., *Science*, vol 335, Feb 2012, p. 551

(c)

Figure 4-4 Super-resolution light microscopy

This series of super-resolution micrographs tracks the rapid changes in nerve cell connections in a living mouse. **(a)** The surface layers of the brain of an anesthetized mouse fitted with an optical coverglass in the top of its skull are viewed through the microscope. The genetically engineered mouse produces a modified form of green fluorescent protein only in its nerve cells. **(b)** An extension of a single brain cell shows its "spine" projections that connect to neighboring nerve cells. **(c)** Video frames spaced 7–8 minutes apart show the changes in shape that occur in a single "spine" over a period of 30 minutes. The white scale bars in the photos represent 1 μm.

(50 to 100 nm thick) with a glass or diamond knife. A section is then placed on a small metal grid. The electron beam passes through the specimen and then falls onto a photographic plate or a fluorescent screen. When you look at TEMs in this chapter (and elsewhere), keep in mind that each represents only a thin cross section of a cell.

Researchers can also detect certain specific molecules in electron microscope images by using antibody molecules to which very tiny gold particles are bound. The dense gold particles block the electron beam and identify the location of the proteins recognized by the antibodies as precise black spots on the electron micrograph.

In the scanning electron microscope, the electron beam does not pass through the specimen. Instead, the specimen is coated with a thin film of gold or some other metal. When the electron beam strikes various points on the surface of the specimen, secondary electrons are emitted whose intensity varies with the contour of the surface. The recorded emission patterns of the secondary electrons give a 3-D picture of the surface (FIG. 4-5c). The SEM provides information about the shape and external features of the specimen that cannot be obtained with the TEM.

Note that the LM, TEM, and SEM are focused by similar principles. A beam of light or an electron beam is directed by the condenser lens onto the specimen, and it is magnified by the objective lens and the eyepiece in the light microscope or by the objective lens and the projector lens in the TEM. The TEM image is focused onto a fluorescent screen, and the SEM image is viewed

on a type of television screen. Lenses in electron microscopes are actually electromagnets that bend the beam of electrons.

Biologists use biochemical and genetic methods to connect cell structures with their functions

The EM and light microscopes are powerful tools for studying cell structure, but they have limitations. The methods used to prepare cells for electron microscopy kill them and may alter their structure. Furthermore, electron microscopy provides few clues about the functions of organelles and other cell components. To determine what organelles actually do, researchers use a variety of biochemical techniques.

Cell fractionation is a technique for separating (fractionating) different parts of cells so that they can be studied by physical and chemical methods. Generally, cells are broken apart in a blender. The resulting mixture, called the *cell homogenate*, is subjected to centrifugal force by spinning in a **centrifuge** (FIG. 4-6a). **Differential centrifugation** involves the separation of cell components through a series of centrifugation stages run at increasingly higher speeds. This allows various cell components to be separated on the basis of their different sizes and densities (FIG. 4-6b). At each step centrifugal force separates the extract into two fractions: a pellet and a supernatant. The *pellet* that forms at the bottom of the tube contains heavier materials packed together. (In the first low-speed step, this pellet is typically

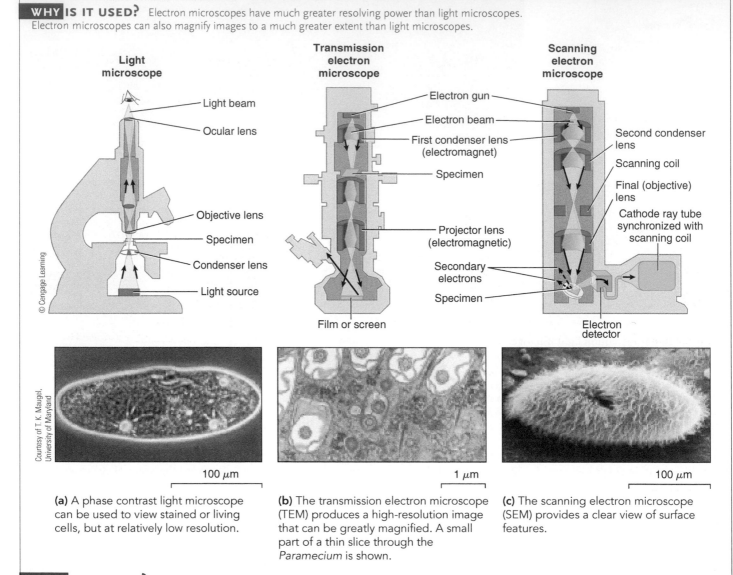

Light microscope

- Light beam
- Ocular lens
- Objective lens
- Specimen
- Condenser lens
- Light source

© Cengage Learning

Transmission electron microscope

- Electron gun
- Electron beam
- First condenser lens (electromagnet)
- Specimen
- Projector lens (electromagnetic)
- Film or screen

Scanning electron microscope

- Second condenser lens
- Scanning coil
- Final (objective) lens
- Cathode ray tube synchronized with scanning coil
- Secondary electrons
- Specimen
- Electron detector

Courtesy of T. K. Maugel, University of Maryland

100 μm

1 μm

100 μm

(a) A phase contrast light microscope can be used to view stained or living cells, but at relatively low resolution.

(b) The transmission electron microscope (TEM) produces a high-resolution image that can be greatly magnified. A small part of a thin slice through the *Paramecium* is shown.

(c) The scanning electron microscope (SEM) provides a clear view of surface features.

HOW IS IT DONE? In an electron microscope, a beam of electrons is focused on or through the specimen. Instead of glass lenses, electromagnetic lenses are used to form the image. Here we compare images of the protist *Paramecium* made using a phase contrast light microscope with images made using two types of electron microscopes. These three microscopes produce distinctive images of cells.

Figure 4-5 *Animation* **Using electron microscopes**

composed of nuclei.) The *supernatant,* the liquid above the pellet, contains lighter organelles, dissolved molecules, and ions.

After the pellet is removed, the supernatant is centrifuged again at a higher speed to obtain a pellet that contains the next-heaviest cell components, for example, mitochondria and chloroplasts. To separate smaller, less dense components, the supernatant is then centrifuged in the powerful ultracentrifuge, which can spin at speeds exceeding 100,000 revolutions per minute (rpm), generating a centrifugal force of 500,000 × *G* (1 *G* is equal to the force of gravity).

Pellets can be resuspended and their components further purified by **density gradient centrifugation**. In this procedure, the ultracentrifuge tube is filled with a series of solutions of decreasing density. For example, sucrose solutions can be used. The concentration of sucrose is highest at the bottom of the tube and decreases gradually so that it is lowest at the top. The resuspended pellet is placed in a layer on top of the density gradient. Because the densities of organelles differ, each migrates during centrifugation to a position in the sucrose gradient that corresponds to its own density (FIG. 4-6c). These purified organelles can then be studied to determine what kinds of proteins and other molecules they might contain, or what types of biochemical reactions take place within them.

Antibodies are also widely used in laboratories to detect specific proteins in subcellular fractions, measure their intracellular

WHY IS IT USED? Cell fractionation is used to separate (fractionate) cell components according to their size and density.

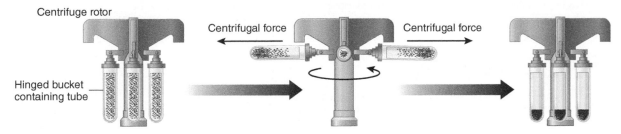

(a) **Centrifugation.** Due to centrifugal force, large or very dense particles move toward the bottom of a tube and form a pellet.

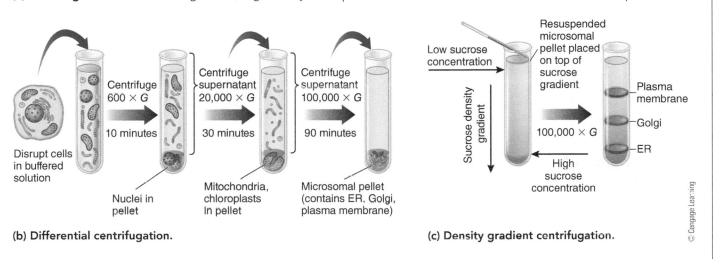

(b) **Differential centrifugation.**

(c) **Density gradient centrifugation.**

HOW IS IT DONE? Cells are broken up in a blender. The cell homogenate (the resulting mixture) is then spun in a centrifuge. As a result of centrifugal force, the heaviest cell components, the nuclei, form a pellet at the bottom of the tube. The supernatant (the liquid above the pellet) can then be spun at a higher speed. The next heaviest component, the mitochondria and chloroplasts, form a pellet, and the supernatant can be spun at a higher speed. This process can be repeated several times. The pellet can be further purified by density gradient centrifugation (see text for further explanation).

Figure 4-6 Cell fractionation

levels, and study how they interact with other proteins. One application involves using antibodies that are coated onto small polymer beads to identify proteins that might bind to and function together with a protein of interest (FIG. 4-7). For example, an antibody that is specific for a microtubule subunit protein might be used to find other proteins that bind to microtubules and regulate their activity. The antibody-coated beads would be added to a cell extract (or a purified cell fraction) and then washed extensively to remove all substances in the extract that did not bind to the antibody-bound microtubule subunit protein. Proteins that remain attached to the antibody-bound subunit molecule can then be released from the antibody and analyzed to determine their identities.

Cell biologists also use genetic methods together with microscopy or biochemical methods to connect cellular proteins with their functions. When a protein has been identified as a critical component in a cell structure, researchers can use genetic engineering methods to alter or delete the gene that encodes that protein, effectively "turning off" its activity. By observing the differences between cells that contain the genetically altered protein with normal cells, researchers can gain insights into its function and how it interacts with other cellular proteins.

CHECKPOINT 4.2

- **CONNECT** *How does resolution limit the effective magnification that can be achieved in microscopy?*

- *What are the advantages of using many varied methods to connect structure and function in cells? Give some examples.*

WHY IS IT USED? An antibody is a protein derived from the immune system that can bind with high specificity to a small region of another protein. Antibodies are widely used to identify the location of a specific protein in a cell by immunofluorescence microscopy. Immunoprecipitation methods employ antibodies to isolate and purify a specific protein from a complex mixture of proteins found in a cellular fraction.

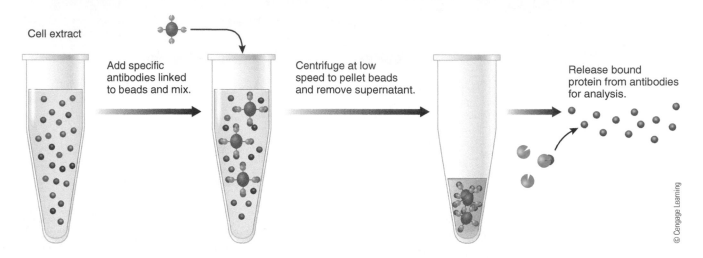

HOW IS IT DONE? Disrupt and fractionate the cells. Suspend a soluble fraction in a buffered solution. Add an antibody that is specific for the protein of interest covalently linked to small polymer beads. Allow the protein to bind to the bead-linked antibodies, and then pellet the beads with low-speed centrifugation (less than $1000 \times G$). After washing the pellet to remove unbound proteins, separate the antibody from its bound protein and subject the released protein to biochemical analysis.

Figure 4-7 Immunoprecipitation

4.3 PROKARYOTIC AND EUKARYOTIC CELLS

LEARNING OBJECTIVES

5 Compare and contrast the general characteristics of prokaryotic and eukaryotic cells, and contrast plant and animal cells.

6 Describe three functions of cell membranes.

Recall from Chapter 1 that two basic types of cells are known: **prokaryotic cells** and **eukaryotic cells**. Bacteria and archaea are prokaryotic cells. All other known organisms consist of one or more eukaryotic cells.

Organelles of prokaryotic cells are not surrounded by membranes

Prokaryotic cells are typically smaller than eukaryotic cells. In fact, the average prokaryotic cell is only about 1/10 the diameter of the average eukaryotic cell. In prokaryotic cells, the DNA is typically located in a limited region of the cell called a **nuclear area,** or **nucleoid.** Unlike the nucleus of eukaryotic cells, the nuclear area is not enclosed by a membrane (**FIG. 4-8**). The term *prokaryotic,* meaning "before the nucleus," refers to this major difference between prokaryotic and eukaryotic cells. Other types of internal membrane–enclosed organelles are also absent in prokaryotic cells.

Like eukaryotic cells, prokaryotic cells have a plasma membrane that surrounds the cell. The plasma membrane confines the contents of the cell to an internal compartment. In some prokaryotic cells, the plasma membrane may be folded inward to form a complex of membranes along which many of the cell's metabolic reactions take place. Most prokaryotic cells have **cell walls**, which are extracellular structures that enclose the entire cell, including the plasma membrane.

Many prokaryotes have **flagella** (sing., *flagellum*), long fibers that project from the surface of the cell. Prokaryotic flagella, which operate like propellers, are important in locomotion. Their structure is different from that of flagella found in eukaryotic cells. Some prokaryotes also have hairlike projections called *fimbriae*, which are used to adhere to one another or to attach to cell surfaces of other organisms.

The dense internal material of the bacterial cell contains **ribosomes**, small complexes of ribonucleic acid (RNA) and protein that synthesize polypeptides. The ribosomes of prokaryotic cells are smaller than those found in eukaryotic cells. Prokaryotic cells also contain storage granules that hold glycogen, lipid, or phosphate compounds. This chapter focuses primarily on eukaryotic cells. Prokaryotes are discussed in more detail in Chapter 25.

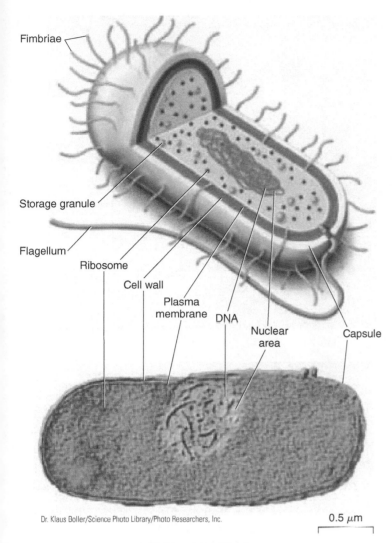

Fimbriae

Storage granule

Flagellum

Ribosome

Cell wall

Plasma membrane

DNA

Nuclear area

Capsule

Dr. Klaus Boller/Science Photo Library/Photo Researchers, Inc.

0.5 μm

Figure 4-8 *Animation* Structure of a prokaryotic cell

This colorized TEM shows a thin lengthwise slice through an *Escherichia coli* bacterium. Note the prominent nuclear area containing the genetic material (DNA). *E. coli* is a normal inhabitant of the human intestine, but under certain conditions some strains can cause infections.

© Cengage Learning

Membranes divide the eukaryotic cell into compartments

Eukaryotic cells are characterized by highly organized membrane-enclosed organelles, including a prominent *nucleus,* which contains DNA, the hereditary material. The term *eukaryotic* means "true nucleus." Early biologists thought that cells consisted of a homogeneous jelly, which they called *protoplasm.* With the electron microscope and other modern research tools, perception of the environment within the cell has been greatly expanded. We now know that the cell is highly organized and complex (**FIGS. 4-9** and 4-10). The eukaryotic cell has its own control center, internal transportation system, power plants, factories for making needed materials, packaging plants, and even a "self-destruct" system.

Biologists refer to the part of the cell outside the nucleus as **cytoplasm** and the part of the cell within the nucleus as **nucleoplasm**. Various organelles are suspended within the fluid component of the cytoplasm, which is called the

cytosol. Eukaryotic proteins are synthesized in the cytoplasmic compartment by ribosomes. These large macromolecular complexes can function as components of the cytosol when they produce soluble proteins. Alternatively, they can be firmly bound to the cytosolic surfaces of membranes, where they form proteins that are either attached to membranes or enclosed in compartments bounded by membranes. The term *cytoplasm* includes both the cytosol and all the organelles other than the nucleus.

The many specialized organelles of eukaryotic cells solve some of the problems associated with large size, so eukaryotic cells can be larger than prokaryotic cells. Eukaryotic cells also differ from prokaryotic cells in having a supporting framework, or cytoskeleton, important in maintaining shape and transporting materials within the cell.

Some organelles are present only in specific cells. For example, *chloroplasts,* structures that trap sunlight for energy conversion, are only in cells that carry on photosynthesis, such as certain plant or algal cells. Cells of fungi and plants are surrounded by a *cell wall* external to the plasma membrane. Plant cells also contain a large, membrane-enclosed *vacuole.* We discuss these and other differences among major types of cells throughout this chapter.

The unique properties of biological membranes allow eukaryotic cells to carry on many diverse functions

Cell membranes have unique properties that enable membranous organelles to carry out a wide variety of functions. For example, cell membranes never have free ends. As a result, a membranous organelle always contains at least one enclosed internal space or compartment. These membrane-enclosed compartments allow certain cell activities to be localized within specific regions of the cell. Reactants confined to only a small part of the total cell volume are far more likely to come in contact, dramatically increasing the rate of the reaction. Membrane-enclosed compartments also keep certain reactive compounds away from other parts of the cell that they might adversely affect, allowing many different activities to go on simultaneously.

Membranes serve as important work surfaces. For example, many chemical reactions in cells are carried out by enzymes that are bound to membranes. Because the enzymes that carry out successive steps of a series of reactions are organized close together on a membrane surface, certain series of chemical reactions occur more rapidly.

Membranes allow cells to store energy. The membrane serves as a barrier that is somewhat analogous to a dam on a river. As we will discuss in Chapter 5, there is both an electric charge difference and a concentration difference of ions on the two sides of certain cell membranes. These differences constitute an *electrochemical gradient.* Such gradients store energy and so have *potential energy* (discussed in Chapter 7). As particles of a substance move across the membrane from the side of higher concentration to the side of lower concentration, the cell can convert some of this potential energy to the chemical energy of

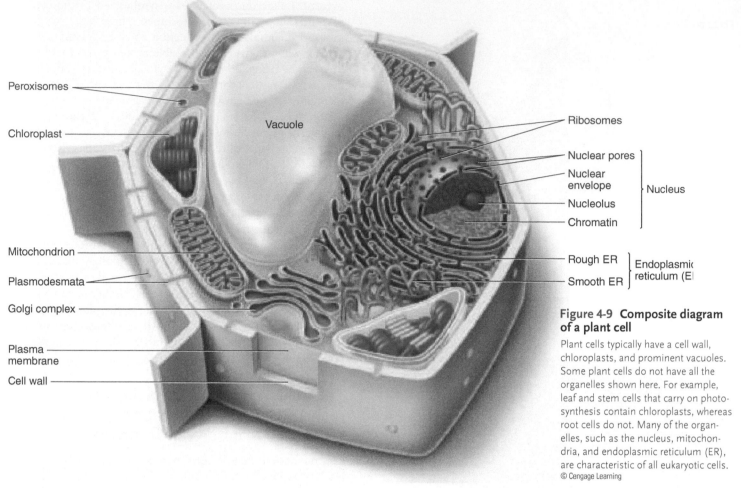

Peroxisomes

Chloroplast

Vacuole

Ribosomes

Nuclear pores

Nuclear envelope

Nucleolus

Chromatin

Nucleus

Mitochondrion

Plasmodesmata

Golgi complex

Rough ER

Smooth ER

Endoplasmic reticulum (ER)

Plasma membrane

Cell wall

Figure 4-9 Composite diagram of a plant cell

Plant cells typically have a cell wall, chloroplasts, and prominent vacuoles. Some plant cells do not have all the organelles shown here. For example, leaf and stem cells that carry on photosynthesis contain chloroplasts, whereas root cells do not. Many of the organelles, such as the nucleus, mitochondria, and endoplasmic reticulum (ER), are characteristic of all eukaryotic cells.
© Cengage Learning

ATP molecules. This process of energy conversion (discussed in Chapters 7, 8, and 9) is a basic mechanism that cells use to capture and convert the energy necessary to sustain life.

CHECKPOINT 4.3

- *What features do prokaryotic and eukaryotic cells have in common?*
- *What are three ways that a plant cell might differ from an animal cell?*
- *In what ways do membrane-enclosed organelles facilitate cell metabolism?*

4.4 THE CELL NUCLEUS

LEARNING OBJECTIVE

7 Relate the structure of the nucleus to its function as the control center of the eukaryotic cell.

The **nucleus** is typically the most prominent organelle in the cell. It is usually spherical or oval in shape and averages 5 μm in diameter. Most of the cell's DNA is located inside the nucleus. Unlike prokaryotic cells, whose DNA is in the form of circular molecules, eukaryotic DNA molecules are very long, linear

molecules (much longer than the diameter of the cell), and they have distinctive ends (see Chapter 10).

The **nuclear envelope** consists of two concentric membranes that separate the nuclear contents from the surrounding cytoplasm (FIG. 4-11). These membranes are separated by about 20 to 40 nm. At intervals the membranes come together to form **nuclear pores,** which are the largest and most complex assembly of proteins in most eukaryotic cells. Each nuclear pore consists of 500–1000 molecules made up of many copies of about 30 different proteins. A typical vertebrate cell that is not growing or dividing will usually have several thousand pores distributed across its nuclear surface. These complexes regulate the passage of large materials (including large proteins as well as macromolecular complexes such as ribosomes) across the nuclear membranes; however, ions and biological molecules (including small proteins) can pass freely through the nuclear pores. Each protein from the cytoplasm that must be actively transported through the pore contains a *nuclear localization signal (NLS)* as part of its amino acid sequence. Special proteins called *importins* bind with the NLS sequence, forming a "cargo complex" that can then be captured by the nuclear pore machinery and transported through the pore into the nucleus. These sequences are not only found on soluble proteins synthesized by ribosomes, but also on proteins that are embedded in cytoplasmic membranes and must then be moved to the inner nuclear membrane (FIG. 4-12).

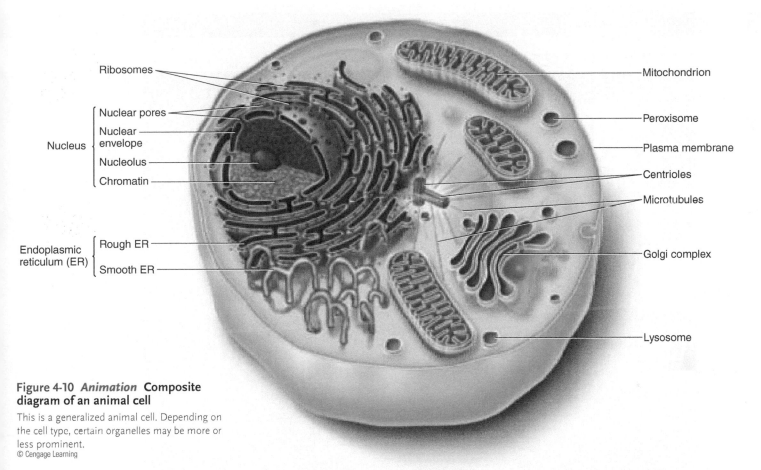

Ribosomes

Nuclear pores

Nuclear envelope

Nucleolus

Chromatin

Nucleus

Endoplasmic reticulum (ER)

Rough ER

Smooth ER

Mitochondrion

Peroxisome

Plasma membrane

Centrioles

Microtubules

Golgi complex

Lysosome

Figure 4-10 *Animation* **Composite diagram of an animal cell**

This is a generalized animal cell. Depending on the cell type, certain organelles may be more or less prominent.
© Cengage Learning

The transport mechanism through nuclear pores can be very fast. Fluorescent-labeled proteins containing an NLS sequence have been observed moving through the nuclear pores at rates approaching 2000 molecules/second, whereas deletion of the NLS sequence from the same protein has been shown to effectively block its entry into the nucleus.

A fibrous network of protein filaments, called the nuclear lamins, forms the nuclear lamina, an inner lining for the nuclear envelope. The *nuclear lamina* supports the inner nuclear membrane and helps organize the nuclear contents. It also plays a role in DNA duplication and in regulating the cycle of growth and division (the *cell cycle*; see Chapter 10). Mutations in genes encoding proteins that make up the nuclear lamina are associated with several human genetic diseases, including some muscular dystrophies and premature aging (progeria).

When a cell divides, the information stored in DNA must be duplicated exactly through a process called replication (discussed in Chapter 12). Each copy is then passed intact to one of the two daughter cells. DNA molecules include sequences of nucleotides called **genes,** which contain the chemically coded instructions for producing the proteins and specialized RNA molecules needed by the cell. The nucleus controls protein synthesis by transcribing its information from DNA into **messenger RNA (mRNA)** molecules, which are then moved into the cytoplasm, where proteins are manufactured by ribosomes.

DNA in the nucleus is associated with RNA and certain proteins, forming a complex known as **chromatin** (see Chapter 10). In the light microscope this complex appears as a network of

granules and strands in nondividing cells. Although chromatin appears disorganized, it is not. Because DNA molecules are extremely long and thin, each molecule is packed inside the nucleus in a regular fashion as part of a structure called a **chromosome**. In dividing cells, the chromosomes become visible as distinct threadlike structures. If the DNA molecules in the 46 chromosomes of one human cell could be stretched end to end, they would extend for 2 meters!

Most nuclei have one or more compact structures called **nucleoli** (sing., *nucleolus*). A nucleolus, which is *not* enclosed by a membrane, usually stains differently than the surrounding chromatin. Each nucleolus contains a *nucleolar organizer,* made up of overlapping regions of DNA from several chromosomes. This DNA contains instructions for making the type of RNA found in ribosomes. This **ribosomal RNA (rRNA)** is synthesized in the nucleolus.

Although it is tempting to think of the nucleus as a relatively quiet region that is reserved for information storage (much like a library), it is a center of constant activity, and there is a very high volume of traffic in both directions through the nuclear pores.

Large amounts of energy are consumed in the nucleus in the form of ATP and other nucleoside triphosphate molecules that are used to synthesize mRNA and rRNA molecules. Energy is also used to transport the large and small materials that are constantly moving in and out of the nucleus through the nuclear pores. This movement can be illustrated by considering the assembly of ribosomes, organelles that function in the cytoplasm but are assembled in the nucleolus.

The nucleus contains DNA and is the control center of the cell.

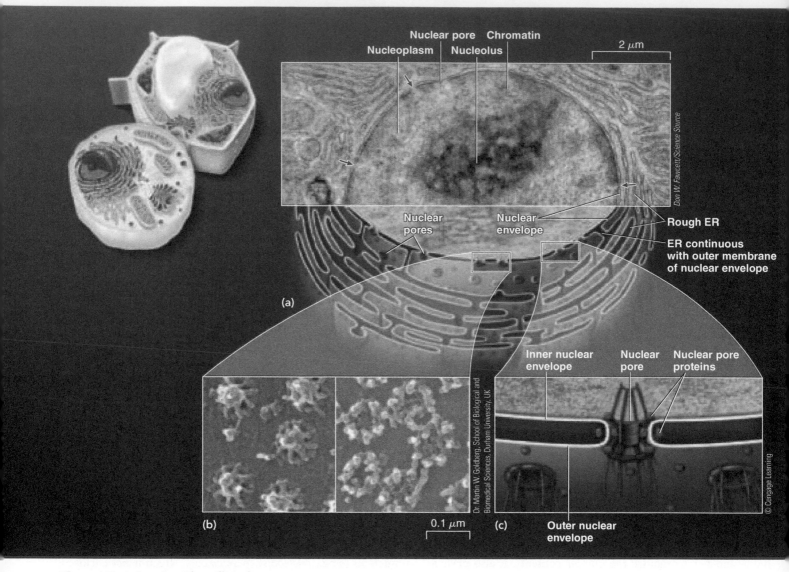

Figure 4-11 *Animation* **The cell nucleus**

(a) The TEM and interpretive drawing show that the nuclear envelope is composed of two concentric membranes connected through nuclear pores that perforate both membranes. The outer membrane of the nuclear envelope is continuous with the membrane of the ER (endoplasmic reticulum) and is usually covered with attached ribosomes. The nucleolus is not enclosed by a membrane. **(b)** SEM images of the nuclear pores show the inner nucleoplasmic face (*left*), which forms a basket-like structure, and the outer (cytoplasmic) face (*right*), which consists of eight subunits with fibers that extend into the cytoplasm. **(c)** The nuclear pores, which are made up of many copies of more than 30 different proteins, form channels between the nucleoplasm and the cytoplasm.

PREDICT In which direction would you expect ribosomes to pass through the nuclear pores?

Ribosomes manufacture proteins in the cytoplasm

Ribosomes are organelles that can be found free in the cytosol or attached to certain cytoplasmic membranes. These small particles contain the enzyme activities necessary to form peptide bonds, which join amino acids to produce proteins (see Chapter 3). Each ribosome has two main components: a large subunit and a small subunit. When the two ribosome subunits join in a complex with an mRNA molecule, they function as manufacturing plants that assemble polypeptides. Cells that actively produce large amounts of proteins may have millions of ribosomes, and the cell can change the number of ribosomes present to meet its metabolic needs. We will discuss much more about ribosomes in Chapter 13.

Ribosomes are molecular machines made up of both proteins and RNA molecules. The two subunits of each eukaryotic ribosome actually consist of more than 80 different proteins and three different rRNA molecules. The mRNAs that encode the ribosomal proteins are first copied from their respective genes in the nucleus. They must then be transported through

Do large inner nuclear membrane proteins need the nuclear pore machinery to move from the rough ER to their location on the inside of the nucleus?

HYPOTHESIS: Large inner nuclear membrane proteins are transported from their cytoplasmic sites of synthesis to their inner membrane locations by the nuclear pore machinery.

EXPERIMENT: Previous experiments had shown that soluble proteins move into the nucleus only after they are bound to specialized "importin" proteins to form a "cargo complex" that can then be captured and transported through the nuclear pore. Megan King, Patrick Lusk, and Günter Blobel of Rockefeller University wanted to know if large proteins incorporated in the inner nuclear membrane are transported from their site of synthesis in the cytoplasm to the inner nuclear membrane by the same mechanism. They engineered a gene that encodes a GFP-tagged form of a large inner nuclear membrane protein and placed it into mutant yeast cells that contain a mutation in an importin protein. This mutant form

of importin is active in cells grown at 25°C, but becomes unfolded and inactive in cells exposed to 34°C. The researchers then used confocal and immuno-gold-transmission electron microscopy to compare the location of this protein in cells grown at the different temperatures.

RESULTS AND CONCLUSION: At 25°C, the GFP-tagged protein and the antibody-linked gold particles are concentrated at the inner nuclear membrane. In the cells grown at 34°C, with defective importin proteins, the GFP-tagged protein accumulates at the outer nuclear membrane and on cytoplasmic ER membranes. Thus, the nuclear pore machinery is required for the membrane protein to move to its correct cellular location within the nucleus.

SOURCE: King, M.C., Lusk, C.P., and Blobel, G. "Karyopherin-Mediated Import of Integral Inner Nuclear Membrane Proteins." *Nature*, Vol. 442, 2006, 1003–1007.

**25°C
(importin proteins active)**

**34°C
(importin proteins inactive)**

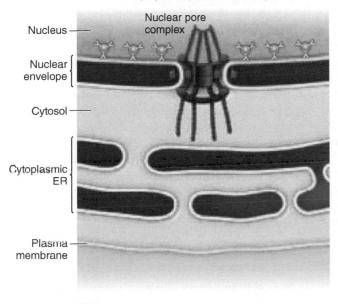
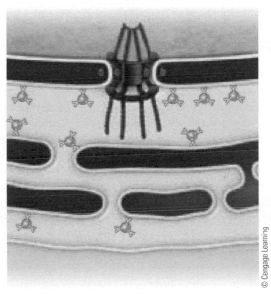

KEY

GFP-labeled protein fluorescence

Antibody-linked gold particle

© Cengage Learning

Figure 4-12 Translocation of membrane-bound proteins through the nuclear pore

PREDICT Soluble proteins that are actively transported through the nuclear pore contain a short series of amino acids called a nuclear localization signal that binds to importin proteins. The researchers identified a similar, but not identical, sequence on the inner nuclear membrane protein that they described in this experiment. If that sequence were a true importin binding site, what would you predict would happen if you were to mix importin-coated beads with an extract of inner nuclear membrane proteins?

the nuclear pores into the cytoplasm, where they are translated by ribosomes to synthesize their corresponding protein. Then, these newly formed ribosomal proteins must be imported back into the nucleus. Many of these proteins include an NLS sequence that is recognized by the nuclear import machinery. It is then packaged as cargo bound to carrier proteins that

allow it to be translocated through the pore. In the nucleus, these ribosomal proteins are assembled with rRNAs into ribosomal subunits. Once assembled, the newly formed ribosome subunit is then transported from the nucleolar region to the inside of the nuclear envelope, where it exits the nucleus through a nuclear pore.

- **CONNECT** *How does the structure of the nucleus affect how information stored in DNA is used by the cell?*
- *In what ways is transport through the nuclear pores selective?*
- *How does the movement of small molecules and large macromolecular structures between the nucleoplasmic and the cytoplasmic compartments differ?*

4.5 MEMBRANOUS ORGANELLES IN THE CYTOPLASM

LEARNING OBJECTIVES

8 Distinguish between smooth and rough endoplasmic reticulum in terms of both structure and function.

9 Trace the path of proteins synthesized in the rough endoplasmic reticulum as they are processed, modified, and sorted by the Golgi complex and then transported to specific destinations.

10 Compare the functions of lysosomes, vacuoles, and peroxisomes.

11 Contrast the functions of mitochondria and chloroplasts, and discuss ATP synthesis by each of these organelles.

Cell biologists have identified many types of membrane-enclosed organelles in the cytoplasm of eukaryotic cells (TABLE 4-1). Among these are the endoplasmic reticulum, Golgi complex, lysosomes, peroxisomes, vacuoles, mitochondria, and chloroplasts. Most of the cytoplasmic organelles in a typical cell—with the exception of mitochondria and chloroplasts—are components of the **endomembrane system** (see Fig. 4-15), a network of organelles (including the plasma membrane) that exchange materials through small membrane-enclosed **transport vesicles.**

In living cells, there is a constant flow of transport vesicle "traffic" between components of the endomembrane system. These vesicles, which are formed from "buds" on the surface membrane of the "donor" organelle, contain "cargo" proteins derived from the organelle's internal compartment or **lumen.** Each vesicle has proteins embedded in its membrane that are specific routing signals for its destination organelle. The vesicle is then transported on cytoskeletal "tracks" by molecular motors (which we will discuss later in this chapter) to the surface of its "target" organelle membrane. On contact, the transport vesicle fuses with the target membrane, releasing its contents into the compartment of the acceptor organelle. This fusion of the two membranes results from interactions between targeting proteins in the vesicle and receptor proteins on the acceptor membrane. As the two membranes fuse, the surface area of the acceptor membrane is expanded by the integration of the vesicle membrane.

The endoplasmic reticulum is a multifunctional network of membranes

One of the most prominent features in the electron micrographs in Figure 4-11 is a maze of parallel internal membranes that encircle the nucleus and extend into many regions of the cytoplasm. This complex of membranes, the **endoplasmic reticulum (ER),** forms a network that makes up a significant part of the total volume of the cytoplasm in many cells. A higher magnification TEM of the ER is shown in FIGURE 4-13. Remember that a TEM represents only a thin cross section of the cell, so there is a tendency to interpret the ER as a series of tubes. In fact, ER membranes consist of a number of different domains that have distinct structures and functions. Many are a series of tightly packed and flattened, saclike structures that form interconnected compartments within the cytoplasm; others are highly curved and tubular; and other parts assume shapes that come in contact with most every other organelle in the cell, including the plasma membrane. Although ER domains have different functions, their membranes are connected, and they enclose a continuous internal compartment called the *ER lumen.* The membranes of other organelles in the endomembrane system are not directly connected to the ER; they form distinct and separate compartments within the cytoplasm.

Each functional domain of the ER membrane and its corresponding region of the ER lumen contains a unique set of enzymes that catalyze many different types of chemical reactions. In some cases, the membranes serve as a framework for enzymes that carry out sequential biochemical reactions. The two surfaces of the membrane (cytosolic and luminal) contain different sets of enzymes and represent regions of the cell with different synthetic capabilities, just as different regions of a factory make different parts of a particular product. Still other enzymes are located within the ER lumen. One common feature throughout the entire ER lumen, however, is that it is the storage site of high levels of calcium, which is used for a number of functions involving intracellular signaling (see Chapter 6).

Two prominent types of ER can usually be easily distinguished in TEMs: *rough ER* and *smooth ER,* each of which has several different types of functional domains.

Smooth ER synthesizes lipids and breaks down toxins

Smooth ER has a tubular appearance, and its membrane surfaces appear smooth. Enzymes in the membranes on the cytosolic surface of the smooth ER catalyze the synthesis of many lipids and carbohydrates. The smooth ER is the primary site for the synthesis of phospholipids and cholesterol needed to make cell membranes. In some cells, such as those found in fat tissue, a region of the smooth ER will have enzymes that form lipid droplets, which store energy reserves in the form of triacylglycerols. Other domains of the smooth ER synthesize steroid hormones, including reproductive hormones, from cholesterol. In liver cells, smooth ER is also important in enzymatically breaking down stored glycogen. (The liver helps regulate the concentration of glucose in the blood. See Chapter 49.)

Whereas smooth ER may be a minor membrane component in some cells, extensive amounts of smooth ER are present in others. For example, large amounts of smooth ER are present in human liver cells where, in addition to lipid biosynthesis, it serves as a major detoxification site. Enzymes located along the smooth ER membrane of liver cells break down toxic chemicals such as carcinogens (cancer-causing agents) and many drugs, including alcohol, amphetamines, and barbiturates. The cell

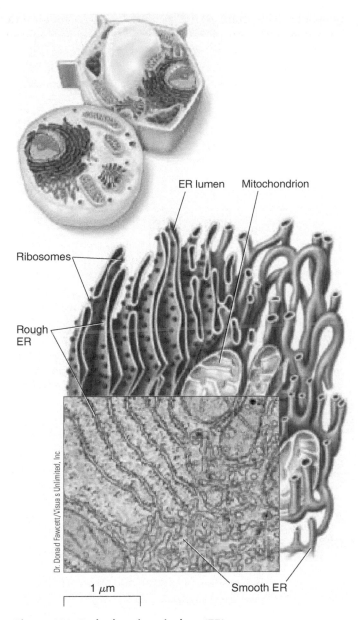

Figure 4-13 Endoplasmic reticulum (ER)

The TEM shows both rough and smooth ER in a liver cell.
© Cengage Learning

ER lumen   Mitochondrion

Ribosomes

Rough ER

Dr. Donald Fawcett/Visuals Unlimited, Inc

1 μm

Smooth ER

The nuclear envelope is one functional domain of the rough ER. Figure 4-11 shows that the outer and inner nuclear membranes are actually continuous with the rough ER. Ribosomes are typically present on the outer (cytosolic) surface of the nuclear envelope, but are not found on the inner (nucleoplasmic) surface.

The rough ER plays a central role in the synthesis and assembly of proteins, including those that are exported from the cell (such as digestive enzymes), proteins destined for the compartments of other organelles, and proteins that function as an integral part of a membrane. All are synthesized by ribosomes bound to the ER membrane. When an mRNA encoding one of these types of proteins enters the cytosol, it first associates with a ribosome. The ribosome is then transported to the ER membrane cytosolic surface, where it forms a tight seal with the membrane. As the polypeptide is synthesized, it passes through a tunnel within the ribosome and into an ER pore. Polypeptides that are destined for export from the cell or to the compartment of another organelle pass directly into the ER lumen. Proteins that are destined to become embedded in the ER membrane will only partially pass through the ER pore before being integrated into the membrane lipid bilayer (see Chapter 5).

In the ER lumen, proteins are assembled and may be modified by enzymes that add carbohydrates or lipids to them. Other enzymes, called **molecular chaperones**, in the ER lumen catalyze the efficient folding of proteins into proper conformations. Proteins that are not processed correctly—for example, proteins that are misfolded—are transported back to the cytosol. There they are degraded by **proteasomes**, protein complexes that direct the destruction of defective proteins. Properly processed proteins that are to be routed to other compartments within the cell, however, are packaged into the small transport vesicles that bud off the ER membrane. They are then transported to and fused with the membrane of the appropriate target organelle.

The ER is the primary site of membrane assembly for components of the endomembrane system

Most cell membranes are first assembled in the endoplasmic reticulum. As we noted in Chapter 3 (and discuss in more detail in Chapter 5), the core of biological membranes consists of a phospholipid bilayer. These phospholipids are synthesized on the cytosolic surface of the smooth ER and then integrated into the membrane bilayer, causing the surfaces of the membrane to expand. Proteins that are to be embedded into newly formed membrane are synthesized by ribosomes attached to the cytosolic surface of the rough ER membrane. By contrast, membranes in other organelles within the endomembrane system grow when transport vesicles from the ER fuse with them.

The Golgi complex processes, sorts, and routes proteins from the ER to different parts of the endomembrane system

The **Golgi complex** (also known as the *Golgi body* or *Golgi apparatus*) was first described in 1898 by Italian microscopist

then converts these compounds to water-soluble products that it excretes. Interestingly, alcohol and many other drugs stimulate liver cells to produce additional smooth ER, increasing the rate that these cells can detoxify the drugs. This mechanism is of limited value, however, because alcohol abuse causes liver inflammation that can lead to cirrhosis and eventual liver failure.

Rough ER is involved in the synthesis of secreted and membrane proteins The outer surface of the **rough ER** is studded with ribosomes that appear as dark granules. Notice in Figure 4-13 that the lumen side of the rough ER appears bare, whereas the outer surface (the cytosolic side) looks rough. The ribosomes attached to the rough ER are known as *bound ribosomes* to differentiate them from *free ribosomes*, which are suspended in the cytosol.

STRUCTURE	DESCRIPTION	FUNCTION
CELL NUCLEUS		
Nucleus 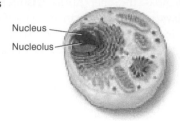	Large structure surrounded by double membrane; contains nucleolus and chromosomes	Information in DNA is transcribed in RNA synthesis; specifies cell proteins
Nucleolus	Granular body within nucleus; consists of RNA and protein	Site of ribosomal RNA synthesis; ribosome subunit assembly
Chromosomes	Composed of chromatin, a complex of DNA and protein; condense during cell division, becoming visible as rodlike structures	Contain genes (units of hereditary information) that govern structure and activity of cell
CYTOPLASMIC ORGANELLES		
Plasma membrane 	Membrane boundary of cell	Encloses cell contents; regulates movement of materials in and out of cell; helps maintain cell shape; communicates with other cells (also present in prokaryotes)
Ribosomes 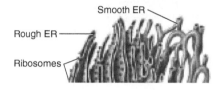	Granules composed of RNA and protein; some attached to ER, some free in cytosol	Synthesize polypeptides in both prokaryotes and eukaryotes
Endoplasmic reticulum (ER)	Network of internal membranes extending through cytoplasm	Synthesizes lipids and modifies many proteins; origin of intracellular transport vesicles that carry proteins
Smooth	Lacks ribosomes on outer surface	Lipid synthesis; drug detoxification; calcium ion storage
Rough	Ribosomes stud outer surface	Manufactures proteins
Golgi complex 	Stacks of flattened membrane sacs	Modifies proteins; packages secreted proteins; sorts other proteins to vacuoles and other organelles
Lysosomes 	Membranous sacs (in animals)	Contain enzymes that break down ingested materials; break down damaged or unneeded organelles and proteins
Vacuoles 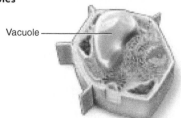	Membranous sacs (mostly in plants, fungi, algae)	Store materials, wastes, water; maintain hydrostatic pressure

TABLE 4-1	Eukaryotic Cell Structures and Their Functions		
STRUCTURE		**DESCRIPTION**	**FUNCTION**
Peroxisomes		Membranous sacs containing a variety of enzymes	Site of many diverse metabolic reactions; e.g., break down fatty acids
Mitochondria		Sacs consisting of two membranes; inner membrane is folded to form cristae and encloses matrix	Site of most reactions of cellular respiration; transformation of energy originating from glucose or lipids into ATP energy
Plastids (e.g., chloroplasts)		Double-membrane structure enclosing internal thylakoid membrane; chloroplasts contain chlorophyll in thylakoid membrane	Chloroplasts are site of photosynthesis; chlorophyll captures light energy; ATP and other energy-rich compounds are produced and then used to convert CO_2 to carbohydrate
CYTOSKELETON			
Microtubules		Hollow tubes made of subunits of tubulin protein	Provide structural support; have role in cell and organelle movement and cell division; components of cilia, flagella, centrioles, basal bodies
Microfilaments		Solid, rodlike structures consisting of actin protein	Provide structural support; play role in cell and organelle movement and cell division
Intermediate filaments		Tough fibers made of protein	Help strengthen cytoskeleton; stabilize cell shape
Centrioles		Pair of hollow cylinders located near nucleus; each centriole consists of nine microtubule triplets (9×3 structure)	Mitotic spindle forms between centrioles during animal cell division; may anchor and organize microtubule formation in animal cells; absent in most plant cells
Cilia		Relatively short projections extending from surface of cell; covered by plasma membrane; made of two central and nine pairs of peripheral microtubules ($9 + 2$ structure)	Movement of some unicellular organisms; used to move materials on surface of some tissues; important in cell signaling
Flagella		Long projections made of two central and nine pairs of peripheral microtubules ($9 + 2$ structure); extend from surface of cell; covered by plasma membrane	Cell locomotion by sperm cells and some unicellular organisms

© Cengage Learning

Camillo Golgi, who found a way to specifically stain this organelle. This membrane system modifies and sorts proteins that it receives from the ER and then packages them into transport vesicles destined to different components of the endomembrane system. Researchers have studied the function of the ER, Golgi complex, and other interacting organelles by radioactively labeling newly manufactured molecules and observing the timing of their movement through the cell. The radiolabeled proteins are first detected in the lumen of the rough ER. They then pass to the Golgi complex and then to some final destination such as the plasma membrane or lysosomes.

In many cells, the Golgi complex consists of stacks of flattened membranous sacs called **cisternae** (sing., *cisterna*). Each cisterna has an internal space, or lumen. The Golgi complex contains a number of separate compartments as well as some that are interconnected.

Each Golgi stack has three areas, referred to as the *cis face*, the *trans face*, and a *medial region* in between. Typically, the *cis* face (the entry surface) is located nearest the nucleus and receives materials from transport vesicles bringing molecules from the ER. The *trans* face (the exit surface) is closest to the plasma membrane. It packages molecules in vesicles and transports them out of the Golgi.

In a cross-sectional view like that in the TEM in FIGURE 4-14, many ends of the sheetlike layers of Golgi membranes are distended because they are filled with cell products, an arrangement characteristic of well-developed Golgi complexes in many cells. In some animal cells, the Golgi complex lies at one side of the nucleus; other animal cells and plant cells have many Golgi complexes dispersed throughout the cell.

Cells that secrete large amounts of *glycoproteins* have many Golgi stacks. (Recall from Chapter 3 that a glycoprotein is a

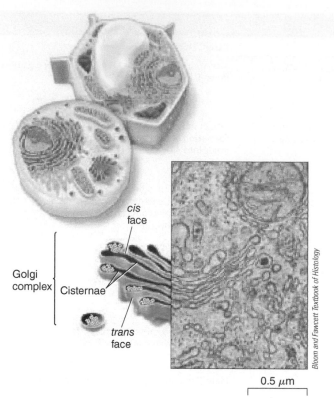

cis
face

Golgi
complex Cisternae

trans
face

Bloom and Fawcett Textbook of Histology

0.5 μm

Figure 4-14 TEM and an interpretive drawing of the Golgi complex
© Cengage Learning

protein with a covalently attached carbohydrate.) Golgi complexes of plant cells produce extracellular polysaccharides that are used as components of the cell wall. In animal cells, the Golgi complex manufactures lysosomes and complex glycoproteins that are secreted to form the extracellular matrix as well as mucus that coats epithelial cells.

Secretory proteins that are assembled in the rough ER lumen are first transported to the *cis* face of the Golgi complex as cargo in the small transport vesicles formed from the ER membrane. These proteins then progress through the Golgi stack, undergoing successive modifications until they reach the *trans* face of the Golgi, where they are packaged into vesicles and shipped to their destination membranes. Vesicles formed from the *cis* Golgi have also been found that move back to the ER as a way of recycling proteins involved in ER packaging and vesicle formation.

What are the mechanisms that move these proteins through the different components of the Golgi complex? One hypothesis holds that the glycoproteins are enclosed in new vesicles that shuttle them from one compartment to another within the Golgi complex. A competing hypothesis postulates that the cisternae themselves may move from *cis* to *trans* positions. In the latter case, new *cis* Golgi compartments would be continuously formed by the fusion of vesicles originating from the ER. As each new *cis* compartment is formed, the previous one moves outward in the *trans* direction until it becomes the *trans* compartment. Both hypotheses may be correct: glycoproteins may be transported by both methods.

Regardless of how proteins are moved through the Golgi complex, while there they are modified in different ways, resulting in the formation of complex biological molecules. For example, the carbohydrate part of a glycoprotein (first added to

proteins in the rough ER) may be modified. In some cases, the carbohydrate component may be a "sorting signal," a cellular zip code that tags the protein, routing it to a specific organelle.

Glycoproteins are packaged in transport vesicles in the *trans* face. These vesicles pinch off from the Golgi membrane and transport their contents to a specific destination. Vesicles transporting products for export from the cell fuse with the plasma membrane. The vesicle membrane becomes part of the plasma membrane, and the glycoproteins are secreted from the cell. Other vesicles may store glycoproteins for secretion at a later time, and still others are routed to various organelles of the endomembrane system such as the lysosomes. **FIGURE 14-15** illustrates the multiple paths followed by proteins that are processed through the Golgi complex. In summary, here is a typical sequence followed by a glycoprotein destined for secretion from the cell.

polypeptides synthesized on ribosomes → protein assembled and carbohydrate component added in lumen of ER → transport vesicles move glycoprotein to Golgi (*cis* face) → glycoprotein further modified in Golgi → in *trans* face, glycoproteins packaged in transport vesicles → glycoproteins transported to plasma membrane → contents released from cell

Lysosomes are compartments for digestion

Lysosomes are small sacs of digestive enzymes dispersed in the cytoplasm of most animal cells (**FIG. 4-16**). Researchers have identified about 40 different digestive enzymes in lysosomes.

Because lysosomal enzymes are active under rather acidic conditions, the lysosome maintains a pH of about 5 in its interior. The powerful enzymes and low pH that the lysosome maintains provide an excellent example of the importance of separating functions within the cell into different compartments. Under most normal conditions, the lysosome membrane confines its enzymes and their actions. However, some forms of tissue damage are related to "leaky" lysosomes.

Primary lysosomes are formed by budding from the Golgi complex. Their hydrolytic enzymes are synthesized in the rough ER. As these enzymes pass through the lumen of the ER, sugars attach to each molecule, identifying it as bound for a lysosome. This signal permits the Golgi complex to sort the enzyme to the lysosomes rather than to export it from the cell.

Lysosomes act by fusing their membranes with vesicles that contain material to be digested. For example, bacteria (or cellular debris) that are engulfed by scavenger cells are captured from the exterior by endocytotic vesicles (see Chapter 5) that form from the plasma membrane (see Figs. 4-16, 5-20, and 5-22). One or more primary lysosomes fuse with a vesicle containing the ingested material, forming a larger vesicle called a *secondary lysosome*. Powerful enzymes in the secondary lysosome come in contact with the ingested molecules and degrade them into their components. Lysosomes can also break down damaged organelles (such as mitochondria) that have been captured in vesicles, allowing their components to be recycled or used as an energy source.

In certain genetic diseases of humans, known as *lysosomal storage diseases*, one of the digestive enzymes normally present in lysosomes is absent. Its substrate (a substance the enzyme would normally break down) accumulates in the cell, which eventually

Proteins are routed through the endomembrane system by membrane-bound targeting signals.

① Membrane-bound ribosomes insert proteins into the rough ER lumen.

② Sugars are added in the ER lumen, forming glycoproteins.

③ Transport vesicles containing *cis* Golgi targeting signals on their surface dock with receptor molecules on the *cis* Golgi surface. Fusion of the vesicle with the Golgi membrane releases glycoproteins into a Golgi cisterna.

④ Glycoprotein sugars on proteins modified further in Golgi.

⑤ Glycoproteins are packaged on Golgi *trans* face into transport vesicles with targeting signals for the plasma membrane (secretory vesicles) or for lysosomes.

⑥ Secretory vesicles dock with targeting signals on the plasma membrane, triggering membrane fusion and release of contents from cell. Proteins and lipids from the secretory transport vesicle membrane become part of plasma membrane.

⑦ Endocytic vesicles containing lysosome targeting signals bud from plasma membrane.

⑧ Lysosomes released from *trans* Golgi fuse with endocytic vesicles.

⑨ Lysosomes released from *trans* Golgi may also fuse with vesicles containing damaged organelles, degrading and recycling contents.

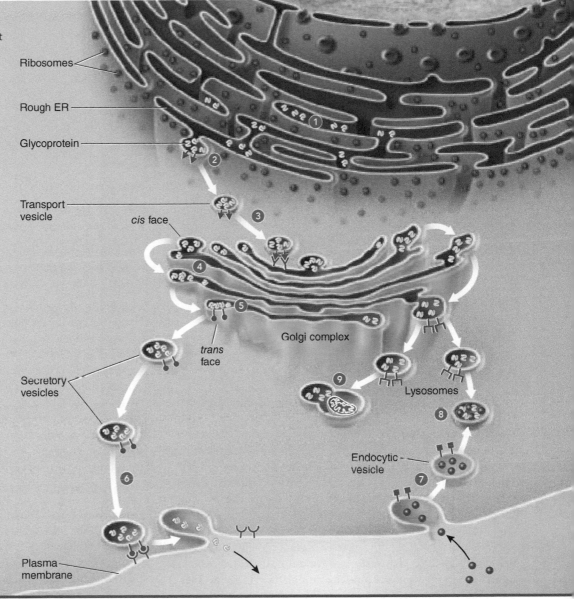

Ribosomes
Rough ER
Glycoprotein
Transport vesicle
cis face
trans face
Golgi complex
Secretory vesicles
Lysosomes
Endocytic vesicle
Plasma membrane

Figure 4-15 *Animation* **The endomembrane system**

This diagram illustrates the sorting and passage of glycoproteins destined for secretion or for packaging in lysosomes. Proteins synthesized by membrane-bound ribosomes are inserted into the ER lumen where sugars are added, forming glycoproteins. They are packaged into vesicles and transported to the *cis* Golgi membrane surface. Targeting signals on the vesicle membrane surface dock with receptor proteins on the Golgi membrane. Following membrane fusion, the vesicle cargo glycoproteins are released into the Golgi complex, where their sugars are further modified. At the Golgi *trans* face, the glycoproteins are sorted into vesicles containing targeting signals either for the plasma membrane or for lysosomes. Vesicles containing secretory proteins dock with appropriate targeting signals on the plasma membrane, triggering membrane fusion and release of the proteins to the exterior. Vesicles containing lysosomal proteins are packaged in lysosomal vesicles, which can fuse with either endocytic vesicles or membranes that enclose damaged organelles.

PREDICT What would happen to proteins destined for secretion if the targeting signal on their vesicles derived from the *trans* Golgi were missing?
© Cengage Learning

interferes with cell activities. An example is Tay-Sachs disease, an inherited disease in which a normal lipid cannot be broken down (discussed in Chapter 16). The accumulation of this lipid in brain cells causes severe intellectual disability, blindness, and death before age 4.

Vacuoles are large, fluid-filled sacs with a variety of functions

Although lysosomes have been identified in almost all kinds of animal cells, biologists have not identified them in plant

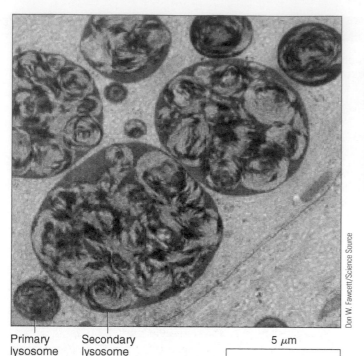

Primary | Secondary | 5 μm
lysosome | lysosome

Figure 4-16 Lysosomes
The dark vesicles in this TEM are lysosomes, compartments that separate powerful digestive enzymes from the rest of the cell. Primary lysosomes bud off from the Golgi complex. After a lysosome takes in material to be digested, it is known as a secondary lysosome. The large vesicles shown here are secondary lysosomes containing various materials being digested.

Don W. Fawcett/Science Source

Food vacuoles containing diatoms

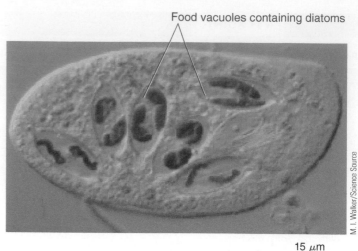

15 μm

M. I. Walker/Science Source

Figure 4-17 LM of food vacuoles
This protist, *Chilodonella*, has ingested many small, photosynthetic protists called diatoms (*dark areas*) that have been enclosed in food vacuoles. From the number of diatoms scattered about its cell, one might conclude that *Chilodonella* has a rather voracious appetite.

and fungal cells. Many functions carried out in animal cells by lysosomes are performed in plant and fungal cells by a large, single, membrane-enclosed sac called a **vacuole**. The membrane of the vacuole, part of the endomembrane system, is called the **tonoplast**. The term *vacuole*, which means "empty," refers to the fact that these organelles have no internal structure. Although some biologists use the terms *vacuole* and *vesicle* interchangeably, vacuoles are usually larger structures, sometimes produced by the merging of many vesicles.

Vacuoles play a significant role in plant growth and development. Immature plant cells are generally small and contain numerous small vacuoles. As water accumulates in these vacuoles, they tend to coalesce, forming a large central vacuole. Because the vacuole contains a high concentration of solutes (dissolved materials), it takes in water and pushes outward on the cell wall. This hydrostatic pressure, called *turgor pressure,* provides much of the mechanical strength of plant cells. A plant cell increases in size mainly by adding water to this central vacuole. As much as 80% of the volume of a plant cell may be occupied by a large central vacuole containing water, stored food, salts, pigments, and metabolic wastes (see Fig. 4-9). The vacuole is important in maintaining the intracellular environment. For example, it helps maintain appropriate pH by taking in excess hydrogen ions. The vacuole may serve as a storage compartment for inorganic compounds. In seeds, vacuoles store molecules such as proteins.

Plants lack organ systems for disposing of toxic metabolic waste products. Plant vacuoles are like lysosomes in that they contain hydrolytic enzymes and break down wastes as well as unneeded organelles and other cell components. Wastes may be recycled in the vacuole, or they may aggregate and form small crystals inside the vacuole. Compounds that are noxious to herbivores (animals that eat plants) may be stored in some plant vacuoles as a means of defense.

Vacuoles are also present in many types of animal cells and in unicellular protists such as protozoa. Most protozoa have *food vacuoles,* which fuse with lysosomes that digest the food (**FIG. 4-17**). Some protozoa also have **contractile vacuoles**, which remove excess water from the cell (discussed in Chapter 26).

Peroxisomes metabolize small organic compounds

Peroxisomes are membrane-enclosed organelles containing enzymes that catalyze a diverse assortment of metabolic reactions in which hydrogen is transferred from various compounds to oxygen (**FIG. 4-18**). They are formed by budding from a specialized domain in the smooth ER. Peroxisomes get their name from the fact that during these oxidation reactions, they produce hydrogen peroxide (H_2O_2). Hydrogen peroxide detoxifies certain compounds, but were this compound to escape from the peroxisome, it would damage other membranes in the cell. Peroxisomes contain the enzyme *catalase*, which rapidly splits excess hydrogen peroxide to water and oxygen, rendering it harmless.

Peroxisomes are found in large numbers in cells that synthesize, store, or degrade lipids. One of their main functions is to break down fatty acid molecules. Peroxisomes synthesize certain phospholipids that are components of the insulating covering of nerve cells. In fact, certain neurological disorders occur when peroxisomes do not perform this function. Mutations that cause synthesis of abnormal membrane lipids by peroxisomes are linked to some forms of intellectual disability.

When yeast cells are grown in an alcohol-rich medium, they manufacture large peroxisomes containing an enzyme that degrades the alcohol. Peroxisomes in human liver and kidney

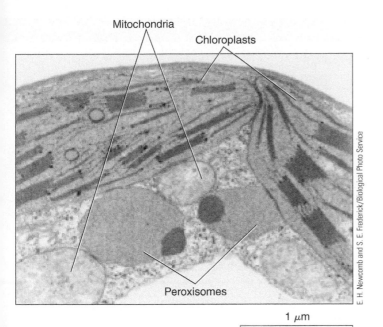

Mitochondria

Chloroplasts

Peroxisomes

1 μm

E. H. Newcomb and S. E. Frederick/Biological Photo Service

Figure 4-18 Peroxisomes

In this TEM of a tobacco (*Nicotiana tabacum*) leaf cell, peroxisomes are in close association with chloroplasts and mitochondria. These organelles may cooperate in carrying out some metabolic activities.

cells detoxify certain toxic compounds, including ethanol, the alcohol in alcoholic beverages.

In plant seeds, specialized peroxisomes, called *glyoxysomes*, contain enzymes that convert stored fats to sugars. The sugars are used by the young plant as an energy source and as a component for synthesizing other compounds. Animal cells lack glyoxysomes and cannot convert fatty acids into sugars.

Mitochondria and chloroplasts are energy-converting organelles

The energy a cell obtains from its environment is usually in the form of chemical energy in food molecules (such as glucose) or in the form of light energy. These types of energy must be converted to forms that cells can use more conveniently. Some energy conversions occur in the cytosol, but other types take place in **mitochondria** and **chloroplasts**, organelles specialized to facilitate the conversion of energy from one form to another.

Chemical energy is most commonly stored in ATP. Recall from Chapter 3 that the chemical energy of ATP can be used to drive a variety of chemical reactions in the cell. FIGURE 4-19 summarizes the main activities relating to energy conversion that take place in mitochondria, found in almost all eukaryotic cells, and in chloroplasts, found only in algae and certain plant cells.

Mitochondria and chloroplasts grow and reproduce themselves. They contain small amounts of DNA that code for a small number of the proteins found in these organelles. These proteins are synthesized by mitochondrial or chloroplast ribosomes. Interestingly, these ribosomes are similar to the ribosomes of prokaryotes. The existence of a separate set of ribosomes and DNA molecules in mitochondria and chloroplasts and their similarity in size to many bacteria provide support for **serial endosymbiosis** (discussed in Chapters 21 and 26; see Figs. 21-8

and 26-2). According to this hypothesis, mitochondria and chloroplasts evolved from prokaryotes that took up residence inside larger eukaryotic cells. Eventually, these symbiotic prokaryotes lost the ability to function as autonomous organisms.

Mitochondria make ATP through aerobic respiration

Virtually all eukaryotic cells (plant, animal, fungal, and protist) contain complex organelles called **mitochondria** (sing., *mitochondrion*). These organelles are the site of **aerobic respiration**, an oxygen-requiring process that includes most of the reactions that convert the chemical energy present in certain foods to ATP (discussed in Chapter 8). During aerobic respiration, carbon, hydrogen, and oxygen atoms are removed from food molecules, such as glucose, and converted to carbon dioxide and water.

Mitochondria are most numerous in cells that are very active and therefore have high energy requirements. More than 1000 mitochondria have been counted in a single liver cell! These organelles vary in size, ranging from 2 to 8 μm in length, and change size and shape rapidly. Mitochondria usually give rise to other mitochondria by growth and subsequent division.

Each mitochondrion is enclosed by a double membrane, which forms two *different* compartments within the organelle: the intermembrane space and the matrix (FIG. 4-20; we will provide more detailed descriptions of mitochondrial structure in Chapter 8). The **intermembrane space** is the compartment formed between the outer and inner mitochondrial membranes. The **matrix,** the compartment enclosed by the inner mitochondrial membrane, contains enzymes that break down food molecules and convert their energy to other forms of chemical energy.

The *outer mitochondrial membrane* is smooth and allows many small molecules to pass through it. By contrast, the *inner mitochondrial membrane* has numerous folds and strictly regulates the types of molecules that can move across it. The folds, called **cristae** (sing., *crista*), extend into the matrix. Cristae greatly increase the surface area of the inner mitochondrial membrane, providing a surface for the chemical reactions that transform the chemical energy in food molecules into the energy of ATP. The membrane contains the enzymes and other proteins needed for these reactions.

Mitochondria play an important role in programmed cell death, or **apoptosis**. Unlike **necrosis,** which is uncontrolled cell death that causes inflammation and damages other cells, apoptosis is a normal part of development and maintenance. For example, during the metamorphosis of a tadpole to a frog, the cells of the tadpole tail must die. The hand of a human embryo is webbed until apoptosis destroys the tissue between the fingers. Cell death also occurs in the adult. For example, cells that are no longer functional because they have aged or become damaged are destroyed by apoptotic mechanisms and replaced by new cells.

Mitochondria initiate cell death in several different ways. For example, they can interfere with energy metabolism or activate enzymes that mediate cell destruction. When a mitochondrion is injured, large pores open in its membrane, and cytochrome *c*, a protein important in energy conversions, is released into the cytoplasm. Cytochrome *c* triggers apoptosis by activating

Mitochondria and chloroplasts convert energy into forms that can be used by cells.

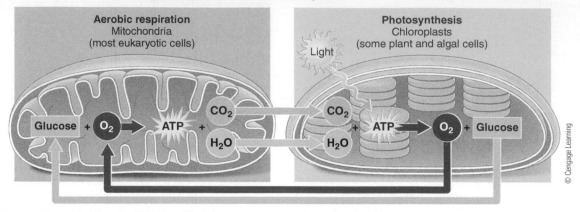

© Cengage Learning

Figure 4-19 Aerobic respiration and photosynthesis

Aerobic respiration takes place in the mitochondria of virtually all eukaryotic cells. In this process, some of the chemical energy in glucose is transferred to ATP. Photosynthesis, which is carried out in chloroplasts in some plant and algal cells, converts light energy to ATP and to other forms of chemical energy. This energy is used to synthesize glucose from carbon dioxide and water.

PREDICT What do you think would happen in the leaf cells of a plant placed in the dark (but supplied with O_2, CO_2, and H_2O) for several days?

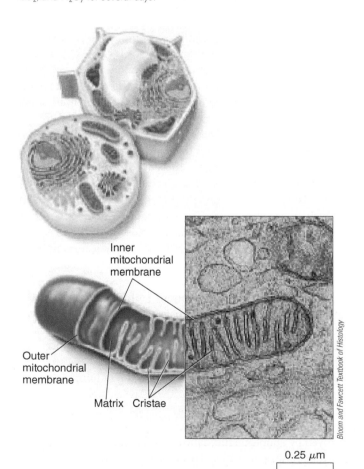

Inner
mitochondrial
membrane

Outer
mitochondrial
membrane

Matrix Cristae

Bloom and Fawcett Textbook of Histology

0.25 μm

Figure 4-20 *Animation* Mitochondria

Aerobic respiration takes place within mitochondria. Cristae are evident in the TEM as well as in the drawing. The drawing shows the relationship between the inner and outer mitochondrial membranes.
© Cengage Learning

enzymes known as **caspases**, which cut up vital compounds in the cell.

Inappropriate inhibition of apoptosis may contribute to a variety of diseases, including cancer. On the other hand, too much apoptosis may deplete needed cells and lead to death of brain cells associated with Alzheimer's disease, Parkinson's disease, and stroke. Mutations that promote apoptosis may be an important mechanism in mammalian aging. Pharmaceutical companies are developing drugs that block apoptosis. However, cell dynamics are extremely complex, and blocking apoptosis could lead to a worse fate, including cancer.

Each mitochondrion in a mammalian cell has 5 to 10 identical, circular molecules of DNA, accounting for up to 1% of the total DNA in the cell. Mitochondrial DNA mutates far more frequently than nuclear DNA. Mutations in mitochondrial DNA have been associated with certain genetic diseases, including a form of young adult blindness, and certain types of progressive muscle degeneration. Mitochondria also affect health and aging by leaking electrons. These electrons form **free radicals**, which are toxic, highly reactive compounds with unpaired electrons. The electrons bond with other compounds in the cell, interfering with normal function.

Chloroplasts convert light energy to chemical energy through photosynthesis

Certain plant and algal cells carry on **photosynthesis**, a set of reactions during which light energy is transformed into the chemical energy of glucose and other carbohydrates. **Chloroplasts** are organelles that contain **chlorophyll**, a green pigment that traps light energy for photosynthesis. Chloroplasts also contain a variety of light-absorbing yellow and orange pigments known as **carotenoids** (see Chapter 3). A unicellular alga may have only

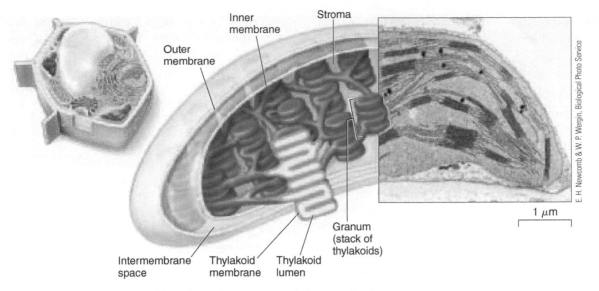

Outer membrane

Inner membrane

Stroma

Granum (stack of thylakoids)

Intermembrane space

Thylakoid membrane

Thylakoid lumen

1 μm

E. H. Newcomb & W. P. Wergin, Biological Photo Service

Figure 4-21 *Animation* **A chloroplast, the organelle of photosynthesis**

This TEM shows part of a chloroplast from a corn leaf cell. Chlorophyll and other photosynthetic pigments are in the thylakoid membranes. One granum is cut open to show the thylakoid lumen. The inner chloroplast membrane may or may not be continuous with the thylakoid membrane (*as shown*).

© Cengage Learning

a single large chloroplast, whereas a leaf cell may have 20 to 100. Chloroplasts tend to be somewhat larger than mitochondria, with lengths usually ranging from about 5 to 10 μm or longer.

Chloroplasts are typically disc-shaped structures and, like mitochondria, have a system of folded membranes (FIG. 4-21; we will provide a more detailed description of chloroplast structure in Chapter 9). Two membranes enclose the chloroplast and separate it from the cytosol. The inner membrane encloses a fluid-filled space called the **stroma,** which contains enzymes that produce carbohydrates from carbon dioxide and water, using energy trapped from sunlight. A system of internal membranes, which consists of an interconnected set of flat, disclike sacs called **thylakoids**, is suspended in the stroma. The thylakoids are arranged in stacks called **grana** (sing., *granum*).

The thylakoid membrane encloses the innermost compartments within the chloroplast, the **thylakoid lumen.** Chlorophyll is present in the thylakoid membrane, which, like the inner mitochondrial membranes, is involved in the formation of ATP. Energy absorbed from sunlight by the chlorophyll molecules excites electrons; the energy in these excited electrons is then used to produce ATP and other molecules that transfer chemical energy.

Chloroplasts belong to a group of organelles, known as **plastids**, that produce and store food materials in cells of plants and algae. All plastids develop from **proplastids**, precursor organelles found in less specialized plant cells, particularly in growing, undeveloped tissues. Depending on the specific functions a cell will eventually have, its proplastids can develop into a variety of specialized mature plastids. They are extremely versatile organelles; in fact, under certain conditions even mature plastids can convert from one form to another.

Chloroplasts are produced when proplastids are stimulated by exposure to light. **Chromoplasts** contain pigments that give certain flowers and fruits their characteristic colors, and these colors attract animals that serve as pollinators or as seed dispersers. **Leukoplasts** are unpigmented plastids; they include

amyloplasts (see Fig. 3-9), which store starch in the cells of many seeds, roots, and tubers (such as white potatoes).

CHECKPOINT 4.5

- *How do the structure and function of rough ER differ from those of smooth ER?*
- *How does the structure of the Golgi complex allow it to carry out its functions?*
- **CONNECT** *Outline the sequence of events that must take place for a protein to be manufactured and then secreted from the cell.*
- **CONNECT** *In what ways are chloroplasts like mitochondria? How are they different?*

4.6 THE CYTOSKELETON

LEARNING OBJECTIVES

12 Contrast the structure and functions of the cytoskeleton with the structure and functions of the membranous components of the cell.

13 Relate the structure of cilia and flagella to their functions.

Scientists watching cells growing in the laboratory see that they frequently change shape and that many types of cells move about. The **cytoskeleton,** a dense network of protein fibers, gives cells mechanical strength, shape, and their ability to move (FIG. 4-22). The cytoskeleton also functions in cell division and in the transport of materials within the cell.

The cytoskeleton is highly dynamic and constantly changing. Its framework is made of three major types of protein filaments: microtubules, microfilaments, and intermediate filaments. Both microfilaments and microtubules are formed from beadlike, globular protein subunits, which can be rapidly assembled and disassembled. Intermediate filaments are made from fibrous protein subunits and are more stable than microtubules and microfilaments.

Microtubules are hollow cylinders

Microtubules, the thickest filaments of the cytoskeleton, are rigid, hollow rods about 25 nm in outside diameter and up to several micrometers in length. In addition to playing a structural role in the cytoskeleton, these extremely adaptable structures are involved in the movement of chromosomes during cell division. They serve as tracks for several other kinds of intracellular movement and are the major structural components of cilia and flagella, specialized structures used in some cell movements.

Microtubules consist of two forms of the protein **tubulin:** α-tubulin and β-tubulin. These proteins combine to form a dimer. (Recall from Chapter 3 that a dimer forms from the association of two simpler units, referred to as monomers.) A microtubule elongates by the addition of tubulin dimers (**FIG. 4-23**). Microtubules are disassembled by the removal of dimers, which are recycled to form new microtubules. Each microtubule has polarity, and its two ends are referred to as *plus* and *minus*. The plus end elongates more rapidly.

Other proteins are important in microtubule function. **Microtubule-associated proteins (MAPs)** are classified into two

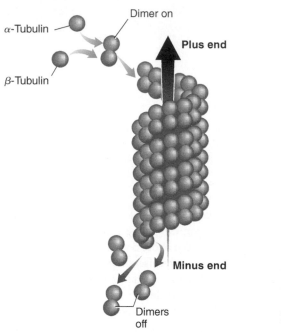

(a) Microtubules are manufactured in the cell by adding dimers of α-tubulin and β-tubulin to an end of the hollow cylinder. Notice that the cylinder has polarity. The end shown at the top of the figure is the fast-growing, or plus, end; the opposite end is the minus end. Each turn of the spiral requires 13 dimers.

The cytoskeleton consists of networks of several types of fibers that support the cell and are important in cell movement.

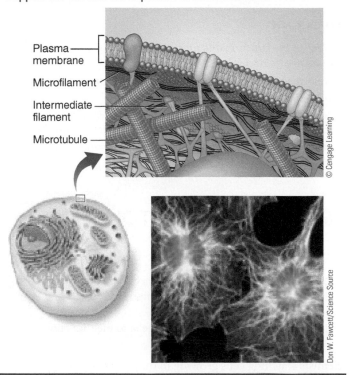

Figure 4-22 The cytoskeleton

The cytoskeleton of eukaryotic cells consists of networks of several types of fibers, including microtubules, microfilaments, and intermediate filaments. The cytoskeleton contributes to the shape of the cell, anchors organelles, and sometimes rapidly changes shape during cell locomotion. This fluorescent LM shows the cytoskeleton of two fibroblast cells (microtubules, *yellow*; microfilaments, *blue*; nuclei, *green*).

PREDICT What might happen in a cell in which all the cytoskeletal fibers associated with the plasma membrane were removed?

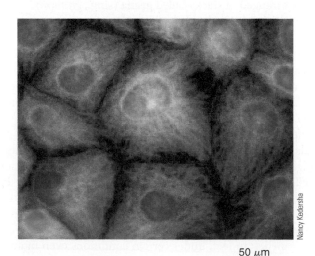

50 μm

(b) Fluorescent LM showing microtubules in *green*. A microtubule-organizing center (*pink dot*) is visible beside or over most of the cell nuclei (*blue*).

Figure 4-23 Organization of microtubules

groups: structural MAPs and motor MAPs. *Structural MAPs* may help regulate microtubule assembly, and they cross-link microtubules to other cytoskeletal polymers. *Motor MAPs* use ATP energy to produce movement.

What are the mechanisms by which organelles and other materials move within the cell? Nerve cells typically have long extensions called axons that transmit signals to other nerve cells, muscle cells, or cells that produce hormones. Because of the axon's length and accessibility and because other cells use similar transport mechanisms, researchers have used the axon as a model for studying the transport of organelles within the cell. Many organelles, including mitochondria, transport vesicles, and secretory vesicles, are attached by molecular motor proteins to microtubules that serve as tracks to different cellular locations.

One motor protein, **kinesin**, moves organelles toward the plus end of a microtubule (**FIG. 4-24**). **Dynein,** another motor protein, transports organelles in the opposite direction, toward the minus end. This dynein movement is referred to as *retrograde transport*. A protein complex called *dynactin* is also required for retrograde transport. Dynactin is an adapter protein that links dynein to the microtubule and the organelle. At times, for example, during peroxisome transport, kinesins and dyneins may work together.

Centrosomes and centrioles function in cell division

For microtubules to act as a structural framework or participate in cell movement, they must be anchored to other parts of the cell. In nondividing cells, the minus ends of microtubules appear to be anchored in regions called **microtubule-organizing centers** (**MTOCs;** see Fig. 4-23b). In animal cells, the main MTOC is the cell center, or **centrosome**.

In many cells, including almost all animal cells, the centrosome contains two structures called **centrioles** (**FIG. 4-25**). These structures are oriented within the centrosome at right angles to each other. They are known as *9 × 3 structures* because they consist of nine sets of three attached microtubules arranged to form a hollow cylinder. The centrioles are duplicated before cell division and may play a role in some types of microtubule assembly. Most plant cells and fungal cells have an MTOC but lack centrioles, which suggests that centrioles are not essential to most microtubule assembly processes and that alternative assembly mechanisms are present.

The ability of microtubules to assemble and disassemble rapidly is seen during cell division, when much of the cytoskeleton disassembles (discussed in Chapter 10). At that time, tubulin subunits organize into a structure called the **mitotic spindle**, which serves as a framework for the orderly distribution of chromosomes during cell division.

Cilia and flagella are composed of microtubules

Thin, movable structures, important in cell movement, project from surfaces of many cells. If a cell has one, or only a few, of these appendages and if they are long (typically about 200 μm)

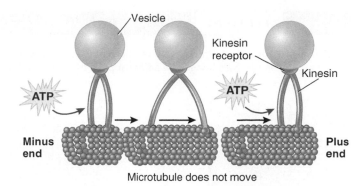

Figure 4-24 *Animation* **A model of a kinesin motor**

A kinesin molecule attaches to a specific receptor on the vesicle. Energy from ATP powers the kinesin molecule so that it changes its conformation and "walks" along the microtubule, carrying the vesicle along. (Size relationships are exaggerated for clarity.)

© Cengage Learning

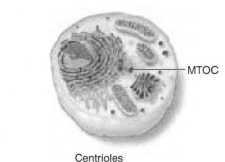

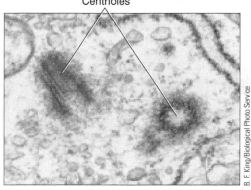

0.25 μm

(a) In the TEM, the centrioles are positioned at right angles to each other, near the nucleus of a nondividing animal cell.

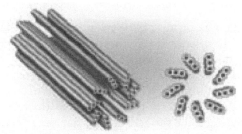

(b) Note the 9 × 3 arrangement of microtubules. The centriole on the right has been cut transversely.

Figure 4-25 Centrioles
© Cengage Learning

A cilium consists of a 9 + 2 arrangement of microtubules surrounded by the plasma membrane; dynein proteins move the microtubules by forming and breaking cross bridges on adjacent pairs of microtubules.

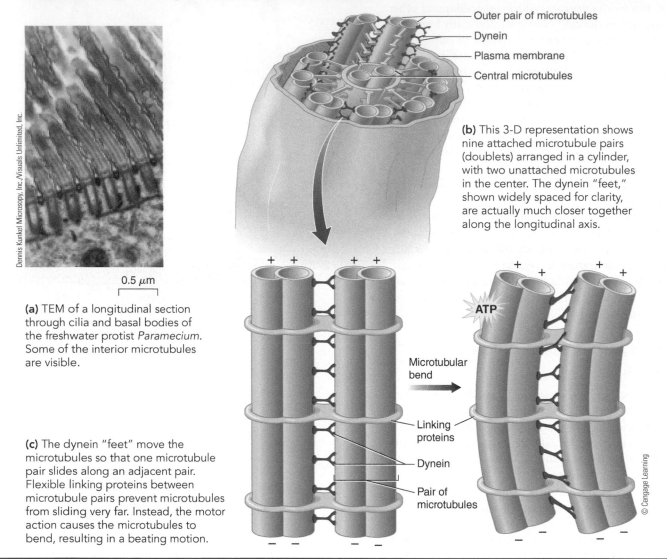

Outer pair of microtubules

Dynein

Plasma membrane

Central microtubules

(b) This 3-D representation shows nine attached microtubule pairs (doublets) arranged in a cylinder, with two unattached microtubules in the center. The dynein "feet," shown widely spaced for clarity, are actually much closer together along the longitudinal axis.

ATP

Microtubular bend

Linking proteins

Dynein

Pair of microtubules

0.5 µm

(a) TEM of a longitudinal section through cilia and basal bodies of the freshwater protist *Paramecium.* Some of the interior microtubules are visible.

(c) The dynein "feet" move the microtubules so that one microtubule pair slides along an adjacent pair. Flexible linking proteins between microtubule pairs prevent microtubules from sliding very far. Instead, the motor action causes the microtubules to bend, resulting in a beating motion.

Dennis Kunkel Microscopy, Inc./Visuals Unlimited, Inc.

© Cengage Learning

Figure 4-26 Structure and movement of cilia

PREDICT How might the action of cilia be affected if the linking proteins were inflexible? if they were absent?

relative to the size of the cell, they are called **flagella** (sing., *flagellum*). If the cell has many short (typically 2 to 10 µm long) appendages, they are called **cilia** (sing., *cilium*).

Cilia and flagella help unicellular and small multicellular organisms move through a watery environment. In animals and certain plants, flagella serve as the tails of sperm cells. In animals, cilia occur on the surfaces of cells that line internal ducts of the body (such as respiratory passageways). Cells use cilia to move liquids and particles across the cell surface. Investigators have shown that cilia also serve as the cell's antenna and play important roles in cell signaling.

Eukaryotic cilia and flagella are structurally alike (but different from bacterial flagella). Each consists of a slender, cylindrical stalk covered by an extension of the plasma membrane. The core of the stalk contains a group of microtubules arranged so that there are nine attached pairs of microtubules around the circumference and two unpaired microtubules in the center (FIG. 4-26). This *9 + 2 arrangement* of microtubules is characteristic of virtually all eukaryotic cilia and flagella.

The microtubules in cilia and flagella move by sliding in pairs past each other. The sliding force is generated by dynein proteins, powered by ATP. The dynein "feet" move the microtubule pairs by forming and breaking cross bridges on adjacent pairs of microtubules. Each microtubule pair "walks" along its neighbor. Flexible linking proteins between microtubule pairs prevent microtubules from sliding very far. As a result, the motor action causes the microtubules to bend, resulting in a beating motion (see Fig. 4-26c). Cilia typically move like the arms of a swimmer, alternating a power stroke in one direction with a recovery stroke in the opposite direction. They exert a force that is parallel to the cell surface. In contrast, a flagellum moves like a whip, exerting a force perpendicular to the cell surface.

Each cilium or flagellum is anchored in the cell by a **basal body**, which has nine sets of three attached microtubules in a cylindrical array (9 × 3 *structure*). The basal body appears to be the organizing structure for the cilium or flagellum when it first begins to form. However, experiments have shown that as growth proceeds, the tubulin subunits are added much faster to the tips of the microtubules than to the base.

Basal bodies and centrioles may be functionally related as well as structurally similar. In fact, centrioles are typically found in the cells of eukaryotic organisms that produce flagellated or ciliated cells; they include animals, certain protists, a few fungi, and a few plants. Both basal bodies and centrioles replicate themselves.

Almost every vertebrate cell has a **primary cilium**, a single cilium on the cell surface that serves as a cellular antenna. The primary cilium has receptors on its surface that bind with specific molecules outside the cell or on surfaces of other cells. Primary cilia play important roles in many signaling pathways that regulate growth and specialization of cells during embryonic development. They also help maintain healthy tissues. Malfunction of primary cilia has been associated with several human disorders, including developmental defects, degeneration of the retina, and polycystic kidney disease.

Microfilaments consist of intertwined strings of actin

Microfilaments, also called *actin filaments*, are flexible, solid fibers about 7 nm in diameter. Each microfilament consists of two intertwined polymer chains of beadlike **actin** molecules (FIG. 4-27). Microfilaments are linked with one another and with other proteins by linker proteins. They form bundles of fibers that provide mechanical support for various cell structures.

In many cells, a network of microfilaments is visible just inside the plasma membrane, a region called the *cell cortex.* Microfilaments give the cell cortex a gel-like consistency compared to the more fluid state of the cytosol deeper inside the cell. The microfilaments in the cell cortex help determine the shape of the cell and are important in its movement.

Microfilaments themselves cannot contract, but they can generate movement in two ways: by rapidly assembling and disassembling or by functioning with molecular motors. Muscle cells have two types of specialized filaments: one composed mainly of the protein **myosin** and another composed mainly of the protein actin. ATP bound to myosin provides energy for

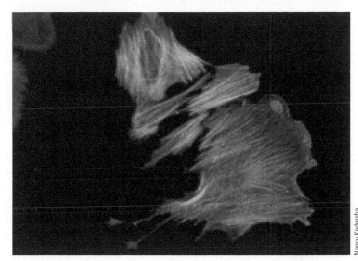

(a) A microfilament consists of two intertwined strings of beadlike actin molecules.

100 μm

Nancy Kedersha

(b) Many bundles of microfilaments (*green*) are evident in this fluorescent LM of fibroblasts, cells found in connective tissue.

Figure 4-27 Microfilaments
© Cengage Learning

muscle contraction. When ATP is hydrolyzed to ADP, myosin binds to actin and causes the microfilament to slide. When thousands of filaments slide in this way, the muscle cell shortens. Thus, ATP, actin, and myosin generate the forces that contract muscles (discussed in Chapter 40).

In nonmuscle cells, actin also associates with myosin, forming contractile structures involved in various cell movements. For example, in animal cell division, contraction of a ring of actin associated with myosin constricts the cell, forming two daughter cells (discussed in Chapter 10).

Some cells change their shape quickly in response to changes in the outside environment. Amoebas, human white blood cells, and cancer cells are among the many cell types that can creep along a surface, a process that includes changes in shape. Such responses depend on external signals that affect microfilament, as well as microtubule, assembly. Actin filaments push the plasma membrane outward, forming cytoplasm-filled bulges called **pseudopodia** ("false feet"). The pseudopodia adhere to the surface. Contractions of microfilaments at the opposite end of the cell force the cytoplasm forward in the direction of locomotion. Microtubules, myosin, and other proteins also appear necessary for cell creeping.

As mentioned earlier in the chapter, some types of cells have microvilli, projections of the plasma membrane that increase the surface area of the cell for transporting materials across the plasma membrane. Composed of bundles of microfilaments, microvilli extend and retract as the microfilaments assemble and disassemble.

Intermediate filaments help stabilize cell shape

Intermediate filaments are tough, flexible fibers about 10 nm in diameter (FIG. 4-28). They provide mechanical strength and help stabilize cell shape. These filaments are abundant in regions of a cell that may be subject to mechanical stress applied from outside the cell. Intermediate filaments prevent the cell from stretching excessively in response to outside forces. Certain proteins cross-link intermediate filaments with other types of filaments and mediate interactions between them.

All eukaryotic cells have microtubules and microfilaments, but only some animal groups, including vertebrates, are known to have intermediate filaments. Even when present, intermediate filaments vary widely in protein composition and size among different cell types and different organisms. Examples of intermediate filaments are the keratins found in the epithelial cells of vertebrate skin and neurofilaments found in vertebrate nerve cells.

Certain mutations in genes coding for intermediate filaments weaken the cell and are associated with several diseases. For example, in the neurodegenerative disease amyotrophic lateral sclerosis (ALS, or Lou Gehrig's disease), abnormal neurofilaments have been identified in nerve cells that control muscles. This condition interferes with normal transport of materials in the nerve cells and leads to degeneration of the cells. The resulting loss of muscle function is typically fatal.

CHECKPOINT 4.6

- *In what ways do the functions of the cytoskeleton differ from those of the endomembrane system?*
- *How are microfilaments and microtubules similar? How are they different?*
- *What roles do microtubules play in movement by cilia and flagella?*

4.7 CELL COVERINGS

LEARNING OBJECTIVE

14 Compare the roles of the glycocalyx, extracellular matrix, and cell wall.

Many cells are surrounded by a **glycocalyx,** or *cell coat,* formed by polysaccharide side chains of proteins and lipids that are part of the plasma membrane. The glycocalyx protects the cell and may help keep other cells at a distance. Certain molecules of the glycocalyx enable cells to recognize one another, to make contact, and in some cases to form adhesive or communicating

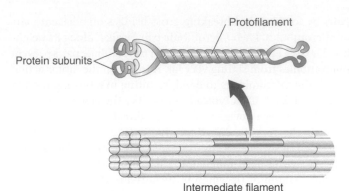

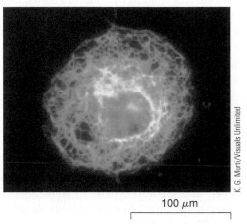

(a) Intermediate filaments are flexible rods about 10 nm in diameter. Each intermediate filament consists of components, called protofilaments, composed of coiled protein subunits.

K. G. Murti/Visuals Unlimited

100 μm

(b) Intermediate filaments are stained *green* in this human cell isolated from a tissue culture.

Figure 4-28 *Animation* **Intermediate filaments**
© Cengage Learning

associations (discussed in Chapter 5). Other molecules of the cell coat contribute to the mechanical strength of multicellular tissues.

Many animal cells are also surrounded by an **extracellular matrix (ECM),** which they secrete. The ECM consists of a gel of carbohydrates and fibrous proteins (FIG. 4-29). The main structural protein in the ECM is *collagen*, a protein that forms very tough fibers (see Fig. 3-23b). Certain glycoproteins of the ECM, called **fibronectins**, organize the matrix and help cells attach to it. Fibronectins bind to protein receptors that extend from the plasma membrane.

Integrins are receptor proteins in the plasma membrane. They maintain adhesion between the ECM and the intermediate filaments and microfilaments inside the cell. These proteins activate many cell signaling pathways that communicate information from the ECM, and they control signals inside the cell that regulate the differentiation and survival of the cell. When cells are not appropriately anchored, apoptosis is initiated. Integrins are also important in organizing the cytoskeleton so that cells assume a definite shape.

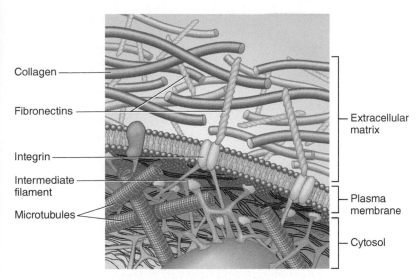

Collagen
Fibronectins
Integrin
Intermediate filament
Microtubules

Extracellular matrix
Plasma membrane
Cytosol

Figure 4-29 The extracellular matrix (ECM)
Fibronectins, glycoproteins of the ECM, bind to integrins and other receptors in the plasma membrane.
© Cengage Learning

Cell 1

Middle lamella

Primary cell wall

Multiple layers of secondary cell wall

Cell 2

Biophoto Associates/Science Source

2.5 μm

The cells of most bacteria, archaea, fungi, and plant cells are surrounded by a cell wall. Plant cells have thick cell walls that contain tiny fibers composed of the polysaccharide **cellulose** (see Fig. 3-10). Other polysaccharides in the plant cell wall form cross links between the bundles of cellulose fibers. Cell walls provide structural support, protect plant cells from disease-causing organisms, and prevent them from bursting due to increased hydrostatic pressure.

A growing plant cell secretes a thin, flexible *primary cell wall*. As the cell grows, the primary cell wall increases in size (FIG. 4-30). After the cell stops growing, either new wall material is secreted that thickens and solidifies the primary wall, or multiple layers of a *secondary cell wall* with a different chemical composition are formed between the primary wall and the plasma membrane. Wood is made mainly of secondary cell walls. The **middle lamella**, a layer of gluelike polysaccharides called *pectins*, lies between the primary cell walls of adjacent cells. The middle lamella causes the cells to adhere tightly to one another. (For more information on plant cell walls, see the discussion of the ground tissue system in Chapter 33.)

CHECKPOINT 4.7

- *What are the functions of the glycocalyx?*
- *How do the functions of fibronectins and integrins differ?*

Figure 4-30 *Animation* **Plant cell walls**
The cell walls of two adjacent plant cells are labeled in this TEM. The cells are cemented together by the middle lamella, a layer of gluelike polysaccharides called pectins. A growing plant cell first secretes a thin primary wall that is flexible and can stretch as the cell grows. The thicker layers of the secondary wall are secreted inside the primary wall after the cell stops elongating.

SUMMARY: FOCUS ON LEARNING OBJECTIVES

4.1 The Cell: Basic Unit of Life *(page 72)*

1 Connect the cell theory to the evolution of life.

- The **cell theory** holds that (1) cells are the basic living units of organization and function in all organisms and (2) all cells come from other cells. It explains that the ancestry of all the cells alive today can be traced back to ancient times. Evidence that all living cells have evolved from a common ancestor is supported by the basic similarities in their structures and in their molecular composition.

2 Relate the organizational similarities of all cells to the need to conduct essential life functions.

- Every cell is surrounded by a **plasma membrane** that separates it from its external environment. The plasma membrane allows the cell to maintain internal conditions that may be very

different from those of the outer environment. The plasma membrane also allows the cell to selectively exchange materials with its outer environment. Cells have many **organelles**, internal structures that carry out specific functions.

- All cells have similar mechanisms for information transfer and chemical reactions that convert energy from one form to another.

3 Explain the functional significance of cell size and cell shape.

- A critical factor in determining cell size is the ratio of the plasma membrane (surface area) to the cell's volume. The plasma membrane must be large enough relative to the cell volume to regulate the passage of materials into and out of the cell. For this reason, most cells are microscopic.

- The size and shape of a cell are largely dictated by the functions it must perform.

4.2 Methods for Studying Cells *(page 74)*

4 Compare methods that biologists use to study cells and point out the ways in which many of these approaches are complementary.

- Biologists use **light microscopes, electron microscopes,** and a variety of chemical methods, including the binding of specific antibodies, to study cells and learn about cell structure. The electron microscope has superior **resolving power,** enabling investigators to see details of cell structures not observable with conventional microscopes. Fluorescence microscopy can be used to track the locations and movements of specific tagged molecules within cells.

- Cell biologists use the technique of **cell fractionation** for purifying organelles as well as genetic methods to gain information about the function of cell structures.

4.3 Prokaryotic and Eukaryotic Cells *(page 80)*

5 Compare and contrast the general characteristics of prokaryotic and eukaryotic cells, and contrast plant and animal cells.

- **Prokaryotic cells** are enclosed by a plasma membrane but have little or no internal membrane organization. They have a **nuclear area** rather than a membrane-enclosed nucleus. Prokaryotic cells typically have a **cell wall** and **ribosomes,** and may have propeller-like **flagella.**

- **Eukaryotic cells** have a membrane-enclosed nucleus, and their **cytoplasm** contains a variety of organelles; the fluid component of the cytoplasm is the **cytosol.**

- Plant cells differ from animal cells in that plant cells have rigid cell walls, plastids, and large vacuoles, which are important in plant growth and development.

6 Describe three functions of cell membranes.

- Membranes divide the eukaryotic cell into compartments, allowing it to conduct specialized activities within small areas of the cytoplasm, concentrate reactants, and organize metabolic reactions. Small membrane-enclosed sacs, called **vesicles**, transport materials between compartments.

- Membranes are important in energy storage and conversion.

- Membranes serve as work surfaces for certain chemical reactions.

4.4 The Cell Nucleus *(page 82)*

7 Relate the structure of the nucleus to its function as the control center of the eukaryotic cell.

- The **nucleus** contains genetic information coded in DNA. The nucleus is bounded by a **nuclear envelope**, consisting of a double membrane perforated with **nuclear pores** that communicate with the cytoplasm.

- DNA in the nucleus associates with protein to form **chromatin,** which is organized into **chromosomes.** During cell division, the chromosomes condense and become visible as threadlike structures.

- DNA transcribes its information in messenger RNA (mRNA) molecules, which enter the cytoplasm to provide information for protein synthesis by ribosomes.

- The **nucleolus** is a region in the nucleus that is the site of ribosomal RNA (rRNA) synthesis and ribosome assembly.

4.5 Membranous Organelles in the Cytoplasm *(page 86)*

8 Distinguish between smooth and rough endoplasmic reticulum in terms of both structure and function.

- The **endoplasmic reticulum (ER)** is a network of folded internal membranes in the cytosol. **Smooth ER** is the site of lipid synthesis, calcium ion storage, and detoxifying enzymes.

- **Rough ER** is studded along its outer surface with **ribosomes** that manufacture polypeptides. Polypeptides synthesized on

rough ER may be moved into the ER lumen, where they are assembled into proteins and modified by the addition of a carbohydrate or lipid. These proteins may then be transferred to other compartments within the cell by small transport vesicles that bud off from the ER membrane.

9 Trace the path of proteins synthesized in the rough endoplasmic reticulum as they are processed, modified, and sorted by the Golgi complex and then transported to specific destinations.

- The **Golgi complex** consists of stacks of flattened membranous sacs called **cisternae** that process, sort, and modify proteins synthesized on the rough ER. The Golgi complex also manufactures lysosomes.

- Glycoproteins are transported from the ER to the *cis* face of the Golgi complex by transport vesicles, which are formed by membrane budding. The Golgi complex modifies carbohydrates and lipids that were added to proteins by the ER and packages them in vesicles.

- Glycoproteins exit the Golgi through vesicles that are formed at its *trans* face. The Golgi routes some proteins to the plasma membrane for export from the cell. Others are transported to lysosomes or other organelles within the cytoplasm.

10 Compare the functions of lysosomes, vacuoles, and peroxisomes.

- **Lysosomes** contain enzymes that break down worn-out cell structures, bacteria, and debris taken into cells.

- **Vacuoles** store materials, water, and wastes. They maintain hydrostatic pressure in plant cells.

- **Peroxisomes** are important in lipid metabolism and detoxify harmful compounds such as ethanol. They produce hydrogen peroxide, but contain the enzyme catalase, which degrades this toxic compound.

11 Contrast the functions of mitochondria and chloroplasts, and discuss ATP synthesis by each of these organelles.

- **Mitochondria,** organelles enclosed by a double membrane, are the sites of aerobic respiration. The inner membrane is folded, forming **cristae** that increase its surface area.

- The cristae and the compartment enclosed by the inner membrane, the **matrix,** contain enzymes for the reactions of **aerobic respiration.** During aerobic respiration, nutrients are broken down in the presence of oxygen. Energy captured from nutrients is packaged in ATP, and carbon dioxide and water are produced as byproducts.

- **Plastids** are organelles that produce and store food in the cells of plants and algae.

- **Chloroplasts** are plastids that carry out **photosynthesis.**

- The inner membrane of the chloroplast encloses a fluid-filled space, the **stroma.**

- **Grana,** stacks of interconnected disclike membranous sacs called **thylakoids,** are suspended in the stroma.

- During photosynthesis, **chlorophyll,** the green pigment found in the thylakoid membranes, traps light energy. This energy is converted to chemical energy in ATP and used to synthesize carbohydrates from carbon dioxide and water.

4.6 The Cytoskeleton *(page 95)*

12 Contrast the structure and functions of the cytoskeleton with the structure and functions of the membranous components of the cell.

- The **cytoskeleton** is a dynamic internal protein fiber framework that includes microtubules, microfilaments, and intermediate filaments. The cytoskeleton provides structural support and functions in various types of cell movement, including transport of materials in the cell.

- **Microtubules** are hollow cylinders assembled from subunits of the protein **tubulin.** In cells that are not dividing, the minus ends of microtubules are anchored in **microtubule-organizing centers (MTOCs).** The main MTOC of animal cells is the **centrosome,** which usually contains two centrioles. Each centriole has a 9 × 3 arrangement of microtubules.
- **Microfilaments,** or **actin** filaments, formed from subunits of the protein actin, are important in cell movement.
- **Intermediate filaments** strengthen the cytoskeleton and stabilize cell shape.

13 Relate the structure of cilia and flagella to their functions.
- **Cilia** and **flagella** are thin, movable structures that project from the cell surface and function in movement. Each consists of a 9 + 2 arrangement of microtubules, and each is anchored in the cell by a basal body that has a 9 × 3 organization of microtubules. Cilia are short, and flagella are long.

4.7 Cell Coverings (page 100)

14 Compare the roles of the glycocalyx, extracellular matrix, and cell wall.
- Most cells are surrounded by a **glycocalyx,** or *cell coat,* formed by polysaccharides extending from the plasma membrane.
- Many animal cells are also surrounded by an **extracellular matrix (ECM)** consisting of carbohydrates and protein. **Fibronectins** are glycoproteins of the ECM that bind to **integrins,** receptor proteins in the plasma membrane.
- Cells of most bacteria, archaea, fungi, and plant cells are surrounded by a cell wall made mainly of carbohydrates. Plant cells secrete **cellulose** and other polysaccharides that form rigid cell walls.

TEST YOUR UNDERSTANDING

Know and Comprehend

1. Which of the following is the most fundamental feature that enables the cell to function as a distinct entity, separate from its environment? (a) nucleus (b) ribosomes (c) nucleic acids (d) plasma membrane (e) protein

2. Which of the following is/are too small to have been discovered before the invention of the electron microscope? (a) chloroplasts (b) mitochondria (c) nucleus (d) ribosomes (e) central vacuole

3. Which of the following would *not* be found in prokaryotic cells? (a) cell wall (b) ribosomes (c) plasma membrane (d) nucleus (e) propeller-like flagellum

4. Which of the following would you expect to find passing through a nuclear pore? (a) ribosome subunit (b) ribosomal protein (c) messenger RNA (d) water (e) all of the preceding

5. Select the sequence that most accurately describes glycoprotein processing in the eukaryotic cell. 1. *cis* face of Golgi 2. smooth ER 3. rough ER 4. *trans* face of Golgi 5. transport vesicle (a) 1, 2, 3, 4, 5 (b) 1, 4, 5, 3, 2 (c) 2, 3, 4, 5, 1 (d) 3, 5, 1, 4 (e) 2, 5, 1, 4

6. To carry out its life functions, every plant cell requires (a) chloroplasts and ribosomes (b) mitochondria and ribosomes (c) mitochondria, chloroplasts, and lysosomes (d) mitochondria and chloroplasts (e) chloroplasts and a vacuole

7. Microtubules (a) have constant diameters, but vary in length (b) vary in diameter, but are constant in length (c) vary in both length and diameter (d) are constant in both length and diameter

8. All of the following are true of integrins *except* (a) they are receptor proteins (b) they help organize the cytoskeleton (c) they are part of the ECM (d) they are important in cell signaling (e) they are located in the plasma membrane

Apply and Analyze

9. **VISUALIZE** Illustrate the relationships among the membranes and compartments of (a) mitochondria and (b) chloroplasts by sketching simple concentric circles to represent the membranes. Choose the appropriate labels for each sketch from the following list: inner membrane, outer membrane, thylakoid membrane, stroma, thylakoid lumen, matrix.

10. Three observers independently measured the same cells and reported their results in the table:

Observer	Average Diameter of 10 cells
1	0.02 μm
2	0.002 mm
3	2×10^4 nm

Which, if any, of their measurements agree? Which observer is most likely to be correct if the cells are prokaryotic cells? if they are eukaryotic cells?

Evaluate and Synthesize

11. Why does a eukaryotic cell need both membranous organelles and fibrous cytoskeletal components? Justify your answer.

12. **INTERPRET DATA** An investigator has isolated two mutant strains of yeast that fail to secrete a short polypeptide. She fractionated the cells and compared the concentrations of this polypeptide in the different cellular fractions with those found in normal cells. What point in the secretory pathway would you expect would be defective for mutant a and mutant b?

Yeast Strain	Secretory Vesicles	Golgi Complex	ER
Normal	90	5	5
Mutant a	4	2	94
Mutant b	2	85	13

13. **EVOLUTION LINK** What types of similarities in cell structure and function tell biologists about the common origin of organisms? Explain.

14. **SCIENCE, TECHNOLOGY, AND SOCIETY** Students majoring in one of the life sciences also take courses in chemistry, physics, and mathematics. Based on what you've learned in this chapter, do you think that these requirements are justified?

 To access course materials, such as Aplia and other companion resources, please visit **www.cengagebrain.com.**

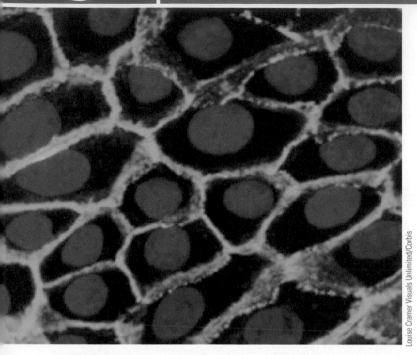

5 | Biological Membranes

Membrane proteins. Cadherins, proteins that span the plasma membrane and participate in adhering junctions with adjacent cells, are stained *green* in this fluorescence LM. Nuclei are stained *purple*.

Louise Cramer Visuals Unlimited/Corbis

The evolution of biological membranes that separate the cell from its external environment was an essential step in the origin of life. Later, these membranes made the evolution of complex cells possible. The extensive internal membranes of eukaryotic cells form multiple compartments with unique chemical environments that allow highly specialized activities to take place.

Membrane proteins are critical molecules in cellular activities. Some proteins associated with the plasma membrane transport materials, whereas others transmit information or serve as enzymes. Still others, known as *cell adhesion molecules,* are important in connecting cells to one another to form tissues.

In Chapter 4 we discussed a variety of cell organelles and how they interact to perform cell activities. In this chapter we focus on the structure and functions of the plasma membrane that surrounds the cell and on the membranes that surround many organelles. We first consider what is known about the composition and structure of biological membranes. Then we provide an overview of the many vital functions of cell membranes, including transport of materials and information transfer. We discuss how cells transport various materials, from ions to complex molecules and even bacteria, across membranes. Finally, we examine specialized structures that allow membranes of different cells to interact. Although much of our discussion centers on the structure and functions of plasma membranes, many of the concepts apply to other cell membranes.

KEY CONCEPTS

5.1 Biological membranes are composed of fluid phospholipid bilayers that form closed cellular compartments. Proteins embedded in the lipid core of the membrane maintain internal cellular environments by selectively controlling the movement of molecules across the lipid bilayers.

5.2 Membrane proteins have many functions, including transport of materials, enzymatic activity, transfer of information, and recognition of other cells.

5.3 Transport proteins move ions and small polar molecules through cell membranes.

5.4 Many small molecules, including water, move through biological membranes by diffusion, the net movement of particles from a region of higher to a region of lower concentration.

5.5 Cells must internalize many substances at higher concentrations than they are outside the cell. These substances must be actively transported against a concentration gradient, requiring a direct expenditure of energy.

5.6 Cells eject products by exocytosis and import materials by endocytosis; both processes require cells to expend energy.

5.7 Cells in close contact may form specialized junctions with one another between their plasma membranes.

5.1 THE STRUCTURE OF BIOLOGICAL MEMBRANES

LEARNING OBJECTIVES

1 Evaluate the importance of membranes to cells, emphasizing their various functions.
2 Describe the fluid mosaic model of cell membrane structure.
3 Relate properties of the lipid bilayer to properties and functions of cell membranes.
4 Describe the ways that membrane proteins associate with the lipid bilayer.

To carry out the many chemical reactions necessary to sustain life, the cell must maintain an appropriate internal environment. Every cell is surrounded by a **plasma membrane** that physically separates it from the outside world and defines it as a distinct entity. By regulating passage of materials into and out of the cell, the plasma membrane helps maintain a life-supporting internal environment. As we discussed in Chapter 4, eukaryotic cells are characterized by numerous organelles that are surrounded by membranes. Some of these organelles—including the nuclear envelope, endoplasmic reticulum (ER), Golgi complex, lysosomes, vesicles, and vacuoles—form the endomembrane system, which extends throughout the cell.

Biological membranes are complex, dynamic structures made of lipid and protein molecules that are in constant motion. The properties of membranes allow them to perform many vital functions. They regulate the passage of materials, divide the cell into compartments, serve as surfaces for chemical reactions, adhere to and communicate with other cells, and transmit signals between the environment and the interior of the cell. Membranes are also an essential part of energy transfer and storage systems. How do the properties of cell membranes enable the cell to carry on such varied functions?

Long before the development of the electron microscope, scientists knew that membranes consist of both lipids and proteins. Work by researchers in the 1920s and 1930s had provided clues that the core of cell membranes consists of lipids, mostly phospholipids (see Chapter 3). Mammalian red blood cells have only a plasma membrane and no internal membrane compartments. By comparing their surface area with the total number of lipid molecules per cell, early investigators had calculated that the membrane is no more than two phospholipid molecules thick. Studies by early researchers also showed that when purified membrane lipids were dispersed in water they could form flexible, self-sealing bilayers that would spontaneously round up to form closed compartments or vesicles.

Phospholipids form bilayers in water

Phospholipid molecules have unique attributes that allow them to form bilayered structures, and they are primarily responsible for the physical properties of biological membranes. Recall from Chapter 3 that phospholipids are **amphipathic molecules,** consisting of two *hydrophobic* ("water-fearing") fatty acid chains linked to two of the three carbons of a glycerol molecule (see Fig. 3-13). Bonded to the third carbon of the glycerol is a negatively charged, *hydrophilic* ("water-loving") phosphate group, which in turn is linked to a polar, hydrophilic organic group. Molecules of this type have distinct hydrophobic and hydrophilic regions, and all lipids that make up the core of biological membranes have amphipathic characteristics that cause them to interact with water in predictable ways (FIG. 5-1).

Because one end of each phospholipid associates freely with water and the opposite end does not, the most stable orientation for them to assume in water results in the formation of a bilayer structure (see Fig. 5-1a). This arrangement allows the hydrophilic heads of the phospholipids to be in contact with the aqueous medium, while their oily tails, the hydrophobic fatty

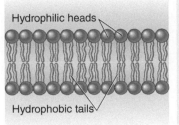
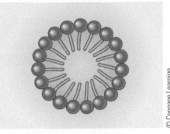

(a) Phospholipids in water. Phospholipids associate as bilayers in water because they are roughly cylindrical amphipathic molecules. The flexible hydrophobic fatty acid chains are not exposed to water, whereas the hydrophilic phospholipid heads are in contact with water.

(b) Detergent in water. Detergent molecules are roughly cone-shaped amphipathic molecules that associate in water as spherical structures.

© Cengage Learning

Figure 5-1 *Animation* **Properties of lipids in water**

acid chains, are buried in the interior of the structure away from the water molecules. This hydrophobic core of the bilayer is the barrier that prevents many types of small, hydrophilic molecules (including ions, amino acids, and organic metabolites) from passing from one side of a membrane to the other, and it allows a cell to maintain different chemical environments within each membrane compartment.

Physical studies on artificial vesicles formed from isolated membrane lipids also revealed another important property associated with the hydrophobic core: at normal biological temperatures, the fatty acid chains in the core are in constant motion as parts of hydrocarbon chains rotate around the C—C bonds. This constant hydrocarbon chain motion gives the bilayer the property of a *liquid crystal,* or a 2-dimensional fluid. The bilayers are crystal-like in that the lipids form an ordered array, with the head groups on the outer surfaces of the bilayer and the fatty acid chains on the inside. Thus, the molecules are free to rotate and can move laterally within their single layer, or *leaflet* of the bilayer. Under normal conditions a single phospholipid exchanges places with its neighbor in about 10^{-7} seconds and can travel laterally across the surface of the cell in seconds. By contrast, the "flip-flop" movement of a phospholipid molecule from one leaflet of an artificial bilayer to the other side is a rare event (on the order of days) because it requires the large, hydrophilic head group to pass through the hydrophobic core of the membrane (FIG. 5-2). In cells, this trans-bilayer movement is facilitated by special membrane proteins commonly referred to as "flippases."

Note that amphipathic properties alone do not predict the ability of lipids to associate as a bilayer. Shape is also important. Phospholipids tend to have uniform widths; their roughly cylindrical shapes, together with their amphipathic properties, are responsible for bilayer formation. By contrast, many common detergents are amphipathic molecules, each containing a single hydrocarbon chain (like a fatty acid) at one end and a hydrophilic region at the other. These molecules are roughly cone-shaped, with the hydrophilic end forming the broad base and the hydrocarbon tail leading to the point. Because of their

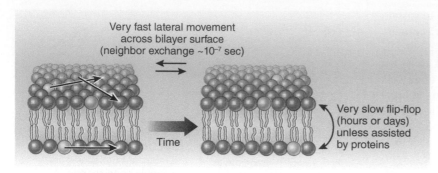

Very fast lateral movement
across bilayer surface
(neighbor exchange ~10^{-7} sec)

Time

Very slow flip-flop
(hours or days)
unless assisted
by proteins

Figure 5-2 Membrane fluidity

The ordered arrangement of phospholipid molecules makes the cell membrane a liquid crystal. The hydrocarbon chains are in constant motion, allowing each molecule to rapidly move laterally on the same side of the bilayer. Flip-flop from one side of the bilayer to the other is a rare event, and in cells it is facilitated by special membrane proteins.
© Cengage Learning

shapes, these molecules do not associate as bilayers but instead tend to form spherical structures in water (see Fig. 5-1b). Detergents can "solubilize" oil because the oil molecules associate with the hydrophobic interiors of the spheres.

The fluid mosaic model explains membrane structure

With the development of the electron microscope in the 1950s, cell biologists were able to see the plasma membrane for the first time. One of their most striking observations was how uniform and thin the membranes appeared to be. The electron microscope revealed a three-layered structure, something like a railroad track, suggesting that the plasma membrane was a uniform structure no more than 10 nm thick (FIG. 5-3). This finding was surprising because membrane proteins were found to be far from uniform, and they vary widely in composition and size.

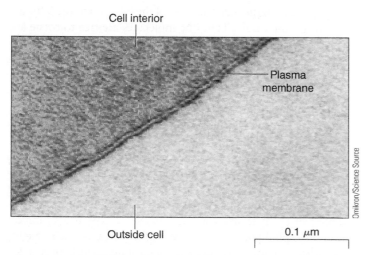

Cell interior

Plasma membrane

Omikron/Science Source

Outside cell

0.1 μm

Figure 5-3 TEM of the plasma membrane of a mammalian red blood cell

The plasma membrane separates the cytosol (*darker region*) from the external environment (*lighter region*). The hydrophilic heads of the phospholipids are the parallel dark lines, and the hydrophobic tails are the light zone between them.

Some of these membrane-bound proteins are quite large, with diameters much greater than 10 nm.

Studies of many membrane proteins showed that one region (or domain) of the molecule could always be found on one side of the bilayer, whereas another part of the protein might be located on the opposite side. These studies indicated that many membrane proteins extend completely through the lipid bilayer and that membranes contain many types of proteins of different shapes and sizes.

In 1972, S. Jonathan Singer and Garth Nicolson of the University of California at San Diego proposed a model of membrane structure that represented a synthesis of the known properties of biological membranes. According to their **fluid mosaic model,** a cell membrane consists of a fluid bilayer of phospholipid molecules in which the proteins are embedded or otherwise associated, much like the tiles in a mosaic picture. This mosaic pattern is not static, however, because the positions of many of the proteins are constantly changing as they move about like icebergs in a fluid sea of phospholipids. FIGURE 5-4 depicts the plasma membrane of a eukaryotic cell according to the fluid mosaic model; prokaryotic plasma membranes are discussed in Chapter 25.

Biological membranes are two-dimensional fluids

The fluid qualities of lipid bilayers also allow molecules embedded in them to move along the plane of the membrane (as long as they are not anchored in some way), as David Frye and Michael Edidin elegantly demonstrated in 1970. They conducted experiments in which they followed the movement of membrane proteins on the surface of two cells that had been joined (FIG. 5-5). When the plasma membranes of a mouse cell and a human cell are fused, within minutes at least some of the membrane proteins from each cell migrate and become randomly distributed over the single, continuous plasma membrane that surrounds the joined cells. Frye and Edidin showed that the fluidity of the lipids in the membrane allows many of the proteins to move, producing an ever-changing configuration. Not all plasma membrane proteins exhibit this behavior, however. Membrane proteins that are physically anchored to the cytoskeleton (see Figs. 4-29 and 5-4) or the extracellular matrix tend to remain in fixed positions on the cell surface.

For a membrane to function properly, its hydrophobic core must be in an optimal fluid state. At normal growing temperatures, cell membranes are fluids with a consistency similar to a vegetable oil at room temperature. If cells are rapidly cooled to lower than normal temperatures, however, membrane functions, such as the transport of certain substances, are inhibited or cease because the motion of the fatty acid chains is slowed and the lipid bilayer becomes too rigid.

Certain properties of membrane lipids have significant effects on the fluidity of the bilayer. Recall from Chapter 3 that fats

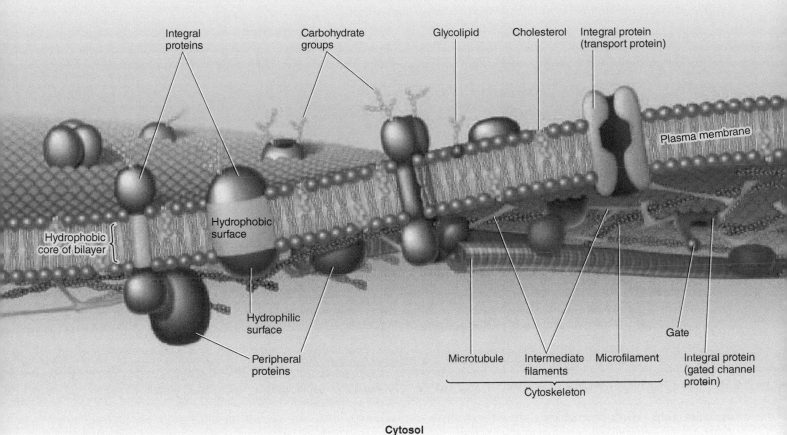

Outside cell

Integral proteins

Carbohydrate groups

Glycolipid

Cholesterol

Integral protein (transport protein)

Plasma membrane

Hydrophobic surface

Hydrophobic core of bilayer

Hydrophilic surface

Peripheral proteins

Microtubule

Intermediate filaments

Microfilament

Cytoskeleton

Gate

Integral protein (gated channel protein)

Cytosol

Figure 5-4 Detailed structure of the plasma membrane

Cell membranes are composed of a fluid bilayer of phospholipids in which proteins move about like icebergs in a sea. Although the lipid bilayer consists mainly of phospholipids, other lipids, such as cholesterol and glycolipids, are present. Peripheral proteins are loosely associated with the bilayer, whereas integral proteins are tightly bound. The integral proteins shown here are transmembrane proteins that extend through the bilayer. They have hydrophilic regions on both sides of the bilayer connected by a hydrophobic membrane-spanning region. Some types of integral membrane proteins are anchored in the membrane by proteins that attach them to the cytoskeleton or the extracellular matrix. Glycolipids (carbohydrates attached to lipids) and glycoproteins (carbohydrates attached to proteins) are exposed on the extracellular surface; they play roles in cell recognition and adhesion to other cells.

© Cengage Learning

containing large amounts of saturated fatty acids tend to be solid at room temperature due to the effects of many van der Waals interactions that occur between closely aligned fatty acid chains. Fats or oils with mono or polyunsaturated fatty acids, however, tend to be liquid at room temperature due to the presence of double bonds that produce kinks in their fatty acid chains. Such kinks prevent the close packing necessary for these interactions to occur.

Many organisms have regulatory mechanisms for maintaining cell membranes in an optimally fluid state. Some organisms compensate for environmental temperature differences by altering the fatty acid content of their membrane lipids. Arctic fish, for example, tend to have higher levels of unsaturated fatty acids in their membrane lipids than tropical species in order to maintain optimal membrane fluidity at the lower

ocean temperatures. Other organisms, such as plants and many microorganisms, will adjust the ratios of saturated and unsaturated fatty acids in their membrane lipids to optimize fluidity in response to changes in environmental temperatures that occur during the growing season.

Some membrane lipids stabilize membrane fluidity within certain limits. One such "fluidity buffer" is cholesterol, a steroid found in animal cell membranes. A cholesterol molecule is largely hydrophobic but is slightly amphipathic because of the presence of a single hydroxyl group (see Fig. 3-15a). In a phospholipid bilayer, this hydroxyl group associates with the hydrophilic heads of the phospholipids; the hydrophobic remainder of the cholesterol molecule fits between the fatty acid hydrocarbon chains (see Fig. 5-4).

Do proteins embedded in a biological membrane move about?

HYPOTHESIS: Proteins are able to move laterally in the plasma membrane.

EXPERIMENT: Larry Frye and Michael Edidin labeled membrane proteins of mouse and human cells using different-colored fluorescent dyes to distinguish between them. They then fused mouse and human cells to produce hybrid cells.

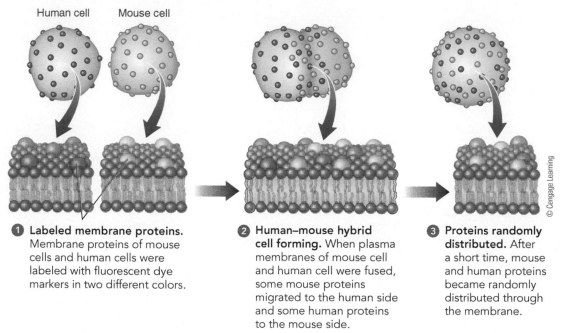

1 **Labeled membrane proteins.** Membrane proteins of mouse cells and human cells were labeled with fluorescent dye markers in two different colors.

2 **Human–mouse hybrid cell forming.** When plasma membranes of mouse cell and human cell were fused, some mouse proteins migrated to the human side and some human proteins to the mouse side.

3 **Proteins randomly distributed.** After a short time, mouse and human proteins became randomly distributed through the membrane.

RESULTS AND CONCLUSION: After a brief period of incubation, mouse and human cells intermixed over the surface of the hybrid cells. After about 40 minutes, the proteins of each species had become randomly distributed through the entire hybrid plasma membrane. This experiment demonstrated that proteins in the plasma membrane do move.

Figure 5-5 *Animation* **Frye and Edidin's experiment**

PREDICT What would be the expected distribution of fluorescence in the fused cell if a membrane protein linked to a microtubule on its cytoplasmic side were the protein that was labeled with the green fluorescent antibody?

SOURCE: Frye, L.D., and M. Edidin. "The Rapid Intermixing of Cell Surface Antigens after Formation of Mouse-Human Heterokaryons." *Journal of Cell Science*, Vol. 7, 319–335, 1970.

At low temperatures cholesterol molecules act as "spacers" between the hydrocarbon chains, restricting van der Waals interactions that would promote solidifying. Cholesterol also helps prevent the membrane from becoming weakened or unstable at higher temperatures. The reason is that the cholesterol molecules interact strongly with the portions of the hydrocarbon chains closest to the phospholipid head. This interaction restricts motion in these regions. Plant cells have steroids other than cholesterol that carry out similar functions.

Biological membranes fuse and form closed vesicles

Lipid bilayers, particularly those in the liquid-crystalline state, have additional important physical properties. Bilayers tend to resist forming free ends; as a result, they are self-sealing and under most conditions spontaneously round up to form closed vesicles. Lipid bilayers are also flexible, allowing cell membranes to change shape without breaking, and under appropriate conditions lipid bilayers fuse with other bilayers.

Membrane fusion is an important cell process. When a vesicle fuses with another membrane, both membrane bilayers and their compartments become continuous. Various transport vesicles form from, and also merge with, membranes of the ER and Golgi complex, facilitating the transfer of materials from one compartment to another. A vesicle fuses with the plasma membrane when a product is secreted from the cell.

Membrane proteins include integral and peripheral proteins

The two major classes of membrane proteins, integral proteins and peripheral proteins, are defined by how tightly they are associated with the lipid bilayer (FIG. 5-6). **Integral membrane**

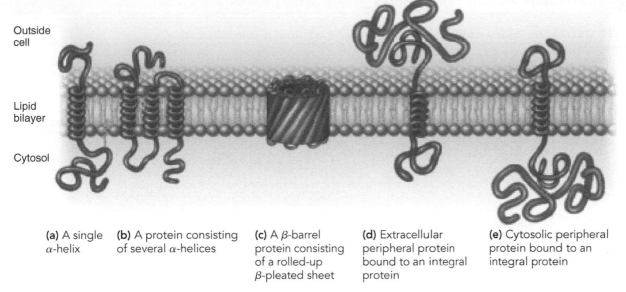

(a) A single α-helix

(b) A protein consisting of several α-helices

(c) A β-barrel protein consisting of a rolled-up β-pleated sheet

(d) Extracellular peripheral protein bound to an integral protein

(e) Cytosolic peripheral protein bound to an integral protein

Figure 5-6 *Animation* **Membrane proteins**

Three transmembrane proteins are shown in **(a)**, **(b)**, and **(c)**. Water molecules and ions pass through specific types of protein pores in the membrane formed between groups of α-helices or through β-barrel structures formed as in **(c)**. Peripheral proteins are bound to integral proteins by noncovalent interactions **(d, e)**.
© Cengage Learning

proteins are firmly bound to the membrane. Cell biologists usually can release them only by disrupting the bilayer with detergents. These proteins are amphipathic. Their hydrophilic regions extend out of the cell or into the cytoplasm, whereas their hydrophobic regions interact with the fatty acid tails of the membrane phospholipids.

Some integral proteins do not extend all the way through the membrane. Many others, called **transmembrane proteins**, extend completely through the membrane. Some span the membrane only once, whereas others wind back and forth as many as 24 times. The most common kind of transmembrane region of a membrane protein is an α-helix (see Chapter 3) with hydrophobic amino acid side chains that project out from the helix into the hydrophobic region of the lipid bilayer. Some proteins span the membrane in the form of rolled-up β-pleated sheets. These protein formations are barrel-shaped and form pores through which water and other substances can pass.

Peripheral membrane proteins are not embedded in the lipid bilayer. They are located on the inner or outer surface of the plasma membrane, usually bound to exposed regions of integral proteins by noncovalent interactions. Peripheral proteins can be easily removed from the membrane without disrupting the structure of the bilayer.

One of the most remarkable demonstrations that proteins are actually embedded in the lipid bilayer comes from *freeze–fracture* electron microscopy, a technique that splits the membrane into halves. The researcher can literally see the two halves of the membrane from "inside out." When cell biologists examine membranes in this way, they observe numerous particles on the fracture faces (**FIG. 5-7**). The particles are clearly integral membrane proteins because researchers never see them in freeze–fractured artificial lipid bilayers. These findings profoundly influenced the development of the fluid mosaic model.

Proteins are oriented asymmetrically across the bilayer

Figure 5-4 shows that membrane protein molecules are *asymmetrically oriented*. A specific external domain of an intrinsic membrane protein is always found on the same side of the membrane. For example, domains with attached carbohydrate groups of plasma membrane proteins are only found on the external side of the membrane. This asymmetry is produced by the highly specific way in which each protein is inserted into the bilayer. Integral membrane proteins that will be associated with the cell's outer surface are manufactured like proteins destined to be exported from the cell.

As discussed in Chapter 4, proteins destined to be exported through the cell's outer surface are initially manufactured by ribosomes on the rough ER. They pass through the ER membrane into the ER lumen, where sugars are added, making them **glycoproteins.** For integral membrane proteins, only a part of each protein passes through the ER membrane, so each completed protein has some regions that are located in the ER lumen and other regions that remain in the cytosol. Because the enzymes that attach the sugars to certain amino acids of the

WHY IS IT USED? The freeze–fracture method is used to split the lipid bilayer apart so that its components can be analyzed.

HOW IS IT DONE?

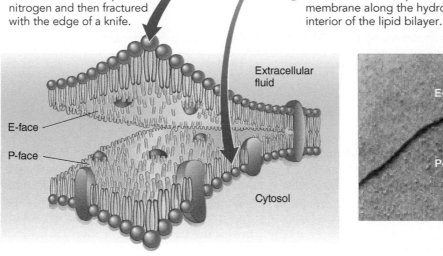

① Cells are frozen in liquid nitrogen and then fractured with the edge of a knife.

② The fracture often splits the membrane along the hydrophobic interior of the lipid bilayer.

③ Two complementary fracture faces result. The inner half-membrane presents the P-face (or protoplasmic face), and the outer half-membrane presents the E-face (or external face). Integral proteins, including transmembrane proteins, are inserted through the lipid bilayer.

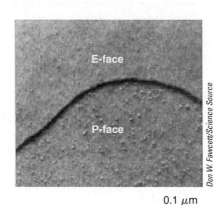

④ An electron microscope is used to view the interior surfaces (faces) of the two layers. In this TEM the particles (which appear as bumps) represent large integral proteins.

Figure 5-7 Freeze–fracture method

---

protein are found only in the ER lumen, carbohydrates can be added only to the parts of the membrane proteins that protrude into that compartment.

In **FIGURE 5-8** follow from top to bottom the vesicle budding and membrane fusion events that are part of the transport process. You can see that the same region of the protein that protruded into the ER lumen is also transported to the lumen of the Golgi complex. There additional enzymes further modify the carbohydrate chains. Within the Golgi complex, the glycoprotein is sorted and directed to the plasma membrane. The modified region of the protein remains inside the membrane compartment of a transport vesicle as it buds from the Golgi

complex. Note that when the transport vesicle fuses with the plasma membrane, the inside layer of the transport vesicle becomes the outside layer of the plasma membrane. The carbohydrate chain extends to the exterior of the cell surface.

In summary, here is the sequence:

sugars added to protein in ER lumen → glycoprotein transported to Golgi complex, where it is further modified → glycoprotein transported to plasma membrane → transport vesicle fuses with plasma membrane → inside layer of transport vesicle becomes outer layer of plasma membrane

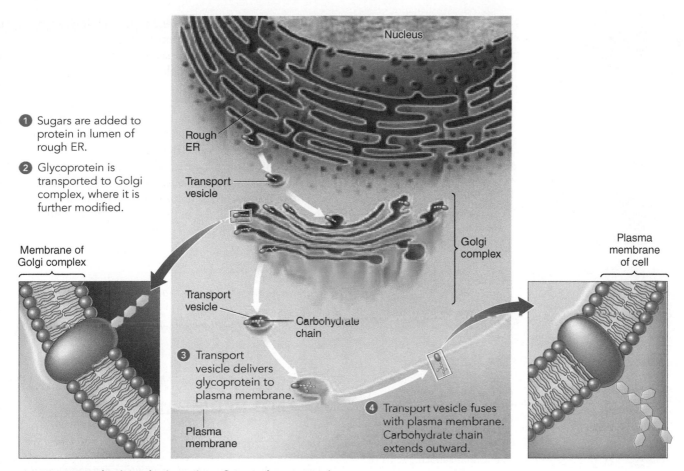

1 Sugars are added to protein in lumen of rough ER.

2 Glycoprotein is transported to Golgi complex, where it is further modified.

Nucleus

Rough ER

Transport vesicle

Golgi complex

Plasma membrane of cell

Membrane of Golgi complex

Transport vesicle

Carbohydrate chain

3 Transport vesicle delivers glycoprotein to plasma membrane.

Plasma membrane

4 Transport vesicle fuses with plasma membrane. Carbohydrate chain extends outward.

Figure 5-8 Synthesis and orientation of a membrane protein

The orientation of a protein in the plasma membrane is determined by the pathway of its synthesis and transport. The surface of the rough ER membrane that faces the lumen of the rough ER also faces the lumen of the Golgi complex and membrane transport vesicles. However, when a vesicle fuses with the plasma membrane, the inner surface of the vesicle becomes the extracellular surface of the plasma membrane.

© Cengage Learning

CHECKPOINT 5.1

- *What molecules are responsible for the physical properties of a cell membrane?*
- **VISUALIZE** *Draw a simple sketch illustrating how a transmembrane protein might be positioned in a lipid bilayer.*
- *What is the pathway used by cells to place carbohydrates on plasma membrane proteins?*

5.2 OVERVIEW OF MEMBRANE PROTEIN FUNCTIONS

LEARNING OBJECTIVE

5 Summarize the functions of membrane proteins.

Why does the plasma membrane require so many different proteins? This diversity reflects the multitude of activities that take place in or on the membrane. Proteins associated with the membrane are essential for most of these activities. Generally, plasma membrane proteins fall into several broad functional categories, as shown in **FIGURE 5-9**. Some membrane proteins anchor the cell to its substrate. For example, *integrins,* proteins bound to microfilaments inside the cell, attach the cell to the extracellular matrix (Fig. 5-9a). Integrins also serve as receptors, or docking sites, for proteins of the extracellular matrix (see Fig. 4-29).

Many membrane proteins are involved in the transport of molecules across the membrane. Some form channels that selectively allow the passage of specific ions or molecules (Fig. 5-9b). Other proteins are pumps that use ATP, or other energy sources, to actively transport solutes across the membrane (Fig. 5-9c).

Certain membrane proteins are enzymes that catalyze reactions near the cell surface (Fig. 5-9d). In mitochondrial or chloroplast membranes, enzymes that catalyze a series of reactions in cellular respiration or photosynthesis may be organized together in sequence to allow the organelle to efficiently regulate those reactions.

Some membrane proteins are receptors that receive information from other cells in the form of chemical or electrical signals. Most vertebrate cells have receptors for hormones released by endocrine glands. Information may be transmitted from

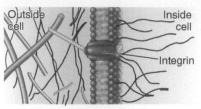

(a) Anchoring. Some membrane proteins, such as integrins, anchor the cell to the extracellular matrix; they also connect to microfilaments within the cell.

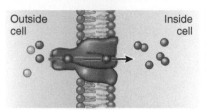

(b) Passive transport. Certain proteins form channels for selective passage of ions or molecules.

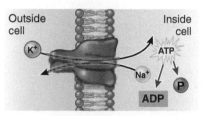

(c) Active transport. Some transport proteins pump solutes across the membrane, which requires a direct input of energy.

(d) Enzymatic activity. Many membrane-bound enzymes catalyze reactions that take place within or along the membrane surface.

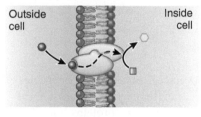

(e) Signal transduction. Some receptors bind with signal molecules such as hormones and transmit information into the cell.

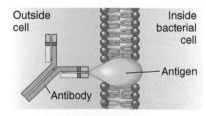

(f) Cell recognition. Some glycoproteins function as identification tags. For example, bacterial cells have surface proteins, or antigens, that human cells recognize as foreign.

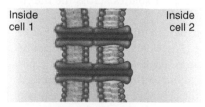

(g) Intercellular junction. Cell adhesion proteins attach membranes of adjacent cells.

Figure 5-9 Some functions of membrane proteins

Cell proteins perform many functions, including transporting materials, serving as enzymes for chemical reactions, and transmitting information.
© Cengage Learning

proteins in the plasma membrane to the cell interior by *signal transduction* (discussed in Chapter 6; Fig. 5-9e).

Some membrane proteins serve as identification tags that other cells recognize. For example, certain cells recognize the surface proteins, or *antigens,* of bacterial cells as foreign. Antigens stimulate immune defenses that destroy the bacteria (Fig. 5-9f).

When certain cells recognize one another, they connect to form tissues. Some membrane proteins form junctions between adjacent cells (Fig. 5-9g). These proteins may also serve as anchoring points for networks of cytoskeletal elements. In the remaining sections of this chapter, we will discuss the functions of cell membrane proteins in transporting material into and out of the cell, and we will discuss junctions between cells. We will discuss other functions of cell membranes in many of the chapters that follow.

CHECKPOINT 5.2

- *How do proteins function in transporting materials into the cell?*
- *What roles do membrane proteins play in cell interactions?*

5.3 CELL MEMBRANE STRUCTURE AND PERMEABILITY

LEARNING OBJECTIVE

6 Describe the importance of selectively permeable membranes and compare the functions of carrier proteins and channel proteins.

A membrane is *permeable* to a given substance if it allows that substance to pass through and impermeable if it does not. The fluid mosaic structure of biological membranes allows them to function as **selectively permeable membranes;** that is, they let some, but not all, substances pass through them. In response to varying environmental conditions or cell needs, a membrane may be a barrier to a particular substance at one time and actively promote its passage at another time. By regulating chemical traffic across its plasma membrane, a cell controls its volume and its internal ionic and molecular composition. This regulation allows the molecular composition of the cell to be quite different from that of its external environment.

Biological membranes present a barrier to polar molecules

In general, biological membranes are most permeable to small nonpolar (hydrophobic) molecules. Such molecules can pass through the hydrophobic lipid bilayer. Gases such as oxygen and carbon dioxide are small, nonpolar molecules that cross the lipid bilayer rapidly. Although they are polar, water molecules are small enough to pass through gaps that occur as a fatty acid chain momentarily moves out of the way. As a result, water molecules slowly cross the lipid bilayer.

The lipid bilayer of the plasma membrane is relatively impermeable to charged ions of any size, so ions and most large polar molecules pass through the bilayer slowly. Ions are important in cell signaling and many other physiological processes. For example, many cell processes, such as muscle contraction, depend on changes in the cytoplasmic concentration of calcium ions. Glucose, amino acids, and most other compounds required in metabolism are polar molecules that also pass through the lipid bilayer slowly. This property is advantageous to cells because the impermeability of the plasma membrane prevents them from diffusing out. How then do cells obtain the ions and polar molecules they require?

Transport proteins transfer molecules across membranes

Systems of *transport proteins* that move ions, amino acids, sugars, and other needed polar molecules through membranes apparently evolved very early in the origin of cells. These transmembrane proteins have been found in all biological membranes. Two main types of membrane transport proteins are carrier proteins and channel proteins. Each type of transport protein transports a specific type of ion or molecule or a group of related substances.

Carrier proteins, also called *transporters*, bind specific ions or molecules and undergo changes in shape, resulting in movement of the solute across the membrane. Transfer of solutes by carrier proteins located within the membrane is called **carrier-mediated transport.** As we will discuss, the two forms of carrier mediated transport—facilitated diffusion and carrier-mediated active transport—differ in their capabilities and energy sources.

ABC transporters make up a large, important group of carrier proteins. The acronym *ABC* stands for ATP-binding cassette. Found in the cell membranes of all species, ABC transporters use energy donated by ATP to transport certain ions, sugars, and polypeptides across cell membranes. Scientists have identified about 48 ABC transporters in human cells. Mutations in the genes encoding these proteins cause or contribute to many human disorders, including cystic fibrosis and certain neurological diseases. ABC transporters transport hydrophobic drugs out of the cell. This response can be a problem clinically because certain transporters remove antibiotics, antifungal drugs, and anticancer drugs.

Channel proteins form tunnels, called pores, through the membrane. Many of these channels are *gated,* which means that they can be opened and closed. Cells regulate the passage of materials through the channels by opening and closing the gates in response to electrical changes, chemical stimuli, or mechanical stimuli. Water and specific types of ions are transported through channels. There are numerous ion channels in every membrane of every cell.

Porins are transmembrane channel proteins that allow various solutes or water to pass through membranes. These channel proteins are rolled-up, barrel-shaped β-pleated sheets that form pores. Researchers Peter Agre of the Johns Hopkins School of Medicine in Baltimore, Maryland, and Roderick MacKinnon of the Howard Hughes Medical Institute at Rockefeller University in New York City shared the 2003 Nobel Prize in Chemistry for their work on transport proteins. Agre identified transmembrane proteins called **aquaporins** that function as gated water channels.

Aquaporins facilitate the rapid transport of water through the plasma membrane. About a billion water molecules per second can pass through an aquaporin! These channels are very selective and do not permit passage of ions and other small molecules. In some cells, such as those lining the kidney tubules of mammals, aquaporins respond to specific signals from hormones. Aquaporins help prevent dehydration by returning water from the kidney tubules into the blood.

CHECKPOINT 5.3

- *What types of molecules pass easily through the plasma membrane?*
- *What are the two main types of transport proteins? What are their functions?*
- *What are aquaporins? What is their function?*

5.4 PASSIVE TRANSPORT

LEARNING OBJECTIVES

7 Contrast simple diffusion with facilitated diffusion.

8 Define *osmosis* and solve simple problems involving osmosis; for example, predict whether cells will swell or shrink under various osmotic conditions.

Passive transport does not require the cell to expend metabolic energy. Many ions and small molecules move through membranes by *diffusion*. Two types of diffusion are simple diffusion and facilitated diffusion.

Diffusion occurs down a concentration gradient

Some substances pass into or out of cells and move about within cells by **diffusion,** a physical process based on random motion. All atoms and molecules possess kinetic energy, or energy of motion, at temperatures above absolute zero (0 K, $-273°C$, or $-459.4°F$). Matter may exist as a solid, liquid, or gas, depending on the freedom of movement of its constituent particles (atoms, ions, or molecules). The particles of a solid are closely packed, and the forces of attraction between them let them vibrate but not move around. In a liquid the particles are farther apart; the intermolecular attractions are weaker, and the particles move about with considerable freedom. In a gas the particles are so far apart that intermolecular forces are negligible; molecular movement is restricted only by the walls of the container that encloses the gas. Atoms and molecules in liquids and gases move in a kind of "random walk," changing directions as they collide.

① When lump of sugar is dropped into beaker of pure water, sugar molecules begin to dissolve and diffuse through water.

② Sugar molecules continue to dissolve and diffuse through water.

③ Eventually, sugar molecules become distributed randomly throughout water.

Figure 5-10 Diffusion
© Cengage Learning

Although the movement of individual particles is undirected and unpredictable, we can nevertheless make predictions about the behavior of groups of particles. If the particles are not evenly distributed, at least two regions exist: one with a higher concentration of particles and the other with a lower concentration. Such a difference in the concentration of a substance from one place to another establishes a **concentration gradient.**

In diffusion the random motion of particles results in their net movement "down" their own concentration gradient, from the region of higher concentration to the one of lower concentration. This motion does not mean that individual particles are prohibited from moving "against" the gradient. However, because there are initially more particles in the region of high concentration, it logically follows that more particles move randomly from there into the low-concentration region than the reverse (FIG. 5-10).

Thus, if a membrane is permeable to a substance, there is net movement from the side of the membrane where it is more highly concentrated to the side where it is less concentrated. Such a gradient across the membrane is a form of stored energy. Stored energy is *potential energy,* which is the capacity to do work as a result of position or state. The stored energy of the concentration gradient is released when ions or molecules move from a region of high concentration to one of low concentration. For this reason, movement down a concentration gradient is spontaneous. (Forms of energy and spontaneous processes are discussed in greater detail in Chapter 7.)

Diffusion occurs rapidly over very short distances. The rate of diffusion is determined by the movement of the particles, which in turn is a function of their size and shape, their electric charges, and the temperature. As the temperature rises, particles move faster, and the rate of diffusion increases.

Particles of different substances in a mixture diffuse independently of one another. Diffusion moves solutes toward a state of equilibrium. If particles are not added to or removed from the system, a state of **dynamic equilibrium** is reached. In this condition, the particles are uniformly distributed, and there is no net change in the system. Particles continue to move back and forth across the membrane, but they move at equal rates and in both directions.

In organisms equilibrium is rarely attained. For example, human cells continually produce carbon dioxide as sugars and other molecules are metabolized during aerobic respiration. Carbon dioxide readily diffuses across the plasma membrane but then is rapidly removed by the blood. This limits the opportunity for the molecules to re-enter the cell, so a sharp concentration gradient of carbon dioxide molecules always exists across the plasma membrane.

In **simple diffusion** through a biological membrane, small, nonpolar (uncharged) solute molecules move directly through the membrane down their concentration gradient. Oxygen and carbon dioxide can rapidly diffuse through the membrane. The rate of simple diffusion is directly related to the concentration of the solute; the more concentrated the solute, the more rapid the diffusion.

Osmosis is diffusion of water across a selectively permeable membrane

Osmosis is a special kind of diffusion that involves the net movement of water (the principal *solvent* in biological systems) through a selectively permeable membrane from a region of higher concentration of water to a region of lower concentration. Water molecules pass freely in both directions, but as in all types of diffusion, *net* movement is from the region where the water molecules are more concentrated to the region where they are less concentrated. Most *solute molecules* (such as sugar and salt) cannot diffuse freely through the selectively permeable membranes of the cell.

The principles involved in osmosis can be illustrated using an apparatus called a U-tube (FIG. 5-11). The U-tube is divided into two sections by a selectively permeable membrane that allows solvent (water) molecules to pass freely but excludes solute molecules. A water/solute solution is placed on one side, and pure water is placed on the other. The side containing the solute has a lower *effective water concentration* than the pure water side does. The reason is that the solute particles, which are charged (ionic) or polar, interact with the partial electric charges on the polar water molecules. Many of the water molecules are thus "bound up" and no longer free to diffuse across the membrane.

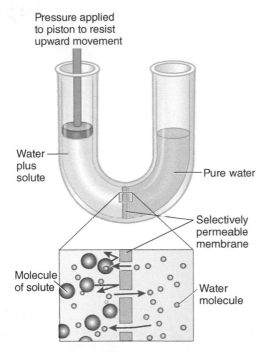

Pressure applied to piston to resist upward movement

Water plus solute

Pure water

Selectively permeable membrane

Molecule of solute

Water molecule

Figure 5-11 Animation Osmosis

The U-tube contains pure water on the right and water plus a solute on the left, separated by a selectively permeable membrane. Water molecules cross the membrane in both directions (*blue arrows*). Solute molecules cannot cross (*red arrows*). The fluid level would normally rise on the left and fall on the right because net movement of water would be to the left. However, the piston prevents the water from rising. The force that must be exerted by the piston to prevent the rise in fluid level is equal to the osmotic pressure of the solution.
© Cengage Learning

Because of the difference in effective water concentration, there is net movement of water molecules from the pure water side (with a high effective concentration of water) to the water/solute side (with a lower effective concentration of water). As a result, the fluid level drops on the pure water side and rises on the water/solute side. Because the solute molecules do not diffuse across the membrane, equilibrium is never attained. Net movement of water continues, and the fluid level rises on the side containing the solute. The weight of the rising column of fluid eventually exerts enough pressure to stop further changes in fluid levels, although water molecules continue to pass through the selectively permeable membrane in both directions.

We define the **osmotic pressure** of a solution as the pressure that must be exerted on the side of a selectively permeable membrane containing the higher concentration of solute to prevent the diffusion of water (by osmosis) from the side containing the lower solute concentration. In the U-tube example, you could measure the osmotic pressure by inserting a piston on the water/solute side of the tube and measuring how much pressure must be exerted by the piston to prevent the rise of fluid on that side of the tube. A solution with a high solute concentration has a low effective water

concentration and a high osmotic pressure; conversely, a solution with a low solute concentration has a high effective water concentration and a low osmotic pressure.

Two solutions may be isotonic Salts, sugars, and other substances are dissolved in the fluid compartment of every cell. These solutes give the cytosol a specific osmotic pressure. TABLE 5-1 summarizes the movement of water into and out of a solution (or cell) depending on relative solute concentrations.

When a cell is placed in a fluid with exactly the same osmotic pressure, no net movement of water molecules occurs, either into or out of the cell. The cell neither swells nor shrinks. Such a fluid is of equal solute concentration, or **isotonic,** to the fluid within the cell. Normally, your blood plasma (the fluid component of blood) and all your other body fluids are isotonic to your cells; they contain a concentration of water equal to that in the cells. A solution of 0.9% sodium chloride (sometimes called *physiological saline*) is isotonic to the cells of humans and other mammals. Human red blood cells placed in 0.9% sodium chloride neither shrink nor swell (FIG. 5-12a).

One solution may be hypertonic and the other hypotonic If the surrounding fluid has a concentration of dissolved substances greater than the concentration within the cell, the fluid has a higher osmotic pressure than the cell and is said to be **hypertonic** to the cell. Because a hypertonic solution has a lower effective water concentration, a cell placed in such a solution shrinks as it loses water by osmosis. Human red blood cells placed in a solution of 1.3% sodium chloride shrivel (FIG. 5-12b).

If the surrounding fluid contains a lower concentration of dissolved materials than does the cell, the fluid has a lower osmotic pressure and is said to be **hypotonic** to the cell; water then enters the cell and causes it to swell. Red blood cells placed in a solution of 0.6% sodium chloride gain water, swell (FIG. 5-12c), and may eventually burst. Many cells that normally live in hypotonic environments have adaptations to prevent excessive water accumulation. For example, *Paramecium* and certain other ciliates (members of the supergroup Chromalveolates) have contractile vacuoles that expel excess water (see Fig. 26-8).

Turgor pressure is the internal hydrostatic pressure usually present in walled cells The cells of most prokaryotes, algae, plants, and fungi have relatively rigid cell walls. These cells can withstand, without bursting, an external medium that is very dilute, containing only a very low concentration of solutes. Because of the substances dissolved in the cytoplasm, the cells are hypertonic to the outside medium (conversely, the

TABLE 5-1	Osmotic Terminology		
SOLUTE CONCENTRATION IN SOLUTION A	SOLUTE CONCENTRATION IN SOLUTION B	TONICITY	DIRECTION OF NET MOVEMENT OF WATER
Greater	Less	A hypertonic to B; B hypotonic to A	B to A
Less	Greater	B hypertonic to A; A hypotonic to B	A to B
Equal	Equal	A and B are isotonic to each other	No net movement

© Cengage Learning

outside medium is hypotonic to the cytoplasm).

Water moves into the cells by osmosis, filling their central vacuoles and distending the cells. The cells swell, building up **turgor pressure** against the rigid cell walls (FIG. 5-13a). The cell walls stretch only slightly, and a steady state is reached when their resistance to stretching prevents any further increase in cell size and thereby halts the *net movement* of water molecules into the cells. (Of course, molecules continue to move back and forth across the plasma membrane.) Turgor pressure in the cells is an important factor in supporting the body of nonwoody plants.

If a cell that has a cell wall is placed in a hypertonic medium, the cell loses water to its surroundings. Its contents shrink, and the plasma membrane separates from the cell wall, a process known as **plasmolysis** (FIGS. 5-13b and 5-13c). Plasmolysis occurs in plants when the soil or water around them contains high concentrations of salts or fertilizers. It also explains why lettuce becomes limp in a salty salad dressing and why a picked flower wilts from lack of water.

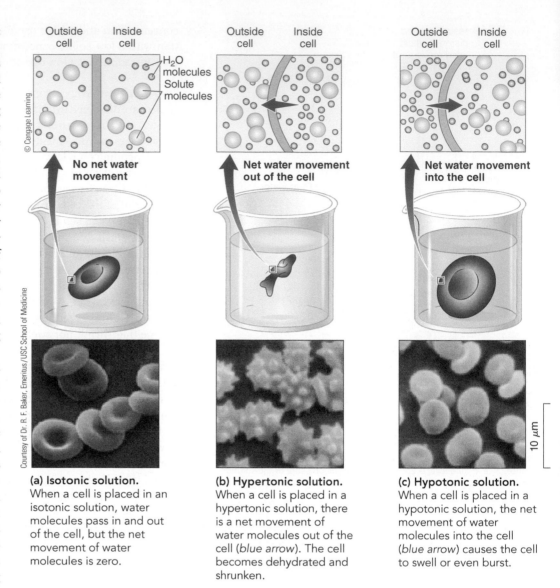

(a) **Isotonic solution.** When a cell is placed in an isotonic solution, water molecules pass in and out of the cell, but the net movement of water molecules is zero.

(b) **Hypertonic solution.** When a cell is placed in a hypertonic solution, there is a net movement of water molecules out of the cell (*blue arrow*). The cell becomes dehydrated and shrunken.

(c) **Hypotonic solution.** When a cell is placed in a hypotonic solution, the net movement of water molecules into the cell (*blue arrow*) causes the cell to swell or even burst.

Figure 5-12 *Animation* **The responses of animal cells to osmotic pressure differences**

Facilitated diffusion occurs down a concentration gradient

In all processes in which substances move across membranes by diffusion, the net transfer of those molecules from one side to the other occurs as a result of a concentration gradient. We have seen that small, uncharged (nonpolar) solute molecules, such as oxygen and carbon dioxide, move directly through the membrane down their concentration gradient by simple diffusion. In **facilitated diffusion,** a specific transport protein makes the membrane permeable to a particular solute, such as a specific ion or polar molecule. A specific solute can be transported from inside the cell to the outside or from the outside to the inside, but net movement is always from a region of higher solute concentration to a region of lower concentration. Channel proteins and carrier proteins facilitate diffusion by different mechanisms.

Channel proteins form hydrophilic channels through membranes Most channel proteins form narrow channels that transport specific ions down their gradients (FIG. 5-14). (As we will discuss, because ions are charged particles, these gradients are electrochemical gradients.) These *ion channels* are referred to as *gated channels* because they can open and close. As many as 100 million ions per second can pass through an open ion channel! Channels can facilitate transport only down a concentration gradient. They cannot actively transport ions from a region of lower concentration to a region of higher concentration.

Carrier proteins undergo a change in shape Transport of solutes through carrier proteins is slower than through channel proteins. The carrier protein binds with one or more solute molecules on one side of the membrane. The protein then undergoes a conformational change (change in shape) that moves the solute to the other side of the membrane.

As an example of facilitated diffusion by a carrier protein, let us consider glucose transport. A carrier protein known as *glucose transporter 1,* or *GLUT 1,* transports glucose into red blood cells (FIG. 5-15). Each red blood cell has approximately

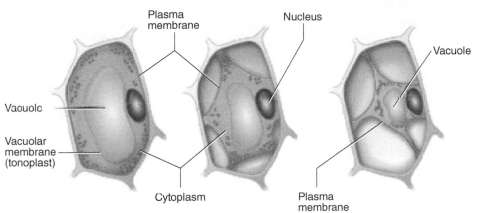

(a) In hypotonic surroundings, the vacuole of a plant cell fills with water, but the rigid cell walls prevent the cell from expanding. The cells of this healthy plant are turgid.

(b) When the plant is exposed to a hypertonic solution, its cells become plasmolyzed as they lose water.

(c) The plant wilts and eventually dies.

Figure 5-13 *Animation* **Turgor pressure and plasmolysis**
© Cengage Learning

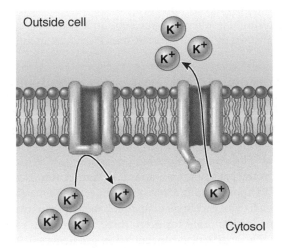

Figure 5-14 Facilitated diffusion of potassium ions

In response to an electrical stimulus, the gate of the potassium ion channel opens, allowing potassium to diffuse out of the cell.
© Cengage Learning

200,000 GLUT 1 transporters in its plasma membrane. The concentration of glucose is higher in the blood plasma than in red blood cells, so glucose diffuses down its concentration gradient into these blood cells. The GLUT 1 transporter facilitates glucose diffusion, allowing glucose to enter the cell about 50,000 times as rapidly as it could by simple diffusion.

Red blood cells keep the internal concentration of glucose low by immediately adding a phosphate group to entering glucose molecules, converting them to highly charged glucose phosphates that cannot pass back through the membrane. Because glucose phosphate is a different molecule, it does not contribute to the glucose concentration gradient. Thus, a steep concentration gradient for glucose is continually maintained, and glucose rapidly diffuses into the cell, only to be immediately changed to the phosphorylated form. Facilitated diffusion is powered by the concentration gradient.

Researchers have studied facilitated diffusion of glucose using *liposomes,* artificial vesicles enclosed by phospholipid bilayers. The phospholipid membrane of a liposome does not allow the passage of glucose unless a glucose transporter has been incorporated into the liposome membrane. Glucose transporters and similar carrier proteins temporarily bind to the molecules they transport. This mechanism appears to be similar to the way an enzyme binds with its substrate, the molecule on which it acts (discussed in Chapter 7). In addition, as in enzyme action, binding apparently changes the shape of the carrier protein. This change allows the glucose molecule to be released on the inside of the cell. According to this model, when the glucose is released into the cytoplasm, the carrier protein reverts to its original shape and is available to bind another glucose molecule on the outside of the cell.

Because carrier proteins bind to their substrate and undergo changes in shape, they operate at a defined maximum rate, which ranges from about 100 to 10,000 ions (or molecules) per second. Unlike channel proteins, carrier proteins become saturated when there is a high concentration of the molecule being transported because each cell has a finite number of each type of carrier protein. When the concentration of solute molecules to be transported reaches a certain level, all the carrier proteins are working at their maximum rate.

It is a common misconception that diffusion, whether simple or facilitated, is somehow "free of cost" and that only active transport mechanisms require energy. Because diffusion always

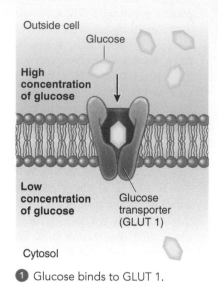 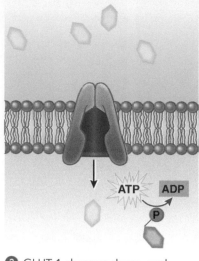 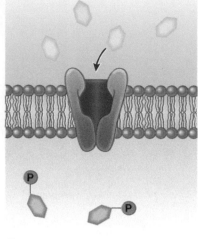

1 Glucose binds to GLUT 1.

2 GLUT 1 changes shape, and glucose is released inside cell. Internalized glucose is rapidly phosphorylated by ATP.

3 GLUT 1 returns to its original shape. Phosphorylation of internalized glucose molecules maintains a large concentration gradient across the plasma membrane.

Figure 5-15 *Animation* **Facilitated diffusion of glucose molecules**
Facilitated diffusion requires the potential energy of a concentration gradient.
© Cengage Learning

involves the net movement of a substance down its concentration gradient, we say that the concentration gradient "powers" the process. However, energy is required to do the work of establishing and maintaining the gradient. In our example of facilitated diffusion of glucose, the cell maintains a steep concentration gradient (high outside, low inside) by phosphorylating the glucose molecules once they enter the cell. One ATP molecule is spent for every glucose molecule phosphorylated, and there are additional costs, such as the energy required to make the enzymes that carry out the reaction.

CHECKPOINT 5.4

- **PREDICT** *What would happen if a plant cell were placed in an isotonic solution? a hypertonic environment? a hypotonic environment? How would you modify your predictions for an animal cell?*

- *What is the immediate source of energy for simple diffusion? for facilitated diffusion?*

- *In what direction is there a net movement of particles along their concentration gradient? Would your answers be different for facilitated diffusion compared with simple diffusion?*

5.5 ACTIVE TRANSPORT

LEARNING OBJECTIVE

9 Describe active transport, including cotransport.

Although adequate amounts of a few substances move across cell membranes by diffusion, cells must actively transport many solutes *against* a concentration gradient. The reason is that cells require many substances in higher concentrations than their concentration outside the cell.

Both diffusion and active transport require energy. The energy for diffusion is provided by a concentration gradient for the substance being transported. Active transport requires the cell to expend metabolic energy directly to power the process.

An **active transport** system can pump materials from a region of low concentration to a region of high concentration. The energy stored in the concentration gradient not only is unavailable to the system but actually works against it. For this reason, the cell needs some other source of energy. In many cases, cells use ATP energy directly. However, active transport may be coupled to ATP indirectly. In indirect active transport, a concentration gradient for one substance provides energy for the cotransport of some other substance, such as an ion.

Active transport systems "pump" substances against their concentration gradients

One of the most striking examples of an active transport mechanism is the **sodium–potassium pump** found in all animal cells (**FIG. 5-16**). The pump is an ABC transporter, a specific carrier protein in the plasma membrane. This transporter uses energy from ATP to pump sodium ions out of the cell and potassium ions into the cell. The exchange is unequal: usually only two potassium ions are imported for every three sodium ions exported. Because these particular concentration gradients involve ions, an electrical potential (separation of electric charges) is generated across the membrane; that is, the membrane is *polarized*.

Both sodium and potassium ions are positively charged, but because there are fewer potassium ions inside relative to the

The sodium–potassium pump is a carrier protein that maintains an electrochemical gradient across the plasma membrane.

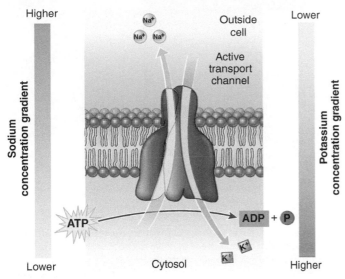

(a) The sodium–potassium pump is a carrier protein that requires energy from ATP. In each complete pumping cycle, the energy of one molecule of ATP is used to export three sodium ions (Na^+) and import two potassium ions (K^+).

Figure 5-16 A model for the pumping cycle of the sodium–potassium pump

PREDICT What would be the effect on the membrane's electrochemical gradient if the Na^+/K^+ pump moved an equal number of Na^+ and K^+ ions in each pump cycle? Would this produce an electrical gradient? Would this produce an ion (or chemical) gradient?

© Cengage Learning

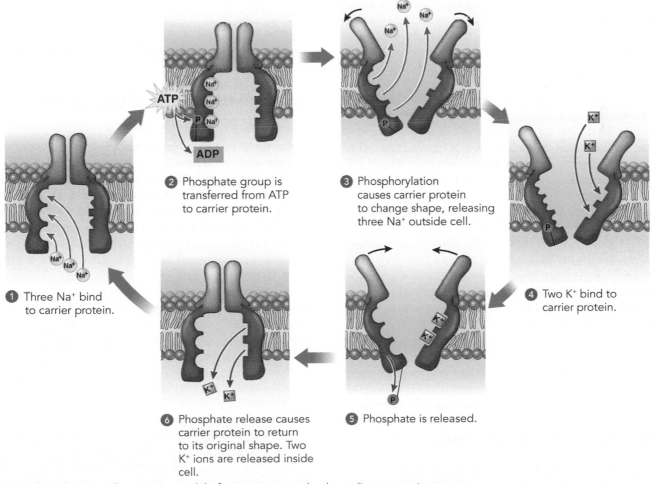

❶ Three Na^+ bind to carrier protein.

❷ Phosphate group is transferred from ATP to carrier protein.

❸ Phosphorylation causes carrier protein to change shape, releasing three Na^+ outside cell.

❹ Two K^+ bind to carrier protein.

❺ Phosphate is released.

❻ Phosphate release causes carrier protein to return to its original shape. Two K^+ ions are released inside cell.

(b) Follow the steps illustrating a model of active transport by the sodium–potassium pump.

sodium ions outside, the inside of the cell is negatively charged relative to the outside. The unequal distribution of ions establishes an *electrical gradient* that drives ions across the plasma membrane. Sodium–potassium pumps help maintain a separation of charges across the plasma membrane. This separation is called a **membrane potential.** Because there is both an electric charge difference and a concentration difference on the two sides of the membrane, the gradient is called an **electrochemical gradient.** Such gradients store energy that is used to drive other transport systems. So important is the electrochemical gradient produced by these pumps that some cells (such as nerve cells) expend more than 25% of their total available energy just to power this one transport system.

Sodium–potassium pumps (as well as all other ATP-driven pumps) are transmembrane proteins that extend entirely through the membrane. By undergoing a series of conformational changes, the pumps exchange sodium for potassium across the plasma membrane. Unlike what occurs in facilitated diffusion, at least one of the conformational changes in the pump cycle requires energy, which is provided by ATP. The shape of the pump protein changes as a phosphate group from ATP first binds to it and is subsequently removed later in the pump cycle.

The use of electrochemical membrane potentials for energy storage is not confined to the plasma membranes of animal cells. Cells of bacteria, fungi, and plants use carrier proteins, known as proton pumps, to actively transport hydrogen ions (which are protons) out of the cell. These ATP-driven membrane pumps transfer protons from the cytosol to the outside (FIG. 5-17). Removal of positively charged protons from the cytoplasm of these cells results in a large difference in the concentration of protons between the outside and inside of the cell. The outside of the cells is positively charged relative to the inside of the plasma membrane. The energy stored in these electrochemical gradients can be used to do many kinds of cell work.

Other proton pumps are used in "reverse" to synthesize ATP. Bacteria, mitochondria, and chloroplasts use energy from food or sunlight to establish proton concentration gradients (discussed in Chapters 8 and 9). When the protons diffuse through the proton carriers from a region of high proton concentration to one of low concentration, ATP is synthesized. These electrochemical gradients form the basis for the major energy conversion systems in virtually all cells.

Ion pumps have other important roles. For example, they are instrumental in the ability of an animal cell to equalize the osmotic pressures of its cytoplasm and its external environment. If an animal cell does not control its internal osmotic pressure, its contents become hypertonic relative to the exterior. Water enters by osmosis, causing the cell to swell and possibly burst (see Fig. 5-12c). By controlling the ion distribution across the membrane, the cell indirectly controls the movement of water, because when ions are pumped out of the cell, water leaves by osmosis.

Carrier proteins can transport one or two solutes

You may have noticed that some carrier proteins, such as proton pumps, transport one type of substance in one direction. These

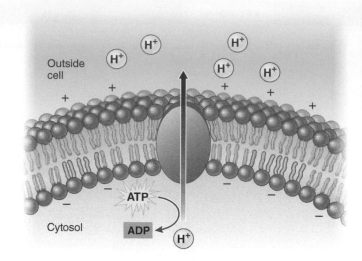

Figure 5-17 A model of a proton pump
Proton pumps use the energy of ATP to transport protons (hydrogen ions) across membranes. The energy of the electrochemical gradient established can then be used for other processes.
© Cengage Learning

carrier proteins are called **uniporters.** Other carrier proteins, **symporters,** move two types of substances in one direction. For example, a specific carrier protein transports both sodium and glucose into the cell. Still other carrier proteins, **antiporters,** move two substances in opposite directions. Sodium–potassium pumps are antiporters that transport sodium ions out of the cell and potassium ions into the cell. Both symporters and antiporters cotransport solutes.

Cotransport systems indirectly provide energy for active transport

A **cotransport** system moves solutes across a membrane by *indirect active transport.* Two solutes are transported at the same time. The movement of one solute down its concentration gradient provides energy for transport of some other solute up its concentration gradient. However, an energy source such as ATP is required to power the pump that produces the concentration gradient.

Sodium–potassium pumps (and other pumps) generate electrochemical concentration gradients. Sodium is pumped out of the cell and then diffuses back in by moving down its concentration gradient. This process generates sufficient energy to power the active transport of other essential substances. In these systems, a carrier protein *cotransports* a solute *against* its concentration gradient while sodium, potassium, or hydrogen ions move *down* their gradient. Energy from ATP produces the ion gradient. Then the energy of this gradient drives the active transport of a required substance, such as glucose, against its gradient.

We have seen how glucose can be moved into the cell by facilitated diffusion. Glucose can also be cotransported into the cell. The sodium concentration inside the cell is kept low by the ATP-requiring sodium–potassium pumps that actively transport sodium ions out of the cell. In glucose cotransport, a carrier protein transports both sodium and glucose (FIG. 5-18).

A carrier protein transports sodium ions down their concentration gradient and uses that energy to cotransport glucose molecules against their concentration gradient.

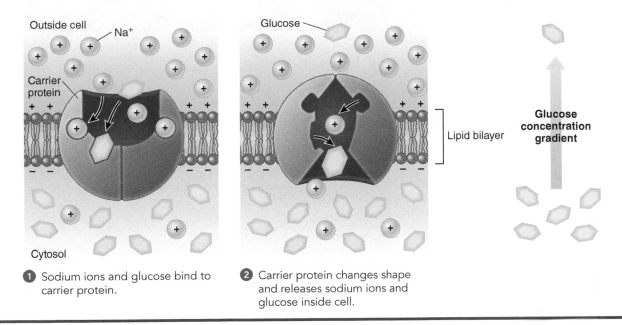

① Sodium ions and glucose bind to carrier protein.

② Carrier protein changes shape and releases sodium ions and glucose inside cell.

Figure 5-18 A model for the cotransport of glucose and sodium ions

This carrier protein is a symporter.

PREDICT What would be the effect on glucose transport through this system if the cell in the figure were treated with a drug that inhibited the Na⁺/K⁺ pump?

© Cengage Learning

As sodium moves into the cell along its concentration gradient, the carrier protein captures the energy released and uses it to transport glucose into the cell. Thus, this indirect active transport system for glucose is "driven" by the cotransport of sodium.

CHECKPOINT 5.5

- *What is the immediate energy source for active transport?*
- *What is the immediate energy source for cotransport?*

5.6 EXOCYTOSIS AND ENDOCYTOSIS

LEARNING OBJECTIVE

10 Compare exocytotic and endocytotic transport mechanisms.

Individual molecules and ions pass through the plasma membrane by simple and facilitated diffusion and by carrier-mediated active transport. Some larger materials, such as large molecules, particles of food, and even small cells, are also moved into or out of cells. They are transported by exocytosis and endocytosis. Like active transport, these processes require cells to expend energy directly.

In exocytosis, vesicles export large molecules

In **exocytosis,** a cell ejects waste products, or specific products of secretion such as hormones, by the fusion of a vesicle with the plasma membrane (FIG. 5-19). As the contents of the vesicle are released from the cell, the membrane of the secretory vesicle is incorporated into the plasma membrane. This process is the primary mechanism by which plasma membranes grow larger.

In endocytosis, the cell imports materials

In **endocytosis,** materials are taken into the cell. Several types of endocytotic mechanisms operate in biological systems, including phagocytosis, pinocytosis, and receptor-mediated endocytosis.

In **phagocytosis** (literally, "cell eating"), the cell ingests large solid particles such as food or bacteria (FIG. 5-20). Certain protists ingest food by phagocytosis. Some types of vertebrate cells, including certain white blood cells, ingest bacteria and other particles by phagocytosis. During ingestion, folds of the plasma membrane enclose the cell or particle. When the membrane has encircled the particle, the membrane fuses at the point of contact, forming a vacuole. The vacuole may then fuse with lysosomes, which degrade the ingested material.

In **pinocytosis** ("cell drinking"), the cell takes in dissolved materials (FIG. 5-21). Tiny droplets of fluid are trapped by folds in the plasma membrane, which pinch off into the cytosol as tiny

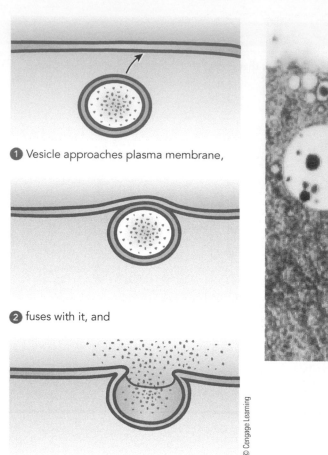

1 Vesicle approaches plasma membrane,

2 fuses with it, and

3 releases its contents outside cell.

© Cengage Learning

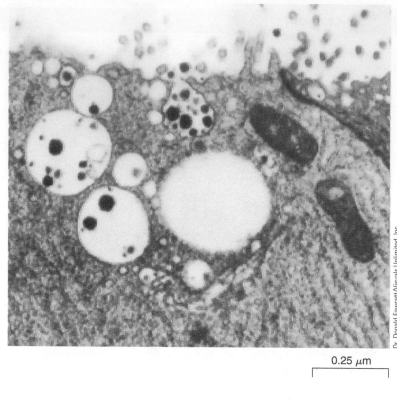

Dr. Donald Fawcett/Visuals Unlimited, Inc.

0.25 μm

Figure 5-19 Exocytosis

The TEM shows exocytosis of the protein components of milk by a mammary gland cell.

vesicles. As the liquid contents of these vesicles are slowly transferred into the cytosol, the vesicles become progressively smaller.

In a third type of endocytosis, **receptor-mediated endocytosis,** specific molecules combine with receptor proteins in the plasma membrane. Receptor-mediated endocytosis is the main mechanism by which eukaryotic cells take in macromolecules. As an example, let us look at how mammalian cells take up cholesterol from the blood. Cells use cholesterol as a component of cell membranes and as a precursor of steroid hormones. Cholesterol is transported in the blood as part of particles called *low-density lipoproteins* (*LDLs;* popularly known as "bad cholesterol").

Much of the receptor-mediated endocytosis pathway was detailed through studies at the University of Texas Health Science Center by Michael Brown and Joseph Goldstein on the LDL receptor. These researchers were awarded the Nobel Prize in Physiology or Medicine in 1985 for their pioneering work. Their findings have important medical implications because cholesterol that remains in the blood instead of entering the cells can be deposited in the artery walls, which increases the risk of cardiovascular disease.

When it needs cholesterol, the cell makes LDL receptors. The receptors are concentrated in *coated pits,* depressed regions on the cytoplasmic surface of the plasma membrane. Each pit is coated by a layer of a protein, called *clathrin,* found just below the plasma membrane. A molecule that binds specifically to a receptor is called a **ligand.** In this case, LDL is the ligand. After the LDL binds with a receptor, the coated pit forms a *coated vesicle* by endocytosis.

FIGURE 5-22 shows the uptake of an LDL particle. Seconds after the vesicle moves into the cytoplasm, the coating dissociates from it, leaving an uncoated vesicle. The vesicles fuse with small compartments called *endosomes.* The LDL and LDL receptors separate, and the receptors are transported to the plasma membrane, where they are recycled. LDL is transferred to a lysosome, where it is broken down. Cholesterol is released into the cytosol for use by the cell. A simplified summary of receptor-mediated endocytosis follows:

ligand molecules bind to receptors in coated pits of plasma membrane → coated vesicle forms by endocytosis → coating detaches from vesicle → uncoated vesicle fuses with endosome → ligands separate from receptors, which are recycled; endosome fuses with primary lysosome, forming secondary lysosome → contents of secondary lysosome are digested and released into the cytosol

The recycling of LDL receptors to the plasma membrane through vesicles causes a problem common to all cells that use endocytotic and exocytotic mechanisms: the plasma membrane changes size as the vesicles bud off from it or fuse with it. A type of phagocytic cell known as a *macrophage,* for example, ingests the equivalent of its entire plasma membrane in about 30 minutes, requiring an equivalent amount of recycling or new membrane synthesis for the cell to maintain its surface area. On the other hand, cells that are constantly

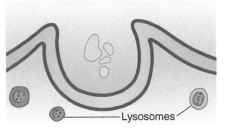

① Folds of plasma membrane surround particle to be ingested, forming small vacuole around it.

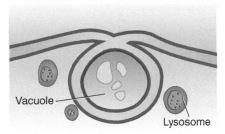

② Vacuole then pinches off inside cell.

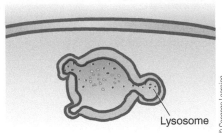

③ Lysosomes fuse with vacuole and pour potent hydrolytic enzymes onto ingested material.

© Cengage Learning

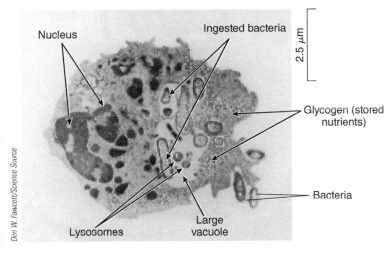

Den W. Fawcett/Science Source

Figure 5-20 *Animation* **Phagocytosis**

In this type of endocytosis, a cell ingests relatively large solid particles. The white blood cell (a neutrophil) shown in the TEM is phagocytizing bacteria. The vacuoles contain bacteria that have already been ingested. Lysosomes contain digestive enzymes that break down the ingested material. Other bacteria are visible outside the cell.

involved in secretion must return an equivalent amount of membrane to the interior of the cell for each vesicle that fuses with the plasma membrane; if not, the cell surface would continue to expand even though the growth of the cell itself may be arrested.

CHECKPOINT 5.6

- *In what ways are exocytosis and endocytosis similar?*
- *How are the processes of phagocytosis and pinocytosis different?*
- *What is the sequence of events in receptor-mediated endocytosis?*

5.7 CELL JUNCTIONS

LEARNING OBJECTIVE

11 Compare the structures and functions of anchoring junctions, tight junctions, gap junctions, and plasmodesmata.

Cells in close contact with one another typically develop specialized intercellular junctions. These structures may allow neighboring cells to form strong connections with one another, prevent the passage of materials, or establish rapid communication between adjacent cells. Several types of junctions connect animal cells, including anchoring junctions, tight junctions, and gap junctions. Plant cells are connected by plasmodesmata.

Anchoring junctions connect cells of an epithelial sheet

Adjacent epithelial cells, such as those found in the outer layer of the mammalian skin, are so tightly bound to each other by *anchoring junctions* that strong mechanical forces are required to separate them. These junctions do not prevent the passage of materials between adjacent cells. Two common types of anchoring junctions are desmosomes and adhering junctions.

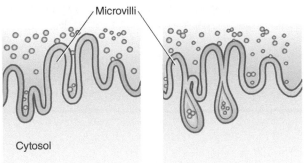

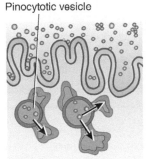

① Tiny droplets of fluid are trapped by folds of plasma membrane.

② These pinch off into cytosol as small fluid-filled vesicles.

③ Contents of these vesicles are then slowly transferred to cytosol.

Figure 5-21 Pinocytosis, or "cell drinking"
© Cengage Learning

In receptor-mediated endocytosis, specific macromolecules bind to receptor proteins, accumulate in coated pits, and enter the cell in clathrin-coated vesicles.

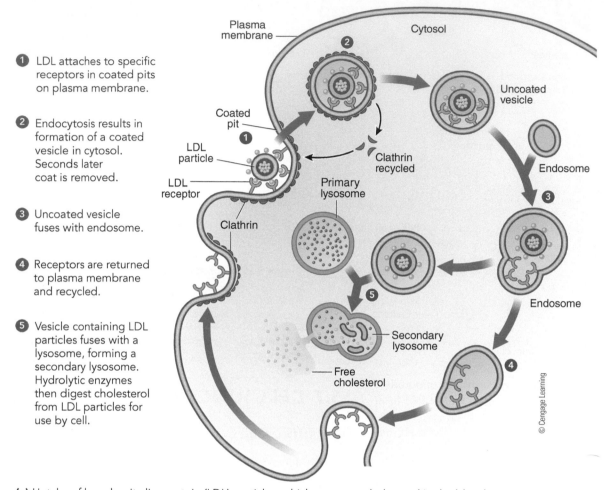

1. LDL attaches to specific receptors in coated pits on plasma membrane.

2. Endocytosis results in formation of a coated vesicle in cytosol. Seconds later coat is removed.

3. Uncoated vesicle fuses with endosome.

4. Receptors are returned to plasma membrane and recycled.

5. Vesicle containing LDL particles fuses with a lysosome, forming a secondary lysosome. Hydrolytic enzymes then digest cholesterol from LDL particles for use by cell.

(a) Uptake of low-density lipoprotein (LDL) particles, which transport cholesterol in the blood.

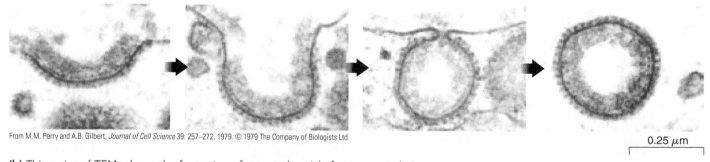

From M.M. Perry and A.B. Gilbert, *Journal of Cell Science* 39: 257–272, 1979. © 1979 The Company of Biologists Ltd.

0.25 μm

(b) This series of TEMs shows the formation of a coated vesicle from a coated pit.

Figure 5-22 Receptor-mediated endocytosis

PREDICT In some humans, the membrane-spanning region of the LDL receptor protein is missing. How would that affect the ability of the cell to take up needed cholesterol? What would be the effect on cholesterol levels in the bloodstream?

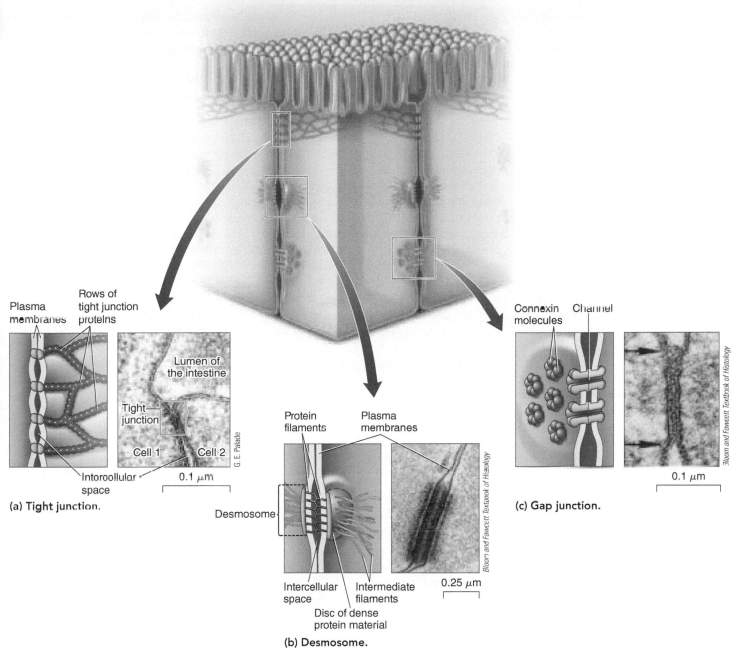

Plasma membranes

Rows of tight junction proteins

Lumen of the intestine

Tight junction

Cell 1 Cell 2

Intercellular space

0.1 μm

G. E. Palade

(a) Tight junction.

Protein filaments **Plasma membranes**

Desmosome

Intercellular space **Intermediate filaments**

Disc of dense protein material

0.25 μm

Bloom and Fawcett Textbook of Histology

(b) Desmosome.

Connexin molecules **Channel**

0.1 μm

Bloom and Fawcett Textbook of Histology

(c) Gap junction.

Figure 5-23 *Animation* **Cellular junctions are protein complexes that join sections of membranes between adjacent cells.**

Not all three types of junctions depicted in this composite drawing would be present between the same two cells. **(a) Tight junctions prevent the passage of materials through spaces between cells. (b) Desmosomes anchor cells together in strong sheets.** The dense structure in the TEM is a desmosome. Each desmosome consists of a pair of buttonlike discs associated with the plasma membranes of adjacent cells plus the intercellular protein filaments that connect them. Intermediate filaments in the cells are attached to the discs and to other desmosomes that connect other adjoining cells. **(c) Gap junctions allow the transfer of small molecules and ions between adjacent cells.** The model of a gap junction shown above is based on electron microscopic and X-ray diffraction data.

Desmosomes are points of attachment between cells (FIG. 5-23b). They hold cells together at one point as a rivet or a spot weld does. Desmosomes allow cells to form strong sheets, and substances still pass freely through the spaces between the plasma membranes. Each desmosome is made up of regions of dense material associated with the cytosolic sides of the two plasma membranes, plus protein filaments that cross the narrow intercellular space between them. Desmosomes are anchored to systems of intermediate filaments inside the cells. Thus, the intermediate filament networks of adjacent cells are connected. As a result, mechanical stresses are distributed throughout the tissue.

Adhering junctions cement cells together. **Cadherins,** transmembrane proteins that are components of these junctions, form a continuous adhesion belt around each cell, binding the cell to neighboring cells. These junctions connect to microfilaments of the cytoskeleton. The cadherins of adhering junctions are a potential path for signals from the outside environment to be transmitted to the cytoplasm.

Tight junctions seal off intercellular spaces between some animal cells

Tight junctions are literally areas of tight connections between the membranes of adjacent cells. These connections are so tight that no space remains between the cells and substances cannot leak between them. TEMs of tight junctions show that in the region of the junction the plasma membranes of the two cells are held together by proteins in actual contact with each other. However, as shown in FIGURE 5-23a, tight junctions are located intermittently. The plasma membranes of the two cells are not fused over their entire surface.

Cells connected by tight junctions seal off body cavities. For example, tight junctions between cells lining the intestine prevent substances in the intestine from passing between the cells and directly entering the blood. The sheet of cells thus acts as a selective barrier. Food substances must be transported across the plasma membranes and *through* the intestinal cells before they enter the blood. This arrangement helps prevent toxins and other unwanted materials from entering the blood and also prevents nutrients from leaking out of the intestine. Tight junctions are also present between the cells that line capillaries in the brain. They form the *blood–brain barrier*, which prevents many substances in the blood from passing into the brain.

Gap junctions allow the transfer of small molecules and ions

A **gap junction** is like a desmosome in that it bridges the space between cells; however, the space it spans is somewhat narrower (FIG. 5-23c). Gap junctions also differ in that they are communicating junctions. They not only connect the plasma membranes but also contain channels connecting the cytoplasm of adjacent cells.

Gap junctions are composed of *connexin,* an integral membrane protein. Groups of six connexin molecules cluster to form a cylinder that spans the plasma membrane. The connexin cylinders on adjacent cells become tightly joined. The two cylinders form a channel about 1.5 nm in diameter. Small inorganic particles (such as ions) and some regulatory molecules (such as cyclic AMP, which is illustrated in Figure 3-26) pass through the channels, but larger molecules are excluded. When a marker substance is injected into one of a group of cells connected by gap junctions, the marker passes rapidly into the adjacent cells but does not enter the space between the cells.

Gap junctions provide for rapid chemical and electrical communication between cells. Cells control the passage of materials through gap junctions by opening and closing the channels. Cells in the pancreas, for example, are linked by gap junctions in such a way that if one of a group of cells is stimulated to secrete insulin, the signal is passed through the junctions to the other cells in the cluster. This mechanism ensures a coordinated response to the initial signal. Gap junctions allow

some nerve cells to be electrically coupled. Cardiac muscle cells are linked by gap junctions that permit the flow of ions necessary to synchronize contractions of the heart.

Plasmodesmata allow certain molecules and ions to move between plant cells

Because plant cells have walls, they do not need desmosomes for strength. Plant cells have connections that are functionally equivalent to the gap junctions of some animal cells. **Plasmodesmata** (sing., *plasmodesma*) are channels 20 to 40 nm wide that pass through the cell walls of adjacent plant cells, connecting the cytoplasm of neighboring cells (FIG. 5-24). The plasma membranes of adjacent cells are continuous with one another through the plasmodesmata. Most plasmodesmata contain a narrow cylindrical structure, called the *desmotubule,* which runs through the channel and connects the smooth ER of the two adjacent cells.

Plasmodesmata generally allow molecules and ions, but not organelles, to pass through the openings from cell to cell. The movement of ions through the plasmodesmata allows for a very slow type of electrical signaling in plants. Whereas the channels of gap junctions have a fixed diameter, plant cells can dilate the plasmodesmata channels. Certain proteins and RNA can pass through plasmodesmata. Some plant viruses spread infection by passing through these junctions.

CHECKPOINT 5.7

- *How are desmosomes and tight junctions functionally similar? How do they differ?*
- **CONNECT** *What is the justification for considering gap junctions and plasmodesmata to be functionally similar? How do they differ structurally?*

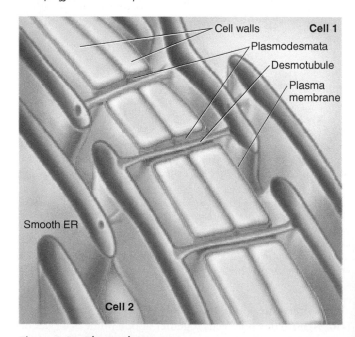

Figure 5-24 Plasmodesmata

Most plant cells have plasmodesmata that connect the cytoplasm of adjacent cells. Cytoplasmic channels through the cell walls of adjacent plant cells allow passage of water, ions, and small molecules. The channels are lined with the fused plasma membranes of the two adjacent cells.

© Cengage Learning

5.1 The Structure of Biological Membranes *(page 104)*

1 Evaluate the importance of membranes to cells, emphasizing their various functions.

- The **plasma membrane** physically separates the interior of the cell from the extracellular environment, receives information about changes in the environment, regulates the passage of materials into and out of the cell, and communicates with other cells.

- Biological membranes form compartments within eukaryotic cells that allow a variety of separate functions. Membranes participate in and serve as surfaces for biochemical reactions.

2 Describe the fluid mosaic model of cell membrane structure.

- According to the **fluid mosaic model,** membranes consist of a fluid phospholipid bilayer in which a variety of proteins are embedded. The phospholipid molecules are **amphipathic:** they have hydrophobic and hydrophilic regions. The hydrophilic heads of the phospholipids are at the two surfaces of the bilayer, and their hydrophobic fatty acid chains are in the interior.

3 Relate properties of the lipid bilayer to properties and functions of cell membranes.

- In almost all biological membranes, the lipids of the bilayer are in a fluid or liquid-crystalline state, which allows the lipid molecules to move rapidly in the plane of the membrane. Proteins also move within the membrane.

- Lipid bilayers are flexible and self-sealing and can fuse with other membranes. These properties allow the cell to transport materials from one region of the cell to another; materials are transported in vesicles that bud from one cell membrane and then fuse with some other membrane.

4 Describe the ways that membrane proteins associate with the lipid bilayer.

- **Integral membrane proteins** are embedded in the bilayer with their hydrophilic surfaces exposed to the aqueous environment and their hydrophobic surfaces in contact with the hydrophobic interior of the bilayer. **Transmembrane proteins** are integral proteins that extend completely through the membrane.

- **Peripheral membrane proteins** are associated with the surface of the bilayer, usually bound to exposed regions of integral proteins, and are easily removed without disrupting the structure of the membrane.

5.2 Overview of Membrane Protein Functions *(page 111)*

5 Summarize the functions of membrane proteins.

- Membrane proteins anchor cells, transport materials, act as enzymes or receptors, recognize cells and communicate with them, and structurally link cells.

5.3 Cell Membrane Structure and Permeability *(page 112)*

6 Describe the importance of selectively permeable membranes and compare the functions of carrier proteins and channel proteins.

- Biological membranes are **selectively permeable membranes:** they allow the passage of some substances but not others. By regulating passage of molecules that enter and leave the cell and its compartments, the cell controls its volume and the internal composition of ions and molecules.

- Membrane *transport proteins* facilitate the passage of certain ions and molecules through biological membranes. *Carrier proteins* are transport proteins that undergo a series of conformational changes as they bind and transport a specific solute. **ABC transporters** are carrier proteins that use energy from ATP to transport solutes.

- *Channel proteins* are transport proteins that form passageways through which water and certain ions travel through the membrane. *Porins* are channel proteins that form relatively large pores through the membrane for passage of water and certain solutes.

5.4 Passive Transport *(page 113)*

7 Contrast simple diffusion with facilitated diffusion.

- **Diffusion** is the net movement of a substance down its **concentration gradient** from a region of greater concentration to one of lower concentration. Diffusion and osmosis are physical processes that do not require the cell to directly expend metabolic energy.

- In **simple diffusion** through a biological membrane, solute molecules or ions move directly through the membrane down their concentration gradient. **Facilitated diffusion** uses specific transport proteins to move solutes across a membrane. As in simple diffusion, net movement is always from a region of higher to a region of lower solute concentration. Facilitated diffusion cannot work against a concentration gradient.

8 Define *osmosis* and solve simple problems involving osmosis; for example, predict whether cells will swell or shrink under various osmotic conditions.

- **Osmosis** is a kind of diffusion in which molecules of water pass through a selectively permeable membrane from a region where water has a higher effective concentration to a region where its effective concentration is lower.

- The concentration of dissolved substances (solutes) in a solution determines its **osmotic pressure.** Cells regulate their internal osmotic pressures to prevent shrinking or bursting.

- An **isotonic** solution has an equal solute concentration compared with that of another fluid, for example, the fluid within the cell.

- When placed in a **hypertonic** solution, one that has a greater solute concentration than that of the cell, a cell loses water to its surroundings; plant cells undergo **plasmolysis,** a process in which the plasma membrane separates from the cell wall.

- When cells are placed in a **hypotonic** solution, one that has a lower solute concentration than the solute concentration of the cell, water enters the cells and causes them to swell.

- Plant cells withstand high internal hydrostatic pressure because their cell walls prevent them from expanding and bursting. Water moves into plant cells by osmosis and fills the central vacuoles. The cells swell, building up **turgor pressure** against the supportive cell walls.

5.5 Active Transport *(page 118)*

9 Describe active transport, including cotransport.

- In **active transport,** the cell expends metabolic energy to move ions or molecules across a membrane against a concentration gradient. For example, the **sodium–potassium pump** uses ATP to pump sodium ions out of the cell and potassium ions into the cell.

- In **cotransport,** also called *indirect active transport,* two solutes are transported at the same time. An ATP-powered pump maintains a concentration gradient. Then a carrier protein cotransports two solutes. It transports one solute down its concentration gradient and uses the energy released to move another solute against its concentration gradient.

5.6 Exocytosis and Endocytosis *(page 121)*

10 Compare exocytotic and endocytotic transport mechanisms.

- The cell expends metabolic energy to carry on exocytosis and endocytosis. In **exocytosis,** the cell ejects waste products or secretes substances such as mucus by fusion of vesicles with the plasma membrane. This process increases the surface area of the plasma membrane.

- In **endocytosis,** materials such as food particles are moved into the cell. A portion of the plasma membrane envelops the material, enclosing it in a vesicle or vacuole that is then released inside the cell. This process decreases the surface area of the plasma membrane.

- Three types of endocytosis are phagocytosis, pinocytosis, and receptor-mediated endocytosis.

- In **phagocytosis,** the plasma membrane encloses a large particle such as a bacterium, forms a vacuole around it, and moves it into the cell. In **pinocytosis,** the cell takes in dissolved materials by forming tiny vesicles around droplets of fluid trapped by folds of the plasma membrane.

- In **receptor-mediated endocytosis,** specific receptors in coated pits along the plasma membrane bind **ligand** molecules. These pits, coated by the protein clathrin, form coated vesicles by endocytosis. The vesicles fuse with lysosomes, and their contents are digested and released into the cytosol.

5.7 Cell Junctions *(page 123)*

11 Compare the structures and functions of anchoring junctions, tight junctions, gap junctions, and plasmodesmata.

- Cells in close contact with one another may form intercellular junctions. *Anchoring junctions* include desmosomes and adhering junctions; they are found between cells that form a sheet of tissue. **Desmosomes** spot-weld adjacent animal cells together. **Adhering junctions** are formed by **cadherins,** transmembrane proteins that cement cells together.

- **Tight junctions** seal membranes of adjacent animal cells together, preventing substances from moving through the spaces between the cells.

- **Gap junctions,** composed of the protein connexin, form channels that allow communication between the cytoplasm of adjacent animal cells.

- **Plasmodesmata** are channels connecting adjacent plant cells. Openings in the cell walls allow the plasma membranes and cytosol to be continuous; certain molecules and ions can pass from cell to cell.

TEST YOUR UNDERSTANDING

Know and Comprehend

1. Transmembrane proteins (a) are peripheral proteins (b) are receptor proteins (c) extend completely through the membrane (d) extend along the surface of the membrane (e) are secreted from the cell

2. Which of the following is *not* a function of the plasma membrane? (a) transports materials (b) helps structurally link cells (c) has receptors that relay signals (d) anchors the cell to the extracellular matrix (e) manufactures proteins

3. ABC transporters (a) use the energy of ATP hydrolysis to transport certain ions and sugars (b) are important in facilitated diffusion of certain ions (c) are a small group of channel proteins (d) are found mainly in plant cell membranes (e) permit passive diffusion through their channels

4. When plant cells are in a hypotonic medium, they (a) undergo plasmolysis (b) build up turgor pressure (c) wilt (d) decrease pinocytosis (e) lose water to the environment

5. Which of the following processes requires the cell to expend metabolic energy directly (e.g., from ATP)? (a) osmosis (b) facilitated diffusion (c) all forms of carrier-mediated transport (d) active transport (e) simple diffusion

6. Electrochemical gradients (a) power simple diffusion (b) are established by pinocytosis (c) are necessary for transport by aquaporins (d) are established by concentration gradients (e) are a result of both an electric charge difference and a concentration difference between the two sides of the membrane

7. In cotransport (indirect active transport) (a) a uniporter moves a solute across a membrane against its concentration gradient (b) the movement of one solute down its concentration gradient provides energy for transport of some other solute up its concentration gradient (c) a channel protein moves ions by facilitated diffusion (d) osmosis powers the movement of ions against their concentration gradient (e) sodium is directly transported in one direction, and potassium is indirectly transported in the same direction

8. Junctions that permit the transfer of water, ions, and molecules between adjacent plant cells are (a) tight junctions (b) adhering junctions (c) desmosomes (d) gap junctions (e) plasmodesmata

Apply and Analyze

9. **PREDICT** A laboratory technician accidentally places red blood cells in a hypertonic solution. What happens? (a) They undergo plasmolysis (b) They build up turgor pressure (c) They swell (d) They pump solutes out (e) They become dehydrated and shrunken

Evaluate and Synthesize

10. **INTERPRET DATA** GLUT 4 is a glucose transporter that functions in adipose (fat) cell plasma membranes. An analysis of adipose cells exposed to insulin showed that a single cell could import glucose at a maximum rate of about 1×10^8 molecules/second. Under the same conditions, unstimulated cells could only transport a maximum of about 1×10^7 molecules/second. What does this finding tell you about the relative number of GLUT 4 transporters functioning in the plasma membranes of stimulated versus unstimulated cells?

11. **CONNECT** Most adjacent plant cells are connected by plasmodesmata, whereas only certain adjacent animal cells are connected through gap junctions. What might account for this difference?

12. **EVOLUTION LINK** Explain to your roommate why the evolution of biological membranes was an essential step in the origin of life. Give arguments supporting (or challenging) this hypothesis.

13. **EVOLUTION LINK** Transport proteins have been found in all biological membranes. What hypothesis could you make regarding whether these molecules evolved early or later in the history of cells? Argue in support of your hypothesis.

 To access course materials, such as Aplia and other companion resources, please visit **www.cengagebrain.com.**

Cell Communication 6

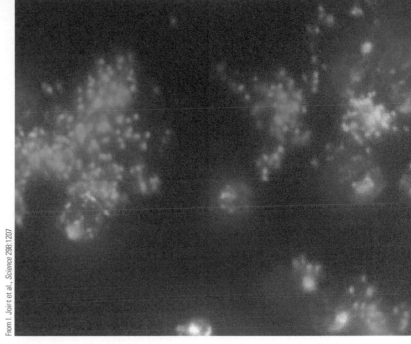

From I. Joint et al., *Science* 298:1207

To maintain homeostasis, the cells of a multicellular organism must continuously communicate with one another. Many different mechanisms for transmitting information between cells, tissues, and organs have evolved, including electrical signaling and many types of chemical signaling. Organisms also communicate with other members of their species by secreting chemical signals. For example, bacteria release chemical signals that diffuse among nearby bacteria. As the population of bacteria increases, the concentration of the chemical signal increases. Through a process known as *quorum sensing*, the bacteria sense when a certain critical concentration of a signal molecule is reached. The bacteria respond by activating a specific biological process. For example, they may form a **biofilm,** a community of microorganisms attached to a solid surface. Forming a biofilm requires the coordinated activity of numerous bacteria.

Over billions of years, elaborate systems of cell signaling have evolved. Organisms of different species, and even different kingdoms and domains, communicate with one another. For example, the chemical signals released by bacteria can be intercepted by other organisms. During its life cycle, the green seaweed *Enteromorpha* produces spores that move about and temporarily attach to a surface. The spores sense a chemical signal released by bacteria that form biofilms. In response to the chemical signal, the spores move toward the biofilm and attach to individual bacteria that are part of the biofilm surface (see photograph).

Thousands of chemical reactions are involved in responding to signal molecules and regulating the communication among molecules necessary to maintain homeostasis. Many researchers are working on the molecular level to understand how proteins receive messages and relay signals. They are learning how proteins act as molecular switches, activating and deactivating molecules in complex signaling pathways.

Some cell biologists are using a systems biology approach to understand the intricate, dynamic interactions involved in cell communication. Biologists, biochemists, physicists, and scientists from many other disciplines are working together to understand how elaborate signaling systems within the cell interact to regulate cell functions. They are studying how information is transferred between cells at the tissue and organ levels, and

Cell-to-cell communication across the prokaryote–eukaryote boundary. Spores of the green seaweed *Enteromorpha* (Domain Eukarya) attach to biofilm-forming bacteria (Domain Bacteria) in response to chemical compounds released by the bacteria. The bacteria (*blue*) were stained and visualized with blue light. The spores appear *red* because of the fluorescence of chlorophyll within them.

KEY CONCEPTS

6.1 Cells communicate by signaling one another, a complex process that involves production of signaling molecules, reception of the signal, signal transduction, and a response.

6.2 Cells signal one another using chemical compounds such as neurotransmitters, hormones, and other signaling molecules.

6.3 A signaling molecule binds to a receptor molecule on the cell surface or inside the target cell.

6.4 In signal transduction, a cell converts an extracellular signal into an amplified intracellular signal that triggers some change in the cell (the response).

6.5 Cells respond to signals in many different ways: by opening or closing ion channels, altering enzyme activities that activate or inhibit specific genes, modifying metabolic activity, or triggering changes in cellular structure or functions such as growth and motility.

6.6 Similarities in cell communication among diverse organisms suggest that the molecules and mechanisms used in information transfer evolved long ago.

throughout the organism. Faulty signaling in cells and between cells can cause a variety of diseases, including cancer and diabetes.

In Chapter 1 we introduced five basic themes of biology. One theme, transmission of information, is the main focus of this chapter. In this chapter we discuss how cells send and receive signals. We consider how information crosses the plasma membrane and is transmitted through signaling systems. We describe some of the responses that cells make. Finally, we discuss the evolution of cell communication. Increased understanding of the mechanisms of cell communication may suggest new strategies for preventing and treating diseases.

6.1 CELL COMMUNICATION: AN OVERVIEW

LEARNING OBJECTIVE

1   Describe the four main processes essential for cells to communicate.

When food is scarce, the amoeba-like cellular slime mold *Dictyostelium* secretes the compound **cyclic adenosine monophosphate (cAMP).** This chemical compound diffuses through the cell's environment and binds to *receptors* on the surfaces of nearby cells. The activated receptors send signals into the cells that result in movement toward the cAMP. Hundreds of slime molds come together and form a multicellular slug-shaped colony (**FIG. 6-1**; also see Fig. 26-20). (When conditions are favorable, the cells of the slug form a stalked fruiting body with spores at the top; when released, each spore gives rise to an amoeba-like cell.)

Even though they do not move from one place to another, plants also communicate with one another. For example, diseased maple trees send airborne chemical signals that are received by uninfected trees nearby. Cells of the uninfected trees respond by increasing their chemical defenses so that they are more resistant to the disease-causing organisms. Plants also send signals to insects. When tobacco plants are attacked by herbivorous insects, the plants release volatile chemicals. In response to these signals, the insects lay fewer eggs, thus reducing the number of insects feeding on the plants. Predator insects that eat the eggs of the herbivorous insects respond to the plant signals by eating more of the herbivorous insect eggs. Thus, natural selection has resulted in plant signals that herbivorous insects detect and avoid and that carnivorous insects detect and approach. This system of information transfer helps protect plants from herbivorous insects.

To survive, organisms must receive signals from the outside environment and effectively respond to them. To grow, develop, and function, the cells of a multicellular organism must also communicate with one another. In plants and animals, *hormones* and other regulatory molecules serve as important chemical signals between various cells and organs. In animals, neurons (nerve cells) transmit information electrically and chemically.

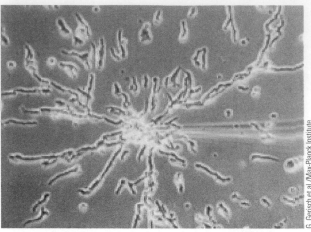

16.6 mm

Figure 6-1 Cell signaling in cellular slime molds
When food is scarce, the amoeba-like cellular slime mold *Dictyostelium* secretes the chemical compound cyclic AMP (cAMP). The slime molds respond to this chemical signal by aggregating. Converging streams of hundreds of individuals come together and form a multicellular colony.

G. Gerisch et al./Max-Planck Institute

The term **cell signaling** refers to the mechanisms by which cells communicate with one another. If the cells are physically close to one another, a signaling molecule on one cell may combine with a *receptor* (a macromolecule that binds with signaling molecules) on another cell. Most commonly, cells communicate by sending chemical signals over some distance. As we will discuss, cell signaling must be precisely regulated. Cell signaling involves a sequence of four main processes (**FIG. 6-2**). We summarize them here and discuss them in more detail in the following sections of this chapter.

1.   **Signal transmission.** In chemical signaling, a cell must synthesize and release signaling molecules. For example, specialized cells in the vertebrate pancreas secrete the hormone insulin. If the **target cells,** the cells that can respond to the signal, are not in close proximity, the signal must be transported to them. The circulatory system transports insulin to target cells throughout the body. Next, target cells must receive, relay, and respond to the information signaled.

2.   **Reception.** Reception is the process of receiving an incoming signal. **Receptors** are large proteins or glycoproteins that bind with signaling molecules. Many types of signaling molecules do not actually enter the target cell. They bind to specific receptors on the surface of the target cell. Insulin, for example, binds to insulin receptors, which are transmembrane proteins.

3.   **Signal transduction** is the process by which a cell converts an extracellular signal into an intracellular signal (or signals) that causes a response. Signal transduction typically involves a chain of molecules that relay information. When insulin binds to an insulin receptor, the signal is relayed through several different signaling pathways.

4.   **Response.** The final molecule in the signaling pathway converts the signal into a response that alters some cell process.

For example, as we will discuss in Chapter 49, insulin stimulates cells to take up glucose from the blood. This response lowers the concentration of glucose in the blood. In some cell types, insulin is also involved in the regulation of fat and protein metabolism. Many signaling molecules stimulate ion channels in the plasma membrane to open or close. Still other signaling molecules activate or inhibit specific genes in the nucleus. These responses can result in changes in cell division and other aspects of cell development. After a signaling molecule has done its job, its action must be stopped, and as part of the signaling process, certain mechanisms operate to terminate the signal.

CHECKPOINT 6.1

- *What is the sequence of events that takes place in cell signaling?*
- **CONNECT** *What key role does signal transduction play in the signaling process?*

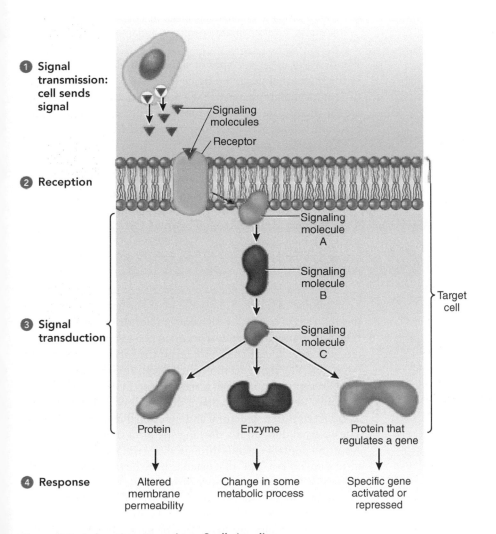

① **Signal transmission: cell sends signal**

Signaling molecules

Receptor

② **Reception**

Signaling molecule A

Signaling molecule B

Target cell

③ **Signal transduction**

Signaling molecule C

Protein

Enzyme

Protein that regulates a gene

④ **Response**

Altered membrane permeability

Change in some metabolic process

Specific gene activated or repressed

Figure 6-2 *Animation* Overview of cell signaling

When a signaling molecule binds to a receptor molecule on a target cell, the receptor activates a signal transduction pathway, leading to some response in the cell.

PREDICT What would happen if the cell were exposed to a drug that blocked the activity of signaling molecule A?

© Cengage Learning

6.2 SENDING SIGNALS

LEARNING OBJECTIVE

2 Compare three types of signaling molecules: neurotransmitters, hormones, and local regulators.

Cells communicate in several ways, including directly through cell junctions, by way of electrical signals, temporary cell-to-cell contact, and chemical signals. Recall from Chapter 5 that gap junctions in animal cells allow rapid chemical and electrical communication between adjacent cells. For example, the gap junctions between cardiac muscle cells of the heart wall allow the rapid flow of ions necessary for synchronized contraction. Plasmodesmata between adjacent plant cells also allow signal molecules to pass quickly from one cell to another.

Cells that are not directly connected also communicate with one another. In animals, some neurons communicate with electrical signals. Most neurons, however, signal one another by releasing chemical compounds called **neurotransmitters** (FIGS. 6-3a and 41-11). Neurotransmitter molecules diffuse across *synapses,* tiny gaps between neurons. More than 60 different neurotransmitters have been identified, including acetylcholine, norepinephrine, dopamine, serotonin, and several amino acids and peptides.

Cells synthesize many different types of chemical signals and deliver them in various ways. In animals certain cells in the immune system produce specific chemical compounds that are displayed on the cell surface. These cells recognize the chemical signals and communicate with one another by making direct contact (FIGS. 6-3b, 45-6, and 45-7).

Specialized cells in plants and animals produce signaling molecules called **hormones.** Hormones may be synthesized by neighboring cells or by specialized organs or tissues some distance from the target cells. In animals many hormones are produced by **endocrine glands.** These glands have no ducts; they secrete their hormones into the surrounding interstitial fluid. Typically, hormones diffuse into capillaries and are transported by the blood to target cells (FIG. 6-3c).

Some cells produce local regulators that signal cells in close proximity. A **local regulator** is a signaling molecule that diffuses through the **interstitial fluid,** the fluid surrounding the cells, and acts on nearby cells. This process is called **paracrine regulation** (FIG. 6-3d). Some local regulators are considered hormones.

Local regulators include local chemical mediators such as growth factors, histamine, nitric oxide, and prostaglandins.

Histamine is a local regulator that is stored in certain cells of the immune system and is released in response to allergic reactions, injury, or infection. Histamine causes blood vessels to dilate and capillaries to become more permeable. **Nitric oxide (NO),** another local regulator, is a gas produced by many types of cells, including plant and animal cells. Nitric oxide released by cells lining blood vessels relaxes smooth muscle in the blood vessel walls. As a result, the blood vessels dilate, decreasing blood pressure.

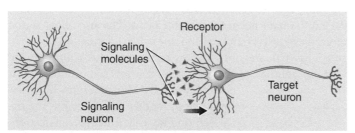

(a) Neurons transmit signals across synapses. (Distances across the synapses are exaggerated for clarity.)

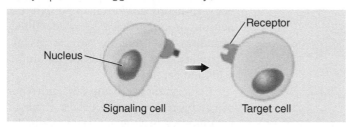

(b) Some cells signal one another by making direct contact.

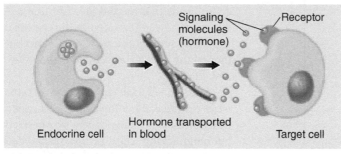

(c) Many hormones are transported by the blood to target cells.

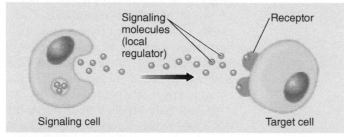

(d) In paracrine regulation a local regulator diffuses to target cells.

Figure 6-3 Some types of cell signaling

Different types of cells may communicate in different ways.
© Cengage Learning

Prostaglandins are local hormones that are paracrine regulators. Prostaglandins modify cAMP levels and interact with other signaling molecules to regulate metabolic activities. For example, some prostaglandins stimulate smooth muscle to contract.

CHECKPOINT 6.2

- *What are neurotransmitters?*
- *How are animal hormones typically transported to target cells?*
- **CONNECT** *How is paracrine regulation similar to endocrine regulation? How does it differ?*

6.3 RECEPTION

LEARNING OBJECTIVES

3 Identify mechanisms that make reception a highly specific process.
4 Briefly compare ion channel–linked receptors, G protein–linked receptors, enzyme-linked receptors, and intracellular receptors.

Hundreds of different types of signaling molecules are present in the interstitial fluid, the tissue fluid that surrounds the cells of a multicellular organism. How do cells know which messages are for them? The answer is that each type of cell is genetically programmed to receive and respond to specific types of signals. Which signals a cell responds to depends on the specific receptors it is programmed to synthesize.

A signaling molecule, such as insulin, that binds to a specific receptor acts as a **ligand.** A ligand is a molecule, other than an enzyme, that binds specifically to a macromolecule (usually a protein), forming a macromolecule-ligand complex. The complex triggers a biological response. Most ligands are hydrophilic molecules that bind to protein receptors on the surface of target cells (FIG. 6-4a).

Some signaling molecules are small enough or sufficiently hydrophobic to move through the plasma membrane and enter the cell (FIG. 6-4b). These signaling molecules bind with intracellular receptors. Reception occurs when a signaling molecule binds to a specific receptor protein on the surface of, or inside, a target cell. The signaling molecule activates the receptor.

A receptor on the cell surface generally has at least three domains. Recall from Chapter 3 that in biochemistry, the term *domain* refers to a structural and functional region of a protein. The external domain is a docking site for a signaling molecule. A second domain extends through the plasma membrane, and a third domain is a "tail" that extends into the cytoplasm. The tail transmits the signal to a molecule inside the cell.

Reception is highly selective. Each type of receptor has a specific shape. The receptor binding site is somewhat like a lock, and signaling molecules are like different keys. Only the signaling molecule that fits the specific receptor can influence the metabolic machinery of the cell. Receptors are important in determining the specificity of cell communication.

Different types of cells can produce different types of receptors. Any one cell makes many different receptors. Furthermore, a cell may synthesize different kinds of receptors at different stages in its life cycle or in response to different conditions. Another consideration is that the same signal can have different meanings for various target cells.

Some receptors are specialized to respond to signals other than chemical signals. For example, in the vertebrate eye, a receptor called **rhodopsin** is activated by light. Rhodopsin is part of a signal transduction pathway that leads to vision in dim light. Plants and some algae have **phytochromes,** a family of blue-green pigment proteins that are activated by red light. Activation can lead to changes such as flowering. Plants, some algae, and at least some animals have **cryptochromes,** pigments that absorb blue light. Cryptochromes play a role in biological rhythms.

Cells regulate reception

An important mechanism that cells use to regulate reception is increasing or decreasing the number of each type of receptor. Depending on the needs of the cell, receptors are synthesized or degraded. For example, when the concentration of the hormone insulin is too high for an extended period, cells decrease the number of their insulin receptors. This process is called **receptor down-regulation.** In the case of insulin, receptor down-regulation suppresses the sensitivity of target cells to the hormone. Insulin stimulates cells to take in glucose by facilitated diffusion, so receptor down-regulation decreases the ability of cells to take in glucose. Receptor down-regulation often involves transporting receptors to lysosomes, where they are destroyed.

Receptor up-regulation occurs in response to low hormone concentrations. In this process, a greater number of receptors are synthesized, and their increased numbers on the plasma membrane make it more likely that the signal will be received by a receptor on the cell. Receptor up-regulation thus *amplifies* the signaling molecule's effect on the cell. Receptor up-regulation and down-regulation are controlled in part by signals to genes that code for the receptors.

Three types of receptors occur on the cell surface

Three main types of receptors on the cell surface are ion channel–linked receptors, G protein–linked receptors, and enzyme-linked receptors.

Ion channel–linked receptors convert chemical signals into electrical signals Ion channel–linked receptors are found in the plasma membrane. These receptors, which have been extensively studied in neurons and muscle cells, convert chemical signals into electrical signals (FIG. 6-5a). The receptor itself serves as a channel.

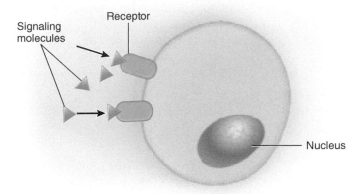

(a) Hydrophilic (water soluble) signaling molecules cannot pass through the plasma membrane. They bind to receptors in the plasma membrane.

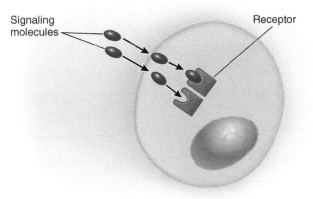

(b) Hydrophobic (lipid soluble) signaling molecules cross the plasma membrane and bind with receptors inside the cell (cytosol or nucleus).

Figure 6-4 Cell-surface and intracellular receptors
© Cengage Learning

Ion channel–linked receptors are also called **ligand-gated channels,** which means that the ion channel opens or closes in response to the binding of the signaling molecule (ligand). A part of the receptor (protein) that makes up the channel forms the gate. The receptor responds to certain signals by changing its shape, opening or closing the gate. Typically, the gate of an ion channel remains closed until a ligand binds to the receptor.

For example, **acetylcholine** is a neurotransmitter that binds to an acetylcholine receptor. This receptor is a ligand-gated sodium ion channel that is important in muscle contraction. When acetylcholine binds to the receptor, the channel opens, allowing sodium ions to enter the cell. The influx of sodium ions decreases the electric charge difference across the membrane (depolarization), which can lead to muscle contraction. After a brief time, the ligand dissociates from the receptor and the gate

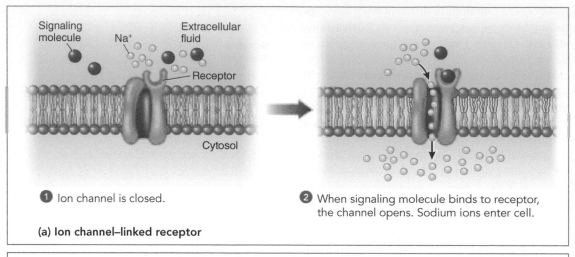

① Ion channel is closed.

② When signaling molecule binds to receptor, the channel opens. Sodium ions enter cell.

(a) Ion channel–linked receptor

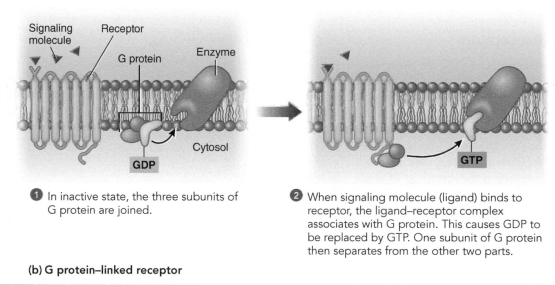

① In inactive state, the three subunits of G protein are joined.

② When signaling molecule (ligand) binds to receptor, the ligand–receptor complex associates with G protein. This causes GDP to be replaced by GTP. One subunit of G protein then separates from the other two parts.

(b) G protein–linked receptor

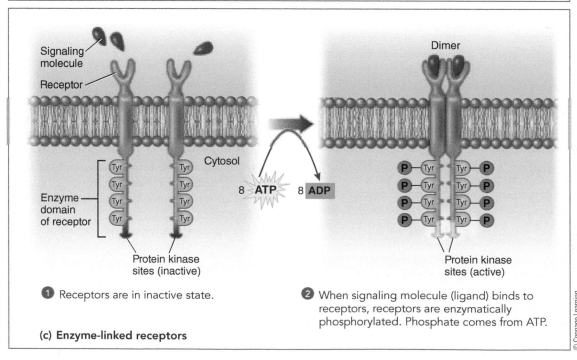

① Receptors are in inactive state.

② When signaling molecule (ligand) binds to receptors, receptors are enzymatically phosphorylated. Phosphate comes from ATP.

(c) Enzyme-linked receptors

Figure 6-5 **Three types of cell-surface receptors**

closes the channel. As we will discuss in Chapter 41, some ion channels, called voltage-activated channels, are regulated by electrical signals.

G protein–linked receptors link signaling molecules to signal transduction pathways

G protein–linked receptors (also called G protein–coupled receptors) are a large family of transmembrane proteins that loop back and forth through the plasma membrane seven times (**FIG. 6-5b**). The receptor consists of seven transmembrane helices connected by loops that extend into the cytosol or outside the cell. G protein–linked receptors couple certain signaling molecules to various signal transduction pathways inside the cell. The outer part of the receptor has a binding site for a signaling molecule, and the part of the receptor that extends into the cytosol has a binding site for a specific **G protein.**

G proteins bind *guanine nucleotides.* When a signaling molecule binds with a G protein–linked receptor, the receptor changes shape. This change allows the G protein to associate with the receptor.

G protein–linked receptors are found in all eukaryotes. These receptors bind with hundreds of different signaling molecules. Some of the many critical processes that depend on G protein–linked receptors are vision, sense of smell, regulation of mood and behavior, and regulation of the immune system. As you might imagine, understanding how G protein–linked receptors work is medically important. About 60% of prescription medications currently in use act on these receptors. More than 900 G protein–linked receptors have been identified in mammals, and more than 400 of these receptors are potential targets for pharmaceutical interventions.

Enzyme-linked receptors function directly as enzymes or are linked to enzymes

Enzyme-linked receptors are transmembrane proteins with a binding site for a signaling molecule outside the cell and an enzyme component inside the cell. Recall from Chapter 3 that *enzymes* catalyze specific chemical reactions; most enzymes are proteins.

Proteins called *tyrosine kinases* make up a major group of enzyme-linked receptors found on the plasma membrane. The domain of the protein that extends into the cytosol is a **tyrosine kinase** enzyme that transfers the terminal phosphate group from ATP to the amino acid *tyrosine* that is part of a protein. This process is called **phosphorylation.** Tyrosine kinase receptors bind certain hormones that regulate many cellular processes and are important in development. They include insulin and *growth factors,* such as nerve growth factor.

Before the tyrosine kinase can phosphorylate a signaling protein in the cell, it must first be activated. When signal molecules bind to two tyrosine kinase receptors, the receptor proteins move closer together in the plasma membrane and pair, forming a *dimer.* A conformational change (change in shape) takes place, which allows the tyrosine kinase part of each receptor to add a phosphate from an ATP molecule to certain tyrosines on the other member of the dimer (**FIG. 6-5c**). Once activated, tyrosine kinase enzymes can phosphorylate signaling proteins inside the cell (discussed in the next section).

Many plant cell-surface receptors are enzyme-linked receptors. **Brassinosteroids (BRs),** a group of plant steroid hormones, regulate many plant processes, including cell division, cell elongation, and flower development (discussed in Chapter 38). Unlike animal steroid hormones, which typically bind with intracellular receptors, BRs bind with a protein kinase receptor in the plasma membrane. In plant protein kinase receptors, serine and threonine, rather than tyrosine, appear to be the amino acids that are phosphorylated.

The gas **ethylene** is a plant hormone that regulates a variety of processes, including seed germination and ripening of fruit. Ethylene is also important in plant responses to stressors. The ethylene receptor has two components. Each component has a domain that is an enzyme, a histidine kinase, that extends into the cell. Receptors with histidine kinase domains are also present in bacterial and yeast cells.

Some receptors are located inside the cell

Certain receptors are found in the cytosol or in the nucleus. Most of these intracellular receptors are **transcription factors,** proteins that regulate the expression of specific genes. The signaling molecules that bind with intracellular receptors are small, hydrophobic molecules that can diffuse across the membranes of target cells (see Fig. 6-4b).

In animal cells most steroid hormones, such as the molting hormone *ecdysone* in insects and *cortisol* in vertebrates, enter target cells and combine with receptor molecules in the cytosol. Vitamins A and D and nitric oxide also bind with intracellular receptors. After binding, the ligand–receptor complex moves into the nucleus. *Thyroid hormones* (which are not steroids) bind to receptors already bound to DNA inside the nucleus.

CHECKPOINT 6.3

- *How does a receptor "know" which signaling molecules to bind?*
- **PREDICT** *Under what conditions might receptor up-regulation occur? receptor down-regulation?*
- **CONNECT** *What do the three main types of cell-surface receptors have in common? How do they differ?*
- **CONNECT** *What is the function of most intracellular receptors?*

6.4 SIGNAL TRANSDUCTION

LEARNING OBJECTIVES

5   Compare the actions of the main types of receptors in signal transduction.
6   Trace the sequence of events in signal transduction for each of the following second messengers: cyclic AMP, inositol trisphosphate (IP$_3$), diacylglycerol (DAG), and calcium ions.

Many regulatory molecules transmit information to the cell's interior without physically crossing the plasma membrane. Instead, they activate membrane proteins, which then *transduce* the signal. The first component in a signal transduction pathway is typically the receptor, which may be a transmembrane protein with a domain exposed on the extracellular surface. Each type of receptor activates a different signal transduction pathway.

In a typical signaling pathway, a signaling molecule binds with a cell-surface receptor and activates it by changing the shape of the receptor tail that extends into the cytoplasm. The signal may then be relayed through a sequence of proteins that are intracellular signaling molecules. Typically, the proteins in this chain are protein kinases that relay and amplify the original signal by adding phosphates to the next protein molecule in the pathway. This chain of signaling molecules in the cell that relays and intensifies the signal is called a *signaling pathway* or *signaling cascade* (FIG. 6-6).

More than 3000 signaling proteins have been identified in the cells of mammals alone. Malfunctions in signal transduction pathways have been linked to major diseases, including cancer, heart disease, diabetes, and autoimmune diseases.

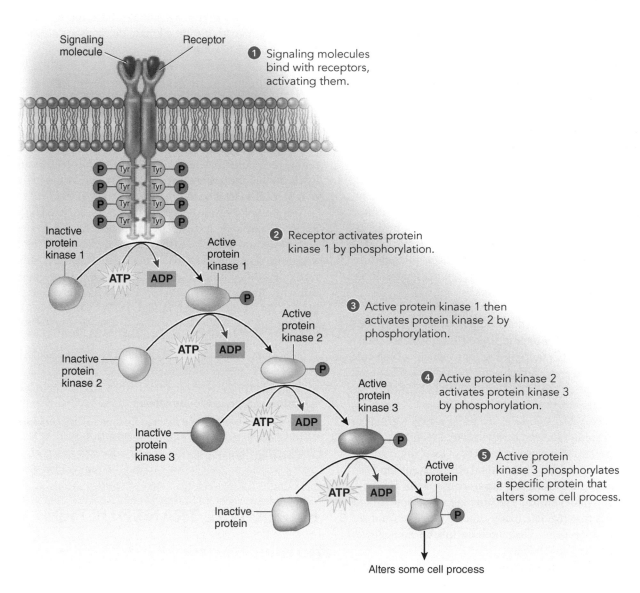

Figure 6-6 A phosphorylation cascade

Many signaling pathways are protein kinase cascades. When the receptor is activated, each protein kinase activates the next protein kinase in the pathway by phosphorylation of one or more of its threonine, serine, or tyrosine residues. Addition of a phosphate group typically changes the shape of the molecule. Activation of the last protein in the chain changes some cell process or turns on (or turns off) specific genes. (*P* represents phosphate.) Note that the number of protein kinases varies from pathway to pathway.
© Cengage Learning

Signaling molecules can act as molecular switches

Each component in a signaling pathway acts as a molecular "switch," which can be in an active ("on") state or an inactive ("off") state. When an intracellular signaling molecule receives a signal, it is activated (turned on). Another process then occurs that inactivates (turns off) the signaling molecule. To transmit a new signal, every activated molecule in a signaling pathway must be inactivated. Molecular switches are typically regulated by the addition or removal of phosphate groups.

Each time a signal molecule binds to a receptor, a signaling pathway is turned on. As the signal is transmitted to each protein kinase in the chain, the protein is phosphorylated. Recall that in phosphorylation, an enzyme transfers phosphate groups from one molecule to another. As phosphate is transferred, the signal passes from protein kinase 1 to protein kinase 2 to protein kinase 3 and on down the chain (see Fig. 6-6). Each protein kinase enzyme in the pathway will specifically phosphorylate one or more tyrosine, serine, or threonine residues on its target protein. Phosphorylation typically activates a protein kinase, although in some cases it inhibits protein kinase activity. A signaling pathway in which a series of protein kinase molecules are phosphorylated is referred to as a *protein kinase cascade*. The last protein kinase in the cascade activates the target protein by phosphorylation. The target protein alters some process in the cell.

After the signal passes from protein kinase 1 to protein kinase 2, protein kinase 1 is usually inactivated so that it can be available to transmit a new signal. A **phosphatase** is an enzyme that catalyzes the removal of a phosphate group by hydrolysis in a process called *dephosphorylation*. Protein phosphatases help regulate protein kinase cascades. Just as a cell contains hundreds of different protein kinases, it also contains many types of protein phosphatases. Rapid removal of phosphate groups by protein phosphatases is an important regulatory mechanism for protein kinase cascades. Such regulation ensures that these pathways operate only in response to the binding of a signal molecule to a receptor.

Ion channel–linked receptors open or close channels

The gates of many ion channels remain closed until a ligand binds to the receptor. For example, when the neurotransmitter acetylcholine binds to an acetylcholine receptor (which is an ion channel–linked receptor), the channel opens, allowing sodium ions to enter the cell (see Fig. 6-5a). Depending on the type of cell, the influx of sodium ions can result in transmission of a neural impulse or in muscle contraction.

Gamma-aminobutyric acid (GABA) is a neurotransmitter that binds to GABA receptors. One class of GABA receptors consists of ligand-gated chloride ion channels. When GABA binds to the receptor, the channel opens. Chloride ions, which are negatively charged, rush out of or into the neuron, depending on the conditions (electrochemical gradient) in the cell. Typically, chloride ions enter the cell, which inhibits transmission

of neural impulses. Thus, GABA *inhibits* neural signaling. Barbiturates and benzodiazepine drugs such as Valium bind to GABA receptors. When that occurs, lower amounts of GABA are required to open the chloride channels and inhibit neural impulses. This action results in a tranquilizing effect. (Not all GABA receptors are *themselves* ion channels; some are G protein–linked receptors or enzyme-linked receptors that trigger a series of reactions resulting in activation of other proteins that serve as ion channels.)

G protein–linked receptors initiate signal transduction

As discussed in the last section, G protein–linked receptors activate G proteins, a group of regulatory proteins important in many signal transduction pathways. These proteins are found in fungi (yeasts), protists, plants, and animals. They are involved in the action of some plant and many animal hormones. Some G proteins regulate channels in the plasma membrane, allowing ions to enter or exit the cell. Other G proteins are involved in the perception of sight and smell. In 1994, Alfred G. Gilman of the University of Texas and Martin Rodbell of the National Institute of Environmental Health Sciences were awarded the Nobel Prize in Physiology or Medicine for their discovery of G proteins and their role in signal transduction. In 2012, the Nobel Prize in Chemistry was awarded to Robert Lefkowitz at the Howard Hughes Medical Institute of Duke University and Brian Kobilka of Stanford University for their work on the structure and function of G protein–linked receptors.

In its inactive state, the G protein consists of three subunits that are joined (see Fig. 6-5b). One subunit is linked to a molecule of **guanosine diphosphate (GDP)**, a molecule similar to ADP but containing the base guanine instead of adenine. When a signaling molecule binds with the receptor, the GDP is released and is replaced by **guanosine triphosphate (GTP)**, a nucleotide that, like ATP, functions in energy transactions.

Binding of GTP to the subunit of the G protein alters its shape, allowing it to separate from the other two subunits and bind with its protein target. The G protein subunit linked to the GTP, however, is also a GTPase, an enzyme that catalyzes the hydrolysis of GTP to GDP. This action, a process that releases energy, deactivates the G protein. In its inactive state, the G protein subunit rejoins the other two subunits.

When activated, a G protein initiates signal transduction by binding with a specific protein in the cell. In some cases, G proteins *directly* activate enzymes that catalyze changes in certain proteins. These changes lead to alterations in cell function. More commonly, the G protein relays the information from the signaling molecule, now referred to as the **first messenger,** to a *second messenger.*

Second messengers are intracellular signaling agents

Second messengers are ions or small molecules that relay signals inside the cell. When receptors are activated, second messengers

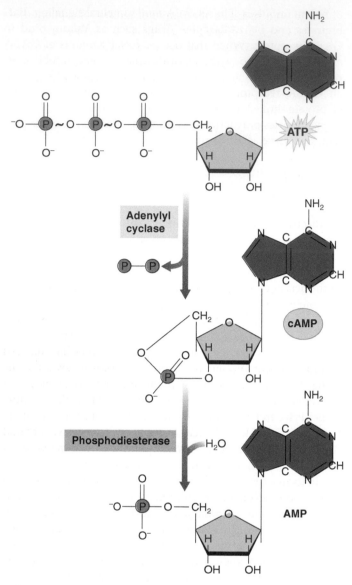

Figure 6-7 Synthesis and inactivation of cyclic AMP

Cyclic AMP (cAMP) is a second messenger produced from ATP that relays a signal from the plasma membrane to the cytosol, affecting many cellular processes. The enzyme adenylyl cyclase catalyzes the reaction. Cyclic AMP is inactivated by the enzyme phosphodiesterase, which converts it to adenosine monophosphate (AMP).

© Cengage Learning

are produced in large quantities. Second messengers rapidly diffuse through the cell (or membrane), relaying the signal. Thus, second messengers amplify the signal.

Second messengers pass the signal along to other signaling proteins or target proteins. The signal typically passes through a chain of proteins and other molecules. The last molecule in the sequence activates the final response. Second messengers are not enzymes, but some regulate specific enzymes, such as protein kinases. Others bind to ion channels, opening or closing them.

Cyclic AMP is a second messenger

Most G proteins shuttle a signal between the receptor and a second messenger. In many signaling cascades in prokaryotic and animal cells, the second messenger is cyclic AMP (cAMP) (**FIG. 6-7**). Researcher Earl Sutherland identified cAMP as a second messenger in the 1960s

and was awarded the 1971 Nobel Prize in Physiology or Medicine for his pioneering work.

When the G protein undergoes a conformational change (change in shape), it binds with and activates **adenylyl cyclase,** an enzyme on the cytoplasmic side of the plasma membrane. The type of G protein that activates adenylyl cyclase is known as a stimulatory G protein, or G_s. (Some G proteins, denoted as G_i, inhibit enzymes.) Note that the G protein couples the ligand–receptor complex to adenylyl cyclase action (**FIG. 6-8**).

When activated, adenylyl cyclase catalyzes the production of cAMP from ATP. By coupling the signaling molecule–receptor complex to an enzyme that rapidly generates multiple cAMP molecules, G proteins rapidly amplify the effects of the original signaling molecule. The pathway is regulated in part by **phosphodiesterase,** an enzyme that converts cAMP to adenosine monophosphate (AMP) (see Fig. 6-7). This action is an off switch that rapidly inactivates cAMP when the receptor becomes inactive.

Figure 6-8 illustrates the sequence of events in a signaling pathway involving G protein and cyclic AMP that activates a group of protein kinase enzymes, referred to as *protein kinase A.* Recall that protein kinases add phosphate groups to target proteins. When a protein is phosphorylated, its function is altered and it triggers a chain of reactions leading to some response in the cell, such as a metabolic change.

The **substrates** (the substances on which an enzyme acts) for protein kinases are different in various cell types. Consequently, the effect of the enzyme varies depending on the substrate. For example, in skeletal muscle cells, protein kinase A activates enzymes that break down glycogen to glucose, providing the muscle cells with energy. In certain neurons in the brain, the same enzyme activates the reward system by regulating action of the neurotransmitter dopamine.

We can summarize the sequence of events during signal transduction involving a G protein and cyclic AMP, beginning with the binding of the signaling molecule to the receptor and leading to a change in some cell function:

signaling molecule (first messenger) binds to G protein–linked receptor → activates G protein → activates adenylyl cyclase → catalyzes the formation of cAMP (second messenger) → activates protein kinase → phosphorylates proteins → response in cell

Some G proteins use phospholipids as second messengers

Certain signaling molecule–receptor complexes activate a G protein that then activates the membrane-bound enzyme *phospholipase C* (**FIG. 6-9**). This enzyme splits a membrane phospholipid, PIP_2 (phosphotidylinositol-4,5-bisphosphate), into two products: **inositol trisphosphate (IP_3)** and **diacylglycerol (DAG).** Both act as second messengers.

DAG remains in the plasma membrane, where in combination with calcium ions it activates *protein kinase C* enzymes. Depending on the type of cell and the specific protein kinase C, the response of the cell can include growth, a change in cell pH, or regulation of certain ion channels. Protein kinase C stimulates contraction of smooth muscle in the digestive system and in other organs of the body.

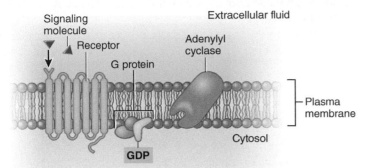

① Signaling molecule binds with G protein–linked receptor in plasma membrane.

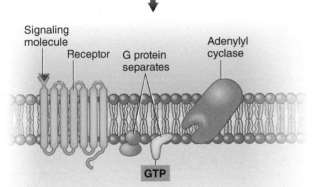

② Signaling molecule–receptor complex activates G protein. GDP is replaced by GTP.

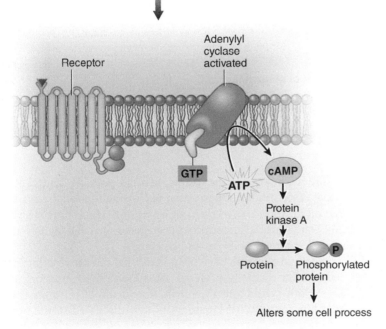

③ G protein activates adenylyl cyclase, which then catalyzes synthesis of cAMP. cAMP activates protein kinase A, which then phosphorylates specific proteins, leading to some response in cell.

Figure 6-8 Signal transduction involving a G protein and cyclic AMP

When a signaling molecule binds to a G protein–linked receptor, a G protein is activated. In this pathway the second messenger, cyclic AMP, is produced and activates a protein kinase.
© Cengage Learning

IP_3 is a member of a family of inositol phosphate messengers, some of which can donate phosphate groups to proteins. IP_3 binds to calcium channels in the endoplasmic reticulum (ER), causing them to open and release calcium ions into the cytosol. We can summarize this sequence of events as follows:

signaling molecule binds to G protein–linked receptor → activates G protein → activates phospholipase → splits PIP_2 → inositol trisphosphate (IP_3) + diacylglycerol (DAG)

DAG → activates protein kinase enzymes → phosphorylates proteins→ some response in the cell

IP_3 → binds to calcium channels in ER → calcium ions released into the cytosol → some response in the cell

Calcium ions are important messengers Calcium ions (Ca^{2+}) have important functions in many cell processes, including microtubule disassembly, muscle contraction, blood clotting, secretion, and activation of certain cells in the immune system. Calcium ions are critical in neural signaling, including the pathways involved in learning. These ions are also essential in fertilization of an egg and in the initiation of development.

Ion pumps in the plasma membrane normally maintain a low calcium ion concentration in the cytosol compared to its concentration in the extracellular fluid. Calcium ions are also stored in the endoplasmic reticulum. When Ca^{2+} gates open in the plasma membrane or endoplasmic reticulum, the Ca^{2+} concentration rises in the cytosol.

Calcium ions can act alone, but typically they exert their effects by binding to certain proteins. **Calmodulin,** found in all eukaryotic cells, is an important Ca^{2+} binding protein. When 4 Ca^{2+} bind to a calmodulin molecule, the molecule changes shape and can then activate certain enzymes. Calmodulin combines with a number of different enzymes, including protein kinases and protein phosphatases, and alters their activity.

Many activated intracellular receptors are transcription factors

Some hydrophobic signaling molecules diffuse across the membranes of target cells and bind with intracellular receptors in the cytosol or in the nucleus. For example, cortisol receptors are located in the cytosol. (Cortisol is a steroid hormone produced in the adrenal glands; its structure is shown in Figure 3-15b.) Thyroid hormones pass into the nucleus and bind with receptors that are bound to DNA in the nucleus. Many intracellular receptors are transcription factors that regulate the expression of specific genes. When a signaling molecule binds to a receptor, the receptor is activated. The ligand–receptor complex binds to a specific region of DNA and activates or represses specific genes (FIG. 6-10).

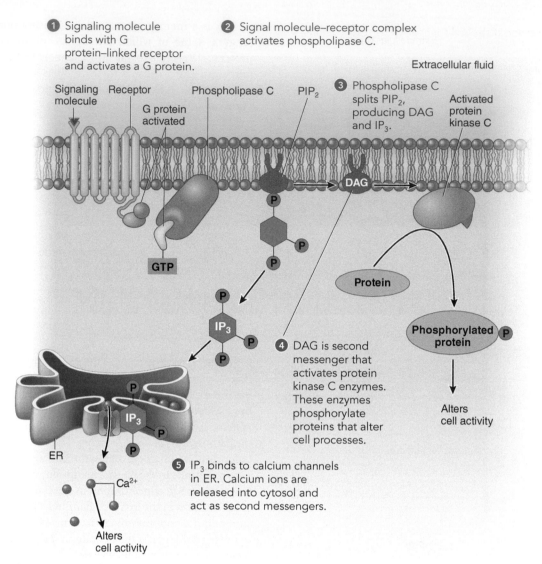

1 Signaling molecule binds with G protein–linked receptor and activates a G protein.

2 Signal molecule–receptor complex activates phospholipase C.

Extracellular fluid

Signaling molecule

Receptor

G protein activated

Phospholipase C

PIP₂

3 Phospholipase C splits PIP₂, producing DAG and IP₃.

Activated protein kinase C

DAG

GTP

P

P

P

IP₃

P

P

Protein

4 DAG is second messenger that activates protein kinase C enzymes. These enzymes phosphorylate proteins that alter cell processes.

Phosphorylated protein

P

P

IP₃

P

ER

P

Alters cell activity

Ca²⁺

5 IP₃ binds to calcium channels in ER. Calcium ions are released into cytosol and act as second messengers.

Alters cell activity

Figure 6-9 Signal transduction involving a G protein activation of phospholipase C

Activated phospholipase C splits PIP₂, producing two second messengers: IP₃ and DAG. IP₃ binds to calcium channels in the endoplasmic reticulum (ER); calcium ions are released into the cytosol and act as second messengers. DAG activates protein kinase C, a family of enzymes that activates signaling pathways by phosphorylating proteins; calcium ions are needed for the activation of protein kinase C.
© Cengage Learning

Gene activation can take place quickly, within about 30 minutes. Messenger RNA is produced and carries the code for synthesis of a particular protein into the cytoplasm. In combination with ribosomes, messenger RNA manufactures specific proteins that can alter cell activity.

Scaffold proteins increase efficiency

Signal transduction is a rapid, precise process. Enzymes must be organized so that they are available as needed for signaling pathways. **Scaffold proteins** organize groups of intracellular signaling molecules into signaling complexes (FIG. 6-11). Many kinases, phosphatases, and other signal transduction proteins are components of multiple signal transduction pathways. Scaffold proteins position enzymes close to the proteins they regulate, increasing the probability that they will react with one another in the correct pathway appropriate for the cell's physiological

condition. In yeast, for example, scaffold proteins control the activities of protein kinases that act in multiple pathways so that they respond correctly to either mating signals or to starvation conditions. Thus, scaffold proteins ensure that signals are relayed accurately, rapidly, and efficiently.

Scaffold proteins have been identified in many pathways, and similar scaffold proteins are found in diverse organisms. Both yeasts and mammals have scaffold proteins that bind kinases in MAP kinase pathways (discussed in the next section).

Signals can be transmitted in more than one direction

Integrins, transmembrane proteins that connect the cell to the extracellular matrix, transduce signals in two directions. They transmit signals from outside the cell to the cell interior and also transmit information about the cell interior to the extracellular matrix.

Cell biologists have demonstrated that when certain signaling molecules bind to integrins in the plasma membrane, specific signal transduction pathways are activated. Interestingly, growth factors and certain molecules of the extracellular matrix may modulate one another's messages. Integrins also respond to information received from inside the cell. This *inside-out signaling* affects how selective integrins are with respect to the molecules to which they bind and how strongly they bind to them.

CHECKPOINT 6.4

- *How is an extracellular signal converted to an intracellular signal in signal transduction? Give a specific example.*
- CONNECT *What feature do all second messengers have in common?*
- PREDICT *How might a signaling pathway be affected if a scaffold protein specific to that pathway were absent?*

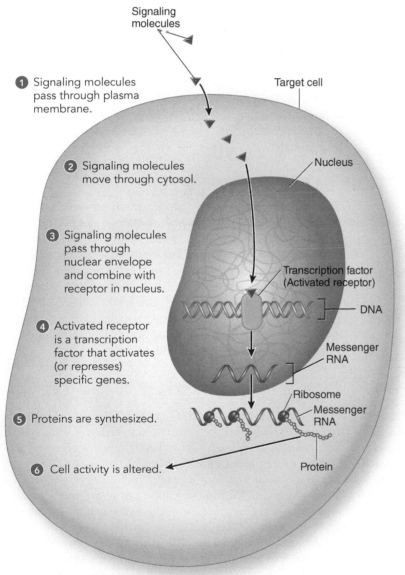

Figure 6-10 Intracellular receptors

Many intracellular receptors are transcription factors; when activated, they activate or repress specific genes.

© Cengage Learning

6.5 RESPONSES TO SIGNALS

LEARNING OBJECTIVES

7 Describe three types of responses that cells make to signaling molecules.

8 Contrast signal amplification with signal termination.

As we have learned, signaling molecules activate signal transduction pathways that bring about specific responses in the cell. Most of these responses fall into three categories: ion channels open or close; enzyme activity is altered, leading to metabolic changes and other effects; and specific gene activity may be turned on or off. Various mechanisms and pathways interact to produce specific actions that are responsible for the structure and function of the cell. They are responsible for metabolic activity, movement, growth, cell division, development, and further information transfer.

In animals neurons release neurotransmitters that excite or inhibit other neurons or muscle cells by affecting ion channels. For example, when acetylcholine binds with a receptor on a target neuron, an ion channel opens and allows passage of sodium and potassium ions. The resulting change in ion permeability can activate the neuron so that it transmits a neural impulse. Serotonin and some other neurotransmitters work indirectly through G proteins and cyclic AMP. In this chain of events, cAMP activates a kinase that phosphorylates a protein, which then closes potassium ion channels. This action leads to transmission of a neural impulse. Some G proteins directly open or close ion channels.

Some receptors directly affect enzyme activity, whereas others initiate signal transduction pathways in which enzymes are altered by components of the pathway. When bacteria infect the body, they release certain peptides. Neutrophils, a type of white blood cell, have cell-surface receptors that detect these peptides. When the bacterial peptides bind to a neutrophil's receptors, enzymes are activated that lead to assembly of microfilaments (actin filaments) and microtubules. Contractions of microfilaments at the far end of the neutrophil force the cytoplasm forward. This action allows the neutrophil to move toward the invading bacteria and destroy them. Microtubules and a variety of proteins, including the contractile protein myosin, appear necessary for this movement.

Some signaling molecules affect gene activity. For example, some signaling molecules activate genes that lead to the manufacture of proteins needed for growth and cell division. In both plants and animals, steroid hormones regulate development by causing changes in the

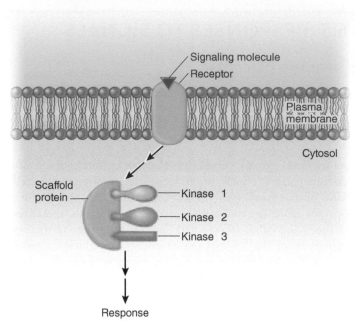

Figure 6-11 Scaffold proteins

These proteins direct signaling traffic by organizing groups of signaling molecules into a complex to make signal transduction faster, more precise, and more efficient. Scaffold proteins are involved in regulating the activity of protein kinases that are used in multiple signal transduction pathways, ensuring that the correct pathway is used for a given physiological condition.
© Cengage Learning

expression of specific genes. In animal cells some steroid hormones bind to nuclear receptors and directly regulate expression of specific target genes. In plant cells steroid hormones bind to receptors on the cell surface. The signal is then transmitted through a chain of molecules, eventually leading to changes in gene expression. Plant hormones will be discussed in greater detail in Chapter 38, and animal hormones are the focus of Chapter 49.

Ras pathways involve tyrosine kinase receptors and G proteins

Some tyrosine kinase receptors activate G proteins. For example, when growth factors bind to tyrosine kinase receptors, **Ras proteins** are activated. Ras proteins are a group of small G proteins that were originally isolated from **Ra**t **s**arcoma cancer cells. Like other G proteins, Ras proteins are active when bound to GTP. Ras proteins are molecular switches that regulate signaling networks inside the cell. When activated, Ras triggers a cascade of reactions called the Ras pathway. In this pathway a tyrosine in specific kinase proteins is phosphorylated, leading to critical cell responses.

Ras pathways are important in gene expression, cell division, cell movement, cell differentiation, cell adhesion, embryonic development, and apoptosis. For example, to initiate DNA synthesis, fibroblasts (a type of connective tissue cell) require the presence of two growth factors, epidermal growth factor and platelet-derived growth factor. In one study investigators injected fibroblasts with antibodies that inactivate Ras proteins by binding to them. The fibroblasts no longer synthesized DNA

in response to growth factors. Data from this and similar experiments led to the conclusion that Ras proteins are important in signal transduction involving growth factors.

Ras genes code for Ras proteins. Certain mutations in *Ras* genes result in mutant Ras proteins that bind GTP but cannot hydrolyze it. The mutant Ras proteins are stuck in the "on" state, resulting in unregulated cell division. This condition is associated with several types of human cancer. In fact, mutations in *Ras* genes have been identified in about one-third of all human cancers. Drugs that inhibit specific tyrosine kinase receptors and Ras pathways are being developed to treat cancer.

One Ras pathway that has been extensively studied is the *MAP kinase pathway*, also known as the *ERK pathway*; *MAP* is an acronym for "mitogen-activated protein" (mitogens induce mitosis, the nuclear division associated with eukaryotic cell division). *ERK* is an acronym for "extracellular signal-regulated kinases." Several distinct groups of MAP kinases have been described. The pathway illustrated in **FIGURE 6-12** shows three main MAP protein kinases: Raf, Mek, and ERK. Proteins in the MAP pathway phosphorylate a nuclear protein that combines with other proteins to form a transcription factor. When specific genes are activated, proteins needed for cell growth, cell division, and cell differentiation (specialization) are synthesized. The MAP kinase cascade is the main signaling pathway for cell division and differentiation. As illustrated in **FIGURE 6-13**, the signaling proteins ERK 1 and ERK 2 are important in fertility in mammals.

The response to a signal is amplified

Signaling molecules are typically present in very low concentrations, yet their effects on the cell are often profound. This situation is possible because the signal is *amplified*, as it is relayed through a signaling pathway. For example, let us examine how the action of a signaling molecule such as the hormone epinephrine is magnified as a signal passes through a series of proteins inside the cell. Epinephrine is released by the adrenal glands in response to danger or other stress. Among its many actions, epinephrine increases heart rate, blood flow to skeletal muscle, and glucose concentration in the blood.

Epinephrine binds to a G protein–linked receptor, causing the receptor to change shape and activate a G protein. A single molecule of a hormone such as epinephrine can activate many G proteins. Each G protein activates an adenylyl cyclase molecule and then returns to its inactive state. Before it becomes inactive, each adenylyl cyclase can catalyze the production of numerous cAMP molecules (**FIG. 6-14**). Then, each cAMP molecule can activate many molecules of a particular protein kinase. That protein kinase can phosphorylate many molecules of the next kinase in the pathway and so on down the cascade.

As a result of **signal amplification,** a single signaling molecule can lead to changes in millions of molecules at the end of a signaling cascade. The response is much greater than would be possible if each signaling molecule acted alone. This process of magnifying the strength of a signaling molecule explains how just a few signaling molecules can lead to major responses in the cell.

When growth factors bind to their receptors, they activate the G protein Ras; Ras activates a MAP-kinase signaling pathway, leading to activation (or repression) of specific genes and ultimately to protein activity that affects some cell process.

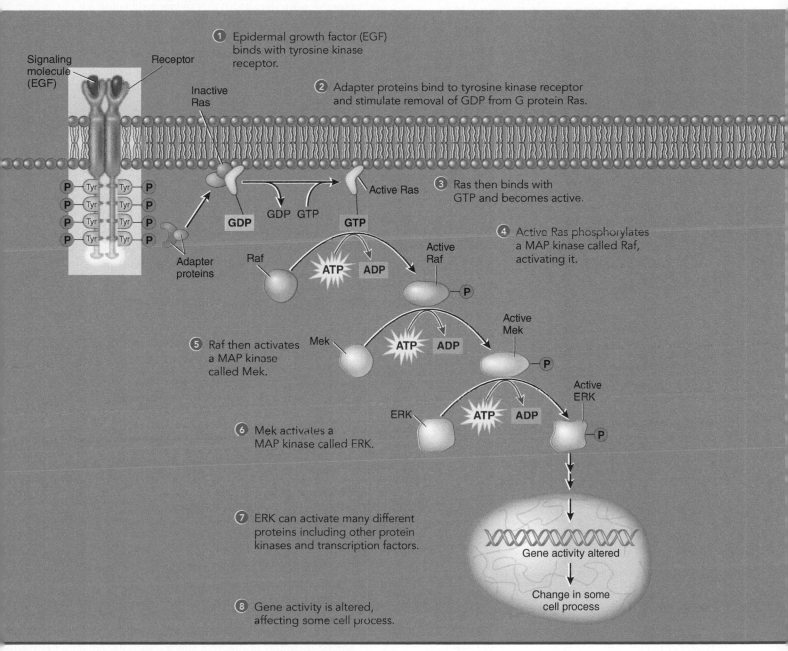

① Epidermal growth factor (EGF) binds with tyrosine kinase receptor.

② Adapter proteins bind to tyrosine kinase receptor and stimulate removal of GDP from G protein Ras.

③ Ras then binds with GTP and becomes active.

④ Active Ras phosphorylates a MAP kinase called Raf, activating it.

⑤ Raf then activates a MAP kinase called Mek.

⑥ Mek activates a MAP kinase called ERK.

⑦ ERK can activate many different proteins including other protein kinases and transcription factors.

⑧ Gene activity is altered, affecting some cell process.

Gene activity altered

Change in some cell process

Figure 6-12 A highly simplified Ras/MAP kinase signaling pathway

In the pathway illustrated here, epidermal growth factor (EGF) binds with a tyrosine kinase receptor, leading to activation of the small G protein Ras. Then, Ras activates a MAP-kinase signaling pathway. A series of MAP kinases in the pathway are activated by phosphorylation. The final MAP kinase can regulate several transcription factors, leading to changes in gene expression that affect cell processes.

PREDICT In many cancers the Ras protein is mutated so that it is always active, promoting continuous cell growth and division. Starting with the EGF receptor, what proteins in the signaling pathway might be good targets for an inhibitory drug that would prevent the mutant Ras protein from promoting cancerous growth?
© Cengage Learning

Signals must be terminated

Once a signal has done its job, it must be terminated. *Signal termination* returns the receptor and each of the components of the signal transduction pathway to their inactive states. This action allows the magnitude of the response to reflect the strength of the signal. Molecules in the system must also be ready to respond to new signals.

We have seen that after a G protein is activated, a subunit of the G protein, a GTPase, catalyzes the hydrolysis of GTP to GDP. This action inactivates the G protein. In the cyclic AMP pathway, any increase in cAMP concentration is temporary. Cyclic AMP

Do the signaling molecules ERK 1 and ERK 2 have key functions in signaling pathways leading to maturation of oocytes (eggs) and ovulation (release of a mature egg from the ovary) in mammals?

HYPOTHESIS: The signaling molecules ERK 1 and ERK 2 are key target molecules of the signal sent by the reproductive hormone, luteinizing hormone (LH), and thus are important in oocyte maturation and ovulation in mammals.

EXPERIMENT: The researchers produced a line of mice that were deficient in both ERK 1 and ERK 2. They performed biochemical analyses on the signaling pathway activated by LH. They also examined the ovaries of the mice.

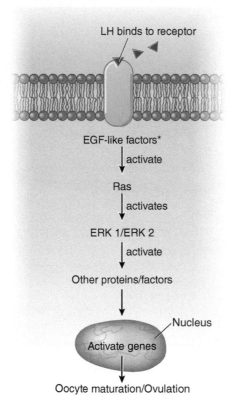

RESULTS AND CONCLUSION: In mice deficient in both ERK 1 and ERK 2, the signaling pathway from LH was disrupted. As a result, genes regulating oocyte maturation and ovulation were not activated. Oocytes failed to mature and ovulate, and the mice also exhibited reproductive disorders associated with changes in levels of reproductive hormones.

This experiment demonstrates that ERK 1 and ERK 2 are key molecules in a signaling pathway that regulates reproduction in mice. These results may lead to greater understanding of certain ovarian disorders that result in infertility in humans.

*EGF = epidermal growth factor

SOURCE: Fan, H.-Y. et al., *Science*, Vol. 324, 938–941, 2009.

Figure 6-13 Identifying key molecules in a signaling pathway that regulates reproduction in mammals

PREDICT What do you think would happen if an altered receptor were to become activated in the absence of LH?

© Cengage Learning

is rapidly inactivated by a phosphodiesterase, which converts it to adenosine monophosphate (AMP). Thus, the concentration of cAMP depends on the activity of both adenylyl cyclase, which produces it, and of phosphodiesterase, which breaks it down (see Fig. 6-8). Recall also that in many signaling pathways, each protein kinase activates the next protein kinase in the chain by phosphorylating it; a phosphatase then inactivates it by removing the phosphate group.

Failure to terminate signals can lead to dire consequences. For example, the bacterium that causes cholera is ingested when people drink contaminated water. Cholera is prevalent in areas where water is contaminated with human feces. The cholera bacterium releases a toxin that activates G proteins in the epithelial cells lining the intestine. The toxin chemically changes the G protein so that it no longer switches off. As a result, the G protein continues to stimulate adenylyl cyclase to make cAMP. The cells lining the intestine malfunction, allowing a large flow of chloride ions into the intestine. Water and other ions follow, leading to the severe, watery diarrhea that characterizes cholera. The disease is treated by replacing the lost fluid. If untreated, this G protein malfunction can cause death.

CHECKPOINT 6.5

- *What are some cell responses to signals?*
- **VISUALIZE** *Draw a simple sketch illustrating signal amplification.*
- **PREDICT** *What are some of the potential consequences of failure of signal termination?*

6.6 EVOLUTION OF CELL COMMUNICATION

LEARNING OBJECTIVE

9 Cite evidence supporting a long evolutionary history for cell signaling molecules.

In this chapter we have examined how the cells of a multicellular organism signal one another and have described a few of the many signal transduction pathways within cells. We have described quorum sensing and other examples of communication between members of a species. We have also discussed communication among members of different species, such as signaling between plants and insects. In our discussion we have noted many similarities in the types of signals used and in the molecules that cells use to relay signals from the cell surface to the molecules that carry out a specific response. Some signal transduction pathways found in organisms as diverse as yeasts and animals are quite similar.

G proteins, protein kinases, and phosphatases have been highly conserved and are part of signaling pathways in most organisms. Certain disease-causing bacteria have signal transduction pathways similar to those found in eukaryotes. Bacteria may use some of these signal mechanisms to interfere with normal function in the eukaryotic cells they infect. Such similarities in many species suggest evolutionary relationships.

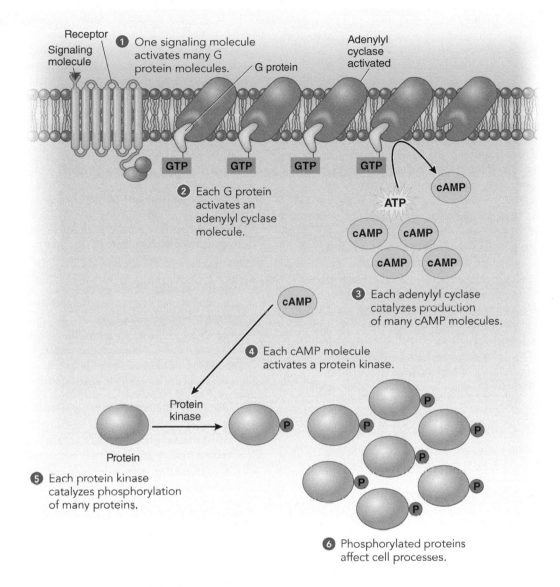

Figure 6-14 Signal amplification

The signal is amplified at each step in the pathway so that one activated receptor can give rise to thousands of final products (proteins at the end of the pathway). The response is far greater than what you might expect from a single receptor.

© Cengage Learning

Similarities in cell signaling suggest that the molecules and mechanisms used in cell communication are very old. The evidence suggests that cell communication first evolved in prokaryotes and continued to change over time as new types of organisms evolved. However, some cell signaling molecules have not changed very much over time, which suggests that the importance of these pathways to cell survival has restricted any evolutionary changes that might have made them less effective. Thus, these pathways have weathered the demands of natural selection through millions of years of evolution.

Choanoflagellates, unicellular protists (see Chapter 26) that are thought to be the most recent ancestors of animals, are used as models for studying the early evolution of animals.

Choanoflagellates have many of the same proteins found in animals. These tiny organisms have protein kinases similar to those of animals, and a G protein–linked receptor has been identified. These findings indicate that important proteins necessary for cell communication in animals had evolved long before the evolution of animals. As we will discuss in later chapters, similarities and differences in basic molecules, such as G proteins, can be used to trace evolutionary pathways.

CHECKPOINT 6.6

- **CONNECT** *Choanoflagellates and animals have similar protein kinases. What does that suggest about their cell signaling mechanisms?*

6.1 Cell Communication: An Overview *(page 130)*

1 Describe the four main processes essential for cells to communicate.

- Cells communicate by **cell signaling,** which consists of four main processes: (1) synthesis, release, and transport of signaling molecules; (2) **reception** of information by **target cells;** (3) **signal transduction,** the process by which a receptor converts an extracellular signal into an intracellular signal and relays the signal, leading to a cellular response; and (4) **response** by the cell, for example, some metabolic process may be altered.

6.2 Sending Signals *(page 131)*

2 Compare three types of signaling molecules: neurotransmitters, hormones, and local regulators.

- Most neurons (nerve cells) signal one another by releasing chemical compounds called **neurotransmitters.**

- **Hormones** are chemical messengers in plants and animals. In animals they are secreted by **endocrine glands,** glands that have no ducts. Most hormones diffuse into capillaries and are transported by the blood to target cells.

- **Local regulators** diffuse through the interstitial fluid and act on nearby cells. This process is called **paracrine regulation.** Histamine, growth factors, **prostaglandins** (a type of local hormone), and **nitric oxide** (a gaseous signaling molecule that passes into target cells) are examples of local regulators.

6.3 Reception *(page 132)*

3 Identify mechanisms that make reception a highly specific process.

- Each type of receptor has a specific shape, and only the signaling molecule that fits the specific receptor can affect the cell. A cell can have many different types of receptors and can make different receptors at different stages in its life cycle or in response to different conditions. Different types of cells can have different types of receptors.

4 Briefly compare ion channel–linked receptors, G protein–linked receptors, enzyme-linked receptors, and intracellular receptors.

- When a signaling molecule binds to an **ion channel–linked receptor,** the ion channel opens or, in some cases, closes.

- **G protein–linked receptors** are transmembrane proteins that extend into the cytosol or outside the cell. These receptors couple specific signaling molecules to signal transduction pathways inside the cell. The tail of the receptor that extends into the cytosol has a binding site for a specific **G protein,** a regulatory protein that binds to GTP.

- **Enzyme-linked receptors** are transmembrane proteins with a binding site for a signaling molecule outside the cell and a binding site for an enzyme inside the cell. Many enzyme-linked receptors are *tyrosine kinases* in which the enzyme is part of the receptor.

- *Intracellular receptors* are located in the cytosol or in the nucleus. Their ligands are small, hydrophobic molecules that diffuse across the plasma membrane.

6.4 Signal Transduction *(page 135)*

5 Compare the actions of the main types of receptors in signal transduction.

- Ion channel–linked receptors convert chemical signals into electrical signals. The gates of many ion channels remain closed until ligands bind to them.

- Many enzyme-linked receptors are tyrosine kinases, enzymes that phosphorylate proteins. Tyrosine kinase receptors activate several different signal transduction pathways. In a *protein kinase cascade,* each molecule in the signaling pathway is phosphorylated by the preceding protein kinase in the chain. The last protein kinase in the cascade activates the target protein by phosphorylation. The target protein alters some process in the cell.

- G protein–linked receptors activate G proteins. A G protein consists of three subunits. It is linked to a molecule of **guanosine diphosphate (GDP),** a molecule similar to ADP but containing the base guanine instead of adenine. When a ligand binds with the receptor, the GDP is released and is replaced by **guanosine triphosphate (GTP).** Then one subunit of the G protein separates from the other two subunits. The activated G protein may initiate a signal transduction pathway by binding with a specific protein in the cell. Some G proteins directly activate enzymes that catalyze changes in certain proteins, leading to changes in cell function.

- Intracellular receptors are located in the cytosol or nucleus. These receptors are **transcription factors** that activate or repress the expression of specific genes.

6 Trace the sequence of events in signal transduction for each of the following second messengers: cyclic AMP, inositol trisphosphate (IP_3), diacylglycerol (DAG), and calcium ions.

- In many signaling systems, the signaling molecule serves as the **first messenger.** Information is relayed by the G protein to a **second messenger,** an intracellular signaling molecule.

- When certain G proteins undergo a conformational change, they bind with and activate **adenylyl cyclase,** an enzyme on the cytoplasmic side of the plasma membrane. Adenylyl cyclase catalyzes the formation of **cyclic AMP (cAMP)** from ATP. Cyclic AMP is a second messenger that activates certain **protein kinase** enzymes that phosphorylate certain proteins. The phosphorylated protein triggers a chain of reactions that lead to some response in the cell.

- Certain G proteins activate the membrane-bound enzyme phospholipase C. This enzyme splits a phospholipid, PIP_2 (phosphotidylinositol-4,5-bisphosphate), into two products, **inositol trisphosphate (IP_3)** and **diacylglycerol (DAG).** IP_3 is a second messenger that can donate phosphate groups to proteins. IP_3 binds to calcium channels in the endoplasmic reticulum, which causes the channels to open and release calcium ions into the cytosol. DAG is a second messenger that activates certain protein kinase enzymes. These enzymes phosphorylate a variety of target proteins.

- Calcium ions can also act as second messengers. They typically combine with the protein **calmodulin,** which then affects the activity of protein kinases and protein phosphatases.

6.5 Responses to Signals *(page 141)*

7 Describe three types of responses that cells make to signaling molecules.

- In response to signaling molecules, ion channels open or close, enzyme activity changes, leading to metabolic changes and other effects, and specific genes are activated or repressed. These responses can affect cell shape, cell growth, cell division, cell differentiation, and metabolism.

8 Contrast signal amplification with signal termination.

- **Signal amplification** is the process of enhancing the cell's response to a signal as the signal is relayed through a signal transduction pathway. Before it becomes inactive, each enzyme can catalyze the production of numerous product molecules.
- *Signal termination* is the process of inactivating the receptor and each component of the signal transduction pathway once

they have done their jobs. Signal termination allows molecules in the system to respond to new signals.

6.6 Evolution of Cell Communication *(page 144)*

9 Cite evidence supporting a long evolutionary history for cell signaling molecules.

- Molecules important in cell signaling first evolved in prokaryotes. G proteins, protein kinases, and phosphatases have been highly conserved and are part of most signaling pathways.

TEST YOUR UNDERSTANDING

Know and Comprehend

1. During signal transduction (a) the cell converts an extracellular signal into an intracellular signal that leads to a change in some cell process (b) a signaling molecule directly activates or represses several genes (c) each enzyme catalyzes production of one molecule of product (d) enzymes in the signal cascade remain active until the last component of the pathway alters a cellular process (e) the signal is terminated by cyclic AMP

2. When a signaling molecule binds with a receptor, (a) G proteins are inactivated (b) a third messenger is activated (c) cell signaling is terminated (d) cAMP is produced by the receptor (e) the receptor becomes activated

3. G protein–linked receptors (a) inactivate G proteins (b) activate first messengers (c) consist of 18 transmembrane alpha helices (d) have a tail that extends into the cytosol with a binding site for a G protein (e) are located in the cytoplasm or nucleus

4. An enzyme-linked receptor (a) is a cytoplasmic protein (b) would not be found on plant cell surfaces (c) forms a dimer with another enzyme-linked receptor when a ligand binds to it (d) is typically an adenylyl cyclase molecule (e) typically activates ion channels

5. G proteins (a) relay a message from an activated receptor to an enzyme that activates a second messenger (b) are GTP molecules (c) terminate cell signaling (d) directly activate protein kinases (e) function as first messengers

6. Calcium ions (a) can act as second messengers (b) split calmodulin (c) are kept at higher concentration in the cytosol than in the extracellular fluid (d) are produced in the ER by protein kinases and protein phosphatases (e) typically terminate signaling cascades

7. When growth hormone binds to an enzyme-linked receptor, (a) G proteins are amplified into a cascade of molecules (b) the enzyme portion of the receptor becomes dephosphorylated (c) the receptor becomes activated and phosphorylates signaling proteins in the cell (d) an ion channel is opened (e) an immediate signal is sent into the nucleus, and specific genes are activated or inhibited

8. Scaffold proteins (a) release kinases and phosphatases into the extracellular fluid (b) bind G proteins to cell membranes (c) increase accuracy but slow signaling cascades (d) organize groups of intracellular signaling molecules into signaling complexes (e) are transcription factors found mainly in plant cells

9. Each adenylyl cyclase molecule produces many cAMP molecules in an example of (a) receptor up-regulation (b) receptor down-regulation (c) signal amplification (d) scaffolding (e) similarities produced by evolution

Apply and Analyze

10. In response to a hormone secreted by a cell of the opposite mating type, a yeast cell undergoes a complex series of physiological changes involving the activity of about 200 genes and

cytoplasmic proteins. They include blocking DNA synthesis, growing toward the mating partner, fusion of the plasma membranes of the two cells, and fusion of their nuclear membranes. Explain how all these events can be controlled through a complex signaling cascade that is triggered by the binding of the hormone to a G protein–linked receptor.

11. More than five hundred genes have been identified in the human genome that code for protein kinases. What does such identification imply regarding the role of protein kinases in cellular functions? Explain your answer.

12. Which is the correct sequence? 1. protein kinase activated 2. adenylyl cyclase activated 3. cAMP produced 4. proteins phosphorylated 5. G protein activated (a) 1, 2, 3, 5, 4 (b) 5, 3, 2, 1, 4 (c) 5, 2, 3, 4, 1 (d) 5, 2, 3, 1, 4 (e) 2, 3, 1, 4, 5

13. Which is the correct sequence? 1. phospholipase activated 2. G protein activated 3. PIP$_2$ split 4. proteins phosphorylated 5. DAG produced (a) 1, 2, 5, 3, 4 (b) 2, 1, 3, 5, 4 (c) 4, 2, 3, 1, 5 (d) 5, 2, 3, 1, 4 (e) 2, 3, 5, 4, 1

Evaluate and Synthesize

14. **EVOLUTION LINK** Cell signaling in plant and animal cells is similar in some ways and different in others. Offer one or more hypotheses for these similarities and differences, and cite specific examples.

15. **EVOLUTION LINK** Some of the same G protein–linked receptors and signal transduction pathways found in plants and animals have been identified in fungi and algae. What does that suggest about the evolution of these molecules? What does it suggest about these molecules and pathways?

16. **SCIENCE, TECHNOLOGY, AND SOCIETY** Mutant tyrosine kinase signaling proteins are implicated in many types of human cancer. Hundreds of millions of dollars are required for the basic research and development of each new drug; consequently, many of these drugs are very expensive when used for cancer treatments. In 2012, eight tyrosine kinase inhibitors were approved for cancer treatments by the U.S. Food and Drug Administration, and more than one hundred potential inhibitors were undergoing clinical trials for approval. What do you think would be some of the difficulties of finding these drugs given that similar kinases are active in normal cells? Do you think new medications of this type should be developed through government-sponsored research? Why or why not? If not, what alternatives do you propose?

 To access course materials, such as Aplia and other companion resources, please visit **www.cengagebrain.com**.

Energy and Metabolism

Giant panda (*Ailuropoda melanoleuca*). The chemical energy produced by photosynthesis and stored in bamboo leaves transfers to the panda as it eats.

Keren Su/Corbis

7.1 Energy, the capacity to do work, can be kinetic energy (energy of motion) or potential energy (energy due to position or state).

7.2 Energy cannot be created or destroyed (the first law of thermodynamics), but the total amount of energy available to do work in a closed system decreases over time (the second law of thermodynamics). Organisms do not violate the laws of thermodynamics because, as open systems, they use energy obtained from their surroundings to do work.

7.3 In cells energy-releasing (exergonic) processes drive energy-requiring (endergonic) processes.

7.4 ATP plays a central role in cell energy metabolism by linking exergonic and endergonic reactions. ATP transfers energy by transferring a phosphate group.

7.5 The transfer of electrons in redox reactions is another way that cells transfer energy.

7.6 As biological catalysts, enzymes increase the rate of specific chemical reactions. The activity of an enzyme is influenced by temperature, pH, the presence of cofactors, and inhibitors and activators.

All living things require energy to carry out life processes. It may seem obvious that cells need energy to grow and reproduce, but even nongrowing cells need energy simply to maintain themselves. Cells obtain energy in many forms, but that energy can seldom be used directly to power cell processes. For this reason, cells have mechanisms that convert energy from one form to another. The ordered systems of the cell provide the information that makes these energy transformations possible. Because most components of these energy conversion systems evolved very early in the history of life, many aspects of energy metabolism tend to be similar in a wide range of organisms.

The sun is the ultimate source of almost all the energy that powers life; this *radiant energy* flows from the sun as electromagnetic waves. Plants and other photosynthetic organisms capture about 0.02% of the sun's energy that reaches Earth. As discussed in Chapter 9, photosynthetic organisms convert radiant energy to *chemical energy* in the bonds of organic molecules. This chemical energy becomes available to plants, animals such as the giant panda shown in the photograph, and other organisms through the process of cellular respiration. In cellular respiration, discussed in Chapter 8, organic molecules are broken apart, and their energy is converted to more immediately usable forms.

This chapter focuses on some of the basic principles that govern how cells capture, transfer, store, and use energy. We discuss the functions of adenosine triphosphate (ATP) and other molecules used in energy conversions, including those that transfer electrons in oxidation–reduction (redox) reactions. We also pay particular attention to the essential role of enzymes in cell energy dynamics. The flow of energy in ecosystems is discussed in Chapter 55.

7.1 BIOLOGICAL WORK

LEARNING OBJECTIVES

1 Define *energy*, emphasizing how it is related to work and to heat.
2 Use examples to contrast potential energy and kinetic energy.

Energy, one of the most important concepts in biology, can be understood in the context of **matter,** which is anything that has mass and takes up space. **Energy** is defined as the capacity to do work, which is any change in the state or motion of matter. Technically, mass is a form of energy, which is the basis behind the energy generated by the sun and other stars. More than 4 billion kilograms of matter per second are converted into energy in the sun.

Biologists generally express energy in units of work, or **kilojoules (kJ).** It can also be expressed in units of *heat energy*—**kilocalories (kcal)**—thermal energy that flows from an object with a higher temperature to an object with a lower temperature. One kilocalorie is equal to 4.184 kJ. Heat energy cannot do cell work because a cell is too small to have regions that differ in temperature. For that reason, the unit most biologists prefer today is the kilojoule. However, we will use both units because references to the kilocalorie are common in the scientific literature.

Organisms carry out conversions between potential energy and kinetic energy

When an archer draws a bow, **kinetic energy,** the energy of motion, is used and work is performed (FIG. 7-1). The resulting tension in the bow and string represents stored, or potential, energy. **Potential energy** is the capacity to do work as a result of position or state. When the string is released, this potential energy is converted to kinetic energy in the motion of the bow, which propels the arrow.

Most actions of an organism involve a series of energy transformations that occur as kinetic energy is converted to potential energy or as potential energy is converted to kinetic energy. *Chemical energy,* potential energy stored in chemical bonds, is of particular importance to organisms. In our example the chemical energy of food molecules is converted to kinetic energy in the muscle cells of the archer. The contraction of the archer's muscles, like many of the activities performed by an organism, is an example of *mechanical energy,* which performs work by moving matter.

CHECKPOINT 7.1

- **VISUALIZE** *Draw simple sketches showing (1) a person stretching a spring, (2) the stretched spring, and (3) the release of tension. Label work that is done, potential energy, and kinetic energy.*

7.2 THE LAWS OF THERMODYNAMICS

LEARNING OBJECTIVE

3   State the first and second laws of thermodynamics, and discuss the implications of these laws as they relate to organisms.

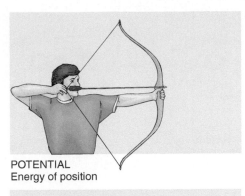

POTENTIAL
Energy of position

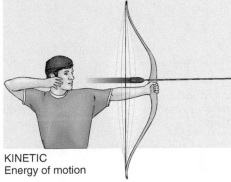

KINETIC
Energy of motion

Figure 7-1 Potential versus kinetic energy
The potential chemical energy released by cellular respiration is converted to kinetic energy in the muscles, which do the work of drawing the bow The potential energy stored in the drawn bow is transformed into kinetic energy as the bowstring pushes the arrow toward its target.
© Cengage Learning

Thermodynamics, the study of energy and its transformations, governs all activities of the universe, from the life and death of cells to the life and death of stars. When considering thermodynamics, scientists use the term *system* to refer to an object that they are studying, whether a cell, an organism, or planet Earth. The rest of the universe other than the system being studied constitutes the *surroundings.* A **closed system** does not exchange energy with its surroundings, whereas an **open system** can exchange energy with its surroundings (FIG. 7-2). Biological systems are open systems. Two laws about energy—the first and second laws of thermodynamics—apply to all things in the universe.

The total energy in the universe does not change

According to the **first law of thermodynamics,** energy cannot be created or destroyed, although it can be transferred or converted from one form to another, including conversions between matter and energy. As far as we know, the total mass-energy present in the universe when it formed, almost 14 billion years ago, equals the amount of energy present in the universe today. It is all the energy that can ever be present in the universe. Similarly, the energy of any system plus its surroundings is constant.

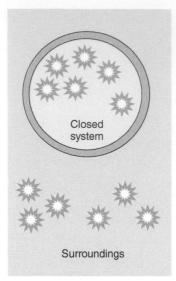

(a) A closed system does not exchange energy with its surroundings.

(b) An open system exchanges energy with its surroundings.

Figure 7-2 Closed and open systems
© Cengage Learning

A system may absorb energy from its surroundings or may give up some energy to its surroundings, but the total energy content of that system plus its surroundings is always the same.

As specified by the first law of thermodynamics, organisms cannot create the energy they require to live. Instead, they must capture energy from the environment and transform it to a form that can be used for biological work.

The entropy of the universe is increasing

The **second law of thermodynamics** states that when energy is converted from one form to another, some usable energy—that is, energy available to do work—is converted into heat that disperses into the surroundings (see Figure 55-1 for an illustration of energy flow through an ecosystem). As you learned in Chapter 2, **heat** is the kinetic energy of randomly moving particles. Unlike *heat energy*, which flows from an object with a higher temperature to one with a lower temperature, this random motion cannot perform work. As a result, the amount of usable energy available to do work in the universe decreases over time.

It is important to understand that the second law of thermodynamics is consistent with the first law; that is, the total amount of energy in the universe is *not* decreasing with time. However, the total amount of energy in the universe that is available to do work is decreasing over time.

Less-usable energy is more diffuse, or disorganized. **Entropy** (S) is a measure of this disorder, or randomness; organized, usable energy has a low entropy, whereas disorganized energy, such as heat, has a high entropy.

Entropy is continuously increasing in the universe in all natural processes. Maybe at some time, billions of years from now, all energy will exist as heat uniformly distributed throughout the universe. If that happens, the universe will cease to operate because no work will be possible. Everything will be at the same temperature, so there will be no way to convert the thermal energy of the universe into usable mechanical energy.

As a consequence of the second law of thermodynamics, no process requiring an energy conversion is ever 100% efficient because much of the energy is dispersed as heat, increasing entropy. For example, an automobile engine, which converts the chemical energy of gasoline to mechanical energy, is between 20% and 30% efficient. Thus, only 20% to 30% of the original energy stored in the chemical bonds of the gasoline molecules is actually transformed into mechanical energy; the other 70% to 80% dissipates as waste heat. Energy use in your cells is about 40% efficient, with the remaining energy given to the surroundings as heat.

Organisms have a high degree of organization, and at first glance they may appear to refute the second law of thermodynamics. As organisms grow and develop, they maintain a high level of order and do not appear to become more disorganized. However, organisms are open systems; they maintain their degree of order over time only with the constant input of energy from their surroundings. That is why plants must photosynthesize and animals must eat. Although the order within organisms may tend to increase temporarily, the total entropy of the universe (organisms plus surroundings) always increases over time.

CHECKPOINT 7.2

- *What is the first law of thermodynamics? the second law?*
- **CONNECT** *Life is sometimes described as a constant struggle against the second law of thermodynamics. How do organisms succeed in this struggle without violating the second law?*

7.3 ENERGY AND METABOLISM

LEARNING OBJECTIVES

4 Discuss how changes in free energy in a reaction are related to changes in entropy and enthalpy.

5 Distinguish between exergonic and endergonic reactions, and give examples of how they may be coupled.

6 Compare the energy dynamics of a reaction at equilibrium with the dynamics of a reaction not at equilibrium.

The chemical reactions that enable an organism to carry on its activities—to grow, move, maintain and repair itself; reproduce; and respond to stimuli—together make up its metabolism. Recall from Chapter 1 that **metabolism** is the sum of all the chemical activities taking place in an organism. An organism's metabolism consists of many intersecting series of chemical reactions, or pathways. Two main types of metabolism are anabolism and catabolism. **Anabolism** includes the various pathways in which complex molecules are synthesized from simpler substances, such as in the linking of amino acids to form proteins. **Catabolism** includes the pathways in which larger molecules are broken down into smaller ones, such as in the degradation of starch to form monosaccharides.

As you will see, these changes involve not only alterations in the arrangement of atoms but also various energy transformations. Catabolism and anabolism are complementary processes; catabolic pathways involve an overall release of energy, some of which powers anabolic pathways, which have an overall energy requirement. In the following sections, we discuss how to predict whether a particular chemical reaction requires energy or releases it.

Enthalpy is the total potential energy of a system

In the course of any chemical reaction, including the metabolic reactions of a cell, chemical bonds break and new and different bonds may form. Every specific type of chemical bond has a certain amount of *bond energy*, defined as the energy required to break that bond. The total bond energy is essentially equivalent to the total potential energy of the system, a quantity known as **enthalpy (*H*)**.

Free energy is available to do cell work

Entropy and enthalpy are related by a third type of energy, termed **free energy (*G*)**, which is the amount of energy available to do work under the conditions of a biochemical reaction. (*G*, also known as "Gibbs free energy," is named for J.W. Gibbs, a Yale professor who was one of the founders of the science of thermodynamics.) Free energy, the only kind of energy that can do cell work, is the aspect of thermodynamics of greatest interest to a biologist. Enthalpy, free energy, and entropy are related by the equation

$$H = G + TS$$

in which *H* is enthalpy; *G* is free energy; *T* is the absolute temperature of the system, expressed in Kelvin units; and *S* is entropy. Disregarding temperature for the moment, enthalpy (the total energy of a system) is equal to free energy (the usable energy) plus entropy (the unusable energy).

A rearrangement of the equation shows that as entropy increases, the amount of free energy decreases:

$$G = H - TS$$

If we assume that entropy is zero, the free energy is simply equal to the total potential energy (enthalpy); an increase in entropy reduces the amount of free energy.

What is the significance of the temperature (*T*)? Remember that as the temperature increases, there is an increase in random molecular motion, which contributes to disorder and multiplies the effect of the entropy term.

Chemical reactions involve changes in free energy

Biologists analyze the role of energy in the many biochemical reactions of metabolism. Although the total free energy of a system (*G*) cannot be effectively measured, the equation $G = H - TS$ can be extended to predict whether a particular chemical reaction will release

energy or require an input of energy. The reason is that *changes* in free energy can be measured. Scientists use the Greek capital letter delta (Δ) to denote any change that occurs in the system between its initial state before the reaction and its final state after the reaction. To express what happens with respect to energy in a chemical reaction, the equation becomes

$$\Delta G = \Delta H - T\Delta S$$

Notice that the temperature does not change; it is held constant during the reaction. Thus, the change in free energy (Δ*G*) during the reaction is equal to the change in enthalpy (Δ*H*) minus the product of the absolute temperature (*T*) in Kelvin units multiplied by the change in entropy (Δ*S*). Scientists express Δ*G* and Δ*H* in kilojoules or kilocalories per mole; they express Δ*S* in kilojoules or kilocalories per Kelvin unit.

Free energy decreases during an exergonic reaction

An **exergonic reaction** releases energy and is said to be a spontaneous or a "downhill" reaction, from higher to lower free energy (FIG. 7-3a). Because the total free energy in its final state is less than the total free energy in its initial state, Δ*G* is a negative number for exergonic reactions.

The term *spontaneous* may give the false impression that such reactions are always instantaneous. In fact, spontaneous reactions do not necessarily occur readily; some are extremely slow. The reason is that energy, known as *activation energy*, is required to initiate every reaction, even a spontaneous one. We discuss activation energy later in the chapter.

Free energy increases during an endergonic reaction

An **endergonic reaction** is a reaction in which there is a gain of free energy (FIG. 7-3b). Because the free energy of the products is greater than the free energy of the reactants, Δ*G* has a positive value. Such a reaction cannot take place in isolation. Instead, it must occur in such a way that energy can be supplied from the

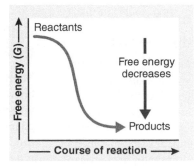

(a) In an exergonic reaction, there is a net loss of free energy. The products have less free energy than was present in the reactants, and the reaction proceeds spontaneously.

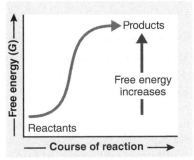

(b) In an endergonic reaction, there is a net gain of free energy. The products have more free energy than was present in the reactants.

Figure 7-3 *Animation* **Exergonic and endergonic reactions**

Concentration gradient

Exergonic process
(occurs
spontaneously)

(a) A concentration gradient is a form of potential energy.

(b) When molecules are evenly distributed, they have high entropy.

Figure 7-4 Entropy and diffusion

The tendency of entropy to increase can be used to produce work, in this case, diffusion.

© Cengage Learning

surroundings. Of course, many energy-requiring reactions take place in cells, and as you will see, metabolic mechanisms have evolved that supply the energy to "drive" these nonspontaneous cell reactions in a particular direction.

Diffusion is an exergonic process

In Chapter 5, you saw that randomly moving particles diffuse down their own concentration gradient (FIG. 7-4). Although the movements of the individual particles are random, net movement of the group of particles seems to be directional. What provides energy for this apparently directed process? A **concentration gradient,** with a region of higher concentration and another region of lower concentration, is an orderly state. A cell must expend energy to produce a concentration gradient. Because work is done to produce this order, a concentration gradient is a form of potential energy. As the particles move about randomly, the gradient becomes degraded. Thus, free energy decreases as entropy increases.

In cellular respiration and photosynthesis, the potential energy stored in a concentration gradient of hydrogen ions (H^+) is transformed into chemical energy in adenosine triphosphate (ATP) as the hydrogen ions pass through a membrane down their concentration gradient. This important concept, known as *chemiosmosis,* is discussed in detail in Chapters 8 and 9.

Free-energy changes depend on the concentrations of reactants and products

According to the second law of thermodynamics, any process that increases entropy can do work. As we have discussed, differences in the concentration of a substance, such as between two different parts of a cell, represent a more orderly state than that when the substance is diffused homogeneously throughout the cell. Free-energy changes in any chemical reaction depend mainly on the difference in bond energies (enthalpy, *H*) between reactants and products. Free energy also depends on *concentrations* of both reactants and products.

In most biochemical reactions, there is little intrinsic free-energy difference between reactants and products. Such reactions are reversible, indicated by drawing double arrows:

$$A \rightleftharpoons B$$

At the beginning of a reaction, only the reactant molecules (A) may be present. As the reaction proceeds, the concentration of the reactant molecules decreases and the concentration of the product molecules (B) increases. As the concentration of the product molecules increases, they may have enough free energy to initiate the reverse reaction. The reaction thus proceeds in both directions simultaneously; if undisturbed, it eventually reaches a state of **dynamic equilibrium,** in which the rate of the reverse reaction equals the rate of the forward reaction. At equilibrium there is no net change in the system; a reverse reaction balances every forward reaction.

At a given temperature and pressure, each reaction has its own characteristic equilibrium. For any given reaction, chemists can perform experiments and calculations to determine the relative concentrations of reactants and products present at equilibrium. If the reactants have much greater intrinsic free energy than the products, the reaction goes almost to completion; that is, it reaches equilibrium at a point at which most of the reactants have been converted to products. Reactions in which the reactants have much less intrinsic free energy than the products reach equilibrium at a point where very few of the reactant molecules have been converted to products.

If you increase the initial concentration of A, the reaction will "shift to the right," and more A will be converted to B. A similar effect can be obtained if B is removed from the reaction mixture. The reaction always shifts in the direction that reestablishes equilibrium so that the proportions of reactants and products characteristic of that reaction at equilibrium are restored. The opposite effect occurs if the concentration of B increases or if A is removed; here the system "shifts to the left." The actual free-energy change that occurs during a reaction is defined mathematically to include these effects, which stem from the relative initial concentrations of reactants and products. Cells use energy to manipulate the relative concentrations of reactants and products of almost every reaction. Cell reactions are virtually never at equilibrium. By displacing their reactions far from equilibrium, cells supply energy to endergonic reactions and direct their metabolism according to their needs.

Cells drive endergonic reactions by coupling them to exergonic reactions

Many metabolic reactions, such as protein synthesis, are anabolic and endergonic. Because an endergonic reaction cannot take place without an input of energy, endergonic reactions are coupled to exergonic reactions. In **coupled reactions,** the thermodynamically favorable exergonic reaction provides the energy required to drive the thermodynamically unfavorable endergonic reaction. The endergonic reaction proceeds only if it absorbs free energy released by the exergonic reaction to which it is coupled.

Consider the free-energy change, ΔG, in the reaction

(1) A $\longrightarrow$ B ΔG = +20.9 kJ/mol (+5 kcal/mol)

Because ΔG has a positive value, you know that the product of this reaction has more free energy than the reactant. It is an endergonic reaction. It is not spontaneous and does not take place without an energy source.

By contrast, consider the reaction

$$(2)\ C \longrightarrow D \qquad \Delta G = -33.5\ \text{kJ/mol}\ (-8\ \text{kcal/mol})$$

The negative value of ΔG tells you that the free energy of the reactant is greater than the free energy of the product. This exergonic reaction proceeds spontaneously.

You can add reactions 1 and 2 as follows:

$(1)\ A \longrightarrow B$	$\Delta G = +20.9\ \text{kJ/mol}\ (+5\ \text{kcal/mol})$	
$(2)\ C \longrightarrow D$	$\Delta G = -33.5\ \text{kJ/mol}\ (-8\ \text{kcal/mol})$	
Overall	$\Delta G = -12.6\ \text{kJ/mol}\ (-3\ \text{kcal/mol})$	

Because thermodynamics considers the overall changes in these two reactions, which show a net negative value of ΔG, the two reactions taken together are exergonic.

That scientists can write reactions this way is a useful bookkeeping device, but it does not mean that an exergonic reaction mysteriously transfers energy to an endergonic "bystander" reaction. However, these reactions are coupled if their pathways are altered so a common intermediate links them. Reactions 1 and 2 might be coupled by an intermediate (I) in the following way:

$(3)\ A + C \longrightarrow I$	$\Delta G = -8.4\ \text{kJ/mol}\ (-2\ \text{kcal/mol})$	
$(4)\ I \longrightarrow B + D$	$\Delta G = -4.2\ \text{kJ/mol}\ (-1\ \text{kcal/mol})$	
Overall	$\Delta G = -12.6\ \text{kJ/mol}\ (-3\ \text{kcal/mol})$	

Note that reactions 3 and 4 are sequential. Thus, the reaction pathways have changed, but overall the reactants (A and C) and products (B and D) are the same, and the free-energy change is the same.

Generally, for each endergonic reaction occurring in a living cell there is a coupled exergonic reaction to drive it. Often the exergonic reaction involves the breakdown of ATP. Now let's examine specific examples of the role of ATP in energy coupling.

CHECKPOINT 7.3

- **CONNECT** *Consider the free-energy change in a reaction in which enthalpy decreases and entropy increases. Is ΔG zero, or does it have a positive value or a negative value? Is the reaction endergonic or exergonic?*

- **PREDICT** *Reaction 1 is at equilibrium; reaction 2 is not. Can either reaction do work? If so, which one?*

7.4 ATP, THE ENERGY CURRENCY OF THE CELL

LEARNING OBJECTIVE

7 Explain how the chemical structure of ATP allows it to transfer a phosphate group and discuss the central role of ATP in the overall energy metabolism of the cell.

In all living cells, energy is temporarily packaged within a remarkable chemical compound called **adenosine triphosphate (ATP),** which holds readily available energy for very short periods. We may think of ATP as the energy currency of the cell. When you work to earn money, you might say that your energy is symbolically stored in the money you earn. The energy the cell requires for immediate use is temporarily stored in ATP, which is like cash. When you earn extra money, you may deposit some in the bank; similarly, a cell may deposit energy in the chemical bonds of lipids, starch, or glycogen. Moreover, just as you dare not make less money than you spend, the cell must avoid energy bankruptcy, which would mean its death. Finally, just as you probably do not keep money you earn very long, the cell continuously spends its ATP, which must be replaced immediately.

ATP is a nucleotide consisting of three main parts: adenine, a nitrogen-containing organic base; ribose, a five-carbon sugar; and three phosphate groups, identifiable as phosphorus atoms surrounded by oxygen atoms (**FIG. 7-5**). Notice that the phosphate groups are bonded to the end of the molecule in a series,

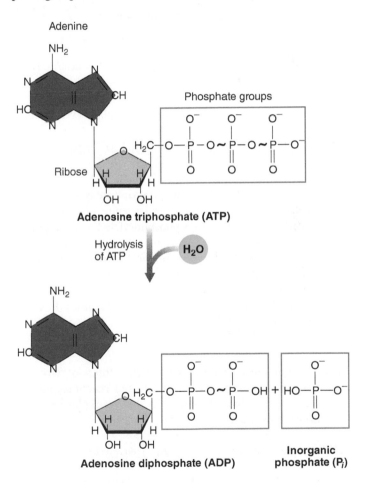

Figure 7-5 ATP and ADP

ATP, the energy currency of all living things, consists of adenine, ribose, and three phosphate groups. The hydrolysis of ATP, an exergonic reaction, yields ADP and inorganic phosphate. (The black wavy lines indicate unstable bonds. These bonds allow the phosphates to be transferred to other molecules, making them more reactive.)
© Cengage Learning

rather like three cars behind a locomotive, and, like the cars of a train, they can be attached and detached.

ATP donates energy through the transfer of a phosphate group

When the terminal phosphate is removed from ATP, the remaining molecule is adenosine diphosphate (ADP) (see Fig. 7-5). If the phosphate group is not transferred to another molecule, it is released as inorganic phosphate (P_i). This exergonic reaction has a relatively large negative value of ΔG. (Calculations of the free energy of ATP hydrolysis vary somewhat, but range between about -28 and -37 kJ/mol, or -6.8 to -8.7 kcal/mol.)

$$(5)\ ATP + H_2O \longrightarrow ADP + P_i$$

$$\Delta G = -32 \text{ kJ/mol } (-7.6 \text{ kcal/mol})$$

Reaction 5 can be coupled to endergonic reactions in cells. Consider the following endergonic reaction, in which two monosaccharides, glucose and fructose, form the disaccharide sucrose:

$$(6)\ glucose + fructose \longrightarrow sucrose + H_2O$$

$$\Delta G = +27 \text{ kJ/mol } (+6.5 \text{ kcal/mol})$$

With a free-energy change of -32 kJ/mol (-7.6 kcal/mol), the hydrolysis of ATP in reaction 5 can drive reaction 6, but only if the reactions are coupled through a common intermediate.

The following series of reactions is a simplified version of an alternative pathway that some bacteria use:

$$(7)\ glucose + ATP \longrightarrow glucose\text{-}P + ADP$$

$$(8)\ glucose\text{-}P + fructose \longrightarrow sucrose + P_i$$

Recall from Chapter 6 that **phosphorylation** is a reaction in which a phosphate group is transferred to some other compound. In reaction 7 glucose becomes phosphorylated to form glucose phosphate (glucose-P), the intermediate that links the two reactions. Glucose-P, which corresponds to I in reactions 3 and 4, reacts exergonically with fructose to form sucrose. For energy coupling to work in this way, reactions 7 and 8 must occur in sequence. It is convenient to summarize the reactions thus:

$$(9)\ glucose + fructose + ATP \longrightarrow sucrose + ADP + P_i$$

$$\Delta G = -5 \text{ kJ/mol } (-1.2 \text{ kcal/mol})$$

When you encounter an equation written in this way, remember that it is actually a summary of a series of reactions and that transitory intermediate products (in this case, glucose-P) are sometimes not shown.

ATP links exergonic and endergonic reactions

We have just discussed how the transfer of a phosphate group from ATP to some other compound is coupled to endergonic reactions in the cell. Conversely, adding a phosphate group to adenosine monophosphate, or AMP (forming ADP), or to ADP (forming ATP) requires coupling to exergonic reactions in the cell.

$$AMP + P_i + energy \longrightarrow ADP$$

$$ADP + P_i + energy \longrightarrow ATP$$

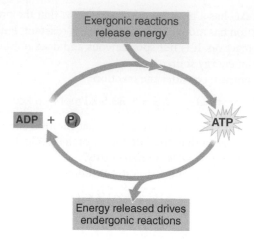

Figure 7-6 ATP links exergonic and endergonic reactions

Exergonic reactions in catabolic pathways (*top*) supply energy to drive the endergonic formation of ATP from ADP. Conversely, the exergonic hydrolysis of ATP supplies energy to endergonic reactions in anabolic pathways (*bottom*).
© Cengage Learning

Thus, ATP occupies an intermediate position in the metabolism of the cell and is an important link between exergonic reactions, which are generally components of *catabolic pathways*, and endergonic reactions, which are generally part of *anabolic pathways* (FIG. 7-6).

The cell maintains a very high ratio of ATP to ADP

The cell maintains a ratio of ATP to ADP far from the equilibrium point. ATP is constantly formed from ADP and inorganic phosphate as nutrients break down in cellular respiration or as photosynthesis traps the radiant energy of sunlight. At any time, a typical cell contains more than 10 ATP molecules for each ADP molecule. Because the cell maintains the ATP concentration at such a high level (relative to the concentration of ADP), its hydrolysis reaction is even more strongly exergonic and more able to drive the endergonic reactions to which it is coupled.

Although the cell maintains a high ratio of ATP to ADP, the cell cannot store large quantities of ATP. The concentration of ATP is always very low, less than 1 mmol/L. In fact, studies suggest that a bacterial cell has no more than a 1-second supply of ATP. Thus, it uses ATP molecules almost as quickly as they are produced. A healthy adult human at rest uses about 45 kg (100 lb) of ATP each day, but the amount present in the body at any given moment is less than 1 g (0.035 oz). Each second in every cell, an estimated 10 million molecules of ATP are made from ADP and phosphate, and an equal number of ATPs transfer their phosphate groups, along with their energy, to whatever chemical reactions need them.

CHECKPOINT 7.4

- *The conversion of substance X to substance Y is an endergonic reaction, but it can be driven if coupled to the hydrolysis of ATP. Write simple equations illustrating how that can occur.*
- **PREDICT** *What would likely happen in a cell if the ratio of ATP to ADP were to become 1:1?*

7.5 ENERGY TRANSFER IN REDOX REACTIONS

LEARNING OBJECTIVE

8 Relate the transfer of electrons (or hydrogen atoms) to the transfer of energy.

You have seen that cells transfer energy through the transfer of a phosphate group from ATP. Energy is also transferred through the transfer of electrons. As discussed in Chapter 2, oxidation is the chemical process in which a substance loses electrons, whereas reduction is the complementary process in which a substance gains electrons. Because electrons released during an oxidation reaction cannot exist in the free state in living cells, every oxidation reaction must be accompanied by a reduction reaction in which the electrons are accepted by another atom, ion, or molecule. Oxidation and reduction reactions are often called redox reactions because they occur simultaneously. The substance that becomes oxidized gives up energy as it releases electrons, and the substance that becomes reduced receives energy as it gains electrons.

Redox reactions often occur in a series as electrons are transferred from one molecule to another. These electron transfers, which are equivalent to energy transfers, are an essential part of cellular respiration, photosynthesis, and many other chemical processes. Redox reactions, for example, release the energy stored in food molecules so that ATP can be synthesized using that energy.

Most electron carriers transfer hydrogen atoms

Generally, it is not easy to remove one or more electrons from a covalent compound; it is much easier to remove a whole atom. For this reason, redox reactions in cells usually involve the transfer of a hydrogen atom rather than just an electron. A hydrogen atom contains an electron, plus a proton that does not participate in the oxidation–reduction reaction.

When an electron, either singly or as part of a hydrogen atom, is removed from an organic compound, it takes with it some of the energy stored in the chemical bond of which it was a part. That electron, along with its energy, is transferred to an acceptor molecule. An electron progressively loses free energy as it is transferred from one acceptor to another.

One of the most common acceptor molecules in cellular processes is **nicotinamide adenine dinucleotide (NAD$^+$).** When NAD$^+$ becomes reduced, it temporarily stores large amounts of free energy. Here is a generalized equation showing the transfer of hydrogen from a compound, which we call X, to NAD$^+$:

$$XH_2 + NAD^+ \longrightarrow X + NADH + H^+$$

$$\text{Oxidized} \qquad\qquad \text{Reduced}$$

Note that the NAD$^+$ becomes reduced when it combines with hydrogen. NAD$^+$ is an ion with a net charge of +1. When 2 electrons and 1 proton are added, the charge is neutralized and the reduced form of the compound, **NADH,** is produced (FIG. 7-7). (Although the correct way to write the reduced form of NAD$^+$ is NADH + H$^+$, for simplicity we present the reduced form as NADH in this book.) Some energy stored in the bonds holding the hydrogen atoms to molecule X has been transferred by this

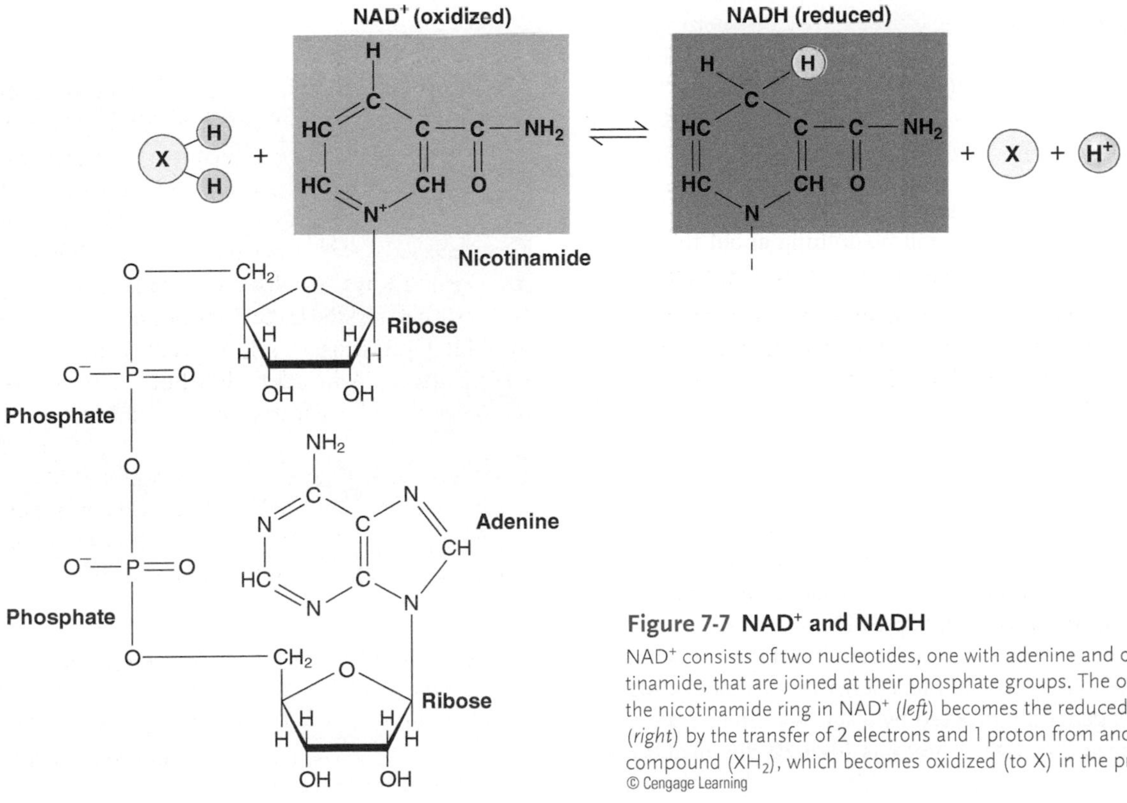

Figure 7-7 NAD$^+$ and NADH

NAD$^+$ consists of two nucleotides, one with adenine and one with nicotinamide, that are joined at their phosphate groups. The oxidized form of the nicotinamide ring in NAD$^+$ (*left*) becomes the reduced form in NADH (*right*) by the transfer of 2 electrons and 1 proton from another organic compound (XH$_2$), which becomes oxidized (to X) in the process.
© Cengage Learning

redox reaction and is temporarily held by NADH. When NADH transfers the electrons to some other molecule, some of their energy is transferred. This energy is usually then transferred through a series of reactions that ultimately result in the formation of ATP (discussed in Chapter 8).

Nicotinamide adenine dinucleotide phosphate (NADP⁺) is a hydrogen acceptor that is chemically similar to NAD⁺ but has an extra phosphate group. Unlike NADH, the reduced form of NADP⁺, abbreviated **NADPH,** is not involved in ATP synthesis. Instead, the electrons of NADPH are used more directly to provide energy for certain reactions, including certain essential reactions of photosynthesis (discussed in Chapter 9).

Other important hydrogen acceptors or electron acceptors are FAD and the cytochromes. Flavin adenine dinucleotide (FAD) is a nucleotide that accepts hydrogen atoms and their electrons; its reduced form is $FADH_2$. The cytochromes are proteins that contain iron; the iron component accepts electrons from hydrogen atoms and then transfers these electrons to some other compound. Like NAD⁺ and NADP⁺, FAD and the cytochromes are electron transfer agents. Each exists in a *reduced state,* in which it has more free energy, or in an *oxidized state,* in which it has less. Each is an essential component of many redox reaction sequences in cells.

CHECKPOINT 7.5

- **PREDICT** *Which has the most energy, the oxidized form of a substance or its reduced form? What is responsible for the difference?*

7.6 ENZYMES

LEARNING OBJECTIVES

9 Explain how an enzyme lowers the required energy of activation for a reaction.

10 Describe specific ways enzymes are regulated.

The principles of thermodynamics help us predict whether a reaction can occur, but they tell us nothing about the speed of the reaction. The breakdown of glucose, for example, is an exergonic reaction, yet a glucose solution stays unchanged virtually indefinitely in a bottle if it is kept free of bacteria and molds and not subjected to high temperatures or strong acids or bases. Cells cannot wait for centuries for glucose to break down, nor can they use extreme conditions to cleave glucose molecules. Cells regulate the rates of chemical reactions with **enzymes,** which are biological **catalysts** that increase the speed of a chemical reaction without being consumed by the reaction. Although most enzymes are proteins, scientists have learned that some types of RNA molecules have catalytic activity as well (catalytic RNA is discussed in Chapter 13).

Cells require a steady release of energy, and they must regulate that release to meet metabolic energy requirements. Metabolic processes generally proceed by a series of steps such that a molecule may go through as many as 20 or 30 chemical transformations before it reaches some final state. Even then, the seemingly completed molecule may enter yet another chemical pathway and become totally transformed or consumed to release energy. The changing needs of the cell require a system of flexible metabolic control. The key directors of this control system are enzymes.

The catalytic ability of some enzymes is truly impressive. For example, hydrogen peroxide (H_2O_2) breaks down extremely slowly if the reaction is uncatalyzed, but a single molecule of the enzyme *catalase* brings about the decomposition of 40 million molecules of hydrogen peroxide per second! Catalase has the highest catalytic rate known for any enzyme. It protects cells by destroying hydrogen peroxide, a poisonous substance produced as a byproduct of some cell reactions. The bombardier beetle uses the enzyme catalase as a defense mechanism (FIG. 7-8).

All reactions have a required energy of activation

All reactions, whether exergonic or endergonic, have an energy barrier known as the **energy of activation (E_A),** or **activation energy,** which is the energy required to break the existing bonds and begin the reaction. In a population of molecules of any kind, some have a relatively high kinetic energy, whereas others have a lower energy content. Only molecules with a relatively high kinetic energy are likely to react to form the product.

Even a strongly exergonic reaction, one that releases a substantial quantity of energy as it proceeds, may be prevented from proceeding by the activation energy required to begin the reaction. For example, molecular hydrogen and molecular oxygen can react explosively to form water:

$$2\,H_2 + O_2 \longrightarrow 2\,H_2O$$

Dr. Thomas Eisner/Visuals Unlimited, Inc.

Figure 7-8 *Animation* **Catalase as a defense mechanism**

When threatened, a bombardier beetle (*Stenaptinus insignis*) uses the enzyme catalase to decompose hydrogen peroxide. The oxygen gas formed in the decomposition ejects water and other chemicals with explosive force. Because the reaction releases a great deal of heat, the water comes out as steam. (A wire attached by a drop of adhesive to the beetle's back immobilizes it. The researcher prodded its leg with the dissecting needle on the left to trigger the ejection.)

This reaction is spontaneous, yet hydrogen and oxygen can be safely mixed as long as all sparks are kept away because the required activation energy for this particular reaction is relatively high. A tiny spark provides the activation energy that allows a few molecules to react. Their reaction liberates so much heat that the rest react, producing an explosion. Such an explosion occurred on the space shuttle *Challenger* on January 28, 1986 (FIG. 7-9). The failure of a rubber O-ring to seal properly caused the liquid hydrogen in the tank attached to the shuttle to leak and start burning. When the hydrogen tank ruptured a few seconds later, the resulting force burst the nearby oxygen tank as well, mixing hydrogen and oxygen and igniting a huge explosion.

An enzyme lowers a reaction's activation energy

Like all catalysts, enzymes affect the rate of a reaction by lowering the activation energy (E_A) necessary to initiate a chemical reaction (FIG. 7-10). If molecules need less energy to react because the activation barrier is lowered, a larger fraction of the reactant molecules reacts at any one time. As a result, the reaction proceeds more quickly.

Although an enzyme lowers the activation energy requirement for a reaction, it has no effect on the overall free-energy change; that is, an enzyme can promote only a chemical reaction

Figure 7-9 The space shuttle *Challenger* explosion
This disaster resulted from an explosive exergonic reaction between hydrogen and oxygen. All seven crew members died in the accident on January 28, 1986.

An enzyme lowers the activation energy of a reaction but does not alter the free-energy change.

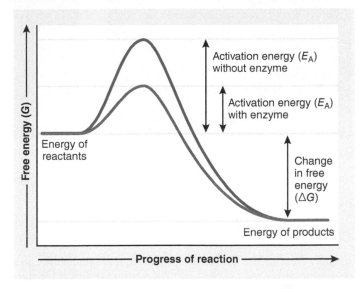

Figure 7-10 *Animation* **Activation energy and enzymes**
An enzyme speeds up a reaction by lowering its activation energy (E_A). In the presence of an enzyme, reacting molecules require less kinetic energy to complete a reaction.
PREDICT Could this reaction have proceeded if ΔG had a positive value?
© Cengage Learning

that could proceed without it. If the reaction goes to equilibrium, no catalyst can cause it to proceed in a thermodynamically unfavorable direction or can influence the final concentrations of reactants and products. Enzymes simply speed up reaction rates.

An enzyme works by forming an enzyme–substrate complex

An uncatalyzed reaction depends on random collisions among reactants. Because of its ordered structure, an enzyme reduces this reliance on random events. It controls the reaction by forming an unstable intermediate complex with the **substrate,** the substance on which it acts. When the **enzyme–substrate complex,** or *ES complex,* breaks up, the product is released; the original enzyme molecule is regenerated and is free to form a new ES complex:

enzyme + substrate(s) ⟶ ES complex

ES complex ⟶ enzyme + product(s)

The enzyme itself is not permanently altered or consumed by the reaction and can be reused.

As shown in **FIGURE 7-11a,** every enzyme contains one or more **active sites,** regions to which the substrate binds, to form the ES complex. The active sites of some enzymes are grooves or cavities in the enzyme molecule, formed by amino acid side chains. The active sites of most enzymes are located close to the

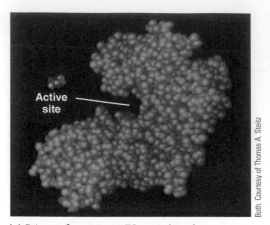

(a) Prior to forming an ES complex, the enzyme's active site is the furrow where the substrate will bind.

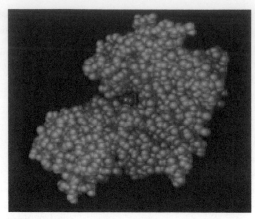

(b) The binding of the substrate to the active site induces a change in the conformation of the active site.

Both: Courtesy of Thomas A. Steitz

Figure 7-11 *Animation* **An enzyme–substrate complex**

This computer graphic model shows the enzyme hexokinase (*blue*) and its substrate, glucose (*red*).

surface. During the course of a reaction, substrate molecules occupying these sites are brought close together and react with one another.

The shape of the enzyme does not seem exactly complementary to that of the substrate. The binding of the substrate to the enzyme molecule causes a change, known as **induced fit,** in the shape of the enzyme (**FIG. 7-11b**). Usually, the shape of the substrate also changes slightly, in a way that may distort its chemical bonds. The proximity and orientation of the reactants, together with strains in their chemical bonds, facilitate the breakage of old bonds and the formation of new ones. Thus, the substrate is changed into a product, which diffuses away from the enzyme. The enzyme is then free to catalyze the reaction of more substrate molecules to form more product molecules.

Enzymes are specific

Enzymes catalyze virtually every chemical reaction that takes place in an organism. Because the shape of the active site is closely related to the shape of the substrate, most enzymes are highly specific. Most catalyze only a few closely related chemical reactions or, in many cases, only one particular reaction. The enzyme urease, which decomposes urea to ammonia and carbon dioxide, attacks no other substrate. The enzyme sucrase splits only sucrose; it does not act on other disaccharides, such as maltose or lactose. A few enzymes are specific only to the extent that they require the substrate to have a certain kind of chemical bond. For example, lipase, secreted by the pancreas, splits the ester linkages connecting the glycerol and fatty acids of a wide variety of fats.

Scientists usually name enzymes by adding the suffix *-ase* to the name of the substrate. The enzyme sucrase, for example, splits sucrose into glucose and fructose. A few enzymes retain traditional names that do not end in *-ase;* some of these end in *-zyme.* For example, lysozyme (from the Greek *lysis,* "a loosening") is an enzyme found in tears and saliva; it breaks down bacterial cell walls. Other examples of enzymes with traditional names are pepsin and trypsin, which break peptide bonds in proteins.

Scientists classify enzymes that catalyze similar reactions into groups, although each particular enzyme in the group may catalyze only one specific reaction. **TABLE 7-1** describes the six classes of enzymes that biologists recognize. Each class is divided into many subclasses. For example, sucrase, mentioned earlier, is called a glycosidase because it cleaves a glycosidic linkage. Glycosidases are a subclass of the hydrolases (see Figure 3-8b for the hydrolysis of sucrose). Phosphatases, enzymes that remove phosphate groups by hydrolysis, are also hydrolases. Kinases, enzymes that transfer phosphate groups to substrates, are transferases.

Many enzymes require cofactors

Some enzymes consist only of a protein. The enzyme pepsin, which is secreted by the animal stomach and digests dietary protein by breaking certain peptide bonds, is exclusively a protein molecule. Other enzymes have two components: a protein called the *apoenzyme* and an additional chemical component called a **cofactor.** Neither the apoenzyme nor the cofactor alone has catalytic activity; only when the two are combined does the enzyme function. A cofactor may be inorganic, or it may be an organic molecule.

Some enzymes require a specific metal ion as a cofactor. Two very common inorganic cofactors are magnesium ions and calcium ions. Most of the trace elements, such as iron, copper, zinc, and manganese—all of which organisms require in very small amounts—function as cofactors.

An organic, nonpolypeptide compound that binds to the apoenzyme and serves as a cofactor is called a **coenzyme.** Most coenzymes are carrier molecules that transfer electrons or part of a substrate from one molecule to another. We have already

TABLE 7-1	Important Classes of Enzymes
ENZYME CLASS	**FUNCTION**
Oxidoreductases	Catalyze oxidation–reduction reactions
Transferases	Catalyze the transfer of a functional group from a donor molecule to an acceptor molecule
Hydrolases	Catalyze hydrolysis reactions
Isomerases	Catalyze conversion of a molecule from one isomeric form to another
Ligases	Catalyze certain reactions in which two molecules become joined in a process coupled to the hydrolysis of ATP
Lyases	Catalyze certain reactions in which double bonds form or break

© Cengage Learning

introduced some examples of coenzymes in this chapter. NADH, NADPH, and $FADH_2$ are coenzymes; they transfer electrons.

ATP functions as a coenzyme; it is responsible for transferring phosphate groups. Yet another coenzyme, coenzyme A, is involved in the transfer of groups derived from organic acids. Most vitamins, which are organic compounds that an organism requires in small amounts but cannot synthesize itself, are coenzymes or components of coenzymes (see descriptions of vitamins in Table 47-3).

Enzymes are most effective at optimal conditions

Enzymes generally work best under certain narrowly defined conditions, such as appropriate temperature, pH (FIG. 7-12), and ion concentration. Any departure from optimal conditions adversely affects enzyme activity.

Each enzyme has an optimal temperature Most enzymes have an optimal temperature, at which the rate of reaction is fastest. For human enzymes, the temperature optima are near

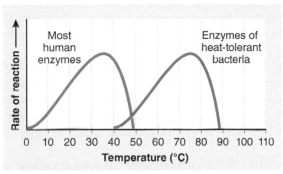

(a) **Generalized curves for the effect of temperature on enzyme activity.** As temperature increases, enzyme activity increases until it reaches an optimal temperature. Enzyme activity abruptly falls after it exceeds the optimal temperature because the enzyme, being a protein, denatures.

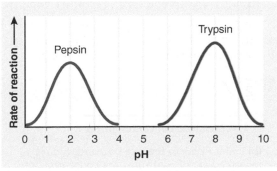

(b) **Enzyme activity is very sensitive to pH.** Pepsin is a protein-digesting enzyme in the very acidic stomach juice. Trypsin, secreted by the pancreas into the slightly basic small intestine, digests polypeptides.

Figure 7-12 The effects of temperature and pH on enzyme activity

Substrate and enzyme concentrations are held constant in the reactions illustrated.
© Cengage Learning

the human body temperature (35°C to 40°C). Enzymatic reactions occur slowly or not at all at low temperatures. As the temperature increases, molecular motion increases, resulting in more molecular collisions. The rates of most enzyme-controlled reactions therefore increase as the temperature increases, within limits (see Fig. 7-12a). High temperatures rapidly denature most enzymes. The molecular conformation (3-D shape) of the protein becomes altered as the hydrogen bonds responsible for its secondary, tertiary, and quaternary structures are broken. Because this inactivation is usually not reversible, activity is not regained when the enzyme is cooled.

Most organisms are killed by even a short exposure to high temperature; their enzymes arc denatured, and they are unable to continue metabolism. There are a few stunning exceptions to this rule. Certain species of archaea (see Chapter 1 for a description of the archaea), and also some bacteria, can survive in the waters of hot springs, such as those in Yellowstone National Park, where the temperature is almost 100°C; these organisms are responsible for the brilliant colors in the terraces of the hot springs (FIG. 7-13). Still other archaea live at temperatures not much above that of boiling water, near deep-sea vents, where the extreme pressure keeps water in its liquid state (see Chapter 25 for a discussion of archaea that live in extreme habitats; see also Chapter 55).

Each enzyme has an optimal pH Most enzymes are active only over a narrow pH range and have an optimal pH, at which the rate of reaction is fastest. The optimal pH for most human enzymes is between 6 and 8. Recall from Chapter 2 that *buffers* minimize pH changes in cells so that the pH is maintained within a narrow limit. Pepsin, a protein-digesting enzyme secreted by cells lining the stomach, is an exception; it works only in a very acidic medium, optimally at pH 2 (see Fig. 7-12b). In contrast, trypsin, a protein-splitting enzyme secreted by the pancreas, functions best under the slightly basic conditions found in the small intestine.

Figure 7-13 Grand Prismatic Spring in Yellowstone National Park
The world's third-largest spring, about 61 m (200 ft) in diameter, the Grand Prismatic Spring teems with heat-tolerant archaea. The rings around the perimeter, where the water is slightly cooler, get their distinctive colors from the various kinds of archaea living there.

The activity of an enzyme may be markedly changed by any alteration in pH, which in turn alters electric charges on the enzyme. Changes in charge affect the ionic bonds that contribute to tertiary and quaternary structure, thereby changing the protein's conformation and activity. Many enzymes become inactive, and usually irreversibly denatured, when the medium is made very acidic or very basic.

Enzymes are organized into teams in metabolic pathways

Enzymes play an essential role in reaction coupling because they usually work in sequence, with the product of one enzyme-controlled reaction serving as the substrate for the next. You can picture the inside of a cell as a factory with many different assembly (and disassembly) lines operating simultaneously. An assembly line consists of a number of enzymes. Each enzyme carries out one step, such as changing molecule A into molecule B. Then molecule B is passed along to the next enzyme, which converts it into molecule C, and so on. Such a series of reactions is called a **metabolic pathway.**

$$A \xrightarrow{\text{Enzyme 1}} B \xrightarrow{\text{Enzyme 2}} C$$

Each of these reactions is reversible, even though an enzyme catalyzes it. An enzyme does not itself determine the direction of the reaction it catalyzes. However, the overall reaction sequence is portrayed as proceeding from left to right. Recall that if there is little intrinsic free-energy difference between the reactants and products for a particular reaction, the direction of the reaction is determined mainly by the relative concentrations of reactants and products.

In metabolic pathways, both intermediate and final products are often removed and converted to other chemical compounds. Such removal drives the sequence of reactions in a particular direction. Let us assume that reactant A is continually supplied and that its concentration remains constant. Enzyme 1 converts reactant A to product B. The concentration of B is always lower than the concentration of A because B is removed as it is converted to C in the reaction catalyzed by enzyme 2. If C is removed as quickly as it is formed (perhaps by leaving the cell), the entire reaction pathway is "pulled" toward C.

In some cases, the enzymes of a metabolic pathway bind to one another to form a multienzyme complex that efficiently transfers intermediates in the pathway from one active site to another. An example of one such multienzyme complex, pyruvate dehydrogenase, is discussed in Chapter 8.

The cell regulates enzymatic activity

Enzymes regulate the chemistry of the cell, but what controls the enzymes? One regulatory mechanism involves controlling the amount of enzyme produced. A specific gene directs the synthesis of each type of enzyme. The gene, in turn, may be switched on by a signal from a hormone or by some other signal molecule. When the gene is switched on, the enzyme is synthesized. The total amount of enzyme present then influences the overall cell reaction rate.

If the pH and temperature are kept constant (as they are in most cells), the rate of the reaction can be affected by the substrate concentration or by the enzyme concentration. If an excess of substrate is present, the enzyme concentration is the rate-limiting factor. The initial rate of the reaction is then directly proportional to the enzyme concentration (**FIG. 7-14a**).

If the enzyme concentration is kept constant, the rate of an enzymatic reaction is proportional to the concentration of substrate present. Substrate concentration is the rate-limiting factor at lower concentrations; the rate of the reaction is therefore directly proportional to the substrate concentration. However, at higher substrate concentrations, the enzyme molecules become saturated with substrate; that is, substrate molecules are bound to all available active sites of enzyme molecules. In this situation, increasing the substrate concentration does not increase the net reaction rate (**FIG. 7-14b**).

The product of one enzymatic reaction may control the activity of another enzyme, especially in a sequence of enzymatic reactions. For example, consider the metabolic pathway

$$A \xrightarrow{\text{Enzyme 1}} B \xrightarrow{\text{Enzyme 2}} C \xrightarrow{\text{Enzyme 3}} D \xrightarrow{\text{Enzyme 4}} E$$

A different enzyme catalyzes each step, and the final product E may inhibit the activity of enzyme 1. When the concentration of E is low, the sequence of reactions proceeds rapidly. However, an increasing concentration of E serves as a signal for enzyme 1

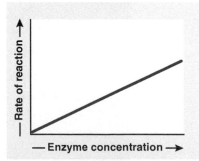

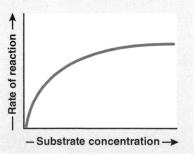

(a) In this example the rate of reaction is measured at different enzyme concentrations, with an excess of substrate present. (Temperature and pH are constant.) The rate of the reaction is directly proportional to the enzyme concentration.

(b) In this example the rate of the reaction is measured at different substrate concentrations, and enzyme concentration, temperature, and pH are constant. If the substrate concentration is relatively low, the reaction rate is directly proportional to substrate concentration. However, higher substrate concentrations do not increase the reaction rate because the enzymes become saturated with substrate.

Figure 7-14 The effects of enzyme concentration and substrate concentration on the rate of a reaction
© Cengage Learning

to slow down and eventually to stop functioning. Inhibition of enzyme 1 stops the entire reaction sequence. This type of enzyme regulation, in which the formation of a product inhibits an earlier reaction in the sequence, is called **feedback inhibition** (FIG. 7-15).

Another method of enzymatic control focuses on the activation of enzyme molecules. In their inactive form, the active sites of the enzyme are inappropriately shaped, so the substrates do not fit. Among the factors that influence the shape of the enzyme are pH, the concentration of certain ions, and the addition of phosphate groups to certain amino acids in the enzyme.

Some enzymes have a receptor site, called an **allosteric site,** on some region of the enzyme molecule other than the active site. (The word *allosteric* means "another space.") When a substance binds to an enzyme's allosteric site, the conformation of the enzyme's active site changes, thereby modifying the enzyme's activity. Substances that affect enzyme activity by binding to allosteric sites are called **allosteric regulators.** Some allosteric regulators are allosteric inhibitors that keep the enzyme in its inactive shape. Conversely, the activities of allosteric activators result in an enzyme with a functional active site.

The enzyme *cyclic AMP–dependent protein kinase* is an allosteric enzyme regulated by a protein that binds reversibly to the allosteric site and inactivates the enzyme. Protein kinase is in this inactive form most of the time (FIG. 7-16). When protein kinase activity is needed, the compound cyclic AMP (cAMP; see Figure 3-26 for the structure) contacts the enzyme–inhibitor complex and removes the inhibitory protein, thereby activating the protein kinase. Activation of protein kinases by cAMP is an important aspect of the mechanism of cell signaling, including the action of certain hormones (see Chapters 6 and 49 for discussions of cell signaling).

Enzymes are inhibited by certain chemical agents

Most enzymes are inhibited or even destroyed by certain chemical agents. Enzyme inhibition may be reversible or irreversible.

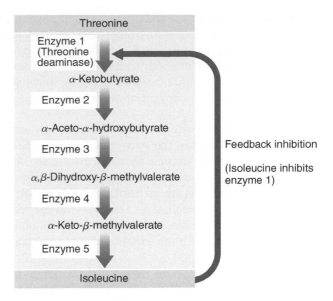

Figure 7-15 Feedback inhibition

Bacteria synthesize the amino acid isoleucine from the amino acid threonine. The isoleucine pathway involves five steps, each catalyzed by a different enzyme. When enough isoleucine accumulates in the cell, the isoleucine inhibits threonine deaminase, the enzyme that catalyzes the first step in this pathway.
© Cengage Learning

Reversible inhibition occurs when an inhibitor forms weak chemical bonds with the enzyme. Reversible inhibition can be competitive or noncompetitive.

In **competitive inhibition,** the inhibitor competes with the normal substrate for binding to the active site of the enzyme (FIG. 7-17a). Usually, a competitive inhibitor is structurally similar to the normal substrate and fits into the active site and combines with the enzyme. However, it is not similar enough to substitute fully for the normal substrate in the chemical reaction, and the enzyme cannot convert it to product molecules. A competitive inhibitor occupies the active site only temporarily and does not permanently damage the enzyme. In competitive inhibition an active site is occupied by

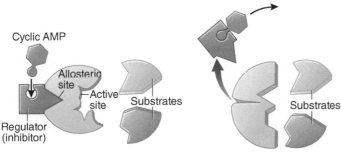

(a) Inactive form of the enzyme. The enzyme protein kinase is inhibited by a regulatory protein that binds reversibly to its allosteric site. When the enzyme is in this inactive form, the shape of the active site is modified so that the substrate cannot combine with it.

(b) Active form of the enzyme. Cyclic AMP removes the allosteric inhibitor and activates the enzyme.

(c) Enzyme–substrate complex. The substrate can then combine with the active site.

Figure 7-16 *Animation* An allosteric enzyme
© Cengage Learning

the inhibitor part of the time and by the normal substrate part of the time. If the concentration of the substrate is increased relative to the concentration of the inhibitor, the active site is usually occupied by the substrate. Biochemists demonstrate competitive inhibition experimentally by showing that increasing the substrate concentration reverses competitive inhibition.

In **noncompetitive inhibition** the inhibitor binds with the enzyme at a site other than the active site (FIG. 7-17b). Such an inhibitor inactivates the enzyme by altering its shape so that the active site cannot bind with the substrate. Many important noncompetitive inhibitors are metabolic substances that regulate enzyme activity by combining reversibly with the enzyme. Allosteric inhibition, discussed previously, is a type of noncompetitive inhibition in which the inhibitor binds to a special site, the allosteric site.

In *irreversible inhibition* an inhibitor permanently inactivates or destroys an enzyme when the inhibitor combines with one of the enzyme's functional groups, either at the active site or elsewhere. Many poisons are irreversible enzyme inhibitors. For example, heavy metals such as mercury and lead bind irreversibly to and denature many proteins, including enzymes. Certain nerve gases poison the enzyme acetylcholinesterase, which is important for the functioning of nerves and muscles. Cytochrome oxidase, one of the enzymes that transports electrons in cellular respiration, is especially sensitive to cyanide. Death results from cyanide poisoning because cytochrome oxidase is irreversibly inhibited and no longer transfers electrons from its substrate to oxygen.

Some drugs are enzyme inhibitors

Physicians treat many bacterial infections with drugs that directly or indirectly inhibit bacterial enzyme activity. For example, sulfa drugs have a chemical structure similar to that of the nutrient *para-aminobenzoic acid (PABA)* (FIG. 7-18). When PABA is available, microorganisms can synthesize the vitamin *folic acid,* which is necessary for growth. Humans do not synthesize folic acid from PABA. For this reason, sulfa drugs selectively affect bacteria. When a sulfa drug is present, the drug competes with PABA for the active site of the bacterial enzyme. When bacteria use the sulfa drug instead of PABA, they synthesize a compound that cannot be used to make folic acid. Therefore, the bacterial cells are unable to grow.

Penicillin and related antibiotics irreversibly inhibit a bacterial enzyme called *transpeptidase.* This enzyme establishes some of the chemical linkages in the bacterial cell wall. Bacteria susceptible to these antibiotics cannot produce properly constructed cell walls and are prevented from multiplying effectively. Human cells do not have cell walls and therefore do not use this enzyme. Thus, except for individuals allergic to it, penicillin is harmless to humans. Unfortunately, during the years since it was introduced, resistance to penicillin has evolved in many bacterial strains. The resistant bacteria fight back with an enzyme of their own, penicillinase, which breaks down the penicillin and renders it ineffective. Because bacteria evolve at such a rapid rate, drug resistance is a growing problem in medical practice.

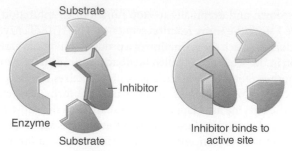

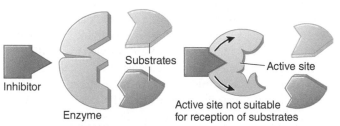

(a) Competitive inhibition. The inhibitor competes with the normal substrate for the active site of the enzyme. A competitive inhibitor occupies the active site only temporarily.

(b) Noncompetitive inhibition. The inhibitor binds with the enzyme at a site other than the active site, altering the shape of the enzyme and thereby inactivating it.

Figure 7-17 *Animation* **Competitive and noncompetitive inhibition**
© Cengage Learning

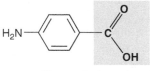

Para-aminobenzoic acid
(PABA)

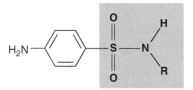

Generic sulfonamide
(Sulfa drug)

Figure 7-18 Para-aminobenzoic acid and sulfonamides

Sulfa drugs inhibit an enzyme in bacteria necessary for the synthesis of folic acid, an important vitamin required for growth. (Note the unusual structure of the sulfonamide molecule; sulfur, which commonly forms two covalent bonds, forms six instead.)
© Cengage Learning

CHECKPOINT 7.6

- CONNECT *What effect does an enzyme have on the required activation energy of a reaction?*
- *How does the function of the active site of an enzyme differ from that of an allosteric site?*
- CONNECT *How are temperature and pH optima of an enzyme related to its structure and function?*
- *Is allosteric inhibition competitive or noncompetitive?*

7.1 Biological Work (page 148)

1 Define *energy*, emphasizing how it is related to work and to heat.

- **Energy** is the capacity to do work (expressed in **kilojoules, kJ**). Energy can be conveniently measured as *heat energy*, thermal energy that flows from an object with a higher temperature to an object with a lower temperature; the unit of heat energy is the **kilocalorie (kcal),** which is equal to 4.184 kJ. Heat energy cannot do cell work.

2 Use examples to contrast potential energy and kinetic energy.

- **Potential energy** is stored energy; **kinetic energy** is energy of motion.

- All forms of energy are interconvertible. For example, photosynthetic organisms capture radiant energy and convert some of it to *chemical energy,* a form of potential energy that powers many life processes, such as muscle contraction.

7.2 The Laws of Thermodynamics (page 149)

3 State the first and second laws of thermodynamics, and discuss the implications of these laws as they relate to organisms.

- A **closed system** does not exchange energy with its surroundings. Organisms are **open systems** that do exchange energy with their surroundings.

- The **first law of thermodynamics** states that energy cannot be created or destroyed but can be transferred and changed in form. The first law explains why organisms cannot produce energy; but as open systems, they continuously capture it from the surroundings.

- The **second law of thermodynamics** states that disorder (entropy) in the universe, a closed system, is continuously increasing. No energy transfer is 100% efficient; some energy is dissipated as **heat,** random motion that contributes to **entropy (S),** or disorder. As open systems, organisms maintain their ordered states at the expense of their surroundings.

7.3 Energy and Metabolism (page 150)

4 Discuss how changes in free energy in a reaction are related to changes in entropy and enthalpy.

- As entropy increases, the amount of **free energy** decreases, as shown in the equation $G = H - TS$, in which G is the free energy, H is the **enthalpy** (total potential energy of the system), T is the absolute temperature (expressed in Kelvin units), and S is entropy.

- The equation $\Delta G = \Delta H - T\Delta S$ indicates that the change in free energy (ΔG) during a chemical reaction is equal to the change in enthalpy (ΔH) minus the product of the absolute temperature (T) multiplied by the change in entropy (ΔS).

5 Distinguish between exergonic and endergonic reactions, and give examples of how they may be coupled.

- An **exergonic reaction** has a negative value of ΔG; that is, free energy decreases. Such a reaction is spontaneous; it releases free energy that can perform work.

- Free energy increases in an **endergonic reaction.** Such a reaction has a positive value of ΔG and is nonspontaneous. In a **coupled reaction,** the input of free energy required to drive an endergonic reaction is supplied by an exergonic reaction.

6 Compare the energy dynamics of a reaction at equilibrium with the dynamics of a reaction not at equilibrium.

- When a chemical reaction is in a state of **dynamic equilibrium,** the rate of change in one direction is exactly the same as the rate of change in the opposite direction; the system can do no work because the free-energy difference between the reactants and products is zero.

- When the concentration of reactant molecules is increased, the reaction shifts to the right and more product molecules are formed until equilibrium is re-established.

7.4 ATP, the Energy Currency of the Cell (page 153)

7 Explain how the chemical structure of ATP allows it to transfer a phosphate group and discuss the central role of ATP in the overall energy metabolism of the cell.

- **Adenosine triphosphate (ATP)** is the immediate energy currency of the cell. It donates energy by means of its terminal phosphate group, which is easily transferred to an acceptor molecule. ATP is formed by the **phosphorylation** of **adenosine diphosphate (ADP),** an endergonic process that requires an input of energy.

- ATP is the common link between exergonic and endergonic reactions and between **catabolism** (degradation of large complex molecules into smaller, simpler molecules) and **anabolism** (synthesis of complex molecules from simpler molecules).

7.5 Energy Transfer in Redox Reactions (page 155)

8 Relate the transfer of electrons (or hydrogen atoms) to the transfer of energy.

- Energy is transferred in **oxidation–reduction (redox) reactions.** A substance becomes oxidized as it gives up one or more electrons to another substance, which becomes reduced in the process. Electrons are commonly transferred as part of hydrogen atoms.

- NAD^+ and $NADP^+$ accept electrons as part of hydrogen atoms and become reduced to form **NADH** and **NADPH,** respectively. These electrons (along with some of their energy) can be transferred to other acceptors.

7.6 Enzymes (page 156)

9 Explain how an enzyme lowers the required energy of activation for a reaction.

- An **enzyme** is a biological **catalyst;** it greatly increases the speed of a chemical reaction without being consumed.

- An enzyme works by lowering the **activation energy (E_A),** the energy necessary to get a reaction going. The **active site** of an enzyme is a 3-D region where **substrates** come into close contact and thereby react more readily. When a substrate binds to an active site, an **enzyme–substrate complex** forms in which the shapes of the enzyme and substrate change slightly. This **induced fit** facilitates the breaking of bonds and formation of new ones.

10 Describe specific ways enzymes are regulated.

- Enzymes work best at specific temperature and pH conditions.

- Some enzymes can only function if an additional chemical component, called a **cofactor,** is present. A cofactor may be inorganic (e.g., a certain metal ion), or it may be a non-polypeptide organic molecule referred to as a **coenzyme.**

- A cell can regulate enzymatic activity by controlling the amount of enzyme produced and by regulating metabolic conditions that influence the shape of the enzyme.

- Some enzymes have **allosteric sites,** noncatalytic sites to which an **allosteric regulator** binds, changing the enzyme's activity. Some allosteric enzymes are subject to **feedback** inhibition, in which the formation of an end product inhibits an earlier reaction in the metabolic pathway.

- *Reversible inhibition* occurs when an inhibitor forms weak chemical bonds with the enzyme. Reversible inhibition may be **competitive,** in which the inhibitor competes with the substrate for the active site, or **noncompetitive,** in which the inhibitor binds with the enzyme at a site other than the active site. *Irreversible inhibition* occurs when an inhibitor combines with an enzyme and permanently inactivates it.

TEST YOUR UNDERSTANDING

Know and Comprehend

1. Which of the following can do work in a cell? (a) entropy (b) heat (c) heat energy (d) all the preceding (e) none of the preceding
2. In a chemical reaction occurring in a cell, free energy is equivalent to (a) heat energy (b) heat (c) disorder (d) potential energy (e) more than one of the preceding options are true
3. Cells are able to function because they (a) are closed systems (b) have mechanisms that transform energy from the environment into useful forms (c) can use enzymes to convert endergonic reactions into spontaneous reactions (d) all the preceding
4. Diffusion is an (a) endergonic process because free energy increases (b) endergonic process because free energy decreases (c) exergonic process because entropy increases (d) exergonic process because entropy decreases (e) more than one of the preceding options are true
5. A spontaneous reaction is one in which the change in free energy (ΔG) has a _____ value. (a) positive (b) negative (c) positive or negative (d) none of the preceding (ΔG has no measurable value)
6. Healthy living cells maintain (a) ATP and ADP at equilibrium (b) equal concentrations of ATP and ADP (c) an ATP/ADP ratio of at least 10:1 (d) an ATP/ADP ratio of no more than 1:10 (e) most of the cell's stored energy in the form of ATP
7. The required energy of activation of a reaction (a) is fixed and cannot be altered (b) can be lowered by a specific enzyme (c) can be raised by a specific enzyme (d) b or c, depending on the enzyme (e) none of the preceding
8. "Induced fit" means that when a substrate binds to an enzyme's active site, (a) it fits perfectly, like a key in a lock (b) the substrate and enzyme undergo conformational changes (c) a site other than the active site undergoes a conformational change (d) the substrate and the enzyme become irreversibly bound to each other (e) c and d
9. The function of a biochemical pathway is to (a) supply energy to reactions (b) drive a sequence of reactions in a particular direction (c) maintain chemical equilibrium (d) make energy available to endergonic reactions (e) any of the preceding, depending on the pathway

Apply and Analyze

10. **PREDICT** Which of the following reactions could be coupled to an endergonic reaction with $\Delta G = +3.56$ kJ/mol?
    - (a) A ⟶ B, $\Delta G = +6.08$ kJ/mol
    - (b) C ⟶ D, $\Delta G = +3.56$ kJ/mol
    - (c) E ⟶ F, $\Delta G = 0$ kJ/mol
    - (d) G ⟶ H, $\Delta G = -1.22$ kJ/mol
    - (e) I ⟶ J, $\Delta G = -5.91$ kJ/mol

Evaluate and Synthesize

11. **PREDICT** In the following reaction series, which enzyme(s) is/are most likely to have an allosteric site to which the end product E binds? (a) enzyme 1 (b) enzyme 2 (c) enzyme 3 (d) enzyme 4 (e) enzymes 3 and 4

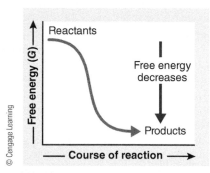

12. **EVOLUTION LINK** All organisms use ATP/ADP as central links between exergonic and endergonic reactions. What does that suggest about the evolution of energy metabolism?
13. **EVOLUTION LINK** Some have argued that "evolution is impossible because the second law of thermodynamics states that entropy always increases; therefore natural processes cannot give rise to greater complexity." In what ways is this statement a misunderstanding of the laws of thermodynamics?
14. **INTERPRET DATA** Does the figure illustrate an exergonic reaction or an endergonic reaction? How do you know?

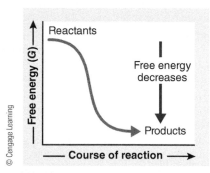

15. **INTERPRET DATA** Reactions 1 and 2 happen to have the same standard free-energy change: $\Delta G = -41.8$ kJ/mol (-10 kcal/mol). Reaction 1 is at equilibrium, but reaction 2 is far from equilibrium. Is either reaction capable of performing work? If so, which one?
16. **INTERPRET DATA** You are performing an experiment in which you are measuring the rate at which succinate is converted to fumarate by the enzyme succinic dehydrogenase. You decide to add a little malonate to make things interesting. You observe that the reaction rate slows markedly and hypothesize that malonate is inhibiting the reaction. Design an experiment that will help you decide whether malonate is acting as a competitive inhibitor or a noncompetitive inhibitor.

 To access course materials, such as Aplia and other companion resources, please visit **www.cengagebrain.com.**

How Cells Make ATP: Energy-Releasing Pathways

Cells are tiny factories that use the information inherent in their orderly systems to enable them to process materials on the molecular level, through thousands of metabolic reactions. Cells exist in a dynamic state and are continuously building up and breaking down the many different cell constituents. As you learned in Chapter 7, metabolism has two complementary components: **catabolism,** which releases energy by splitting complex molecules into smaller components; and **anabolism,** the synthesis of complex molecules from simpler building blocks. Anabolic reactions produce proteins, nucleic acids, lipids, polysaccharides, and other molecules that help maintain the cell or the organism. Most anabolic reactions are endergonic and require ATP or some other energy source to drive them.

Every organism must extract energy from food molecules that it either manufactures by photosynthesis or obtains from the environment. Grizzly bears, such as the one in the photograph, obtain organic molecules from their varied plant and animal diets. How do they obtain energy from these organic molecules? First, the food molecules are broken down by digestion into simpler components that are absorbed into the blood and transported to all the cells. The catabolic processes that convert the energy in the chemical bonds of nutrients to chemical energy stored in ATP subsequently occur inside cells, usually through a process known as **cellular respiration.**

Cellular respiration may be either aerobic or anaerobic. *Aerobic respiration* requires oxygen, whereas *anaerobic pathways,* which include anaerobic respiration and fermentation, do not require oxygen. In the process of *organismal respiration* (discussed in Chapter 46), your lungs provide a steady supply of oxygen that enables your cells to capture energy through aerobic respiration, which is by far the most common pathway and the main subject of this chapter. All three pathways—aerobic respiration, anaerobic respiration, and fermentation—are exergonic and release free energy that can be captured by the cell.

Digital Vision/Getty Images

Grizzly bear (*Ursus arctos*). This grizzly, shown attempting to eat a jumping salmon, may also eat fruit, nuts, roots, insects, and small vertebrates such as mice and ground squirrels.

KEY CONCEPTS

8.1 Aerobic respiration is an exergonic redox process in which glucose becomes oxidized, oxygen becomes reduced, and energy is captured to make ATP.

8.2 Aerobic respiration consists of four stages: glycolysis, formation of acetyl coenzyme A, the citric acid cycle, and the electron transport chain and chemiosmosis.

8.3 Nutrients other than glucose, including many carbohydrates, lipids, and amino acids, can be oxidized by aerobic respiration.

8.4 Anaerobic respiration and fermentation are ATP-yielding redox processes in which glucose becomes oxidized, but oxygen does not become reduced. Instead, these processes involve the reduction of inorganic substances (in anaerobic respiration) or organic substances (in fermentation).

8.1 REDOX REACTIONS

Most eukaryotes and prokaryotes carry out **aerobic respiration,** a form of cellular respiration requiring molecular oxygen (O_2). During aerobic respiration, nutrients are catabolized to carbon dioxide and water. Most cells use aerobic respiration to obtain energy from glucose, which enters the cell through a specific transport protein in the plasma membrane (see discussion of facilitated diffusion in Chapter 5). The overall reaction pathway for the aerobic respiration of glucose is summarized as follows:

$$C_6H_{12}O_6 + 6\,O_2 + 6\,H_2O \longrightarrow$$
$$6\,CO_2 + 12\,H_2O + \text{energy (in the chemical bonds of ATP)}$$

Note that water is shown on both sides of the equation because it is a reactant in some reactions and a product in others. For purposes of discussion, the equation for aerobic respiration can be simplified to indicate that there is a net yield of water:

$$\overset{\text{Oxidation}}{C_6H_{12}O_6 + 6\,O_2 \rightarrow 6\,CO_2 + 6\,H_2O} + \text{energy (in the chemical}$$
$$\underset{\text{Reduction}}{\qquad\qquad\qquad} \text{bonds of ATP)}$$

If we analyze this summary reaction, it appears that CO_2 is produced by the removal of hydrogen atoms from glucose. Conversely, water seems to be formed as oxygen accepts the hydrogen atoms. Because the transfer of hydrogen atoms is equivalent to the transfer of electrons, this process is a **redox reaction** in

which glucose becomes *oxidized* and oxygen becomes *reduced* (see discussion of redox reactions in Chapters 2 and 7).

The products of the reaction would be the same if the glucose were simply placed in a test tube and burned in the presence of oxygen. However, if a cell were to burn glucose, its energy would be released all at once as heat, which not only would be unavailable to the cell but also would actually destroy it. For this reason, cells do not transfer hydrogen atoms directly from glucose to oxygen. Aerobic respiration includes a series of redox reactions in which electrons associated with the hydrogen atoms in glucose are transferred to oxygen in a series of steps (**FIG. 8-1**). During this process, the free energy of the electrons is coupled to ATP synthesis.

CHECKPOINT 8.1

- *Does glucose become oxidized or reduced in aerobic respiration?*
- **CONNECT** *What is the specific role of oxygen in most cells?*

8.2 THE FOUR STAGES OF AEROBIC RESPIRATION

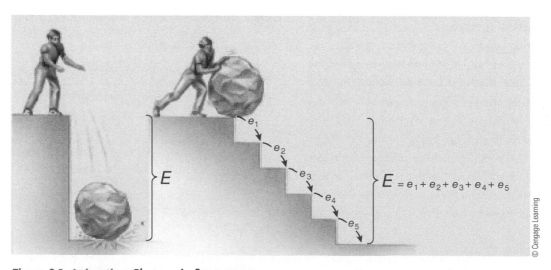

Figure 8-1 *Animation* **Changes in free energy**
The release of energy from a glucose molecule is analogous to the liberation of energy by a falling object. The total energy released (E) is the same whether it occurs all at once or in a series of steps.

The chemical reactions of the aerobic respiration of glucose are grouped into four stages (FIG. 8-2 and TABLE 8-1; see also the summary equations at the end of this chapter). In eukaryotes the first stage (glycolysis) takes place in the cytosol, and the remaining stages take place inside mitochondria. Most bacteria and archaea also carry out these processes, but because prokaryotic cells lack mitochondria, the reactions of aerobic respiration occur in the cytosol and in association with the plasma membrane.

1. *Glycolysis.* A six-carbon glucose molecule is converted to two three-carbon molecules of pyruvate.[1] Some of the energy of glucose is captured with the formation of two kinds of energy carriers, ATP and NADH.[2] See Chapter 7 to review how ATP transfers energy by transferring a phosphate group (see Figs. 7-5 and 7-6). NADH is a reduced molecule that transfers energy by transferring electrons (see Fig. 7-7).

2. *Formation of acetyl coenzyme A.* Each pyruvate enters a mitochondrion and is oxidized to a two-carbon group (an acetyl group) that combines with coenzyme A, forming

acetyl coenzyme A. NADH is produced, and carbon dioxide is released as a waste product.

3. *The citric acid cycle.* The acetyl group of acetyl coenzyme A combines with a four-carbon molecule (oxaloacetate) to form a six-carbon molecule (citrate). In the course of the cycle, citrate is recycled to oxaloacetate, and carbon dioxide is released as a waste product. Energy is captured as ATP and the reduced, high-energy compounds NADH and $FADH_2$ (see Chapter 7 to review $FADH_2$).

4. *Electron transport and chemiosmosis.* The electrons removed from glucose during the preceding stages are transferred from NADH and $FADH_2$ to a chain of electron acceptor

---

[1] Pyruvate and many other compounds in cellular respiration exist as anions at the pH found in the cell. They sometimes associate with H^+ to form acids. For example, pyruvate forms pyruvic acid. In some textbooks these compounds are presented in the acid form.

[2] Although the correct way to write the reduced form of NAD^+ is NADH + H^+, for simplicity we present the reduced form as NADH throughout this book.

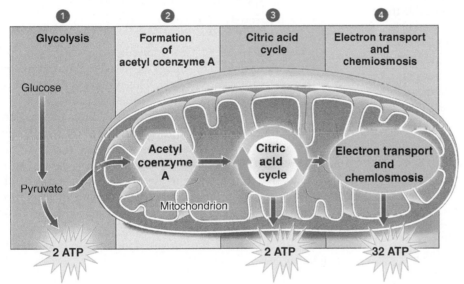

Figure 8-2 *Animation* **The four stages of aerobic respiration**

The stages of aerobic respiration occur in specific locations. Glycolysis, the first stage, occurs in the cytosol. Pyruvate, the product of glycolysis, enters a mitochondrion, where cellular respiration continues with the formation of acetyl CoA, the citric acid cycle, and electron transport and chemiosmosis. Most ATP is synthesized by chemiosmosis.

© Cengage Learning

TABLE 8-1	Summary of Aerobic Respiration			
STAGE	**SUMMARY**		**SOME STARTING MATERIALS**	**SOME END PRODUCTS**
1. Glycolysis (in cytosol)	Series of reactions in which glucose is degraded to pyruvate; net profit of 2 ATPs; electrons are transferred to carriers; can proceed anaerobically		Glucose, ATP, NAD^+, ADP, P_i	Pyruvate, ATP, NADH
2. Formation of acetyl CoA (in mitochondria)	Pyruvate is degraded and combined with coenzyme A to form acetyl CoA; electrons are transferred to carriers; CO_2 is released		Pyruvate, coenzyme A, NAD^+	Acetyl CoA, CO_2, NADH
3. Citric acid cycle (in mitochondria)	Series of reactions in which the acetyl portion of acetyl CoA is degraded to CO_2; electrons are transferred to carriers; ATP is synthesized		Acetyl CoA, H_2O, NAD^+, FAD, ADP, P_i	CO_2, NADH, $FADH_2$, ATP
4. Electron transport and chemiosmosis (in mitochondria)	Chain of several electron transport molecules; electrons are passed along chain; released energy is used to form a proton gradient; ATP is synthesized as protons diffuse down the gradient; oxygen is final electron acceptor		NADH, $FADH_2$, O_2, ADP, P_i	ATP, H_2O, NAD^+, FAD

© Cengage Learning

compounds. These electrons are ultimately passed to the final electron acceptor, oxygen, and water is formed. As the electrons are passed from one electron acceptor to another, some of their energy is used to transport hydrogen ions (protons) across the inner mitochondrial membrane, forming a proton gradient. In a process known as *chemiosmosis* (described later), the energy of this proton gradient is used to produce ATP.

Most reactions involved in aerobic respiration are one of three types: dehydrogenations, decarboxylations, and those we informally categorize as preparation reactions. **Dehydrogenations** are reactions in which two hydrogen atoms (actually, 2 electrons plus 1 or 2 protons) are removed from the substrate and transferred to NAD^+ or FAD. **Decarboxylations** are reactions in which part of a carboxyl group (—COOH) is removed from the substrate as a molecule of CO_2. The carbon dioxide you exhale with each breath is derived from decarboxylations that occur in your cells. The rest of the reactions are preparation reactions in which molecules undergo rearrangements and other changes so that they can undergo further dehydrogenations or decarboxylations. As you examine the individual reactions of aerobic respiration, you will encounter these three basic types.

In following the reactions of aerobic respiration, it helps to do some bookkeeping as you go along. Because glucose is the starting material, it is useful to express changes on a per glucose basis. We will pay particular attention to changes in the number of carbon atoms per molecule and to steps in which some type of energy transfer takes place.

In glycolysis, glucose yields two pyruvates

The word **glycolysis** comes from Greek words meaning "sugar splitting," which refers to the sugar glucose being metabolized. Glycolysis does not require oxygen and proceeds under aerobic or anaerobic conditions. FIGURE 8-3 shows a simplified overview of glycolysis, in which a glucose molecule consisting of 6 carbons is converted to 2 molecules of **pyruvate,** a three-carbon molecule. Some of the energy in the glucose is captured; there is a net yield of 2 ATP molecules and 2 NADH molecules. The reactions of glycolysis take place in the cytosol, where the necessary reactants, such as ADP, NAD^+, and inorganic phosphate, float freely and are used as needed.

The glycolysis pathway consists of a series of reactions, each of which is catalyzed by a specific enzyme (FIG. 8-4, pages 172–173). Glycolysis is divided into two major phases: the first includes endergonic reactions that require ATP, and the second includes exergonic reactions that yield ATP and NADH.

The first phase of glycolysis requires an investment of ATP The first phase of glycolysis is sometimes called the "energy investment phase" (see Fig. 8-4, steps 1 to 5). Glucose is a relatively stable molecule and is not easily broken down. In two separate **phosphorylation** reactions, a phosphate group is transferred from ATP to the sugar. The resulting phosphorylated sugar (fructose-1,6-bisphosphate) is less stable and is broken enzymatically into 2 three-carbon molecules, dihydroxyacetone phosphate and glyceraldehyde-3-phosphate (G3P). The dihydroxyacetone phosphate is enzymatically converted to G3P, so the products at this point in glycolysis are 2 molecules of G3P per glucose. We can summarize this portion of glycolysis as follows:

$$\text{glucose} + 2\ \text{ATP} \longrightarrow 2\ \text{G3P} + 2\ \text{ADP}$$

Six-carbon compound   Three-carbon compound

The second phase of glycolysis yields NADH and ATP The second phase of glycolysis is sometimes called the "energy capture phase" (see Fig. 8-4, steps 6 to 10). Each G3P is converted to pyruvate. In the first step of this process, each G3P is oxidized by the removal of 2 electrons (as part of 2 hydrogen atoms). These immediately combine with the hydrogen carrier molecule, NAD^+:

$$NAD^+ + 2\,H \longrightarrow NADH + H^+$$

Oxidized   (From G3P)   Reduced

Because there are 2 G3P molecules for every glucose, 2 NADH are formed. The energy of the electrons carried by NADH is used to form ATP later. This process is discussed in conjunction with the electron transport chain.

In two of the reactions leading to the formation of pyruvate, ATP forms when a phosphate group is transferred to ADP from a phosphorylated intermediate (see Fig. 8-4, steps 7 and 10). This process is called **substrate-level phosphorylation.** Note that in the energy investment phase of glycolysis 2 molecules of ATP are consumed, but in the energy capture phase 4 molecules of ATP are produced. Thus, glycolysis yields a net energy profit of *2 ATPs* per glucose.

We can summarize the energy capture phase of glycolysis as follows:

$$2\ \text{G3P} + 2\ NAD^+ + 4\ \text{ADP} \longrightarrow$$
$$2\ \text{pyruvate} + 2\ \text{NADH} + 4\ \text{ATP}$$

Pyruvate is converted to acetyl CoA

In eukaryotes the pyruvate molecules formed in glycolysis enter the mitochondria, where they are converted to **acetyl coenzyme A (acetyl CoA).** These reactions occur in the cytosol of aerobic prokaryotes. In this series of reactions, pyruvate undergoes a process known as *oxidative decarboxylation*. First, a carboxyl group is removed as carbon dioxide, which diffuses out of the cell (FIG. 8-5). Then the remaining two-carbon fragment becomes oxidized, and NAD^+ accepts the electrons removed during the oxidation. Finally, the oxidized two-carbon fragment, an acetyl group, becomes attached to **coenzyme A,** yielding acetyl

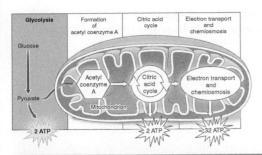

CoA. *Pyruvate dehydrogenase,* the enzyme that catalyzes these reactions, is an enormous multienzyme complex consisting of 72 polypeptide chains! Recall from Chapter 7 that coenzyme A transfers groups derived from organic acids. In this case, coenzyme A transfers an acetyl group, which is related to acetic acid. Coenzyme A is manufactured in the cell from one of the B vitamins, pantothenic acid.

The overall reaction for the formation of acetyl coenzyme A is

$$2 \text{ pyruvate} + 2 \text{ NAD}^+ + 2 \text{ CoA} \longrightarrow$$
$$2 \text{ acetyl CoA} + 2 \text{ NADH} + 2 \text{ CO}_2$$

Note that the original glucose molecule has now been partially oxidized, yielding 2 acetyl groups and 2 CO_2 molecules. The electrons removed have reduced NAD^+ to NADH. At this point in aerobic respiration, 4 NADH molecules have been formed as a result of the catabolism of a single glucose molecule: 2 during glycolysis and 2 during the formation of acetyl CoA from pyruvate. Keep in mind that these NADH molecules will be used later (during electron transport) to form additional ATP molecules.

The citric acid cycle oxidizes acetyl groups derived from acetyl CoA

The **citric acid cycle** is also known as the **tricarboxylic acid (TCA) cycle** and the **Krebs cycle,** after Hans Krebs, a German biochemist who assembled the accumulated contributions of many scientists and worked out the details of the cycle in the 1930s. He received a Nobel Prize in Physiology or Medicine in 1953 for this contribution. A simplified overview of the citric acid cycle, which takes place in the matrix of the mitochondria, is given in FIGURE 8-6 on page 174. The 8 steps of the citric acid cycle are shown in FIGURE 8-7 on page 175. A specific enzyme catalyzes each reaction.

The first reaction of the cycle occurs when acetyl CoA transfers its two-carbon acetyl group to the four-carbon acceptor compound **oxaloacetate,** forming **citrate,** a six-carbon compound.

oxaloacetate	+	acetyl CoA	⟶	citrate	+	CoA
Four-carbon compound		Two-carbon compound		Six-carbon compound		

The citrate then goes through a series of chemical transformations, losing first one and then a second carboxyl group as CO_2. One ATP is formed (per acetyl group) by substrate-level

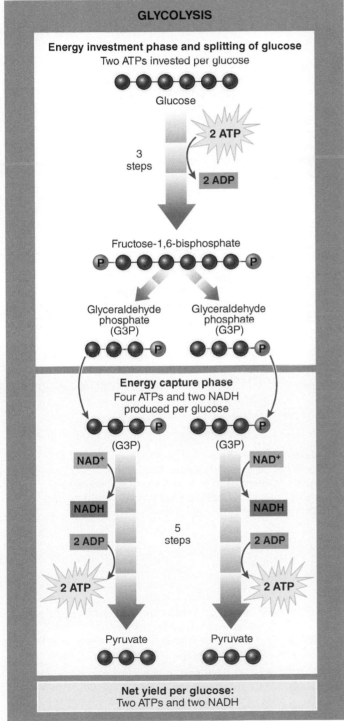

Figure 8-3 *Animation* **An overview of glycolysis**

Glycolysis includes both energy investment and energy capture. The black spheres represent carbon atoms. The energy investment phase of glycolysis leads to the splitting of sugar; ATP and NADH are produced during the energy capture phase. During glycolysis, each glucose molecule is converted to 2 pyruvates, with a net yield of 2 ATP molecules and 2 NADH molecules.

PREDICT Which do you think has more energy value to the cell, 1 molecule of glucose or 2 molecules of G3P? 2 molecules of G3P or 2 molecules of pyruvate?
© Cengage Learning

Figure 8-4
Animation **A detailed look at glycolysis**

A specific enzyme catalyzes each of the reactions in glycolysis. Note the net yield of 2 ATP molecules and 2 NADH molecules. (The black wavy lines indicate bonds that permit the phosphates to be readily transferred to other molecules, in this case, ADP.)
© Cengage Learning

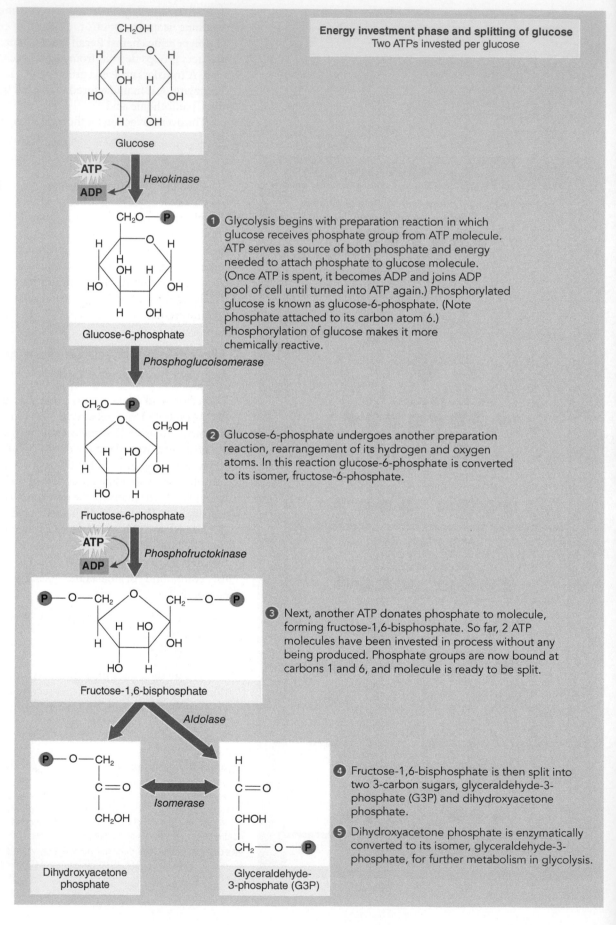

Energy investment phase and splitting of glucose
Two ATPs invested per glucose

Glucose

ATP → ADP   *Hexokinase*

Glucose-6-phosphate

1 Glycolysis begins with preparation reaction in which glucose receives phosphate group from ATP molecule. ATP serves as source of both phosphate and energy needed to attach phosphate to glucose molecule. (Once ATP is spent, it becomes ADP and joins ADP pool of cell until turned into ATP again.) Phosphorylated glucose is known as glucose-6-phosphate. (Note phosphate attached to its carbon atom 6.) Phosphorylation of glucose makes it more chemically reactive.

Phosphoglucoisomerase

Fructose-6-phosphate

2 Glucose-6-phosphate undergoes another preparation reaction, rearrangement of its hydrogen and oxygen atoms. In this reaction glucose-6-phosphate is converted to its isomer, fructose-6-phosphate.

ATP → ADP   *Phosphofructokinase*

Fructose-1,6-bisphosphate

3 Next, another ATP donates phosphate to molecule, forming fructose-1,6-bisphosphate. So far, 2 ATP molecules have been invested in process without any being produced. Phosphate groups are now bound at carbons 1 and 6, and molecule is ready to be split.

Aldolase

Isomerase

Dihydroxyacetone phosphate

Glyceraldehyde-3-phosphate (G3P)

4 Fructose-1,6-bisphosphate is then split into two 3-carbon sugars, glyceraldehyde-3-phosphate (G3P) and dihydroxyacetone phosphate.

5 Dihydroxyacetone phosphate is enzymatically converted to its isomer, glyceraldehyde-3-phosphate, for further metabolism in glycolysis.

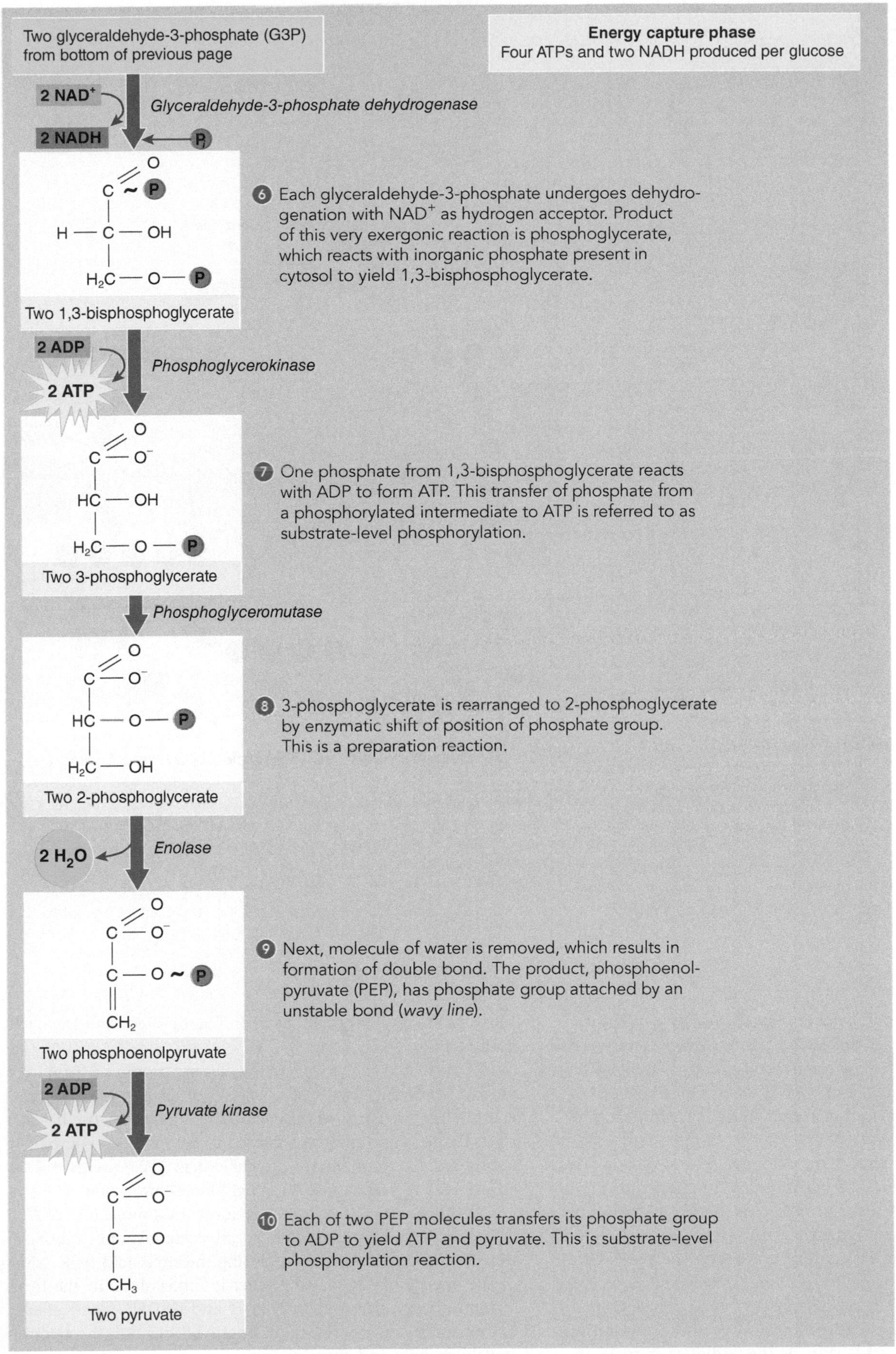

Two glyceraldehyde-3-phosphate (G3P) from bottom of previous page
Energy capture phase
Four ATPs and two NADH produced per glucose
2 NAD+
2 NADH
Glyceraldehyde-3-phosphate dehydrogenase
Pi
Two 1,3-bisphosphoglycerate
6 Each glyceraldehyde-3-phosphate undergoes dehydrogenation with NAD+ as hydrogen acceptor. Product of this very exergonic reaction is phosphoglycerate, which reacts with inorganic phosphate present in cytosol to yield 1,3-bisphosphoglycerate.
2 ADP
2 ATP
Phosphoglycerokinase
Two 3-phosphoglycerate
7 One phosphate from 1,3-bisphosphoglycerate reacts with ADP to form ATP. This transfer of phosphate from a phosphorylated intermediate to ATP is referred to as substrate-level phosphorylation.
Phosphoglyceromutase
Two 2-phosphoglycerate
8 3-phosphoglycerate is rearranged to 2-phosphoglycerate by enzymatic shift of position of phosphate group. This is a preparation reaction.
2 H2O
Enolase
Two phosphoenolpyruvate
9 Next, molecule of water is removed, which results in formation of double bond. The product, phosphoenolpyruvate (PEP), has phosphate group attached by an unstable bond (wavy line).
2 ADP
2 ATP
Pyruvate kinase
Two pyruvate
10 Each of two PEP molecules transfers its phosphate group to ADP to yield ATP and pyruvate. This is substrate-level phosphorylation reaction.

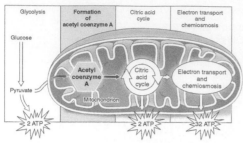

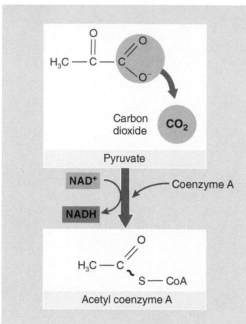

Figure 8-5 *Animation* The formation of acetyl CoA

This series of reactions is catalyzed by the multienzyme complex pyruvate dehydrogenase. Pyruvate, a three-carbon molecule that is the end product of glycolysis, enters the mitochondrion and undergoes oxidative decarboxylation. First, the carboxyl group is split off as carbon dioxide. Then, the remaining two-carbon fragment is oxidized, and its electrons are transferred to NAD^+. Finally, the oxidized two-carbon group, an acetyl group, is attached to coenzyme A. CoA has a sulfur atom that forms a bond, shown as a black wavy line, with the acetyl group. When this bond is broken, the acetyl group can be readily transferred to another molecule.
© Cengage Learning

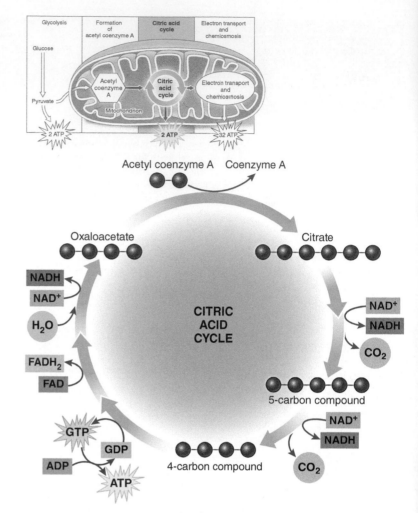

Figure 8-6 Overview of the citric acid cycle

For every glucose, 2 acetyl groups enter the citric acid cycle (*top*). Each two-carbon acetyl group combines with a four-carbon compound, oxaloacetate, to form the six-carbon compound citrate. Two CO_2 molecules are removed, and energy is captured as 1 ATP, 3 NADH, and 1 $FADH_2$ per acetyl group (or 2 ATPs, 6 NADH, and 2 $FADH_2$ per glucose molecule).
© Cengage Learning

phosphorylation. Most of the energy made available by the oxidative steps of the cycle is transferred as energy-rich electrons to NAD^+, forming NADH. For each acetyl group that enters the citric acid cycle, 3 molecules of NADH are produced (steps 3, 4, and 8). Electrons are also transferred to the electron acceptor FAD, forming $FADH_2$.

In the course of the citric acid cycle, 2 molecules of CO_2 and the equivalent of 8 hydrogen atoms (8 protons and 8 electrons) are removed, forming 3 NADH and 1 $FADH_2$. You may wonder why more hydrogen equivalents are generated by these reactions than entered the cycle with the acetyl CoA molecule. These hydrogen atoms come from water molecules that are added during the reactions of the cycle. The CO_2 produced accounts for the 2 carbon atoms of the acetyl group that entered the citric acid cycle. At the end of each cycle, the

four-carbon oxaloacetate has been regenerated, and the cycle continues.

Because two acetyl CoA molecules are produced from each glucose molecule, two cycles are required per glucose molecule. After two turns of the cycle, the original glucose has lost all its carbons and may be regarded as having been completely consumed. To summarize, the citric acid cycle yields 4 CO_2, 6 NADH, 2 $FADH_2$, and 2 ATPs per glucose molecule.

At this point in aerobic respiration, only 4 molecules of ATP have been formed per glucose by substrate-level phosphorylation: 2 during glycolysis and 2 during the citric acid cycle. Most of the energy of the original glucose molecule is in the form of high-energy electrons in NADH and $FADH_2$. Their energy will be used to synthesize additional ATP through the electron transport chain and chemiosmosis.

Figure 8-7 A detailed look at the citric acid cycle

Begin with step 1, in the upper right corner, where an acetyl group donated by acetyl coenzyme A attaches to oxaloacetate. Follow the steps in the citric acid cycle to see that the entry of a two-carbon acetyl group is balanced by the release of 2 molecules of CO_2. Electrons are transferred to NAD^+ or FAD, yielding NADH and $FADH_2$, respectively, and ATP is formed by substrate-level phosphorylation.
© Cengage Learning

1 Unstable bond attaching acetyl group to coenzyme A breaks. 2-carbon acetyl group becomes attached to 4-carbon oxaloacetate molecule, forming citrate, a 6-carbon molecule with three carboxyl groups. Coenzyme A is free to combine with another 2-carbon group and repeat process.

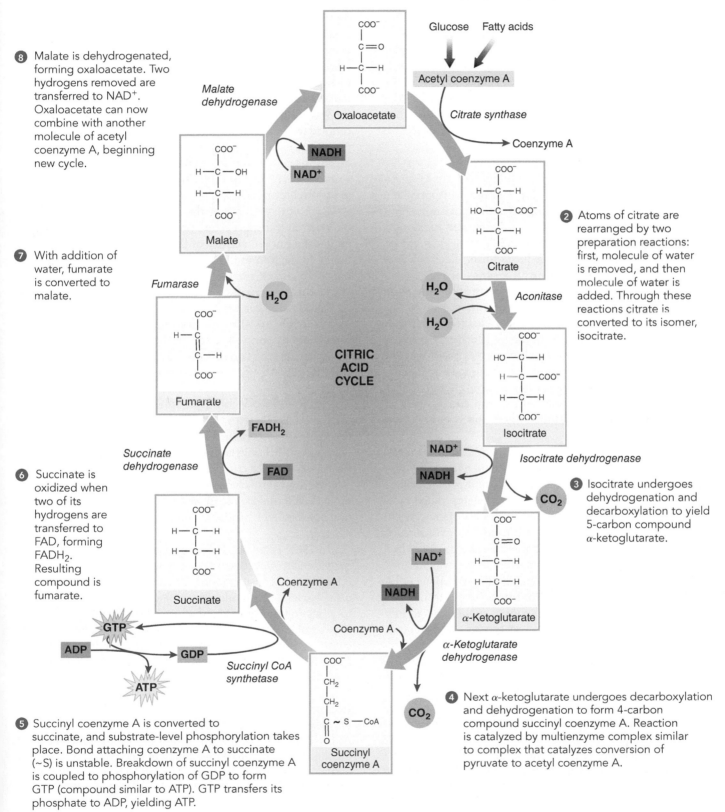

8 Malate is dehydrogenated, forming oxaloacetate. Two hydrogens removed are transferred to NAD^+. Oxaloacetate can now combine with another molecule of acetyl coenzyme A, beginning new cycle.

7 With addition of water, fumarate is converted to malate.

6 Succinate is oxidized when two of its hydrogens are transferred to FAD, forming $FADH_2$. Resulting compound is fumarate.

5 Succinyl coenzyme A is converted to succinate, and substrate-level phosphorylation takes place. Bond attaching coenzyme A to succinate (~S) is unstable. Breakdown of succinyl coenzyme A is coupled to phosphorylation of GDP to form GTP (compound similar to ATP). GTP transfers its phosphate to ADP, yielding ATP.

2 Atoms of citrate are rearranged by two preparation reactions: first, molecule of water is removed, and then molecule of water is added. Through these reactions citrate is converted to its isomer, isocitrate.

3 Isocitrate undergoes dehydrogenation and decarboxylation to yield 5-carbon compound α-ketoglutarate.

4 Next α-ketoglutarate undergoes decarboxylation and dehydrogenation to form 4-carbon compound succinyl coenzyme A. Reaction is catalyzed by multienzyme complex similar to complex that catalyzes conversion of pyruvate to acetyl coenzyme A.

The electron transport chain is coupled to ATP synthesis

Let us consider the fate of all the electrons removed from a molecule of glucose during glycolysis, acetyl CoA formation, and the citric acid cycle. Recall that these electrons were transferred as part of hydrogen atoms to the acceptors NAD^+ and FAD, forming NADH and $FADH_2$. These reduced compounds now enter the **electron transport chain,** where the high-energy electrons of their hydrogen atoms are shuttled from one acceptor to another. As the electrons are passed along in a series of exergonic redox reactions, some of their energy is used to drive the synthesis of ATP, which is an endergonic process. Because ATP synthesis (by phosphorylation of ADP) is coupled to the redox reactions in the electron transport chain, the entire process is known as **oxidative phosphorylation.**

The electron transport chain transfers electrons from NADH and $FADH_2$ to oxygen

The electron transport chain is a series of electron carriers embedded in the inner mitochondrial membrane of eukaryotes and in the plasma membrane of aerobic prokaryotes. Like NADH and $FADH_2$, each carrier exists in an oxidized form or a reduced form. Electrons pass down the electron transport chain in a series of redox reactions that works much like a bucket brigade, the old-time chain of people who passed buckets of water from a stream to one another to a building that was on fire. In the electron transport chain, each acceptor molecule becomes alternately reduced as it accepts electrons and oxidized as it gives them up. The electrons entering the electron transport chain have a relatively high energy content. They lose some of their energy at each step as they pass along the chain of electron carriers (just as some of the water spills out of the bucket as it is passed from one person to another).

Members of the electron transport chain include the flavoprotein *flavin mononucleotide (FMN),* the lipid *ubiquinone* (also called *coenzyme Q or CoQ),* several *iron–sulfur proteins,* and a group of closely related iron-containing proteins called *cytochromes* (FIG. 8-8). Each electron carrier has a different mechanism for accepting and passing electrons. As cytochromes accept and donate electrons, for example, the charge on the iron atom, which is the electron carrier portion of the cytochromes, alternates between Fe^{2+} (reduced) and Fe^{3+} (oxidized).

Scientists have extracted and purified the electron transport chain from the inner mitochondrial membrane as four large, distinct protein complexes, or groups, of acceptors. *Complex I (NADH–ubiquinone oxidoreductase)* accepts electrons from NADH molecules that were produced during glycolysis, the formation of acetyl CoA, and the citric acid cycle. *Complex II (succinate–ubiquinone reductase)* accepts electrons from $FADH_2$ molecules that were produced during the citric acid cycle. Complexes I and II both produce the same product, reduced ubiquinone, which is the substrate of *complex III (ubiquinone–cytochrome c oxidoreductase).* That is, complex III accepts electrons from reduced ubiquinone and passes them on to cytochrome *c. Complex IV (cytochrome c oxidase)* accepts electrons from cytochrome *c* and uses these electrons to reduce molecular oxygen, forming water in the process. The electrons simultaneously unite with protons from the surrounding medium to form hydrogen, and the chemical reaction between hydrogen and oxygen produces water.

Because oxygen is the final electron acceptor in the electron transport chain, organisms that respire aerobically require oxygen. What happens when cells that are strict aerobes are deprived of oxygen? The last cytochrome in the chain retains its electrons when no oxygen is available to accept them. When that occurs, each acceptor molecule in the chain retains its electrons (each remains in its reduced state), and the entire chain is blocked all the way back to NADH. Because oxidative phosphorylation is coupled to electron transport, no additional ATP is produced by way of the electron transport chain. Most cells of multicellular organisms cannot live long without oxygen because the small amount of ATP they produce by glycolysis alone is insufficient to sustain life processes.

Lack of oxygen is not the only factor that interferes with the electron transport chain. Some poisons, including cyanide, inhibit the normal activity of the cytochromes. Cyanide binds tightly to the iron in the last cytochrome in the electron transport chain, making it unable to transport electrons to oxygen. It blocks the further passage of electrons through the chain, and ATP production ceases.

Although the flow of electrons in electron transport is usually tightly coupled to the production of ATP, some organisms uncouple the two processes to produce heat (see *Inquiring About: Electron Transport and Heat*).

The chemiosmotic model explains the coupling of ATP synthesis to electron transport in aerobic respiration

For decades, scientists were aware that oxidative phosphorylation occurs in mitochondria, and many experiments had shown that the transfer of 2 electrons from each NADH to oxygen (via the electron transport chain) usually results in the production of up to 3 ATP molecules. However, for a long time, the connection between ATP synthesis and electron transport remained a mystery.

In 1961, Peter Mitchell, a British biochemist, proposed the *chemiosmotic model,* which was based on his experiments and on theoretical considerations. One type of experiment involved using bacteria as a model system (FIG. 8-9). Because the respiratory electron transport chain is located in the plasma membrane of an aerobic bacterial cell, the bacterial plasma membrane can be considered comparable to the inner mitochondrial membrane. Mitchell demonstrated that if bacterial cells were placed in an acidic environment (i.e., an environment with a high hydrogen ion, or proton, concentration), the cells synthesized ATP even if electron transport was not taking place. On the basis of these and other experiments, Mitchell proposed that electron transport and ATP synthesis are coupled by means of a proton gradient across the inner mitochondrial membrane in eukaryotes (or across the plasma membrane in bacteria). His model was so radical that it

Electron carriers in the mitochondrial inner membrane transfer electrons from NADH and FADH$_2$ to oxygen.

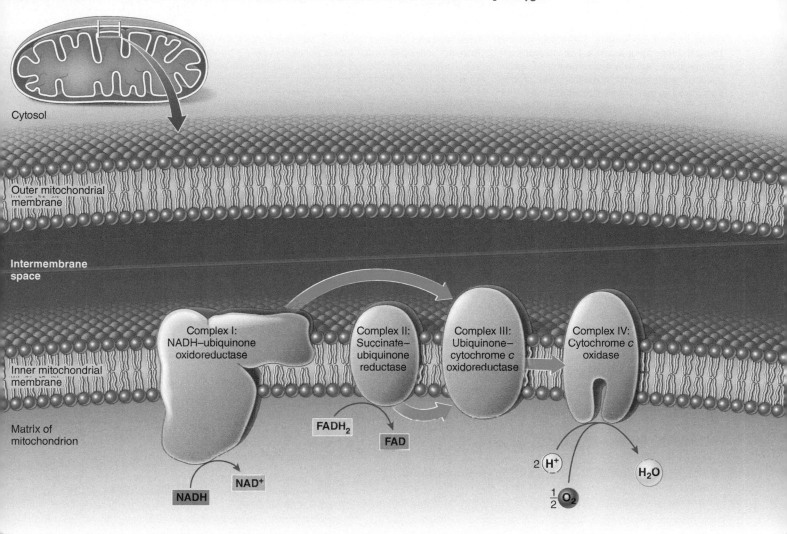

Figure 8-8 *Animation* **An overview of the electron transport chain**

Electrons fall to successively lower energy levels as they are passed along the four complexes of the electron transport chain located in the inner mitochondrial membrane. (The *blue arrows* indicate the pathway of electrons.) The carriers within each complex become alternately reduced and oxidized as they accept and donate electrons. The terminal acceptor is oxygen; one of the 2 atoms of an oxygen molecule (written as ¹/₂ O$_2$) accepts 2 electrons, which are added to 2 protons from the surrounding medium to produce water.

PREDICT How would the flow of electrons be affected if complex III were missing?
© Cengage Learning

was not immediately accepted, but by 1978, so much evidence had accumulated in support of **chemiosmosis** that Mitchell was awarded the Nobel Prize in Chemistry that year.

The electron transport chain establishes the proton gradient; some of the energy released as electrons pass down the electron transport chain is used to move protons (H$^+$) across a membrane. In eukaryotes the protons are moved across the

inner mitochondrial membrane into the intermembrane space (FIG. 8-10). Hence, the inner mitochondrial membrane separates a space with a higher concentration of protons (the intermembrane space) from a space with a lower concentration of protons (the mitochondrial matrix).

Protons are moved across the inner mitochondrial membrane by three of the four electron transport complexes (complexes I,

Electron Transport and Heat

What is the source of our body heat? Essentially, it is a byproduct of various exergonic reactions, especially those involving the electron transport chains in our mitochondria. Some cold-adapted animals, hibernating animals, and newborn animals produce unusually large amounts of heat by uncoupling electron transport from ATP production. These animals have adipose tissue (tissue in which fat is stored) that is brown. The brown color comes from the large number of mitochondria found in the brown adipose tissue cells. The inner mitochondrial membranes of these mitochondria contain an uncoupling protein that produces a passive proton channel through which protons flow into the mitochondrial matrix. As a consequence, most of the energy of glucose is converted to heat rather than to chemical energy in ATP.

Certain plants, which are not generally considered "warm" organisms, also have the ability to produce large amounts of heat. Skunk cabbage (*Symplocarpus foetidus*), for example, lives in North American swamps and wet woodlands

and generally flowers during February and March when the ground is still covered with snow (see figure). Its uncoupled mitochondria generate large amounts of heat, enabling the plant to melt the snow and attract insect pollinators by vaporizing certain odiferous molecules into the surrounding air. The flower temperature of skunk cabbage is 15° to 22°C (59° to 72°F) when the air surrounding it is −15° to 10°C (5° to 50°F). Skunk cabbage flowers maintain this temperature for two weeks or more. Other plants, such as split leaf philodendron (*Philodendron selloum*) and sacred lotus (*Nelumbo nucifera*), also generate heat when they bloom and maintain their temperatures within precise limits.

Some plants generate as much or more heat per gram of tissue than animals in flight, which have long been considered the greatest heat producers in the living world. The European plant lords-and-ladies (*Arum maculatum*), for example, produces 0.4 J (0.1 cal) of heat per second per gram of tissue, whereas a hummingbird in

flight produces 0.24 J (0.06 cal) per second per gram of tissue.

Ed Reschke/Getty Images

Skunk cabbage (*Symplocarpus foetidus*)
This plant not only produces a significant amount of heat when it flowers but also regulates its temperature within a specific range.

KEY EXPERIMENT

What is the mechanism of oxidative phosphorylation?

HYPOTHESIS: Peter Mitchell proposed that the cell uses energy released during electron transport to create a proton gradient across a membrane. The potential energy inherent in that gradient then drives the synthesis of ATP.

EXPERIMENT: Aerobic bacteria were placed in an acid (high H^+ concentration) environment, thus creating a proton gradient across the plasma membrane. It was done under conditions in which no electron transport was occurring.

RESULTS AND CONCLUSION: The bacteria synthesized ATP in the absence of aerobic respiration. These results supported Mitchell's view that a proton gradient across a membrane is an essential link in the conversion of the electrical energy of the electron transport chain to chemical energy in ATP.

SOURCE: Mitchell, P. "David Keilin's Respiratory Chain Concept and Its Chemiosmotic Consequences." *Nobel Lectures, Chemistry 1971–1980.* Singapore: World Scientific, 1993. http://www.nobelprize.org/nobel_prizes/chemistry/laureates/1978/mitchell-lecture.html

Figure 8-9 Evidence for chemiosmosis

PREDICT What do you think would happen if the cells were placed in a basic (low H^+ concentration) environment?
© Cengage Learning

Bacterial cytoplasm (low acid)

ATP Synthesized

H^+

Plasma membrane

Acidic environment

III, and IV) (FIG. 8-11a). Like water behind a dam, the resulting proton gradient is a form of potential energy that can be harnessed to provide the energy for ATP synthesis.

Diffusion of protons from the intermembrane space, where they are highly concentrated, through the inner mitochondrial membrane to the matrix of the mitochondrion is limited to specific channels formed by a fifth enzyme complex, **ATP synthase,** a transmembrane protein. Portions of these complexes project from the inner surface of the membrane (the surface that faces the matrix) and are visible by electron microscopy (FIG. 8-11b). Diffusion of the protons down their gradient, through the ATP synthase complex, is exergonic because the entropy of the system increases. This exergonic process provides the energy for ATP production, although the exact mechanism by which ATP synthase catalyzes the phosphorylation of ADP is still not completely understood.

In 1997, Paul Boyer of the University of California at Los Angeles and John Walker of the Medical Research Council Laboratory of Molecular Biology, Cambridge, England, shared the Nobel Prize in Chemistry for the discovery that ATP synthase functions in an unusual way. Experimental evidence strongly suggests that ATP synthase acts like a highly efficient molecular motor. During the production of ATP from ADP and inorganic phosphate, a central structure of ATP synthase rotates, possibly in response to the force of protons moving through the enzyme complex. The rotation apparently alters the conformation of the catalytic subunits in a way that drives ATP synthesis.

Chemiosmosis is a fundamental mechanism of energy coupling in cells; it allows exergonic redox reactions to drive the endergonic reaction in which ATP is produced by phosphorylating ADP. In photosynthesis (discussed in Chapter 9), ATP is produced by a comparable process.

Aerobic respiration of one glucose yields a maximum of 36 to 38 ATPs

Let us now review where biologically useful energy is captured in aerobic respiration and calculate the total energy yield from the complete oxidation of glucose. FIGURE 8-12 summarizes the arithmetic involved.

1. In glycolysis glucose is activated by the addition of phosphates from 2 ATP molecules and converted ultimately to 2 pyruvates + 2 NADH + 4 ATPs, yielding a net profit of 2 ATPs.
2. The 2 pyruvates are metabolized to 2 acetyl CoA + 2 CO_2 + 2 NADH.
3. In the citric acid cycle, the 2 acetyl groups from CoA are metabolized to 4 CO_2 + 6 NADH + 2 $FADH_2$ + 2 ATPs.

Because the oxidation of NADH in the electron transport chain yields up to 3 ATPs per molecule, the total of 10 NADH molecules can yield up to 30 ATPs. The 2 NADH molecules from glycolysis, however, yield either 2 or 3 ATPs each. The reason is that certain types of eukaryotic cells must expend energy to shuttle the electrons from NADH produced by glycolysis across the mitochondrial membrane (to be discussed shortly). Prokaryotic cells lack mitochondria; hence, they have no need to shuttle electrons. For this reason, bacteria are able to generate 3 ATPs for every NADH, even those produced during glycolysis. Thus, the maximum number of ATPs formed using the energy from NADH is 28 to 30, depending on the cell.

The oxidation of $FADH_2$ yields 2 ATPs per molecule (recall that electrons from $FADH_2$ enter the electron transport chain at a different location than those from NADH), so the 2 $FADH_2$ molecules produced in the citric acid cycle yield 4 ATPs.

4. Summing all the ATPs (2 from glycolysis, 2 from the citric acid cycle, and 32 to 34 from electron transport and chemiosmosis), you can see that the complete aerobic metabolism of one molecule of glucose yields a maximum of 36 to 38 ATPs. Most ATP is generated by oxidative phosphorylation, which involves the electron transport chain and chemiosmosis. Only 4 ATPs are formed by substrate-level phosphorylation in glycolysis and the citric acid cycle.

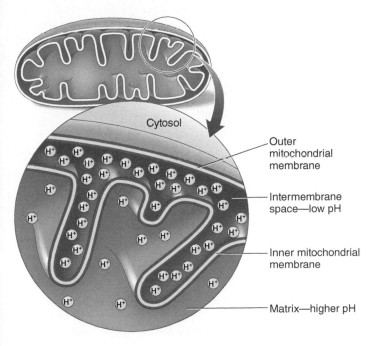

Cytosol

Outer mitochondrial membrane

Intermembrane space—low pH

Inner mitochondrial membrane

Matrix—higher pH

Figure 8-10 The accumulation of protons (H^+) within the intermembrane space

As electrons move down the electron transport chain, the electron transport complexes move protons (H^+) from the matrix to the intermembrane space, creating a proton gradient. The high concentration of H^+ in the intermembrane space lowers the pH.

© Cengage Learning

The electron transport chain forms a concentration gradient for H⁺, which diffuses through ATP synthase complexes, producing ATP.

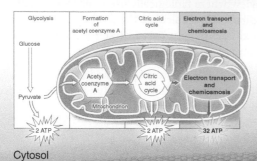

Cytosol

(a) The electron transport chain in the inner mitochondrial membrane includes three proton pumps that are located in three of the four electron transport complexes. (The *blue arrows* indicate the pathway of electrons; and the *white arrows*, the pathway of protons.) The energy released during electron transport is used to transport protons (H⁺) from the mitochondrial matrix to the intermembrane space, where a high concentration of protons accumulates. The protons cannot diffuse back into the matrix except through special channels in ATP synthase in the inner membrane. The flow of the protons through ATP synthase provides the energy for generating ATP from ADP and inorganic phosphate (P_i). In the process, the inner part of ATP synthase rotates (*thick purple arrows*) like a motor.

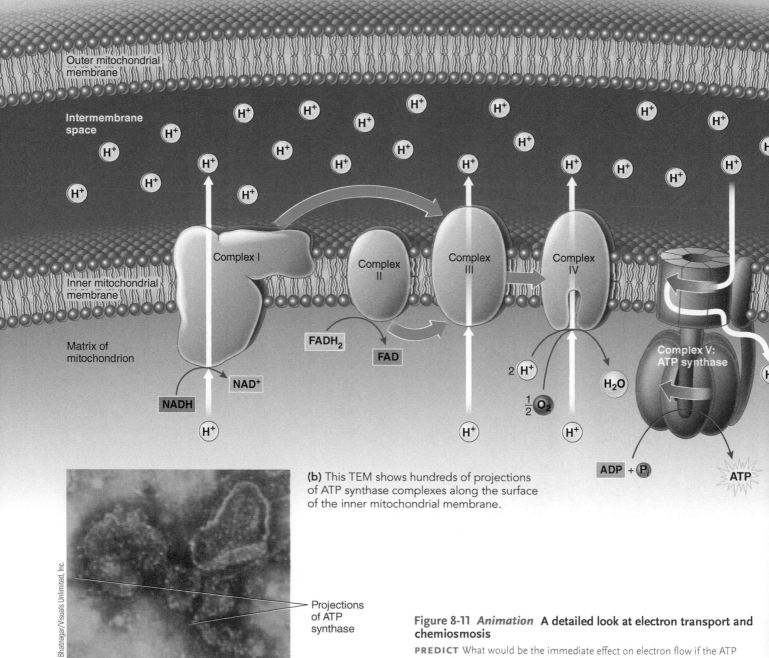

(b) This TEM shows hundreds of projections of ATP synthase complexes along the surface of the inner mitochondrial membrane.

Projections of ATP synthase

250 nm

R. Bhatnagar/Visuals Unlimited, Inc.

Figure 8-11 *Animation* **A detailed look at electron transport and chemiosmosis**

PREDICT What would be the immediate effect on electron flow if the ATP synthase complexes were removed?

© Cengage Learning

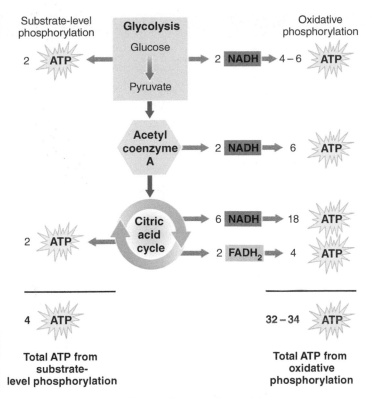

Figure 8-12 Energy yield from the complete oxidation of glucose by aerobic respiration

Most ATP is produced by electron transport and chemiosmosis (oxidative phosphorylation).

© Cengage Learning

We can analyze the efficiency of the overall process of aerobic respiration by comparing the free energy captured as ATP to the total free energy in a glucose molecule. Recall from Chapter 6 that although heat energy cannot power biological reactions, it is convenient to measure energy as heat. This is done through the use of a calorimeter, an instrument that measures the heat of a reaction. A sample is placed in a compartment surrounded by a chamber of water. As the sample burns (becomes oxidized), the temperature of the water rises, providing a measure of the heat released during the reaction.

When 1 mol of glucose is burned in a calorimeter, some 686 kcal (2870 kJ) are released as heat. The free energy temporarily held in the phosphate bonds of ATP is about 7.6 kcal (31.8 kJ) per mole. When 36 to 38 ATPs are generated during the aerobic respiration of glucose, the free energy trapped in ATP amounts to 7.6 kcal/mol × 36, or about 274 kcal (1146 kJ) per mole. Thus, the efficiency of aerobic respiration is 274/686, or about 40%. (By comparison, a steam power plant has an efficiency of 35% to 36% in converting its fuel energy into electricity.) The remainder of the energy in the glucose is released as heat.

Mitochondrial shuttle systems harvest the electrons of NADH produced in the cytosol The inner mitochondrial membrane is not permeable to NADH, which is a large molecule. Therefore, the NADH molecules produced in the cytosol during glycolysis cannot diffuse into the mitochondria to transfer their electrons to the electron transport chain. Unlike ATP

and ADP, NADH does not have a carrier protein to transport it across the membrane. Instead, several systems have evolved to transfer just the *electrons* of NADH, not the NADH molecules themselves, into the mitochondria.

In liver, kidney, and heart cells, a special shuttle system transfers the electrons from NADH through the inner mitochondrial membrane to an NAD^+ molecule in the matrix. These electrons are transferred to the electron transport chain in the inner mitochondrial membrane, and up to 3 molecules of ATP are produced per pair of electrons.

In skeletal muscle, brain, and some other types of cells, another type of shuttle operates. Because this shuttle requires more energy than the shuttle in liver, kidney, and heart cells, the electrons are at a lower energy level when they enter the electron transport chain. They are accepted by ubiquinone rather than by NAD^+ and so generate a maximum of 2 ATP molecules per pair of electrons. For this reason, the number of ATPs produced by aerobic respiration of 1 molecule of glucose in skeletal muscle cells is 36 rather than 38.

Cells regulate aerobic respiration

Aerobic respiration requires a steady input of fuel molecules and oxygen. Under normal conditions these materials are adequately provided and do not affect the rate of respiration. Instead, the rate of aerobic respiration is regulated by how much ADP and phosphate are available, with ATP synthesis continuing until most of the ADP has been converted to ATP. At this point oxidative phosphorylation slows considerably, which in turn slows down the citric acid cycle.

Glycolysis is partly controlled by feedback regulation (see Figure 7-15 for an illustration of feedback regulation) exerted on the enzyme phosphofructokinase, which catalyzes an early reaction of glycolysis (see Fig. 8-4). The active site of phosphofructokinase binds ATP and fructose-6-phosphate. However, the enzyme has two allosteric sites: an inhibitor site to which ATP binds when present at very high levels and an activator site to which AMP (adenosine monophosphate, a molecule formed when two phosphates are removed from ATP) binds. Therefore, this enzyme is inactivated when ATP levels are high and activated when they are low. Respiration proceeds when the enzyme becomes activated, thus generating more ATP.

⬤HECKPOINT 8.2

- *How much ATP is made available to the cell from a single glucose molecule by the operation of (1) glycolysis, (2) the formation of acetyl CoA, (3) the citric acid cycle, and (4) the electron transport chain and chemiosmosis? Where does each of these processes take place in a eukaryotic cell?*

- **CONNECT** *What essential role does each of the following play in chemiosmotic ATP synthesis: (1) electron transport chain, (2) proton gradient, and (3) ATP synthase complex?*

- **CONNECT** *What are the roles of NAD^+, FAD, and oxygen in aerobic respiration?*

- **PREDICT** *What do you expect would happen to the rate of oxidative phosphorylation if most of the ADP in the cell were to become converted to ATP?*

8.3 ENERGY YIELD OF NUTRIENTS OTHER THAN GLUCOSE

LEARNING OBJECTIVE

7 Summarize how the products of protein and lipid catabolism enter the same metabolic pathway that oxidizes glucose.

Many organisms, including humans, depend on nutrients other than glucose as a source of energy. In fact, you usually obtain more of your energy by oxidizing fatty acids than by oxidizing glucose. Amino acids derived from protein digestion are also used as fuel molecules. Such nutrients are transformed into one of the metabolic intermediates that are fed into glycolysis or the citric acid cycle (FIG. 8-13).

Amino acids are metabolized by reactions in which the amino group (—NH$_2$) is first removed, a process called **deamination.** In mammals and some other animals, the amino group is converted to urea (see Figure 48-1 for the biochemical pathway) and excreted, but the carbon chain is metabolized and eventually is used as a reactant in one of the steps of aerobic respiration. The amino acid alanine, for example, undergoes deamination to become pyruvate, the amino acid glutamate is converted to α-ketoglutarate, and the amino acid aspartate yields oxaloacetate. Pyruvate enters aerobic respiration as the end product of glycolysis, and α-ketoglutarate and oxaloacetate both enter aerobic respiration as intermediates in the citric acid cycle. Ultimately, the carbon chains of all the amino acids are metabolized in this way.

Each gram of lipid in the diet contains 9 kcal (38 kJ), more than twice as much energy as 1 g of glucose or amino acids, which have about 4 kcal (17 kJ) per gram. Lipids are rich in energy because they are highly reduced; that is, they have many hydrogen atoms and few oxygen atoms. When completely oxidized in aerobic respiration, a molecule of a six-carbon fatty acid generates up to 44 ATPs (compared with 36 to 38 ATPs for a molecule of glucose, which also has 6 carbons).

Both the glycerol and fatty acid components of a triacylglycerol (see Figure 3-12 for structures) are used as fuel; phosphate is added to glycerol, converting it to G3P or another compound that enters glycolysis. Fatty acids are oxidized and split enzymatically into two-carbon acetyl groups that are bound to coenzyme A; that is, fatty acids are converted to acetyl CoA. This process, which occurs in the mitochondrial matrix, is called **β-oxidation** (beta-oxidation). Acetyl groups from CoA molecules formed by β-oxidation enter the citric acid cycle.

CHECKPOINT 8.3

- **CONNECT** *How can a person obtain energy from a low-carbohydrate diet?*
- *What process must occur before amino acids enter the aerobic respiratory pathway?*
- **VISUALIZE** *Draw a simple diagram indicating where fatty acids enter the aerobic respiratory pathway.*

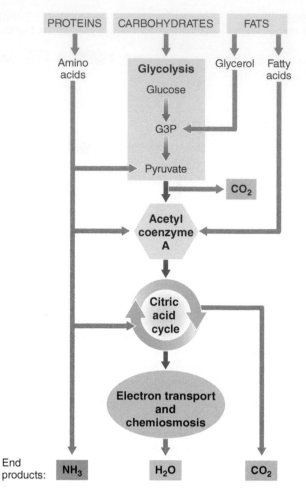

Figure 8-13 *Animation* **Energy from proteins, carbohydrates, and fats**

Products of the catabolism of proteins, carbohydrates, and fats enter glycolysis or the citric acid cycle at various points. This diagram is greatly simplified and illustrates only a few of the principal catabolic pathways.
© Cengage Learning

8.4 ANAEROBIC RESPIRATION AND FERMENTATION

LEARNING OBJECTIVE

8 Compare and contrast anaerobic respiration and fermentation. Include the mechanism of ATP formation, the final electron acceptor, and the end products.

Anaerobic respiration, which does not use oxygen as the final electron acceptor, is performed by some prokaryotes that live in anaerobic environments, such as waterlogged soil, stagnant ponds, and animal intestines. As in aerobic respiration, electrons are transferred in anaerobic respiration from glucose to NADH; they then pass down an electron transport chain that is coupled to ATP synthesis by chemiosmosis. However, an inorganic substance such as nitrate (NO_3^-) or sulfate (SO_4^{2-})

replaces molecular oxygen as the terminal electron acceptor. The end products of this type of anaerobic respiration are carbon dioxide, one or more reduced inorganic substances, and ATP. The following equation summarizes one representative type of anaerobic respiration, which is part of the biogeochemical cycle known as the **nitrogen cycle** (discussed in Chapter 55).

$$C_6H_{12}O_6 + 12\,KNO_3 \longrightarrow$$
Potassium nitrate

$$6\,CO_2 + 6\,H_2O + 12\,KNO_2 + \text{energy}$$
Potassium nitrite **(in the chemical bonds of ATP)**

Certain other bacteria, as well as some fungi, regularly use **fermentation,** an anaerobic pathway that does not involve an electron transport chain. During fermentation only 2 ATPs are formed per glucose (by substrate-level phosphorylation during glycolysis). One might expect that a cell that obtains energy from glycolysis would produce pyruvate, the end product of glycolysis. However, that cannot happen because every cell has a limited supply of NAD$^+$ and NAD$^+$ is required for glycolysis to continue. If virtually all NAD$^+$ becomes reduced to NADH during glycolysis, glycolysis stops and no more ATP is produced.

In fermentation, NADH molecules transfer their hydrogen atoms to organic molecules, thus regenerating the NAD$^+$ needed to keep glycolysis going. The resulting relatively reduced organic molecules (commonly, alcohol or lactate) tend to be toxic to the cells and are essentially waste products.

TABLE 8-2 compares aerobic respiration, anaerobic respiration, and fermentation.

Alcohol fermentation and lactate fermentation are inefficient

Yeasts are **facultative anaerobes** that carry out aerobic respiration when oxygen is available but switch to *alcohol fermentation* when deprived of oxygen (**FIG. 8-14a**). These eukaryotic, unicellular fungi have enzymes that decarboxylate pyruvate, releasing carbon dioxide and forming a two-carbon compound called *acetaldehyde.* NADH produced during glycolysis transfers hydrogen atoms to acetaldehyde, reducing it to *ethyl alcohol* (**FIG. 8-14b**). Alcohol fermentation is the basis for the production of beer, wine, and other alcoholic beverages. Yeast cells are also used in baking to produce the carbon dioxide that causes dough to rise; the alcohol evaporates during baking.

Certain fungi and bacteria perform *lactate (lactic acid) fermentation*. In this alternative pathway, NADH produced during glycolysis transfers hydrogen atoms to pyruvate, reducing it to *lactate* (**FIG. 8-14c**). The ability of some bacteria to produce lactate is exploited by humans, who use these bacteria to make yogurt and ferment cabbage for sauerkraut.

Vertebrate muscle cells also produce lactate. Exercise can cause fatigue and muscle cramps possibly due to insufficient oxygen, the depletion of fuel molecules, and the accumulation of lactate during strenuous activity. This buildup of lactate occurs because muscle cells shift briefly to lactate fermentation if the amount of oxygen delivered to muscle cells is insufficient to support aerobic respiration. The shift is only temporary, however, and oxygen is required for sustained work. About 80% of the lactate is eventually exported to the liver, where it is used to regenerate more glucose for the muscle cells. The remaining 20% of the lactate is metabolized in muscle cells in the presence of oxygen. For this reason, you continue to breathe heavily after you have stopped exercising: the additional oxygen is needed to oxidize lactate, thereby restoring the muscle cells to their normal state.

Although humans use lactate fermentation to produce ATP for only a few minutes, a few animals can live without oxygen for much longer periods. The red-eared slider, a freshwater turtle, remains underwater for as long as two weeks. During this time, it is relatively inactive and therefore does not expend a great deal of energy. It relies on lactate fermentation for ATP production.

Both alcohol fermentation and lactate fermentation are highly inefficient because the fuel is only partially oxidized. Alcohol, the end product of fermentation by yeast cells, can be burned and is even used as automobile fuel; obviously, it

TABLE 8-2	A Comparison of Aerobic Respiration, Anaerobic Respiration, and Fermentation		
	AEROBIC RESPIRATION	**ANAEROBIC RESPIRATION**	**FERMENTATION**
Immediate fate of electrons in NADH	Transferred to electron transport chain	Transferred to electron transport chain	Transferred to organic molecule
Terminal electron acceptor of electron transport chain	O_2	Inorganic substances such as NO_3^- or SO_4^{2-}	No electron transport chain
Reduced product(s) formed	Water	Relatively reduced inorganic substances	Relatively reduced organic compounds (commonly, alcohol or lactate)
Mechanism of ATP synthesis	Oxidative phosphorylation/ chemiosmosis; also substrate-level phosphorylation	Oxidative phosphorylation/chemiosmosis; also substrate-level phosphorylation	Substrate-level phosphorylation only (during glycolysis)

Fermentation regenerates NAD⁺ needed for glycolysis.

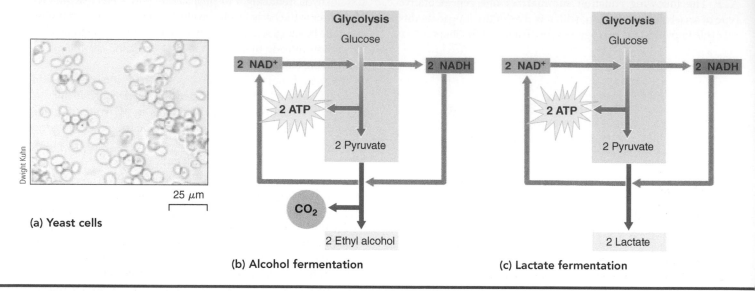

(a) Yeast cells

25 μm

(b) Alcohol fermentation

(c) Lactate fermentation

Figure 8-14 *Animation* **Fermentation**

(a) Light micrograph of live brewer's yeast (*Saccharomyces cerevisiae*). Yeast cells have mitochondria and carry on aerobic respiration when O_2 is present. In the absence of O_2, yeasts carry on alcohol fermentation. **(b, c)** Glycolysis is the first part of fermentation pathways. In alcohol fermentation **(b)**, CO_2 is split off, and the two-carbon compound ethyl alcohol is the end product. In lactate fermentation **(c)**, the final product is the three-carbon compound lactate. In both alcohol and lactate fermentation, there is a net gain of only 2 ATPs per molecule of glucose. Note that the NAD⁺ used during glycolysis is regenerated during both alcohol fermentation and lactate fermentation.

CONNECT Which is more efficient in terms of yield of ATP per glucose, anaerobic respiration or fermentation?
© Cengage Learning

contains a great deal of energy that the yeast cells cannot extract using anaerobic methods. Lactate, a three-carbon compound, contains even more energy than the two-carbon alcohol. In contrast, all available energy is removed during aerobic respiration because the fuel molecules become completely oxidized to CO_2. A net profit of only 2 ATPs is produced by the fermentation of 1 molecule of glucose, compared with up to 36 to 38 ATPs when oxygen is available.

The inefficiency of fermentation necessitates a large supply of fuel. To perform the same amount of work, a cell engaged in fermentation must consume up to 20 times as much glucose or other carbohydrate per second as a cell using aerobic respiration. For this reason, your skeletal muscle cells store large

quantities of glucose in the form of glycogen, which enables them to metabolize anaerobically for short periods.

CHECKPOINT 8.4

- **CONNECT** *What is the fate of hydrogen atoms removed from glucose during glycolysis when oxygen is present in muscle cells? How does it compare with the fate of hydrogen atoms removed from glucose when the amount of available oxygen is insufficient to support aerobic respiration?*

- *What accounts for the ATP yield of fermentation being only a tiny fraction of the yield from aerobic respiration?*

- *Is chemiosmosis involved in fermentation? in anaerobic respiration?*

SUMMARY: FOCUS ON LEARNING OBJECTIVES

8.1 Redox Reactions (page 166)

1 Write a summary reaction for aerobic respiration that shows which reactant becomes oxidized and which becomes reduced.

$$\underset{\text{Reduction}}{\overset{\text{Oxidation}}{C_6H_{12}O_6 + 6\,O_2 \longrightarrow 6\,CO_2 + 6\,H_2O + energy}}$$

- **Aerobic respiration** is a catabolic process in which a fuel molecule such as glucose is broken down to form carbon dioxide and water. It includes **redox reactions** that result in the transfer of electrons from glucose (which becomes *oxidized*) to oxygen (which becomes *reduced*).

- Energy released during aerobic respiration is used to produce up to 36 to 38 ATPs per molecule of glucose.

8.2 The Four Stages of Aerobic Respiration (page 166)

2 List and give a brief overview of the four stages of aerobic respiration.

- The chemical reactions of aerobic respiration occur in four stages: glycolysis, formation of acetyl CoA, the citric acid cycle, and the electron transport chain and chemiosmosis.
- During **glycolysis** a molecule of glucose is degraded to 2 molecules of **pyruvate. Substrate-level phosphorylation** produces 2 ATP molecules during glycolysis, and 4 hydrogen atoms are removed and used to produce 2 NADH.
- During the formation of **acetyl CoA,** the 2 pyruvate molecules each lose a molecule of carbon dioxide, and the remaining acetyl groups each combine with **coenzyme A,** producing 2 molecules of acetyl CoA; 1 NADH is produced per pyruvate.
- Each acetyl group from acetyl CoA enters the **citric acid cycle** by combining with a four-carbon compound, **oxaloacetate,** to form **citrate,** a six-carbon compound. Two acetyl CoA molecules enter the cycle for every glucose molecule. For every 2 carbons that enter the cycle as part of an acetyl CoA molecule, 2 leave as carbon dioxide. For every acetyl CoA, hydrogen atoms are transferred to 3 NAD^+ and 1 FAD; only 1 ATP is produced by substrate-level phosphorylation.
- Hydrogen atoms (or their electrons) removed from fuel molecules are transferred from one electron acceptor to another down an **electron transport chain** located in the mitochondrial inner membrane; ultimately, these electrons reduce molecular oxygen, forming water. In **oxidative phosphorylation** the redox reactions in the electron transport chain are coupled to synthesis of ATP through the mechanism of **chemiosmosis.**

3 Indicate where each stage of aerobic respiration takes place in a eukaryotic cell.

- Glycolysis occurs in the cytosol, and the remaining stages of aerobic respiration take place in the mitochondria.

4 Add up the energy captured (as ATP, NADH, and $FADH_2$) in each stage of aerobic respiration.

- In glycolysis each glucose molecule produces 2 NADH and 2 ATPs (net). The conversion of 2 pyruvates to acetyl CoA results in the formation of 2 NADH. In the citric acid cycle, the 2 acetyl CoA molecules are metabolized to form 6 NADH, 2 $FADH_2$, and 2 ATPs. To summarize, we have 4 ATPs, 10 NADH, and 2 $FADH_2$.
- When electrons donated by the 10 NADH and 2 $FADH_2$ pass through the electron transport chain, 32 to 34 ATPs are produced by chemiosmosis. Therefore, each glucose molecule yields a total of up to 36 to 38 ATPs.

5 Define *chemiosmosis* and explain how a gradient of protons is established across the inner mitochondrial membrane.

- In chemiosmosis some of the energy of the electrons in the electron transport chain is used to pump protons across the inner mitochondrial membrane into the intermembrane space. This pumping establishes a proton gradient across the inner mitochondrial membrane. Protons (H^+) accumulate within the intermembrane space, lowering the pH.

6 Describe the process by which the proton gradient drives ATP synthesis in chemiosmosis.

- The diffusion of protons through channels formed by the enzyme **ATP synthase,** which extends through the inner mitochondrial membrane from the intermembrane space to the mitochondrial matrix, provides the energy to synthesize ATP.

8.3 Energy Yield of Nutrients Other Than Glucose (page 180)

7 Summarize how the products of protein and lipid catabolism enter the same metabolic pathway that oxidizes glucose.

- Amino acids undergo **deamination,** and their carbon skeletons are converted to metabolic intermediates of aerobic respiration.
- Both the glycerol and fatty acid components of lipids are oxidized as fuel. Fatty acids are converted to acetyl CoA molecules by the process of β-**oxidation.**

8.4 Anaerobic Respiration and Fermentation (page 180)

8 Compare and contrast anaerobic respiration and fermentation. Include the mechanism of ATP formation, the final electron acceptor, and the end products.

- In **anaerobic respiration** electrons are transferred from fuel molecules to an electron transport chain that is coupled to ATP synthesis by chemiosmosis; the final electron acceptor is an inorganic substance such as nitrate or sulfate, not molecular oxygen.
- **Fermentation** is an anaerobic process that does not use an electron transport chain. There is a net gain of only 2 ATPs per glucose; they are produced by substrate-level phosphorylation during glycolysis. To maintain the supply of NAD^+ essential for glycolysis, hydrogen atoms are transferred from NADH to an organic compound derived from the initial nutrient.
- Yeast cells carry out *alcohol fermentation,* in which ethyl alcohol and carbon dioxide are the final waste products.
- Certain fungi, prokaryotes, and animal cells carry out *lactate (lactic acid) fermentation,* in which hydrogen atoms are added to pyruvate to form lactate, a waste product.

Summary Reactions for Aerobic Respiration

Summary reaction for the complete oxidation of glucose:

$$C_6H_{12}O_6 + 6\ O_2 + 6\ H_2O \longrightarrow 6\ CO_2 + 12\ H_2O + energy\ (36\ to\ 38\ ATP)$$

Summary reaction for glycolysis:

$$C_6H_{12}O_6 + 2\ ATP + 2\ ADP + 2\ P_i + 2\ NAD^+ \longrightarrow 2\ pyruvate + 4\ ATP + 2\ NADH + H_2O$$

Summary reaction for the conversion of pyruvate to acetyl CoA:

$$2\ pyruvate + 2\ coenzyme\ A + 2\ NAD^+ \longrightarrow 2\ acetyl\ CoA + 2\ CO_2 + 2\ NADH$$

Summary reaction for the citric acid cycle:

$$2\ acetyl\ CoA + 6\ NAD^+ + 2\ FAD + 2\ ADP + 2\ P_i + 2\ H_2O \longrightarrow 4\ CO_2 + 6\ NADH + 2\ FADH_2 + 2\ ATP + 2\ CoA$$

Summary reactions for the processing of the hydrogen atoms of NADH and $FADH_2$ in the electron transport chain:

$$NADH + 3\ ADP + 3\ P_i + \tfrac{1}{2}\ O_2 \longrightarrow NAD^+ + 3\ ATP + H_2O$$

$$FADH_2 + 2\ ADP + 2\ P_i + \tfrac{1}{2}O_2 \longrightarrow FAD^+ + 2\ ATP + H_2O$$

Summary Reactions for Fermentation

Summary reaction for lactate fermentation:

$$C_6H_{12}O_6 \longrightarrow 2\ lactate + energy\ (2\ ATP)$$

Summary reaction for alcohol fermentation:

$$C_6H_{12}O_6 \longrightarrow 2\ CO_2 + 2\ ethyl\ alcohol + energy\ (2\ ATP)$$

Know and Comprehend

1. A chemical process during which a substance gains electrons and energy is called (a) oxidation (b) oxidative phosphorylation (c) deamination (d) reduction (e) dehydrogenation

2. The reactions of ___ take place within the cytosol of eukaryotic cells. (a) glycolysis (b) oxidation of pyruvate (c) the citric acid cycle (d) chemiosmosis (e) the electron transport chain

3. Before pyruvate enters the citric acid cycle, it is decarboxylated, oxidized, and combined with coenzyme A, forming acetyl CoA, carbon dioxide, and one molecule of (a) NADH (b) FADH$_2$ (c) ATP (d) ADP (e) C$_6$H$_{12}$O$_6$

4. In the first step of the citric acid cycle, an acetyl group from acetyl CoA reacts with oxaloacetate to form (a) pyruvate (b) citrate (c) NADH (d) ATP (e) CO$_2$

5. Which of the following is the major source of electrons that flow through the mitochondrial electron transport chain? (a) H$_2$O (b) ATP (c) NADH (d) ATP synthase (e) coenzyme A

6. The "aerobic" part of aerobic cellular respiration occurs during (a) glycolysis (b) the conversion of pyruvate to acetyl CoA (c) the citric acid cycle (d) electron transport (e) all the preceding are aerobic processes

7. Substrate-level phosphorylation (a) occurs through a chemiosmotic mechanism (b) accounts for most of the ATP formed during aerobic cellular respiration (c) occurs during the conversion of pyruvate to acetyl CoA (d) occurs during glycolysis and the citric acid cycle (e) requires high energy electrons from NADH

8. A net profit of only 2 ATPs can be produced anaerobically from the ___ of one molecule of glucose, compared with a maximum of 38 ATPs produced in ___. (a) fermentation; anaerobic respiration (b) aerobic respiration; fermentation (c) aerobic respiration; anaerobic respiration (d) dehydrogenation; decarboxylation (e) fermentation; aerobic respiration

9. When deprived of oxygen, yeast cells obtain energy by fermentation, producing carbon dioxide, ATP, and (a) acetyl CoA (b) ethyl alcohol (c) lactate (d) pyruvate (e) citrate

Apply and Analyze

10. Which of the following is a correct ranking of molecules with respect to their energy value in glycolysis (*note: >* means "greater than")? (a) two pyruvates > one glucose (b) one glucose > one fructose-1,6-bisphosphate (c) two glyceraldehyde-3-phosphates (G3P) > one glucose (d) two pyruvates > one fructose-1,6-bisphosphate (e) two pyruvates > two glyceraldehyde-3-phosphates (G3P)

11. Which of the following is a correct ranking of molecules, according to their energy value in oxidative phosphorylation (*note: >* means "greater than")? (a) ATP > NADH (b) NAD$^+$ > NADH (c) FAD > FADH$_2$ (d) NADH > ATP

Evaluate and Synthesize

12. **CONNECT** Explain why the proton gradient formed during chemiosmosis represents a state of low entropy. (You may wish to refer to the discussion of entropy in Chapter 7.)

13. **CONNECT** How are the endergonic reactions of the first phase of glycolysis coupled to the hydrolysis of ATP, which is exergonic? How are the exergonic reactions of the second phase of glycolysis coupled to the endergonic synthesis of ATP and NADH?

14. **PREDICT** Could the inner mitochondrial membrane carry out its functions in the coupling of electron transport and ATP synthesis if its lipid bilayer were readily permeable to hydrogen ions (protons)?

15. **VISUALIZE** Draw a simple sketch illustrating an inner mitochondrial membrane that is actively involved in chemiosmosis and label the two compartments it separates. Add the ATP synthase complex, indicate the proton gradient, and specify in which compartment ATP is synthesized.

16. **CONNECT** When you lose weight, where does it go?

17. **EVOLUTION LINK** The reactions of glycolysis are identical in *all* organisms—prokaryotes, protists, fungi, plants, and animals—that obtain energy from glucose catabolism. What does this universality suggest about the evolution of glycolysis?

18. **EVOLUTION LINK** Molecular oxygen is so reactive that it would not exist in Earth's atmosphere today if it were not constantly replenished by organisms that release oxygen as a waste product of photosynthesis. What does that fact suggest about the evolution of aerobic respiration and oxygen-releasing photosynthetic processes?

 To access course materials, such as Aplia and other companion resources, please visit **www.cengagebrain.com**.

Photosynthesis: Capturing Light Energy

9

©vovan/Shutterstock.com

Photosynthesis. These trees use light energy to power the processes that incorporate CO_2 into organic molecules.

Look at all the living things that surround you: the trees, your pet goldfish, your own body. Most of that biomass is made up of carbon-based biological molecules. What is the ultimate source of all that carbon? Surprising to some, the source is carbon dioxide from the air. Your cells cannot take carbon dioxide from the air and incorporate it into organic molecules, but some plant cells can. They do so through **photosynthesis,** the sequence of events in which the orderly systems in these cells provide the information needed to convert light energy into the stored chemical energy of organic molecules. Photosynthesis is the first step in the flow of energy through most of the living world, capturing the vast majority of the energy that living organisms use. Photosynthesis not only sustains plants (see photograph) and other photosynthetic organisms such as algae and photosynthetic prokaryotes but also indirectly supports most non-photosynthetic organisms such as animals, fungi, protozoa, and most prokaryotes.

Each year photosynthetic organisms convert CO_2 into billions of tons of organic molecules. These molecules have two important roles in both photosynthetic and non-photosynthetic organisms: they are both the building blocks of cells and, as we saw in Chapter 8, a source of chemical energy that fuels the metabolic reactions that sustain almost all life. Photosynthesis also releases O_2, which is essential to aerobic cellular respiration, the process by which plants, animals, and most other organisms convert this chemical energy to ATP to power cellular processes.

In this chapter we first examine how light energy is used in the synthesis of ATP and other molecules that temporarily hold chemical energy but are unstable and cannot be stockpiled in the cell. We then see how their energy powers the anabolic pathway by which a photosynthetic cell synthesizes stable organic molecules from the simple inorganic compounds CO_2 and water. Finally, we explore the role of photosynthesis in plants and in Earth's environment.

KEY CONCEPTS

9.1 Light energy powers photosynthesis, which is essential to plants and most life on Earth.

9.2 Photosynthesis occurs in chloroplasts and requires the pigment chlorophyll.

9.3 Photosynthesis is a redox process.

9.4 Light-dependent reactions convert light energy to the chemical energy of NADPH and ATP.

9.5 Carbon fixation reactions incorporate CO_2 into organic molecules.

9.6 Most photosynthetic organisms are photoautotrophs.

9.7 Photosynthesis is important to plants and also other organisms.

9.1 LIGHT AND PHOTOSYNTHESIS

1   Describe the physical properties of light and explain the relationship between a wavelength of light and its energy.

Because most life on this planet depends on light, either directly or indirectly, it is important to understand the nature of light and its essential role in photosynthesis. Visible light represents a very small portion of a vast, continuous range of radiation called the *electromagnetic spectrum* (FIG. 9-1). All radiation in this spectrum travels as waves. A **wavelength** is the distance from one wave peak to the next.

At one end of the electromagnetic spectrum are gamma rays, which have very short wavelengths measured in fractions of nanometers, or nm (1 nanometer equals 10^{-9} m, one-billionth of a meter). At the other end of the spectrum are radio waves, with wavelengths so long they can be measured in kilometers. The portion of the electromagnetic spectrum from 380 to 760 nm is called the *visible spectrum* because we humans can see it. The visible spectrum includes all the colors of the rainbow (FIG. 9-2); violet has the shortest wavelength, and red has the longest.

Light is composed of small particles, or packets, of energy called **photons.** The energy of a photon is inversely proportional to its wavelength: shorter-wavelength light has more energy per photon than longer-wavelength light.

Why does photosynthesis depend on light detectable by the human eye (visible light) rather than on some other wavelength(s) of radiation? We know that radiation within the visible-light portion of the spectrum excites certain types of biological molecules, moving electrons into higher energy levels. Radiation with wavelengths longer than those of visible light does not have enough energy to excite these biological molecules. Radiation with wavelengths shorter than those of visible light is so energetic that it disrupts the bonds of many biological molecules. Thus, visible light has just the right amount of energy to cause the kinds of reversible changes in the molecules that are useful in photosynthesis.

When a molecule absorbs a photon of light energy, one of its electrons becomes energized, which means that the electron shifts from a lower-energy atomic orbital to a high-energy orbital that is more distant from the atomic nucleus. One of two things then happens to the energized electron, depending on the atom and its surroundings (FIG. 9-3). The atom may return to its **ground state,** which is the condition in which all its electrons are in their normal, lowest-energy levels. When an electron returns to its ground state, its energy dissipates as heat, and/or as an emission of light of a longer wavelength than the absorbed light; this emission of light is called **fluorescence.** Alternatively, the energized electron may leave the atom and be accepted by an electron acceptor molecule, which becomes reduced in the process; this is what occurs in photosynthesis.

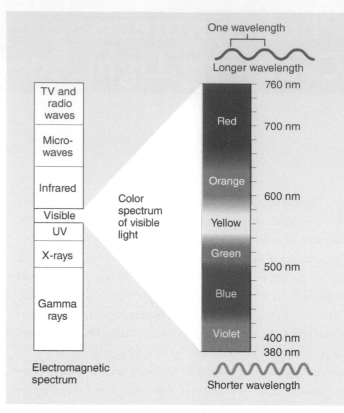

Figure 9-1 The electromagnetic spectrum

Waves in the electromagnetic spectrum have similar properties but different wavelengths. Radio waves are the longest (and least energetic) waves, with wavelengths as long as 20 km. Gamma rays are the shortest (and most energetic) waves. Visible light represents a small fraction of the electromagnetic spectrum and consists of a mixture of wavelengths ranging from about 380 to 760 nm. The energy from visible light is used in photosynthesis.
© Cengage Learning

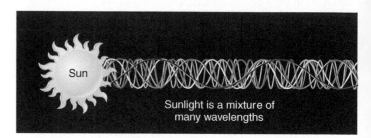

Figure 9-2 Visible radiation emitted from the sun

Electromagnetic radiation from the sun includes ultraviolet radiation and visible light of varying colors and wavelengths.
© Cengage Learning

Now that you understand some of the properties of light, let us consider the organelles that use light for photosynthesis.

CHECKPOINT 9.1

*   *Which color of light has the longer wavelength, violet or red?*
*   **CONNECT** *Which color of light has the higher energy per photon, violet or red?*

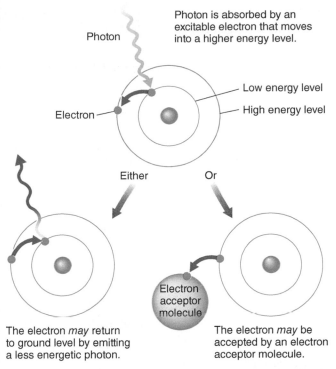

Photon

Photon is absorbed by an excitable electron that moves into a higher energy level.

Electron

Low energy level

High energy level

Either   Or

Electron acceptor molecule

The electron *may* return to ground level by emitting a less energetic photon.

The electron *may* be accepted by an electron acceptor molecule.

Figure 9-3 Interactions between light and atoms or molecules

(*Top*) When a photon of light energy strikes an atom or a molecule of which the atom is a part, the energy of the photon may push an electron to an orbital farther from the nucleus (i.e., into a higher energy level). (*Lower left*) If the electron returns to the lower, more stable energy level, the energy may be released as a less energetic, longer-wavelength photon, known as fluorescence (*shown*), or as heat. (*Lower right*) If the appropriate electron acceptors are available, the electron may leave the atom. During photosynthesis, an electron acceptor captures the energetic electron and passes it to a chain of acceptors.

© Cengage Learning

9.2 CHLOROPLASTS

LEARNING OBJECTIVES

2 Diagram the internal structure of a chloroplast and explain how its components interact and facilitate the process of photosynthesis.

3 Describe what happens to an electron in a biological molecule such as chlorophyll when a photon of light energy is absorbed.

If you examine a section of leaf tissue in a microscope, you see that the green pigment, chlorophyll, is not uniformly distributed in the cell but is confined to organelles called chloroplasts. In plants, **chloroplasts** lie mainly inside the leaf in the cells of the **mesophyll,** a layer that includes many air spaces and a very high concentration of water vapor (FIG. 9-4a). The interior of the leaf exchanges gases with the outside through microscopic pores, called **stomata** (sing., *stoma*). Each mesophyll cell has 20 to 100 chloroplasts.

The chloroplast, like the mitochondrion, is enclosed by outer and inner membranes (FIG. 9-4b). The inner membrane encloses a fluid-filled region called the **stroma,** which contains most of

the enzymes required to produce carbohydrate molecules. Suspended in the stroma is a third system of membranes that forms an interconnected set of flat, disclike sacs called **thylakoids.**

The thylakoid membrane encloses a fluid-filled interior space, the **thylakoid lumen.** In some regions of the chloroplast, thylakoid sacs are arranged in stacks called **grana** (sing., *granum*). Each granum looks something like a stack of coins, with each "coin" being a thylakoid. Some thylakoid membranes extend from one granum to another. Thylakoid membranes, like the inner mitochondrial membrane (see Chapter 8), are involved in ATP synthesis. (Photosynthetic prokaryotes have no chloroplasts, but thylakoid membranes are often arranged around the periphery of the cell as infoldings of the plasma membrane.)

Chlorophyll is found in the thylakoid membrane

Thylakoid membranes contain several kinds of *pigments,* which are substances that absorb visible light. Different pigments absorb light of different wavelengths. **Chlorophyll,** the main pigment of photosynthesis, absorbs light primarily in the blue and red regions of the visible spectrum. Green light is not appreciably absorbed by chlorophyll. Plants usually appear green because some of the green light that strikes them is scattered or reflected.

A chlorophyll molecule has two main parts, a complex ring and a long side chain (FIG. 9-5). The ring structure, called a *porphyrin ring,* is made up of joined smaller rings composed of carbon and nitrogen atoms; the porphyrin ring absorbs light energy. The porphyrin ring of chlorophyll is strikingly similar to the heme portion of the red pigment hemoglobin in red blood cells. However, unlike heme, which contains an atom of iron in the center of the ring, chlorophyll contains an atom of magnesium in that position. The chlorophyll molecule also contains a long, hydrocarbon side chain that makes the molecule extremely nonpolar and anchors the chlorophyll in the membrane.

All chlorophyll molecules in the thylakoid membrane are associated with specific *chlorophyll-binding proteins;* biologists have identified about 15 different kinds. Each thylakoid membrane is filled with precisely oriented chlorophyll molecules and chlorophyll-binding proteins that facilitate the transfer of energy from one molecule to another.

There are several kinds of chlorophyll. The most important is **chlorophyll a,** the pigment that initiates the light-dependent reactions of photosynthesis. **Chlorophyll b** is an accessory pigment that also participates in photosynthesis. It differs from chlorophyll a only in a functional group on the porphyrin ring: the methyl group ($-CH_3$) in chlorophyll a is replaced in chlorophyll b by a terminal carbonyl group ($-CHO$). This difference shifts the wavelengths of light absorbed and reflected by chlorophyll b, making it appear yellow-green, whereas chlorophyll a appears bright green.

Chloroplasts have other accessory photosynthetic pigments, such as **carotenoids,** which are yellow and orange (see Fig. 3-14). Carotenoids absorb different wavelengths of light than chlorophyll, thereby expanding the spectrum of light that provides energy for photosynthesis. Chlorophyll may be excited by light directly by energy passed to it from the light source or indirectly by energy passed to it from accessory pigments that have become excited by light. When a carotenoid molecule is excited, its energy can be transferred to chlorophyll *a*.

In addition, carotenoids are antioxidants that inactivate highly reactive forms of oxygen generated in the chloroplasts.

Chlorophyll is the main photosynthetic pigment

As you have seen, the thylakoid membrane contains more than one kind of pigment. An instrument called a *spectrophotometer* measures the relative abilities of different pigments to absorb different wavelengths of light. The **absorption spectrum** of a pigment is a plot of its absorption of light of different wavelengths. FIGURE 9-6a shows the absorption spectra for chlorophylls *a* and *b*.

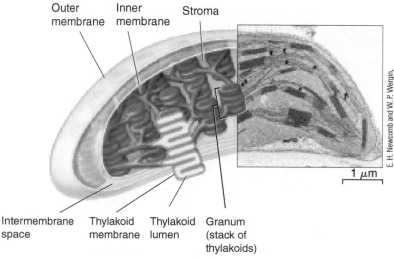

(a) This leaf cross section reveals that the mesophyll is the photosynthetic tissue. CO_2 enters the leaf through tiny pores or stomata, and H_2O is carried to the mesophyll in veins.

(b) In the chloroplast, pigments necessary for the light-capturing reactions of photosynthesis are part of thylakoid membranes, whereas the enzymes for the synthesis of carbohydrate molecules are in the stroma.

Figure 9-4 *Animation* **The site of photosynthesis**
© Cengage Learning

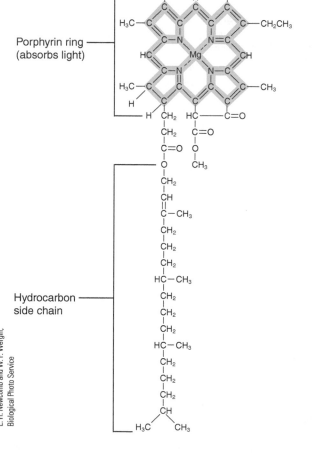

E. H. Newcomb and W. P. Wergin, Biological Photo Service

Figure 9-5 The structure of chlorophyll

Chlorophyll consists of a porphyrin ring and a hydrocarbon side chain. The porphyrin ring, with a magnesium atom in its center, contains a system of alternating double and single bonds; these bonds are commonly found in molecules that strongly absorb certain wavelengths of visible light and reflect others (chlorophyll reflects green). Note that at the top right corner of the diagram, the methyl group (—CH₃) distinguishes chlorophyll *a* from chlorophyll *b*, which has a carbonyl group (—CHO) in this position. The hydrophobic hydrocarbon side chain anchors chlorophyll to the thylakoid membrane.
© Cengage Learning

An **action spectrum** of photosynthesis is a graph of the relative effectiveness of different wavelengths of light. To obtain an action spectrum, scientists measure the rate of photosynthesis at each wavelength for leaf cells or tissues exposed to monochromatic light (light of one wavelength) (FIG. 9-6b).

In a classic biology experiment, German biologist T. W. Engelmann obtained the first action spectrum in 1882. Engelmann's experiment, described in FIGURE 9-7, took advantage of the shape of the chloroplast in a species of a filamentous green alga. Engelmann exposed these cells, each of which contained a long chloroplast that filled most of the cell, to a color spectrum produced by passing light through a prism. He hypothesized that if chlorophyll were indeed responsible for photosynthesis, the process would take place most rapidly in the areas where the chloroplast was illuminated by the colors most strongly absorbed by chlorophyll.

Yet how could photosynthesis be measured in those technologically unsophisticated days? Engelmann knew that photosynthesis produces oxygen and that certain motile bacteria are

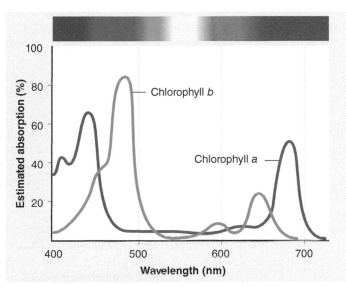

(a) Chlorophylls *a* and *b* absorb light mainly in the blue (422 to 492 nm) and red (647 to 760 nm) regions.

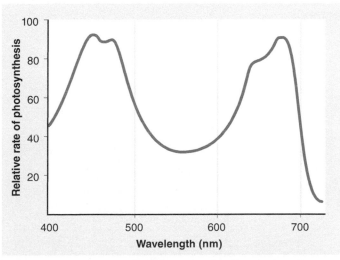

(b) The action spectrum of photosynthesis indicates the effectiveness of various wavelengths of light in powering photosynthesis. Many plant species have action spectra for photosynthesis that resemble the generalized action spectrum shown here.

Figure 9-6 A comparison of the absorption spectra for chlorophylls *a* and *b* with the action spectrum for photosynthesis
© Cengage Learning

Is a pigment in the chloroplast responsible for photosynthesis?

HYPOTHESIS: Engelmann hypothesized that chlorophyll was the main photosynthetic pigment. Accordingly, he predicted that he would observe differences in the amount of photosynthesis, as measured by the amount of oxygen produced, depending on the wavelengths of light used and that these wavelengths would be consistent with the known absorption spectrum of chlorophyll.

EXPERIMENT: Engelmann used the filamentous alga *Cladophora*, in which each cell has a long chloroplast, in his experiments. He used a prism to expose the cells to light that had been separated into various wavelengths. He estimated the formation of oxygen (which he knew was a product of photosynthesis) by exploiting that certain aerobic bacteria would be attracted to the oxygen. As a control (*not shown*), he also exposed the bacteria to the spectrum of light in the absence of the algal cells.

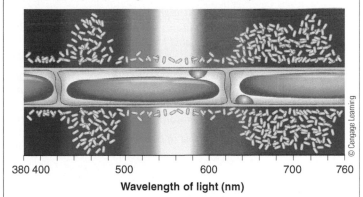

© Cengage Learning

RESULTS AND CONCLUSION: Although the bacteria alone (*control*) showed no preference for any particular wavelength, large numbers were attracted to the photosynthesizing cells in red or blue light, wavelengths that are strongly absorbed by chlorophyll (see Fig. 9-6). Thus, Engelmann concluded that chlorophyll is responsible for photosynthesis.

SOURCE: Englemann's work is reviewed by R.P. Hangarter and H. Gest, "Pictorial Demonstrations of Photosynthesis," in J. Govindjee, T. Beatty, H. Gest, and J. F. Allen (eds.), *Discoveries in Photosynthesis* (The Netherlands: Springer, 2005).

Figure 9-7 *Animation* The first action spectrum of photosynthesis
PREDICT What would have been the distribution of bacteria if the main photosynthetic pigment had turned out to be one with maximal absorption in the yellow and green parts of the spectrum, and very low absorption in other wavelengths?

attracted to areas of high oxygen concentration. He determined the action spectrum of photosynthesis by observing that the bacteria swam toward the parts of the algal filaments in the blue and red regions of the spectrum. How did Engelmann know bacteria were not simply attracted to blue or red light? Engelmann exposed bacteria to the spectrum of visible light in the absence of algal cells as a control. The bacteria showed no preference for any particular wavelength of light. Because the action spectrum of photosynthesis closely matched the absorption spectrum of chlorophyll, Engelmann concluded that chlorophyll in the chloroplasts (and not another compound in another organelle) is responsible for photosynthesis. Numerous studies using sophisticated instruments have since confirmed Engelmann's conclusions.

If you examine Figure 9-6 closely, you will observe that the action spectrum of photosynthesis does not parallel the absorption spectrum of chlorophyll exactly. This difference occurs because accessory pigments, such as carotenoids, transfer some of the energy of excitation produced by green light to chlorophyll molecules. The presence of these accessory photosynthetic pigments can be demonstrated by chemical analysis of almost any leaf, although it is obvious in temperate climates when leaves change color in the fall. Toward the end of the growing season, chlorophyll breaks down (and its magnesium is stored in the permanent tissues of the tree), leaving orange and yellow accessory pigments in the leaves.

CHECKPOINT 9.2

- VISUALIZE *Draw a simple straight line to represent the chloroplast membrane that contains the photosynthetic pigments. What color should it be? Label the two compartments it separates.*

- CONNECT *What is the significance that the combined absorption spectra of chlorophylls a and b roughly match the action spectrum of photosynthesis? Would photosynthesis be more efficient if their individual absorption spectra coincided exactly?*

- *Does fluorescence play a role in photosynthesis?*

9.3 OVERVIEW OF PHOTOSYNTHESIS

LEARNING OBJECTIVES

4   Describe photosynthesis as a redox process.
5   Distinguish between the light-dependent reactions and carbon fixation reactions of photosynthesis.

During photosynthesis a cell uses light energy captured by chlorophyll to power the synthesis of carbohydrates. The overall reaction of photosynthesis can be summarized as

$$6\,CO_2 + 12\,H_2O \xrightarrow[\text{Chlorophyll}]{\text{Light energy}} C_6H_{12}O_6 + 6\,O_2 + 6\,H_2O$$

Carbon dioxide   Water   Glucose   Oxygen   Water

The equation is most accurately written in the form just given, with H_2O on both sides, because water is a reactant in some reactions and a product in others. Furthermore, all the oxygen produced comes from water, so 12 water molecules are required to produce 12 oxygen atoms. However, because there is no net yield of H_2O, we can simplify the summary equation of photosynthesis for purposes of discussion:

$$6\,CO_2 + 6\,H_2O \xrightarrow[\text{Chlorophyll}]{\text{Light}} C_6H_{12}O_6 + 6\,O_2$$

When you analyze this process, it appears that hydrogen atoms are transferred from H_2O to CO_2 to form carbohydrate, so you can recognize it as a redox reaction. Recall from Chapter 7 that in a redox reaction one or more electrons, usually as part of one or more hydrogen atoms, are transferred from an electron donor (a reducing agent) to an electron acceptor (an oxidizing agent).

$$6\,CO_2 + 6\,H_2O \xrightarrow[\text{Chlorophyll}]{\text{Light}} C_6H_{12}O_6 + 6\,O_2$$

When the electrons are transferred, some of their energy is transferred as well. However, the summary equation of photosynthesis is somewhat misleading because no direct transfer of hydrogen atoms actually occurs. The summary equation describes *what* happens but not *how* it happens. The *how* is more complex and involves multiple steps, many of which are redox reactions.

The reactions of photosynthesis are divided into two phases: the light-dependent reactions (the *photo* part of photosynthesis) and the carbon fixation reactions (the *synthesis* part of photosynthesis). Each set of reactions occurs in a different part of the chloroplast: the light-dependent reactions in association with the thylakoids and the carbon fixation reactions in the stroma (FIG. 9-8).

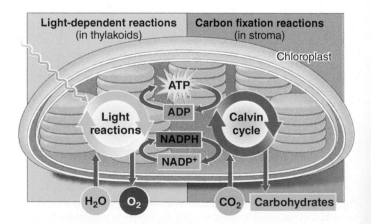

Figure 9-8 *Animation* An overview of photosynthesis
The light-dependent reactions in the thylakoids capture energy as ATP and NADPH, which power the carbon fixation reactions in the stroma.
© Cengage Learning

ATP and NADPH are the products of the light-dependent reactions: An overview

Light energy is converted to chemical energy in the **light-dependent reactions,** which are associated with the thylakoids. The light-dependent reactions begin as chlorophyll captures light energy, which causes one of its electrons to move to a higher energy state. The energized electron is transferred to an acceptor molecule and is replaced by an electron from H_2O. When that happens, H_2O is split and molecular oxygen is released (FIG. 9-9). Some energy of the energized electrons is used to phosphorylate **adenosine diphosphate (ADP),** forming **adenosine triphosphate (ATP).** In addition, the coenzyme **nicotinamide adenine dinucleotide phosphate ($NADP^+$)** becomes reduced, forming **NADPH.**[1] NADPH is an electron carrier similar to NADH, differing by the addition of a phosphate group. Unlike NADH, which is generally associated with catabolic pathways like aerobic cellular respiration, NADPH has the ability to provide high-energy electrons to power certain reactions in anabolic pathways, such as the carbon fixation reactions of photosynthesis. Thus, the products of the light-dependent reactions, ATP and NADPH, are both needed in the energy-requiring carbon fixation reactions.

Carbohydrates are produced during the carbon fixation reactions: An overview

The ATP and NADPH molecules produced during the light-dependent phase are suited for transferring chemical energy but not for long-term energy storage. For this reason, some of their energy is transferred to chemical bonds in carbohydrates, which can be produced in large quantities and stored for future use. Known as **carbon fixation,** these reactions "fix" carbon atoms from CO_2 to existing skeletons of organic molecules. Because the

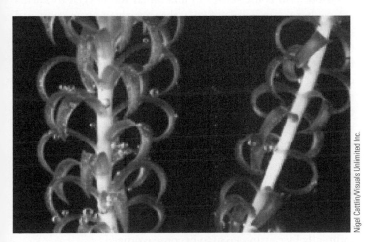

Figure 9-9 Oxygen produced by photosynthesis

On sunny days, the oxygen released by aquatic plants is sometimes visible as bubbles in the water. This plant (*Elodea*) is actively carrying on photosynthesis.

carbon fixation reactions have no direct requirement for light, they were previously referred to as the "dark" reactions. However, they do not require darkness; in fact, many of the enzymes involved in carbon fixation are much more active in the light than in the dark. Furthermore, carbon fixation reactions depend on the products of the light-dependent reactions. Carbon fixation reactions take place in the stroma of the chloroplast.

Now that we have presented an overview of photosynthesis, let us examine the entire process more closely.

CHECKPOINT 9.3

- CONNECT *Which is more oxidized, oxygen that is part of a water molecule or molecular oxygen?*
- CONNECT *In what ways do the carbon fixation reactions depend on the light-dependent reactions?*

9.4 THE LIGHT-DEPENDENT REACTIONS

LEARNING OBJECTIVES

6 Describe the flow of electrons through photosystems I and II in the noncyclic electron transport pathway and the products produced. Contrast this flow with cyclic electron transport.

7 Explain how a proton (H^+) gradient is established across the thylakoid membrane and how this gradient functions in ATP synthesis.

In the light-dependent reactions, the radiant energy from sunlight phosphorylates ADP, producing ATP, and reduces $NADP^+$, forming NADPH. The light energy that chlorophyll captures is temporarily stored in these two compounds. The light-dependent reactions are summarized as follows:

$$12\ H_2O + 12\ NADP^+ + 18\ ADP + 18\ P_i \xrightarrow[\text{Chlorophyll}]{\text{Light}}$$

$$6\ O_2 + 12\ NADPH + 18\ ATP$$

Photosystems I and II each consist of a reaction center and multiple antenna complexes

The light-dependent reactions of photosynthesis begin when chlorophyll *a* and/or accessory pigments absorb light. According to the currently accepted model, chlorophylls *a* and *b* and accessory pigment molecules are organized with pigment-binding proteins in the thylakoid membrane into units called **antenna complexes.** The pigments and associated proteins are arranged as highly ordered groups that include about 250 chlorophyll molecules associated with specific enzymes and other proteins. Each antenna complex absorbs light energy and transfers it to its **reaction center,** which consists of chlorophyll molecules and

---

[1] Although the correct way to write the reduced form of $NADP^+$ is NADPH + H^+, for simplicity's sake we present the reduced form as NADPH throughout this book.

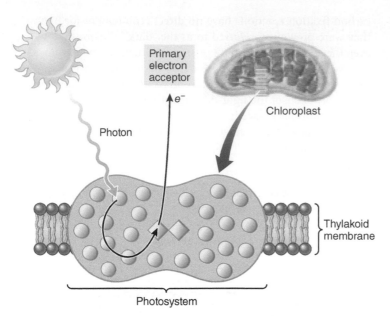

Figure 9-10 *Animation* **Schematic view of a photosystem**

Chlorophyll molecules (*green circles*) and accessory pigments (*not shown*) are arranged in light-harvesting arrays, or antenna complexes. A portion of one such complex within a photosystem is depicted. Each complex consists of several hundred pigment molecules, in association with special proteins (*not shown*). These proteins hold the pigments in a highly ordered spatial array such that when a molecule in an antenna complex absorbs a photon, energy derived from that photon is readily passed from one pigment molecule to another (*black arrow*). When this energy reaches one of the two chlorophyll molecules in the reaction center (*green diamonds*), an electron becomes energized and is accepted by a primary electron acceptor.

© Cengage Learning

proteins, including electron transfer components, that participate directly in photosynthesis (FIG. 9-10). Energy derived from light is converted to chemical energy in the reaction centers by a series of electron transfer reactions.

Two types of photosynthetic units, designated photosystem I and photosystem II, are involved in photosynthesis. Their reaction centers are distinguishable because they are associated with proteins in a way that causes a slight shift in their absorption spectra. Ordinary chlorophyll *a* has a strong absorption peak at about 660 nm. In contrast, the reaction center of **photosystem I** consists of a pair of chlorophyll *a* molecules with an absorption peak at 700 nm and is referred to as **P700.** The reaction center of **photosystem II** is made up of a pair of chlorophyll *a* molecules with an absorption peak of about 680 nm and is referred to as **P680.**

When a pigment molecule absorbs light energy, that energy is passed, through a process known as *resonance,* directly from one pigment molecule to another within the antenna complex until it reaches the reaction center. When the energy reaches a molecule of P700 (in a photosystem I reaction center) or P680 (in a photosystem II reaction center), an electron is then raised to a higher energy level. As we explain in the next section, this energized electron can be donated to an electron acceptor that becomes reduced in the process.

Noncyclic electron transport produces ATP and NADPH

Let us begin our discussion of **noncyclic electron transport** with the events associated with photosystem I (FIG. 9-11). A pigment molecule in an antenna complex associated with photosystem I absorbs a photon of light. The absorbed energy is transferred from one pigment molecule to another until it reaches the reaction center, where it excites an electron in a molecule of P700. This energized electron is transferred to a primary electron acceptor, a special molecule of chlorophyll *a,* which is the first of several electron acceptors in a series. The energized electron is passed along an **electron transport chain** from one electron acceptor to another, until it is passed to *ferredoxin,* an iron-containing protein. Ferredoxin transfers the electron to NADP⁺ in the presence of the enzyme *ferredoxin–NADP⁺ reductase.*

Although single electrons pass down the electron transport chain, two are needed to reduce NADP⁺. When NADP⁺ accepts two electrons, they unite with a proton (H⁺); thus, the reduced form of NADP⁺ is NADPH, which is released into the stroma. P700 becomes positively charged when it gives up an electron to the primary electron acceptor; the missing electron is replaced by one donated by photosystem II.

As in photosystem I, photosystem II becomes activated when a pigment molecule in an antenna complex absorbs a photon of light energy. The energy is transferred to the reaction center, where it causes an electron in a molecule of P680 to move to a higher energy level. This energized electron is accepted by a primary electron acceptor (a highly modified chlorophyll molecule known as *pheophytin*) and then passes along an electron transport chain until it is donated to P700 in photosystem I.

How is the electron that has been donated to the electron transport chain replaced? This process occurs through **photolysis** (light splitting) of water, which not only yields electrons but also is the source of almost all the oxygen in Earth's atmosphere. A molecule of P680 that has given up an energized electron to the primary electron acceptor is positively charged (P680⁺). P680⁺ is an oxidizing agent so strong that it pulls electrons away from an oxygen atom that is part of an H_2O molecule. In a reaction catalyzed by a unique, manganese-containing enzyme, water is broken into its components: two electrons, two protons, and oxygen. Each electron is donated to a P680 molecule, which then loses its positive charge; the protons are released into the thylakoid lumen. Because oxygen does not exist in atomic form, the oxygen produced by splitting one H_2O molecule is written ½ O_2. Two water molecules must be split to yield one oxygen molecule. The photolysis of water is a remarkable reaction, but its name is somewhat misleading because it implies that water is broken by light. Actually, light splits water indirectly by causing P680 to become oxidized.

Noncyclic electron transport is a continuous linear process In the presence of light, there is a continuous, one-way flow of electrons from the ultimate electron source, H_2O, to the terminal electron acceptor, NADP⁺. Water undergoes enzymatically catalyzed photolysis to replace energized electrons donated to the electron transport chain by molecules of P680

Noncyclic electron transport converts light energy to chemical energy in ATP and NADPH.

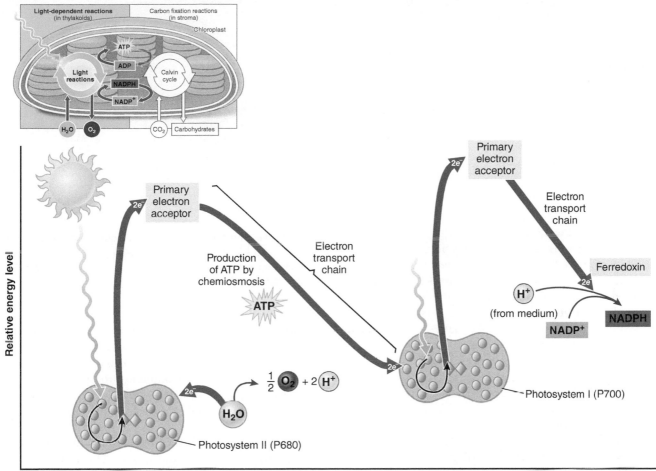

① Electrons are supplied to system from the splitting of H_2O by photosystem II, with release of O_2 as byproduct. When photosystem II is activated by absorbing photons, electrons are passed along the electron transport chain and are eventually donated to photosystem I.

② Electrons in photosystem I are "re-energized" by absorption of additional light energy and are passed to $NADP^+$, forming NADPH.

Figure 9-11 *Animation* **Noncyclic electron transport**

In noncyclic electron transport, the formation of ATP is coupled to one-way flow of energized electrons (*orange arrows*) from H_2O (*lower left*) to $NADP^+$ (*far right*). Single electrons actually pass down the electron transport chain; two are shown in this figure because two electrons are required to form one molecule of NADPH.

PREDICT What would happen if photosystem I were missing?

© Cengage Learning

in photosystem II. These electrons travel down the electron transport chain that connects photosystem II with photosystem I. Thus, they provide a continuous supply of replacements for energized electrons that have been given up by P700.

As electrons are transferred along the electron transport chain that connects photosystem II with photosystem I, they lose energy. Some of the energy released is used to pump protons across the thylakoid membrane, from the stroma to the thylakoid lumen, producing a proton gradient. The energy of this proton gradient is harnessed to produce ATP from ADP by *chemiosmosis,* which we discuss later in this chapter. ATP and NADPH, the products of the light-dependent reactions, are

released into the stroma, where both are required by the carbon fixation reactions.

Cyclic electron transport produces ATP but no NADPH

Only photosystem I is involved in **cyclic electron transport,** the simplest light-dependent reaction. The pathway is cyclic because energized electrons that originate from P700 at the reaction center eventually return to P700. In the presence of light, electrons flow continuously through an electron transport chain within the thylakoid membrane. As they pass from one

TABLE 9-1   A Comparison of Noncyclic and Cyclic Electron Transport

	NONCYCLIC ELECTRON TRANSPORT	CYCLIC ELECTRON TRANSPORT
Electron source	H_2O	None—electrons cycle through the system
Oxygen released?	Yes (from H_2O)	No
Terminal electron acceptor	$NADP^+$	None—electrons cycle through the system
Form in which energy is temporarily captured	ATP (by chemiosmosis); NADPH	ATP (by chemiosmosis)
Photosystem(s) required	PS I (P700) and PS II (P680)	PS I (P700) only

© Cengage Learning

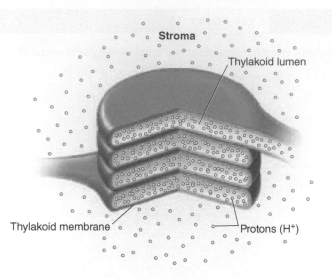

Figure 9-12   The accumulation of protons in the thylakoid lumen
As electrons move down the electron transport chain, protons (H^+) move from the stroma to the thylakoid lumen, creating a proton gradient. The greater concentration of H^+ in the thylakoid lumen lowers the pH.
© Cengage Learning

acceptor to another, the electrons lose energy, some of which is used to pump protons across the thylakoid membrane. An enzyme (ATP synthase) in the thylakoid membrane uses the energy of the proton gradient to manufacture ATP. NADPH is not produced, H_2O is not split, and oxygen is not generated. By itself, cyclic electron transport could not serve as the basis of photosynthesis because, as we explain later in this chapter, NADPH is required to reduce CO_2 to carbohydrate.

The significance of cyclic electron transport to photosynthesis in plants is unclear. Cyclic electron transport may occur in plant cells when there is too little $NADP^+$ to accept electrons from ferredoxin. There is evidence that cyclic electron flow may help maintain the optimal ratio of ATP to NADPH required for carbon fixation as well as provide extra ATP to power other ATP-requiring processes in chloroplasts. Biologists generally agree that ancient bacteria used this process to produce ATP from light energy. A reaction pathway analogous to cyclic electron transport in plants is present in some modern photosynthetic prokaryotes. Noncyclic and cyclic electron transport are compared in TABLE 9-1.

ATP synthesis occurs by chemiosmosis

Each member of the electron transport chain that links photosystem II to photosystem I can exist in an oxidized (lower-energy) form and a reduced (higher-energy) form. The electron accepted from P680 by the primary electron acceptor is highly energized; it is passed from one carrier to the next in a series of exergonic redox reactions, losing some of its energy at each step. Some of the energy given up by the electron is not lost by the system, however; it is used to provide energy for ATP synthesis. Because the synthesis of ATP (i.e., the phosphorylation of ADP) is coupled to the transport of electrons that have been energized by photons of light, the process is called **photophosphorylation.**

The chemiosmotic model explains the coupling of ATP synthesis and electron transport As discussed earlier, the pigments and electron acceptors of the light-dependent reactions are embedded in the thylakoid membrane. Energy released from electrons traveling through the chain of acceptors

is used to pump protons from the stroma, across the thylakoid membrane, and into the thylakoid lumen (FIG. 9-12). Thus, the pumping of protons results in the formation of a proton gradient across the thylakoid membrane. Protons also accumulate in the thylakoid lumen as water is split during noncyclic electron transport. Because protons are actually hydrogen ions (H^+), the accumulation of protons causes the pH of the thylakoid interior to fall to a pH of about 5 in the thylakoid lumen, compared with a pH of about 8 in the stroma. This difference of about 3 pH units across the thylakoid membrane means that there is an approximately thousand-fold difference in hydrogen ion concentration.

The proton gradient has a great deal of free energy because of its state of low entropy. How does the chloroplast convert that energy to a more useful form? According to the general principles of diffusion, the concentrated protons inside the thylakoid might be expected to diffuse out readily. However, they are prevented from doing so because the thylakoid membrane is impermeable to H^+ except through certain channels formed by the enzyme **ATP synthase.** This enzyme, a transmembrane protein also found in mitochondria, forms complexes so large they can be seen in electron micrographs (see Fig. 8-11b). ATP synthase complexes project into the stroma. As the protons diffuse through an ATP synthase complex, free energy decreases as a consequence of an increase in entropy. Each ATP synthase complex couples this exergonic process of diffusion down a concentration gradient to the endergonic process of phosphorylation of ADP to form ATP, which is released into the stroma (FIG. 9-13). The movement of protons through ATP synthase is thought to induce changes in the conformation of the enzyme that are necessary for the synthesis of ATP. It is estimated that for every four protons that move through ATP synthase, one ATP molecule is synthesized.

Electron carriers associated with the thylakoid membrane transfer energized electrons from water to NADP$^+$, forming NADPH. ATP is generated by chemiosmosis.

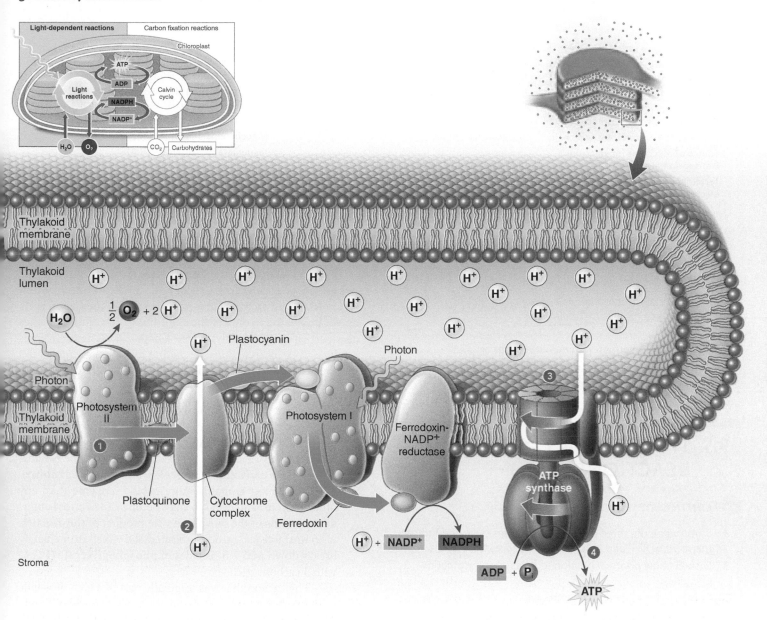

① Blue arrows indicate pathway of electrons along electron transport chain in thylakoid membrane. Electron carriers within membrane become alternately reduced and oxidized as they accept and donate electrons.

② Energy released during electron transport is used to transport H$^+$ from the stroma to the thylakoid lumen, where a high concentration of H$^+$ accumulates.

③ H$^+$ are prevented from diffusing back into stroma except through special channels in ATP synthase in the thylakoid membrane.

④ H$^+$ flows through ATP synthase, generating ATP.

Figure 9-13 *Animation* **A detailed look at electron transport and chemiosmosis**

PREDICT What would be the result if the cytochrome complex were able to transport electrons to photosystem I but an inhibitor prevented it from pumping protons across the thylakoid membrane?
© Cengage Learning

The mechanism by which the phosphorylation of ADP is coupled to diffusion down a proton gradient is called **chemiosmosis.** As the essential connection between the electron transport chain and the phosphorylation of ADP, chemiosmosis is a basic mechanism of energy coupling in cells. You may recall from Chapter 8 that chemiosmosis also occurs in aerobic respiration (see **TABLE 9-2**).

TABLE 9-2 A Comparison of Photosynthesis and Aerobic Respiration

	PHOTOSYNTHESIS	AEROBIC RESPIRATION
Type of metabolic reaction	Anabolism	Catabolism
Raw materials	CO_2, H_2O	$C_6H_{12}O_6$, O_2
End products	$C_6H_{12}O_6$, O_2	CO_2, H_2O
Which cells have these processes?	Cells that contain chlorophyll (certain cells of plants, algae, and some prokaryotes)	Every actively metabolizing cell has aerobic respiration or some other energy-releasing pathway
Sites involved (in eukaryotic cells)	Chloroplasts	Cytosol (glycolysis); mitochondria
ATP production	By photophosphorylation (a chemiosmotic process)	By substrate-level phosphorylation and by oxidative phosphorylation (a chemiosmotic process)
Principal electron transfer compound	$NADP^+$ is reduced to form NADPH*	NAD^+ is reduced to form NADH*
Location of electron transport chain	Thylakoid membrane	Mitochondrial inner membrane (cristae)
Source of electrons for electron transport chain	In noncyclic electron transport: H_2O (undergoes photolysis to yield electrons, protons, and oxygen)	Immediate source: NADH, $FADH_2$ Ultimate source: glucose or other carbohydrate
Terminal electron acceptor for electron transport chain	In noncyclic electron transport: $NADP^+$ (becomes reduced to form NADPH)	O_2 (becomes reduced to form H_2O)

*NADPH and NADH are very similar hydrogen (i.e., electron) carriers, differing only in a single phosphate group. However, NADPH generally works with enzymes in anabolic pathways, such as photosynthesis. NADH is associated with catabolic pathways, such as cellular respiration.

© Cengage Learning

CHECKPOINT 9.4

- **CONNECT** *What role does molecular oxygen play in photosynthesis? in aerobic cellular respiration?*
- **CONNECT** *Describe the series of processes that link light absorption with ATP synthesis (photophosphorylation).*
- **PREDICT** *Can cyclic electron transport alone support photosynthesis? Explain your answer.*

9.5 THE CARBON FIXATION REACTIONS

LEARNING OBJECTIVES

8 Summarize the three phases of the Calvin cycle and indicate the roles of ATP and NADPH in the process.

9 Discuss how photorespiration reduces photosynthetic efficiency.

10 Compare the C_4 and CAM pathways.

In carbon fixation, the energy of ATP and NADPH is used in the formation of organic molecules from CO_2. The carbon fixation reactions may be summarized as follows:

$$12 \text{ NADPH} + 18 \text{ ATP} + 6 \text{ } CO_2 \longrightarrow$$
$$C_6H_{12}O_6 + 12 \text{ NADP}^+ + 18 \text{ ADP} + 18 \text{ P}_i + 6 \text{ } H_2O$$

Most plants use the Calvin cycle to fix carbon

Carbon fixation occurs in the stroma through a sequence of 13 reactions known as the **Calvin cycle.** During the 1950s, University of California researchers Melvin Calvin, Andrew Benson, and others elucidated the details of this cycle. Calvin was awarded a Nobel Prize in Chemistry in 1961.

The 13 reactions of the Calvin cycle are divided into three phases: CO_2 uptake, carbon reduction, and RuBP regeneration (**FIG. 9-14**). All 13 enzymes that catalyze steps in the Calvin cycle are located in the stroma of the chloroplast. Ten of the enzymes also participate in glycolysis (see Chapter 8). These enzymes catalyze reversible reactions, degrading carbohydrate molecules in cellular respiration and synthesizing carbohydrate molecules in photosynthesis.

1. *CO_2 uptake.* The first phase of the Calvin cycle consists of a single reaction in which a molecule of CO_2 reacts with a phosphorylated five-carbon compound, **ribulose bisphosphate (RuBP).** This reaction is catalyzed by the enzyme *ribulose bisphosphate carboxylase/oxygenase,* also known as **rubisco.** The chloroplast contains more rubisco enzyme than any other protein, and rubisco may be one of the most abundant proteins in the biosphere. The product of this reaction is an unstable six-carbon intermediate, which immediately breaks down into 2 molecules of **phosphoglycerate (PGA)** with 3 carbons each.

   The carbon that was originally part of a CO_2 molecule is now part of a carbon skeleton; the carbon has been "fixed." The Calvin cycle is also known as the C_3 **pathway** because the product of the initial carbon fixation reaction is a three-carbon compound. Plants that initially fix carbon in this way are called C_3 **plants.**

2. *Carbon reduction.* The second phase of the Calvin cycle consists of two steps in which the energy and reducing power from ATP and NADPH (both produced in the light-dependent reactions) are used to convert the PGA molecules to **glyceraldehyde-3-phosphate (G3P).** As shown in Figure 9-14, for every 6 carbons that enter the cycle as CO_2, 6 carbons can leave the system as 2 molecules of G3P, to be used in carbohydrate synthesis. Each of these three-carbon molecules of G3P is essentially half a hexose (six-carbon sugar) molecule. (In fact, you may recall that G3P is a key intermediate in the splitting of sugar in glycolysis; see Figs. 8-3 and 8-4.)

ATP and NADPH provide the energy that drives carbon fixation in the Calvin cycle.

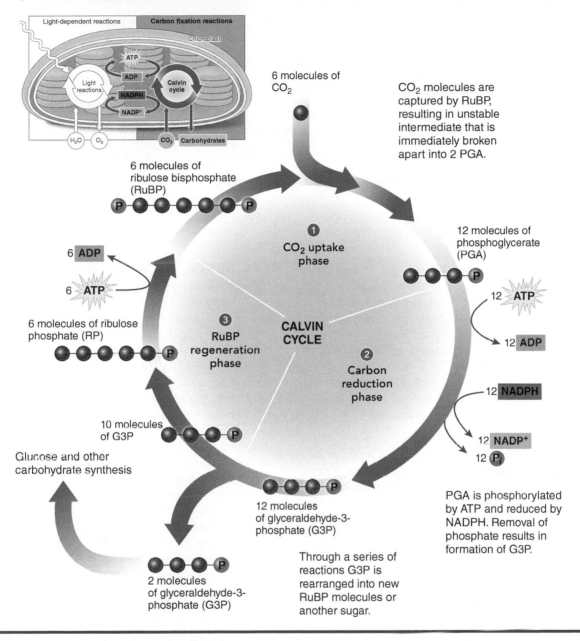

Figure 9-14 *Animation* **A detailed look at the Calvin cycle**

❶ This diagram, in which carbon atoms are black spheres, shows that 6 molecules of CO_2 must be "fixed" (incorporated into pre-existing carbon skeletons) in the CO_2 uptake phase to produce one molecule of a six-carbon sugar such as glucose. ❷ Glyceraldehyde-3-phosphate (G3P) is formed in the carbon reduction phase. For every glucose formed, 2 G3P molecules "leave" the cycle. ❸ Ribulose bisphosphate (RuBP) is regenerated, and a new cycle

can begin. Although these reactions do not require light directly, the energy that drives the Calvin cycle comes from ATP and NADPH, which are the products of the light-dependent reactions.

PREDICT What would happen if the 2:10 ratio of G3P molecules leaving the cycle to those remaining to regenerate RuBP were to become a 4:8 ratio?
© Cengage Learning

The reaction of 2 molecules of G3P is exergonic and leads to the formation of glucose or fructose. In some plants glucose and fructose are then joined to produce sucrose (common table sugar). (Sucrose can be harvested from sugarcane, sugar beets, and maple sap.) The plant cell also uses glucose to produce starch or cellulose.

TABLE 9-3 Summary of Photosynthesis

REACTION SERIES	SUMMARY OF PROCESS	NEEDED MATERIALS	END PRODUCTS
Light-dependent reactions (take place in thylakoid membranes)	Energy from sunlight used to split water, manufacture ATP, and reduce $NADP^+$		
Photochemical reactions	Chlorophyll-activated; reaction center gives up photoexcited electron to electron acceptor	Light energy; pigments (chlorophyll)	Electrons
Electron transport	Electrons transported along chain of electron acceptors in thylakoid membranes; electrons reduce $NADP^+$; splitting of water provides some H^+ that accumulates inside thylakoid space	Electrons, $NADP^+$, H_2O, electron acceptors	NADPH, O_2
Chemiosmosis	H^+ permitted to diffuse across the thylakoid membrane down their gradient; they cross the membrane through special channels in ATP synthase complex; energy released is used to produce ATP	Proton gradient, $ADP + P_i$, ATP synthase	ATP
Carbon fixation reactions (take place in stroma)	Carbon fixation: carbon dioxide used to make carbohydrate	Ribulose bisphosphate, CO_2, ATP, NADPH, necessary enzymes	Carbohydrates, $ADP + P_i$, $NADP^+$

© Cengage Learning

3. *RuBP regeneration.* Note that although 2 G3P molecules are removed from the cycle, 10 G3P molecules remain; this represents a total of 30 carbon atoms. Through a series of ten reactions that make up the third phase of the Calvin cycle, these 30 carbons and their associated atoms become rearranged into 6 molecules of ribulose phosphate, each of which becomes phosphorylated by ATP to produce RuBP, the five-carbon compound with which the cycle started. These RuBP molecules begin the process of CO_2 fixation and eventual G3P production once again.

In summary, the inputs required for the carbon fixation reactions are 6 molecules of CO_2 (the source of both the carbons and the oxygens in carbohydrate), phosphates transferred from ATP, and electrons (as hydrogen) provided by NADPH (but ultimately derived from the photolysis of water). In the end, the 6 carbons from the CO_2 are accounted for by the harvest of a hexose molecule. The remaining G3P molecules are used to synthesize the RuBP molecules with which more CO_2 molecules may combine. TABLE 9-3 provides a summary of photosynthesis.

Photorespiration reduces photosynthetic efficiency

Many C_3 plants, including certain agriculturally important crops such as soybeans, wheat, and potatoes, do not yield as much carbohydrate from photosynthesis as might be expected, especially during periods of very hot temperature in summer. This phenomenon is a consequence of trade-offs between the plant's need for CO_2 and its need to prevent water loss. Recall that most photosynthesis occurs in mesophyll cells inside the leaf and that the entry and exit of gases from the interior of the leaf are regulated by stomata, tiny pores concentrated on the underside of the leaf (see Fig. 9-4a). On hot, dry days, plants close their stomata to conserve water. Once the stomata close, photosynthesis rapidly uses up the CO_2 remaining in the leaf and produces O_2, which accumulates in the chloroplasts.

Recall that the enzyme RuBP carboxylase/oxygenase (rubisco) catalyzes CO_2 fixation in the Calvin cycle by attaching CO_2 to RuBP. As its full name implies, rubisco acts not only as a carboxylase but also as an oxygenase because high levels of O_2 compete with CO_2 for the active site of rubisco. Some of the intermediates involved in the Calvin cycle are degraded to CO_2 and H_2O in a process that is called **photorespiration** because (1) it occurs in the presence of light, and as in aerobic respiration, (2) it requires oxygen and (3) produces CO_2 and H_2O. However, photorespiration does not produce ATP, and it reduces photosynthetic efficiency because it removes some of the intermediates used in the Calvin cycle.

The reasons for photorespiration are incompletely understood, although scientists hypothesize that it reflects the origin of rubisco at an ancient time when CO_2 levels were high and molecular oxygen levels were low. This view is supported by recent evidence that some amino acid sequences in rubisco are similar to sequences in certain bacterial proteins that apparently evolved prior to the evolution of the Calvin cycle. Genetic engineering to produce plants with rubisco that has a much lower affinity for oxygen is a promising area of research to improve yields of certain valuable crop plants.

The initial carbon fixation step differs in C_4 plants and in CAM plants

Photorespiration is not the only problem faced by plants engaged in photosynthesis. Because CO_2 is not a very abundant gas (composing only 0.04% of the atmosphere), it is not easy for plants to obtain the CO_2 they need. As you have learned, when conditions are hot and dry, the stomata close to reduce the loss of water vapor, greatly diminishing the supply of CO_2. Ironically, CO_2 is potentially less available at the very times when maximum sunlight is available to power the light-dependent reactions.

Many plant species living in hot, dry environments have adaptations that facilitate carbon fixation. **C_4 plants** first fix CO_2 into a four-carbon compound, **oxaloacetate. CAM plants** initially fix carbon at night through the formation of oxaloacetate. These special pathways found in C_4 and CAM plants precede the Calvin cycle (C_3 pathway); they do not replace it.

The C_4 pathway efficiently fixes CO_2 at low concentrations The **C_4 pathway,** in which CO_2 is fixed through the formation of oxaloacetate, occurs not only before the C_3 pathway but also in different cells. Leaf anatomy is usually distinctive in C_4 plants. The photosynthetic mesophyll cells are closely associated with prominent, chloroplast-containing **bundle sheath** cells, which tightly encircle the veins of the leaf (FIG. 9-15). The C_4 pathway occurs in the mesophyll cells, whereas the Calvin cycle takes place within the bundle sheath cells.

The key component of the C_4 pathway is a remarkable enzyme that has an extremely high affinity for CO_2, binding it effectively even at unusually low concentrations. This enzyme, **PEP carboxylase,** catalyzes the reaction by which CO_2 reacts with the three-carbon compound *phosphoenolpyruvate (PEP)*, forming oxaloacetate (FIG. 9-16).

In a step that requires NADPH, oxaloacetate is converted to some other four-carbon compound, usually malate. The malate then passes to chloroplasts within bundle sheath cells, where a different enzyme catalyzes the decarboxylation of malate to yield pyruvate (which has three carbons) and CO_2. NADPH is formed, replacing the one used earlier.

$$\text{malate} + \text{NADP}^+ \longrightarrow \text{pyruvate} + CO_2 + \text{NADPH}$$

The CO_2 released in the bundle sheath cell combines with ribulose bisphosphate in a reaction catalyzed by rubisco and goes through the Calvin cycle in the usual manner. The pyruvate formed in the decarboxylation reaction returns to the mesophyll cell, where it reacts with ATP to regenerate phosphoenolpyruvate.

Because the C_4 pathway captures CO_2 and provides it to the bundle sheath cells so efficiently, CO_2 concentration within the bundle sheath cells is about 10 to 60 times as great as its concentration in the mesophyll cells of plants having only the C_3 pathway. Photorespiration is negligible in C_4 plants such as crabgrass because the concentration of CO_2 in bundle sheath cells (where rubisco is present) is always high.

The combined C_3–C_4 pathway involves the expenditure of 30 ATPs per hexose rather than the 18 ATPs used by the C_3 pathway alone. The extra energy expense required to regenerate PEP from pyruvate is worthwhile at high light intensities because it ensures a high concentration of CO_2 in the bundle sheath cells and permits them to carry on photosynthesis at a rapid rate. At lower light intensities and temperatures, C_3 plants are favored. For example, winter rye, a C_3 plant, grows lavishly in cool weather, when crabgrass cannot because it requires more energy to fix CO_2.

CAM plants fix CO_2 at night Plants living in dry, or *xeric*, conditions have a number of structural adaptations that enable them to survive. Many xeric plants have physiological adaptations as well, including a special carbon fixation pathway, the **crassulacean acid metabolism (CAM) pathway.** The name comes from the stonecrop plant family (the Crassulaceae), which uses the CAM pathway, although the pathway has evolved independently in some members of more than 25 other plant

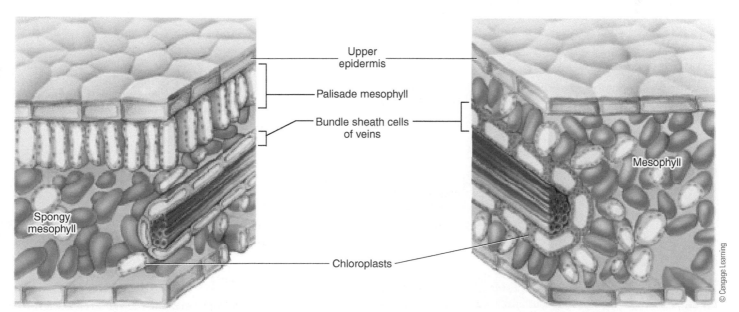

(a) In C_3 plants, the Calvin cycle takes place in the mesophyll cells and the bundle sheath cells are nonphotosynthetic.

(b) In C_4 plants, reactions that fix CO_2 into four-carbon compounds take place in the mesophyll cells. The four-carbon compounds are transferred from the mesophyll cells to the photosynthetic bundle sheath cells, where the Calvin cycle takes place.

Figure 9-15 **C_3 and C_4 plant structure compared**

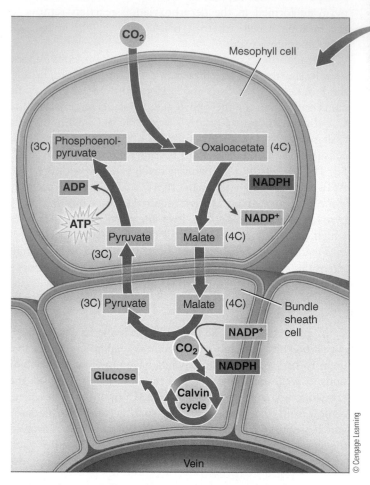

Figure 9-16 *Animation* **Summary of the C₄ pathway**

CO_2 combines with phosphoenolpyruvate (PEP) in the chloroplasts of mesophyll cells, forming a four-carbon compound that is converted to malate. Malate goes to the chloroplasts of bundle sheath cells, where it is decarboxylated. The CO_2 released in the bundle sheath cell is used to make carbohydrate by way of the Calvin cycle.

Figure 9-17 *Animation* **A typical CAM plant**

Prickly pear cactus (*Opuntia*) is a CAM plant. The more than 200 species of *Opuntia* living today originated in various xeric habitats in North and South America.

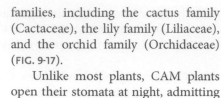

families, including the cactus family (Cactaceae), the lily family (Liliaceae), and the orchid family (Orchidaceae) (FIG. 9-17).

Unlike most plants, CAM plants open their stomata at night, admitting CO_2 while minimizing water loss. They use the enzyme PEP carboxylase to fix CO_2, forming oxaloacetate, which is converted to malate and stored in cell vacuoles. During the day, when stomata are closed and gas exchange cannot occur between the plant and the atmosphere, CO_2 is removed from malate by a decarboxylation reaction. Now the CO_2 is available within the leaf tissue to be fixed into sugar by the Calvin cycle (C_3 pathway).

The CAM pathway is very similar to the C_4 pathway but with important differences. C_4 plants initially fix CO_2 into four-carbon organic acids in mesophyll cells. The acids are later decarboxylated to produce CO_2, which is fixed by the C_3 pathway in the bundle sheath cells. In other words, the C_4 and C_3 pathways occur in *different locations* within the leaf of a C_4 plant. In CAM plants the initial fixation of CO_2 occurs at night. Decarboxylation of malate and subsequent production of sugar from CO_2 by the normal C_3 photosynthetic pathway occur during the day. In other words, the CAM and C_3 pathways occur at *different times* within the same cell of a CAM plant.

Although it does not promote rapid growth the way that the C_4 pathway does, the CAM pathway is a very successful adaptation to xeric conditions. CAM plants can exchange gases for photosynthesis and reduce water loss significantly. Plants with CAM photosynthesis survive in deserts where neither C_3 nor C_4 plants can.

CHECKPOINT 9.5

- *Describe what happens in each of the three phases of the Calvin cycle.*
- **CONNECT** *A decrease in entropy occurs during the CO_2 uptake phase of the Calvin cycle, as freely moving CO_2 molecules become fixed into a carbon skeleton. How can this occur without direct participation by NADPH and/or ATP?*
- *In what ways does photorespiration differ from aerobic cellular respiration?*
- **CONNECT** *Do C_3, C_4, and CAM plants all have rubisco? PEP carboxylase?*

9.6 METABOLIC DIVERSITY

LEARNING OBJECTIVE

11 Contrast photoautotrophs and chemoheterotrophs with respect to their energy and carbon sources.

Land plants, algae, and certain prokaryotes are known as **photoautotrophs.** They are **phototrophs** because they use light energy to make ATP and NADPH, which temporarily hold chemical energy but are unstable and cannot be stockpiled in the cell. They are **autotrophs** (from the Greek *auto*, which means "self," and *trophos*, which means "nourishing") that synthesize complex organic compounds from simpler, inorganic raw materials. The chemical energy of ATP and NADPH then drives carbon fixation, the anabolic pathway in which stable organic molecules are synthesized from CO_2 and water. These organic compounds are used not only as starting materials to synthesize all the other organic compounds the photosynthetic organism needs (such as complex carbohydrates, amino acids, and lipids) but also for energy storage. Glucose and other carbohydrates produced during photosynthesis are relatively reduced compounds that can be subsequently oxidized by aerobic respiration or by some other catabolic pathway (see Chapter 8).

In contrast, animals, fungi, and most prokaryotes are known as **chemoheterotrophs.** They are **chemotrophs** because they obtain energy from chemicals, typically by redox reactions (see Chapters 7 and 8). They are **heterotrophs** (from the Greek *heter*, which means "other," and *trophos*, which means "nourishing") because they cannot fix carbon; they use organic molecules produced by *other* organisms as the building blocks from which they synthesize the carbon compounds they need.

We are so familiar with plants as photoautotrophs and animals such as ourselves as chemoheterotrophs that we tend to think that all organisms should fit into these two "mainstream" categories. Two other types of nutrition are found in certain prokaryotes. A few bacteria, known as nonsulfur purple bacteria, are **photoheterotrophs,** able to use light energy but unable to carry out carbon fixation, so they must obtain carbon from organic compounds. Some other prokaryotes are **chemoautotrophs,** which obtain their energy from the oxidation of reduced inorganic molecules such as hydrogen sulfide (H_2S), nitrite (NO_2^+), or ammonia (NH_3). Some of this captured energy is subsequently used to carry out carbon fixation.

CHECKPOINT 9.6

- **CONNECT** *How does a green plant obtain energy? carbon? How does your body obtain these things?*

9.7 PHOTOSYNTHESIS IN PLANTS AND IN THE ENVIRONMENT

LEARNING OBJECTIVE

12 State the importance of photosynthesis both in a plant and to other organisms.

Although we characterize plants as photoautotrophs, not all plant cells carry out photosynthesis, and even cells with chloroplasts also possess mitochondria and carry out aerobic respiration. In fact, respiration using the organic molecules the plant has made for itself is the direct source of ATP needed for most plant metabolism.

Several mechanisms regulate the relative activities of photosynthesis and aerobic respiration in plants. Although the enzymes of the Calvin cycle do not require light to function, they are actually regulated by light. As a consequence of the light-requiring reactions, the stroma becomes more basic (approximately pH 8), activating rubisco and other Calvin cycle enzymes. In contrast, light tends to inhibit the enzymes of glycolysis in the cytosol. Hence, photosynthesis, not aerobic respiration, is favored in the light. When light is very dim, at a point known as the *light compensation point,* photosynthesis still occurs, but it is not evident because the rate of CO_2 fixation by photosynthesis is equal to the rate of CO_2 release through aerobic respiration. On the other hand, when light is very bright, photorespiration can significantly diminish photosynthetic yields.

As we have seen in this chapter, the reactions of the Calvin cycle provide a net yield of the three-carbon phosphorylated sugar, G3P. What are the various fates of G3P in the plant? Consider a leaf cell actively conducting photosynthesis. A series of enzymes may convert some of the G3P to glucose and then to starch. This starch is stored in starch granules that form inside chloroplasts. It has been recently shown that when this starch is broken down, the disaccharide maltose is typically formed (see Fig. 3-8a). Maltose is transported out of the chloroplast and then cleaved in the cytosol, providing glucose for aerobic respiration. Not all G3P ends up as carbohydrate; some is ultimately converted to amino acids, fatty acids, and other organic molecules needed by the photosynthetic cell.

Some of the G3P is exported to the cytosol, where enzymes convert it to the disaccharide sucrose (see Fig. 3-8b). Sucrose is then actively transported out of the cell, moves through the vascular system of the plant (see Chapter 35 for a discussion of plant transport), and is actively transported into the various cells. Sucrose can be broken down into glucose and fructose, which are used in aerobic respiration or as starting points for the synthesis of the various organic molecules the cells need, such as amino acids, lipids, and carbohydrates. Important carbohydrates include cellulose for cell walls (see Fig. 3-10) and starch, particularly in starch-storing structures such as roots (see Fig. 3-9a) and developing seeds and tubers (such as potatoes).

The benefits of photosynthesis in the environment are staggering. Of course, by fixing carbon, photoautotrophs are the ultimate source of virtually all organic molecules used as energy and carbon sources by chemoheterotrophs such as ourselves (for an exception, see *Inquiring About: Life without the Sun* in Chapter 55). In carrying out carbon fixation, photoautotrophs remove CO_2 from the atmosphere, thereby slowing climate change (see Chapter 57). Also of prime importance is that photolysis of water by photosystem II releases the O_2 that all aerobic organisms require for aerobic respiration. Molecular oxygen is so reactive that it could not be maintained in the atmosphere if it were not constantly replenished in this way.

As discussed in Chapter 21, the evolution of oxygen-producing photosynthesis was a critical event in the history of life on Earth. It not only permitted the evolution of aerobic organisms, but it also made terrestrial life possible because in the stratosphere O_2 is converted to ozone (O_3), which shields the planet from damaging ultraviolet light.

CHECKPOINT 9.7

- **CONNECT** *How does a root cell obtain energy? organic molecules?*
- **CONNECT** *What is the source of molecular oxygen in Earth's atmosphere?*

SUMMARY: FOCUS ON LEARNING OBJECTIVES

9.1 Light and Photosynthesis *(page 186)*

1 Describe the physical properties of light and explain the relationship between a wavelength of light and its energy.

- Light consists of particles called **photons** that move as waves.
- Photons with shorter **wavelengths** have more energy than those with longer wavelengths.

9.2 Chloroplasts *(page 187)*

2 Diagram the internal structure of a chloroplast and explain how its components interact and facilitate the process of photosynthesis.

- In plants **photosynthesis** occurs in chloroplasts, which are located mainly within **mesophyll** cells inside the leaf.
- **Chloroplasts** are organelles enclosed by a double membrane; the inner membrane encloses the **stroma** in which membranous, saclike **thylakoids** are suspended. Thylakoids enclose the **thylakoid lumen.** Thylakoids arranged in stacks are called **grana.**
- **Chlorophyll *a*, chlorophyll *b*, carotenoids,** and other photosynthetic pigments are components of the thylakoid membranes of chloroplasts.

3 Describe what happens to an electron in a biological molecule such as chlorophyll when a photon of light energy is absorbed.

- Photons excite biological molecules such as chlorophyll and other photosynthetic pigments, causing one or more electrons to become energized. These energized electrons may be accepted by electron acceptor compounds.
- The combined **absorption spectra** of chlorophylls *a* and *b* are similar to the **action spectrum** for photosynthesis.

9.3 Overview of Photosynthesis *(page 190)*

4 Describe photosynthesis as a redox process.

- During photosynthesis, light energy is captured and converted to the chemical energy of carbohydrates; hydrogens from water are used to reduce carbon, and oxygen derived from water becomes oxidized, forming molecular oxygen.

5 Distinguish between the light-dependent reactions and carbon fixation reactions of photosynthesis.

- In the **light-dependent reactions,** electrons energized by light are used to generate **ATP** and **NADPH;** these compounds provide energy for the formation of carbohydrates during the **carbon fixation reactions.**

9.4 The Light-Dependent Reactions *(page 191)*

6 Describe the flow of electrons through photosystems I and II in the noncyclic electron transport pathway and the products produced. Contrast this flow with cyclic electron transport.

- **Photosystems I** and **II** are the two types of photosynthetic units involved in photosynthesis. Each photosystem includes chlorophyll molecules and accessory pigments organized with pigment-binding proteins into **antenna complexes.**
- Only a special pair of chlorophyll *a* molecules in the **reaction center** of an antenna complex give up energized electrons to a nearby electron acceptor. **P700** is in the reaction center for photosystem I; **P680** is in the reaction center for photosystem II.

- During the noncyclic light-dependent reactions, known as **noncyclic electron transport,** ATP and NADPH are formed.
- Electrons in photosystem I are energized by the absorption of light and passed through an **electron transport chain** to $NADP^+$, forming NADPH. Electrons given up by P700 in photosystem I are replaced by electrons from P680 in photosystem II.
- A series of redox reactions takes place as energized electrons are passed along the electron transport chain from photosystem II to photosystem I. Electrons given up by P680 in photosystem II are replaced by electrons made available by the **photolysis** of H_2O; oxygen is released in the process.
- During **cyclic electron transport,** electrons from photosystem I are eventually returned to photosystem I. ATP is produced by **chemiosmosis,** but no NADPH or oxygen is generated.

7 Explain how a proton (H^+) gradient is established across the thylakoid membrane and how this gradient functions in ATP synthesis.

- **Photophosphorylation** is the synthesis of ATP coupled to the transport of electrons energized by photons of light. Some of the energy of the electrons is used to pump protons across the thylakoid membrane, providing the energy to generate ATP by chemiosmosis.
- As protons diffuse through **ATP synthase,** an enzyme complex in the thylakoid membrane, ADP is phosphorylated to form ATP.

9.5 The Carbon Fixation Reactions *(page 196)*

8 Summarize the three phases of the Calvin cycle and indicate the roles of ATP and NADPH in the process.

- The carbon fixation reactions proceed by way of the **Calvin cycle,** also known as the **C_3 pathway.**
- In the CO_2 uptake phase of the Calvin cycle, CO_2 is combined with **ribulose bisphosphate (RuBP),** a five-carbon sugar, by the enzyme ribulose bisphosphate carboxylase/oxygenase, commonly known as **rubisco,** forming the three-carbon molecule **phosphoglycerate (PGA).**
- In the carbon reduction phase of the Calvin cycle, the energy and reducing power of ATP and NADPH are used to convert PGA molecules to **glyceraldehyde-3-phosphate (G3P).** For every 6 CO_2 molecules fixed, 12 molecules of G3P are produced, and 2 molecules of G3P leave the cycle to produce the equivalent of 1 molecule of glucose.
- In the RuBP regeneration phase of the Calvin cycle, the remaining G3P molecules are modified to regenerate RuBP.

9 Discuss how photorespiration reduces photosynthetic efficiency.

- In **photorespiration** C_3 plants consume oxygen and generate CO_2 by degrading Calvin cycle intermediates but do not produce ATP. Photorespiration is significant on bright, hot, dry days when plants close their stomata, conserving water but preventing the passage of CO_2 into the leaf.

10 Compare the C_4 and CAM pathways.

- In the **C_4 pathway,** the enzyme **PEP carboxylase** binds CO_2 effectively, even when CO_2 is at a low concentration. C_4

reactions take place within mesophyll cells. The CO_2 is fixed in oxaloacetate, which is then converted to malate. The malate moves into a **bundle sheath** cell, and CO_2 is removed from it. The released CO_2 then enters the Calvin cycle.

- The **crassulacean acid metabolism (CAM)** pathway is similar to the C_4 pathway. PEP carboxylase fixes carbon at night in the mesophyll cells, and the Calvin cycle occurs during the day in the same cells.

9.6 Metabolic Diversity (page 200)

11 Contrast photoautotrophs and chemoheterotrophs with respect to their energy and carbon sources.

- **Photoautotrophs** use light as an energy source and are able to incorporate atmospheric CO_2 into pre-existing carbon skeletons.
- **Chemoheterotrophs** obtain energy by oxidizing chemicals and obtain carbon as organic molecules from other organisms.

9.7 Photosynthesis in Plants and in the Environment (page 201)

12 State the importance of photosynthesis both in a plant and to other organisms.

- Photosynthesis is the ultimate source of all chemical energy and organic molecules available to photoautotrophs, such

as plants, and to virtually all other organisms as well. It also constantly replenishes the supply of oxygen in the atmosphere, vital to all aerobic organisms.

Summary Reactions for Photosynthesis

The light-dependent reactions (noncyclic electron transport):

$$12\ H_2O + 12\ NADP^+ + 18\ ADP + 18\ P_i \xrightarrow[\text{Chlorophyll}]{\text{Light}}$$
$$6\ O_2 + 12\ NADPH + 18\ ATP$$

The carbon fixation reactions (Calvin cycle):

$$12\ NADPH + 18\ ATP + 6\ CO_2 \longrightarrow$$
$$C_6H_{12}O_6 + 12\ NADP^+ + 18\ ADP + 18\ P_i + 6\ H_2O$$

By canceling the common items on opposite sides of the arrows in these two coupled equations, we obtain the simplified overall equation for photosynthesis:

$$6\ CO_2 + 12\ H_2O \xrightarrow[\text{Chlorophyll}]{\text{Light energy}} C_6H_{12}O_6 + 6\ O_2 + 6\ H_2O$$

Carbon dioxide   Water   Glucose   Oxygen   Water

TEST YOUR UNDERSTANDING

Know and Comprehend

1. Where is chlorophyll located in the chloroplast? (a) thylakoid membranes (b) stroma (c) matrix (d) thylakoid lumen (e) between the inner and outer membranes
2. In photolysis some of the energy captured by chlorophyll is used to split (a) CO_2 (b) ATP (c) NADPH (d) H_2O (e) both b and c
3. In plants, the final electron acceptor in noncyclic electron transport is (a) $NADP^+$ (b) CO_2 (c) H_2O (d) O_2 (e) G3P
4. In ___, electrons that have been energized by light contribute their energy to add phosphate to ADP, producing ATP. (a) crassulacean acid metabolism (b) the Calvin cycle (c) photorespiration (d) C_4 pathways (e) photophosphorylation
5. The Calvin cycle begins when CO_2 reacts with (a) phosphoenolpyruvate (b) glyceraldehyde-3-phosphate (c) ribulose bisphosphate (d) oxaloacetate (e) phosphoglycerate
6. The enzyme directly responsible for almost all carbon fixation on Earth is (a) rubisco (b) PEP carboxylase (c) ATP synthase (d) phosphofructokinase (e) maltase
7. In C_4 plants C_4 and C_3 pathways occur at different ___, whereas in CAM plants CAM and C_3 pathways occur at different ___. (a) times of day; locations within the leaf (b) seasons; locations (c) locations; times of day (d) locations; seasons (e) times of day; seasons
8. An organism characterized as a photoautotroph obtains energy from ___ and carbon from ___. (a) light; organic molecules (b) light; CO_2 (c) organic molecules; organic molecules (d) organic molecules; CO_2 (e) O_2; CO_2

Apply and Analyze

9. **VISUALIZE** Draw a simple sketch illustrating a thylakoid membrane that is actively involved in chemiosmosis and label the two compartments it separates. Add the ATP synthase complex, indicate the proton gradient, and specify in which compartment ATP is synthesized.
10. **CONNECT** Compare the sketch you drew for question 9 (above) with the one you drew for Chapter 8, Question 15. In each sketch, are protons being pumped into the innermost compartment or out of it? Does it matter?
11. **CONNECT** Must all autotrophs use light energy? Explain.

12. **CONNECT** Only some plant cells have chloroplasts, but all actively metabolizing plant cells have mitochondria. Explain.
13. **CONNECT** High-energy electrons from glucose are used to drive ATP synthesis in aerobic respiration. How did these electrons become so energetic?

Evaluate and Synthesize

14. **PREDICT** What would life be like for photoautotrophs if there were no chemoheterotrophs? for chemoheterotrophs if there were no photoautotrophs?
15. **EVOLUTION LINK** Propose an explanation for bacteria, chloroplasts, and mitochondria all having ATP synthase complexes.
16. **INTERPRET DATA** The figure depicts the absorption spectrum of a plant pigment. What colors or wavelengths does it absorb? What is the color of this pigment?

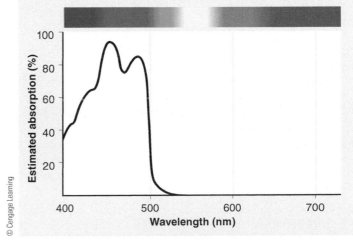

17. **SCIENCE, TECHNOLOGY, AND SOCIETY** What strategies may be employed in the future to increase world food supply? Base your answer on your knowledge of photosynthesis and related processes.

aplia To access course materials, such as Aplia and other companion resources, please visit **www.cengagebrain.com**.

10 | Chromosomes, Mitosis, and Meiosis

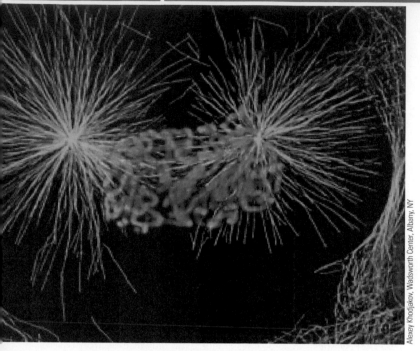

Alexey Khodjakov, Wadsworth Center, Albany, NY

Fluorescence LM of a cultured newt lung cell in mitosis (early prometaphase). The nuclear envelope has broken down, and the microtubules of the mitotic spindle (*green*) now interact with the chromosomes (*blue*).

KEY CONCEPTS

10.1 In eukaryotic cells, DNA is wound around specific proteins to form chromatin, which in turn is folded and packaged to make individual chromosomes.

10.2 In mitosis, duplicated chromosomes separate (split apart) and are evenly distributed into two daughter nuclei. Mitosis is an important part of the cell cycle, which consists of the successive stages through which a cell passes.

10.3 An internal genetic program interacts with external signals to regulate the cell cycle.

10.4 Meiosis, which reduces the number of chromosome sets from diploid to haploid, is necessary to maintain the normal chromosome number when two cells join during sexual reproduction. Meiosis helps increase genetic variation among offspring.

10.5 Meiosis and gamete production precede fertilization in the life cycles of sexually reproducing organisms.

re-existing cells divide to form new cells. This remarkable process enables an organism to grow, repair damaged parts, and reproduce. Cells serve as the essential link between generations. Even the simplest cell contains a large amount of precisely coded genetic information in the form of deoxyribonucleic acid (DNA). When a cell divides, the information contained in the DNA must be faithfully replicated and the copies then transmitted to each daughter cell through a precisely choreographed series of steps (see photograph).

DNA is a very long, thin molecule that could easily become tangled and broken, and a eukaryotic cell's nucleus contains a huge amount of DNA. In this chapter we consider how eukaryotes accommodate the genetic material by packaging each DNA molecule with proteins to form a structure called a *chromosome*, each of which contains large amounts of genetic information.

We then consider *mitosis*, the highly regimented process that ensures a parent cell transmits one copy of every chromosome to each of its two daughter cells. In this way, the chromosome number is preserved through successive mitotic divisions. Most *somatic cells* (body cells) of eukaryotes divide by mitosis. Mitosis is an active area of biological research, and for good reason: errors in mitosis can result in a host of disorders and diseases such as cancer, a disease condition in which cells divide at an inappropriate rate and become invasive. Thus, a clearer understanding of mitosis has the potential to improve our treatment of many diseases.

Finally, we discuss *meiosis*, a process that reduces the chromosome number by half. Sexual life cycles in eukaryotes require meiosis. Sexual reproduction involves the fusion of two sex cells, or *gametes*, to form a fertilized egg called a *zygote*. Meiosis makes it possible for each gamete to contain only half the number of chromosomes in the parent cell, thereby preventing the zygotes from having twice as many chromosomes as the parents.

10.1 EUKARYOTIC CHROMOSOMES

1 Discuss the significance of chromosomes in terms of their information content.
2 Explain how DNA is packed into chromosomes in eukaryotic cells.

The major carriers of genetic information in eukaryotes are the **chromosomes,** which lie within the cell nucleus. Although *chromosome* means "colored body," chromosomes are virtually colorless; the term refers to their ability to be stained by certain dyes. In the 1880s, light microscopes had been improved to the point that scientists such as German biologist Walther Fleming began to observe chromosomes during cell division. In 1903, American biologist Walter Sutton and German biologist Theodor Boveri noted independently that chromosomes were the physical carriers of genes, the genetic factors Gregor Mendel discovered in the 19th century (discussed in Chapter 11).

Chromosomes are made of **chromatin,** a material consisting of DNA and associated proteins. When a cell is not dividing, the chromosomes are present but in an extended, partially unraveled form. Chromatin consists of long, thin threads that are somewhat aggregated, giving them a granular appearance when viewed with the electron microscope (see Fig. 4-11a). During cell division, the chromatin fibers condense and the chromosomes become visible as distinct structures (**FIG. 10-1**).

DNA is organized into informational units called genes

An organism may have thousands of *genes*. For example, humans have more than 20,000 genes that code for proteins. The concept of the gene has changed considerably since the science of genetics began, but our traditional definitions have always centered on the gene as an informational unit. By providing information needed to carry out one or more specific cell functions, a gene affects some characteristic of the organism. For example, genes govern eye color in humans, wing length in flies, and seed color in peas. As you will learn in later chapters, these concepts are being expanded as scientists study the many ways information stored in DNA controls the workings of the cell.

DNA is packaged in a highly organized way in chromosomes

Prokaryotic and eukaryotic cells differ markedly in their DNA content as well as in the organization of DNA molecules. The bacterium *Escherichia coli* normally contains about 4×10^6 base pairs (almost 1.35 mm) of DNA in its single, circular DNA molecule. In fact, the total length of its DNA is about 1000 times as

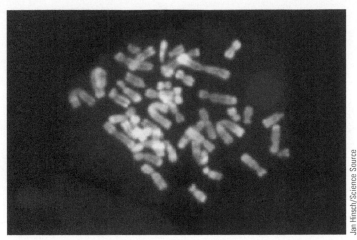

Figure 10-1 **Chromosomes**
Human chromosomes from an unidentified cell are shown in this fluorescence LM.

10 μm

Jan Hinsch/Science Source

long as the length of the cell itself. Therefore, the DNA molecule is, with the help of proteins, twisted and folded compactly to fit inside the bacterial cell (see Fig. 25-2).

A typical eukaryotic cell contains much more DNA than a bacterium does, and it is organized in the nucleus as multiple chromosomes that vary widely in size and number among different species. Although a human nucleus is about the size of a large bacterial cell, it contains more than 1000 times the amount of DNA found in *E. coli*. The DNA content of a human sperm cell is about 3×10^9 base pairs; stretched end to end, it would measure almost 1 m long. Remarkably, this DNA fits into a nucleus with a diameter of only 10 μm.

How does a eukaryotic cell pack its DNA into the chromosomes? Chromosome packaging is facilitated by certain proteins known as **histones.**[1] Histones have a positive charge because they have a high proportion of amino acids with basic side chains (see Chapter 3). The positively charged histones associate with DNA, which has a negative charge because of its phosphate groups, to form structures called **nucleosomes.** The fundamental unit of each nucleosome consists of a beadlike structure with 146 base pairs of DNA wrapped around a disc-shaped core of eight histone molecules (two each of four different histone types) (**FIG. 10-2**). Although the nucleosome was originally defined as a bead plus a DNA segment that links it to an adjacent bead, today the term more commonly refers only to the bead itself (i.e., the eight histones and the DNA wrapped around them).

Nucleosomes function like tiny spools, preventing DNA from becoming tangled. You can see the importance of this role in **FIGURE 10-3**, which illustrates the enormous length of DNA that unravels from a mouse chromosome after researchers have removed the histones. The role of histones is more than simply

---

[1] A few types of eukaryotic cells lack histones. Conversely, histones occur in one group of prokaryotes, the archaea (see Chapter 25).

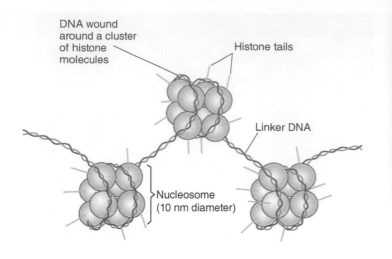

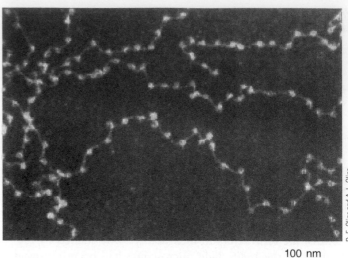

100 nm

D. E. Olins and A. L. Olins

(a) A model for the structure of a nucleosome. Each nucleosome bead contains a set of eight histone molecules, forming a protein core around which the double-stranded DNA winds. The DNA surrounding the histones consists of 146 nucleotide pairs; another segment of DNA, about 60 nucleotide pairs long, links nucleosome beads.

Figure 10-2 Nucleosomes
© Cengage Learning

(b) TEM of nucleosomes from the nucleus of a chicken cell. Normally, nucleosomes are packed more closely together, but the preparation procedure has spread them apart, revealing the DNA linkers.

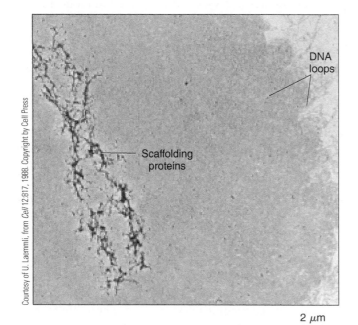

Courtesy of U. Laemmli, from *Cell* 12.817, 1988. Copyright by Cell Press

2 μm

Figure 10-3 TEM of a mouse chromosome depleted of histones
Notice how densely packed the DNA strands are, even though they have been released from the histone proteins that organize them into tightly coiled structures.

structural because their arrangement also affects the activity of the DNA with which they are associated. Histones are increasingly viewed as an important part of the regulation of gene expression, that is, whether genes are turned off or on. We discuss gene regulation by histones in Chapter 14.

The wrapping of DNA into nucleosomes represents the first level of chromosome structure. FIGURE 10-4 shows the higher-order structures of chromatin leading to the formation of a condensed chromosome. The nucleosomes themselves are 10 nm in diameter. The packed nucleosome state occurs when a fifth type of histone, known as *histone H1*, associates with the linker DNA, packing adjacent nucleosomes together to form a compacted 30 nm chromatin fiber. In extended chromatin these fibers form large, coiled loops held together by **scaffolding proteins,** nonhistone proteins that help maintain chromosome structure. The loops then interact to form the condensed chromatin found in a chromosome. Cell biologists have identified a group of proteins, collectively called **condensin,** required for chromosome compaction. Condensin binds to DNA and wraps it into coiled loops that are compacted into a chromosome.

Chromosome number and informational content differ among species

Every individual of a given species has a characteristic number of chromosomes in the nuclei of its somatic (body) cells. However, it is not the number of chromosomes that makes each species unique but the information the genes specify. Most human somatic cells have exactly 46 chromosomes, but humans are not humans merely because we have 46 chromosomes. Some other species—the olive tree, for example—also have 46. Some

When a cell prepares to divide, its chromosomes become thicker and shorter as their long chromatin fibers are compacted.

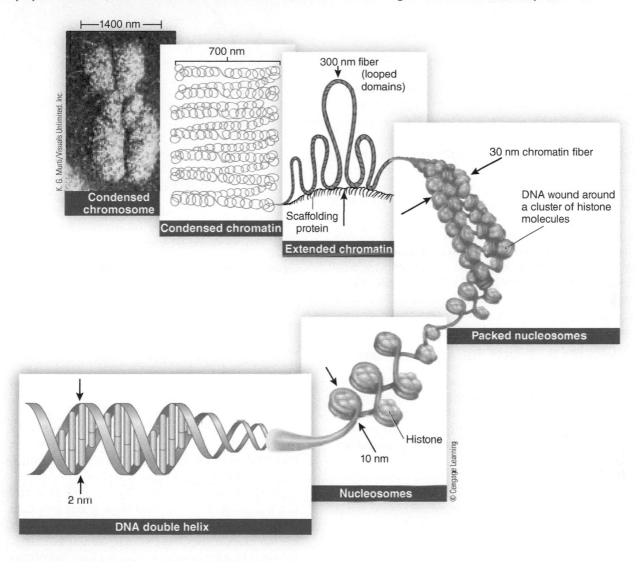

Figure 10-4 *Animation* **Organization of a eukaryotic chromosome**

This diagram shows how DNA is packaged into highly condensed metaphase chromosomes. First, DNA is wrapped around histone proteins to form nucleosomes. Then, the nucleosomes are compacted into chromatin fibers, which are coiled into looped domains. The looped domains are compacted, ultimately forming chromosomes.

VISUALIZE For which of the states of chromatin illustrated is histone H1 most responsible?

humans have an abnormal chromosome composition with more or fewer than 46 (see Fig. 16-5).

Other species have different chromosome numbers. A certain species of roundworm has only 2 chromosomes in each cell, whereas some crabs have as many as 200, and some ferns have more than 1000. Most animal and plant species have between 8 and 50 chromosomes per somatic cell. Quantities above and below these numbers are uncommon. The number of

chromosomes a species has does not indicate the species' complexity or its status within a particular domain or kingdom.

CHECKPOINT 10.1

- *What are the informational units on chromosomes called? Of what do these informational units consist?*
- **CONNECT** *How is the large discrepancy between DNA length and nucleus size addressed in eukaryotic cells?*

10.2 THE CELL CYCLE AND MITOSIS

LEARNING OBJECTIVES

3   Identify the stages in the eukaryotic cell cycle and describe their principal events.

4   Describe the structure of a duplicated chromosome, including the sister chromatids, centromeres, and kinetochores.

5   Explain the significance of mitosis and describe the process.

When cells reach a certain size, they usually either stop growing or divide. Not all cells divide; some, such as skeletal muscle and red blood cells, do not normally divide once they are mature. Other cells undergo a sequence of activities required for growth and cell division.

The stages through which a cell passes from one cell division to the next are collectively referred to as the **cell cycle.** Timing of the cell cycle varies widely, but in actively growing plant and animal cells, it is about 8 to 20 hours. The cell cycle consists of two main phases, interphase and M phase, both of which can be distinguished under a light microscope (**FIG. 10-5**).

Chromosomes duplicate during interphase

Most of a cell's life is spent in **interphase,** the time when no cell division is occurring. A cell is metabolically active during interphase, synthesizing needed materials (proteins, lipids, and other biologically important molecules) and growing. Here is the sequence of interphase and M phase in the eukaryotic cell cycle:

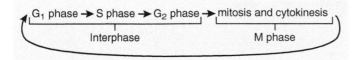

The time between the end of mitosis and the beginning of the S phase is termed the **G_1 phase** (*G* stands for *gap*, an interval during which no DNA synthesis occurs). Growth and normal metabolism take place during the G_1 phase, which is typically the longest phase. Cells that are not dividing usually become arrested in this part of the cell cycle and are said to be in a state called G_0. Toward the end of G_1, the enzymes required for DNA synthesis become more active. Synthesis of these enzymes, along with proteins needed to initiate cell division (discussed later in this chapter), enable the cell to enter the S phase.

During the **synthesis phase,** or **S phase,** DNA replicates and histone proteins are synthesized so that the cell can make duplicate copies of its chromosomes. How did researchers identify the S phase of the cell cycle? In the early 1950s, researchers demonstrated that cells preparing to divide duplicate their chromosomes at a relatively restricted time interval during interphase and not during early mitosis, as previously hypothesized. These

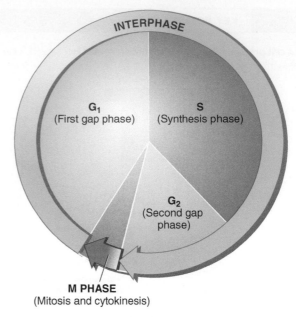

Figure 10-5 *Animation* **The eukaryotic cell cycle**

The cell cycle, a successive series of events in the life of a cell, includes interphase (G_1, S, and G_2) and M phase (mitosis and cytokinesis). Proportionate amounts of time spent at each stage vary among species, cell types, and growth conditions. If the cell cycle were a period of 12 hours, G_1 would be about 5 hours, S would be 4.5 hours, G_2 would be 2 hours, and M phase would be 30 minutes.
© Cengage Learning

investigators used isotopes, such as ^{3}H, to synthesize radioactive thymidine, a nucleotide that is incorporated specifically into DNA as it is synthesized. After radioactive thymidine was supplied for a brief period (such as 30 minutes) to actively growing cells, *autoradiography* (see Fig. 2-3) on exposed film showed that a fraction of the cells had silver grains over their chromosomes. The nuclei of these cells were radioactive because during the experiment DNA had replicated. DNA replication was not occurring in the cells that did not have radioactively labeled chromosomes. Researchers therefore inferred that the proportion of labeled cells out of the total number of cells provides a rough estimate of the length of the S phase relative to the rest of the cell cycle.

After it completes the S phase, the cell enters a second gap phase, the **G_2 phase.** At this time, increased protein synthesis occurs as the final steps in the cell's preparation for division take place. For many cells, the G_2 phase is short relative to the G_1 and S phases.

M phase involves two main processes, mitosis and cytokinesis. **Mitosis,** the nuclear division that produces two nuclei containing chromosomes identical to the parental nucleus, begins at the end of the G_2 phase. Cytokinesis, which generally begins before mitosis is complete, is the division of the cell cytoplasm to form two cells.

Mitosis is a continuous process, but for descriptive purposes, it is divided into five stages:

prophase → prometaphase → metaphase→ anaphase → telophase

Study FIGURE 10-6 while you read the following descriptions of these stages as they occur in a typical plant or animal cell.

During prophase, duplicated chromosomes become visible with the microscope

The first stage of mitosis, **prophase,** begins with chromosome compaction, when the long chromatin fibers that make up the chromosomes begin a coiling process that makes them shorter and thicker. The compacted chromatin can then be distributed to the daughter cells with less likelihood of tangling.

When stained with certain dyes and viewed through the light microscope, chromosomes become visible as darkly stained bodies as prophase progresses. It is now apparent that each chromosome was duplicated during the preceding S phase and consists of a pair of **sister chromatids**, which contain identical, double-stranded DNA sequences. Each chromatid includes a constricted region called the **centromere.** Sister chromatids are tightly associated in the vicinity of their centromeres (FIG. 10-7). The chemical basis for this close association at the centromeres consists of precise DNA sequences that are tightly bound to specific proteins.

For example, sister chromatids are physically linked by a ring-shaped protein complex called **cohesin.** Cohesins extend along the length of the sister chromatid arms and are particularly concentrated at the centromere (FIG. 10-8). These cohesins, which hold the duplicated chromosomes together from their synthesis in S phase onward, help ensure accurate chromosome separation during mitosis.

Attached to each centromere is a **kinetochore,** a multiprotein complex to which **microtubules** can bind. These microtubules function in chromosome distribution during mitosis, in which one copy of each chromosome is delivered to each daughter cell.

A dividing cell can be described as a globe, with an equator that determines the midplane (equatorial plane) and two opposite poles. This terminology is used for all cells regardless of their actual shape. Microtubules radiate from each pole, and some of these protein fibers elongate toward the chromosomes, forming the **mitotic spindle,** a structure that separates the duplicated chromosomes during anaphase (FIG. 10-9). The *minus* ends of these microtubules are at the poles, and the *plus* ends extend to the cell's midplane. It might be helpful to review Figure 4-23a, which shows the organization of microtubules as linear polymers of the protein *tubulin.* The organization and function of the spindle require the presence of motor proteins and a variety of signaling molecules.

Animal cells differ from plant cells in the details of mitotic spindle formation. In both types of dividing cells, each pole contains a region, the **microtubule-organizing center,** from which extend the microtubules that form the mitotic spindle. The electron microscope shows that microtubule-organizing centers in certain plant cells consist of fibrils with little or no discernible structure.

In contrast, animal cells have a pair of **centrioles** in the middle of each microtubule-organizing center (see Fig. 4-25). The centrioles are surrounded by fibrils that make up the **pericentriolar material.** The spindle microtubules terminate in the pericentriolar material, but they do not actually touch the centrioles. Although cell biologists once thought spindle formation in animal cells required centrioles, their involvement is probably coincidental. Current evidence suggests that centrioles organize the pericentriolar material and ensure its duplication when the centrioles duplicate.

Each of the two centrioles is duplicated during the S phase of interphase, yielding two centriole pairs. Late in prophase, microtubules radiate from the pericentriolar material surrounding the centrioles; these clusters of microtubules are called **asters.** The two asters migrate to opposite sides of the nucleus, establishing the two poles of the mitotic spindle.

Prometaphase begins when the nuclear envelope breaks down

During **prometaphase,** the nuclear envelope fragments so that the spindle microtubules come into contact with the chromosomes; units of the disassembled nuclear envelope are sequestered in vesicles to be used later, to assemble nuclear envelopes for the daughter cells. The nucleolus shrinks and usually disappears, and the mitotic spindle is completely assembled. At the start of prometaphase, the duplicated chromosomes are scattered throughout the nuclear region (see the chapter-opening photograph, which shows early prometaphase). The spindle microtubules grow and shrink as they move toward the center of the cell in a "search and capture" process. Their random, dynamic movements give the appearance that they are "searching" for the chromosomes. If a microtubule comes near a centromere, one of the kinetochores of a duplicated chromosome "captures" it. As the now-tethered chromosome continues moving toward the cell's midplane, the unattached kinetochore of its sister chromatid becomes connected to a spindle microtubule from the cell's other pole.

During the chromosomes' movements toward the cell's midplane, long microtubules are shortened by the removal of tubulin subunits, and short microtubules are lengthened by the addition of tubulin subunits. Evidence indicates that shortening and lengthening occur at the kinetochore end (the plus end) of the microtubule, not at the spindle pole end (the minus end). This shortening or lengthening occurs while the spindle microtubule remains firmly tethered to the kinetochore. Motor proteins located at the kinetochores may be involved in this tethering of the spindle microtubule. These motor proteins may work in a similar fashion to the kinesin motor shown in Figure 4-24.

To summarize the events of prometaphase, sister chromatids of each duplicated chromosome become attached at their kinetochores to spindle microtubules extending from opposite

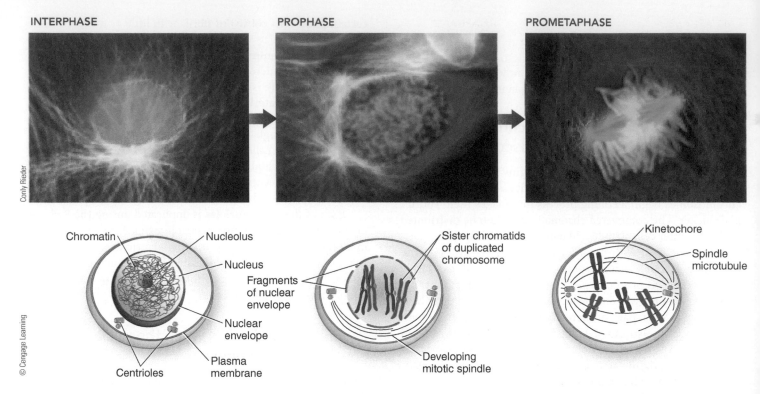

INTERPHASE

PROPHASE

PROMETAPHASE

Chromatin · Nucleolus · Nucleus · Fragments of nuclear envelope · Nuclear envelope · Plasma membrane · Centrioles · Sister chromatids of duplicated chromosome · Developing mitotic spindle · Kinetochore · Spindle microtubule

(a) Cell carries out normal life activities. Chromosomes become duplicated.

(b) Long fibers of chromatin condense as compact mitotic chromosomes, each consisting of two chromatids attached at their centromeres. Cytoskeleton is disassembled, and mitotic spindle forms between centrioles, which have moved to poles of cell. Nuclear envelope begins to disassemble.

(c) Spindle microtubules attach to kinetochores of chromosomes. Chromosomes begin to move toward cell's midplane.

Figure 10-6 *Animation* **Interphase and the stages of mitosis**

The fluorescence LMs are of cultured lung cells of a newt, *Taricha granulosa*. (Chromosomes and chromatin, *blue*; microtubules, *yellow/green*.) The drawings depict generalized animal cells with a diploid chromosome number of 4; the sizes of the nuclei and chromosomes are exaggerated to show the structures more clearly. Cells of most plants lack centrioles.

poles of the cell, and the chromosomes begin to move toward the cell's midplane. As the cell transitions from prometaphase to metaphase, cohesins dissociate from the sister chromatid arms, freeing them from one another, although some cohesins remain in the centromere regions.

Duplicated chromosomes line up on the midplane during metaphase

During **metaphase**, all the cell's chromosomes align at the cell's midplane, or **metaphase plate**. As already mentioned, one of the two sister chromatids of each chromosome is attached by its kinetochore to microtubules from one pole, and its sister chromatid is attached by its kinetochore to microtubules from the opposite pole.

The mitotic spindle has three types of microtubules: polar microtubules, kinetochore microtubules, and astral microtubules (see **FIG. 10-9**). *Polar microtubules*, also known as *nonkinetochore microtubules,* extend from each pole to the equatorial region, where they overlap and interact with nonkinetochore microtubules from the opposite pole. *Kinetochore microtubules* extend from each pole and attach to chromosomes at their kinetochores. *Astral microtubules* are the short microtubules that form asters at each pole.

Each chromatid is completely condensed and appears distinct during metaphase. Because individual chromosomes are more obvious at metaphase than at any other time, the **karyotype,** or chromosome composition, is usually checked at this stage for chromosome abnormalities (see Chapter 16). As the mitotic cell transitions from metaphase to anaphase, the remaining cohesin proteins joining the sister chromatids at their centromere dissociate.

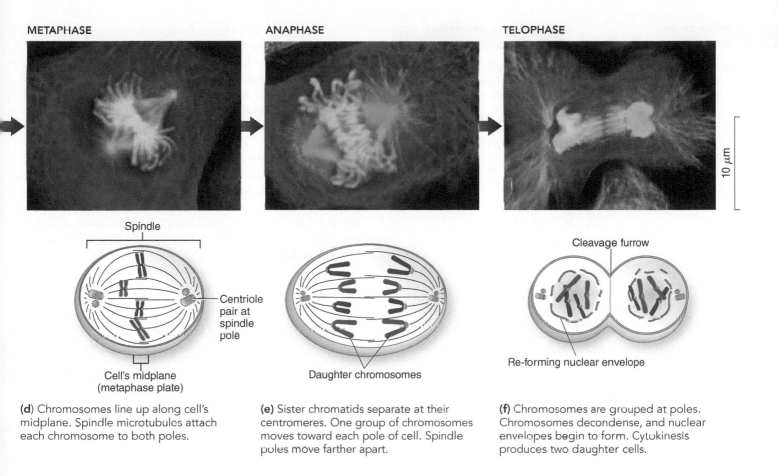

METAPHASE

ANAPHASE

TELOPHASE

10 μm

Spindle

Centriole pair at spindle pole

Cell's midplane (metaphase plate)

Cleavage furrow

Daughter chromosomes

Re-forming nuclear envelope

(d) Chromosomes line up along cell's midplane. Spindle microtubules attach each chromosome to both poles.

(e) Sister chromatids separate at their centromeres. One group of chromosomes moves toward each pole of cell. Spindle poles move farther apart.

(f) Chromosomes are grouped at poles. Chromosomes decondense, and nuclear envelopes begin to form. Cytokinesis produces two daughter cells.

Figure 10-6 *Continued*

During anaphase, chromosomes move toward the poles

Anaphase begins as the sister chromatids separate. Once the chromatids are no longer attached to their duplicates, each chromatid is called a *chromosome*. The now-separate chromosomes move to opposite poles, using the spindle microtubules as tracks. The kinetochores, still attached to kinetochore microtubules, lead the way, with the chromosome arms trailing behind. Anaphase ends when all the chromosomes have reached the poles.

Cell biologists are making significant progress in understanding the overall mechanism of chromosome movement in anaphase. Chromosome movements are studied in several ways. The number of microtubules at a particular stage or after certain treatments is determined by carefully analyzing electron micrographs. Researchers also physically perturb living cells that are

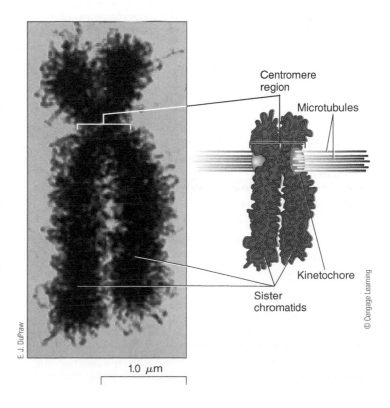

Centromere region

Microtubules

Kinetochore

Sister chromatids

© Cengage Learning

E. J. DuPraw

1.0 μm

Figure 10-7 Sister chromatids and centromeres

The sister chromatids, each consisting of tightly coiled chromatin fibers, are tightly associated at their centromere regions, indicated by the brackets. Associated with each centromere is a kinetochore, which serves as a microtubule attachment site. Kinetochores and microtubules are not visible in this TEM of a metaphase chromosome.

When chromosomes duplicate, sister chromatids are initially linked to one another by protein complexes called cohesins. Cohesin linkages are particularly concentrated in the vicinity of the centromere.

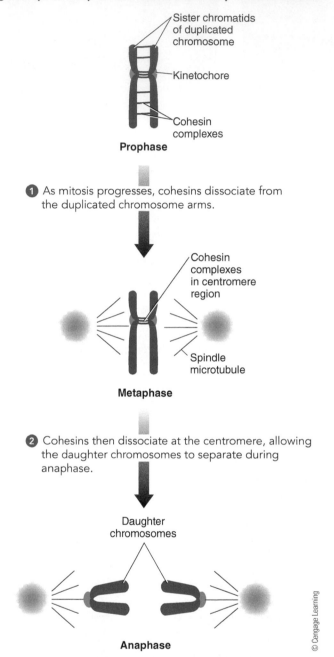

Prophase

1 As mitosis progresses, cohesins dissociate from the duplicated chromosome arms.

Metaphase

2 Cohesins then dissociate at the centromere, allowing the daughter chromosomes to separate during anaphase.

Anaphase

© Cengage Learning

Figure 10-8 Cohesins

CONNECT As you learn more about mitosis, consider what would happen if the cohesins failed to dissociate or if they were to dissociate prematurely, in late prophase.

dividing, using microlaser beams or mechanical devices known as *micromanipulators*. A skilled researcher can move chromosomes, break their connections to microtubules, and even remove them from the cell entirely.

Microtubules lack elastic or contractile properties. Then how do the chromosomes move apart? Are they pushed or pulled, or do other forces operate? Microtubules are dynamic structures, with *tubulin* subunits constantly being removed from their ends and others being added. Evidence indicates that during anaphase, kinetochore microtubules shorten, or *depolymerize*, at their *plus* ends, that is, closest toward the midplane of the cell (FIG. 10-10). This shortening mechanism pulls the chromosomes toward the poles.

A second mechanism also plays a role in chromosome separation. During anaphase, the spindle as a whole elongates, at least partly because polar microtubules originating at opposite poles are associated with motors that let them slide past one another at the midplane. The sliding decreases the degree of overlap, thereby "pushing" the poles apart. This mechanism indirectly causes the chromosomes to move apart because they are attached to the poles by kinetochore microtubules.

During telophase, two separate nuclei form

During the final stage of mitosis, **telophase,** chromosomes arrive at the poles, and there is a return to interphase-like conditions. The chromosomes decondense by partially uncoiling. A new nuclear envelope forms around each set of chromosomes, made at least in part from small vesicles and other components derived from the old nuclear envelope. The spindle microtubules disappear, and the nucleoli reorganize.

Cytokinesis forms two separate daughter cells

Cytokinesis, the division of the cytoplasm to yield two daughter cells, is the last step in M phase and usually overlaps mitosis, generally beginning during telophase. Cytokinesis of an animal or fungal cell (e.g., yeast) begins as an *actomyosin contractile ring* is assembled and attached to the plasma membrane. The contractile ring encircles the cell in the equatorial region, at right angles to the spindle (FIG. 10-11a). The contractile ring consists of an association between actin and myosin filaments; it is thought that the motor activity of myosin moves actin filaments to cause the constriction, similar to the way actin and myosin cause muscle contraction (see Fig. 40-11). The ring contracts, producing a **cleavage furrow** that gradually deepens and eventually separates the cytoplasm into two daughter cells, each with a complete nucleus. The contractile ring then disassembles.

In plant cells cytokinesis occurs by forming a **cell plate** (FIG. 10-11b), a partition constructed in the equatorial region of the spindle that grows laterally toward the cell wall. The cell plate forms as a line of vesicles originating in the *Golgi complex*. The vesicles contain materials to construct both a primary cell wall for each daughter cell and a middle lamella that cements the primary cell walls together. The vesicle membranes fuse to become the plasma membrane of each daughter cell.

Multinucleated cells form if mitosis is not followed by cytokinesis; this is a normal condition for certain cell types. For example, the body of plasmodial slime molds consists of a multinucleate mass of cytoplasm (see Fig. 26-19a).

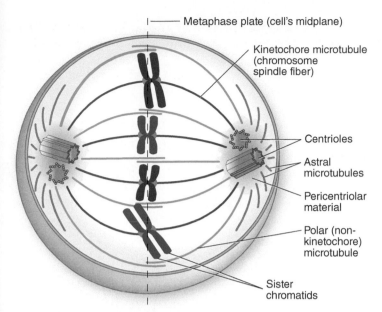

Metaphase plate (cell's midplane)

Kinetochore microtubule (chromosome spindle fiber)

Centrioles

Astral microtubules

Pericentriolar material

Polar (non-kinetochore) microtubule

Sister chromatids

Figure 10-9 The mitotic spindle
One end of each microtubule of this animal cell is associated with one of the poles. Astral microtubules (*green*) radiate in all directions, forming the aster. Kinetochore microtubules (*red*) connect the kinetochores to the poles, and polar (nonkinetochore) microtubules (*blue*) overlap at the midplane.
© Cengage Learning

Mitosis produces two cells genetically identical to the parent cell

The remarkable regularity of the process of cell division ensures that each daughter nucleus receives exactly the same number and kinds of chromosomes that the parent cell had. Thus, with a few exceptions, every cell of a multicellular organism has the same genetic makeup. If a cell receives more or fewer than the characteristic number of chromosomes through some malfunction of the cell division process, the resulting cell may show marked abnormalities and often cannot survive.

Mitosis provides for the orderly distribution of chromosomes (and of centrioles, if present), but what about the various cytoplasmic organelles? For example, all eukaryotic cells, including plant cells, require mitochondria. Likewise, photosynthetic plant cells cannot carry out photosynthesis without chloroplasts. These organelles contain their own DNA and appear to form by the division of previously existing mitochondria or plastids or their precursors. This nonmitotic division process is similar to prokaryotic cell division (discussed in the next section) and generally occurs during interphase. Because many copies of each organelle are present in each cell, organelles are apportioned with the cytoplasm that each daughter cell receives during cytokinesis.

Lacking nuclei, prokaryotes divide by binary fission

Bacteria and archaea contain much less DNA than do most eukaryotic cells, but precise distribution of the genetic material into two daughter cells is still a formidable process.

Do spindle microtubules move chromosomes by a shortening (i.e., depolymerization) of microtubules at the spindle poles or at the kinetochore ends?

HYPOTHESIS: Spindle microtubules move chromosomes toward the spindle poles by a mechanism in which the spindle microtubules are shortened at their kinetochore ends.

EXPERIMENT: Microtubules in pig kidney cells in early anaphase were labeled with a fluorescent dye that specifically attaches to microtubules.

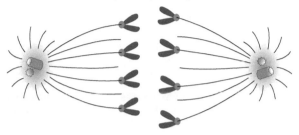

The researchers marked the microtubules by using a laser microbeam to bleach the dye while keeping the microtubules intact.

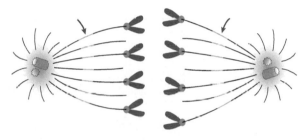

RESULTS AND CONCLUSION: The chromosomes moved toward the bleached areas of the spindle microtubules, indicating a shortening of the microtubules on the kinetochore side. The microtubules on the polar ends did not shorten.

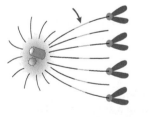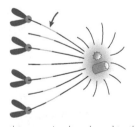

Chromosomes moved poleward because they remained anchored to the kinetochore microtubules as tubulin subunits were removed at the kinetochore ends of the microtubules.

SOURCE: Gorbsky, G.J., P.J. Sammak, and G.G. Borisy (1987) "Chromosomes move poleward in anaphase along stationary microtubules that coordinately disassemble from their kinetochore ends." *Journal of Cell Biology* 104: 9–18.

Figure 10-10 *Animation* **Using laser photobleaching to determine how chromosomes are transported toward the spindle poles during anaphase**

PREDICT How would the spindle microtubules have looked during anaphase if they had disassembled at their polar ends instead of their kinetochore ends?

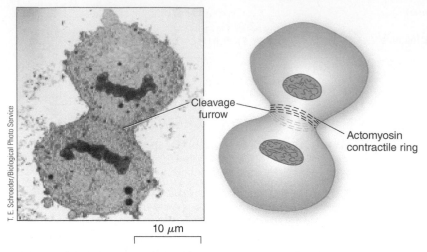

(a) TEM of the equatorial region of a cultured animal cell undergoing cytokinesis. Note the cleavage furrow. Dividing fungal cells also have a contractile ring that causes cytokinesis.

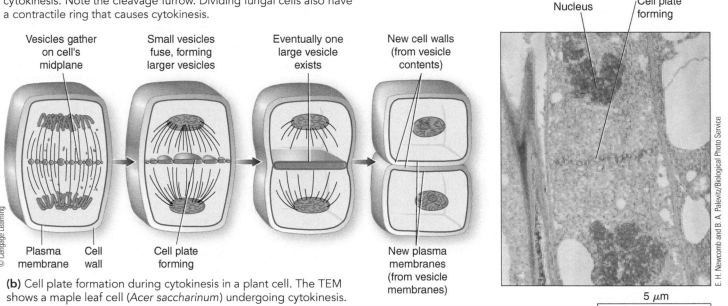

(b) Cell plate formation during cytokinesis in a plant cell. The TEM shows a maple leaf cell (*Acer saccharinum*) undergoing cytokinesis.

Figure 10-11 *Animation* **Cytokinesis in animal and plant cells**
The nuclei in both TEMs are in telophase. The drawings show 3-D relationships.

Prokaryotic DNA usually consists of a single, circular chromosome that is packaged with associated proteins. Although the distribution of genetic material in dividing prokaryotic cells is a simpler process than mitosis, it nevertheless is very precise, to ensure that the daughter cells are genetically identical to the parent cell.

Prokaryotes reproduce asexually, generally by **binary fission,** a process in which one cell divides into two daughter cells (**FIG. 10-12**). The circular DNA molecule replicates, resulting in two identical chromosomes. DNA replication begins at a single site on the bacterial chromosome, called the *origin of replication.* DNA synthesis proceeds from that point in both directions until they eventually meet (see Fig. 12-16).

Following replication, the daughter chromosomes separate and move to opposite ends of the elongating cell. Cytokinesis between the daughter chromosomes is controlled by the **Z ring,** a protein scaffold that holds about ten different proteins around the cell's midsection. There the plasma membrane grows inward between the two DNA copies, dividing the cell's cytoplasm in half, and a new transverse cell wall is synthesized between the two cells. (Bacterial reproduction is described further in Chapter 25.)

CHECKPOINT 10.2

- *What are the stages of the cell cycle? During which stage does DNA replicate?*
- *What are the stages of mitosis, and what happens in each stage?*

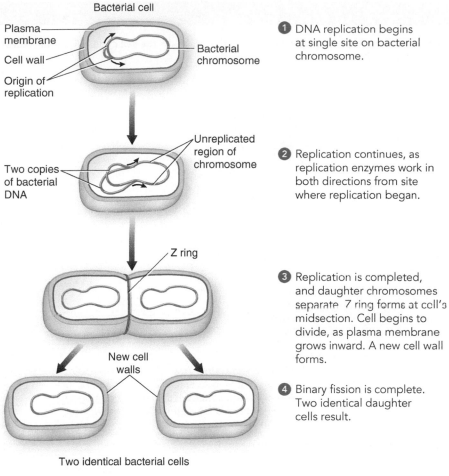

Bacterial cell

Plasma membrane
Cell wall
Origin of replication
Bacterial chromosome

❶ DNA replication begins at single site on bacterial chromosome.

Unreplicated region of chromosome
Two copies of bacterial DNA

❷ Replication continues, as replication enzymes work in both directions from site where replication began.

Z ring

❸ Replication is completed, and daughter chromosomes separate. Z ring forms at cell's midsection. Cell begins to divide, as plasma membrane grows inward. A new cell wall forms.

New cell walls

❹ Binary fission is complete. Two identical daughter cells result.

Two identical bacterial cells

Figure 10-12 Binary fission

Binary fission is a precisely orchestrated sequence of events that ensures each bacterial daughter cell has identical genetic material. The bacterial chromosome is much longer than depicted here and is tethered to the plasma membrane at one spot (not shown).

© Cengage Learning

10.3 REGULATION OF THE CELL CYCLE

LEARNING OBJECTIVE

6 Explain some ways in which the cell cycle is controlled.

When conditions are optimal, some prokaryotic cells can divide every 20 minutes. The generation times of eukaryotic cells are generally much longer, although the frequency of cell division varies widely among different species and among different tissues of the same species. Some skeletal muscle cells usually stop dividing after the first few months of life, whereas blood-forming cells, digestive tract cells, and skin cells divide frequently throughout the life of the organism. Under optimal conditions of nutrition, temperature, and pH, the length of the eukaryotic cell cycle is constant for any given cell type. Under less-favorable conditions, however, the generation time may be longer.

Certain regulatory molecules that control the cell cycle are common to all eukaryotes. Genetically programmed in the cell's nucleus, these regulatory molecules are components of the *cell cycle control system* found in organisms as diverse as yeast, clams, frogs, humans, and plants. Regulatory molecules trigger a specific sequence of events during the cell cycle.

Because the cell cycle consists of hundreds of sequential events that proceed in an orderly manner, a failure to carefully control these events can have disastrous consequences. Control mechanisms in the genetic program, called **cell-cycle checkpoints**, temporarily block key events from being initiated during the cell cycle. Cell-cycle checkpoints ensure that all the events of a particular stage have been completed before the next stage begins (FIG. 10-13). The checkpoints are inactivated after they have done their job so the cell cycle can proceed.

Genes that encode molecules involved in checkpoints are critically important to the cell cycle. If a checkpoint gene is defective, it can result in cancer or other serious diseases. Consider what might happen if the metaphase-anaphase checkpoint molecules were nonfunctional. In this case, anaphase might be initiated too early, before all chromosomes were properly attached to spindle fibers. The resulting daughter cells might have too few or too many chromosomes. An abnormal number of chromosomes is associated with Down syndrome as well as many cancers.

FIGURE 10-14 shows some of the key molecules involved in regulating the cell cycle. Among them are **protein kinases**, enzymes that activate or inactivate other proteins by *phosphorylating* (adding phosphate groups to) them. The protein kinases involved in controlling the cell cycle are **cyclin-dependent kinases (Cdks)**. The activity of various Cdks increases and then decreases as the cell moves through the cell cycle. Cdks are active only when they bind tightly to regulatory proteins called **cyclins.** The cyclins are so named because their levels fluctuate predictably during the cell cycle (i.e., they "cycle," or are alternately synthesized and degraded as part of the cell cycle).

Three scientists who began their research in the 1970s and 1980s on the roles of protein kinases and cyclins in the cell cycle (Leland Hartwell from the United States, and Paul Nurse and Tim Hunt from Great Britain) were awarded the Nobel Prize in Physiology or Medicine in 2001. Their discoveries were cited as important not only in working out the details of the fundamental cell process of mitosis but also in understanding why cancer cells divide when they should not. For example, cyclin levels are often higher than normal in human cancer cells.

When a specific Cdk associates with a specific cyclin, it forms a **cyclin–Cdk complex**. Cyclin–Cdk complexes phosphorylate

When a cell has not completed the steps leading to a cell-cycle checkpoint, the checkpoint is active and halts the cell cycle. When the necessary steps are completed, the checkpoint is inactivated, and the cell cycle proceeds.

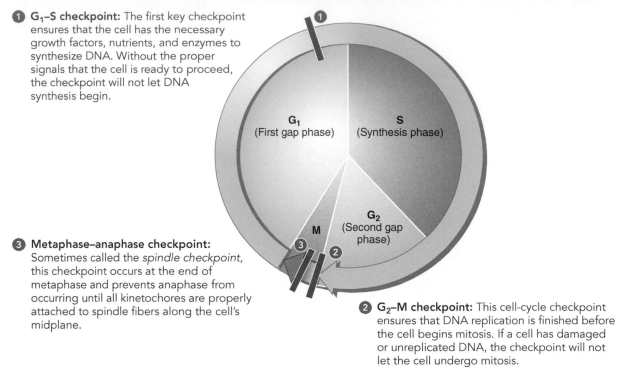

1 **G₁–S checkpoint:** The first key checkpoint ensures that the cell has the necessary growth factors, nutrients, and enzymes to synthesize DNA. Without the proper signals that the cell is ready to proceed, the checkpoint will not let DNA synthesis begin.

3 **Metaphase–anaphase checkpoint:** Sometimes called the *spindle checkpoint*, this checkpoint occurs at the end of metaphase and prevents anaphase from occurring until all kinetochores are properly attached to spindle fibers along the cell's midplane.

2 **G₂–M checkpoint:** This cell-cycle checkpoint ensures that DNA replication is finished before the cell begins mitosis. If a cell has damaged or unreplicated DNA, the checkpoint will not let the cell undergo mitosis.

Figure 10-13 Key checkpoints in the cell cycle

The cell cycle consists of hundreds of sequential events. The *red bars* show three important checkpoints that determine that previous steps are completed so that the next steps may proceed. Each checkpoint is inactivated after it has performed its function, allowing the cell cycle to continue.

VISUALIZE Consider a cell with two chromosomes. Sketch what it might look like if it were arrested at the metaphase–anaphase checkpoint.

© Cengage Learning

enzymes and other proteins. Some of these proteins become activated when they are phosphorylated, and others become inactivated. For example, phosphorylation of the protein p27, known to be a major inhibitor of cell division, is thought to initiate degradation of the protein. As various enzymes are activated or inactivated by phosphorylation, the activities of the cell change. Thus, a decrease in a cell's level of p27 causes a nondividing cell to resume division.

Eukaryotic cells form four major cyclin–Cdk complexes: G₁-Cdk, G₁/S-Cdk, S-Cdk, and M-Cdk. Each cyclin–Cdk complex phosphorylates a different group of proteins. G₁-Cdk prepares the cell to pass from the G₁ phase to the S phase, and then G₁/S-Cdk commits the cell to undergo DNA replication. S-Cdk initiates DNA replication. M-Cdk promotes the events of mitosis, including chromosome condensation, nuclear envelope breakdown, and mitotic spindle formation.

M-Cdk also activates another enzyme complex, the **anaphase-promoting complex (APC),** toward the end of metaphase. APC initiates anaphase by allowing degradation of the cohesins and other proteins that hold the sister chromatids together during metaphase. As a result, the sister chromatids separate as two daughter chromosomes. At this point, cyclin is

degraded to negligible levels and M-Cdk activity drops, allowing the mitotic spindle to disassemble and the cell to exit mitosis.

Certain drugs can stop the cell cycle at a specific checkpoint. Some of them prevent DNA synthesis, whereas others inhibit the synthesis of proteins that control the cycle or inhibit the synthesis of structural proteins that contribute to the mitotic spindle. Because one of the distinguishing features of most cancer cells is their high rate of cell division relative to that of most normal somatic cells, cancer cells are greatly affected by these drugs. Many side effects of certain anticancer drugs (such as nausea and hair loss) are due to the drugs' effects on normal cells that divide rapidly in the digestive system and hair follicles.

In plant cells certain hormones stimulate mitosis. They include the **cytokinins,** a group of plant hormones that promote mitosis both in normal growth and in wound healing (see Chapter 38). Similarly, animal hormones, such as certain steroids, stimulate growth and mitosis (see Chapter 49).

Protein **growth factors,** which are active at extremely low concentrations, stimulate mitosis in some animal cells. Of the approximately 50 protein growth factors known, some act only on specific types of cells, whereas others act on a broad range of cell types. For example, the effects of the growth factor

Cyclin-dependent kinases (Cdks) control the phosphorylation of other proteins, thereby regulating the transitions between phases of the cell cycle.

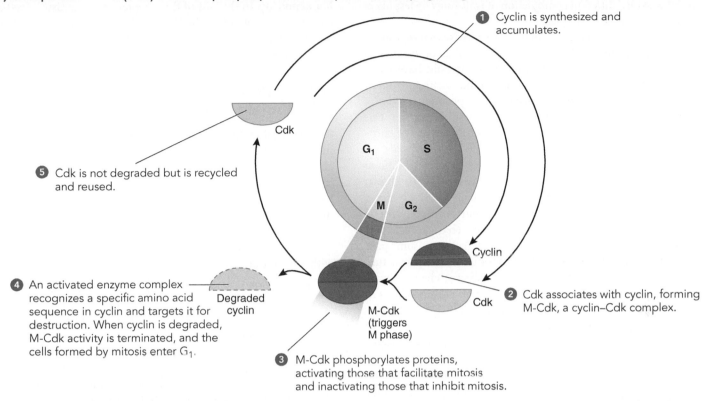

1 Cyclin is synthesized and accumulates.

5 Cdk is not degraded but is recycled and reused.

Cdk

G₁   S

M   G₂

Cyclin

4 An activated enzyme complex recognizes a specific amino acid sequence in cyclin and targets it for destruction. When cyclin is degraded, M-Cdk activity is terminated, and the cells formed by mitosis enter G₁.

Degraded cyclin

Cdk

M-Cdk (triggers M phase)

2 Cdk associates with cyclin, forming M-Cdk, a cyclin–Cdk complex.

3 M-Cdk phosphorylates proteins, activating those that facilitate mitosis and inactivating those that inhibit mitosis.

Figure 10-14 Molecular control of the cell cycle

This diagram is a simplified view of the control system that triggers the cell to move from G₂ to M phase.

PREDICT What might happen if cyclin were not degraded in step 4?

© Cengage Learning

erythropoietin are limited to cells that will develop into red blood cells, but *epidermal growth factor* stimulates many cell types to divide. Many types of cancer cells divide in the absence of growth factors.

CHECKPOINT 10.3

- *What are cell-cycle checkpoints?*
- *What are two molecular controls that trigger the onset of different stages of the cell cycle?*

10.4 SEXUAL REPRODUCTION AND MEIOSIS

LEARNING OBJECTIVES

7 Differentiate between asexual and sexual reproduction.

8 Distinguish between haploid and diploid cells, and define *homologous chromosomes.*

9 Explain the significance of meiosis and describe the process.

10 Contrast mitosis and meiosis, emphasizing the different outcomes.

Although the details of the reproductive process vary greatly among different kinds of eukaryotes, biologists distinguish two basic types of reproduction: asexual and sexual. In **asexual reproduction** a single parent splits, buds, or fragments to produce two or more individuals. In most kinds of eukaryotic asexual reproduction, all the cells are the result of mitotic divisions, so their genes and inherited traits are like those of the parent. Such a group of genetically identical organisms is called a **clone.** In asexual reproduction organisms that are well adapted to their environment produce new generations of similarly adapted organisms. Asexual reproduction occurs rapidly and efficiently, partly because the organism does not need to expend time and energy finding a mate.

In contrast, **sexual reproduction** involves the union of two sex cells, or **gametes,** to form a single cell called a **zygote**. Usually, two different parents contribute the gametes, but in some cases a single parent furnishes both gametes. In the case of animals and plants, the egg and sperm cells are the gametes, and the fertilized egg is the zygote.

Sexual reproduction results in genetic variation among the offspring. (*How* this genetic variation arises is discussed later in this chapter and in Chapter 11.) Because the offspring produced by sexual reproduction are not genetically identical to their parents or to each other, some offspring may be able to survive environmental changes better than either parent does. However, one disadvantage of sexual reproduction is that some offspring with a different combination of traits may be less likely to survive than their parents.

There is a potential problem in eukaryotic sexual reproduction: if each gamete had the same number of chromosomes as the parent cell that produced it, the zygote would have twice as many chromosomes. This doubling would occur generation after generation. How do organisms avoid producing zygotes with ever-increasing chromosome numbers? To answer this question, we need more information about the types of chromosomes found in cells.

Each chromosome in a somatic cell of a plant or animal normally has a partner chromosome. The two partners, known as **homologous chromosomes,** are similar in size, shape, and the position of their centromeres. Furthermore, special chromosome-staining procedures produce a characteristic pattern of bands evident in the members of each chromosome pair. In most species chromosomes vary enough in their structure that cell biologists can distinguish the different chromosomes and match up the homologous pairs. The 46 chromosomes in human cells constitute 23 homologous pairs.

The most important feature of homologous chromosomes is that they carry information about the same genetic traits, although this information is not necessarily identical. For example, each member of a homologous pair may carry a gene that specifies hemoglobin structure. One member, however, may have the information for the normal hemoglobin β chain (see Fig. 3-23a), whereas the other may specify the abnormal form of hemoglobin associated with sickle cell anemia (see Chapter 16). Homologous chromosomes can therefore be contrasted with the two members of a pair of sister chromatids, which are precisely identical to each other.

A set of chromosomes has one of each kind of chromosome; in other words, it contains one member of each homologous pair. If a cell or nucleus contains two sets of chromosomes, it is said to have a **diploid** chromosome number. If it has only a single set of chromosomes, it has the **haploid** number.

In humans the diploid chromosome number is 46 and the haploid number is 23. When a sperm and egg fuse at fertilization, each gamete is haploid, contributing one set of chromosomes; the diploid number is thereby restored in the fertilized egg (zygote). When the zygote divides by mitosis to form the first two cells of the embryo, each daughter cell receives the diploid number of chromosomes, and subsequent mitotic divisions repeat this. Thus, somatic cells are diploid.

An individual whose cells have three or more sets of chromosomes is **polyploid.** Polyploidy is relatively rare among animals but common among plants (see Chapter 20). In fact, polyploidy has been an important mechanism of plant evolution. As many as 80% of all flowering plants are polyploid. Polyploid plants are often larger and hardier than diploid members of the same group. Many commercially important plants, such as wheat and cotton, are polyploid.

The chromosome number found in the gametes of a particular species is represented as n, and the zygotic chromosome number is represented as $2n$. If the organism is not polyploid, the haploid chromosome number is equal to n and the diploid number is equal to $2n$; thus, in humans, $n = 23$ and $2n = 46$. For simplicity, in the rest of this chapter, the organisms used as examples are not polyploid. We use diploid and $2n$ interchangeably, and haploid and n interchangeably, although the terms are not strictly synonymous.

Meiosis produces haploid cells with unique gene combinations

A cell division that reduces chromosome number is called **meiosis.** The term *meiosis* means "to make smaller," and the chromosome number is reduced by one-half. In meiosis a diploid cell undergoes two cell divisions, potentially yielding four haploid cells. It is important to note that the haploid cells produced by this process do not contain just any combination of chromosomes, but one member of each homologous pair.

The events of meiosis are similar to the events of mitosis, with four important differences:

1. Meiosis involves two successive nuclear and cytoplasmic divisions, producing up to four cells.
2. Despite two successive nuclear divisions, the DNA and other chromosome components duplicate only once, during the interphase preceding the first meiotic division.
3. Each of the four cells produced by meiosis contains the haploid chromosome number, that is, only one chromosome set containing only one representative of each homologous pair.
4. During meiosis, each homologous chromosome pair is shuffled, so the resulting haploid cells each have a virtually unique combination of genes.

Meiosis typically consists of two nuclear and cytoplasmic divisions, designated the *first* and *second meiotic divisions,* or simply **meiosis I** and **meiosis II** (FIG. 10-15). Each includes prophase, metaphase, anaphase, and telophase stages. During meiosis I, the partner homologous chromosomes physically pair with each other and subsequently separate and move into different nuclei. In meiosis II, the sister chromatids that make up each duplicated chromosome separate from each other and are distributed to two different nuclei. The following discussion describes meiosis in an organism with a diploid chromosome number of 4. Refer to FIG. 10-16 as you read.

Prophase I includes synapsis and crossing-over

As occurs during mitosis, the chromosomes duplicate in the S phase of interphase, before the complex movements of meiosis actually begin. Each duplicated chromosome consists of two chromatids, which are linked by cohesins. During **prophase I,** while the chromatids are still elongated and thin, the homologous chromosomes come to lie lengthwise side by side. This process is called **synapsis,** which means "fastening together." For example, in an animal cell with a diploid number of four, synapsis results in two homologous pairs.

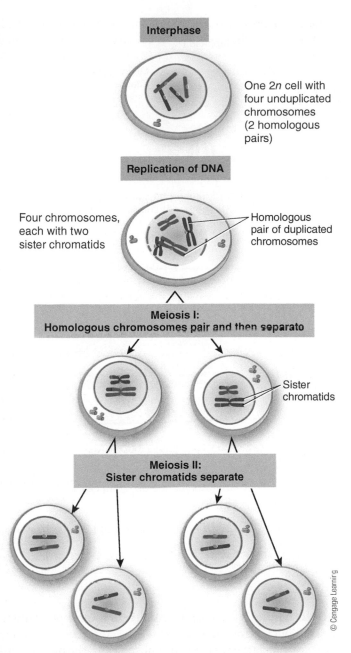

Interphase

One *2n* cell with four unduplicated chromosomes (2 homologous pairs)

Replication of DNA

Four chromosomes, each with two sister chromatids

Homologous pair of duplicated chromosomes

Meiosis I:
Homologous chromosomes pair and then separate

Sister chromatids

Meiosis II:
Sister chromatids separate

Four haploid (*n*) cells, each with two unduplicated chromosomes

Figure 10-15 Overview of meiosis

This figure begins with a diploid cell with four unduplicated chromosomes. The chromosomes derived from one parent are shown in *blue*, and those from the other parent are *red*. Homologous pairs are similar in size and shape.

One member of each homologous pair is called the *maternal homologue* because it was originally inherited from the female parent; the other member of a homologous pair is the *paternal homologue* because it was inherited from the male parent. Because each chromosome duplicated during interphase and now consists of two chromatids, synapsis results in the association of four chromatids. The resulting association is a **tetrad.** The number of tetrads per prophase I cell is equal to the haploid chromosome number. In an animal cell with a diploid number of 4, there are 2 tetrads (and a total of 8 chromatids); in

a human cell at prophase I, there are 23 tetrads (and a total of 92 chromatids).

Homologous chromosomes become closely associated during synapsis. Electron microscopic observations reveal that a characteristic structure, the **synaptonemal complex,** forms along the entire length of the synapsed homologues (**FIG. 10-17**). This proteinaceous structure holds the synapsed homologues together and is thought to play a role in chromosome **crossing-over,** a process in which enzymes break and rejoin DNA molecules, allowing paired homologous chromosomes to exchange genetic material. Crossing-over produces new combinations of genes. The **genetic recombination** from crossing-over greatly enhances the genetic variation—that is, new combinations of traits—among sexually produced offspring. Some biologists think that recombination is the main reason for sexual reproduction in eukaryotes.

In addition to the unique processes of synapsis and crossing-over, events similar to those in mitotic prophase also occur during prophase I. A spindle forms, consisting of microtubules and other components. In animal cells one pair of centrioles moves to each pole, and astral microtubules form. The nuclear envelope disappears in late prophase I, and in cells with large and distinct chromosomes, the structure of the tetrads can be seen clearly with the microscope.

The sister chromatids remain closely aligned along their lengths. However, the centromeres (and kinetochores) of the homologous chromosomes become separated from one another. In late prophase I, the homologous chromosomes are held together only at specific regions, called **chiasmata** (sing., *chiasma*). Each chiasma originates at a crossing-over site, that is, a site at which homologous chromatids exchanged genetic material and rejoined, producing an X-shaped configuration (**FIG. 10-18**). At the chiasmata, cohesins hold homologous chromosomes together after the synaptonemal complex has been disassembled. Later, the cohesins dissociate from the chiasmata, freeing the homologous chromosome arms from one another. The consequences of crossing-over and genetic recombination are discussed in Chapter 11 (e.g., see Fig. 11-12).

During meiosis I, homologous chromosomes separate

Metaphase I occurs when the tetrads align on the midplane. Both sister kinetochores of one duplicated chromosome are attached by spindle fibers to the same pole, and both sister kinetochores of the other duplicated homologous chromosome are attached to the opposite pole. (By contrast, sister kinetochores of each duplicated chromosome are attached to opposite poles in mitosis.)

During **anaphase I,** the paired homologous chromosomes separate, or disjoin, and move toward opposite poles. Each pole receives a random combination of maternal and paternal chromosomes, but only one member of each homologous pair is present at each pole. The sister chromatids remain united at their centromere regions. Again, this process differs from mitotic anaphase, in which the sister chromatids separate and move to opposite poles.

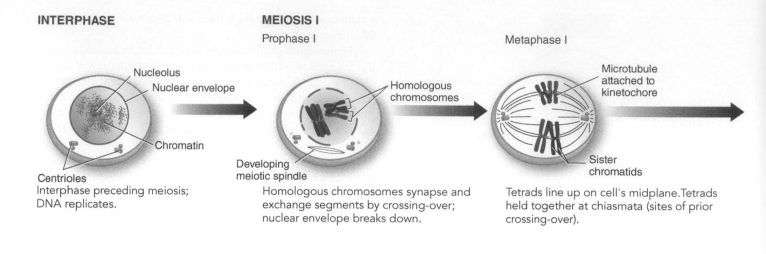

INTERPHASE

MEIOSIS I

Prophase I

Metaphase I

Nucleolus

Nuclear envelope

Chromatin

Centrioles

Interphase preceding meiosis; DNA replicates.

Homologous chromosomes

Developing meiotic spindle

Homologous chromosomes synapse and exchange segments by crossing-over; nuclear envelope breaks down.

Microtubule attached to kinetochore

Sister chromatids

Tetrads line up on cell's midplane. Tetrads held together at chiasmata (sites of prior crossing-over).

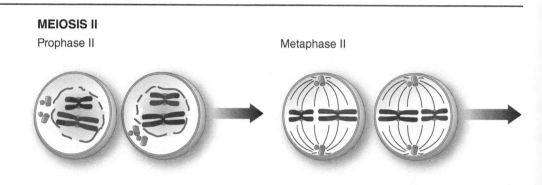

MEIOSIS II

Prophase II

Metaphase II

Chromosomes condense again following brief period of interkinesis. DNA does *not* replicate again.

Chromosomes line up along cell's midplane.

Figure 10-16 *Animation* **Interphase and the stages of meiosis**

Meiosis consists of two nuclear divisions, meiosis I (*top row*) and meiosis II (*bottom row*). The drawings depict generalized animal cells with a diploid chromosome number of 4; the sizes of the nuclei and chromosomes are exaggerated to show the structures more clearly. Cells of most plants lack centrioles.

During **telophase I,** the chromatids generally decondense somewhat, the nuclear envelope may reorganize, and cytokinesis may take place. Each telophase I nucleus contains the haploid number of chromosomes, but each chromosome is a duplicated chromosome (it consists of a pair of chromatids). In our example, 2 duplicated chromosomes lie at each pole, for a total of 4 chromatids; humans have 23 duplicated chromosomes (46 chromatids) at each pole.

An interphase-like stage called **interkinesis** usually follows. Interkinesis is not a true interphase: there is no S phase and therefore no DNA replication. Interkinesis is brief in most organisms and absent in some.

Chromatids separate in meiosis II

Because the chromosomes usually remain partially condensed between divisions, the prophase of the second meiotic division is brief. **Prophase II** is similar to mitotic prophase in many respects. There is no pairing of homologous chromosomes

(indeed, only one member of each pair is present in each nucleus) and no crossing-over.

During **metaphase II,** the chromosomes line up on the midplanes of their cells. You can easily distinguish the first and second metaphases in diagrams; at metaphase I the chromatids are arranged in bundles of four (tetrads), and at metaphase II they are in groups of two (as in mitotic metaphase). This difference is not always so obvious in living cells.

During **anaphase II,** the chromatids, attached to spindle fibers at their kinetochores, separate and move to opposite poles, just as they would at mitotic anaphase. As in mitosis, each former chromatid is now referred to as a *chromosome.* Thus, at **telophase II** there is one representative for each homologous pair at each pole. Each is an unduplicated (single) chromosome. Nuclear envelopes re-form, the chromosomes gradually elongate to form chromatin fibers, and cytokinesis occurs.

The two successive divisions of meiosis yield four haploid nuclei, each containing *one* of each kind of chromosome. Each resulting haploid cell has a different combination of genes.

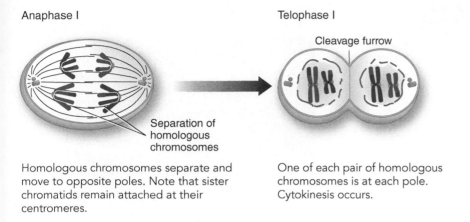

Anaphase I

Separation of homologous chromosomes

Homologous chromosomes separate and move to opposite poles. Note that sister chromatids remain attached at their centromeres.

Telophase I

Cleavage furrow

One of each pair of homologous chromosomes is at each pole. Cytokinesis occurs.

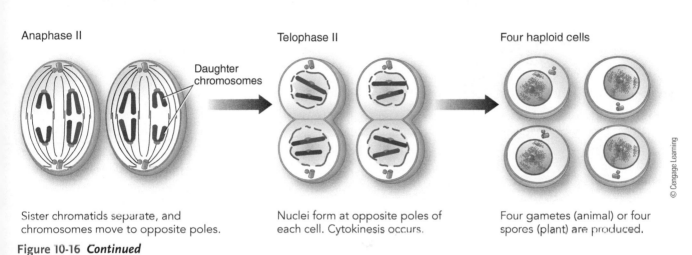

Anaphase II

Daughter chromosomes

Sister chromatids separate, and chromosomes move to opposite poles.

Telophase II

Nuclei form at opposite poles of each cell. Cytokinesis occurs.

Four haploid cells

Four gametes (animal) or four spores (plant) are produced.

© Cengage Learning

Figure 10-16 *Continued*

This genetic variation has two sources: (1) DNA segments are exchanged between maternal and paternal homologues during crossing-over; and (2) during meiosis, the maternal and paternal chromosomes of homologous pairs separate independently, and the chromosomes are "shuffled" so that each member of a pair becomes randomly distributed to one of the poles at anaphase I.

Mitosis and meiosis lead to contrasting outcomes

Although mitosis and meiosis share many similar features, specific distinctions between these processes result in the formation of different types of cells. Mitosis is a single nuclear division in which sister chromatids separate from each other and are distributed to the two daughter cells, which are genetically identical to each other and to the original cell. A diploid cell that undergoes mitosis produces two diploid cells. Similarly, a haploid cell that undergoes mitosis produces

two haploid cells. (Some eukaryotic organisms—e.g., certain yeasts—are haploid, as are plants at certain stages of their life cycles.) Homologous chromosomes do not associate physically at any time in mitosis.

In meiosis, a diploid cell undergoes two successive nuclear divisions, meiosis I and meiosis II. In prophase I of meiosis, the homologous chromosomes undergo synapsis to form tetrads. Homologous chromosomes separate during meiosis I, and sister chromatids separate during meiosis II. Meiosis ends with the formation of four genetically different, haploid daughter cells. The fates of these cells depend on the type of life cycle; in animals they differentiate as gametes, whereas in plants they become spores.

CHECKPOINT 10.4

- *Are homologous chromosome pairs present in a diploid cell? Are they present in a haploid cell?*
- **CONNECT** *How does the outcome of meiosis differ from the outcome of mitosis?*
- *Can haploid cells divide by mitosis? by meiosis?*

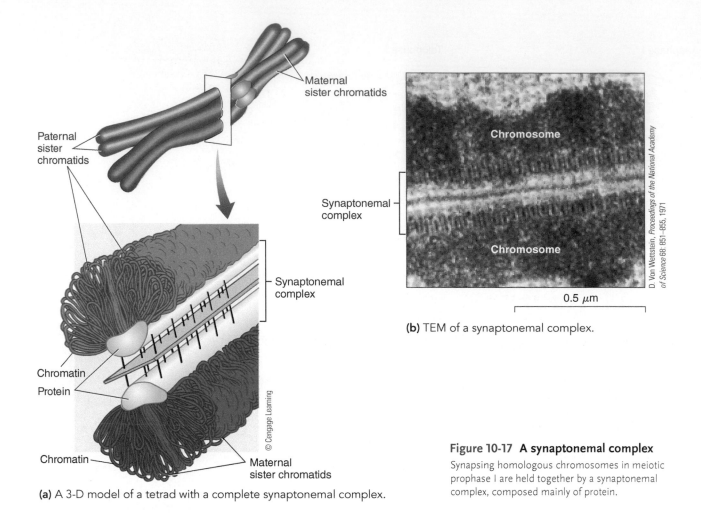

(a) A 3-D model of a tetrad with a complete synaptonemal complex.

(b) TEM of a synaptonemal complex.

Figure 10-17 A synaptonemal complex

Synapsing homologous chromosomes in meiotic prophase I are held together by a synaptonemal complex, composed mainly of protein.

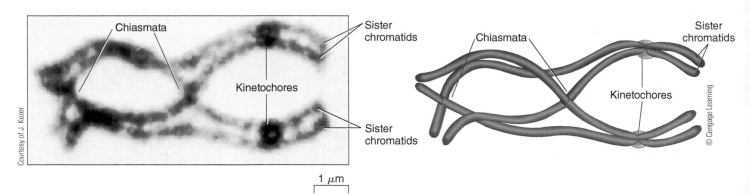

(a) LM of a tetrad during late prophase I of a male meiotic cell (spermatocyte) from a salamander.

(b) A drawing showing the structure of the tetrad. The paternal chromatids are *blue*, and the maternal chromatids are *red*.

Figure 10-18 *Animation* A meiotic tetrad with two chiasmata

The two chiasmata are the result of separate crossing-over events.

10.5 SEXUAL LIFE CYCLES

LEARNING OBJECTIVE

11 Compare the roles of mitosis and meiosis in various generalized life cycles.

Because sexual reproduction is characterized by the fusion of two haploid sex cells to form a diploid zygote, it follows that in a sexual life cycle, meiosis must occur before gametes can form. The timing of meiosis in the life cycle varies among species.

In animals and a few other organisms, meiosis leads directly to gamete production (**FIG. 10-19a**). An organism's somatic cells multiply by mitosis and are diploid; the only haploid cells

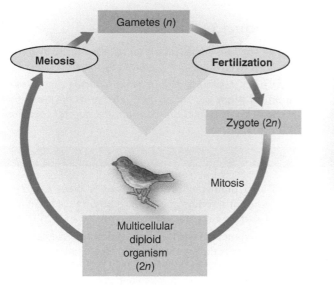

(a) Animals

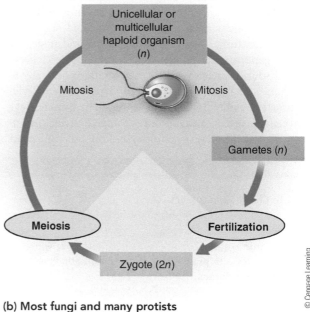

(b) Most fungi and many protists

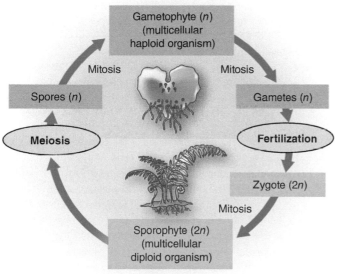

(c) Plants, some algae, and some fungi

Figure 10-19 *Animation* **Representative life cycles**

Each species has a characteristic number of chromosomes that does not change because the doubling of chromosomes that occurs during fertilization is compensated for by the reduction in chromosome number that occurs during meiosis. The color code and design here is used throughout the rest of the book. For example, in all life cycles the haploid (*n*) generation is shown in *purple*, and the diploid (2*n*) generation is *gold*. The processes of meiosis and fertilization always link the haploid and diploid generations.

produced are the gametes. Gametes develop when **germ line cells,** which give rise to the next generation, undergo meiosis.

The formation of gametes is known as **gametogenesis.** Male gametogenesis, called **spermatogenesis**, forms four haploid sperm cells for each cell that enters meiosis. (See Chapter 50 and Fig. 50-5 for a detailed description of spermatogenesis.)

In contrast, female gametogenesis, called **oogenesis,** forms a single egg cell, or *ovum,* for every cell that enters meiosis. In this process, most of the cytoplasm goes to only one of the two cells produced during each meiotic division. At the end of meiosis I, one nucleus is retained and the other, called the first *polar body,* often degenerates. Similarly, at the end of meiosis II, one nucleus becomes another polar body and the other nucleus

survives. In this way, one haploid nucleus receives most of the accumulated cytoplasm and nutrients from the original meiotic cell. (See Chapter 50 and Fig. 50-11 for a detailed description of oogenesis.)

Although meiosis occurs at some point in a sexual life cycle, it does not always *immediately* precede gamete formation. Many eukaryotes, including most fungi and many protists, remain haploid (their cells dividing mitotically) throughout most of their life cycles, with individuals being unicellular or multicellular. Two haploid gametes (produced by mitosis) fuse to form a diploid zygote that undergoes meiosis to restore the haploid state (**FIG. 10-19b**). Examples of these types of life cycles are found in Figures 26-16 and 29-9.

Plants and some algae and fungi have complicated life cycles (FIG. 10-19c). These life cycles, characterized by an **alternation of generations,** consist of a multicellular diploid stage, the **sporophyte generation,** and a multicellular haploid stage, the **gametophyte generation.** Sporophyte cells undergo meiosis to form haploid spores, each of which may divide mitotically to produce a multicellular haploid gametophyte. Gametophytes produce gametes by mitosis. The female and male gametes (egg and sperm cells) fuse to form a diploid zygote that divides mitotically to form a multicellular sporophyte. You can find more detailed descriptions of alternation of generations in plants in Chapters 27 and 28.

CHECKPOINT 10.5

- **CONNECT** *In animals, which cells are produced by mitosis? by meiosis? Which cells are produced by these processes in plants?*
- **CONNECT** *Assuming a sexually reproducing organism such as a protist is haploid throughout most of its life cycle, how do meiosis and fertilization maintain the normal chromosome number?*

SUMMARY: FOCUS ON LEARNING OBJECTIVES

10.1 Eukaryotic Chromosomes *(page 205)*

1 Discuss the significance of chromosomes in terms of their information content.

- Genes are informational units made of DNA. In eukaryotes, DNA associates with protein to form the **chromatin** fibers that make up **chromosomes.**

2 Explain how DNA is packed into chromosomes in eukaryotic cells.

- The organization of eukaryotic DNA into chromosomes allows the DNA to be accurately replicated and sorted into daughter cells without tangling. In eukaryotic cells DNA is associated with **histones** (basic proteins) to form **nucleosomes,** each of which consists of a histone bead with DNA wrapped around it. Nucleosomes are organized into large, coiled loops held together by nonhistone **scaffolding proteins.**

10.2 The Cell Cycle and Mitosis *(page 208)*

3 Identify the stages in the eukaryotic cell cycle and describe their principal events.

- The eukaryotic **cell cycle** is the period from the beginning of one division to the beginning of the next. The cell cycle consists of interphase and M phase.
- **Interphase** consists of the first gap phase (G_1), the synthesis phase (S), and the second gap phase (G_2). During the **G_1 phase,** the cell grows and prepares for the S phase. During the **S phase,** DNA and the chromosome proteins are synthesized, and chromosome duplication occurs. During the **G_2 phase,** protein synthesis increases in preparation for cell division.
- **M phase** consists of **mitosis,** the nuclear division that produces two nuclei identical to the parental nucleus, and **cytokinesis,** the division of the cytoplasm to yield two daughter cells.

4 Describe the structure of a duplicated chromosome, including the sister chromatids, centromeres, and kinetochores.

- A duplicated chromosome consists of a pair of **sister chromatids,** which contain identical DNA sequences. Each chromatid includes a constricted region called a **centromere.** Sister chromatids are tightly associated in the region of their centromeres. Attached to each centromere is a **kinetochore,** a protein structure to which microtubules can bind.

5 Explain the significance of mitosis and describe the process.

- Mitosis assures that the chromosome number is preserved when one eukaryotic cell divides to form two. In mitosis, identical chromosomes are distributed to each pole of the cell, and a nuclear envelope forms around each set.
- During **prophase,** the structure of the duplicated chromosomes becomes apparent as the chromatin condenses; each is composed of a pair of identical sister chromatids. The nuclear envelope begins to disassemble, and the **mitotic spindle** begins to form.

- During **prometaphase,** spindle microtubules attach to kinetochores of chromosomes, and chromosomes begin to move toward the cell's midplane.
- During **metaphase,** the chromosomes are aligned on the cell's midplane, or **metaphase plate;** the mitotic spindle is complete, and the kinetochores of the sister chromatids are attached by microtubules to opposite poles of the cell.
- During **anaphase,** the sister chromatids separate and move to opposite poles. Each former chromatid is now a chromosome.
- During **telophase,** a nuclear envelope re-forms around each set of chromosomes, nucleoli become apparent, the chromosomes uncoil, and the spindle disappears. Cytokinesis generally begins in telophase.

10.3 Regulation of the Cell Cycle *(page 215)*

6 Explain some ways in which the cell cycle is controlled.

- Control mechanisms, called **cell-cycle checkpoints,** temporarily block key events from being initiated during the cell cycle. **Cyclin-dependent kinases (Cdks)** are **protein kinases** involved in regulating the cell cycle. Cdks are active only when they bind tightly to regulatory proteins called **cyclins.** Cyclin levels fluctuate predictably during the cell cycle.

10.4 Sexual Reproduction and Meiosis *(page 217)*

7 Differentiate between asexual and sexual reproduction.

- Offspring produced by **asexual reproduction** usually have hereditary traits identical to those of the single parent. Mitosis is the basis for asexual reproduction in eukaryotic organisms.
- In **sexual reproduction** two haploid sex cells, or **gametes,** fuse to form a single diploid **zygote.** In a sexual life cycle, meiosis must occur before gametes can be produced.

8 Distinguish between haploid and diploid cells, and define *homologous chromosomes.*

- A **diploid** cell has a characteristic number of chromosome pairs per cell. The members of each pair, called **homologous chromosomes,** are similar in length, shape, and other features and carry genes affecting the same kinds of attributes of the organism.
- A **haploid** cell contains only one member of each homologous chromosome pair.

9 Explain the significance of meiosis and describe the process.

- A diploid cell undergoing **meiosis** completes two successive cell divisions, yielding four haploid cells. Sexual life cycles in eukaryotes require meiosis, which makes it possible for each gamete to contain only half the number of chromosomes in the parent cell.
- **Meiosis I** begins with **prophase I,** in which the members of a homologous pair of chromosomes physically join by the process of **synapsis. Crossing-over** is a process of **genetic recombination** during which homologous (nonsister) chromatids exchange segments of DNA strands.

- At **metaphase I**, **tetrads**—each consisting of a pair of homologous chromosomes held together by one or more **chiasmata**—line up on the metaphase plate. The members of each pair of homologous chromosomes separate during meiotic **anaphase I** and are distributed to different nuclei. Each nucleus contains the haploid number of chromosomes; each chromosome consists of two chromatids.
- During **meiosis II**, the two chromatids of each chromosome separate, and one is distributed to each daughter cell. Each former chromatid is now a chromosome.

10 Contrast mitosis and meiosis, emphasizing the different outcomes.

- Mitosis involves a single nuclear division in which the two daughter cells formed are genetically identical to each other and to the original cell. Synapsis of homologous chromosomes does not occur during mitosis.
- Meiosis involves two successive nuclear divisions and forms four haploid cells. Synapsis of homologous chromosomes occurs during prophase I of meiosis.

10.5 Sexual Life Cycles (page 222)

11 Compare the roles of mitosis and meiosis in various generalized life cycles.

- Somatic cells of animals are diploid and are produced by mitosis. The only haploid cells are gametes, produced by **gametogenesis,** which in animals occurs by meiosis.
- Most fungi and many protists are haploid and are produced by mitosis. The only diploid stage is the zygote, which undergoes meiosis to restore the haploid state.
- The life cycle of plants, some algae, and some fungi includes an **alternation of generations.** The multicellular diploid **sporophyte generation** forms haploid spores by meiosis. Each spore divides mitotically to form a multicellular haploid **gametophyte generation,** which produces gametes by mitosis. Two haploid gametes then fuse to form a diploid zygote, which divides mitotically to produce a new sporophyte generation.

TEST YOUR UNDERSTANDING

Know and Comprehend

1. A nucleosome consists of (a) DNA and scaffolding proteins (b) scaffolding proteins and histones (c) DNA and histones (d) DNA, histones, and scaffolding proteins (e) histones only

2. At which of the following stages do human skin cell nuclei have the same DNA content? (a) early mitotic prophase and late mitotic telophase (b) G_1 and G_2 (c) G_1 and early mitotic prophase (d) G_1 and late mitotic telophase (e) G_2 and late mitotic telophase

3. In a cell at ___, each chromosome consists of a pair of attached chromatids. (a) mitotic prophase (b) meiotic prophase II (c) meiotic prophase I (d) meiotic anaphase I (e) all the preceding

4. The molecular tether that links sister chromatids of a duplicated chromosome to each other is (a) condensin (b) actin (c) myosin (d) cohesin (e) actomyosin

5. In an animal cell at mitotic metaphase, you would expect to find (a) two pairs of centrioles located on the metaphase plate (b) a pair of centrioles inside the nucleus (c) a pair of centrioles within each microtubule-organizing center (d) a centriole within each centromere (e) no centrioles

6. A diploid nucleus at early mitotic prophase has ___ set(s) of chromosomes; a diploid nucleus at mitotic telophase has ___ set(s) of chromosomes. (a) 1; 1 (b) 1; 2 (c) 2; 2 (d) 2; 1 (e) not enough information has been given

7. You would expect to find a synaptonemal complex in a cell at (a) mitotic prophase (b) meiotic prophase I (c) meiotic prophase II (d) meiotic anaphase I (e) meiotic anaphase II

8. A chiasma links a pair of (a) homologous chromosomes at prophase II (b) homologous chromosomes at late prophase I (c) sister chromatids at metaphase II (d) sister chromatids at mitotic metaphase (e) sister chromatids at metaphase I

Apply and Analyze

9. **VISUALIZE** Sketch a mitotic prophase chromosome and label sister chromatids, sister centromeres, and sister kinetochores.

10. **CONNECT** Does the DNA content of the cell change from the beginning of interphase to the end of interphase? Does the number of chromosomes change? Explain.

11. Fill out the following table for a cell with 5 chromosomes undergoing mitosis. Is this cell haploid or diploid? How do you know?

	Number of Duplicated Chromosomes	Number of Unduplicated Chromosomes	Number of Kinetochores
Prophase (number per cell)			
Metaphase (number per cell)			
Telophase (number per nucleus)			

12. Fill out the following table for a diploid cell with 14 chromosomes undergoing meiosis.

	Number of Duplicated Chromosomes	Number of Unduplicated Chromosomes	Number of Tetrads
Beginning of prophase I (number per cell)			
End of prophase I (number per cell)			
End of telophase II (number per nucleus)			

In questions 13 and 14, decide whether each is an example of sexual or asexual reproduction, and state why.

13. A diploid queen honeybee produces haploid eggs by meiosis. Some of these eggs are never fertilized and develop into haploid male honeybees (drones).

14. Seeds develop after a flower has been pollinated with pollen from the same plant.

Evaluate and Synthesize

15. **EVOLUTION LINK** How does mitosis provide evidence for relationships among eukaryotes as diverse as mammals and seaweeds?

16. **EVOLUTION LINK** Some organisms—for example, certain fungi—reproduce asexually when the environment is favorable and sexually when the environment becomes unfavorable. What might be the evolutionary advantage of sexual reproduction with the associated process of meiosis during unfavorable conditions?

 aplia To access course materials, such as Aplia and other companion resources, please visit **www.cengagebrain.com.**

11

The Basic Principles of Heredity

Gregor Mendel. This painting shows Mendel with his pea plants in the monastery garden at Brünn, Austria (now Brüno, Czech Republic).

© Pictorial Press Ltd/Alamy

KEY CONCEPTS

11.1 The experiments of Gregor Mendel, a pioneer in the field of genetics, revealed the basic principles of inheritance. In Mendel's principle of segregation, members of a gene pair segregate (separate) from one another prior to gamete formation. In the principle of independent assortment, members of different gene pairs assort independently (randomly) into gametes.

11.2 You can use probability to predict Mendelian inheritance: the product rule shows how to combine the probabilities of independent events, and the sum rule shows how to combine the probabilities of mutually exclusive events.

11.3 Chromosome behavior during meiosis helps explain Mendel's principles of inheritance.

11.4 Distinctive inheritance patterns (i.e., "extensions" to Mendel's principles) characterize some traits.

uman characters such as eye color and hair color, along with a multitude of other characteristics, are passed on from one generation to another. **Heredity,** the transmission of genetic information from parent to offspring, generally follows predictable patterns in organisms as diverse as humans, penguins, baker's yeast, and sunflowers. **Genetics,** the science of heredity, studies both genetic similarities and **genetic variation,** the differences between parents and offspring or among individuals of a population.

The study of inheritance as a modern branch of science began in the mid-19th century with the work of Gregor Mendel (1822–1884), a monk who bred pea plants (see picture). Mendel was the first scientist to effectively apply quantitative methods to the study of inheritance. He did not merely describe his observations; he planned his experiments carefully, recorded the data, and analyzed the results mathematically. Although unappreciated during his lifetime, his work was rediscovered in 1900.

During the decades following the rediscovery of Mendel's findings, geneticists extended Mendel's principles by correlating the transmission of genetic information from generation to generation with the behavior of chromosomes during *meiosis.* By studying a variety of organisms, geneticists verified Mendel's findings and added a growing list of so-called exceptions to his principles.

Geneticists study not only the transmission of genes but also the expression of genetic information. As you will see in this chapter and those that follow, understanding the relationships between an organism's genetic information and its characteristics has become increasingly sophisticated as biologists have learned more about the orderly transmission of information in cells from one generation to another.

11.1 MENDEL'S PRINCIPLES OF INHERITANCE

LEARNING OBJECTIVES

1 Define the terms *phenotype, genotype, locus, allele, dominant allele, recessive allele, homozygous,* and *heterozygous*.

2 Describe Mendel's principles of segregation and independent assortment.

3 Distinguish among monohybrid, dihybrid, and test crosses.

4 Explain Mendel's principles of segregation and independent assortment, given what scientists now know about genes and chromosomes.

Gregor Mendel was not the first plant breeder. At the time he began his work, breeders had long recognized the existence of **hybrid** plants and animals, the offspring of two genetically dissimilar parents. When Mendel began his breeding experiments in 1856, two main concepts about inheritance were widely accepted. First, all hybrid plants that are the offspring of genetically pure, or **true-breeding,** parents are similar in appearance. Second, when these hybrids mate with each other, they do not breed true; their offspring show a mixture of traits. Some look like their parents, and some have features like those of their grandparents.

Mendel's genius lay in his ability to recognize a pattern in the way the parental traits reappear in the offspring of hybrids. Before Mendel, no one had categorized and counted the offspring and analyzed these regular patterns over several generations to the extent he did. Just as geneticists do today, Mendel chose the organism for his experiments very carefully. The garden pea, *Pisum sativum,* had several advantages. Pea plants are easy to grow, and many varieties were commercially available. Another advantage of pea plants is that controlled pollinations are relatively easy to conduct. Pea flowers have both male and female parts and naturally self-pollinate. However, the anthers (the male parts of the flower that produce pollen) can be removed to prevent self-fertilization (FIG. 11-1). Pollen from

RESEARCH METHOD

WHY IS IT USED? Garden peas normally self-fertilize during reproduction; that is, the male and female gametes are from the same flower. Because pea petals completely enclose the reproductive parts, there is little chance of natural cross-pollination between separate flowers. Cross-pollination enables the researcher to study various patterns of inheritance in peas.

HOW IS IT DONE?

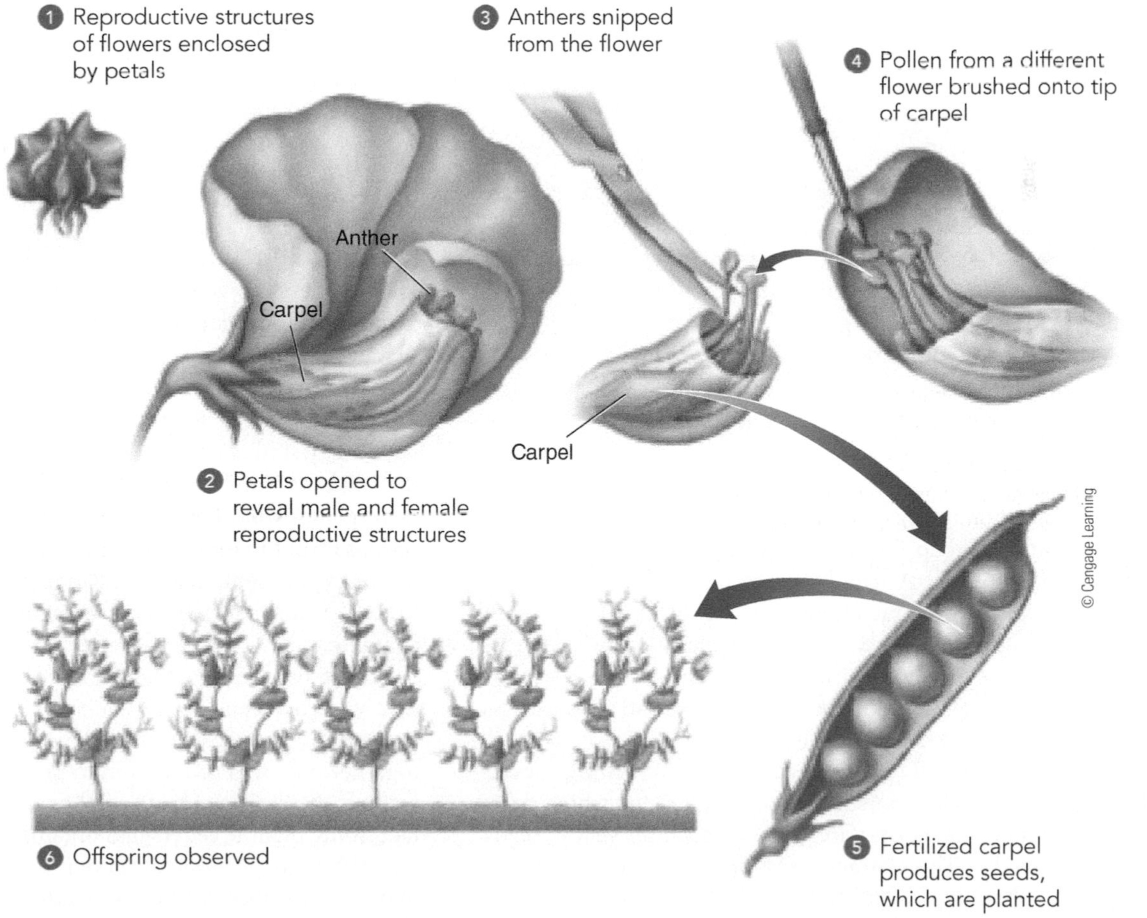

❶ Reproductive structures of flowers enclosed by petals

❸ Anthers snipped from the flower

❹ Pollen from a different flower brushed onto tip of carpel

Anther

Carpel

❷ Petals opened to reveal male and female reproductive structures

Carpel

❺ Fertilized carpel produces seeds, which are planted

❻ Offspring observed

© Cengage Learning

Figure 11-1 *Animation* **How garden peas are cross-pollinated**

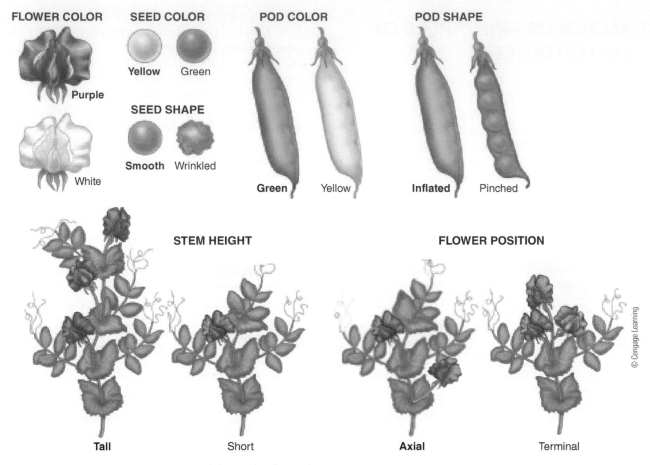

FLOWER COLOR

Purple

White

SEED COLOR

Yellow   Green

SEED SHAPE

Smooth   Wrinkled

POD COLOR

Green   Yellow

POD SHAPE

Inflated   Pinched

STEM HEIGHT

Tall   Short

FLOWER POSITION

Axial   Terminal

© Cengage Learning

Figure 11-2 Seven characters in Mendel's study of pea plants
Each character had two clearly distinguishable phenotypes; the dominant phenotype is boldface.

a different source can then be applied to the stigma (the receptive surface of the carpel, or female part). Pea flowers are easily protected from other sources of pollen because the petals completely enclose the reproductive structures.

Mendel obtained his original pea seeds from commercial sources and did some important preliminary work before starting his actual experiments. For two years he verified that the varieties were true-breeding lines for various inherited features. Today, scientists use the term **phenotype** to refer to the physical appearance of an organism and the term **genotype** to refer to the genetic makeup for that organism, which is most often expressed in symbols. A true-breeding line produces only offspring expressing the same phenotype (e.g., round seeds or tall plants) generation after generation. During this time, Mendel apparently chose those traits of his pea strains that he could study most easily. He probably made the initial observations that later formed the basis of his hypotheses.

Mendel eventually chose strains representing seven **characters**, the attributes (such as seed color) for which heritable differences, or **traits,** are known (such as yellow seeds and green seeds). The characters Mendel selected had clearly contrasting phenotypes (FIG. 11-2). Mendel's results were easy to analyze because he chose easily distinguishable phenotypes and limited the genetic variation studied in each experiment.

Mendel began his experiments by crossing plants from two different true-breeding lines with contrasting phenotypes; these genetically pure individuals constituted the **parental generation**, or **P generation.** In every case, the members of the first generation of offspring all looked alike and resembled one of the two parents. For example, when he crossed tall plants with short plants, all the offspring were tall (FIG. 11-3). These offspring were the first filial generation, or the **F$_1$ generation** (*filial* is from the Latin for "sons and daughters"). The second filial generation, or **F$_2$ generation,** resulted from a cross between F$_1$ individuals or by self-pollination of F$_1$ individuals. Mendel's F$_2$ generation in this experiment included 787 tall plants and 277 short plants. TABLE 11-1 shows Mendel's experimental results for all seven pea characters.

Most breeders in Mendel's time thought that inheritance involved the blending of traits. In *blending inheritance* male and female gametes supposedly contained fluids that blended together during reproduction to produce hybrid offspring with features intermediate between those of the mother and father. In fact, some plant breeders had obtained such hybrids.

Although Mendel observed some intermediate types of hybrids, he chose for further study those F$_1$ hybrids in which "hereditary factors" (as he called them) from one of the parents apparently masked the expression of those factors from the

When the F₁ generation of tall pea plants is self-pollinated, what phenotypes appear in the F₂ generation?

HYPOTHESIS: Although only the "factor" (gene) for tall height is expressed in the F₁ generation, Mendel hypothesized that the factor for short height is not lost. He predicted that the short phenotype would reappear in the F₂ generation.

EXPERIMENT: Mendel crossed true-breeding tall pea plants with true-breeding short pea plants, yielding only tall offspring in the F₁ generation. He then allowed these F₁ individuals to self-pollinate to yield the F₂ generation.

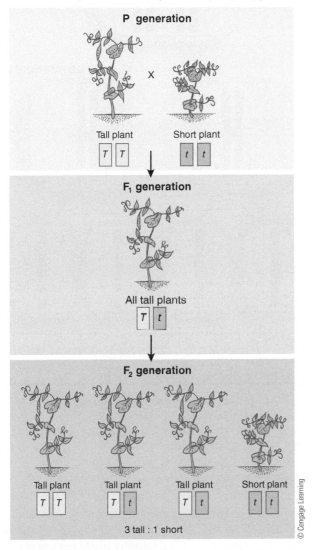

P generation

X

Tall plant   Short plant

T T   t t

F₁ generation

All tall plants

T t

F₂ generation

Tall plant   Tall plant   Tall plant   Short plant

T T   T t   T t   t t

3 tall : 1 short

© Cengage Learning

RESULTS AND CONCLUSION: The F₂ generation included 787 tall and 277 short plants, a ratio of about 3:1. Thus, Mendelian traits pass to successive generations in fixed ratios.

SOURCE: An extensively annotated English translation of Mendel's original 1866 paper is included in *Gregor Mendel's Experiments on Plant Hybrids: A Guided Study* (1993) Corcos, A.F. and F.V. Monaghan, Rutgers University Press.

Figure 11-3 One of Mendel's pea crosses

PREDICT Would you expect to obtain predictable results if you were to cross an F₂ generation tall plant with an F₂ generation short plant? Explain your answer.

TABLE 11-1	Mendel's Experimental Results for Seven Characters				
CHARACTERS AND TRAITS IN PEAS				**F₂ GENERATION**	
CHARACTER	DOMINANT TRAIT	×	RECESSIVE TRAIT	DOMINANT: RECESSIVE	RATIO
Stem height	Tall	×	Short	787:277	2.84:1
Flower color	Purple	×	White	705:224	3.15:1
Flower position	Axial	×	Terminal	651:207	3.14:1
Pod color	Green	×	Yellow	428:152	2.82:1
Pod shape	Inflated	×	Pinched	882:299	2.95:1
Seed color	Yellow	×	Green	6022:2001	3.01:1
Seed shape	Smooth	×	Wrinkled	5474:1850	2.96:1

© Cengage Learning

other parent. Other breeders had also observed these types of hybrids, but they had not explained them. Using modern terms, we say that the factor expressed in the F₁ generation (tallness, in our example) is **dominant;** the one hidden in the F₁ (shortness) is **recessive.** Dominant traits mask recessive ones when both are present in the same individual. Although scientists know today that dominance is not always observed, the realization that dominance can occur was not consistent with the notion of blending inheritance.

Mendel's results were inconsistent with the hypothesis of blending inheritance in a more compelling way. Once two fluids have blended, it is very difficult to imagine how they can separate. However, in the preceding example, in the F₁ generation the hereditary factor(s) that controlled shortness clearly was not lost or blended inseparably with the hereditary factor(s) that controlled tallness because shortness reappeared in the F₂ generation. Mendel was very comfortable with the theoretical side of biology because he was also a student of physics and mathematics. He therefore proposed that each kind of inherited feature of an organism is controlled by two factors that behave like discrete particles and are present in every individual.

To Mendel these hereditary factors were abstractions: he knew nothing about chromosomes and DNA. These factors are essentially what scientists today call **genes,** units of heredity that affect an organism's traits. At the molecular level, a gene has been thought of as a DNA sequence that contains the information to make an RNA or protein product with a specific function. However, as you will see in Chapter 13, this definition of a gene is being reconsidered as more information accumulates about the many functions of DNA in the cell.

Mendel's experiments led to his discovery and explanation of the major principles of heredity, which we now know as the principles of segregation and independent assortment (see **TABLE 11-2** for a summary of Mendel's model of inheritance). We discuss the first principle next and the second later in the chapter.

Alleles separate before gametes are formed: the principle of segregation

Alternative forms of a gene are called **alleles.** In the example in Figure 11-3, each F₁ generation tall plant had two different

TABLE 11-2 | Mendel's Model of Inheritance

1. **Alternative forms of a "factor" (what we now call a *gene*) account for variations in inherited traits.**

Although Mendel observed only two forms (what we now call *alleles*) for each factor he studied, we now know that many genes have more than two alleles.

2. **Inherited traits pass from parents to offspring as unmodified factors.**

Mendel did not observe offspring of intermediate appearance, as a hypothesis of blending inheritance would have predicted. Exceptions to this concept are known today.

3. **Each individual has two sets of factors, one of each pair inherited from the mother and one from the father.**

It does not matter which parent contributes which set of factors.

4. **The paired factors separate prior to the formation of reproductive cells (the principle of segregation).**

Because of *meiosis*, which was discovered after Mendel's time, each parent passes one set of factors to each offspring.

5. **Factors may be expressed or hidden in a given generation, but they are never lost.**

For example, factors not expressed in the F_1 generation reappear in some F_2 individuals.

6. **Each factor is passed to the next generation independently from all other factors (the principle of independent assortment).**

Research since Mendel's time has revealed that exceptions to his model are very common.

© Cengage Learning

Mendel's principle of segregation is related to the events of meiosis: the separation of homologous chromosomes during meiosis results in the segregation of alleles.

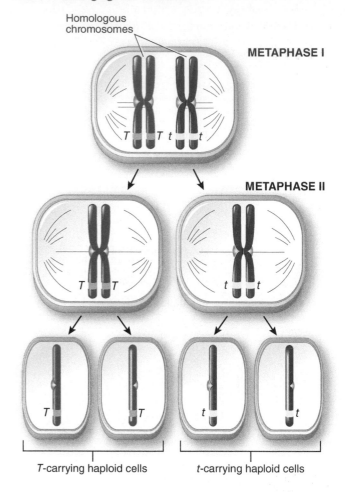

Figure 11-4 *Animation* **Chromosomes and segregation**

Note that half the haploid cells carry *T* and half carry *t*.

CONNECT What kinds of cells would the haploid cells be if meiosis were occurring in a plant? in an animal?

© Cengage Learning

alleles that control plant height: a **dominant allele** for tallness (which we designate *T*) and a **recessive allele** for shortness (designated *t*). Because the tall allele was dominant, these plants were tall. To explain his experimental results, Mendel proposed an idea now known as the **principle of segregation.** Using modern terminology, the principle of segregation states that before sexual reproduction occurs, the two alleles carried by an individual parent must become separated (i.e., segregated).

Recall that during meiosis, homologous chromosomes, and therefore the alleles that reside on them, separate. (You may want to review meiosis in Figure 10-16.) As a result, each sex cell (egg or sperm) formed contains only one allele of each pair. (Later, at the time of fertilization, each haploid gamete contributes one chromosome from each homologous pair and therefore one allele for each gene pair.) An essential feature of meiosis is that the alleles remain intact (one does not mix with or eliminate the other); thus, recessive alleles are not lost and can reappear in the F_2 generation. In our example, before the F_1 plants formed gametes, the allele for tallness segregated from the allele for shortness; so, half the gametes contained a *T* allele, and the other half, a *t* allele (FIG. 11-4).

The random process of fertilization led to three possible combinations of alleles in the F_2 offspring: one-fourth with two tallness alleles (*TT*), one-fourth with two shortness alleles (*tt*), and one-half with one allele for tallness and one for shortness (*Tt*). Because both *TT* and *Tt* plants are tall, Mendel expected approximately three-fourths (787 of the 1064 plants he obtained)

to express the phenotype of the dominant allele (tall) and about one-fourth (277/1064) to express the phenotype of the recessive allele (short). We will explain the mathematical reasoning behind these predictions later in the chapter.

Alleles occupy corresponding loci on homologous chromosomes

Today scientists know that each unduplicated chromosome consists of one long, linear DNA molecule and that each gene is actually a segment of that DNA molecule. We also know that homologous chromosomes not only are similar in size and shape but also usually have the same genes (often with different alleles) located in corresponding positions. The term **locus** (pl., *loci*) originally designated the location of a particular gene on the chromosome (**FIG. 11-5**). We are actually referring to a segment of the DNA that has the information for controlling some aspect of the structure or function of the organism. One locus may govern seed color, another seed shape, another shape of the pods, and so on. Traditional genetic methods can infer the existence of a particular locus only if at least two allelic variants of that locus, producing contrasting phenotypes (e.g., yellow peas versus green peas), are available for study. In the simplest cases, an individual can express one (yellow) or the other (green), but not both.

Alleles are therefore genes that govern variations of the same character (yellow versus green seed color) and occupy corresponding loci on homologous chromosomes. Geneticists assign each allele of a locus a single letter or group of letters as its symbol.[1]

Although geneticists often use more complicated forms of notation, it is customary when working simple genetics problems to indicate a dominant allele with a capital letter. A recessive allele with the same letter is indicated in lowercase.

Remember that the term *locus* designates not only a position on a chromosome but also a type of gene controlling a particular character; thus, *Y* (yellow) and *y* (green) represent a specific pair of alleles of a locus involved in determining seed color in peas. Although you may initially be uncomfortable with geneticists sometimes using the term *gene* to specify a locus and at other times to specify one of the alleles of that locus, the meaning is usually clear from the context.

A monohybrid cross involves individuals with different alleles of a given locus

The basic principles of genetics and the use of genetics terms are best illustrated by examples. In the simplest case, a **monohybrid cross,** the inheritance of two different alleles of a single locus, is studied. FIGURE 11-6 illustrates a monohybrid cross featuring a locus that governs coat color in guinea pigs. The female comes from a true-breeding line of black guinea pigs. We say that she is **homozygous** for black because the two alleles she carries for this locus are identical. The brown male is also from a true-breeding line and is homozygous for brown. What color would you expect the F_1 offspring to be? Actually, it is impossible to make such a prediction without more information.

---

[1] Early geneticists developed their own symbols to represent genes and alleles. Later, groups of scientists met and decided on specific symbols for a given research organism, such as the fruit fly, but each research group had its own rules for assigning symbols. Universally accepted rules for assigning symbols for genes and alleles still do not exist.

A gamete has one set of chromosomes, the *n* number. It carries *one* chromosome of *each* homologous pair. A given gamete can have only *one* gene of any particular pair of alleles.

When the gametes fuse, the resulting zygote is diploid (*2n*) and has homologous pairs of chromosomes. For purposes of illustration, these chromosomes are shown physically paired.

(a) One member of each pair of homologous chromosomes is of maternal origin (*red*), and the other is paternal (*blue*).

Gene loci

A pair of alleles

These genes are not allelic to each other

(b) These chromosomes are nonhomologous. Each chromosome is made up of hundreds or thousands of genes. A locus is the specific place on a chromosome where a gene is located.

(c) These chromosomes are homologous. Alleles are members of a gene pair that occupy corresponding loci on homologous chromosomes.

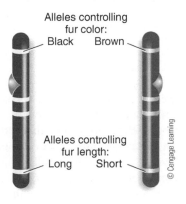

Alleles controlling fur color: Black   Brown

Alleles controlling fur length: Long   Short

© Cengage Learning

(d) Alleles govern the same character but do not necessarily contain the same information.

Figure 11-5 *Animation* **Gene loci and their alleles**

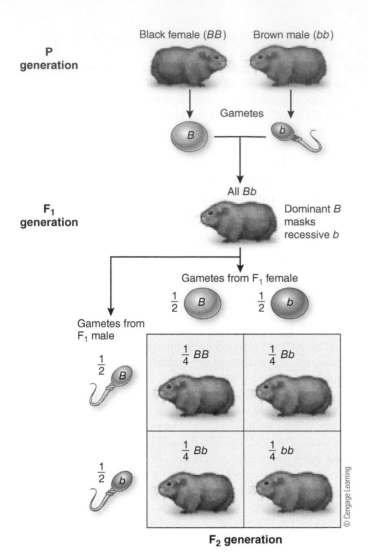

P generation

Black female (*BB*)   Brown male (*bb*)

Gametes

B b

F₁ generation

All *Bb*

Dominant *B* masks recessive *b*

Gametes from F₁ female

$\frac{1}{2}$ B $\frac{1}{2}$ b

Gametes from F₁ male

$\frac{1}{2}$ B

$\frac{1}{4}$ *BB* $\frac{1}{4}$ *Bb*

$\frac{1}{2}$ b

$\frac{1}{4}$ *Bb* $\frac{1}{4}$ *bb*

© Cengage Learning

F₂ generation

Figure 11-6 *Animation* **A monohybrid cross in guinea pigs**

In this example a homozygous black guinea pig is mated with a homozygous brown guinea pig. The F₁ generation includes only black individuals. However, the mating of two of these F₁ offspring yields F₂ generation offspring in the expected ratio of 3 black to 1 brown, indicating that the F₁ individuals are heterozygous.

PREDICT What results would you expect if the P generation female were homozygous brown and the male homozygous black?

In this particular case, the F₁ offspring are black, but they are *heterozygous*, meaning that they carry two different alleles for this locus. The brown allele determines coat color only in a homozygous brown individual; it is a recessive allele. The black allele influences coat color in both homozygous black and heterozygous individuals; it is a dominant allele. On the basis of this information, we can use symbols to designate the dominant black allele *B* and the recessive brown allele *b*.

During meiosis in the female parent (*BB*), the two *B* alleles separate according to Mendel's principle of segregation, so each egg has only one *B* allele. In the male (*bb*) the two *b* alleles separate, so each sperm has only one *b* allele. The fertilization of each *B* egg by a *b* sperm results in heterozygous F₁ offspring, each *Bb*; that is, each individual has one allele for brown coat and one for black coat. Because it is the only possible combination of alleles

present in the eggs and sperm, all the F₁ offspring are *Bb*. Also, note that it does not make any difference whether the offspring receive the dominant allele from the mother or father guinea pig.

A Punnett square predicts the ratios of the various offspring of a cross During meiosis in heterozygous black guinea pigs (*Bb*), the chromosome containing the *B* allele becomes separated from its homologue (the chromosome containing the *b* allele), so each normal sperm or egg contains *B* or *b*, but never both. Heterozygous *Bb* individuals form gametes containing *B* alleles and gametes containing *b* alleles in equal numbers. Because no special attraction or repulsion occurs between an egg and a sperm containing the same allele, fertilization is a random process.

As you can see in Figure 11-6, the possible combinations of eggs and sperm at fertilization can be represented in the form of a grid, or **Punnett square,** devised by early English geneticist Sir Reginald Punnett. The types of gametes (and their expected frequencies) from one parent are listed across the top, and those from the other parent are listed along the left side. The squares are then filled in with the resulting F₂ combinations. Three-fourths of all F₂ offspring have the genetic constitution *BB* or *Bb* and are phenotypically black; one-fourth have the genetic constitution *bb* and are phenotypically brown. The genetic mechanism that governs the approximate 3:1 F₂ ratios obtained by Mendel in his pea-breeding experiments is again evident. These ratios are called *monohybrid F₂* phenotypic ratios.

The phenotype of an individual does not always reveal its genotype As mentioned earlier, an organism's phenotype is its appearance with respect to a certain inherited trait. However, because some alleles may be dominant and others recessive, we cannot always determine, simply by examining its phenotype, which alleles are carried by an organism. In the cross we have been considering, the parents are from true-breeding lines, so the genotype of the female parent is homozygous dominant, *BB*, and her phenotype is black. The genotype of the male parent is homozygous recessive, *bb*, and his phenotype is brown. The genotype of all the F₁ offspring is heterozygous, *Bb*, and their phenotype is black. To prevent confusion, we always indicate the genotype of a heterozygous individual by writing the symbol for the dominant allele first and the recessive allele second (always *Bb*, never *bB*). The expression of dominance partly explains why an individual may resemble one parent more than the other, even though the two parents contribute equally to their offspring's genetic constitution.

Dominance is not predictable; that is, dominance is not an intrinsic part of an allele but is the property of an allele relative to other alleles. Dominance is produced by the mechanism of gene expression and can be determined only by experiment. In one species of animal, black coat may be dominant to brown; in another species, brown may be dominant to black. In a population, the dominant phenotype is not necessarily more common than the recessive phenotype.

A test cross can detect heterozygosity Guinea pigs with the genotypes *BB* and *Bb* are alike phenotypically; they both have black coats. How, then, can we know the genotype of a black guinea pig?

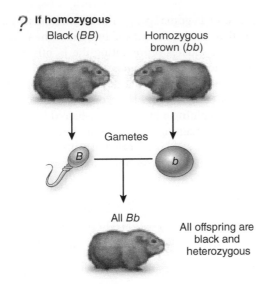

? If homozygous

Black (*BB*) Homozygous brown (*bb*)

Gametes

All *Bb*

All offspring are black and heterozygous

(a) If a black guinea pig is mated with a brown guinea pig and all the offspring are black, the black parent probably has a homozygous genotype.

Figure 11-7 *Animation* **A test cross in guinea pigs**
In this illustration, a test cross is used to determine the genotype of a black guinea pig.
PREDICT If this cross were to produce a single offspring, what might you conclude if it happened to be black? brown?

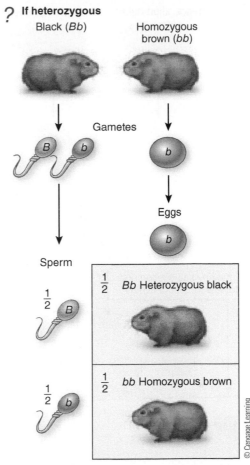

? If heterozygous

Black (*Bb*) Homozygous brown (*bb*)

Gametes

Eggs

Sperm

$\frac{1}{2}$ *B*

$\frac{1}{2}$ *b*

$\frac{1}{2}$ *Bb* Heterozygous black

$\frac{1}{2}$ *bb* Homozygous brown

© Cengage Learning

(b) If any of the offspring is brown, the black guinea pig must be heterozygous. The expected phenotypic ratio is 1 black to 1 brown.

Geneticists find out by performing an experimental cross known as a **test cross,** in which an individual of unknown genotype is crossed with a recessive individual (FIG. 11-7). In a test cross, the alleles carried by the gametes from the parent of unknown genotype are never "hidden" in the offspring by dominant alleles contributed by the other parent. Therefore, you can deduce the genotypes of all offspring directly from their phenotypes.

Mendel conducted several test crosses; for example, he bred F_1 (tall) pea plants with homozygous recessive (*tt*) short ones. He reasoned that the F_1 individuals were heterozygous (*Tt*) and would be expected to produce equal numbers of *T* and *t* gametes. Because the homozygous short parents (*tt*) were expected to produce only *t* gametes, Mendel hypothesized that he would obtain equal numbers of tall (*Tt*) and short (*tt*) offspring. His results agreed with his hypothesis, providing additional evidence for the hypothesis that there is 1:1 segregation of the alleles of a heterozygous parent. Thus, Mendel's principle of segregation not only explained the known facts, such as the 3:1 monohybrid F_2 phenotypic ratio, but also let him successfully anticipate the results of other experiments, in this case, the 1:1 test-cross phenotypic ratio.

A dihybrid cross involves individuals that have different alleles at two loci

Monohybrid crosses involve a pair of alleles of a single locus. Mendel also analyzed crosses involving alleles of two or more loci. A mating between individuals with different alleles at two loci is called a **dihybrid cross.** Consider the case of two pairs of alleles carried on nonhomologous chromosomes (i.e., one pair of alleles is in one pair of homologous chromosomes, and the other pair of alleles is in a different pair of homologous chromosomes). Each pair of alleles is inherited independently; that is, each pair segregates during meiosis independently of the other.

An example of a dihybrid cross carried through the F_2 generation is shown in FIGURE 11-8. In this example black is dominant to brown, and short hair is dominant to long hair. When a homozygous, black, short-haired guinea pig (*BBSS*) and a homozygous, brown, long-haired guinea pig (*bbss*) are mated, the *BBSS* animal produces gametes that are all *BS*, and the *bbss* individual produces gametes that are all *bs*. Each gamete contains one allele for each of the two loci. The union of the *BS* and *bs* gametes yields only individuals with

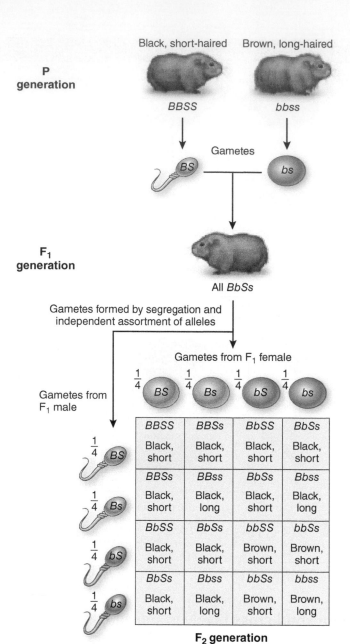

Gametes formed by segregation and
independent assortment of alleles

Gametes from F₁ female

	$\frac{1}{4}$ BS	$\frac{1}{4}$ Bs	$\frac{1}{4}$ bS	$\frac{1}{4}$ bs
$\frac{1}{4}$ BS	BBSS Black, short	BBSs Black, short	BbSS Black, short	BbSs Black, short
$\frac{1}{4}$ Bs	BBSs Black, short	BBss Black, long	BbSs Black, short	Bbss Black, long
$\frac{1}{4}$ bS	BbSS Black, short	BbSs Black, short	bbSS Brown, short	bbSs Brown, short
$\frac{1}{4}$ bs	BbSs Black, short	Bbss Black, long	bbSs Brown, short	bbss Brown, long

Gametes from
F₁ male

F₂ generation

F₂ phenotypes

$\frac{9}{16}$	$\frac{3}{16}$	$\frac{3}{16}$	$\frac{1}{16}$
Black, short-haired	Black, long-haired	Brown, short-haired	Brown, long-haired

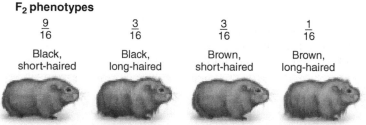

Figure 11-8 *Animation* **A dihybrid cross in guinea pigs**

When a black, short-haired guinea pig is crossed with a brown, long-haired one, all the offspring are black and have short hair. However, when two members of the F₁ generation are crossed, the ratio of phenotypes is 9:3:3:1.

PREDICT Would these results be different if the P generation genotypes were *BBss* and *bbSS*? Explain your answer.

the genotype *BbSs*. All these F₁ offspring are heterozygous for hair color and for hair length, and all are phenotypically black and short-haired.

Each F₁ guinea pig produces four kinds of gametes with equal probability: *BS, Bs, bS,* and *bs*. Hence, the Punnett square has 16 (i.e., 4²) squares representing the F₂ offspring, some of which are genotypically or phenotypically alike. There are 9 chances in 16 of obtaining a black, short-haired individual; 3 chances in 16 of obtaining a black, long-haired individual; 3 chances in 16 of obtaining a brown, short-haired individual; and 1 chance in 16 of obtaining a brown, long-haired individual. This 9:3:3:1 phenotypic ratio is expected in a dihybrid F₂ if the hair color and hair length loci are on nonhomologous chromosomes.

Alleles on nonhomologous chromosomes are randomly distributed into gametes: the principle of independent assortment

On the basis of results similar to the guinea pig example, Mendel formulated the principle of inheritance, now known as Mendel's **principle of independent assortment**, which states that members of any gene pair segregate from each other independently of the members of the other gene pairs. This mechanism occurs in a regular way to ensure that each gamete contains one allele for each locus, but the alleles of different loci are assorted at random with respect to each other in the gametes. The independent assortment of these alleles can result in **genetic recombination** (or simply **recombination**), the process of assorting and passing alleles to offspring in new combinations that are different from those in the parents.

Today we recognize that independent assortment is related to the events of meiosis. It occurs because two pairs of homologous chromosomes can be arranged in two different ways at metaphase I of meiosis (**FIG. 11-9**). These arrangements occur randomly, with approximately half the meiotic cells oriented one way and half oriented the opposite way. The orientation of the homologous chromosomes on the metaphase plate then determines the way they subsequently separate and disperse into the haploid cells. (As you will soon see, however, independent assortment does not always occur.)

Recognition of Mendel's work came during the early 20th century

Mendel reported his findings at a meeting of the Brünn Society for the Study of Natural Science (in what is now the Czech Republic), and he published his results in the society's report in 1866. At that time biology was largely a descriptive science, and biologists had little interest in applying quantitative and experimental methods such as those Mendel had used. Other biologists of the time did not appreciate the importance of his results nor his interpretations of those results. For 34 years, his findings were largely neglected.

In 1900, Hugo DeVries in Holland, Carl Correns in Germany, and Erich von Tschermak in Austria recognized Mendel's principles in their own experiments; they later discovered Mendel's paper and found that it explained their own research observations. By this time biologists had a much greater appreciation of the value of quantitative experimental methods.

Mendel's principle of independent assortment—that factors for different characteristics separate independently of one another prior to gamete formation—is a direct consequence of the events of meiosis.

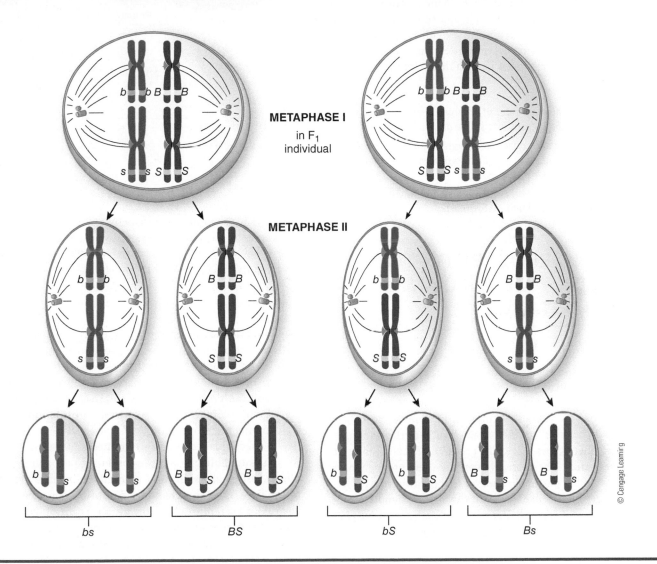

METAPHASE I
in F₁
individual

METAPHASE II

bs   BS   bS   Bs

© Cengage Learning

Figure 11-9 *Animation* Meiosis and independent assortment

Two different pairs of homologous chromosomes can line up two different ways at metaphase I in an F₁ individual and be subsequently distributed. A cell with the orientation shown at the left produces half *BS* and half *bs* gametes. Conversely, the cell at the right produces half *Bs* and half *bS* gametes. Because approximately half of the meiotic cells at metaphase I are of each type, the ratio of the four possible types of gametes is 1:1:1:1.

CONNECT In Figure 11-8 the genotypes of the P generation were *BBSS* and *bbss*. Would this diagram be drawn differently if the P generation genotypes were *BBss* and *bbSS*? Explain your answer.

Correns gave credit to Mendel by naming the basic laws of inheritance after him.

Although gametes and fertilization were known at the time Mendel carried out his research, mitosis and meiosis had not yet been discovered. It is truly remarkable that Mendel formulated his ideas mainly on the basis of mathematical abstractions. Today his principles are much easier to understand because we relate the transmission of genes to the behavior of chromosomes.

The details of mitosis and meiosis were described during the late 19th century, and in 1902, American biologist

Walter Sutton and German biologist Theodor Boveri independently pointed out the connection between Mendel's segregation of alleles and the separation of homologous chromosomes during meiosis. This connection developed into the **chromosome theory of inheritance,** or the *Sutton–Boveri theory*, which stated that inheritance can be explained by assuming that genes are linearly arranged in specific locations along the chromosomes.

The chromosome theory of inheritance was initially controversial because at that time there was no direct evidence that genes are found on chromosomes. However, new research provided the findings necessary for wider acceptance and extension of these ideas and their implications. For example, the work of American geneticist Thomas Hunt Morgan in 1910 provided evidence for the location of a particular gene (white eye color) on a specific chromosome (the X chromosome) in fruit flies. Morgan and his graduate students also provided insight into the way genes are organized on chromosomes; we discuss some of Morgan's research contributions later in the chapter.

CHECKPOINT 11.1

- *What is the maximum number of different alleles for a particular locus that can be present in a single diploid individual?*
- **CONNECT** *Can Mendel's principle of segregation be illustrated by a cross between two homozygous dominant individuals? two homozygous recessive individuals?*
- **CONNECT** *Can a monohybrid cross be used to illustrate Mendel's principle of independent assortment?*

11.2 USING PROBABILITY TO PREDICT MENDELIAN INHERITANCE

LEARNING OBJECTIVE

5   Apply the product rule and sum rule appropriately when predicting the outcomes of genetic crosses.

All genetic ratios are properly expressed in terms of probabilities. In monohybrid crosses the expected ratio of the dominant and recessive phenotypes is 3:1. The probability of an event is its expected frequency. Therefore, we can say there are 3 chances in 4 (or ¾) that any particular individual offspring of two heterozygous individuals will express the dominant phenotype and there is 1 chance in 4 (or ¼) that it will express the recessive phenotype. Although we sometimes speak in terms of percentages, probabilities are calculated as fractions (such as ¾) or decimal fractions (such as 0.75). If an event is certain to occur, its probability is 1; if it is certain *not* to occur, its probability is 0. A probability can be 0, 1, or some number between 0 and 1.

The Punnett square lets you combine two or more probabilities. When you use a Punnett square, you are following two important statistical principles known as the product rule and the sum rule. The **product rule** predicts the combined probabilities of independent events. Events are *independent* if the occurrence of one does not affect the probability that the other will occur. For example, the probability of obtaining heads on the first toss of a coin is ½; the probability of obtaining heads on the second toss (an independent event) is also ½. If two or more events are independent of each other, the probability of both occurring is the product of their individual probabilities. If this concept seems strange, keep in mind that when we multiply two numbers that are less than 1, the product is a smaller number. Therefore, the probability of obtaining heads two times in a row is ½ × ½ = ¼, or 1 chance in 4 (**FIG. 11-10**).

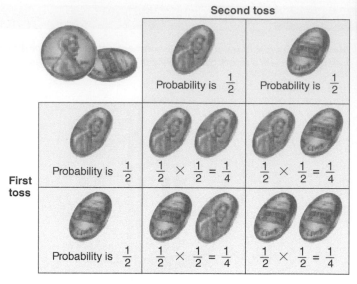

Figure 11-10 The rules of probability

For each coin toss, the probability of heads is ½, and the probability of tails is also ½. Because the outcome of the first toss is independent of the outcome of the second, the combined probabilities of the outcomes of successive tosses are calculated by multiplying their individual probabilities (according to the product rule: ½ × ½ = ¼). These same rules of probability predict genetic events.

© Cengage Learning

Similarly, we can apply the product rule to genetic events. If both parents are *Bb*, what is the probability that they will produce a child who is *bb*? For the child to be *bb*, he or she must receive a *b* gamete from each parent. The probability of a *b* egg is ½, and the probability of a *b* sperm is also ½. Like the outcomes of the coin tosses, these probabilities are independent, so we combine them by the product rule (½ × ½ = ¼). You might like to check this result using a Punnett square.

The **sum rule** predicts the combined probabilities of *mutually exclusive* events. In some cases, there is more than one way to obtain a specific outcome. These different ways are mutually exclusive; if one occurs, the other(s) cannot. For example, if both parents are *Bb*, what is the probability that their first child will also have the *Bb* genotype? There are two different ways these parents can have a *Bb* child: either a *B* egg combines with a *b* sperm (probability ¼) or a *b* egg combines with a *B* sperm (probability ¼).

Naturally, if there is more than one way to get a result, the chances of its being obtained improve; we therefore combine the probabilities of mutually exclusive events by summing (adding) their individual probabilities. The probability of obtaining a *Bb* child in our example is therefore ¼ + ¼ = ½. (Because there is only one way these heterozygous parents can produce a homozygous recessive child, *bb*, that probability is only ¼. The probability of a homozygous dominant child, *BB*, is likewise ¼.)

The rules of probability can be applied to a variety of calculations

The rules of probability have wide applications. For example, what are the probabilities that a family with two (and only two) children will have two girls, two boys, or one girl and one boy? For

How do you solve simple Mendelian genetics problems? Such problems can be fun and easy to work if you follow certain conventions and are methodical in your approach.

1. Always use standard designations for the generations. The generation in which a particular genetic experiment is begun is called the P, or parental, generation. Offspring of this generation are called the F_1, or first filial, generation. The offspring resulting when two F_1 individuals are bred constitute the F_2, or second filial, generation.

2. Write down a key for the symbols you are using for the allelic variants of each locus. Use an uppercase letter to designate a dominant allele and a lowercase letter to designate a recessive allele. Use the same letter of the alphabet to designate both alleles of a particular locus. If you are not told which allele is dominant and which is recessive, the phenotype of the F_1 generation is a good clue.

3. Determine the genotypes of the parents of each cross by using the following types of evidence:
   - Are they from true-breeding lines? If so, they should be homozygous.
   - Can their genotypes be reliably deduced from their phenotypes? Usually they can, if they express the recessive phenotype.
   - Do the phenotypes of their offspring provide any information? An example is included in part 8.

4. Indicate the possible kinds of gametes formed by each of the parents. It is helpful to draw a circle around the symbols for each kind of gamete.

- If it is a monohybrid cross, we apply the principle of segregation; that is, a heterozygote Aa forms two kinds of gametes, A and a. A homozygote, such as aa, forms only one kind of gamete, a.
- If it is a dihybrid cross, we apply the principles of segregation and independent assortment. For example, an individual heterozygous for two loci would have the genotype $AaBb$. Allele A segregates from a, and B segregates from b. The assortment of A and a into gametes is independent of the assortment of B and b. A is equally likely to end up in a gamete with B or b. The same is true for a. Thus, an individual with the genotype $AaBb$ produces four kinds of gametes in equal amounts: AB, Ab, aB, and ab.

5. Set up a Punnett square, placing the possible types of gametes from one parent down the left side and the possible types from the other parent across the top.

6. Fill in the Punnett square. Avoid confusion by consistently placing the dominant allele first and the recessive allele second in heterozygotes (Aa, never aA). If it is a dihybrid cross, always write the two alleles of one locus first and the two alleles of the other locus second. It does not matter which locus you choose to write first, but once you have decided on the order, it is crucial to maintain it consistently. So, if the individual is heterozygous for both loci, you will always use the form $AaBb$. Writing this particular genotype as $aBbA$, or even as $BbAa$, would cause confusion.

7. If you do not need to know the frequencies of all the expected genotypes and phenotypes, you can use the rules of probability as a shortcut instead of making a Punnett square. For example, if both parents are $AaBb$, what is the probability of an $AABB$ offspring? To be AA, the offspring must receive an A gamete from each parent. The probability that a given gamete is A is $\frac{1}{2}$, and each gamete represents an independent event, so combine their probabilities by multiplying ($\frac{1}{2} \times \frac{1}{2} = \frac{1}{4}$). The probability of BB is calculated similarly and is also $\frac{1}{4}$. The probability of AA is independent of the probability of BB, so again, use the product rule to obtain their combined probabilities ($\frac{1}{4} \times \frac{1}{4} = \frac{1}{16}$).

8. Very often the genotypes of the parents can be deduced from the phenotypes of their offspring. In peas, for example, the allele for yellow seeds (Y) is dominant to the allele for green seeds (y). Suppose plant breeders cross two plants with yellow seeds, but you do not know whether the yellow-seeded plants are homozygous or heterozygous. You can designate the cross as: $Y\_ \times Y\_$. The offspring of the cross are allowed to germinate and grow, and their seeds are examined. Of the offspring, 74 produce yellow seeds, and 26 produce green seeds. Knowing that green-seeded plants are recessive, yy, the answer is obvious: Each parent contributed a y allele to the green-seeded offspring, so the parents' genotypes must have been $Yy \times Yy$.

---

purposes of discussion, let's assume male and female births are equally probable. The probability of having a girl first is $\frac{1}{2}$, and the probability of having a girl second is also $\frac{1}{2}$. They are independent events, so we combine their probabilities by multiplying: $\frac{1}{2} \times \frac{1}{2} = \frac{1}{4}$. Similarly, the probability of having two boys is $\frac{1}{4}$.

In families with both a girl and a boy, the girl can be born first or the boy can be born first. The probability that a girl will be born first is $\frac{1}{2}$, and the probability that a boy will be born second is also $\frac{1}{2}$. We use the product rule to combine the probabilities of these two independent events: $\frac{1}{2} \times \frac{1}{2} = \frac{1}{4}$. Similarly, the probability that a boy will be born first and a girl second is $\frac{1}{4}$. These two kinds of families represent mutually exclusive outcomes, that is, two different ways of obtaining a family with one boy and one girl. Having two different ways of obtaining the desired result improves our chances, so we use the sum rule to combine the probabilities: $\frac{1}{4} + \frac{1}{4} = \frac{1}{2}$.

In working with probabilities, keep in mind a point that many gamblers forget: Chance has no memory. If events are truly independent, past events have no influence on the probability of the occurrence of future events. Probability only has predictive value in the long run, over many trials. (Recall that Mendel counted hundreds of offspring for each cross, which was one of the reasons for his success.) When working probability problems, common sense is more important than blindly memorizing rules. Examine your results to see whether they appear reasonable; if they do not, re-evaluate your assumptions. (See *Inquiring About: Solving Genetics Problems* for procedures to solve genetics problems, including when to use the rules of probability.)

CHECKPOINT 11.2

- PREDICT *Use the rules of probability to answer the following question: in a cross between homozygous pea plants with yellow, round seeds (YYRR) and homozygous pea plants with green, wrinkled seeds (yyrr), what is the probability of an F_2 plant having yellow, round seeds?*
- CONNECT *In answering the previous question, did you use the product rule, the sum rule, or both?*

11.3 INHERITANCE AND CHROMOSOMES

LEARNING OBJECTIVES

6 Define *linkage* and relate it to specific events in meiosis.
7 Show how data from a two-point test cross can be used to distinguish between independent assortment and linkage.
8 Discuss the genetic determination of sex and the inheritance of X-linked genes in mammals.

It is a measure of Mendel's genius that he worked out the principles of segregation and independent assortment without knowing anything about meiosis or the chromosome theory of inheritance. The chromosome theory of inheritance also helps explain certain apparent exceptions to Mendelian inheritance. One of these so-called exceptions involves linked genes.

Linked genes do not assort independently

Beginning around 1910, the research of geneticist Thomas Hunt Morgan and his graduate students extended the concept of the chromosome theory of inheritance. Morgan's research organism was the fruit fly (*Drosophila melanogaster*). Just as the garden pea was an excellent model research organism for Mendel's studies, the fruit fly was perfect for extending general knowledge about inheritance. Fruit flies have a short life cycle—just 14 days—and their small size means that thousands can be kept in a research lab. The large number of individuals increases the chance of identifying mutants. Also, fruit flies have just four pairs of chromosomes, one of which is a pair of sex chromosomes.

By carefully analyzing the results of crosses involving fruit flies, Morgan and his students demonstrated that genes are arranged in a linear order on each chromosome. Morgan also showed that independent assortment does not apply if the two loci lie close together in the same pair of homologous chromosomes. In fruit flies there is a locus controlling wing shape: the dominant allele *V* for normal wings and the recessive allele *v* for abnormally short, or vestigial, wings. Another locus controls body color: the dominant allele *B* for gray body and the recessive allele *b* for black body. If a homozygous *BBVV* fly is crossed with a homozygous *bbvv* fly, the F$_1$ flies all have gray bodies and normal wings, and their genotype is *BbVv*.

Because these loci happen to lie close to each other in the *same pair* of homologous chromosomes, their alleles do not assort independently; instead, they are **linked genes** that tend to be inherited together. **Linkage** is the tendency for a group of genes on the same chromosome to be inherited together in successive generations. You can readily observe linkage in the results of a test cross in which heterozygous F$_1$ flies (*BbVv*) are mated with homozygous recessive (*bbvv*) flies (**FIG. 11-11**). Because heterozygous individuals are mated to homozygous recessive individuals, this test cross is similar to the test cross described earlier. However, it is called a **two-point test cross** because alleles of two loci are involved.

If the loci governing these traits were unlinked—that is, on different chromosomes—the heterozygous parent in a test cross would produce four kinds of gametes (*BV*, *Bv*, *bV*, and *bv*) in equal numbers. This independent assortment would produce offspring with new gene combinations not present in the parental generation. Recall that any process that leads to new allele combinations is called genetic recombination. In our example, gametes *Bv* and *bV* are *recombinant types*. The other two kinds of gametes, *BV* and *bv*, are *parental types* because they are identical to the gametes produced by the P generation.

Of course, the homozygous recessive parent produces only one kind of gamete, *bv*. Thus, if independent assortment were to occur in the F$_1$ flies, approximately 25% of the test-cross offspring would be gray-bodied and normal-winged (*BbVv*), 25% black-bodied and normal-winged (*bbVv*), 25% gray-bodied and vestigial-winged (*Bbvv*), and 25% black-bodied and vestigial-winged (*bbvv*). Note that the two-point test cross lets us determine the genotypes of the offspring directly from their phenotypes.

By contrast, the alleles of the loci in our example do not undergo independent assortment because they are linked. Alleles at different loci but close to one another on a given chromosome tend to be inherited together; because chromosomes pair and separate during meiosis as units, the alleles at different loci on a given chromosome tend to be inherited as units. If linkage were complete, only parental-type flies would be produced, with approximately 50% having gray bodies and normal wings (*BbVv*) and 50% having black bodies and vestigial wings (*bbvv*).

However, in our example the offspring also include some gray-bodied, vestigial-winged flies and some black-bodied, normal-winged flies. They are recombinant flies, having received a recombinant-type gamete from the heterozygous F$_1$ parent. Each recombinant-type gamete arose by **crossing-over** between these loci in a meiotic cell of a heterozygous female fly. (Fruit flies are unusual in that crossing-over occurs only in females and not in males; it is far more common for crossing-over to occur in both sexes of a species.) When chromosomes pair and undergo synapsis, crossing-over occurs as homologous (nonsister) chromatids exchange segments of chromosome material by a process of breakage and rejoining catalyzed by enzymes (**FIG. 11-12**). Also see the discussion of prophase I in Chapter 10, Section 10.4.

Calculating the frequency of crossing-over reveals the linear order of linked genes on a chromosome

In our fruit fly example (see Fig. 11-11), 217 of the offspring are recombinant types: gray flies with vestigial wings, *Bbvv* (111 of the total); and black flies with normal wings, *bbVv* (106 of the total). The remaining 1051 offspring are parental types. These data can be used to calculate the percentage of crossing-over between the loci (**TABLE 11-3**). You do this calculation by adding the number of individuals in the two recombinant types of offspring, dividing by the *total number of offspring*, and multiplying by 100: $217 \div 1268 = 0.17$; $0.17 \times 100 = 17\%$. Thus, the *V* locus and the *B* locus have 17% recombination between them.

How can linkage be recognized in fruit flies?

HYPOTHESIS: Linkage can be recognized when an excess of parental-type offspring and a deficiency of recombinant-type offspring are produced in a two-point test cross.

EXPERIMENT: Fruit flies from pure lines with gray bodies and normal wings (*BBVV*) and black bodies and vestigial wings (*bbvv*) (P generation) are crossed. The heterozygous F$_1$ flies with gray, normal wings (*BbVv*) are then crossed with flies that have black, vestigial wings (*bbvv*). If the alleles for color and wing shape are not linked (i.e., the alleles assort independently), the offspring will consist of an equal number of each of four phenotypes.

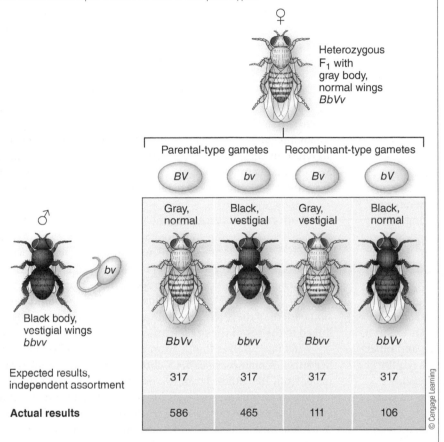

RESULTS AND CONCLUSION: Of the 1268 offspring (*bottom row*) of an actual cross, a total of 1051 belong to one of the two parental types (83%), and 217 belong to one of the two recombinant types (17%). Thus, loci for wing length and body color are linked on a homologous chromosome pair..

SOURCE: Morgan, T.H. (1914) "No crossing over in the male of *Drosophila* of genes in the second and third pairs of chromosomes." *Biological Bulletin* 26: 195–204.

Figure 11-11 A two-point test cross to detect linkage in fruit flies

PREDICT What results would you expect if the P generation flies were *BBvv* and *bbVV*? What would be the genotypes and phenotypes of the parental classes? the recombinant classes?

During a single meiotic division, crossing-over may occur at several different points along the length of each homologous chromosome pair. In general, crossing-over is more likely to occur between two loci if they lie far apart on the chromosome and less likely to occur if they lie close together. Because of this rough correlation between the frequency of recombination of two loci and the linear distance between them, a genetic map of the

chromosome can be generated by converting the percentage of recombination to **map units.** By convention, 1% recombination between two loci equals a distance of 1 map unit, so the loci in our example are 17 map units apart.

Scientists have determined the frequencies of recombination between specific linked loci in many species. All the experimental results are consistent with the hypothesis that genes are present in a linear order in the chromosomes. **FIGURE 11-13** illustrates the traditional method for determining the linear order of genes in a chromosome.

By putting together the results of numerous crosses, scientists have developed detailed linkage maps for many eukaryotes, including the fruit fly, the mouse, yeast, *Neurospora* (a fungus), and many plants, especially those that are important crops. In addition, researchers have used genetic methods to develop a detailed map for *Escherichia coli*—a bacterium with a single, circular DNA molecule—and many other prokaryotes and viruses. They have made much more sophisticated maps of chromosomes of various species by means of recombinant DNA technology (discussed in Chapter 15). Using these techniques, the *Human Genome Project* has produced detailed maps of human chromosomes (discussed in Chapter 16).

Sex is generally determined by sex chromosomes

In some species, environmental factors exert a large control over an individual's sex. However, genes are the most important sex determinants in most eukaryotic organisms. The major sex-determining genes of mammals, birds, and many insects are carried by **sex chromosomes.** Typically, members of one sex have a pair of similar sex chromosomes and produce gametes that are all identical in sex chromosome constitution. The members of the other sex have two different sex chromosomes and produce two kinds of gametes, each bearing a single kind of sex chromosome.

The cells of female mammals, including humans, contain two **X chromosomes.** In contrast, the males have a single X chromosome and a smaller **Y chromosome** that bears only a few active genes (**FIG. 11-14**). For example, human females have 22 pairs of **autosomes,** which are chromosomes other than the sex chromosomes, plus a pair of X chromosomes; males have 22 pairs of autosomes plus one X chromosome and one Y chromosome. Domestic cats have 19 pairs of autosomes, to which are added a pair of X chromosomes

| TABLE 11-3 | How to Determine Recombination Frequency from a Two-Point Test Cross | | | |

| | TEST-CROSS RESULTS (FROM FIG. 11-11) | | | |
TYPE OF OFFSPRING	PARENTAL TYPE		RECOMBINANT TYPE	
Phenotype	Gray, normal	Black, vestigial	Gray, vestigial	Black, normal
Genotype	*BbVv*	*bbvv*	*Bbvv*	*bbVv*
Number of offspring	586	465	111	106
Calculations of recombination frequency	1. Number of parental-type offspring = 1051 2. Number of recombinant-type offspring = 217 3. Total number of offspring = 1051 + 217 =1268 4. Recombination frequency =217/1268 × 100 = 17%			

© Cengage Learning

in females, or an X plus a Y in males. In contrast, sex determination is based on different genetic systems in animals other than mammals (TABLE 11-4).

The Y chromosome determines male sex in most species of mammals

Do male humans have a male phenotype because they have only one X chromosome, or because they have a Y chromosome? Much of the traditional evidence bearing on this question comes from studies of people with abnormal sex chromosome constitutions (see discussion in Chapter 16). A person with an XXY constitution is a nearly normal male in external appearance, although his testes are underdeveloped (Klinefelter syndrome). A person with one X but no Y chromosome has the overall appearance of a female but has defects such as short stature and undeveloped ovaries (Turner syndrome). An embryo with a Y but no X does not survive. Based on these and other observations, biologists concluded that all individuals require at least one X, and the Y is the male-determining chromosome.

Geneticists have identified several genes on the Y chromosome that are involved in determination of the male sex. The *sex reversal on Y (SRY) gene*, the major male-determining gene on the Y chromosome, acts as a "genetic switch" that causes testes to develop in the fetus. The developing testes then secrete the hormone *testosterone*, which causes other male characteristics to develop. Several other genes on the Y chromosome also play a role in sex determination, as do many genes on the X chromosome, which explains why an XXY individual does not have a completely normal male phenotype. Some genes on the autosomes also affect sex development.

Evidence suggests that the X and Y chromosomes of mammals originated as a homologous pair of autosomes. During the evolution of the X and Y chromosomes, almost all of the original functional genes were retained on the X chromosome and lost from the Y chromosome. Today, about 95% of the Y chromosome is male-specific. Either the Y chromosome retained certain genes that coded for proteins that determine maleness or perhaps mutations occurred in existing genes on the Y chromosome that made it the male-determining chromosome.

Thus, the sex chromosomes are not truly homologous in their present forms because they are not similar in size, shape, or genetic constitution. Nevertheless, the Y chromosome has short, homologous "pairing regions" at its tips that lets it synapse and exchange genetic material with the X chromosome during meiosis.

Half the sperm contain an X chromosome, and half contain a Y chromosome. All normal eggs bear a single X chromosome. Fertilization of an X-bearing egg by an X-bearing sperm results in an XX (female) zygote, or fertilized egg; fertilization by a Y-bearing sperm results in an XY (male) zygote.

You might expect to have equal numbers of X- and Y-bearing sperm and a 1:1 ratio of females to males. However, in humans more males are conceived than females, and more males die before birth. Even at birth the ratio is not 1:1; about 106 boys are born for every 100 girls. The Y-bearing sperm appear to have a selective advantage, possibly because sperm containing the Y chromosome are smaller and have less mass than sperm containing the X chromosome; it is hypothesized that, on average, the sperm carrying the Y chromosome can swim slightly faster than X-bearing sperm to reach the egg.

X-linked genes have unusual inheritance patterns

The human X chromosome contains many loci that are required in both sexes. Genes located in the X chromosome, such as those governing color perception and blood clotting, are sometimes called *sex-linked genes*. It is more appropriate, however, to refer to them as **X-linked genes** because they follow the transmission pattern of the X chromosome and, strictly speaking, are not linked to the sex of the organism.

A female receives one X from her mother and one X from her father. A male receives his Y chromosome, which makes him male, from his father. From his mother he inherits a single X chromosome and therefore all his X-linked genes. In the male every allele present on the X chromosome is expressed, whether that allele was dominant or recessive in the female parent.

A male is neither homozygous nor heterozygous for his X-linked alleles; instead, he is always **hemizygous;** that is, he has only one copy of each X-linked gene. The significance of hemizygosity in males, including human males, is that rare, recessive X-linked genes are expressed, making males more likely to be affected by the many genetic disorders associated with the X chromosome. In comparison, only a few genes are located exclusively on the Y chromosome. X and Y chromosomes also have short areas where they carry the same genes, enabling the X and Y to pair during meiosis I.

We will use a simple system of notation for problems involving X linkage, indicating the X chromosome and incorporating specific alleles as superscripts. For example, the symbol X^e signifies a recessive X-linked allele for color blindness and X^E the dominant X-linked allele for normal color vision. The Y chromosome is written without superscripts because it does not carry the locus of interest. Two recessive X-linked alleles must be present in a female for the abnormal phenotype to be expressed (X^eX^e), whereas in the hemizygous male a single recessive allele

The exchange of segments between chromatids of homologous chromosomes is the mechanism of recombination of linked genes.

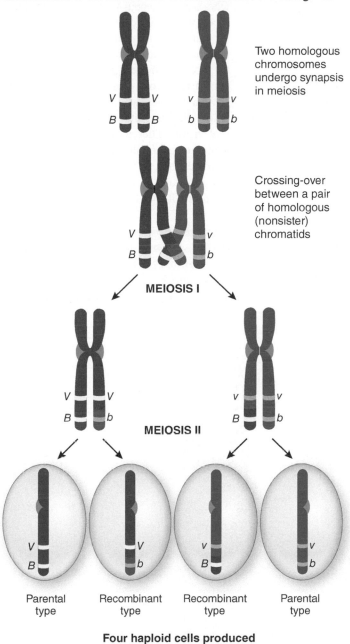

Two homologous chromosomes undergo synapsis in meiosis

Crossing-over between a pair of homologous (nonsister) chromatids

MEIOSIS I

MEIOSIS II

| Parental type | Recombinant type | Recombinant type | Parental type |

Four haploid cells produced

Figure 11-12 *Animation* Crossing-over

Genes located far apart on a chromosome have a greater probability of being separated by crossing-over than do genes that are closer together.

VISUALIZE Draw a series of simple sketches illustrating what would happen in meiosis if the genotypes of the P generation were *BBvv* and *bbVV*.
© Cengage Learning

(X^{e}Y) causes the abnormal phenotype. As a consequence, these abnormal alleles are much more frequently expressed in male offspring. A heterozygous female may be a *carrier*, an individual who possesses one copy of a mutant recessive allele but does not express it in the phenotype (X^{E}X^e).

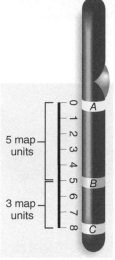

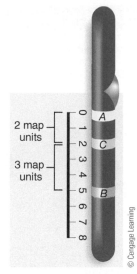

(a) If the recombination between *A* and *C* is 8% (8 map units), then *B* must be in the middle.

(b) If the recombination between *A* and *C* is 2%, then *C* must be in the middle.

Figure 11-13 Gene mapping

Gene order (i.e., which locus lies between the other two) is determined by the percentage of recombination between each of the possible pairs. In this hypothetical example, the percentage of recombination between locus *A* and locus *B* is 5% (corresponding to 5 map units) and between *B* and *C* is 3% (3 map units). There are two alternatives for the linear order of these loci.

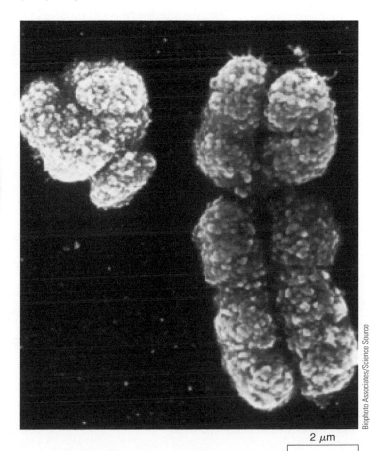

2 μm

Figure 11-14 SEM of human Y chromosome (*left*) and X chromosome (*right*)

Each chromosome is in the duplicated state and consists of two identical chromatids.

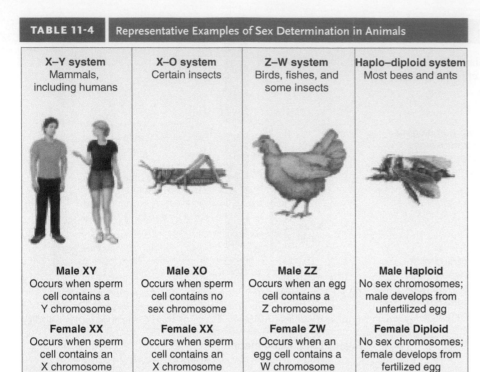

TABLE 11-4	Representative Examples of Sex Determination in Animals		
X–Y system Mammals, including humans	**X–O system** Certain insects	**Z–W system** Birds, fishes, and some insects	**Haplo–diploid system** Most bees and ants
Male XY Occurs when sperm cell contains a Y chromosome	**Male XO** Occurs when sperm cell contains no sex chromosome	**Male ZZ** Occurs when an egg cell contains a Z chromosome	**Male Haploid** No sex chromosomes; male develops from unfertilized egg
Female XX Occurs when sperm cell contains an X chromosome	**Female XX** Occurs when sperm cell contains an X chromosome	**Female ZW** Occurs when an egg cell contains a W chromosome	**Female Diploid** No sex chromosomes; female develops from fertilized egg

© Cengage Learning

To be expressed in a female, a recessive X-linked allele must be inherited from both parents. A color-blind female, for example, must have a color-blind father and a mother who is homozygous or heterozygous for a recessive allele for color blindness (FIG. 11-15).

The homozygous combination is unusual because the frequency of alleles for color blindness is relatively low. In contrast, a color-blind male need only have a mother who is heterozygous for color blindness; his father can have normal vision. Therefore, X-linked recessive traits are generally much more common in males than in females, which may partially explain why human male embryos are more likely to die.

Dosage compensation equalizes the expression of X-linked genes in males and females The X chromosome contains numerous genes required by both sexes, yet a normal female has two copies

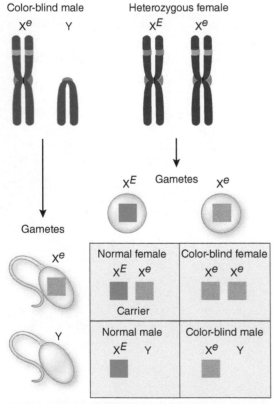

(a) To be color-blind, a female must inherit alleles for color blindness from both parents.

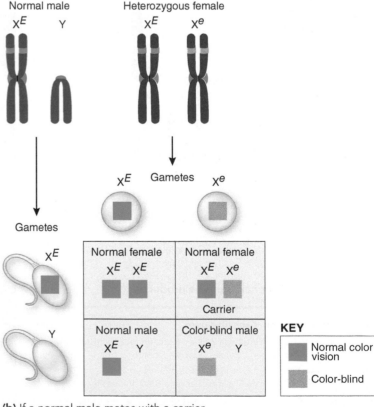

(b) If a normal male mates with a carrier (heterozygous) female, half of their sons would be expected to be color-blind and half of their daughters would be expected to be carriers.

KEY
- ■ Normal color vision
- ■ Color-blind

Figure 11-15 *Animation* X-linked red–green color blindness
Note that the Y chromosome does not carry a gene for color vision.
© Cengage Learning

In female mammals one of the two X chromosomes is randomly inactivated during early development, equalizing the level of expression of genes at loci on the X chromosome in males and females.

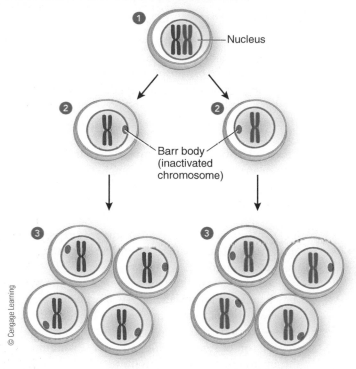

① The zygote and early embryonic cells have two X chromosomes, one from each parent.

② Random inactivation of one X chromosome occurs early in development. Roughly half the cells inactivate one X chromosome (*left cell*), and the other half inactivate the second X chromosome (*right cell*). The inactive X chromosome is visible as a Barr body near the nuclear envelope.

③ Chromosome inactivation persists through subsequent mitotic divisions, resulting in patches of cells in the adult body.

(a) Inactivation of one X chromosome in female cells.

© Cengage Learning

© Sari O'Neal/Shutterstock.com

(b) A calico cat has X-linked genes for both black and yellow (or orange) fur. Because of random X chromosome inactivation, black is expressed in some groups of cells and orange is expressed in others. (The patches of white fur are due to the presence of other genes that affect fur color.)

Figure 11-16 *Animation* Dosage compensation in female mammals

PREDICT What is most likely to be the sex of the cat in the photo? Could you make such a prediction if the cat were black or orange?

("doses") for each locus, whereas a normal male has only one. **Dosage compensation** is a mechanism that makes equivalent the two doses in the female and the single dose in the male. Because of dosage compensation, males and females produce the same amounts of proteins coded by X-linked genes. Male fruit flies accomplish this by making their single X chromosome more active. In most fly tissues, the metabolic activity of a single male X chromosome is equal to the combined metabolic activity of the two X chromosomes present in the female.

Our understanding of dosage compensation in humans and other mammals is incomplete, but the process generally involves the random inactivation of one of the two X chromosomes in the female (FIG. 11-16a). During interphase, a dark spot of chromatin is visible at the edge of the nucleus of each female mammalian cell when stained and observed with a microscope. This dark spot, a **Barr body,** is a dense, metabolically inactive X chromosome. The other X chromosome resembles the metabolically active autosomes; during interphase, it is a greatly extended thread that is not evident in light microscopy. From this and other evidence, British geneticist Mary Lyon hypothesized in 1961 that in most cells of a female mammal, only one of the two X chromosomes is active; the other is inactive and is condensed as a Barr body. Actually, however, X chromosome inactivation is never complete; as many as 25% of the genes on the inactive chromosome are expressed to some degree.

X chromosome inactivation is a random event in each somatic (body) cell of the female embryo. A female mammal that is heterozygous at an X-linked locus expresses one of the alleles in about half her cells and the other allele in the other half. X chromosome inactivation is sometimes evident in the phenotype. Mice and cats have several X-linked genes for certain coat colors. Females that are heterozygous for such genes may show patches of one coat color in the middle of areas of the other coat color. This phenomenon, called *variegation,* is evident in tortoiseshell and calico cats (FIG. 11-16b). Early in development, when relatively few cells are present, X chromosome inactivation occurs randomly in each cell. X inactivation is then maintained during all subsequent divisions of that cell line. When any one of these cells divides by mitosis, the cells of the resulting *clone* (a group of genetically identical cells) all have the same active X chromosome; therefore, a patch of cells that all express the same color develops.

You might wonder why variegation is not always apparent in females heterozygous at X-linked loci. The answer is that although variegation usually occurs, we may need to use special techniques to observe it. For example, color blindness is caused by a defect involving the pigments in the cone cells in the retina of the eye. In at least one type of red–green color blindness, the retina of a heterozygous female actually contains patches of abnormal cones, but the patches of normal cones are enough to provide normal color vision. Variegation can be very hard to observe in cases where cell products become mixed in bodily fluids. For instance, in females heterozygous for the allele that causes hemophilia, only half the cells responsible for producing a specific blood-clotting factor do so, but they produce enough to ensure that the blood clots normally.

CHECKPOINT 11.3

- *What ratio of genotypes to phenotypes is observed in a two-point test cross if genes are unlinked?*
- **CONNECT** *Does the mechanism of recombination of unlinked genes require crossing-over? Explain your answer.*
- **CONNECT** *Two loci exhibit 5% recombination between them. How many map units apart are they?*
- *Which chromosome determines the male sex in humans and other mammals?*
- **CONNECT** *In what way is variegation of X-linked genes related to the mechanism responsible for sex chromosome dosage compensation in humans and other mammals?*

11.4 EXTENSIONS OF MENDELIAN GENETICS

LEARNING OBJECTIVES

9 Explain some of the ways genes may interact to affect the phenotype and discuss how a single gene can affect many features of the organism simultaneously.

10 Distinguish among incomplete dominance, codominance, multiple alleles, epistasis, and polygenic inheritance.

11 Describe *norm of reaction* and give an example.

The relationship between a given locus and the trait it controls may or may not be simple. A single pair of alleles of a locus may regulate the appearance of a single trait (such as tall versus short in garden peas). Alternatively, a pair of alleles may participate in the control of several traits, or alleles of many loci may interact to affect the phenotypic expression of a single character. Not surprisingly, these more complex relationships are quite common.

You can assess the phenotype on one or many levels. It may be a morphological trait, such as shape, size, or color. It may be a physiological trait or even a biochemical trait, such as the presence or absence of a specific enzyme required for the metabolism of some specific molecule. In addition, changes in the environmental conditions under which the organism develops may alter the phenotypic expression of genes.

Dominance is not always complete

Studies of the inheritance of many traits in a wide variety of organisms have shown that one member of a pair of alleles may not be completely dominant over the other. In such instances, it is inaccurate to use the terms *dominant* and *recessive.*

The plants commonly called four o'clocks (*Mirabilis jalapa*) may have red or white flowers. Each color breeds true when these plants are self-pollinated. What flower color might you expect in the offspring of a cross between a red-flowering plant and a white-flowering one? Without knowing which is dominant, you might predict that all would have red flowers or all would have white flowers. German botanist Carl Correns, one of the rediscoverers of Mendel's work, first performed this cross and found that all F_1 offspring have pink flowers!

Does this result in any way indicate that the principles of inheritance that Mendel deduced are wrong? Did the parental traits blend inseparably in the offspring? Quite the contrary, for when two of these pink-flowered plants are crossed, red-flowered, pink-flowered, and white-flowered offspring appear in a ratio of 1:2:1 (FIG. 11-17). In this instance as in all other aspects of the scientific process, results that differ from those hypothesized prompt scientists to re-examine and modify their hypotheses to account for the exceptional results. The pink-flowered plants are clearly the heterozygous individuals, and neither the red allele nor the white allele is completely dominant. When the heterozygote has a phenotype intermediate between those of its two parents, the

In incomplete dominance an F₁ heterozygote has a phenotype intermediate between its parents.

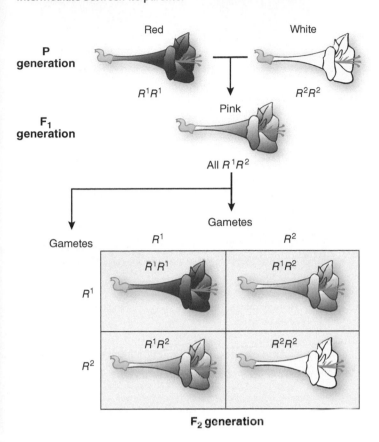

Figure 11-17 *Animation* **Incomplete dominance in four o'clocks**

Two incompletely dominant alleles, R^1 and R^2, are responsible for red, white, and pink flower colors. Red-flowered plants are R^1R^1, white-flowered plants are R^2R^2, and heterozygotes (R^1R^2) are pink. Note that uppercase letters are used for both alleles because neither is recessive to the other.

PREDICT What ratio of offspring would you expect in four o'clocks if you crossed a pink-flowered plant with a white-flowered plant? a pink-flowered plant with a red-flowered plant?

© Cengage Learning

genes show **incomplete dominance.** In these crosses, the genotypic and phenotypic ratios are identical.

Incomplete dominance is not unique to four o'clocks, and additional examples of incomplete dominance are known in both plants and animals. For example, true-breeding white chickens and true-breeding black chickens produce bluish gray offspring, or Andalusian blues, when crossed.

In both cattle and horses, reddish coat color is not completely dominant to white coat color. Heterozygous individuals have a mixture of reddish hairs and white hairs, which is called *roan.* If you saw a white mare nursing a roan foal, what would you guess was the coat color of the foal's father? Because the reddish and white colors are expressed independently (hair by

TABLE 11-5 | ABO Blood Types

PHENOTYPE (BLOOD TYPE)	GENOTYPE	SURFACE ANTIGEN ON RBC	SERUM ANTIBODIES TO A OR B ANTIGENS
A	I^AI^A or I^Ai	A	Anti-B
B	I^BI^B or I^Bi	B	Anti-A
AB	I^AI^B	A, B	None
O	ii	None	Anti-A, anti-B

*This table and the discussion of the ABO system have been simplified somewhat. Note that the body produces antibodies against the antigens *lacking* on its own red blood cells (RBCs). Because of their specificity for the corresponding antigens, these antibodies are used in standard tests to determine blood types.

© Cengage Learning

hair) in the roan heterozygote, scientists sometimes refer to it as a case of **codominance.** Strictly speaking, the term *incomplete dominance* refers to instances in which the heterozygote is intermediate in phenotype, and *codominance* refers to instances in which the heterozygote simultaneously expresses the phenotypes of both types of homozygotes.

Humans have four blood types (A, B, AB, and O), collectively called the *ABO blood group.* The human ABO blood group is an excellent example of codominant alleles. Blood types A, B, AB, and O are controlled by three alleles representing a single locus (**TABLE 11-5**). Allele I^A codes for the synthesis of a specific glycoprotein, antigen A, which is expressed on the surface of red blood cells. (Immune responses are discussed in Chapter 45.) *Antigens* are substances capable of stimulating an immune response. Allele I^B leads to the production of antigen B, a different but related glycoprotein. Allele i is allelic to I^A and I^B, but it does not code for an antigen.

Individuals with the genotype I^AI^A or I^Ai have blood type A. People with genotype I^BI^B or I^Bi have blood type B. Those with genotype I^AI^B have blood type AB, and those with genotype ii have blood type O. These results show that neither allele I^A nor allele I^B is dominant to the other. Both alleles are expressed phenotypically in the heterozygote and are therefore codominant to each other, although each is dominant to allele i.

At one time, determining blood types was used to settle cases of disputed parentage. Although blood-type tests can *exclude* someone as a possible parent of a particular child, they can never prove that a certain person is the parent; they only determine that he or she *could* be. Could a man with blood type AB be the father of a child with blood type O? Could a woman with blood type O be the mother of a child with blood type AB? Could a type B child with a type A mother have a type A father or a type O father?[2]

Multiple alleles for a locus may exist in a population

Most of our examples so far have dealt with situations in which each locus was represented by a maximum of two allelic variants

---

[2] The answer to all these questions is no.

(three in the example of blood types). It is true that a single diploid individual has a maximum of two different alleles for a particular locus and that a haploid gamete has only one allele for each locus. However, if you survey a population, you may find more than two alleles for a particular locus, as you saw with the ABO blood group (see Table 11-5). If three or more alleles for a given locus exist within the population, that locus has **multiple alleles.**

Research has shown that many loci have multiple alleles. Some alleles can be identified by the activity of a certain enzyme or by some other biochemical feature but do not produce an obvious phenotype. Others produce a readily recognizable phenotype, and certain patterns of dominance can be discerned when the alleles are combined in various ways. In other series of multiple alleles, certain alleles may be codominant and others incompletely dominant. In such cases, the heterozygotes commonly have phenotypes intermediate between those of their parents.

A single gene may affect multiple aspects of the phenotype

In our examples the relationship between a gene and its phenotype has been direct, precise, and exact, and the loci have controlled the appearance of single traits. However, the relationship of gene to trait may not have such a simple genetic basis. Most genes affect several different characters. The ability of a single gene to have multiple effects is known as **pleiotropy.** Most cases of pleiotropy can be traced to a single fundamental cause. For example, a defective enzyme may affect the functioning of many types of cells. Pleiotropy is evident in many genetic diseases in which a single pair of alleles causes multiple symptoms. For example, people who are homozygous for the recessive allele that causes cystic fibrosis produce abnormally thick mucus in many parts of the body, including the respiratory, digestive, and reproductive systems (cystic fibrosis is discussed in Chapter 16).

Alleles of different loci may interact to produce a phenotype

Several pairs of alleles may interact to affect a single phenotype, or one pair may inhibit or reverse the effect of another pair. One example of gene interaction is illustrated by the inheritance of combs in chickens, where two genes may interact to produce a novel phenotype (FIG. 11-18). The allele for a rose comb, *R*, is dominant to that for a single comb, *r*. A second, unlinked pair of alleles governs the inheritance of a pea comb, *P*, versus a single comb, *p*. A single-comb chicken is homozygous for the recessive allele at both loci (*pprr*). A rose comb chicken is either *ppRR* or *ppRr*, and a pea comb chicken is either *PPrr* or *Pprr*. When an *R* and *P* occur in the same individual, the phenotype is neither pea comb nor rose comb but a completely different type, a walnut comb. The walnut comb phenotype is produced whenever a chicken has one or two *R* alleles, plus one or two *P* alleles (that is, *PPRR*, *PpRR*, *PPRr*, or *PpRr*).

Epistasis is a common type of gene interaction in which the presence of certain alleles of one locus can prevent or mask the

Walnut comb
PPRR, PpRR, PPRr, or *PpRr*

Pea comb
PPrr or *Pprr*

Rose comb
ppRR or *ppRr*

Single comb
pprr

© Cengage Learning

Figure 11-18 *Animation* **Gene interaction in chickens**

Two gene pairs govern four chicken comb phenotypes. Chickens with walnut combs have the genotype *P_R_*. Chickens with pea combs have the genotype *P_rr*, and those with rose combs have the genotype *ppR_*. Chickens that are homozygous recessive for both loci, *pprr*, have a single comb. (The blanks represent either dominant or recessive alleles.)

PREDICT What types of combs, and in what ratio, would you expect among the offspring of two heterozygous walnut comb chickens, *PpRr*?

expression of alleles of a different locus and express their own phenotype instead. (The term *epistasis* means "standing on.") Unlike the chicken example, no novel phenotypes are produced in epistasis.

Coat color in Labrador retrievers is an example of epistasis that involves a gene for pigment and a gene for depositing color in the coat (FIG. 11-19). The two alleles for the pigment gene are *B* for black coat and its recessive counterpart, *b*, for brown coat. The gene for depositing color in the coat has two alleles, *E* for the expression of black and brown coats and *e*, which is epistatic and blocks the expression of the *B/b* gene. The epistatic allele is recessive and therefore is expressed as a yellow coat only in the homozygous condition (*ee*), regardless of the combination of *B* and *b* alleles in the genotype.

In polygenic inheritance, the offspring exhibit a continuous variation in phenotypes

Many human characters—such as height, body form, and skin pigmentation—are not inherited through alleles at a single locus. The same holds true for many commercially important

Figure 11-19 *Animation* **Epistasis in Labrador retrievers**

Two gene pairs interact to govern coat color in Labrador retrievers. Black Labs (*left*) have the genotype *B_E_*; chocolate Labs (*middle*) have the genotype *bbE_*; and yellow Labs (*right*) have the genotype *B_ee* or *bbee*. (The blanks represent either dominant or recessive alleles.)

PREDICT Can two black Labs have a yellow puppy?

characters in domestic plants and animals, such as milk and egg production. Alleles at several, perhaps many, loci affect each character. The term **polygenic inheritance** is applied when multiple independent pairs of genes have similar and additive effects on the same character.

As many as 60 loci account for the inheritance of skin pigmentation in humans. To keep things simple in this example, we illustrate the principle of polygenic inheritance in human skin pigmentation with pairs of alleles at three unlinked loci. They can be designated *A* and *a*, *B* and *b*, and *C* and *c*. The capital letters represent incompletely dominant alleles producing dark skin. The more capital letters, the darker the skin because the alleles affect skin pigmentation in an additive fashion. A person with the darkest skin possible would have the genotype *AABBCC*, and a person with the lightest skin possible would have the genotype *aabbcc*. The F₁ offspring of an *aabbcc* person and an *AABBCC* person are all *AaBbCc* and have an intermediate skin color. The F₂ offspring of two such triple heterozygotes (*AaBbCc × AaBbCc*) would have skin pigmentation ranging from very dark to very light (**FIG. 11-20**).

Polygenic inheritance is characterized by an F₁ generation that is intermediate between the two completely homozygous parents and by an F₂ generation that shows wide variation between the two parental types. When the number of individuals in a population is plotted against the amount of skin pigmentation and the points are connected, the result is a bell-shaped curve, a *normal distribution curve*. Most of the F₂ generation individuals have one of the intermediate phenotypes; only a few show the extreme phenotypes of the original P generation (i.e., the grandparents). On average, only 1 of 64 is as dark as the very dark grandparent, and only 1 of 64 is as light as the very light grandparent. The alleles *A*, *B*, and *C* each produce about the same amount of darkening of the skin; hence, the genotypes *AaBbCc*, *AABbcc*, *AAbbCc*, *AaBBcc*, *aaBBCc*, *AabbCC*, and *aaBbCC* all produce similar intermediate phenotypes.

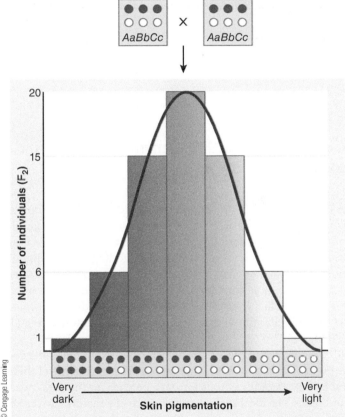

Figure 11-20 Polygenic inheritance in human skin pigmentation

This simplified example assumes that skin pigmentation in humans is governed by alleles of three unlinked loci. The alleles producing dark skin (*A*, *B*, and *C*) are represented by capital letters, but they are not dominant. Instead, their effects are additive. The number of dark dots, each signifying an allele producing dark skin, is counted to determine the phenotype. A wide range of phenotypes is possible when individuals of intermediate phenotype mate and have offspring (*AaBbCc × AaBbCc*). The expected distribution of phenotypes is consistent with the superimposed normal distribution curve.

PREDICT In this simplified model, what are all the possible genotypes of an individual from the class in the middle of the normal distribution curve?

Figure 11-21 Influence of the environment on hydrangea flower color

These hydrangeas are all the same genotype, but their flowers vary in color depending on availability of aluminum, which in turn is dependent on soil pH. Blue flowers develop in a soil pH of 5.5 or less, purple flowers in a soil pH of 5.6 to 6.4, and pink flowers in a soil pH of 6.5 to 7.0.

(a) The Himalayan genotype at warm temperatures.

(b) The Himalayan genotype at cold temperatures.

Figure 11-22 *Animation* Influence of the environment on rabbit coat color

These rabbits have the same genotype for coat color, but have been exposed to different temperatures.
© Cengage Learning

Genes interact with the environment to shape phenotype

Hydrangeas are shrubs grown for their attractive flowers. The color of certain genetically identical hydrangea flowers ranges from blue to purple to pink depending on the level of aluminum in the soil before the flowers begin to develop. It is easy to manipulate the level of aluminum by adding alum or aluminum sulfate to the soil or by lowering the soil pH (in acidic soils, aluminum is more soluble). Under these conditions, hydrangea flowers are blue. In alkaline soils (made by adding limestone to the soil), aluminum is less soluble, and the flowers are pink (FIG. 11-21).

Another example of the effect of environment on gene expression involves Himalayan rabbits. The phenotype of these rabbits is white fur except for dark patches on the ears, nose, and paws. The local surface temperature of a rabbit's ears, nose, and paws is colder in the rabbit's natural environment, and this temperature difference causes the production of dark fur. If you raise rabbits with the Himalayan genotype at a warm temperature (30°C), the rabbits are completely white, with no dark patches on the ears, nose, or paws (FIG. 11-22a). If you raise Himalayan rabbits at a cooler temperature (25°C), however, they develop the characteristic dark patches of fur (FIG. 11-22b). Thus, genes can function differently in different environments.

Now let's examine a human example—height—in the context of genes and the environment. The inheritance of height in humans is polygenic and involves alleles representing ten or more loci. Because many genes are involved and because height is modified by a variety of environmental conditions, such as diet and general health, the height of most adults ranges from 4 ft 2 in. (1.25 m) to 7 ft 2 in. (2.15 m). The genes that affect height set limits for the phenotype—no human is 12 ft tall, for example—but the environment shapes the phenotype within its genetic limits. The range of phenotypic possibilities that can develop from a single genotype under different environmental conditions is known as the **norm of reaction.** In certain genotypes the norm of reaction is quite limited. In other genotypes, such as those involved in human height, the norm of reaction is quite broad.

Although interactions between genes and the environment influence the phenotypes of many characters, it is difficult to determine the exact contributions of genes and the environment to a given phenotype. In some cases, the environment regulates the activity of certain genes, turning them on in some environmental conditions and off in others. Investigators argued for years about the relative importance of *nature* (genetics/biology) versus *nurture* (environmental influences) regarding such human characters as intelligence, depression, bipolar disorder, and schizophrenia. Studies with identical twins raised in different environments indicate that individuals may inherit genetic potential or vulnerabilities, but environmental conditions may influence the expression of the genotype. Thus, phenotypic expression depends on a combination of nature *and* nuture.

CHECKPOINT 11.4

- **CONNECT** *The human ABO blood groups are considered an example of both dominance and codominance. However, flower color in four o'clocks is considered an example of incomplete dominance. Explain.*

- *What is the difference between multiple alleles and polygenic inheritance?*

- *How do examples of pleiotropy and epistasis differ in terms of the minimum number of loci required?*

- **CONNECT** *How is the concept of* norm of reaction *related to the lack of yellow hydrangea flowers illustrated in Figure 11-21?*

11.1 Mendel's Principles of Inheritance *(page 227)*

1 Define the terms *phenotype, genotype, locus, allele, dominant allele, recessive allele, homozygous,* and *heterozygous.*

- **Genes** are in chromosomes, and the site a gene occupies in the chromosome is its **locus.** Different forms of a particular gene are **alleles;** they occupy corresponding loci on homologous chromosomes.

- An individual that carries two identical alleles is **homozygous** for that locus. If the two alleles are different, that individual is **heterozygous** for that locus.

- One allele, the **dominant allele**, may mask the expression of the other allele, the **recessive allele**, in a heterozygous individual. For this reason two individuals with the same appearance, or **phenotype,** may differ from each other in their genetic makeup (i.e., their combination of alleles), or **genotype.**

2 Describe Mendel's principles of segregation and independent assortment.

- According to Mendel's **principle of segregation,** during meiosis the alleles for each locus separate, or segregate, from each other. When haploid gametes are formed, each contains only one allele for each locus.

- According to Mendel's **principle of independent assortment,** alleles of different loci are distributed randomly into gametes. The result can be **genetic recombination,** the production of new allele combinations that were not present in the **parental (P) generation.**

3 Distinguish among monohybrid, dihybrid, and test crosses.

- A cross between homozygous parents (P generation) that differ from each other with respect to their alleles at one locus is called a **monohybrid cross;** if they differ at two loci, it is called a **dihybrid cross.** The first generation of offspring, called the F_1 **generation,** is heterozygous; the generation produced by a cross of two F_1 individuals is the F_2 **generation.**

- A test cross between an individual of unknown genotype and a recessive individual helps determine the unknown genotype.

4 Explain Mendel's principles of segregation and independent assortment, given what scientists now know about genes and chromosomes.

- Segregation of alleles is a direct result of homologous chromosomes separating during meiosis.

- Independent assortment occurs because there are two ways in which two pairs of homologous chromosomes can be arranged at metaphase I of meiosis. The orientation of homologous chromosomes on the metaphase plate determines the way chromosomes are distributed into haploid cells.

11.2 Using Probability to Predict Mendelian Inheritance *(page 236)*

5 Apply the product rule and sum rule appropriately when predicting the outcomes of genetic crosses.

- According to the **product rule,** the probability of two independent events occurring together can be calculated by multiplying the probabilities of each event occurring separately.

- According to the **sum rule,** the probability of an outcome that can be obtained in more than one way can be calculated by adding the separate probabilities.

11.3 Inheritance and Chromosomes *(page 238)*

6 Define *linkage* and relate it to specific events in meiosis.

- **Linkage** is the tendency for a group of genes on the same chromosome to be inherited together. Independent assortment does

not apply if two loci are linked close together on the same pair of homologous chromosomes.

- Recombination of linked genes can result from **crossing-over** (breaking and rejoining of homologous chromatids) in meiotic prophase I. (Recall from Section 11.1 that recombination can also result from independent assortment of unlinked genes.)

7 Show how data from a two-point test cross can be used to distinguish between independent assortment and linkage.

- To distinguish between independent assortment of unlinked genes and linked genes, perform a **two-point test cross** between an individual that is heterozygous at both loci and an individual that is homozygous recessive for both.

- Linkage is recognized when an excess of parental-type offspring and a deficiency of recombinant-type offspring are produced in a two-point test cross.

8 Discuss the genetic determination of sex and the inheritance of X-linked genes in mammals.

- The sex of humans and other mammals is determined by the **X** and **Y chromosomes.** Normal female mammals have two X chromosomes; normal males have one X and one Y. The fertilization of an X-bearing egg by an X-bearing sperm results in a female (XX) zygote. The fertilization of an X-bearing egg by a Y-bearing sperm results in a male (XY) zygote.

- The Y chromosome determines male sex in mammals. The X chromosome contains many important genes unrelated to sex determination that are required by both males and females. A male receives all his **X-linked genes** from his mother. A female receives X-linked genes from both parents.

11.4 Extensions of Mendelian Genetics *(page 244)*

9 Explain some of the ways genes may interact to affect the phenotype and discuss how a single gene can affect many features of the organism simultaneously.

- **Pleiotropy** is the ability of one gene to have several effects on different characters. Most cases of pleiotropy can be traced to a single cause, such as a defective enzyme. Alternatively, alleles of many loci may interact to affect the phenotypic expression of a single character.

10 Distinguish among incomplete dominance, codominance, multiple alleles, epistasis, and polygenic inheritance.

- Dominance does not always apply; some alleles demonstrate **incomplete dominance,** in which the heterozygote is intermediate in phenotype, or **codominance,** in which the heterozygote simultaneously expresses the phenotypes of both homozygotes.

- **Multiple alleles,** three or more alleles that can potentially occupy a particular locus, may exist in a population. A diploid individual has any two of the alleles; a haploid individual or gamete has only one.

- In **epistasis** an allele of one locus can mask the expression of alleles of a different locus.

- In **polygenic inheritance** multiple independent pairs of genes may have similar and additive effects on the phenotype.

11 Describe *norm of reaction* and give an example.

- The range of phenotypic possibilities that can develop from a single genotype under different environmental conditions is known as the **norm of reaction.**

- Many genes are involved in the inheritance of height in humans. Also, height is modified by a variety of environmental conditions, such as diet and general health. The genes that affect height set the norm of reaction—that is, the limits—for the phenotype, and the environment molds the phenotype within its norm of reaction.

Know and Comprehend

1. One of the autosomal loci controlling eye color in fruit flies has two alleles: one for brown eyes and the other for red eyes. Fruit flies from a true-breeding line with brown eyes were crossed with flies from a true-breeding line with red eyes. The F_1 flies had red eyes. What conclusion can be drawn from this experiment? (a) these alleles underwent independent assortment (b) these alleles underwent segregation (c) these genes are X-linked (d) the allele for red eyes is dominant to the allele for brown eyes (e) all the preceding are true

2. The F_1 flies described in question 1 were mated with brown-eyed flies from a true-breeding line. What phenotypes would you expect the offspring to have? (a) all with red eyes (b) all with brown eyes (c) half with red eyes and half with brown eyes (d) red-eyed females and brown-eyed males (e) brown-eyed females and red-eyed males

3. The type of cross described in question 2 is (a) an F_2 cross (b) a dihybrid cross (c) a test cross (d) a two-point test cross (e) none of the preceding

4. Individuals of genotype *AaBb* were crossed with *aabb* individuals. Approximately equal numbers of the following classes of offspring were produced: *AaBb, Aabb, aaBb,* and *aabb*. These results illustrate Mendel's principle(s) of (a) linkage (b) independent assortment (c) segregation (d) a and c (e) b and c

Apply and Analyze

5. Assume that the ratio of females to males is 1:1. A couple already has two daughters and no sons. If they plan to have a total of six children, what is the probability that they will have four more girls? (a) ¼ (b) ⅛ (c) ¹⁄₁₆ (d) ¹⁄₃₂ (e) ¹⁄₆₄

6. Red–green color blindness is an X-linked recessive disorder in humans. Your friend is the daughter of a color-blind father. Her mother had normal color vision, but her maternal grandfather was color-blind. What is the probability that your friend is color-blind? (a) 1 (b) ½ (c) ¼ (d) ¾ (e) 0

7. When two long-winged flies were mated, the offspring included 77 with long wings and 24 with short wings. Is the short-winged condition dominant or recessive? What are the genotypes of the parents?

8. The long hair of Persian cats is recessive to the short hair of Siamese cats, but the black coat color of Persians is dominant to the brown-and-tan coat color of Siamese. Make up appropriate symbols for the alleles of these two unlinked loci. If a pure black, long-haired Persian is mated to a pure brown-and-tan, short-haired Siamese, what will be the appearance of the F_1 offspring? If two of these F_1 cats are mated, what is the chance that a long-haired, brown-and-tan cat will be produced in the F_2 generation? (Use the shortcut probability method to obtain your answer; then check it with a Punnett square.)

9. Mr. and Mrs. Smith are concerned because their own blood types are A and B, respectively, but their new son, Richard, is blood type O. Could Richard be the child of these parents?

10. A walnut comb rooster is mated to three hens. Hen A, which has a walnut comb, has offspring in the ratio of 3 walnut to 1 rose. Hen B, which has a pea comb, has offspring in the ratio of 3 walnut to 3 pea to 1 rose to 1 single. Hen C, which has a walnut comb, has only walnut comb offspring. What are the genotypes of the rooster and the three hens?

11. Individuals of genotype *AaBb* were mated to individuals of genotype *aabb*. One thousand offspring were counted, with the following results: 474 *Aabb,* 480 *aaBb,* 20 *AaBb,* and 26 *aabb*. What type of cross is it? Are these loci linked? What are the two parental classes and the two recombinant classes of offspring? What is the percentage of recombination between these two loci? How many map units apart are they?

12. Genes *A* and *B* are 6 map units apart, and *A* and *C* are 4 map units apart. Which gene is in the middle if *B* and *C* are 10 map units apart? Which is in the middle if *B* and *C* are 2 map units apart?

Evaluate and Synthesize

13. **VISUALIZE** Sketch a series of diagrams showing each of the following, making sure to end each series with haploid cells:
    (a) How a pair of alleles for a single locus segregate in meiosis
    (b) How the alleles of two unlinked loci assort independently in meiosis
    (c) How the alleles of two linked loci undergo genetic recombination

14. Can you always ascertain an organism's genotype for a particular locus if you know its phenotype? Conversely, if you are given an organism's genotype for a locus, can you always reliably predict its phenotype? Explain.

15. **CONNECT** Compare the mechanisms of genetic recombination in linked and unlinked genes.

16. **EVOLUTION LINK** Darwin's theory of evolution by natural selection is based on four observations about the natural world. One of them is that each individual has a combination of traits that makes it uniquely different. Darwin recognized that much of this variation among individuals must be inherited, but he did not know about Mendel's mechanism of inheritance. Based on what you have learned in this chapter, briefly explain the variation among individuals that Darwin observed.

17. **INTERPRET DATA** Using the graph in Figure 11-20, determine how many offspring were involved in the hypothetical cross studying skin color. What percentage had the lightest skin possible? the darkest skin possible?

 To access course materials, such as Aplia and other companion resources, please visit **www.cengagebrain.com**.

16 | Human Genetics and the Human Genome

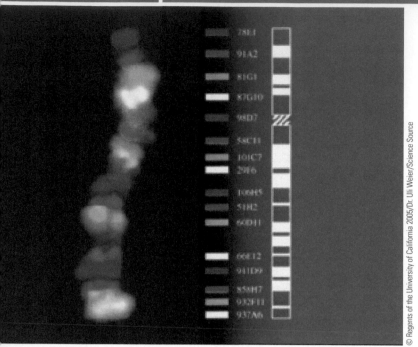

Rapid chromosome mapping. This fluorescent LM of human chromosome 10 (*left*) has different-colored fluorescent probes attached to specific DNA sequences. (Loci and key are at *right*.) This technique allows researchers to efficiently determine certain chromosome rearrangements and abnormalities.

KEY CONCEPTS

16.1 Pedigree analysis and karyotype analysis are traditional methods used to study human genetics; investigations of molecular aspects of the human genome, including genome-wide association studies and comparative genomics, are increasingly used today.

16.2 Chromosome abnormalities such as aneuploidies—the presence or absence of a single chromosome—can cause serious medical conditions.

16.3 Mutations in single genes can produce genetic disorders.

16.4 Researchers are developing gene therapy methods that could potentially correct certain genetic disorders.

16.5 Genetic testing and counseling help individuals make reproductive decisions.

16.6 Certain advances in human genetics raise ethical questions.

The principles of genetics apply to all organisms, including humans. However, important differences separate genetic research on humans and genetic research on other organisms. To study inheritance in other species, geneticists may conduct controlled matings between individuals and raise their offspring under carefully controlled conditions. Of course, setting up experimental matings in humans is unethical and illegal.

Despite the inherent difficulties of studying inheritance in humans, **human genetics,** the science of inherited variation in humans, is progressing rapidly (see figure). The medical attention given to human genetic diseases has expanded our knowledge of human genetics. Our most detailed understanding comes from diseases caused by defects in single genes that exhibit a Mendelian inheritance pattern. Valuable insights have come from studies of other organisms that have similar genes, and many human inheritance questions have been explained using model organisms, such as bacteria, yeasts, worms, fruit flies, and mice.

Researchers also conduct population studies of large extended families with a high incidence of a particular type of human genetic disease. These studies use genetic information and technologies derived from the Human Genome Project to uncover genes associated with many different types of *complex genetic diseases*. For these diseases, many different genes interact to cause various conditions, including susceptibility to certain types of cancer, diabetes, kidney disease, obesity, and behavioral disorders such as schizophrenia, depression, and autism.

In this chapter we first examine the methods of human genetics, including new research directions based on DNA technologies discussed in Chapter 15, and then we discuss a variety of human genetic disorders. We explore the use of gene therapy as well as the application of genetic testing, screening, and counseling for families at risk. The chapter concludes with a discussion of ethical issues related to human genetics.

16.1 STUDYING HUMAN GENETICS

1 Distinguish between karyotyping and pedigree analysis.

2 Discuss how gene databases and genomic methods are used to study human genetic diseases.

3 Discuss the importance of comparative genomics to the study of human genetics.

Human geneticists use a variety of methods that enable them to help identify genetic defects and to make inferences about a trait's mode of inheritance. We consider three of these methods: the identification of chromosomes by karyotyping, the analysis of family inheritance patterns using pedigrees, and DNA sequencing and mapping of genes through genome projects. Investigators often study human inheritance most effectively by combining these and other approaches.

Human chromosomes are studied by karyotyping

Some well-known human genetic disorders involve changes in the structure or number of chromosomes. The normal number of chromosomes for the human species is 46, made up of 44 *autosomes* (22 pairs) and 2 sex chromosomes (1 pair). A *karyotype* (from Greek, meaning "nucleus") illustrates an individual's chromosome composition, showing both the chromosome number and any large structural defects in the chromosomes.

Human chromosomes are visible only in dividing cells (see Chapter 10), which are difficult to obtain directly from the body. Researchers typically use blood because white blood cells can be induced to divide in a culture medium by treating them with certain chemicals. Other sources of dividing cells include skin and, for prenatal chromosome studies, chorionic villi or fetal cells shed into the amniotic fluid (discussed later in this chapter).

In karyotyping biologists culture dividing human cells and then treat them with the drug *colchicine*, which arrests the cells at mitotic metaphase or late prophase, when the chromosomes are most highly condensed. Next, the researchers immerse the cells in a hypotonic solution; the cells swell, and the chromosomes spread out and are easily observed. The investigators then flatten the cells on microscope slides and stain the chromosomes to reveal the patterns of bands, which are unique for each homologous pair. After the microscopic image has been scanned into a computer, the homologous pairs are electronically matched and placed together (FIG. 16-1).

By convention, geneticists identify chromosomes by length; position of the centromere; banding patterns, which are produced by staining chromosomes with dyes that produce dark and light crossbands of varying widths; and other features such as *satellites*, tiny knobs of chromosome material at the tips of

WHY IS IT USED? Researchers use karyotypes to screen individuals for chromosome abnormalities.

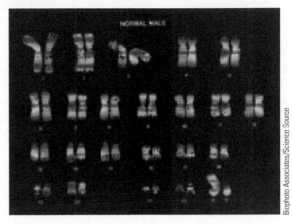

HOW IS IT DONE? Karyotypes are commonly prepared from cultures of white blood cells. Researchers place prepared cells on a slide, and the chromosomes spill out of the ruptured nuclei. The light microscope under which the slide is viewed is connected to a computer with image analysis software, which helps the biologist match homologous chromosomes and organize them by size. Before computers were used, researchers cut and pasted chromosomes from photographs.

The chromosomes in the photograph have been "painted" by different-colored fluorescent dyes that hybridize to specific pairs of homologous chromosomes. Painting helps the researcher identify chromosomes. A normal human male karyotype is shown.

Figure 16-1 *Animation* **Karyotyping**

certain chromosomes. With the exception of the sex chromosomes, all chromosomes but chromosome 21, which is smaller than chromosome 22, are numbered and lined up in order of size. The largest human chromosome (chromosome 1) is about five times as long as the smallest one (chromosome 21), but there are only slight size differences among some of the intermediate-sized chromosomes. The X and Y chromosomes of a normal male are homologous only at their tips; normal females have two X chromosomes and no Y chromosome. Differences from the normal karyotype—that is, deviations in chromosome number or structure—are associated with certain disorders such as Down syndrome (discussed later in the chapter).

Another way to distinguish chromosomes in a karyotype is by **fluorescent in situ hybridization (FISH).** A geneticist tags a DNA strand complementary to DNA in a specific chromosome with a fluorescent dye. The DNA in the chromosome is denatured—that is, the two strands are separated—so the tagged strand can bind to it. A different dye is used for each chromosome, "painting" each with a different color (see Fig. 16-1). A chromosome that is multicolored (*not shown*) indicates breakage and fusion of chromosomes, an abnormality associated with certain genetic diseases and many types of cancer.

Family pedigrees help identify certain inherited conditions

Early studies of human genetics usually dealt with readily identified pairs of contrasting traits and their distribution among members of a family. A "family tree" that shows inheritance patterns—the transmission of genetic traits within a family over several generations—is known as a **pedigree.** Pedigree analysis remains widely used, even in today's world of powerful molecular genetic techniques, because it helps molecular geneticists determine the exact inter-relationships of the DNA molecules they analyze from related individuals. Pedigree analysis is also an important tool of genetic counselors and clinicians. However, because human families tend to be small and information about certain family members, particularly deceased relatives, may not be available, pedigree analysis has limitations.

Pedigrees are produced using standardized symbols. Examine **FIGURE 16-2**, which shows a pedigree for **albinism,** a lack of the pigment melanin in the skin, hair, and eyes. Each horizontal row represents a separate generation, with the earliest generation (Roman numeral I) at the top and the most recent generation at the bottom. Within a given generation, the individuals are usually numbered consecutively, from left to right, using Arabic numbers. A horizontal line connects two parents, and a vertical line drops from the parents to their children. For example, individuals II-3 and II-4 are parents of four offspring (III-1, III-2, III-3, and III-4). Note that individuals in a given generation can be genetically unrelated. For example, II-1, II-2, and II-3 are unrelated to II-4 and II-5. Within a group of siblings, the oldest is on the left, and the youngest is on the right.

The allele for albinism cannot be dominant; if it were, at least one of female III-2's parents would have been an albino. This pedigree is explained if albinism is inherited as an autosomal (not carried on a sex chromosome) recessive allele. In such cases, two phenotypically normal parents could produce an albino offspring because they are heterozygotes and could each transmit a recessive allele.

Studying pedigrees enables human geneticists to predict how phenotypic traits that are governed by the genotype at a single locus are inherited. More than 12,000 traits have been described in humans. Pedigree analysis most often identifies three modes of single-locus inheritance: autosomal dominant, autosomal recessive, and X-linked recessive. We define and discuss examples of these inheritance modes later in this chapter.

Human gene databases allow geneticists to map the locations of genes on chromosomes

Although pedigree analysis can provide information about the type of inheritance associated with a single gene, it does not provide specific information about where it is located or how that form of the gene causes the disease. Furthermore, most genetic diseases involve many genes that produce complex patterns of inheritance. How do you identify a specific gene and find its location in an extremely complex genome if you know nothing about it?

(a) An albino Cuna Indian girl plays with her friends. Albinism is common among the Cuna people living on the San Blas Islands of Panama.

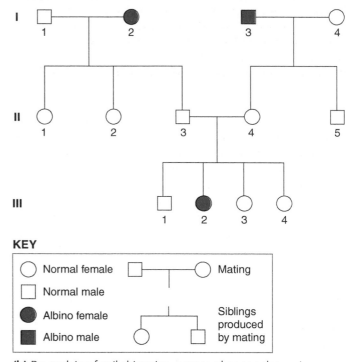

(b) By studying family histories, a researcher can determine the genetic mechanism of an inherited trait. In this example, III-2 represents an albino girl with two phenotypically normal parents, II-3 and II-4.

Figure 16-2 *Animation* **A pedigree for albinism**
© Cengage Learning

Using the database of the **Human Genome Project,** researchers have now generated maps of each chromosome that show the precise location of each gene. These maps allow investigators to locate the region where the gene resides on a specific chromosome and then to analyze genes within that region to determine which one is associated with the disease. Once the disease-causing gene is identified, geneticists can initiate studies to determine its function and how it interacts with other genes associated with the disease.

Single nucleotide polymorphisms are used as genomic landmarks to locate genes linked to genetic disease

Single nucleotide polymorphisms (SNPs, pronounced "snips") are single-letter differences in DNA sequences found every few hundred bases when the genomes of individuals in large populations are compared. In 2012 the **1000 Genomes Project** (see Chapter 15), a group of scientists in eight countries, published data derived from 1092 individuals from 14 different populations, providing a map of 38 million SNPs that span all the human chromosomes. Investigators now use DNA chips to compare the distribution of more than one million SNPs in DNA isolated from individuals affected by a given genetic disease with those who are not affected. By identifying a specific SNP that consistently appears in the affected individuals but that is rare in unaffected persons, researchers can locate a small region of the genome that contains a gene now associated with that disease. FIGURE 16-3 shows the strategy used to locate affected genes using SNP mapping methods. Once the region of an affected gene is identified, investigators use genomic and analytical methods (discussed in Chapter 15) to identify the specific gene that is associated with the disease. For example, researchers would first compare the DNA sequences of genes in the region to determine if one had an unusual mutation that might be the cause of the genetic defect.

Genome-wide association studies demonstrate the genetic complexity of major human diseases

In humans only about 1.5% of the genome specifies the amino acid sequences of polypeptides. However, reports from the **ENCODE Project** have now shown that at least 80% of the human genome is involved in biological functions. These DNA sequences include non-protein-coding regulatory elements and non-protein-coding genes that produce RNAs with unknown functions. Many times, RNA encoding genes are found in introns as well as in the regions between genes that were previously thought to be "gene deserts" or "junk DNA" with no biological functions.

Researchers are now actively engaged in **genome-wide association studies (GWAS)** to compare the genomes of individuals with a particular disease to individuals without that disease. In one study, for example, researchers used SNP analysis to survey the genomes of more than 14,000 British people to compare genetic patterns in healthy people with those in people with one of seven common diseases. The phenotypes of these diseases exhibit complex inheritance patterns, with many different genes contributing to susceptibility. In this particular study, scientists identified 24 SNP variations associated with bipolar disorder, 1 with coronary artery disease, 9 with Crohn's disease, 3 with rheumatoid arthritis, 7 with type 1 diabetes, and 3 with type 2 diabetes.

Many genetic variations associated with complex human diseases are found in non-protein-coding genes

The results of many genome-wide studies conducted since 2005 have shown that almost 90% of SNP variants associated with disease-linked regions are found outside of protein-coding genes. Many of them appear to be associated with enhancer regions or genes that encode regulatory RNAs. For example, one gene associated with one of the highest risks for schizophrenia encodes a microRNA (miRNA; see Chapter 13). Thirty percent of individuals who have a deleted form of this gene develop schizophrenia during adolescence or early childhood. Recent studies in mice and humans have shown that this miRNA regulates the expression of an enzyme in nerve cells involved in memory formation.

How do investigators determine the functions of disease-associated genes? Determining the genomic location of a disease-associated gene is simply the first step toward developing a treatment for the disease. To develop effective treatment strategies, scientists must first identify the specific gene that causes the disease. Then, they must determine its function, how it interacts with other genes, and how its expression is regulated in different tissues. Many of these studies involve the use of comparative genomics with other organisms to identify disease genes that might have highly conserved and identical functions.

Comparative genomics has revealed DNA identical in both mouse and human genomes

A comparison between the mouse and human genomes has shown that about five hundred DNA segments longer than two hundred base pairs are 100% conserved (i.e., identical). This remarkable degree of conservation has interesting evolutionary implications: it means that these segments have not mutated in the past 75 million years, since mice and humans shared a common ancestor. During this time, other DNA sections underwent considerable mutation and selection, allowing mice and humans to diverge to their present states. Although the functions of these unchanged elements are not yet determined, they clearly have a vital role. (If they were not essential in their present form, they would have undergone

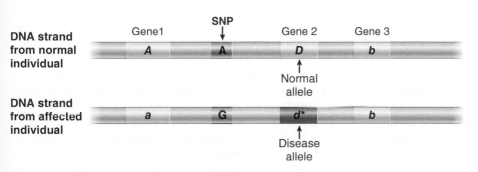

DNA strand from normal individual

Gene1   SNP   Gene 2   Gene 3

A   *A*   *D*   *b*

Normal allele

DNA strand from affected individual

a   *G*   *d**   *b*

Disease allele

Figure 16-3 Single nucleotide polymorphisms (SNPs) as landmarks for locating disease-causing genes

Microarray analysis comparing the DNA from many affected and normal individuals can identify single nucleotide polymorphisms that are closely linked to genes involved in genetic disorders. In this example the SNP polymorphism consists of an A (adenine) base near the normal gene, and a G (guanine) base in that position in the DNA of an affected individual. SNP markers are usually not directly involved in the genetic defect. Researchers use bioinformatics and molecular genetic methods to identify which gene in the region of a SNP is associated with the disease and to investigate its function.

© Cengage Learning

mutation and selection.) These strong evolutionary connections allow investigators to use the mouse as a powerful research tool to detect and investigate the functions of human disease-causing genes that are common between the two species.

Researchers use mouse models to study human genetic diseases Many questions relating to human genetic diseases are difficult to answer because of the ethical issues involved in using humans as test subjects. However, research on any disease is greatly facilitated if an animal model is used for experimentation. A good example is *cystic fibrosis,* a genetic disease caused by a single gene mutation inherited as a recessive allele. Researchers used *gene targeting* to produce strains of mice that were either homozygous or heterozygous for cystic fibrosis by replacing the normal mouse genes with ones containing the same types of mutations found in human cystic fibrosis patients.

The allele that causes cystic fibrosis is a mutant form of a locus involved in controlling the body's water and electrolyte balance. Geneticists have cloned this gene and found that it codes for a protein, the *CFTR protein,* that serves as a chloride ion channel in the plasma membrane. (*CFTR* stands for *cystic fibrosis transmembrane conductance regulator.*) This ion channel transports chloride ions out of the cells lining the digestive tract and the respiratory system. When the chloride ions leave the cells, water follows by osmosis. Thus, the normal secretions of these cells are relatively watery. Because the cells of individuals with cystic fibrosis lack normal chloride ion channels, the individuals' secretions have a low water content, and their sweat is very salty. Cells of heterozygous individuals have only half the usual number of functional CFTR ion channels, but they are enough to maintain the normal fluidity of their secretions.

Using these mouse models, researchers have focused on understanding the way in which the CFTR channel is activated or inactivated. This information is used to design drugs that enhance chloride transport through the CFTR channels. Such drugs have the potential to treat cystic fibrosis in humans by activating the mutant channels.

Sequencing of individual genomes is an emerging strategy for diagnosing and treating rare genetic diseases The completion of the Human Genome Project required the efforts of thousands of scientists over 13 years and cost more than $3 billion. Remarkably, the technological advances gained from this project have dramatically lowered the cost of genomic sequencing to the point that it is now becoming economically feasible to rapidly sequence an individual's genome to diagnose a genetic disease. One recent case involved twins who were born with a severe neuromuscular disorder. Some characteristics of their condition resembled a rare genetic disease caused by mutations in the genes that are involved in the synthesis of the neurotransmitter dopamine, which is used to transmit signals between nerves and muscle cells (see Chapter 41). Providing the patients dopamine, however, did not relieve the symptoms. When the twins were age 14, the genomes of both were sequenced. Analysis of the genomes found a mutation in a gene known as *SPR,* which is required for the synthesis of a cofactor used by enzymes that synthesize both dopamine and a second neurotransmitter, serotonin. (A subsequent analysis of the parent's DNA revealed that both the mother and father were heterozygous for different mutations within the same gene.) When the twins were provided with both dopamine and serotonin, their symptoms were improved to the point that both could participate in athletic programs.

CHECKPOINT 16.1

- *What kinds of information can a human karyotype provide?*
- **CONNECT** *How does pedigree analysis complement other methods for studying human genetics?*
- *Describe two ways in which genome database information is used to study human disease genes.*
- **CONNECT** *How does the evolutionary relationship between mice and humans overcome some of the difficulties in studying human inheritance?*

16.2 ABNORMALITIES IN CHROMOSOME NUMBER AND STRUCTURE

LEARNING OBJECTIVES

4   Explain how nondisjunction in meiosis is responsible for chromosome abnormalities such as Down syndrome, Klinefelter syndrome, and Turner syndrome.

5   Distinguish among the following structural abnormalities in chromosomes: translocations, deletions, and fragile sites.

6   Explain how genomic imprinting influences inheritance patterns.

Polyploidy, the presence of multiple sets of chromosomes, is common in plants but rare in animals. It may arise from the failure of chromosomes to separate during meiosis or from the fertilization of an egg by more than one sperm. When it occurs in all the cells of the body, polyploidy is lethal in humans and many other animals. For example, *triploidy* ($3n$) is sometimes found in human embryos that have been spontaneously aborted in early pregnancy.

Abnormalities caused by the presence of a single extra chromosome or the absence of a chromosome—called **aneuploidy**—are more common than polyploidy. **Disomy** is the normal state: two of each kind of chromosome in a cell or individual. In **trisomy** a cell or individual has two copies of each chromosome except for one, which has three copies; a trisomic chromosome number is designated $2n + 1$. In **monosomy** an individual lacks one member of a pair of chromosomes; a monosomic chromosome number is designated $2n - 1$. **TABLE 16-1** summarizes some disorders that aneuploidies produce.

Aneuploidies generally arise as a result of an abnormal meiotic (or, rarely, mitotic) division in which chromosomes fail to separate at anaphase. This phenomenon, called **nondisjunction,** can occur with the autosomes or with the sex chromosomes.

TABLE 16-1	Chromosome Abnormalities: Disorders Produced by Aneuploidies	
KARYOTYPE	**COMMON NAME**	**CLINICAL DESCRIPTION**
Trisomy 13	Patau syndrome	Multiple defects, with death typically by age 3 months.
Trisomy 18	Edwards syndrome	Ear deformities, heart defects, spasticity, and other damage; death typically by age 1 year, but some survive much longer.
Trisomy 21	Down syndrome	Overall frequency is about 1 in 1000 live births. Most conceptions involving true trisomy occur in older (age 35+) mothers, but translocation resulting in the equivalent of trisomy is not related to age. Trisomy 21 is characterized by a fold of skin above the eye, varying degrees of intellectual disability, short stature, protruding furrowed tongue, transverse palmar crease, cardiac deformities, and increased risk of leukemia and Alzheimer's disease.
X0	Turner syndrome	Short stature, webbed neck, sometimes slight intellectual disability; ovaries degenerate in late embryonic life, leading to rudimentary sexual characteristics; gender is female; no Barr bodies.
XXY	Klinefelter syndrome	Male with slowly degenerating testes, enlarged breasts; one Barr body per cell.
XYY	XYY karyotype	Many males have no unusual symptoms; others are unusually tall, with heavy acne, and some tendency to mild intellectual disability.
XXX	Triplo-X	Despite three X chromosomes, usually fertile females with normal intelligence; two Barr bodies per cell.

© Cengage Learning

In meiosis chromosome nondisjunction may occur during the first or the second meiotic division (or both). For example, two X chromosomes that fail to separate at either the first or the second meiotic division may both enter the egg nucleus. Alternatively, the two joined X chromosomes may go into a *polar body*, leaving the egg with no X chromosome. (Recall from Chapter 10 that a polar body is a nonfunctional haploid cell produced during oogenesis; also see Fig. 50-11).

Nondisjunction of the XY pair during the first meiotic division in the male may lead to the formation of a sperm with both X and Y chromosomes or a sperm with neither an X nor a Y chromosome (FIG. 16-4). Similarly, nondisjunction at the second meiotic division can produce sperm with two Xs or two Ys. When an abnormal gamete unites with a normal one, the resulting zygote has a chromosome abnormality that will be present in every cell of the body.

Meiotic nondisjunction results in an abnormal chromosome number at the zygote stage of development, so all cells in the individual have an abnormal chromosome number. In contrast, nondisjunction during a mitotic division occurs sometime later in development and leads to the establishment of a clone of abnormal cells in an otherwise normal individual. Such a mixture of cells with different chromosome numbers may or may not affect somatic (body) or germ line (reproductive) tissues.

Different numbers of chromosomes are common in many cancer cells, particularly those in solid tumors. Whether aneuploidy is a cause or a consequence of cancer, however, is not yet clear.

Recognizable chromosome abnormalities are seen in less than 1% of all live births, but substantial evidence suggests that the rate at conception is much higher. At least 17% of pregnancies recognized at eight weeks will end in spontaneous abortion (miscarriage). Approximately half of these spontaneously aborted embryos have major chromosome abnormalities, including autosomal trisomies (such as trisomy 21), triploidy, tetraploidy, and Turner syndrome (X0), in which the 0 refers to the absence of a second sex chromosome. Autosomal monosomies are exceedingly rare, possibly because they induce a spontaneous abortion very early in the pregnancy, before a

woman is even aware that she is pregnant. Some investigators give surprisingly high estimates (50% or more) for the loss rate of very early embryos. Chromosome abnormalities probably induce many of these spontaneous abortions.

Down syndrome is usually caused by trisomy 21

Down syndrome is one of the most common chromosome abnormalities in humans. (The term *syndrome* refers to a set of symptoms that usually occur together in a particular disorder.) It was named after J. Langdon Down, the British physician who in 1866 first described the condition. Affected individuals have abnormalities of the face, eyelids, tongue, hands, and other parts of the body and are intellectually disabled (FIG. 16-5a). They are also unusually susceptible to certain diseases, such as leukemia and Alzheimer's disease.

Genetic studies have revealed that most people with Down syndrome have 47 chromosomes because of *autosomal trisomy:* this condition is known as **trisomy 21** (FIG. 16-5b). Nondisjunction during meiosis is responsible for the presence of the extra chromosome. Although no genetic information is missing in these individuals, the extra copies of chromosome 21 genes bring about some type of genetic imbalance that causes abnormal physical and mental development. Down syndrome is quite variable in expression, with some individuals far more severely affected than others.

Researchers using DNA technologies have pinpointed genes on chromosome 21 that affect mental development as well as possible *oncogenes* (cancer-causing genes) and genes that may be involved in Alzheimer's disease. (Like many human conditions, cancer and Alzheimer's disease have both genetic and environmental components.) A study published in 2013 reported that one cause of Down syndrome appears to be the result of the overexpression of a chromosome 21 gene that encodes the micro RNA, miR155. This miRNA negatively regulates the expression of a protein involved in the endomembrane traffic of receptor proteins in the brain. The resulting underexpression of this gene in a mouse model causes severe defects in neuron functions.

Aneuploidy may occur by meiotic nondisjunction, the abnormal segregation of chromosomes during meiosis.

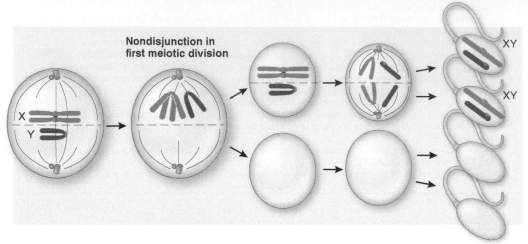

(a) First meiotic division nondisjunction results in two XY sperm and two sperm with neither an X nor a Y.

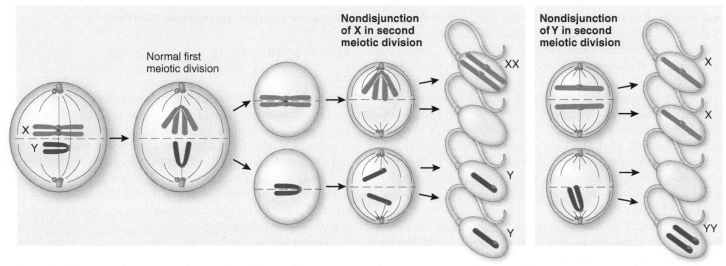

(b) Second meiotic division nondisjunction of the X chromosome results in one sperm with two X chromosomes, two with one Y each, and one with no sex chromosomes. Nondisjunction of the Y chromosome results in one sperm with two Y chromosomes, two with one X each, and one with no sex chromosome (*box on right*).

Figure 16-4 *Animation* **Meiotic nondisjunction**

In these examples of nondisjunction of the sex chromosomes in the human male, only the X (*purple*) and Y (*blue*) chromosomes are shown. (The positions of the metaphase chromosomes have been modified to save space.)

PREDICT Which of the sperm illustrated here could give rise to an offspring with Klinefelter syndrome? Turner syndrome? XYY karyotype?

© Cengage Learning

Down syndrome occurs in all ethnic groups in about 1 out of 1000 live births in the U.S. Its incidence increases markedly with increasing maternal age. The occurrence of Down syndrome is not affected by the father's age (although other disorders are, including schizophrenia and achondroplasia, the most common form of dwarfism). Down syndrome is 68 times as likely in the offspring of mothers of age 45 than in the offspring of mothers age 20. However, most babies with Down syndrome in the United States are born to mothers younger than 35, in

part because these women greatly outnumber older mothers and in part because about 90% of older women who undergo prenatal testing terminate the pregnancy if Down syndrome is diagnosed.

The relationship between increased incidence in Down syndrome and maternal age has been studied for decades, but there is no explanation. Scientists have proposed several hypotheses to explain the maternal age effect, but none is supported unequivocally. One explanation is that older women have held

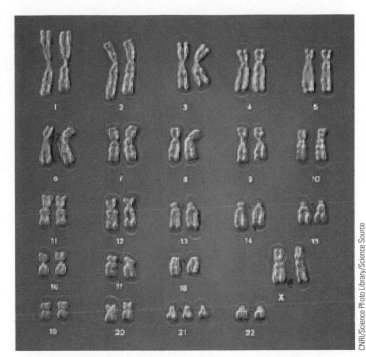

(a) This girl with Down syndrome is working on a math problem with her teacher. Some individuals with Down syndrome learn to read and write.

(b) Note the presence of an extra chromosome 21 in this colorized karyotype of a female with Down syndrome.

Figure 16-5 Down syndrome

eggs in suspended meiosis too long, leading to a deterioration of the meiotic spindle apparatus. (A woman is born with all the oocytes she will ever have; these oocytes remain in prophase I of meiosis until ovulation.) Another possibility is that an aging uterus is less likely to reject an abnormal fetus than a younger uterus.

Most sex chromosome aneuploidies are less severe than autosomal aneuploidies

Sex chromosome aneuploidies are tolerated relatively well (see Table 16-1) at least in part because of the mechanism of **dosage compensation:** mammalian cells compensate for extra X chromosome material by rendering all but one X chromosome inactive. The inactive X is seen as a **Barr body,** a region of darkly stained, condensed chromatin next to the nuclear envelope of an interphase nucleus (see Fig. 11-16). Investigators have used the presence of the Barr body in the cells of normal females as an initial screen to determine whether an individual is genetically female or male. However, as you will see shortly in the context of sex chromosome aneuploidies, the Barr body test has limitations.

Individuals with **Klinefelter syndrome** are males with 47 chromosomes, including two Xs and one Y. They have small testes, produce few or no sperm, and are therefore sterile. The hypothesis that the Y chromosome is the major determinant of the male phenotype has been substantiated by the identification of at least one gene on the Y chromosome that acts as a genetic switch, directing male development. Males with Klinefelter syndrome tend to be unusually tall and have female-like breast development. About half show some intellectual disability, but many live relatively normal lives. However, each of their cells has one Barr body. On the basis of such a test, they would be erroneously classified as females. About 1 in 1000 live-born males has Klinefelter syndrome.

The sex chromosome composition for **Turner syndrome,** in which an individual has only one sex chromosome, an X chromosome, is designated X0. Because they lack the male-determining effect of the Y chromosome, individuals with Turner syndrome develop as females. However, both their internal and their external genital structures are underdeveloped, and they are sterile. Apparently, a second X chromosome is necessary for normal development of ovaries in a female embryo. Examination of the cells of these individuals reveals no Barr bodies because there is no extra X chromosome to be inactivated. Using the standards of the Barr body test, such an individual would be classified erroneously as a male. About 1 in 2500 live-born females has Turner syndrome.

People with an X chromosome plus two Y chromosomes are phenotypically males, and they are fertile. Other characteristics of these individuals (tall, often with severe acne) hardly qualify as a syndrome; hence, the term **XYY karyotype** is used. Some years ago, several widely publicized studies suggested that males with this condition are more likely to display criminal tendencies and thus to be imprisoned than those without this condition. However, these studies were flawed because they were based on small numbers of XYY males, without adequate or well-matched control studies of XY males. The prevailing

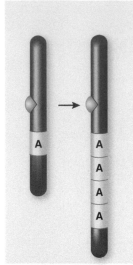
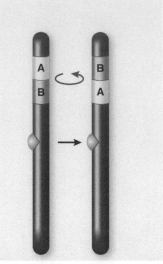
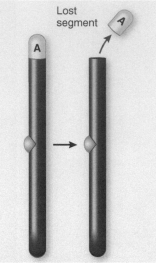
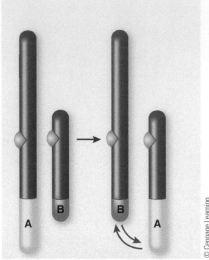

(a) A **duplication** is a repeated segment of a chromosome. In this example, segment A is repeated.

(b) An **inversion** is a chromosome segment with a reversed orientation. An inversion does not change the amount of genetic material in the chromosome, only its arrangement.

(c) A **deletion** is the loss of a chromosome segment. A deletion can occur at the tip (*shown*) or within the chromosome.

(d) A **reciprocal translocation** occurs when two nonhomologous chromosomes exchange segments.

Figure 16-6 *Animation* **Common abnormalities of chromosome structure**

opinion in medical genetics today is that there are many undiagnosed XYY males in the general population who do not have overly aggressive or criminal behaviors and are unlikely to be incarcerated.

Abnormalities in chromosome structure cause certain disorders

Chromosome abnormalities are caused not only by changes in chromosome number but also by distinct changes in the structure of one or more chromosomes. The breakage and rejoining of chromosome parts result in four structural changes within or between chromosomes: duplications, inversions, deletions, and translocations (**FIG. 16-6**). Breaks in chromosomes are the result of errors in replication or recombination. In a **duplication** a segment of the chromosome is repeated one or more times; these repeats often appear in tandem with one another. The orientation of a chromosome segment is reversed in an **inversion.** In a **deletion** breakage causes loss of part of a chromosome along with the genes on that segment. A deletion can occur at the end of a chromosome or on an internal part of the chromosome. In some cases of **translocation,** a chromosome fragment breaks off and attaches to a nonhomologous chromosome. In a *reciprocal translocation,* two nonhomologous chromosomes exchange segments.

Here we consider three simple examples of chromosomal structural changes that result in abnormal phenotypes: translocations, deletions, and *fragile sites,* which are chromosome sites that are susceptible to breakage.

Translocation is the attachment of part of one chromosome to another The consequences of translocations vary

considerably. They include deletions, in which some genes are missing, and duplications, in which extra copies of certain genes are present. In about 4% of individuals with Down syndrome, only 46 chromosomes are present, but one is abnormal. The large arm of chromosome 21 has been translocated to the large arm of another chromosome, usually chromosome 14. Individuals with *translocation Down syndrome* have one chromosome 14, one combined 14/21 chromosome, and two normal copies of chromosome 21. All or part of the genetic material from chromosome 21 is thus present in triplicate. When studying the karyotypes of the parents in such cases, geneticists usually find that either the mother or the father has only 45 chromosomes, although she or he is generally phenotypically normal. The parent with 45 chromosomes has one chromosome 14, one combined 14/21 chromosome, and one chromosome 21; although the karyotype is abnormal, there is no extra genetic material. In contrast to trisomy 21, translocation Down syndrome can run in families, and its incidence is not related to maternal age.

A deletion is the loss of part of a chromosome Sometimes chromosomes break and fail to rejoin. Such breaks result in deletions of as little as a few base pairs to as much as an entire chromosome arm. As you might expect, large deletions are generally lethal, whereas small deletions may have no effect or may cause recognizable human disorders.

One deletion disorder (1 in 20,000–50,000 live births) is **cri du chat syndrome,** in which part of the short arm of chromosome 5 is deleted. As in most deletions, the exact point of breakage in chromosome 5 varies from one individual to another; some cases of cri du chat involve a small loss, whereas others involve a more substantial deletion of base pairs. Infants born with cri du chat syndrome typically have a small head with altered features described as a "moon face" and a distinctive cry that sounds like a kitten mewing. (The name literally means "cry of the cat" in French.) Affected individuals usually survive beyond childhood but exhibit severe intellectual disability.

Fragile sites are weak points at specific locations in chromatids A **fragile site** is a place where part of a chromatid appears to be attached to the rest of the chromosome by a thin thread of DNA. Fragile sites occur at corresponding locations on both chromatids of a chromosome. They have been identified on the X chromosome as well as on certain autosomes. The location of a fragile site is exactly the same in each one of an individual's cells as well as in cells of other family members. Scientists report growing evidence that cancer cells may have breaks at these fragile sites. Whether cancer destabilizes the fragile sites, leading to breakage, or the fragile sites themselves contain genes that contribute to cancer is unknown at this time.

In **fragile X syndrome,** also known as *Martin–Bell syndrome,* a fragile site occurs near the tip of the X chromosome, where the fragile X gene contains a nucleotide triplet CGG that repeats from 200 to more than 1000 times (FIG. 16-7). In a normal chromosome, CGG repeats up to 50 times.

Fragile X syndrome is the most common cause of inherited intellectual disability. The effects of fragile X syndrome, which are more pronounced in males than in females, range from mild learning and attention deficit disorders to severe intellectual disability and hyperactivity. According to the National Fragile X Foundation, about 80% of boys and 35% of girls with fragile X syndrome are at least mildly intellectually disabled. Females with fragile X syndrome are usually heterozygous (because their other X chromosome is normal) and are therefore more likely to have normal intelligence.

The discovery of the fragile X gene in 1991 and the development of the first fragile X mouse model in 1994 have provided researchers with ways to develop and test potential treatments, including gene therapy. At the microscopic level, the nerve cells of individuals with fragile X syndrome have malformed dendrites (the part of the nerve cell that receives nerve impulses from other nerve cells). At the molecular level, the triplet repeats associated with fragile X syndrome disrupt the functioning of a gene that codes for a certain protein, designated *fragile X mental retardation protein (FMRP)*. In normal cells FMRP binds to many different mRNA molecules in nerve cells and regulates their translation. In cells of individuals with fragile X syndrome, the mutated allele does not produce functional FMRP, resulting in excess translation of its mRNA targets.

Genomic imprinting may determine whether inheritance is from the male or female parent

Some traits are the result of **genomic** or **parental imprinting,** in which the expression of a gene in a given tissue or developmental

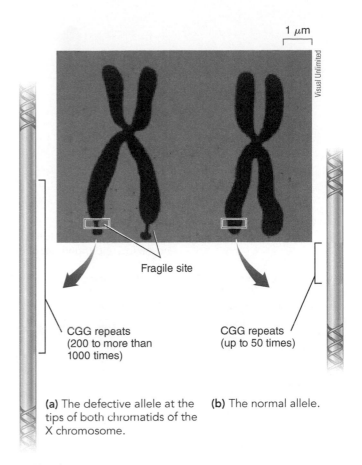

1 μm

(a) The defective allele at the tips of both chromatids of the X chromosome.

(b) The normal allele.

Fragile site

CGG repeats (200 to more than 1000 times)

CGG repeats (up to 50 times)

Figure 16-7 Fragile X syndrome
This colorized SEM shows an X chromosome with a fragile site and a normal X chromosome.
© Cengage Learning

stage is based on its parental origin; that is, it is based on whether the individual inherits the gene from the male or the female parent. For some imprinted genes, the paternally inherited allele is always repressed (not expressed); for other imprinted genes, the maternally inherited allele is always repressed. Thus, maternal and paternal genomes have different imprints that result in differential gene expression in the embryo. As discussed in Chapter 14, *epigenetic inheritance* refers to changes in how a gene is expressed without any change in the coding of the DNA bases. Epigenetic inheritance may cause genomic imprinting.

Two rare genetic disorders provide a fascinating demonstration of genomic imprinting. In *Prader-Willi syndrome (PWS),* individuals become compulsive overeaters and obese; they are also short in stature and have mild to moderate intellectual disabilities. In *Angelman syndrome (AS),* affected individuals are hyperactive, intellectually disabled and unable to speak, and they suffer from seizures. A small *deletion* of several loci from the same region of chromosome 15 causes both PWS and AS (FIG. 16-8a). One of these deleted loci is responsible for PWS, another for AS.

Pedigree analysis has shown that when the person inherits the deletion from the father, PWS occurs, whereas when the person inherits the deletion from the mother, AS occurs. This inheritance pattern suggests that the normal PWS gene is expressed only in the paternal chromosome and that the normal

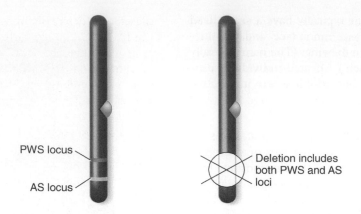

(a) Homologous chromosome 15, showing (*left*) close proximity of the PWS and AS loci and (*right*) site of deletion that includes both PWS and AS loci.

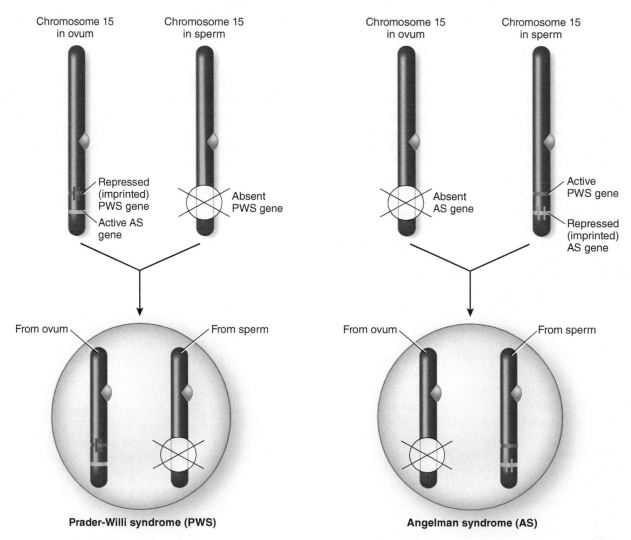

Prader-Willi syndrome (PWS)

Angelman syndrome (AS)

(b) This individual has Prader-Willi syndrome because the sperm contributed a chromosome 15 in which the PWS gene had been deleted. The chromosome with the repressed (imprinted) PWS gene from the egg is unable to compensate for the deletion.

(c) This individual has Angelman syndrome because the egg contributed a chromosome 15 in which the AS gene had been deleted. The chromosome with the repressed (imprinted) AS gene from the sperm is unable to compensate for the deletion.

Figure 16-8 Genomic imprinting and development of Prader-Willi syndrome (PWS) and Angelman syndrome (AS)

The PWS gene is active in the male gamete and repressed (imprinted) in the female gamete. Conversely, the AS gene is active in the female gamete and repressed (imprinted) in the male gamete.

© Cengage Learning

AS gene is expressed only in the maternal chromosome. PWS occurs because the repressed (imprinted) PWS gene from the mother cannot make up for the absent PWS gene in the paternal chromosome (FIG. 16-8b). Similarly, AS occurs because the repressed (imprinted) AS gene from the father cannot make up for the absent AS gene in the maternal chromosome (FIG. 16-8c).

CHECKPOINT 16.2

- VISUALIZE *Draw a simple sketch illustrating how nondisjunction in meiosis can lead to Down syndrome.*
- *What is the chromosome abnormality in cri du chat syndrome?*
- *What is the chromosome abnormality in fragile X syndrome?*
- CONNECT *What types of chemical modifications occur in DNA or histones that result in genomic imprinting? (See Chapter 14.)*

16.3 GENETIC DISEASES CAUSED BY SINGLE-GENE MUTATIONS

LEARNING OBJECTIVE

7   State whether each of the following genetic defects is inherited as an autosomal recessive, autosomal dominant, or X-linked recessive trait: phenylketonuria (PKU), sickle cell anemia, cystic fibrosis, Tay-Sachs disease, Huntington's disease, and hemophilia A.

You have seen that several human disorders involve chromosome abnormalities. Hundreds of human disorders, however, involve enzyme defects caused by mutations of single genes. Alkaptonuria (discussed in Chapter 13) and phenylketonuria (discussed below) are examples of these disorders, each of which is sometimes referred to as an **inborn error of metabolism,** a metabolic disorder caused by the mutation of a gene that codes for an enzyme needed in a biochemical pathway. Both PKU and alkaptonuria involve blocks in the metabolism of specific amino acids.

Many genetic diseases are inherited as autosomal recessive traits

Many human genetic diseases have a simple autosomal recessive inheritance pattern and therefore are expressed only in the homozygous state. Why are these traits recessive? Most recessive mutations result in a mutant allele that encodes a product that no longer works (either there is not enough gene product or it is a defective gene product). In the heterozygous state, there is one functional copy of the gene and one mutated, nonfunctional copy. The normal copy of the gene generally produces enough protein to meet the cell's needs. In homozygous recessive individuals, *both* alleles of the gene are nonfunctional, and the cell's needs are not met. As a result, the person shows symptoms of disease.

Phenylketonuria results from an enzyme deficiency
Phenylketonuria (PKU), which is most common in individuals of western European descent, is an autosomal recessive disease caused by a defect of amino acid metabolism. It affects about 1 in 10,000-15,000 live births in North America. Homozygous recessive individuals lack an enzyme that converts the amino acid phenylalanine to another amino acid, tyrosine. These individuals accumulate high levels of phenylalanine, phenylpyruvic acid, and similar compounds.

The accumulating phenylalanine is converted to phenylketones, which damage the central nervous system, including the brain, in children. The ultimate result in untreated cases is severe intellectual disability. An infant with PKU is usually healthy at birth because its mother, who is heterozygous, breaks down excess phenylalanine for both herself and her fetus. However, during infancy and early childhood, the accumulation of toxic products eventually causes irreversible damage to the central nervous system.

Beginning in the 1950s, infants with PKU have been identified early and placed on a low-phenylalanine diet, dramatically alleviating their symptoms. The diet is difficult to adhere to because it contains no meat, fish, dairy products, breads, or nuts. Also, individuals with PKU should not consume the sugar substitute aspartame, found in many diet drinks and foods, because it contains phenylalanine. Biochemical tests for PKU have been developed, and screening of newborns through a simple blood test is required in the United States. Because of these screening programs and the availability of effective treatment, thousands of PKU-diagnosed children have not developed severe intellectual disability. Most must continue the diet through at least adolescence. Doctors now recommend that patients stay on the diet throughout life because some adults who have discontinued the low-phenylalanine diet experience certain mental problems, such as difficulty in concentration and short-term memory loss.

Ironically, the success of PKU treatment in childhood presents a new challenge today. If a homozygous female who has discontinued the special diet becomes pregnant, the high phenylalanine levels in her blood can damage the brain of the fetus she is carrying, even though that fetus is heterozygous. Therefore, she must resume the diet, preferably before becoming pregnant. This procedure is usually (although not always) successful in preventing the effects of *maternal PKU.* It is especially important for women with PKU to be aware of maternal PKU and to obtain appropriate counseling and medical treatment during pregnancy.

Sickle cell anemia results from a hemoglobin defect
Sickle cell anemia is inherited as an autosomal recessive trait. The disease is most common in people of African descent (approximately 1 in 500 African Americans), and about 1 in 12 African Americans is heterozygous. Under low oxygen conditions, the red blood cells of an individual with sickle cell anemia are shaped like sickles, or half-moons, whereas normal red blood cells are biconcave discs.

The mutation that causes sickle cell anemia was first identified in 1957. The sickled cells contain abnormal hemoglobin molecules, which have the amino acid valine instead of glutamic acid at position 6 (the sixth amino acid from the amino terminal end) in the β-globin chain (see Fig. 3-23a). The substitution of valine for glutamic acid makes the hemoglobin molecules stick to one another to form fiber-like structures that change the shape of some of the red blood cells. This sickling occurs in the veins after the oxygen has been released from the hemoglobin. The blood cells' abnormal sickled shape slows blood flow and blocks small blood vessels (FIG. 16-9), resulting in tissue damage from lack of oxygen and essential nutrients, and in episodes of pain. Because sickled red blood cells also have a shorter lifespan than normal red blood cells, many affected individuals have severe anemia.

Treatments for sickle cell anemia include pain-relief measures, transfusions, and more recently, medicines such as hydroxyurea, which activates the gene for the production of normal fetal hemoglobin (this gene is generally not expressed after birth). The presence of normal fetal hemoglobin in the red blood cells dilutes the sickle cell hemoglobin, thereby minimizing the painful episodes and reducing the need for blood transfusions. The long-term effects of hydroxyurea are not known at this time, but there are concerns that it may induce tumor formation.

Ongoing research is directed toward providing gene therapy for sickle cell anemia using a mouse model for the disease. The first gene therapy treatments in mice used a mouse retrovirus as a *vector*, a carrier that transfers the genetic information. However, the retrovirus did not effectively transport the normal gene for hemoglobin into the bone marrow, where stem cells produce new blood cells. Current research involves the use of other viral vectors to engineer stem cells isolated from the individual to produce fetal hemoglobin in the adult animal.

The reason that the sickle cell allele occurs at a higher frequency in parts of Africa and Asia than in other parts of the world is well established. Individuals who are heterozygous ($Hb^A Hb^S$) and carry alleles for both normal hemoglobin (Hb^A) and sickle cell hemoglobin (Hb^S) are more resistant than others to the malarial parasite, *Plasmodium falciparum,* which causes a severe and often fatal form of malaria. The malarial parasite, which spends part of its life cycle inside red blood cells, does not thrive when sickle cell hemoglobin is present. (An individual heterozygous for sickle cell anemia produces both normal and sickle cell hemoglobin.) Areas in Africa where *falciparum* malaria occurs correlate well with areas in which the frequency of the sickle cell allele is more common in the human population. Thus, $Hb^A Hb^S$ individuals, possessing one copy of the mutant sickle cell allele, have a selective advantage over both types of homozygous individuals, $Hb^A Hb^A$ (who may die of malaria) and $H^b S Hb^S$ (who may die of sickle cell anemia). This phenomenon, known as *heterozygote advantage*, is discussed further in Chapter 19 (see Fig. 19-7).

Cystic fibrosis results from defective ion transport **Cystic fibrosis** is the most common autosomal recessive disorder in children of European descent (1 in 2500 births). About 1 in 25 individuals in the United States is a heterozygous carrier of the mutant cystic fibrosis allele. Abnormal secretions characterize this disorder. The most severe effect is on the respiratory system, where abnormally viscous mucus clogs the airways. The cilia that line the bronchi cannot easily remove the mucus, and it becomes a growth medium for dangerous bacteria. These bacteria or their toxins attack the surrounding tissues, leading to recurring pneumonia and other complications. The heavy mucus also occurs elsewhere in the body, causing digestive difficulties and other effects.

As discussed earlier, the gene responsible for cystic fibrosis codes for CFTR, the protein that regulates the transport of chloride ions across cell membranes. The defective protein, found in plasma membranes of epithelial cells lining the passageways of the lungs, intestines, pancreas, liver, sweat glands, and reproductive organs, results in the production of an unusually thick mucus that eventually leads to tissue damage. Although many forms of cystic fibrosis exist that vary somewhat in the severity of symptoms, the disease is almost always serious.

Antibiotics are used to control bacterial infections, and daily physical therapy is required to clear mucus from the respiratory system (FIG. 16-10). Treatment with *Dornase Alpha (DNase),* an enzyme produced by recombinant DNA technology, helps break down the mucus. Without treatment, death would occur in infancy. With treatment, the average life expectancy for individuals with cystic fibrosis is currently about 38 years. Because of the serious limitations of available treatments, gene therapy for cystic fibrosis is under development.

The most severe mutant allele for cystic fibrosis predominates in northern Europe, and another, somewhat less serious, mutant allele is more prevalent in southern Europe. Presumably, these mutant alleles are independent mutations that have been maintained by natural selection. Some experimental evidence supports the hypothesis that heterozygous individuals are less likely than other individuals to die from infectious diseases that

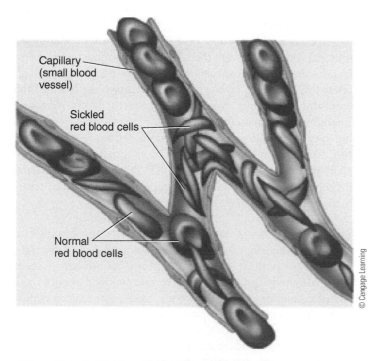

Figure 16-9 *Animation* Sickle cell anemia
Sickled red blood cells do not pass through small blood vessels as easily as unsickled red blood cells do. The sickled cells can cause blockages that prevent oxygen from being delivered to tissues.

Figure 16-10 Treating cystic fibrosis
This brother and sister are being treated for cystic fibrosis with nebulizer therapy, which loosens the mucus. The boy is also wearing a vest that creates chest percussion or gentle pounding on the chest, to clear mucus from clogged airways in the lungs.

cause severe diarrhea, such as cholera, another possible example of heterozygote advantage.

Tay-Sachs disease results from abnormal lipid metabolism in the brain

Tay-Sachs disease is an autosomal recessive disease that affects the central nervous system and results in blindness and severe intellectual disability. The symptoms begin within the first year of life and result in death before the age of five years. Because of the absence of an enzyme, a normal membrane lipid in brain cells fails to break down properly and accumulates in intracellular organelles called *lysosomes* (discussed in Chapter 4). The lysosomes swell and cause nerve cells to malfunction. Although research is ongoing, no effective treatment for Tay-Sachs disease is available at this time.

The abnormal allele is especially common in the United States among Jewish individuals whose ancestors came from eastern and central Europe (Ashkenazi Jews). In contrast, Jewish individuals whose ancestors came from the Mediterranean region (Sephardic Jews) have a very low frequency of the allele.

Some genetic diseases are inherited as autosomal dominant traits

Huntington's disease (HD), named after George Huntington, the U.S. physician who first described it in 1872, is caused by a rare autosomal dominant allele that affects the central nervous system. The disease causes severe mental and physical deterioration, uncontrollable muscle spasms, and personality changes, and death ultimately results. No effective treatment has been found. Every child of an affected individual has a 50% chance

of also being affected (and, if affected, of passing the abnormal allele to his or her offspring). Ordinarily, we would expect a dominant allele with such devastating effects to occur only as a new mutation and not to be transmitted to future generations. Because HD symptoms typically do not appear until relatively late in life (most people do not develop the disease until they are in their 40s), affected individuals are likely to produce children before the disease develops (FIG. 16-11). In North America HD occurs in 1 in 20,000 live births.

The gene responsible for HD is located on the short end of chromosome 4. The mutation is a nucleotide triplet (CAG) that is repeated many times; the normal allele repeats CAG from 6 to 35 times, whereas the mutant allele repeats CAG from 40 to more than 150 times. Because CAG codes for the amino acid glutamine, the resulting protein, called "huntingtin," has a long strand of glutamines. The number of nucleotide triplet repeats seems to be important in determining the age of onset and the severity of the disease; larger numbers of repeats correlate with an earlier age of onset and greater severity.

Much research now focuses on how the mutation is linked to neurodegeneration in the brain. A mouse model of HD is providing valuable clues about the development of the disease. Using this model, researchers have demonstrated that the defective version of huntingtin binds to enzymes called *acetyltransferases* in brain cells, blocking their action. Acetyltransferases are involved in turning genes on for expression, so in the brain cells of HD individuals much of normal transcription cannot occur. Once neurologists better understand HD's mechanism of action on nerve cells, it may be possible to develop effective treatments to slow the progression of the disease.

Cloning of the HD allele became the basis for tests that allow those at risk to learn presymptomatically if they carry the allele. The decision to be tested for any genetic disease is

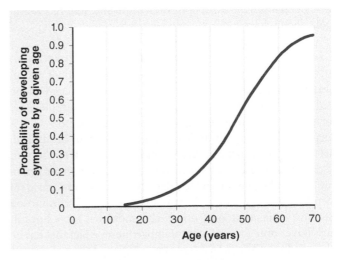

Figure 16-11 Age of onset of Huntington's disease
This graph shows the cumulative probability that an individual carrying a Huntington's disease allele will have developed symptoms at a given age. (Adapted from Harper, P.S., *Genetic Counseling*, 5th ed., Butterworth-Heinemann, Oxford, 1998.)

understandably a highly personal one. The information is, of course, invaluable for those who must decide whether or not to have children. However, someone who tests positive for the HD allele must then live with the virtual certainty of eventually developing this devastating and incurable disease. Researchers hope that information from affected individuals who choose to be identified before the onset of symptoms may ultimately contribute to the development of effective treatments.

Some genetic diseases are inherited as X-linked recessive traits

Hemophilia was once referred to as a disease of royalty because of its high incidence among male descendants of England's Queen Victoria, but it is also found in many nonroyal pedigrees. There are two primary forms of hemophilia. Both are caused by the absence of a blood-clotting protein encoded by genes on the X chromosome. Hemophilia A is the most common form of the disease involving clotting factor VIII. Hemophilia B (in Queen Victoria's lineage) is associated with a clotting factor IX deficiency. Both forms are characterized by severe internal bleeding in the head, joints, and other areas from even a slight wound. The mode of inheritance is X-linked recessive. Thus, affected individuals are almost exclusively male, having inherited the abnormal allele on the X chromosome from their heterozygous carrier mothers. (For a female to be affected by an X-linked trait, she would have to inherit the defective allele from both parents, whereas an affected male need only inherit one defective allele from his mother.)

Treatments for both types of hemophilia consist of blood transfusions and the administration of appropriate clotting factor (the missing gene product) by injection. Unfortunately, these treatments are costly. During the 1980s, many clotting factor preparations made from human plasma were unknowingly contaminated with HIV, and many men with hemophilia subsequently died from AIDS. Since 1992, virus-free clotting factors have been available from both human plasma and recombinant DNA technology.

Geneticists are beginning to unravel X-linked genes affecting intelligence The X chromosome contains a disproportionate number of the more than two hundred genes identified so far that affect cognitive abilities by, for example, coding for proteins required for the brain to function normally. Not surprisingly, many kinds of mental impairment are linked to defects in genes on the X chromosome. By one count, the human X chromosome contains less than 4% of the human genome, yet 10% of the genes in which defects are known to cause some form of intellectual disability are found on the X chromosome. Because males have only one X chromosome, more boys than girls have some form of mental impairment, a fact that has been observed for more than a century.

CHECKPOINT 16.3

- *Which of the following genetic diseases is/are inherited as an autosomal recessive trait: phenylketonuria, Huntington's disease, Tay-Sachs disease?*

- *Which of the following genetic diseases is/are inherited as an autosomal dominant trait: sickle cell anemia, hemophilia A, Huntington's disease?*

- *Which of the following genetic diseases is/are inherited as an X-linked recessive trait: hemophilia A, cystic fibrosis, Tay-Sachs disease?*

16.4 GENE THERAPY

LEARNING OBJECTIVE

8 Briefly discuss the process of gene therapy, including some of its technical challenges.

Because serious genetic diseases are difficult to treat, scientists have dreamed of developing actual cures. One strategy is **gene therapy,** which aims to compensate for a defective, mutant allele by adding a normal, therapeutic allele (and its expressed protein) to certain cells. The rationale is that although a particular allele may be present in all cells, it is expressed only in some. Expression of the normal allele in only the cells that require it may be sufficient to yield a normal phenotype (**FIG. 16-12**).

This approach presents several technical problems. The solutions to these problems must be tailored to the nature of the gene itself as well as to its product and the types of cells in which it is expressed. First, the gene is cloned and the DNA introduced into the appropriate cells.

One of the most successful techniques is packaging the normal allele in a viral vector, a virus that moves the normal allele into target cells that currently have a mutant allele. Ideally, the virus should infect a high percentage of the cells. Most important, the virus should do no harm, especially over the long term. Early gene therapy trials used an adenovirus, which causes the common cold. However, some individuals had a strong immune reaction to the virus, so many current trials use an adeno-associated virus that does not cause side effects.

Gene therapy has had a greater than 90% success rate in restoring the immune systems of children with *severe combined immunodeficiency (SCID)*. (SCID is a group of inherited disorders that seriously compromise the immune system.) This success rate is significantly better than the 50% success rate of the older therapy involving bone marrow transplants. However, serious safety concerns have impeded progress in gene therapy. The death of a young man in a gene therapy trial in 1999 and five cases of cancer (leukemia) in children, one of whom died, led to a temporary shutdown of many trials in 2003, pending the outcome of investigations about health risks. Although the ban was lifted later that year, researchers have continued to proceed cautiously. The main safety concern is the potential toxicity of viral vectors. The vector used in the young man who died was an adenovirus that was required in large doses to transfer enough copies of the normal alleles for effective therapy. Unfortunately, the high viral doses triggered a fatal immune response in the patient's body. The children who developed leukemia were being treated for SCID. The vector in these cases was a retrovirus that inserted itself into and activated an oncogene that can cause childhood leukemia.

WHY IS IT USED? Mice are a model system for the development of gene therapy, the use of normal genes to correct or alleviate the symptoms of a genetic disease caused by defective copies of a particular gene. This procedure is performed on humans for certain types of genetic disease.

HOW IS IT DONE?

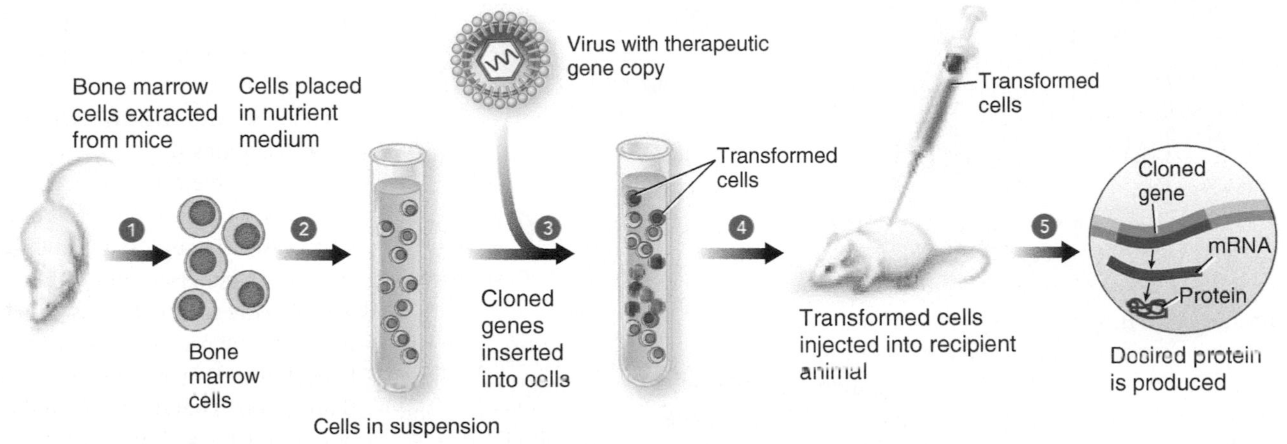

Figure 16-12 **Gene therapy in bone marrow cells of a mouse**
© Cengage Learning

Performing clinical trials on humans always has inherent risks

Researchers carefully select patients and thoroughly explain the potential benefits and risks, as far as they are known, so that the patient—or, in the case of children, the parents—can give informed consent for the procedure. However, the problems in gene therapy trials in recent years have researchers busy developing safer alternatives to viral vectors.

CHECKPOINT 16.4

- *What are the potential concerns regarding the use of viral vectors in gene therapy?*

16.5 GENETIC TESTING AND COUNSELING

LEARNING OBJECTIVES

9 State the relative advantages and disadvantages of amniocentesis, chorionic villus sampling, and preimplantation genetic diagnosis in the prenatal diagnosis of human genetic abnormalities.

10 Distinguish between genetic screening programs for newborns and adults, and discuss the scope and implications of genetic counseling.

Geneticists have made many advances in detecting genetic disorders in individuals in recent years, including in prenatal diagnosis and genetic screening. With these advances comes increased information for couples at risk of having children with genetic diseases. Helping them understand and deal with the genetic information now available is part of the rapidly expanding field of genetic counseling.

Prenatal diagnosis detects chromosome abnormalities and gene defects

Health care professionals are increasingly successful at diagnosing genetic diseases prenatally. In the diagnostic technique called **amniocentesis,** a physician obtains a sample of the *amniotic fluid* surrounding the fetus by inserting a needle through the pregnant woman's abdomen, into the uterus, and then into the amniotic sac surrounding the fetus. Some of the amniotic fluid is withdrawn from the amniotic cavity into a syringe (**FIG. 16-13**). The fetus is normally safe from needle injuries because **ultrasound imaging** helps determine the positions of the fetus, placenta, and the needle. (Figure 51-17 shows an ultrasound of a human fetus.) However, there is a 0.5%, or 1 in 200, chance that amniocentesis will induce a miscarriage.

Amniotic fluid contains living cells sloughed off the body of the fetus and hence genetically identical to the cells of the fetus. After cells grow in culture in the lab, technicians karyotype dividing cells to detect chromosome abnormalities. Other

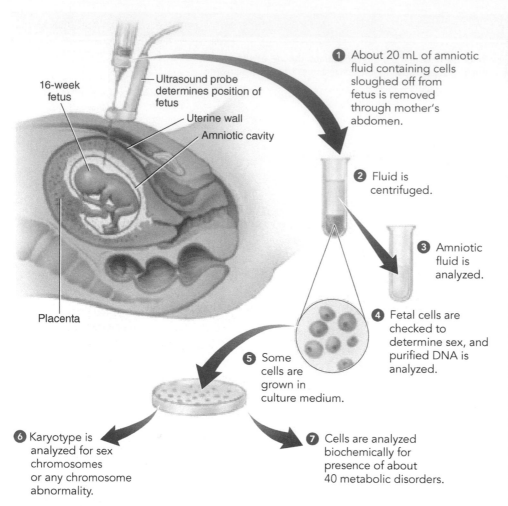

① About 20 mL of amniotic fluid containing cells sloughed off from fetus is removed through mother's abdomen.

16-week fetus

Ultrasound probe determines position of fetus

Uterine wall

Amniotic cavity

Placenta

② Fluid is centrifuged.

③ Amniotic fluid is analyzed.

④ Fetal cells are checked to determine sex, and purified DNA is analyzed.

⑤ Some cells are grown in culture medium.

⑥ Karyotype is analyzed for sex chromosomes or any chromosome abnormality.

⑦ Cells are analyzed biochemically for presence of about 40 metabolic disorders.

Figure 16-13 Amniocentesis

In amniocentesis the fluid surrounding the developing fetus is sampled, usually during the 16th week of pregnancy, to detect genetic and developmental disorders.

© Cengage Learning

DNA tests have also been developed to identify most chromosome abnormalities. Amniocentesis, which has been performed since the 1960s, is routinely offered for pregnant women older than age 35 because their fetuses have a higher-than-normal risk of Down syndrome.

Researchers have developed prenatal tests to detect many genetic disorders with a simple inheritance pattern, but these disorders are rare enough that physicians usually order the tests performed only if they suspect a particular problem. Enzyme deficiencies can often be detected by incubating cells recovered from amniotic fluid with the appropriate substrate and measuring the product; this technique has been useful in prenatal diagnosis of disorders such as Tay-Sachs disease. The tests for several other diseases, including sickle cell anemia, Huntington's disease, and cystic fibrosis, involve directly testing the individual's DNA for the mutant allele.

Amniocentesis is also useful in detecting a condition known as *spina bifida,* in which the spinal cord does not close properly during development. A relatively common malformation (about 1 in 3000 births), this birth defect is associated with abnormally high levels of a normally occurring protein, *a-fetoprotein,* in the amniotic fluid. Some of this protein crosses the placenta into the mother's blood, which is tested for *maternal serum a-fetoprotein (MSAFP)* as a screen for spinal cord defects. If an elevated level of MSAFP is detected, the physician performs diagnostic tests, such as ultrasound imaging and amniocentesis. (Interestingly, abnormally *low* levels of MSAFP are associated with Down syndrome and other trisomies.)

One problem with amniocentesis is that most of the conditions it detects are unpreventable and incurable, and the results are generally not obtained until well into the second trimester, when terminating the pregnancy is both psychologically and medically more difficult than earlier. Therefore, researchers have developed tests that yield results earlier in the pregnancy. **Chorionic villus sampling (CVS)** involves removing and studying cells that will form the fetal contribution to the placenta (FIG. 16-14). CVS, which has been performed in the United States since about 1983, is associated with a slightly greater risk of infection or miscarriage than amniocentesis, but its advantage is that results are obtained earlier in the pregnancy than in amniocentesis, usually within the first trimester.

A relatively new embryo screening process, known as **preimplantation genetic diagnosis (PGD),** is available for potential parents who carry alleles for Tay-Sachs disease, hemophilia, sickle cell anemia, and dozens of other inherited genetic conditions. PGD is an adjunct to assisted reproductive technology. Conception is by *in vitro fertilization (IVF),* in which gametes are collected, eggs are fertilized in a dish in the laboratory, and the resulting embryo is then implanted in the uterus for development (see *Inquiring About: Novel Origins,* in Chapter 50). Prior to implantation, the physician screens single cells of early embryos for one or more genetic diseases before placing a healthy embryo into the woman's uterus. PGD differs from amniocentesis and CVS in that the test is performed *before* a woman is pregnant, so it eliminates the decision of whether or not to terminate the pregnancy if an embryo has a genetic abnormality. However, PGD is not as accurate as amniocentesis or CVS, and it is more expensive. Moreover, PGD is sometimes controversial because some potential parents may use it to choose the gender of their offspring, not to screen for genetic diseases.

Although using amniocentesis, CVS, and PGD can help physicians diagnose certain genetic disorders with a high degree of accuracy, the tests are not foolproof, and many disorders cannot be diagnosed at all. Therefore, the lack of an abnormal finding is no guarantee of a normal baby.

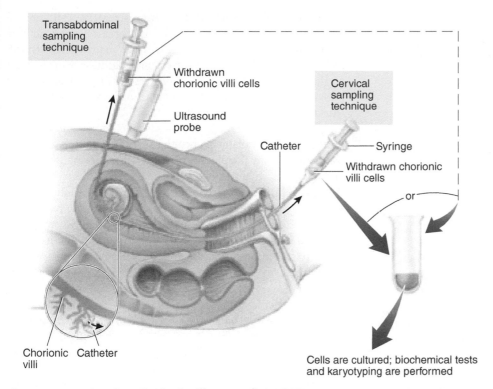

Genetic screening of adults identifies carriers (heterozygotes) of recessive genetic disorders. If both prospective parents are heterozygous, the carriers are counseled about the risks involved in having children. Since the 1970s, about one million young Jewish adults in the United States, Israel, and other countries have been screened voluntarily for Tay-Sachs disease, and about 1 in 30 has been identified as a carrier. Tay-Sachs screening programs have reduced the incidence of Tay-Sachs disease to almost zero.

Genetic counselors educate people about genetic diseases

Prospective parents who are concerned about the risk of abnormality in their children because they have either an abnormal child or a relative affected by a hereditary disease may seek **genetic counseling** for medical and genetic information as well as support and guidance. Genetic clinics, available in most major metropolitan centers, are usually affiliated with medical schools.

Genetic counselors, who have received training in counseling, medicine, and human genetics, provide people with the information they need to make reproductive decisions. They offer advice, tempered with respect and sensitivity, in terms of risk estimates, that is, the *probability* that any given offspring will inherit a particular condition. The counselor analyzes family histories, and a clinical geneticist (a physician who specializes in genetics) may screen for the detection of heterozygous carriers of certain conditions.

When a disease involves only a single gene locus, probabilities can usually be easily calculated. For example, if one prospective parent is affected with a trait that is inherited as an autosomal dominant disorder, such as Huntington's disease, the probability that any given child will have the disease is 0.5, or 50%. The birth to phenotypically normal parents of a child affected with an autosomal recessive trait, such as albinism or PKU, establishes that both parents are heterozygous carriers, and the probability that any subsequent child will be affected is therefore 0.25, or 25%. For a disease inherited through a recessive allele on the X chromosome, such as hemophilia A, a homozygous normal woman and an affected man will have daughters who are carriers and sons who are phenotypically normal. The probability that the son of a carrier mother and a normal father will be affected is 0.5, or 50%; the probability that their daughter will be a carrier is also 0.5, or 50%.

It is important for identified carriers to receive appropriate genetic counseling. A genetic counselor is trained not only to provide information pertaining to reproductive decisions but also to help individuals understand their situation and avoid feeling stigmatized.

Figure 16-14 *Animation* **Chorionic villus sampling (CVS)**
In chorionic villus sampling, chorionic cells genetically identical to the embryo are sampled, usually during the eighth or ninth week of pregnancy, to detect genetic disorders. This test allows the early diagnosis of some genetic abnormalities. Samples may be obtained by inserting a needle through the uterine wall or the cervical opening.

© Cengage Learning

Genetic screening searches for genotypes or karyotypes

Genetic screening is a systematic search through a population for individuals with a genotype or karyotype that might cause a serious genetic disease in themselves or their offspring. There are two main types of genetic screening—one for newborns and one for adults—and each serves a different purpose. Newborns are screened primarily as the first step in preventive medicine, and adults are screened to help them make informed reproductive decisions.

Newborns are screened to detect and treat certain genetic diseases before the onset of serious symptoms. The routine screening of infants for PKU began in 1962 in Massachusetts. Laws in all 50 states of the United States and the District of Columbia, as well as in many other countries, currently require PKU screening. Sickle cell anemia is also more effectively treated with early diagnosis. Screening newborns for sickle cell anemia reduces infant mortality by about 15% because doctors can administer daily doses of antibiotics, thereby preventing bacterial infections common to newborns with the disease. The number of genetic disorders that can be screened in newborns is rapidly increasing, and the March of Dimes organization currently recommends screening newborns for 31 disorders, most of which are genetic.

• CONNECT *What are the relative advantages and disadvantages of amniocentesis, chorionic villus sampling, and preimplantation genetic diagnosis?*

• CONNECT *What are the goals of genetic screening for newborns? for adults?*

16.6 HUMAN GENETICS, SOCIETY, AND ETHICS

LEARNING OBJECTIVE

11 Discuss the controversies of genetic discrimination.

Many misconceptions exist about genetic diseases and their effects on society. Some people erroneously think of certain individuals or populations as genetically unfit and thus responsible for many of society's ills. They argue, for example, that medical treatment of people affected with genetic diseases, especially those who reproduce, increases the frequency of abnormal alleles in the population. However, such notions are incorrect. Genetic disorders are so rare that modern medical treatments will have only a negligible effect on their incidence.

Recessive mutant alleles are present in *all* individuals and *all* ethnic groups; no one is exempt. According to one estimate, each of us is heterozygous for several (3 to 15) harmful recessive alleles, any of which could cause debilitating illness or death in the homozygous state. Why, then, are genetic diseases relatively uncommon? Each of us has many thousands of essential genes, any of which can be mutated. It is very unlikely that the abnormal alleles that one individual carries are also carried by the other parent of that individual's children. Of course, this possibility is more likely if the harmful allele is a relatively common one, such as the one responsible for cystic fibrosis.

Relatives are more likely than nonrelatives to carry the same harmful alleles, having inherited them from a common ancestor. A greater-than-normal frequency of a particular genetic disease among offspring of *consanguineous matings*, matings between genetically related individuals, is often the first clue that the mode of inheritance is autosomal recessive. The offspring of consanguineous matings have a small but significantly increased risk of genetic disease. In fact, they account for a disproportionately high percentage of those individuals in the population with autosomal recessive disorders. Because of this perceived social cost, marriages of close relatives, including first cousins, are prohibited by about half the states in the United States. However, consanguineous marriages are still relatively common in many other countries.

Genetic discrimination provokes heated debate

One of the fastest-growing areas of medical diagnostics is genetic screening and testing, and new genetic tests that screen for diseases such as cystic fibrosis, sickle cell anemia, Huntington's disease, colon cancer, and breast cancer increase each year. However, genetic testing raises many social, ethical, and legal issues that we as a society must address. Not the least of these is *genetic discrimination*, discrimination against an individual or family member because of differences from the "normal" genome in that individual.

One of the most difficult issues is whether genetic information should be available to health insurance and life insurance companies. Many people think that genetic information should not be given to insurance companies, but others, including employers, insurers, and many organizations representing people affected by genetic disorders, say such a view is unrealistic. If people use genetic tests to help them decide when to buy insurance and how much, insurers insist that they should also have access to this information. Insurers say that they need access to genetic data to help calculate equitable premiums (insurance companies average risks over a large population). Physicians argue that people at risk for a particular genetic disease might delay being tested because they fear genetic discrimination from insurers and employers.

Complicating the issue even more is that genetic tests are sometimes difficult to interpret, in part because of the many complex interactions between genes and the environment. If a woman tests positive for an allele that has been linked to breast cancer, for example, she is at significant risk, but testing positive does not necessarily mean that she will develop breast cancer. These uncertainties also make it hard to decide what form of medical intervention—from frequent mammograms to surgical removal of healthy breasts—is appropriate.

The Ethical, Legal, and Social Implications (ELSI) Research Program of the National Human Genome Research Institute has developed principles designed to protect individuals against genetic discrimination. In 2008, the *Genetic Information Nondiscrimination Act (GINA)* extended significant protection against workplace and health discrimination. This law prohibits employers and insurance companies from discriminating on the basis of information derived from genetic tests. For example, neither employers nor insurance companies are permitted to request a genetic test. Employers cannot base employment decisions on genetic information. Also, insurance companies cannot cancel or deny coverage or increase the price of premiums based on genetic information.

Many ethical issues related to human genetics must be addressed

Genetic discrimination is only one example of ethical issues arising from our expanding knowledge of human genetics. Consider the following questions, all of which deal with the broad ethical issue of individual rights: What is the youngest age at which genetic testing should be permitted for adult-onset diseases, such as Huntington's disease? What are the emotional and psychological effects on individuals who are told that they have tested positive for an incurable genetic disease? Should testing be performed when some family members want testing and others do not?

Should parents be able to test their minor children? Should unexpected, but medically significant, results be reported to patients (or to their parents) when they are uncovered in the course of DNA sequencing for an unrelated medical condition? Should access to genetic test data be permitted in cases of paternity or kinship testing? Should states be able to collect genetic data on their residents? Should school administrators or law enforcement agencies have access to genetic data? These questions are only a sample of the many issues that both ethicists and society must consider now and in the future. As human genetics assumes an increasingly important role in society, issues of genetic privacy and the confidentiality of genetic information must be addressed.

CHECKPOINT 16.6

- Why is it incorrect to assume that certain individuals or populations carry most of the abnormal alleles found in humans?

- CONNECT To be expressed, an autosomal recessive genetic disease must be homozygous. What relationship does this fact have to consanguineous matings?

- For what reason do health and life insurance companies want genetic information about their clients?

SUMMARY: FOCUS ON LEARNING OBJECTIVES

16.1 Studying Human Genetics (page 337)

1 Distinguish between karyotyping and pedigree analysis.

- Studies of an individual's *karyotype*, the number and kinds of chromosomes present in the nucleus, enable researchers to identify various chromosome abnormalities.

- A **pedigree** is a "family tree" that shows the transmission of genetic traits within a family over several generations. Pedigree analysis is useful in detecting autosomal dominant mutations, autosomal recessive mutations, X-linked recessive mutations, and defects due to **genomic imprinting**, which is the expression of a gene based on its parental origin.

2 Discuss how gene databases and genomic methods are used to study human genetic diseases.

- The database of the **Human Genome Project** contains the entire sequence of human chromosomal DNA. Large international collaborative efforts such as the **1000 Genomes Project** and the **ENCODE Project** have allowed investigators to construct maps of the human genome showing the location of natural variations in DNA in human populations, such as **single nucleotide polymorphisms (SNPs),** and the locations of DNA sequences involved in biological functions. Researchers use these polymorphisms in **genome-wide association (GWAS) studies** to identify genetic variations associated with complex human diseases. Investigators then use gene database information to identify affected genes and understand the role of each gene, how each gene interacts with other genes, and how the expression of each gene is regulated in different tissues.

3 Discuss the importance of comparative genomics to the study of human genetics.

- Comparative genomics examines the relationships among genes, genomic structures, and functions among different species. The identification of genes and genomic regions in other species that are highly conserved with those in humans allows investigators to study their structure and function in model organisms such as the mouse, *Drosophila, C. elegans,* yeast and *E. coli.* These studies provide important insights into the roles of those genes in humans.

16.2 Abnormalities in Chromosome Number and Structure (page 340)

4 Explain how nondisjunction in meiosis is responsible for chromosome abnormalities such as Down syndrome, Klinefelter syndrome, and Turner syndrome.

- In **aneuploidy** there are either missing or extra copies of certain chromosomes. Aneuploidies include **trisomy,** in which an individual's cells contain an extra chromosome, and **monosomy,** in which one member of a pair of chromosomes is missing.

- **Trisomy 21,** the most common form of **Down syndrome,** and **Klinefelter syndrome** (XXY) are examples of trisomy. **Turner syndrome** (X0) is an example of monosomy.

- Trisomy and monosomy are caused by meiotic **nondisjunction,** in which sister chromatids or homologous chromosomes fail to move apart properly during meiosis.

5 Distinguish among the following structural abnormalities in chromosomes: translocations, deletions, and fragile sites.

- In a **translocation** part of one chromosome becomes attached to another. About 4% of individuals with Down syndrome have a translocation in which the long arm of chromosome 21 is attached to the long arm of one of the larger chromosomes, such as chromosome 14.

- A **deletion** can result in chromosome breaks that fail to rejoin. The deletion may range in size from a few base pairs to an entire chromosome arm. One deletion disorder in humans is **cri du chat syndrome,** in which part of the short arm of chromosome 5 is deleted.

- **Fragile sites** may occur at specific locations on both chromatids of a chromosome. In **fragile X syndrome,** a fragile site occurs near the tip on the X chromosome, where the nucleotide triplet CGG is repeated many more times than is normal. Fragile X syndrome is the most common cause of inherited intellectual disability.

6 Explain how genomic imprinting influences inheritance patterns.

- Genomic imprinting can affect the expression of a gene based on its parental origin. An allele can be repressed or expressed, without any changes to the DNA base sequence, depending on the parent from which it was inherited.

16.3 Genetic Diseases Caused by Single-Gene Mutations (page 347)

7 State whether each of the following genetic defects is inherited as an autosomal recessive, autosomal dominant, or X-linked recessive trait: phenylketonuria (PKU), sickle cell anemia, cystic fibrosis, Tay-Sachs disease, Huntington's disease, and hemophilia A.

- Most human genetic diseases that show a simple inheritance pattern are transmitted as autosomal recessive traits.

Phenylketonuria (PKU) is an autosomal recessive disorder in which toxic phenylketones damage the developing nervous system. **Sickle cell anemia** is an autosomal recessive disorder in which abnormal hemoglobin (the protein that transports oxygen in the blood) is produced. **Cystic fibrosis** is an autosomal recessive disorder in which abnormal secretions are produced primarily in organs of the respiratory and digestive systems. **Tay-Sachs disease** is an autosomal recessive disorder caused by abnormal lipid metabolism in the brain.

- **Huntington's disease** has an autosomal dominant inheritance pattern and results in mental and physical deterioration, usually beginning in adulthood.
- **Hemophilia** is an X-linked recessive disorder that results in a defect in a blood component required for clotting.

16.4 Gene Therapy (page 350)

8 Briefly discuss the process of gene therapy, including some of its technical challenges.

- In **gene therapy** the normal allele is cloned, and the DNA is introduced into certain human cells where its expression may be sufficient to yield a normal phenotype.
- One technical challenge in gene therapy is finding a safe, effective vector, usually a virus, to deliver the gene of interest into the cells.

16.5 Genetic Testing and Counseling (page 351)

9 State the relative advantages and disadvantages of amniocentesis, chorionic villus sampling, and preimplantation genetic diagnosis in the prenatal diagnosis of human genetic abnormalities.

- In **amniocentesis** a physician samples the amniotic fluid surrounding the fetus and then cultures and screens the fetal cells suspended in the fluid for genetic defects. Amniocentesis provides results in the second trimester of pregnancy.

- In **chorionic villus sampling (CVS),** a physician removes and studies some of the fetal cells. CVS provides results in the first trimester of pregnancy but is associated with a slightly greater risk of infection and miscarriage than amniocentesis.
- Couples who conceive by in vitro fertilization may elect to have **preimplantation genetic diagnosis (PGD),** in which a physician screens the embryos for one or more genetic diseases before placing a healthy embryo into the woman's uterus. PGD is not as accurate as amniocentesis or CVS, and it is more expensive.

10 Distinguish between genetic screening programs for newborns and adults, and discuss the scope and implications of genetic counseling.

- **Genetic screening** identifies individuals who might carry a serious genetic disease. Screening of newborns is the first step in preventive medicine, and screening of adults helps them make informed reproductive decisions.
- Couples who are concerned about the risk of abnormality in their children may seek **genetic counseling.** A genetic counselor provides medical and genetic information pertaining to reproductive decisions and helps individuals understand their situation and avoid feeling stigmatized.

16.6 Human Genetics, Society, and Ethics (page 354)

11 Discuss the controversies of genetic discrimination.

- *Genetic discrimination* is discrimination against an individual or family member because of differences from the "normal" genome in that individual.
- One of the most difficult issues in avoiding genetic discrimination is whether genetic information should be available to employers and to health and life insurance companies. The *Genetic Information Nondiscrimination Act (GINA)* prohibits employers and insurance companies from discriminating on the basis of information derived from genetic tests.

TEST YOUR UNDERSTANDING

Know and Comprehend

1. A diagram of a pedigree shows (a) controlled matings between members of different true-breeding strains (b) the total genetic information in human cells (c) a comparison of DNA sequences among genomes of humans and other species (d) the subtle genetic differences among unrelated people (e) the expression of genetic traits in the members of two or more generations of a family
2. An abnormality in which there is one more or one fewer than the normal number of chromosomes is called (a) a karyotype (b) a fragile site (c) an aneuploidy (d) trisomy (e) a translocation
3. The failure of chromosomes to separate normally during cell division is called (a) a fragile site (b) an inborn error of metabolism (c) a satellite knob (d) a translocation (e) nondisjunction
4. The chromosome composition of an individual or cell is called its (a) karyotype (b) nucleotide triplet repeat (c) pedigree (d) DNA microarray (e) translocation
5. An inherited disorder caused by a defective or absent enzyme is called (a) a karyotype (b) trisomy (c) a reciprocal translocation (d) an inborn error of metabolism (e) an aneuploidy

6. In ___, a genetic mutation codes for an abnormal hemoglobin molecule that is less soluble than usual and more likely than normal to deform the shape of the red blood cell. (a) Down syndrome (b) Tay-Sachs disease (c) sickle cell anemia (d) PKU (e) hemophilia A
7. During this procedure, a sample of the fluid that surrounds the fetus is obtained by inserting a needle through the walls of the abdomen and uterus. (a) DNA marking (b) chorionic villus sampling (c) ultrasound imaging (d) preimplantation genetic diagnosis (e) amniocentesis

Apply and Analyze

8. Which pattern of inheritance is associated with a trait that (1) is not usually expressed in the parents, (2) is expressed in about one-fourth of the children, and (3) is expressed in both male and female children? (a) autosomal recessive (b) autosomal dominant (c) X-linked recessive (d) X-linked dominant (e) Y-linked

Examine the following pedigrees. Which is the most likely mode of inheritance of each disorder? (a) autosomal recessive (b) autosomal dominant (c) X-linked recessive (d) a, b, or c (e) a or c

9.   10.  11.

Evaluate and Synthesize

12. **SCIENCE, TECHNOLOGY, AND SOCIETY** Imagine that you are a genetic counselor. What advice or suggestions might you give in the following situations?
    a. A couple has come for advice because the woman had a sister who died of Tay-Sachs disease.
    b. A young man and woman who are not related are engaged to be married. However, they have learned that the man's parents are first cousins, and they are worried about the possibility of increased risk of genetic defects in their own children.
    c. A young woman's paternal uncle (her father's brother) has hemophilia A. Her father is free of the disease, and there has never been a case of hemophilia A in her mother's family. Should she be concerned about the possibility of hemophilia A in her own children?

d. A 20-year-old man is seeking counseling because his father was recently diagnosed with Huntington's disease.
e. A 45-year-old woman has just been diagnosed with Huntington's disease. She says she will not tell her college-age sons because of the burden it will place on them. Given that the woman, not her sons, is your client, do you have a duty to inform the sons? Explain your reasoning.

13. A common belief about human genetics is that an individual's genes alone determine his or her destiny. Explain why this idea is a misconception.

14. **CONNECT** Is a chromosome deletion equivalent to a frameshift mutation (discussed in Chapter 13)? Why or why not?

15. **EVOLUTION LINK** Explain some of the evolutionary implications that one can conclude from mice and humans having about five hundred DNA segments that are completely identical.

16. **INTERPRET DATA** Examine Figure 16-11 and estimate the age at which half of individuals carrying a Huntington's disease allele will have developed symptoms. At what age will three-fourths of these individuals have symptoms?

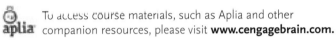 To access course materials, such as Aplia and other companion resources, please visit **www.cengagebrain.com.**

Introduction to Darwinian Evolution

A great deal of evidence suggests that the biological diversity represented by the millions of species currently living on our planet evolved from a single ancestor during Earth's long history. Thus, organisms that are radically different from one another are in fact distantly related, linked through numerous intermediate ancestors to a single, common ancestor. British naturalist Charles Darwin (1809–1882) developed a simple, scientifically testable mechanism to explain the relationship among Earth's diversity of organisms. He argued persuasively that all the species that exist today, as well as the countless extinct species that existed in the past, arose from earlier ones by a process of gradual *divergence* (splitting into separate evolutionary pathways), or *evolution*.

The concept of evolution is the cornerstone of biology because it links all fields of the life sciences into a unified body of knowledge. As stated by U.S. geneticist Theodosius Dobzhansky, "Nothing in biology makes sense except in the light of evolution."[1] Biologists seek to understand both the remarkable variety and the fundamental similarities of organisms within the context of evolution. The science of evolution allows biologists to compare common threads among organisms as seemingly different as bacteria, whales, lilies, slime molds, and tapeworms. Animal behavior, developmental biology, genetics, evolutionary ecology, systematics, and molecular evolution are examples of some of the biological disciplines that are grounded in evolution.

This chapter discusses Charles Darwin and the development of his scientific theory of evolution through the mechanism of natural selection. It also presents evidence that supports evolution, including fossils, biogeography, comparative anatomy, molecular biology, developmental biology, and experimental studies of ongoing evolutionary change in both the laboratory and nature.

Science Source

Charles Darwin. This portrait was made shortly after Darwin returned to England from his voyage around the world.

KEY CONCEPTS

18.1 Evolution is the accumulation of inherited changes within populations over time.

18.2 Ideas about evolution originated long before Darwin's time.

18.3 Darwin's scientific theory of evolution, natural selection, explained how natural forces in the environment could cause evolution. Natural selection occurs because individuals with traits that make them better adapted to local conditions are more likely to survive and produce offspring than are individuals that are not as well adapted. The modern synthesis combines Darwin's scientific theory with the scientific underpinnings of modern genetics.

18.4 The evidence that evolution has taken place and is still occurring is overwhelming. This evidence includes fossils, biogeography, comparative anatomy, molecular biology, developmental biology, and evolutionary experiments with living organisms.

---

[1] Dobzhansky, T. "Nothing in Biology Makes Sense Except in the Light of Evolution," *American Biology Teacher*, Vol. 35, No. 125, pp. 125–129 (1973).

18.1 WHAT IS EVOLUTION?

1 Define the scientific theory of *evolution*.

In beginning our study of evolution, we define **evolution** as the accumulation of genetic changes within populations over time. A **population** is a group of individuals of one species that live in the same geographic area at the same time. Just as the definition of a *gene* changed as you studied genetics, you will find that the definition of *evolution* will become more precise in later chapters.

The term *evolution* does not refer to changes that occur in an individual within its lifetime. Instead, it refers to changes in the characteristics of populations over the course of generations. These changes may be so small that they are difficult to detect or so great that the population differs markedly from its ancestral population.

Eventually, two populations may diverge to such a degree that we refer to them as different species. The concept of species is developed extensively in Chapter 20. For now, a simple working definition is that a **species** is a group of organisms, with similar genetic information, structure, function, and behavior, that are capable of interbreeding with one another.

Evolution has two main perspectives. The minor evolutionary changes of populations (*microevolution,* discussed in Chapter 19) are usually viewed over a few generations, and the major evolutionary events (*macroevolution,* discussed in Chapter 20), such as formation of different species from common ancestors, are usually viewed over a long period.

Evolution has important practical applications. Agriculture must deal with the evolution of pesticide resistance in insects and other pests. Likewise, medicine must respond to the rapid evolutionary potential of disease-causing organisms such as bacteria and viruses (**FIG. 18-1**). (Significant evolutionary change occurs in a very short time period in insects, bacteria, and other organisms with short lifespans.) Medical researchers use evolutionary principles to predict which flu strains are evolving more quickly than others, information that scientists need to make the next year's flu vaccine. Also, researchers developing effective treatment strategies for the human immunodeficiency virus (HIV) must understand its evolution, both within and among hosts (see Fig. 23-12).

The conservation management of rare and endangered species makes use of the evolutionary principles of population genetics. The rapid evolution of bacteria and fungi in polluted soils is used in the field of **bioremediation,** in which microorganisms are employed to clean up hazardous-waste sites. Evolution even has applications beyond biology. For example, certain computer applications make use of algorithms that mimic natural selection in biological systems.

CHECKPOINT 18.1

- **CONNECT** *How is microevolution related to macroevolution?*
- *Do individuals evolve? Explain your answer.*

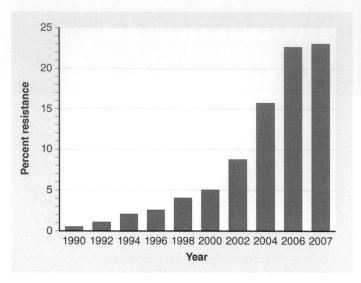

Figure 18-1 *Animation* **Evolution of antibiotic resistance to ciprofloxacin in** *Escherichia coli*

These data show an increased resistance to ciprofloxacin in *E. coli* isolated from blood and cerebrospinal infections in patients in England, Wales, and Northern Ireland, 1990 to 2007. (SOURCE: Livermore, D. "Zietgeist of Resistance." *The Journal of Antimicrobial Chemotherapy*, Vol. 60, i59–i61, 2007. By permission of Oxford University Press.)

18.2 PRE-DARWINIAN IDEAS ABOUT EVOLUTION

2 Discuss the historical development of evolutionary thought.

Although Darwin is universally associated with evolution, ideas of evolution predate Darwin by centuries. Aristotle (384–322 BCE) saw much evidence of natural affinities among organisms, which led him to arrange all the organisms he knew in a "scale of nature" that extended from the exceedingly simple to the most complex. Aristotle visualized organisms as being imperfect but "moving toward a more perfect state." Some scientific historians have interpreted this idea as a forerunner of evolutionary thought, but Aristotle was vague on the nature of this "movement toward perfection" and certainly did not propose that natural processes drove the process of evolution. Furthermore, modern scientific evolutionary theory now recognizes that evolution does not move toward more "perfect" states or even necessarily toward greater complexity.

Long before Darwin's time, fossils had been discovered embedded in rocks. Some of these fossils corresponded to parts of familiar species, but others were strangely unlike any known species. Fossils were often found in unexpected contexts; for example, marine invertebrates (sea animals without backbones) were sometimes discovered in rocks high on mountains. Leonardo da Vinci (1452–1519) was among the first to correctly interpret these unusual finds as the remains of animals that had existed in previous ages but had become extinct.

French naturalist Jean Baptiste de Lamarck (1744–1829) was the first scientist to propose that organisms undergo change over time as a result of some natural phenomenon rather than divine intervention. According to Lamarck, a changing environment caused an organism to alter its behavior, thereby using some organs or body parts more and others less. Over several generations, a given organ or body part would increase in size if it was used a lot or would shrink and possibly disappear if it was used less. Lamarck's hypothesis required that organisms pass traits that they acquired during their lifetimes to their offspring. For example, Lamarck suggested that the long neck of the giraffe developed when a short-necked ancestor stretched its neck to browse on the leaves of trees. Its offspring inherited the longer neck, which stretched even more as they ate. This process, repeated over many generations, resulted in the long necks of modern giraffes. Lamarck also thought that all organisms were endowed with a vital force that drove them to change toward greater complexity and "perfection" over time.

Lamarck's proposed mechanism of evolution is quite different from the mechanism later proposed by Darwin. However, Lamarck's hypothesis remained a reasonable explanation for evolution until Mendel's basis of heredity was rediscovered at the beginning of the 20th century. At that time, Lamarck's ideas were largely discredited.

CHECKPOINT 18.2

- CONNECT *How is Aristotle's "scale of nature" idea linked to early evolutionary thought? In what ways does it differ from modern scientific evolutionary theory?*

- CONNECT *How does Jean Baptiste de Lamarck's proposed mechanism for evolution differ from that of Charles Darwin?*

18.3 DARWIN AND EVOLUTION

LEARNING OBJECTIVES

3 Explain the four premises of evolution by natural selection as proposed by Charles Darwin.

4 Compare the modern synthesis with Darwin's original view of evolution.

Darwin, the son of a prominent physician, was sent at the age of 15 to study medicine at the University of Edinburgh. Finding himself unsuited for medicine, he transferred to Cambridge University to study theology. During that time, he became the protégé of the Reverend John Henslow, who was a professor of botany. Henslow encouraged Darwin's interest in the natural world. Shortly after receiving his degree, Darwin embarked on the HMS *Beagle,* which was taking a five-year exploratory cruise around the world to prepare navigation charts for the British navy.

The *Beagle* left Plymouth, England, in 1831 and cruised along the east and west coasts of South America (FIG. 18-2). While other members of the crew mapped the coasts and harbors, Darwin spent many weeks ashore studying the animals, plants, fossils, and geologic formations of both coastal and inland regions, areas that had not been extensively explored. He collected and cataloged thousands of plant and animal specimens and kept notes of his observations, information that became essential in the development of his ideas.

The *Beagle* spent almost two months at the Galápagos Islands, 965 km (600 mi) west of Ecuador, where Darwin continued his observations and collections. He compared the animals and plants of the Galápagos with those of the South

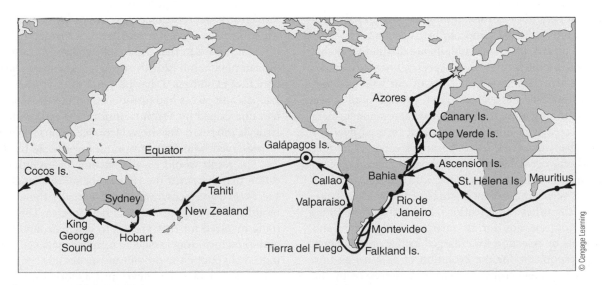

Figure 18-2 The voyage of HMS *Beagle*
The five-year voyage began in Plymouth, England (*star*), in 1831. Observations made in the Galápagos Islands (*bull's-eye*) off the western coast of South America helped Darwin develop a satisfactory mechanism to explain how a population of organisms could change over time.

American mainland. He was particularly impressed by their similarities and wondered why the organisms of the Galápagos should resemble those from South America more than those from other islands in different parts of the world. Moreover, although there were similarities between Galápagos and South American species, there were also distinct differences. There were even recognizable differences in the reptiles and birds from one island to the next. Darwin wondered why these remote islands should have such biological diversity. After he returned home, Darwin pondered these observations and attempted to develop a satisfactory explanation for the distribution of species among the islands.

Darwin drew on several lines of evidence when considering how species might have originated. Despite the work of Lamarck, the general notion in the mid-1800s was that Earth was too young for organisms to have changed significantly since they had first appeared. During the early 19th century, however, geologists advanced the idea that mountains, valleys, and other physical features of Earth's surface did not originate in their present forms. Instead, these features developed slowly over long periods by the geologic processes of volcanic activity, uplift, erosion, and glaciation. On his voyage Darwin took with him *Principles of Geology,* published by English geologist Charles Lyell in 1830, and studied it carefully. Lyell provided an important concept for Darwin: that the slow pace of geologic processes, which still occur today, indicated that Earth was extremely old.

Other important evidence that influenced Darwin was that breeders and farmers could develop many varieties of domesticated animals in just a few generations. They did so by choosing certain traits and breeding only individuals that exhibited the desired traits, a procedure known as **artificial selection.** Breeders, for example, have produced numerous dog varieties—such as bloodhounds, golden retrievers, Chihuahuas, Great Danes, and Pekinese—by artificial selection.

Many plant varieties were also produced by artificial selection. For example, cabbage, broccoli, brussels sprouts, cauliflower, collard greens, kale, and kohlrabi are distinct vegetable crops that are all members of the same species, *Brassica oleracea* (FIG. 18-3). Selective breeding of the colewort, or wild cabbage, a leafy plant native to Europe and Asia, produced all seven vegetables. Beginning more than 4000 years ago, some farmers artificially selected wild cabbage plants that formed overlapping leaves. Over time, these leaves became so prominent that the plants, which resembled modern cabbages, became recognized as separate and distinct from their wild cabbage ancestor. Other farmers selected different features of the wild cabbage, giving rise to the other modifications. For example, kohlrabi was produced by selection for an enlarged storage stem and brussels sprouts by selection for enlarged axillary buds. Thus, humans are responsible for the evolution of *B. oleracea* into seven distinct vegetable crops. Darwin was impressed by the changes induced by artificial selection and hypothesized that a similar selective process occurred in nature. He therefore used artificial selection as a model when he developed the concept of natural selection.

Figure 18-3 Artificial selection in *Brassica oleracea*

An enlarged terminal bud (the "head") was selected in cabbage (*lower left*), flower clusters in broccoli (*upper left*) and cauliflower (*middle right*), axillary buds in brussels sprouts (*bottom middle*), leaves in collards (*upper right*) and kale (*lower right*), and stems in kohlrabi (*middle*).

The ideas of Thomas Malthus (1766–1834), a British clergyman and economist, were another important influence on Darwin. In *An Essay on the Principle of Population as It Affects the Future Improvement of Society,* published in 1798, Malthus noted that population growth is not always desirable, a view contrary to the beliefs of his day. He observed that populations have the capacity to increase geometrically ($1 \rightarrow 2 \rightarrow 4 \rightarrow 8 \rightarrow 16$) and thus outstrip the food supply, which only has the capacity to increase arithmetically ($1 \rightarrow 2 \rightarrow 3 \rightarrow 4 \rightarrow 5$). In the case of humans, Malthus suggested that the conflict between population growth and food supply generates famine, disease, and war, which serve as inevitable brakes on population growth.

Malthus's idea that there is a strong and constant check on human population growth strongly influenced Darwin's explanation of evolution. Darwin's years of observing the habits of animals and plants had introduced him to the struggle for existence described by Malthus. It occurred to Darwin that in this struggle inherited variations favorable to survival would tend to be preserved, whereas unfavorable ones would be eliminated.

The result would be **adaptation,** an evolutionary modification that improves the chances of survival and reproductive success in a given environment. Eventually, the accumulation of modifications might result in a new species. Time was the only thing required for new species to originate, and the geologists of the era, including Lyell, had supplied evidence that Earth was indeed old enough to provide adequate time.

Darwin had at last developed a workable scientific explanation of evolution, that of **natural selection,** in which better adapted organisms are more likely to survive and become the parents of the next generation. As a result of natural selection, the population changes over time; the frequency of favorable traits increases in successive generations, whereas less-favorable traits become scarce or disappear. Darwin spent the next 20 years formulating his arguments for natural selection, accumulating an immense body of evidence to support this explanatory mechanism, and corresponding with other scientists.

As Darwin was pondering his ideas, Alfred Russel Wallace (1823–1913), a British naturalist who had studied the plants and animals of the Malay Archipelago for eight years, was similarly struck by the diversity of species and the peculiarities of their distribution. He wrote a brief essay on this subject and sent it to Darwin, by then a world-renowned biologist, asking his opinion. Darwin recognized his own ideas and realized that Wallace had independently arrived at the same conclusion: that evolution occurs by natural selection. Darwin's colleagues persuaded him to present Wallace's manuscript along with an abstract of his own work, which he had prepared and circulated to a few friends several years earlier. Both papers were presented in July 1858 at a London meeting of the Linnaean Society. Darwin's monumental book, *On the Origin of Species by Natural Selection; or, The Preservation of Favored Races in the Struggle for Life*, was published in 1859. In 1870, Wallace's book, *Contributions to the Theory of Natural Selection*, was published, eight years after he had returned from the Malay Archipelago.

Darwin proposed that evolution occurs by natural selection

Darwin's mechanism of evolution by natural selection consists of observations on four aspects of the natural world: variation; overproduction; limits on population growth, or a struggle for existence; and differential reproductive success.

1. *Variation.* The individuals in a population exhibit variation (FIG. 18-4). Each individual has a unique combination of traits, such as size, color, ability to tolerate harsh environmental conditions, and resistance to certain parasites or infections. Some traits improve an individual's chances of

Figure 18-4 Genetic variation in emerald tree boas

These snakes, all the same species (*Corallus caninus*), were caught in a small section of forest in French Guiana. Many snake species exhibit considerable variation in their coloration and patterns.

survival and reproductive success, whereas others do not. Remember that the variation necessary for evolution by natural selection must be inherited. Although Darwin recognized the importance to evolution of inherited variation, he did not know the mechanism of inheritance.

2. *Overproduction.* The reproductive ability of each species has the potential to cause its population to geometrically increase over time. A female frog lays about 10,000 eggs, and a female cod produces perhaps 40 million eggs! In each case, however, only about two offspring survive to reproduce. Thus, in every generation each species has the capacity to produce more offspring than can survive.

3. *Limits on population growth, or a struggle for existence.* There is only so much food, water, light, growing space, and other resources available to a population, so organisms compete with one another for these limited resources. Because there are more individuals than the environment can support, not all survive to reproduce. Other limits on population growth include predators, disease organisms, and unfavorable weather conditions.

4. *Differential reproductive success.* Those individuals that have the most favorable combination of characteristics (those that make individuals better adapted to their environment) are more likely to survive and reproduce. Offspring tend to resemble their parents because the next generation inherits the parents' genetically based traits. Successful reproduction is the key to natural selection: the best-adapted individuals produce the most offspring, whereas individuals that are less well adapted die prematurely or produce fewer or inferior offspring.

Over time, enough changes may accumulate in geographically separated populations (often with slightly different environments) to produce new species. Darwin noted that the Galápagos finches appeared to have evolved in this way. The 14 species are closely related. All descended from a common ancestor, a single species that found its way from the South American mainland two million to three million years ago. (The closest genetic relatives of the Galápagos finches are small seed-eating birds known as grassquits that live in western South America.)

During this two-million- to three-million-year period, the number of islands increased, the climate changed, and the plant life and food supply changed. The different islands of the Galápagos kept the finches isolated from one another, thereby allowing them to diverge into separate species in response to varying conditions (FIG. 18-5).

Peter Grant, Rosemary Grant, and their colleagues have documented natural selection in the Galápagos finches in their natural environment since the early 1970s. As an example of the evolutionary process in action, consider the sharp-beaked ground finch (*Geospiza difficilis*). This species lives on several different islands, and different beak shapes and sizes have evolved in each population depending on the diet available on the island where it lives.

We revisit the Galápagos finches in later chapters. Some long-term research by Peter Grant, Rosemary Grant, and their colleagues on the microevolution of Galápagos finches when

(a) The cactus finch (*Geospiza scandens*), which feeds on the fleshy parts of cacti such as their flowers, has a long, pointed beak.

(b) The large ground finch (*Geospiza magnirostris*) has an extremely heavy, nutcracker-type beak adapted for eating thick, hard-walled seeds.

(c) The warbler finch (*Certhidia olivacea*) has a slender beak for eating insects.

(d) The woodpecker finch (*Camarhynchus pallidus*) digs insects out of bark and crevices by using spines, twigs, or even dead leaves.

Figure 18-5 *Animation* **Galápagos finches**

Darwin inferred that these birds are derived from a common ancestral population of seed-eating birds from South America. Variation in their beaks is the result of adaptation to the availability of different kinds of food.

droughts affect the food supply is described in Chapter 19; these studies have demonstrated that environmental change can drive natural selection. *Character displacement,* an aspect of evolutionary ecology, is described in Galápagos finches in Chapter 54.

The modern synthesis combines Darwin's scientific theory of evolution with genetics

One premise on which Darwin based his scientific theory of evolution by natural selection is that individuals transmit traits to the next generation. However, Darwin was unable to explain *how* this occurs or *why* individuals vary within a population. As discussed in Chapter 11, Gregor Mendel elucidated the basic patterns of inheritance. Darwin, who was a contemporary of Mendel, was apparently not acquainted with Mendel's work. Indeed, the scientific community did not recognize Mendel's work until the early part of the 20th century.

Beginning in the 1930s and 1940s, biologists experienced a conceptual breakthrough when they combined the principles of Mendelian inheritance with Darwin's principle of natural selection. The result was a unified explanation of evolution known as the **modern synthesis.** In this context, *synthesis* refers to combining parts of several scientific theories to form a unified whole. Some of the founders of the modern synthesis were U.S. geneticist Theodosius Dobzhansky, British geneticist and statistician Ronald Fisher, British geneticist J.B.S. Haldane, British biologist Julian Huxley, U.S. biologist Ernst Mayr, U.S. paleontologist George Gaylord Simpson, U.S. botanist G. Ledyard Stebbins, and U.S. geneticist Sewell Wright.

Today, the modern synthesis incorporates our expanding knowledge in genetics (which on its own makes an irrefutable case for evolution), systematics, paleontology, developmental biology, behavior, and ecology. The modern synthesis explains Darwin's observation of variation among offspring in terms of **mutation,** or changes in DNA, such as nucleotide substitutions. Mutations provide the genetic variability on which natural selection acts during evolution. The modern synthesis, which

emphasizes the genetics of populations as the central focus of evolution, has held up well since it was developed. It has dominated the thinking and research of biologists working in many areas and has resulted in an enormous accumulation of new discoveries that validate evolution by natural selection.

Most biologists not only accept the basic principles of the modern synthesis but also try to better understand the causal processes of evolution. For example, what is the role of chance in evolution? How rapidly do new species evolve? These and other questions have arisen in part from a re-evaluation of the fossil record and in part from new discoveries in molecular aspects of inheritance. Such critical analyses are an integral part of the scientific process because they stimulate additional observation and experimentation along with re-examination of previous evidence. Science is an ongoing process, and information obtained in the future may require modifications to certain parts of the modern synthesis.

We now consider one of the many evolutionary questions currently being addressed by biologists: What are the relative effects of chance and natural selection on evolution?

Biologists study the effect of chance on evolution

Biologists have wondered whether we would get the same results if we were able to repeat evolution by starting with similar organisms exposed to similar environmental conditions. That is, would the same kinds of changes evolve as a result of natural selection, or would the organisms be quite different as a result of random events? Studies of evolution in action suggest that chance may not be as important as natural selection, at least at the population level.

A fruit fly species (*Drosophila subobscura*) native to Europe inhabits areas from Denmark to Spain. Biologists noted that the northern flies have larger wings than southern flies (FIG. 18-6). The same fly species was accidentally introduced to North America in the late 1970s. Ten years after its introduction,

Figure 18-6 Wing size in female fruit flies

In Europe female fruit flies (*Drosophila subobscura*) in southern countries have smaller wings than flies in northern countries. Shown are two flies: one from Spain (*left*) and the other from Denmark (*right*) . The same evolutionary pattern emerged in North America after the accidental introduction of *D. subobscura* to the Americas.

biologists determined that no statistically significant changes in wing size had occurred in the different regions of North America. However, 20 years after its introduction, the fruit flies in North America exhibited the same type of north–south wing changes as in Europe. (It is not known why larger wings evolve in northern areas and smaller wings in southern climates.)

A study of the evolution of fishes known as *sticklebacks* in three coastal lakes of western Canada yielded intriguingly similar results to the fruit fly study. Molecular evidence indicates that when the lakes first formed several thousand years ago, they were populated with the same ancestral species. (Analysis of the mitochondrial DNA of sticklebacks in the three lakes supports the hypothesis of a common ancestor.) In each lake the same two species have evolved from the common ancestral fish. One species is large and consumes invertebrates along the bottom of the lake, whereas the other species is smaller and consumes plankton at the lake's surface. Members of the two species within a single lake do not interbreed with each other, but individuals of the larger species from one lake interbreed in captivity with individuals of the larger species from the other lakes. Similarly, smaller individuals from one lake interbreed in captivity with smaller individuals from the other lakes.

In these examples, natural selection appears to be a more important agent of evolutionary change than chance. If chance were the most important factor influencing the direction of evolution, fruit fly evolution would not have proceeded the same way on two different continents and stickleback evolution would not have proceeded the same way in three different lakes. However, just because we have many examples of the importance of natural selection in evolution, it does not necessarily follow that random events should be discounted as a factor in evolutionary change. Proponents of the role of chance think that it is more important in the evolution of major taxonomic groups (macroevolution) than in the evolution of populations (microevolution). It also may be that random events take place but that their effects on evolution are harder to demonstrate than natural selection.

C HECKPOINT 18.3

- **CONNECT** *What is the relationship between artificial selection and natural selection?*
- *Why are only inherited variations important in the evolutionary process? Explain your answer.*
- **CONNECT** *What was missing in Darwin's explanation of evolution by natural selection? How does the modern synthesis fill this gap?*

18.4 EVIDENCE FOR EVOLUTION

L EARNING OBJECTIVES

5 Summarize the evidence for evolution obtained from the fossil record.
6 Define *biogeography* and describe how the distribution of organisms supports evolution.
7 Describe the evidence for evolution derived from comparative anatomy.
8 Briefly explain how molecular biology and developmental biology provide insights into the evolutionary process.
9 Give an example of how evolutionary hypotheses are tested experimentally.

A vast body of scientific evidence supports evolution, including observations from the fossil record, biogeography, comparative anatomy, molecular biology, and developmental biology. In addition, evolutionary hypotheses are increasingly being tested experimentally. Taken together, this evidence confirms the scientific theory that life unfolded on Earth by the process of evolution.

The fossil record provides strong evidence for evolution

Perhaps the most direct evidence for evolution comes from the discovery, identification, and interpretation of **fossils,** which are the remains or traces typically left in sedimentary rock by previously existing organisms. (The term *fossil* comes from the Latin word *fossilis,* meaning "something dug up.") Sedimentary rock forms by the accumulation and solidification of particles (pebbles, sand, silt, or clay) produced by the weathering of older rocks, such as volcanic rocks. The sediment particles, which are usually deposited on a riverbed, lake bottom, or the ocean floor, accumulate over time and exhibit distinct layers (FIG. 18-7). In an undisturbed rock sequence, the oldest layer is at the bottom, and upper layers are successively younger. The study of sedimentary rock layers, including their composition, arrangement, and similarity from one location to another, enables geologists to place events recorded in rocks in their correct sequence.

The fossil record shows a progression from the earliest unicellular organisms to the many unicellular and multicellular organisms living today (see Table 21-1). The fossil record therefore demonstrates that life has evolved through time. To date, paleontologists (scientists who study extinct species) have

Figure 18-7 Exposed layers of sedimentary rock at the Burgess shale fossil bed

This site, located in the Canadian Rockies, was formed about 500 million years ago when an avalanche of mud buried and preserved diverse and unusual marine animals.

described and named about 300,000 fossil species, and others are still being discovered.

Although most fossils are preserved in sedimentary rock, some more recent remains have been exceptionally well preserved in bogs, tar, amber (ancient tree resin), or ice (**FIG. 18-8**). For example, the remains of a woolly mammoth deep-frozen in Siberian ice for more than 25,000 years were so well preserved that part of its DNA could be analyzed.

Few organisms that die become fossils. The formation and preservation of a fossil require that an organism be buried under conditions that slow or prevent the decay process. These conditions are most likely to occur if an organism's remains are covered quickly by a sediment of fine soil particles suspended in water. In this way, the remains of aquatic organisms may be trapped in bogs, mudflats, sandbars, or deltas. Remains of terrestrial organisms that lived on a floodplain may also be covered by waterborne sediments or, if the organism lived in an arid region, by windblown sand. Over time, the sediments harden to form sedimentary rock, and minerals usually replace the organism's remains so that many details of its structure, even cellular details, are preserved.

The fossil record is not a random sample of past life but instead is biased toward aquatic organisms and those living in the few terrestrial habitats conducive to fossil formation. Relatively few fossils of tropical rainforest organisms have been

found, for example, because their remains decay extremely rapidly on the forest floor, before fossils can develop. Another reason for bias in the fossil record is that organisms with hard body parts such as bones and shells are more likely to form fossils than are those with soft body parts. Also, rocks of different ages are unequally exposed at Earth's surface; some rocks of certain ages are more accessible to paleontologists for fossil study than are rocks of other ages.

Because of the nature of the scientific process, each fossil discovery represents a separate "test" of scientific evolutionary theory. If any of the tests fail, the theory would have to be modified to fit the existing evidence. The verifiable discovery, for example, of fossil remains of modern humans (*Homo sapiens*) in Precambrian rocks, which are more than 570 million years old, would falsify evolutionary theory as currently proposed. However, Precambrian rocks examined to date contain only fossils of simple organisms, such as algae and small, soft-bodied animals, that evolved early in the history of life. The earliest fossils of *H. sapiens* with anatomically modern features do not appear in the fossil record until approximately 195,000 years ago (see Chapter 22).

Fossils provide a record of ancient organisms and some understanding of where and when they lived. Using fossils of organisms from different geologic ages, scientists can sometimes infer the lines of descent (evolutionary relationships) that gave rise to modern-day organisms. In many instances, fossils provide direct evidence of the origin of new species from preexisting species, including many transitional forms.

Transitional fossils document whale evolution Over the past century, biologists have found evidence suggesting that whales and other cetaceans (an order of marine mammals) evolved from land-dwelling mammals. During the 1980s and 1990s, paleontologists discovered several fossil intermediates in whale evolution that help document the whales' transition from land to water.

Fossils of *Ambulocetus natans,* a 50-million-year-old transitional form discovered in Pakistan, have many features of modern whales but also possess hind limbs and feet (**FIG. 18-9a**). (Modern whales do not have hind limbs, although *vestigial* pelvic and hind-limb bones persist. Vestigial structures are discussed later in the chapter.) The vertebrae of *Ambulocetus*'s lower back were very flexible, allowing the back to move dorsoventrally (up and down) during swimming and diving, as with modern whales. This ancient whale could swim but also moved about on land, perhaps as sea lions do today.

Rodhocetus is a fossil whale found in more recent rocks in Pakistan (**FIG. 18-9b**). The vertebrae of *Rodhocetus* were even more flexible than those found in *Ambulocetus*. The flexible vertebrae allowed *Rodhocetus* a more powerful dorsoventral movement during swimming. *Rodhocetus* may have been totally aquatic.

By 40 million years ago (mya), the whale transition from land to ocean was almost complete. Egyptian fossils of *Basilosaurus* show a whale with a streamlined body and front flippers for steering, like those of modern-day whales (**FIG. 18-9c**). *Basilosaurus* retained vestiges of its land-dwelling ancestors—a pair of reduced hind limbs that were disjointed from the backbone

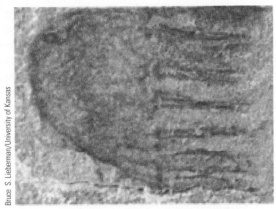

(a) Although some fossils contain traces of organic matter, all that remains in this fossil of a 500-million-year-old jellyfish is an impression, or imprint, in the rock.

(b) Petrified wood from the Petrified Forest National Park in Arizona consists of trees that were buried and infiltrated with minerals. The logs were exposed by erosion of the mudstone layers in which they were buried.

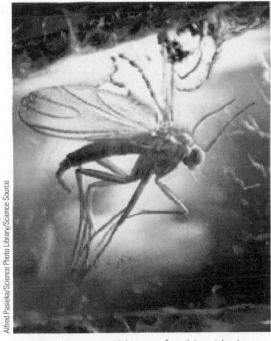

(c) A 2-million-year-old insect fossil (a midge) was embedded in amber.

(d) A cast fossil of ancient echinoderms called *crinoids* formed when the crinoids decomposed, leaving a mold that later filled with dissolved minerals that hardened.

(e) Dinosaur footprints, each 75 to 90 cm (2.5 to 3 ft) in length, provide clues about the posture, gait, and behavior of these extinct animals.

Figure 18-8 Fossils are formed in different ways

(a) *Ambulocetus natans*, a transitional form between modern whale descendants and their terrestrial ancestors, possessed several recognizable whale features. It retained the hind limbs of its four-legged ancestors, however.

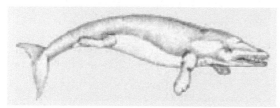

(b) The more recent *Rodhocetus* had flexible vertebrae that permitted a powerful dorsoventral movement during swimming.

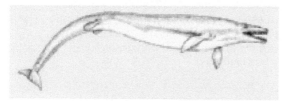

(c) *Basilosaurus* was more streamlined and possessed tiny, nonfunctional hind limbs.

(d) *Balaenoptera*, the modern blue whale, contains vestiges of pelvis and leg bones embedded in its body.

Figure 18-9 Fossil intermediates in whale evolution

Biologists hypothesize that the ancestors of whales had four legs, as shown in these reconstructions of whale intermediates based on fossil evidence. Fossils indicate that ankle bones in whale intermediates match those found in present-day hippos, cows, pigs, and camels. Figures are not drawn to scale. (**a–c:** Adapted with permission from Futuyma, D.J., *Science on Trial: The Case for Evolution*, Fig. 2, pp. 260–261, Sinauer Associates, Sunderland, MA, 1995; **d:** © Cengage Learning)

and probably not used in locomotion—and this reduction in the hind limbs continued to the present. The modern blue whale has vestigial pelvis and femur bones embedded in its body (**FIG. 18-9d**).

Various methods determine the age of fossils Because layers of sedimentary rock occur naturally in the sequence of their deposition, with the more recent layers on top of the older, earlier ones, most fossils are dated by their relative position in

sedimentary rock. However, geologic events occurring after the rocks were initially formed have occasionally changed the relationships of some rock layers. Geologists identify specific sedimentary rocks not only by their positions in layers but also by features such as mineral content and by the fossilized remains of certain organisms, known as **index fossils,** that characterize a specific layer over large geographic areas. Index fossils are fossils of organisms that existed for a relatively short geologic time but were preserved as fossils in large numbers. With this information, geologists can arrange rock layers and the fossils they contain in chronological order and identify comparable layers in widely separated locations.

Radioactive isotopes, also called **radioisotopes,** present in a rock provide a means to accurately measure its age (see Chapter 2). Radioisotopes emit invisible radiations. As radiation is emitted, the nucleus of a radioisotope changes into the nucleus of a different element through a process known as **radioactive decay.** The radioactive nucleus of uranium-235, for example, decays into lead-207.

Each radioisotope has its own characteristic rate of decay. The time required for one-half of the atoms of a radioisotope to change into a different atom is known as its **half-life** (FIG. 18-10). Radioisotopes differ significantly in their half-lives. For example, the half-life of iodine-132 is only 2.4 hours, whereas the half-life of uranium-235 is 704 million years. The half-life of a particular radioisotope is constant and does not vary with temperature, pressure, or any other environmental factor.

The age of a fossil in sedimentary rock is usually estimated by measuring the relative proportions of the original radioisotope and its decay product in volcanic rock intrusions that penetrate the sediments. For example, the half-life of potassium-40 is 1.3 billion years, meaning that in 1.3 billion years half of the radioactive potassium will have decayed into its decay product, argon-40. The radioactive clock begins ticking when the magma solidifies into volcanic rock. The rock initially contains

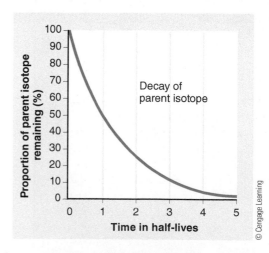

Figure 18-10 *Animation* **Radioisotope decay**

At time zero, the sample is composed entirely of the radioisotope, and the radioactive clock begins ticking. After one half-life, only 50% of the original radioisotope remains. During each succeeding half-life, half of the remaining radioisotope is converted to decay product(s).

some potassium but no argon. Because argon is a gas, it escapes from hot rock as soon as it forms, but when potassium decays in rock that has cooled and solidified, the argon accumulates in the crystalline structure of the rock. If the ratio of potassium-40 to argon-40 in the rock being tested is 1:1, the rock is 1.3 billion years old.

Several radioisotopes are commonly used to date fossils, including potassium-40 (half-life 1.3 billion years), uranium-235 (half-life 704 million years), and carbon-14 (half-life 5730 years). Radioisotopes other than carbon-14 are used to date the *rock* in which fossils are found, whereas carbon-14 is used to date the *carbon remains* of anything that was once living, such as wood, bones, and shells. Whenever possible, the age of a fossil is independently verified using two or more different radioisotopes.

Carbon-14, which is continuously produced in the atmosphere from nitrogen-14 (by cosmic radiation), subsequently decays to nitrogen-14. Because the formation and the decay of carbon-14 occur at constant rates, the ratio of carbon-14 to carbon-12 (a more abundant, stable isotope of carbon) is constant in the atmosphere. Organisms absorb carbon from the atmosphere either directly (by photosynthesis) or indirectly (by consuming photosynthetic organisms). Because each organism absorbs carbon from the atmosphere, its ratio of carbon-14 to carbon-12 is the same as that in the atmosphere. When an organism dies, however, it no longer absorbs carbon, and the proportion of carbon-14 in its remains declines as carbon-14 decays to nitrogen-14. Because of its relatively short half-life, carbon-14 is useful for dating fossils that are 50,000 years old or less. It is particularly useful for dating archaeological sites.

The distribution of plants and animals supports evolution

The study of the past and present geographic distribution of organisms is called **biogeography.** The geographic distribution of organisms affects their evolution. Darwin was interested in biogeography, and he considered why the species found on ocean islands tend to resemble species of the nearest mainland, even if the environment is different. He also observed that species on ocean islands do not tend to resemble species on islands with similar environments in other parts of the world.

Darwin studied the plants and animals of two sets of arid islands: the Cape Verde Islands, nearly 640 km (400 mi) off western Africa; and the Galápagos Islands, about 965 km (600 mi) west of Ecuador, South America. On each group of islands, the plants and terrestrial animals were indigenous (native), but those of the Cape Verde Islands resembled African species and those of the Galápagos resembled South American species. The similarities of Galápagos species to South American species were particularly striking considering that the Galápagos Islands are dry and rocky and that the nearest part of South America is humid and has a lush, tropical rain forest. Darwin concluded that species from the neighboring continent migrated or were carried to the islands, where they

subsequently adapted to the new environment and, in the process, evolved into new species.

If evolution were not a factor in the distribution of species, we would expect to find a given species everywhere it could survive. However, the actual geographic distribution of organisms makes sense in the context of evolution. For example, Australia, which has been a separate landmass for millions of years, has distinctive organisms. Australia has populations of egg-laying mammals (monotremes) and pouched mammals (marsupials) not found anywhere else. Two hundred million years ago, Australia and the other continents were joined in a major landmass. Over the course of millions of years, the Australian continent gradually separated from the others. The monotremes and marsupials in Australia continued to thrive and diversify. The isolation of Australia also prevented placental mammals, which arose elsewhere at a later time, from competing with its monotremes and marsupials. In other areas of the world where placental mammals evolved, most monotremes and marsupials became extinct.

We now consider how Earth's dynamic geology has affected biogeography and evolution.

Biogeography and evolution are related to Earth's geologic history In 1915, German scientist Alfred Wegener, who had noted a correspondence between the geographic shapes of South America and Africa, proposed that all the landmasses had at one time been joined into one huge supercontinent, which he called Pangaea (FIG. 18-11a). He further suggested that Pangaea had subsequently broken apart and that the various landmasses had separated in a process known as **continental drift.** Wegener did not know of any mechanism that could have caused continental drift, so his idea, although debated initially, was largely ignored.

In the 1960s, scientific evidence provided the explanation for continental drift. Earth's crust is composed of seven large plates (plus a few smaller ones) that float on the mantle, which is the mostly solid layer of Earth lying beneath the crust and above the core. (Because of its hotter temperature, the solid rock of the mantle is more plastic than the solid rock of the crust above it.)

The landmasses are situated on some of these plates. As the plates move, the continents change their relative positions (FIGS. 18-11b, c, and d). The movement of the crustal plates is called *plate tectonics.*

Any area where two plates meet is a site of intense geologic activity. Earthquakes and volcanoes are common in such a region. Both San Francisco, noted for its earthquakes, and the Mount St. Helens volcano are situated where two plates meet. If landmasses lie on the edges of two adjacent plates, mountains may form. The Himalayas formed when the plate carrying India rammed into the plate carrying Asia. When two plates grind together, one of them is sometimes buried under the other in a process known as *subduction.* When two plates move apart, a ridge of lava forms between them. The Atlantic Ocean is increasing in size because of the expanding zone of lava along the Mid-Atlantic Ridge, where two plates are separating.

Knowledge that the continents were at one time connected and have since drifted apart is useful in explaining certain

Geologists hypothesize that the breakup of Pangaea is only the latest in a series of continental breakups and collisions that have taken place since early in Earth's history.

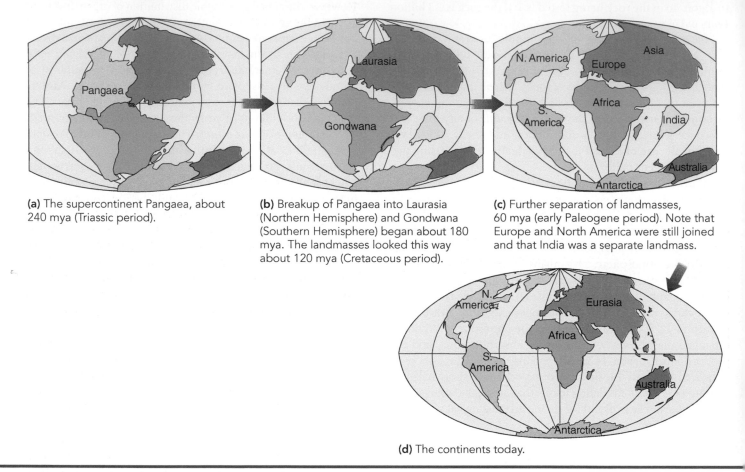

(a) The supercontinent Pangaea, about 240 mya (Triassic period).

(b) Breakup of Pangaea into Laurasia (Northern Hemisphere) and Gondwana (Southern Hemisphere) began about 180 mya. The landmasses looked this way about 120 mya (Cretaceous period).

(c) Further separation of landmasses, 60 mya (early Paleogene period). Note that Europe and North America were still joined and that India was a separate landmass.

(d) The continents today.

Figure 18-11 Continental drift

CONNECT If you were to find 60-million-year-old fossils of a species of land plants on the east coast of the northern part of North America, on what part of which continent would you begin a quest for similar fossils?
© Cengage Learning

aspects of biogeography (FIG. 18-12). Likewise, continental drift has played a major role in the evolution of different organisms. When Pangaea originally formed during the late Permian period, it brought together terrestrial species that had evolved separately from one another, leading to competition and some extinction. Marine life was adversely affected, in part because, with the continents joined as one large mass, less coastal area existed. (Shallow coastal areas contain a greater diversity of marine species than deep-water environments.)

Pangaea separated into several landmasses approximately 180 mya. As the continents began to drift apart, populations became geographically isolated, were exposed to different environmental conditions, and began to diverge along separate evolutionary pathways. As a result, the plants, animals, and other organisms of previously connected continents—South America and Africa, for example—differ. Continental drift also caused gradual changes in ocean and atmospheric currents that have profoundly influenced the biogeography and evolution of organisms. (Biogeography is discussed further in Chapter 56.)

Comparative anatomy of related species demonstrates similarities in their structures

Comparing the structural details of features found in different but related organisms reveals a basic similarity. Such features that are derived from the same structure in a common ancestor are called **homologous features;** the condition is known as **homology.** For example, consider the limb bones of mammals. A human arm, a cat forelimb, a whale front flipper, and a bat wing, although quite different in appearance, have strikingly similar arrangements of bones, muscles, and nerves. FIGURE 18-13 shows a comparison of their skeletal structures. Each has a single bone (the humerus) in the part of the limb nearest the trunk of the body, followed by the two bones (radius and ulna) of the forearm, a group of bones (carpals) in the wrist, and a variable number of digits (metacarpals and phalanges). This similarity is particularly striking because arms, forelimbs, flippers, and wings are used for different types of locomotion, and there is no overriding mechanical

Knowledge that the continents were united at one time explains the unique distribution of certain fossil plants and animals.

(a) *Cynognathus* was a carnivorous reptile found in Triassic rocks in South America and Africa.

(b) *Lystrosaurus* was a herbivorous reptile found in Triassic rocks in Africa, India, and Antarctica.

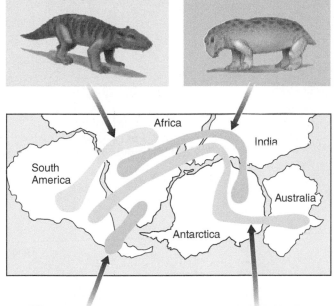

Mesosaurus

Glossopteris

(c) *Mesosaurus* was a freshwater reptile found in Permian rocks in South America and Africa.

(d) *Glossopteris* was a seed-bearing tree found in Permian rocks in South America, Africa, India, Antarctica, and Australia.

Adapted from E.H. Colbert, *Wandering Lands and Animals,* Hutchinson, London, 1973.

Figure 18-12 Distribution of fossils on continents that were joined during the Permian and Triassic periods (286 mya to 213 mya)

CONNECT Examine Figure 18-11. With which continent is Antarctica most likely to share 60-million-year-old fossils of a particular species of land animals?

reason for them to be so similar structurally. Similar arrangements of parts of the forelimb are evident in ancestral birds, reptiles, and amphibians and even in the first fishes that came out of water onto land hundreds of millions of years ago (see Fig. 32-17).

Leaves provide an example of homology in plants. In many plant species, leaves have been modified for functions other than photosynthesis. A cactus spine and a pea tendril, although quite different in appearance, are homologous because both are modified leaves (FIG. 18-14). The spine protects the succulent stem tissue of the cactus, whereas the tendril, which winds around a small object once it makes contact, helps support the climbing stem of the pea plant. Such modifications in organs used in different ways are the expected outcome of a common evolutionary origin. The basic structure present in a common ancestor was modified in different ways for different functions as various descendants subsequently evolved.

Not all species with "similar" features have descended from a recent common ancestor, however. Sometimes similar environmental conditions result in the evolution of similar adaptations. Such independent evolution of similar structures in distantly related organisms is known as **convergent evolution.** Aardvarks, anteaters, and pangolins are an excellent example of convergent evolution (FIG. 18-15). They resemble one another in lifestyle and certain structural features. All have strong, sharp claws to dig open ant and termite mounds and elongated snouts with long, sticky tongues to catch these insects. Yet aardvarks, anteaters, and pangolins evolved from three distantly related orders of mammals. (See Figure 32-28, which shows several examples of convergent evolution in placental and marsupial mammals.)

Structurally similar features that are not homologous but have similar functions that evolved independently in distantly related organisms are said to be **homoplastic features.** Such similarities in different species that are independently acquired by convergent evolution and not by common descent are called **homoplasy.**[2]

For example, the wings of various distantly related flying animals, such as insects and birds, resemble one another superficially; they are homoplastic features that evolved over time to meet the common function of flight, although they differ in more fundamental aspects. Bird wings are modified forelimbs supported by bones, whereas insect wings may have evolved from gill-like appendages present in the aquatic ancestors of insects.

Spines, which are modified leaves, and thorns, which are modified stems, are an example of homoplasy in plants. Spines and thorns resemble each other superficially but are homoplastic features that evolved independently to solve the common need for protection from herbivores (FIG. 18-16).

Like homology, homoplasy offers crucial evidence of evolution. Homoplastic features are of evolutionary interest because they demonstrate that organisms with separate ancestries may adapt in similar ways to similar environmental demands.

Comparative anatomy also reveals the existence of **vestigial** structures. Many organisms contain organs or parts of organs that are seemingly nonfunctional and degenerate, often undersized or lacking some essential part. Vestigial structures are remnants of more developed structures that were present and functional in ancestral organisms. In the human body, more than one hundred structures are considered vestigial, including

---

[2] An older, less precise term that some biologists still use for nonhomologous features with similar functions is *analogy.*

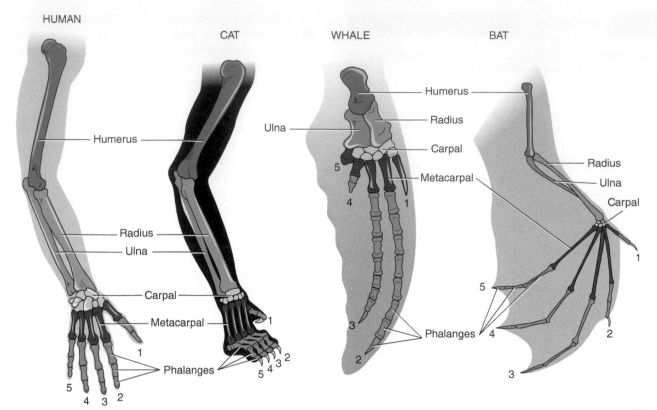

Figure 18-13 *Animation* **Structural homology in vertebrates**
The human arm, cat forelimb, whale flipper, and bat wing have a basic under-
lying similarity of structure because they are derived from a common ancestor.
The five digits are numbered in each drawing.
© Cengage Learning

the coccyx (fused tailbones), third molars (wisdom teeth), and
the muscles that move our ears. Whales and pythons (FIG. 18-17)
have vestigial hind-limb bones; pigs have vestigial toes that do
not touch the ground; wingless birds such as the kiwi have vestigial wing bones; and many blind, burrowing, or cave-dwelling
animals have nonfunctioning, vestigial eyes.

The occasional presence of a vestigial structure is to be
expected as a species adapts to a changing mode of life. Some
structures become much less important for survival and may
end up as vestiges. When a structure no longer confers a selective advantage, it may become smaller and lose all or much of its
function with the passage of time. Because the presence of the
vestigial structure is usually not harmful to the organism, however, selective pressure for completely eliminating it is weak, and
the vestigial structure is found in many subsequent generations.

Molecular comparisons among organisms provide evidence for evolution

Fossils, biogeography, and comparative anatomy provided Darwin
with important clues about the evolutionary history of life. Today,
similarities and differences in the biochemistry and molecular
biology of various organisms provide additional compelling
evidence for evolutionary relationships. Molecular evidence for
evolution includes the universal genetic code and the conserved
sequences of amino acids in proteins and of nucleotides in DNA.

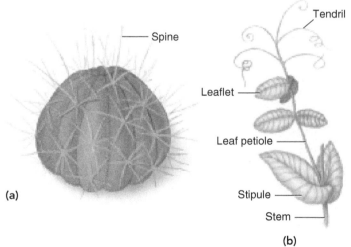

Figure 18-14 Homology in plants
(a) The spines of the fishhook cactus (*Ferocactus wislizenii*) are modified
leaves, as are **(b)** the tendrils of the garden pea (*Pisum sativum*). Leaves of
the garden pea are compound; that is, they are divided into smaller components called leaflets. The terminal leaflets are modified into tendrils that are
frequently branched.
© Cengage Learning

The genetic code is virtually universal Organisms owe
their characteristics to the types of proteins they possess, which
in turn are determined by the sequence of nucleotides in their
messenger ribonucleic acid (mRNA) as specified by the order
of nucleotides in their DNA. Evidence that all life is related
comes from all organisms using a genetic code that is virtually
identical. (There is some minor variation in the genetic code.
For example, some mitochondria have several deviations from
the standard code.)

(a) The aardvark (*Orycteropus afer*) is native to central, southern, and eastern Africa.

(b) A giant anteater (*Myrmecophaga tridactyla*) at a termite mound. The anteater is native to Latin America, from southern Mexico to northern Argentina.

(c) The pangolin (*Manis crassicaudata*) is native to Africa and to southern and southeastern Asia.

Figure 18-15 Convergent evolution

Three distantly related mammals adapted independently to eat ants and termites in similar grassland/forest environments in different parts of the world.

Recall from Chapter 13 that the genetic code specifies a triplet (a sequence of three nucleotides in DNA) that codes for a particular codon (a sequence of three nucleotides in mRNA). The codon then codes for a particular amino acid in a polypeptide chain. For example, AAA in DNA codes for UUU in mRNA, which codes for the amino acid phenylalanine in organisms as diverse as shrimp, humans, bacteria, and tulips. In fact, AAA codes for phenylalanine in all organisms examined to date.

The universality of the genetic code—no other code has been found in any organism—is convincing evidence that all organisms arose from a common ancestor. The genetic code has been maintained and transmitted through all branches of the evolutionary tree since its origin in some extremely early (and successful) organism.

Proteins and DNA contain a record of evolutionary change Researchers have carried out thousands of comparisons of protein and DNA sequences from various species since the late 1970s. Moreover, the recent explosion in DNA sequencing information (more than 1000 species have now had their genomes sequenced) is beginning to provide a wealth of evolutionary data as these genomes are compared. Sequence-based relationships generally agree with earlier studies, which based evolutionary relationships on similarities in structure among living organisms and on fossil data of extinct organisms.

Investigations of the sequence of amino acids in proteins that play the same roles in many species have revealed both great similarities and certain specific differences. Even organisms that are only remotely related share some proteins, such as cytochrome *c*, which is part of the electron transport chain in aerobic respiration. To survive, all aerobic organisms need a respiratory protein with the same basic structure and function as the cytochrome *c* of their common ancestor. Consequently, not all amino acids that confer the structural and functional features of cytochrome *c* are free to change. Any mutations that changed the amino acid sequence at structurally important sites of the cytochrome *c* molecule would have been harmful, and natural selection would have prevented such mutations from being passed to future generations. However, in the course of the long, independent evolution of different organisms, mutations have resulted in the substitution of many amino acids at less important locations in the cytochrome *c* molecule. The greater the differences in the amino acid sequences of their cytochrome *c* molecules, the longer it has been since two species diverged.

Because a protein's amino acid sequences are coded in DNA, the differences in amino acid sequences indirectly reflect the nature and number of underlying DNA base-pair changes that must have occurred during evolution. Of course, not all DNA codes for proteins (witness the regulatory RNAs summarized in Table 13-1, as well as ribosomal RNA and transfer RNA genes). **DNA sequencing,** i.e., determining the order of nucleotide bases in both protein-coding DNA and non-protein-coding DNA, is proving invaluable in determining evolutionary relationships.

Generally, the more closely species are considered related on the basis of other scientific evidence, the greater the percentage of nucleotide sequences that their DNA molecules have in common. By using the DNA sequence data in **FIGURE 18-18,** for example, you can conclude that the closest living relative of humans is the chimpanzee (because its DNA has the lowest percentage of differences in the sequence examined). (Primate evolution is discussed in Chapter 22.)

In some cases, molecular evidence challenges traditional evolutionary ideas that were based on structural comparisons among living species and/or on studies of fossil skeletons.

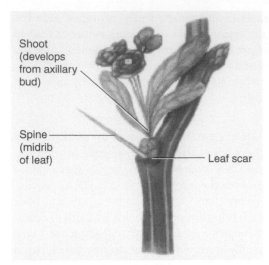

Shoot (develops from axillary bud)

Spine (midrib of leaf)

Leaf scar

(a) A spine of Japanese barberry (*Berberis thunbergii*) is a modified leaf. (In this example, the spine is actually the midrib of the original leaf, which has been shed.)

Thorn (develops from axillary bud)

© Cengage Learning

(b) Thorns of downy hawthorn (*Crataegus mollis*) are modified stems that develop from axillary buds.

Figure 18-16 Homoplasy in plants

Consider even-toed hoofed mammals such as pigs, camels, deer, antelope, cattle, and hippos. Whales lack toes and were traditionally not classified as close relatives of hoofed mammals.

FIGURE 18-19 depicts a **cladogram,** or **phylogenetic tree,** based on molecular data for whales and selected hoofed mammals. Such cladograms—diagrams showing lines of descent—can be derived from differences in a given DNA nucleotide sequence. This diagram indicates that whales are more closely related to hippos than to any other hoofed mammal. The branches representing whales and hippos probably diverged relatively recently because of the close similarity of DNA

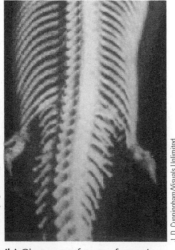

Karlmarx Rajangam/Alamy

J. D. Cunningham/Visuals Unlimited

(a) An Indian python (*Python molurus*).

(b) Close-up of part of a python skeleton showing the hind-limb bones.

Figure 18-17 *Animation* Vestigial structures

All pythons have remnants of hind-limb bones embedded in their bodies.

sequences in these species. In contrast, camels, which have DNA sequences that are less similar to those of whales, diverged much earlier. The molecular evidence indicates that whales and hippos share a recent common ancestor.

The molecular evidence linking whales and even-toed hoofed mammals has led to a re-examination of early fossil whales. Like today's hoofed mammals, early fossil whales had an even number of toes on their appendages. Fossil whales also had the same type of specialized ankle bone (called a double pulley) as hippos and other hoofed mammals.

Developmental biology helps unravel evolutionary patterns

As early as 1975, biologists were suggesting that regulatory changes in gene expression, particularly of genes involved in development, were responsible for many differences between closely related species. Today much evidence supports the idea that regulatory changes—how genes are switched on and off during development—help explain the diversity of form in species with similar genes. Mutations in genes that regulate development often result in dramatically different structures (see Fig. 17-12).

Increasingly, developmental biology, particularly at the molecular level, is providing answers to such questions as how snakes became elongated and lost their limbs. In many cases, evolutionary changes such as the loss of limbs in snakes occur as a result of changes in genes that regulate the orderly sequence of events that occurs during development. In pythons, for example, the loss of forelimbs and elongation of the body are linked to mutations in several *Hox* genes that affect the expression of body patterns and limb formation in a wide variety of animals. (See the discussion of *Hox* gene clusters in Chapter 17.) The hind limbs may not develop because python embryonic tissue does not respond to internal signals that trigger leg elongation.

Developmental geneticists at Harvard Medical School and Princeton University are studying the developmental basis for the different beak shapes of the Galápagos finches. They have determined that a gene that codes for an important signaling molecule, bone morphogenic protein 4 (BMP4), affects the development of the birds' craniofacial skeletons. The gene for BMP4 is turned on earlier in development and has a higher level of expression in finch species with larger, thicker beaks than in finches with smaller beaks.

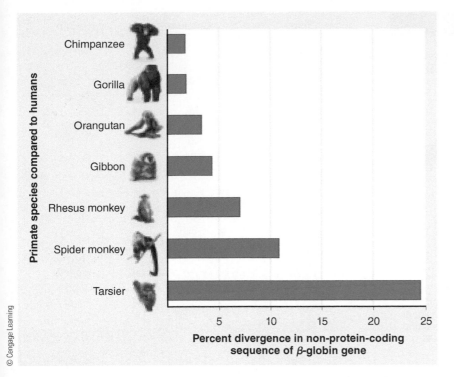

Figure 18-18 Differences in DNA nucleotide sequences as evidence of evolutionary relationships

Comparing the same gene in different organisms provides a window into evolution. Here the differences in the non-protein-coding region of the β-globin gene are compared between humans and other primates. Evolutionary biologists are rapidly expanding such studies from comparing one or several genes to comparing entire genomes.

Scientific evidence overwhelmingly demonstrates that development in different animals is controlled by the same kinds of genes; these genetic similarities in a wide variety of organisms reflect a shared evolutionary history. For example, vertebrates have similar patterns of embryological development that indicate that they share a common ancestor. All vertebrate embryos have segmented muscles, pharyngeal (throat) pouches, a tubular heart without left and right sides, a system of arteries known as *aortic arches* in the pharyngeal region, and many other shared features. All these structures are necessary and functional in the developing fish. The small, segmented muscles of the fish embryo give rise to the segmented muscles used by the adult fish in swimming. The pharyngeal pouches break through to the surface as gill slits. The adult fish heart remains undivided and pumps blood forward to the gills that develop in association with the aortic arches.

Because none of these embryonic features persists in the adults of reptiles, birds, or mammals, why are these fishlike structures present in their embryos? Evolution is a conservative process, and natural selection builds on what has come before rather than starting from scratch. The evolution of new features often does not require the evolution of new developmental genes but instead depends on a modification in developmental genes that already exist (see discussion of preadaptations in Chapter 20). Terrestrial vertebrates are thought to have evolved from fishlike ancestors; therefore, they share some of the early stages of development still found in fishes

today. The accumulation of genetic changes over time in these vertebrates has modified the basic body plan laid out in fish development (**FIG. 18-20**).

Evolutionary hypotheses are tested experimentally

Increasingly, biologists are designing imaginative experiments, often in natural settings, to test evolutionary hypotheses. David Reznick from the University of California, Santa Barbara and John Endler from James Cook University in Australia have studied evolution in guppy populations in Venezuela and in Trinidad, a small island in the southern Caribbean.

Reznick and Endler observed that different streams have different kinds and numbers of fishes that prey on guppies. Predatory fishes that prey on larger guppies are present in all streams at lower elevations; these areas of intense predation pressure are known as *high-predation habitats*. Predators are often excluded from tributaries or upstream areas by rapids and waterfalls. The areas above such barriers are known as *low-predation habitats* because they contain only one species of small predatory fish that occasionally eats smaller guppies.

Differences in predation are correlated with many differences in the guppies, such as male coloration, behavior, and attributes known as *life history traits* (discussed in more detail in Chapter 53). These traits include age and size at sexual maturity, the number of offspring per reproductive event, the size of the offspring, and the frequency of reproduction. For example, guppy adults are larger in streams found at higher elevations and smaller in streams found at lower elevations.

Do predators actually cause these differences to evolve? Reznick and his colleagues tested this evolutionary hypothesis by conducting field experiments in Trinidad. Taking advantage of waterfalls that prevent the upstream movement of guppies, guppy predators, or both, they moved either guppies or guppy predators over such barriers. For example, guppies from a high-predation habitat were introduced into a low-predation habitat by moving them over a barrier waterfall into a section of stream that was free of guppies and large predators. The only fish species that lived in this section of stream before the introduction was the small predatory fish.

Eleven years later, the researchers captured adult females from the introduction site (low-predation habitat) and the control site below the barrier waterfall (high-predation habitat). They bred these females in their laboratory and compared the life history traits of succeeding generations. The descendants of guppies introduced into the low-predation habitat matured at a larger size than did the descendants of guppies from the control site below the waterfall (**FIG. 18-21**). They also produced fewer, but larger, offspring. The introduced fish populations had evolved to have life histories similar to those of fishes typically

This branching diagram, called a *cladogram*, shows proposed evolutionary relationships based on available data. The organisms depicted here share a common ancestor.

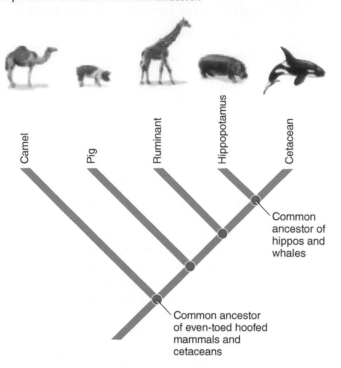

Common ancestor of hippos and whales

Common ancestor of even-toed hoofed mammals and cetaceans

Adapted from Nikaido, M., et al., "Phylogenetic Relationships among Cetartiodactyls Based on Insertions of Short and Long Interspersed Elements: Hippopotamuses Are the Closest Extant Relatives of Whales," *Proceedings of the National Academy of Sciences*, Vol. 96, Aug. 31, 1999.

Figure 18-19 Cladogram of whales and their closest living relatives

DNA sequence differences among selected mammals suggest that hoofed mammals such as hippos and giraffes are the closest living relatives of whales. The hippopotamus is probably the closest living relative of whales and other cetaceans. The nodes (*circles*) represent branch points where a species splits into two or more lineages. (Ruminants are mammals such as cows, sheep, and giraffes that have a multichambered stomach and chew regurgitated plant material to make it more digestible.)

CONNECT According to the cladogram, which animals other than the cetaceans are the closest relatives of ruminants?

found in such low-predation habitats. Similar studies have demonstrated that predators have played an active role in the evolution of other traits, such as the average number of offspring produced during the lifetime of an individual female (fecundity), male coloration, and behavior.

Rapid evolution on a scale of years has also been observed in organisms as diverse as marine snails, mussels, soapberry bugs, mayflies, anole lizards, ʻiʼiwis (scarlet honeycreepers), and wild rabbits. These and other experiments and observations demonstrate not only that evolution is real but also that it is occurring now, driven by selective environmental forces, such as predation, that can be experimentally manipulated. Darwin incorrectly

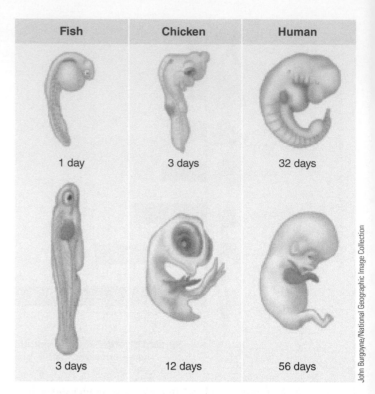

Fish	Chicken	Human
1 day	3 days	32 days
3 days	12 days	56 days

John Burgoyne/National Geographic Image Collection

Figure 18-20 Development of fish fins, chicken wings, and human limbs

Fish, chickens, and humans are vertebrates with strikingly similar genes. Although the early embryos of these organisms are much alike, the areas colored *orange* follow different developmental pathways, resulting in fins, wings, or limbs. (Figures are not to scale.)

assumed evolution to be so gradual that humans cannot observe it. As Jonathan Weiner, author of *The Beak of the Finch: A Story of Evolution in Our Time*, notes, "Darwin did not know the strength of his own theory. He vastly underestimated the power of natural selection. Its action is neither rare nor slow. It leads to evolution daily and hourly, all around us, and we can watch."[3]

CHECKPOINT 18.4

- *How do scientists date fossils?*
- *How can we explain that fossils of Mesosaurus, an extinct reptile that could not swim across open water, are found in the southern parts of both Africa and South America?*
- *How do homologous and homoplastic features provide evidence of evolution?*
- **CONNECT** *How does developmental biology provide evidence of a common ancestry for vertebrates as diverse as reptiles, birds, pigs, and humans?*
- *How do predator preferences drive the evolution of size in guppies?*

_____

[3] Weiner, J. *The Beak of the Finch: A Story of Evolution in Our Time*, p. 9. Alfred A. Knopf. New York (1994).

Can natural selection be observed in a natural population?

HYPOTHESIS: A natural population will respond adaptively to environmental change.

EXPERIMENT: Male and female guppies from a stream in which the predators preferred large adult guppies as prey (*brown bars*) were transferred to a stream in which the predators preferred juveniles and small adults.

RESULTS AND CONCLUSION: After 11 years, the descendants of the transferred guppies (*purple bars*) were measurably larger than their ancestors, indicating that larger guppies had a selective advantage in the new environment.

SOURCE: Data used with permission from Reznick, D.N., et al., "Evaluation of the Rate of Evolution in Natural Populations of Guppies [*Poecilia reticulata*]," *Science*, Vol. 275, Mar. 28, 1997.

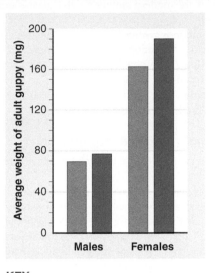

KEY

■ Average initial weight of guppies (control)

■ Average weight of guppies 18 generations after being transferred to stream with different selective predation (experimental)

Figure 18-21 D.N. Reznick's experiment in guppy evolution

CONNECT What do you think would happen next if larger predators were introduced into this low-predation habitat?

SUMMARY: FOCUS ON LEARNING OBJECTIVES

18.1 What Is Evolution? *(page 382)*

1 Define the scientific theory of *evolution*.

- **Evolution** is the accumulation of inherited changes within a **population** over time. Evolution is the unifying concept of biology because it links all fields of the life sciences into a coherent body of knowledge.

18.2 Pre-Darwinian Ideas about Evolution *(page 382)*

2 Discuss the historical development of evolutionary thought.

- Jean Baptiste de Lamarck was the first scientist to propose that organisms undergo change over time as a result of some natural phenomenon rather than divine intervention. Lamarck thought that organisms were endowed with a vital force that drove them to change toward greater complexity over time. He thought that organisms could pass traits acquired during their lifetimes to their offspring.

- Charles Darwin's observations while voyaging on the HMS *Beagle* were the basis for his evolutionary theory. Darwin tried to explain the similarities between animals and plants of the arid Galápagos Islands and the humid South American mainland.

- Darwin was influenced by **artificial selection**, in which breeders develop many varieties of domesticated plants and animals

in just a few generations. Darwin applied Thomas Malthus's ideas on the natural increase in human populations to natural populations. Darwin was influenced by the idea that Earth was extremely old, an idea promoted by Charles Lyell and other geologists.

18.3 Darwin and Evolution *(page 383)*

3 Explain the four premises of evolution by natural selection as proposed by Charles Darwin.

- Charles Darwin and Alfred Russel Wallace independently proposed evolution by **natural selection,** which is based on four observations. First, genetic variation exists among the individuals in a population. Second, the reproductive ability of each species causes its populations to have the potential to geometrically increase in number over time. Third, organisms compete with one another for the resources needed for life, such as food, living space, water, and light. Fourth, offspring with the most favorable combination of inherited characteristics are most likely to survive and reproduce, passing those genetic characteristics to the next generation.

- Natural selection results in **adaptations,** evolutionary modifications that improve the chances of survival and reproductive success in a particular environment. Over time, enough changes may accumulate in geographically separated populations to produce new species.

4 Compare the modern synthesis with Darwin's original view of evolution.

- The **modern synthesis** combines Darwin's evolutionary theory by natural selection with modern genetics to explain why individuals in a population vary and how species adapt to their environment.

- **Mutation** provides the genetic variability that natural selection acts on during evolution.

18.4 Evidence for Evolution *(page 387)*

5 Summarize the evidence for evolution obtained from the fossil record.

- Direct evidence of evolution comes from **fossils,** the remains or traces of ancient organisms. Layers of sedimentary rock normally occur in their sequence of deposition, with the more recent layers on top of the older, earlier ones. **Index fossils** characterize a specific layer over large geographic areas. **Radioisotopes** present in a rock provide a way to accurately measure the rock's age.

6 Define *biogeography* and describe how the distribution of organisms supports evolution.

- **Biogeography,** the geographic distribution of organisms, affects their evolution. Areas that have been separated from the rest of the world for a long time contain organisms that have evolved in isolation and are therefore unique to those areas.

- At one time the continents were joined to form a supercontinent. **Continental drift,** which caused the various landmasses to break apart and separate, has played a major role in evolution.

7 Describe the evidence for evolution derived from comparative anatomy.

- **Homologous features** have basic structural similarities even though the structures may be used in different ways because homologous features derive from the same structure in a common ancestor. Evolutionary affinities exist among the organisms that have homologous features.

- **Homoplastic features** evolved independently to have similar functions in distantly related organisms. Homoplastic features demonstrate **convergent evolution,** in which organisms with separate ancestries adapt in similar ways to comparable environmental demands.

© Cengage Learning

- **Vestigial** structures are nonfunctional or degenerate remnants of structures that were present and functional in ancestral organisms. Structures occasionally become vestigial as species adapt to different modes of life.

8 Briefly explain how molecular biology and developmental biology provide insights into the evolutionary process.

- Molecular evidence for evolution includes the universal genetic code and the conserved sequences of amino acids in proteins and of nucleotides in DNA.

- Evolutionary changes are often the result of mutations in genes that affect the orderly sequence of events during development. Development in different animals is controlled by the same kinds of genes, which indicates that these animals have a shared evolutionary history.

- The accumulation of genetic changes since organisms diverged, or took separate evolutionary pathways, has modified the pattern of development in more complex vertebrate embryos.

9 Give an example of how evolutionary hypotheses are tested experimentally.

- David Reznick and John Endler have studied the effects of predation intensity on the evolution of guppy populations in the laboratory and in nature. Such experiments are a powerful way for investigators to test the underlying processes of natural selection.

TEST YOUR UNDERSTANDING

Know and Comprehend

1. Evolution is based on which of the following concepts? (a) organisms share a common origin (b) over time, organisms have diverged from a common ancestor (c) an animal's body parts can change over its lifetime, and these acquired changes are passed to the next generation (d) a and b (e) a, b, and c

2. Evolution is the accumulation of genetic changes within ___ over time. (a) individuals (b) populations (c) communities (d) a and b (e) a and c

3. Charles Darwin proposed that evolution could be explained by the differential reproductive success of organisms that resulted from their naturally occurring variation. Darwin called this process (a) coevolution (b) convergent evolution (c) natural selection (d) artificial selection (e) homoplasy

4. Which of the following is *not* part of Darwin's mechanism of evolution? (a) differential reproductive success (b) variation in a population (c) inheritance of acquired (nongenetic) traits (d) overproduction of offspring (e) struggle for existence

5. The evolution of beak size in the various species of Galápagos finches is associated with their (a) songs (b) diets (c) body sizes (d) predators (e) none of the preceding

6. The fossil record (a) usually occurs in sedimentary rock (b) sometimes appears fragmentary (c) is relatively complete for tropical rainforest organisms but incomplete for aquatic organisms (d) a and b (e) a, b, and c

7. In ___ the selecting agent is the environment, whereas in ___ the selecting agent is humans. (a) natural selection; convergent evolution (b) mutation; artificial selection (c) homoplasy;

homology (d) artificial selection; natural selection (e) natural selection; artificial selection

8. Aardvarks, anteaters, and pangolins are only distantly related but are similar in structure and form as a result of (a) homology (b) convergent evolution (c) biogeography (d) vestigial structures (e) artificial selection

9. The species of the Galápagos Islands (a) are similar to those on other islands at the same latitude (b) are similar to those on the South American mainland (c) are identical to those on other islands at the same latitude (d) are identical to those on the South American mainland (e) are similar to those on both the African and South American mainlands

Apply and Analyze

10. **CONNECT** In what way does the modern synthesis strengthen scientific understanding of evolution? (a) is based on the sequence of fossils in rock layers (b) uses genetics to explain the source of hereditary variation that is essential to natural selection (c) was first proposed by ancient Greek scholars (d) considers the influence of the geographic distribution of organisms on their evolution (e) is reinforced by homologies that are explained by common descent

11. **CONNECT** What types of gene changes are most associated with the evolution of new anatomical features in a population?

Evaluate and Synthesize

12. **EVOLUTION LINK** The use of model organisms such as the mouse for research and biomedical testing of human diseases is based on the assumption that all organisms share a common ancestor. On what evidence is this assumption based?

13. **EVOLUTION LINK** Charles Darwin once said, "It is not the strongest of the species that survive, nor the most intelligent, but the one most responsive to change." Explain what he meant.

14. **EVOLUTION LINK** Write short paragraphs explaining each of the following statements:
    a. Natural selection chooses from among the individuals in a population those most suited to *current* environmental conditions. It does not guarantee survival under future conditions.
    b. Individuals do not evolve, but populations do.
    c. The organisms that exist today do so because their ancestors had traits that allowed them and their offspring to thrive.

d. At the molecular level, evolution can take place by the replacement of one nucleotide by another.
e. Evolution is said to have occurred within a population when measurable genetic changes are detected.

15. **EVOLUTION LINK** Although most salamanders have four legs, a few species that live in shallow water lack hind limbs and have extremely tiny forelimbs (*see photograph*). Develop a hypothesis to explain how limbless salamanders came about according to Darwin's mechanism of evolution by natural selection. How could you test your hypothesis?

The narrow-striped dwarf siren (*Pseudobranchus striatus axanthus*) is an aquatic salamander that resembles an eel. It is native to Florida.

16. **INTERPRET DATA** Which of the primates in Figure 18-18 is the most distantly related to humans? Explain your answer.

17. **SCIENCE, TECHNOLOGY, AND SOCIETY** Farmers often face a predicament, known as the pesticide treadmill, in which the cost of applying pesticides increases because the pesticides have to be applied more frequently or in larger doses, while their effectiveness decreases. Based on what you have learned in this chapter, offer an explanation for why the pesticides lose their effectiveness.

 To access course materials, such as Aplia and other companion resources, please visit **www.cengagebrain.com.**

21 The Origin and Evolutionary History of Life

Fossil of an Early Permian reptile. This well-preserved fossil of *Orobates pabsti* was matched to well-preserved fossil footprints found nearby. Although the limbs are spread out in death, *Orobates* walked with an upright gait with its limbs under its body. Discovered and photographed in Germany.

© Phil Degginger/Carnegie Museum/Alamy

KEY CONCEPTS

21.1 Although there is no direct fossil evidence of the origin of life, biochemical experiments have demonstrated how the complex organic molecules that are found in all living organisms may have formed.

21.2 The first cells were probably heterotrophic, anaerobic, and prokaryotic. Photosynthesis, aerobic respiration, and eukaryotic cell structure represent several major advances that occurred during the early history of life.

21.3 The fossil record tells us much of what we know about the history of life, such as what kinds of organisms existed and where and when they lived. Scientists identify and demonstrate relationships among fossils in rock layers from different periods of geologic time.

The preceding three chapters were concerned with biological evolution. However, we have not dealt with what many regard as a fundamental question: How did life begin? Although biologists generally accept the hypothesis that life developed from nonliving matter, exactly how this process, called **chemical evolution,** occurred is not certain. Current models suggest that small organic molecules first formed spontaneously and accumulated over time. Large organic macromolecules such as proteins and nucleic acids could have then assembled from the smaller molecules.

The macromolecules interacted, combining into more-complicated structures that could eventually metabolize and replicate, passing their genetic information on to their descendants, which eventually became the first true cells. After the first cells originated, they diverged over several billion years into the rich biological diversity that characterizes our planet today.

Initially, unicellular prokaryotes (archaea and bacteria) predominated, followed by unicellular eukaryotes. The first multicellular eukaryotes were soft-bodied marine animals that did not leave many fossils. Shelled animals and other marine invertebrates (animals without backbones) appeared next, as exemplified by trilobites, primitive aquatic arthropods. Marine invertebrates were followed by the first vertebrates (animals with backbones). The first fishes with jaws appeared and diversified, with some of them giving rise to amphibians, the first vertebrates with limbs that were capable of moving about on land. Amphibians gave rise to reptiles, which diversified and populated the land (see photograph). Reptiles, in turn, gave rise independently to birds and to mammals. Plants underwent a comparable evolutionary history and diversification.

In this chapter we survey life over a vast span of time, starting when our planet was relatively young. We first examine proposed models about how life began and then trace life's long evolutionary history.

21.1 CHEMICAL EVOLUTION ON EARLY EARTH

LEARNING OBJECTIVES

1 Describe the conditions that scientists think existed on early Earth.
2 Compare the prebiotic soup hypothesis with the iron–sulfur world hypothesis.

Scientists generally agree that life's beginnings occurred under environmental conditions quite different from those of today. Therefore, we must examine the conditions of early Earth to understand the origin of life. Evidence from many sources provides us with clues that help us formulate plausible scenarios of the steps in which life originated. Study of the origin of life is an active area of scientific research today, and many important contributions are adding to our understanding of how life began.

Astrophysicists and geologists estimate that Earth is about 4.6 billion years old. The atmosphere of early Earth apparently included carbon dioxide (CO_2), water vapor (H_2O), carbon monoxide (CO), and nitrogen (N_2). It may also have contained some ammonia (NH_3), hydrogen sulfide (H_2S), and methane (CH_4), although ultraviolet radiation from the sun most likely broke these reduced molecules down rapidly. The early atmosphere probably contained little or no free oxygen (O_2).

Four requirements must have existed for the chemical evolution of life: little or no free oxygen, a source of energy, the availability of chemical building blocks, and time. First, life could

have begun only in the absence of free oxygen. Oxygen is quite reactive and would have oxidized the organic molecules that are necessary building blocks in the origin of life. Earth's early atmosphere was probably strongly reducing, which means that any free oxygen would have reacted with other elements to form oxides. Thus, oxygen would have been tied up in compounds.

The origin of life would also have required energy to do the work of building biological molecules from simple inorganic chemicals. Early Earth was a place of high energy with violent thunderstorms; widespread volcanic activity; bombardment from meteorites and other extraterrestrial objects; and intense radiation, including ultraviolet radiation from the sun (FIG. 21-1). The young sun probably produced more ultraviolet radiation than it does today, and ancient Earth had no protective ozone layer to filter it.

A third requirement would have been the presence of the chemical building blocks needed for chemical evolution, including water, dissolved inorganic minerals (present as ions), and the gases present in the early atmosphere. A final requirement for the origin of life was time for molecules to accumulate and react with one another. Earth is approximately 4.6 billion years old, and evidence suggests that life arose early in Earth's history.

Organic molecules formed on primitive Earth

Because organic molecules are the building materials for organisms, it is reasonable to first consider how they may have originated. Two main models seek to explain how the organic precursors of life originated: the **prebiotic soup hypothesis** proposes that these molecules formed near Earth's surface, whereas

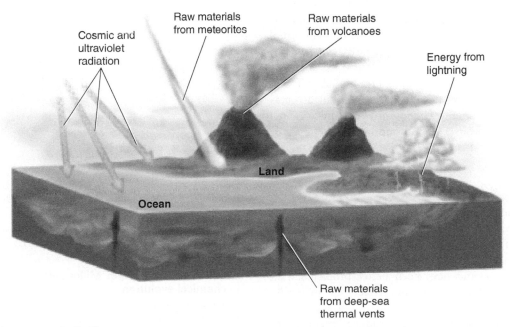

Figure 21-1 Conditions on early Earth

Volcanoes erupted, spewing gases that contributed to the atmosphere, and violent thunderstorms triggered torrential rainfall that washed molecules out of the atmosphere and eroded the land. Meteorites and other extraterrestrial objects bombarded Earth, cataclysmically changing the crust, ocean, and atmosphere. Deep-sea thermal vents, heated by Earth's internal heat, spewed forth chemicals. High-energy radiation from cosmic and ultraviolet rays blasted the planet.

© Cengage Learning

the **iron–sulfur world hypothesis** proposes that organic precursors formed at cracks in the ocean's floor.

Organic molecules may have been produced at Earth's surface

The concept that simple organic molecules such as sugars, nucleotide bases, and amino acids could form spontaneously from simpler raw materials was first advanced in the 1920s by two scientists working independently: A.I. Oparin, a Russian biochemist, and J.B.S. Haldane, a Scottish physiologist and geneticist.

Their hypothesis was tested in the 1950s by U.S. biochemists Stanley Miller and Harold Urey, who designed a closed apparatus that simulated conditions that presumably existed on early Earth (**FIG. 21-2**). They exposed an atmosphere rich in H_2O, CH_4, NH_3, and H_2 to an electric discharge that simulated lightning. Their analysis of the chemicals produced during one week revealed that amino acids and other organic molecules had formed. Although more recent data suggest that Earth's early atmosphere was not rich in methane, ammonia, or hydrogen, similar experiments using different combinations of gases have produced a wide variety of organic molecules that are important in contemporary organisms. They include all 20 amino acids, several sugars, lipids, the nucleotide bases of RNA and DNA, and ATP (when phosphate is present). Thus, before life began, its chemical building blocks were probably accumulating as a necessary step in chemical evolution.

Oparin envisioned that the organic molecules would, over vast spans of time, accumulate in the shallow seas to form a "sea of organic soup." He envisioned smaller organic molecules (monomers) combining to form larger ones (polymers) under such conditions. Evidence gathered since Oparin's time indicates that organic polymers may have formed and accumulated on rock or clay surfaces rather than in the primordial seas. Clay, which consists of microscopic particles of weathered rock, is particularly intriguing as a possible site for early polymerizations because it binds organic monomers and contains zinc and iron ions that may have served as catalysts. Laboratory experiments have confirmed that organic polymers form spontaneously from monomers on hot rock or clay surfaces.

Organic molecules may have formed at hydrothermal vents

Some biologists hypothesize that early polymerizations leading to the origin of life may have occurred in cracks in the deep-ocean floor where hot water, carbon monoxide, and minerals such as sulfides of iron and nickel spew forth; this view is known as the iron–sulfur world hypothesis. Such **hydrothermal vents** would have been better protected than Earth's surface from the catastrophic effects of meteorite bombardment.

Today, these anaerobic hot springs produce precursors of biological molecules and of energy-rich "food," including the highly reduced compounds hydrogen sulfide and methane. These chemicals support a diverse community of microorganisms, clams, crabs, tube worms, and other animals (see *Inquiring About: Life without the Sun*, in Chapter 55).

Could organic molecules have formed in the conditions of early Earth?

HYPOTHESIS: Organic molecules can form in a reducing atmosphere similar to that thought to be present on early Earth.

EXPERIMENT: The apparatus that Miller and Urey used to simulate the reducing atmosphere of early Earth contained water, methane, ammonia, and hydrogen. An electrical spark was produced in the upper right flask to simulate lightning.

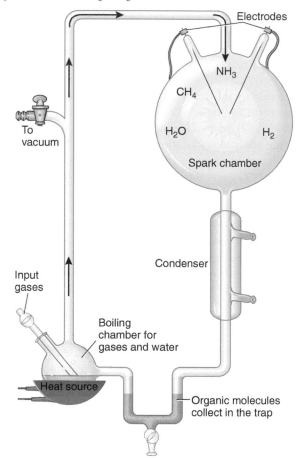

RESULTS AND CONCLUSION: The gases present in the flask reacted together, and in one week a variety of simple organic compounds, such as amino acids, accumulated in the trap at the bottom. Thus, the formation of organic molecules—the first step in the origin of life—can be produced from simple precursors.

SOURCE: Miller, S.L., and H.C. Urey, "Organic Compound Synthesis on the Primitive Earth," *Science*, Vol. 130, July 1959.

Figure 21-2 *Animation* **Miller and Urey's experiment in chemical evolution**

PREDICT Could organic molecules have been produced in this experiment if methane had been omitted?

© Cengage Learning

Testing the iron–sulfur world hypothesis at hydrothermal vents is difficult, but laboratory experiments simulating the high pressures and temperatures at the vents have yielded intriguing results. For example, iron and nickel sulfides catalyze reactions between carbon monoxide and hydrogen sulfide, producing acetic acid and other simple organic compounds. Also, experiments show that ammonia, one of the precursors of proteins and nucleic acids, is produced in abundance, suggesting that vents were ammonia-rich environments in the prebiotic world and that the earliest organisms could have formed in this seemingly inhospitable environment.

CHECKPOINT 21.1

- *What are the four requirements for chemical evolution, and why is each essential?*
- **CONNECT** *How does the iron–sulfur world hypothesis differ from the prebiotic soup hypothesis? What do these hypotheses have in common?*

21.2 THE FIRST CELLS

LEARNING OBJECTIVES

3 Outline the major steps hypothesized to have occurred in the origin of cells.
4 Explain how the evolution of photosynthetic autotrophs affected both the atmosphere and other organisms.
5 Describe the hypothesis of serial endosymbiosis.

After the first polymers formed, could they have assembled spontaneously into more complex structures with an outer membranous boundary? Scientists have synthesized several different **protobionts,** which are vesicle-like assemblages of abiotically produced (i.e., not produced by organisms) organic polymers. These protobionts resemble living cells in several ways, thus providing clues as to how aggregations of complex nonliving molecules took that "giant leap" and became living cells. These protobionts exhibit many functional and structural attributes of living cells. They often divide in half (binary fission) after they have sufficiently "grown." Protobionts maintain an internal chemical environment that is different from the external environment (homeostasis), and some of them show the beginnings of metabolism (catalytic activity). They are highly organized, considering their relatively simple composition.

Microspheres are a type of protobiont formed by adding water to abiotically formed polypeptides (FIG. 21-3). Some microspheres are excitable: they produce an electrical potential across their surfaces, reminiscent of electrochemical gradients in cells. Microspheres can also absorb materials from their surroundings (selective permeability) and respond to changes in osmotic pressure as though membranes enveloped them, even though they contain no lipid.

Scientists have constructed protobionts in which membranes of fatty acids and monoglycerides surround larger DNA-like molecules. These protobionts are impermeable to the genetic molecules but allow smaller organic molecules—that is, "nutrients"—to enter. This study is significant because it suggests how early cells could have held on to their "genes" and absorbed needed nutrients from their environment without the sophisticated membrane structure associated with contemporary cells.

The study of protobionts shows that relatively simple nonliving structures have some of the properties of life. However, it is a major step (or several steps) to go from simple molecular aggregates such as protobionts to living cells.

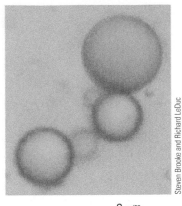

2 μm

Figure 21-3 Microspheres
These tiny protobionts exhibit some of the properties of life.

The origin of a simple metabolism within a membrane boundary may have occurred early in the evolution of cells

Although we have learned many things about how organic molecules may have formed on primitive Earth, the problem of how pre-cells evolved into living cells remains to be solved. Let's examine one possible scenario—the **metabolism first hypothesis**—supported by many chemists, including Robert Shapiro at New York University. Shapiro envisions life beginning as a self-sustaining, organized system consisting of chemical reactions between simple molecules that are enclosed within a boundary, that is, separated from the external environment (FIG. 21-4a).

A source of energy must be available to drive these chemical reactions (thereby maintaining an internal organization different from the external environment). To be self-sustaining, the energy source must be coupled to the chemical reaction sequence (FIG. 21-4b). (Recall how ATP links exergonic and endergonic reactions, shown in Figure 7-6.)

As the pre-cells continue to evolve, their organization increases (FIG. 21-4c). Finally, to survive, the pre-cell system must grow and reproduce. One of the most significant parts of the origin of living cells from pre-cells was the evolution of molecular reproduction (FIG. 21-4d).

Molecular reproduction was a crucial step in the origin of cells

In living cells genetic information is stored in the nucleic acid DNA, which is transcribed into messenger RNA (mRNA), which in turn is translated into the proper amino acid sequence in proteins. All three macromolecules in the DNA → RNA → protein sequence contain precise information. Of these macromolecules, only DNA and RNA are capable of self-replication (although only in the presence of the proper enzymes in cells today). Because both RNA and DNA can form spontaneously on clay in much the same way that other organic polymers

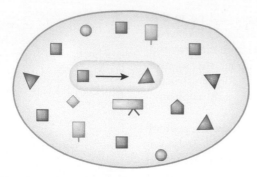

(a) Within a boundary, chemical reactions occur among simple molecules.

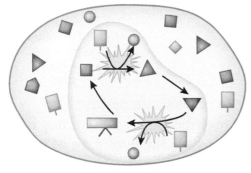

(b) A source of energy is coupled to the chemical reaction sequence.

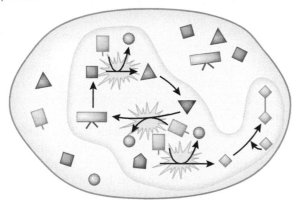

(c) As the pre-cell system continues to evolve, its size and organization increase.

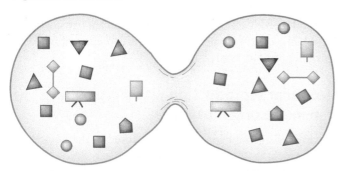

(d) The pre-cell system develops the ability to reproduce.

Figure 21-4 *Animation* **Origin of life: the metabolism first scenario**
© Cengage Learning

do, the question becomes which molecule, DNA or RNA, first appeared in the prebiotic world.

Many scientists have suggested that RNA was the first informational molecule to evolve in the progression toward a self-sustaining, self-reproducing cell and that proteins and DNA came along later. According to a model known as the **RNA world,** the chemistry of prebiotic Earth gave rise to self-replicating RNA molecules that functioned as both enzymes and substrates for their own replication. We represent the replication of RNA in the RNA world scenario as a circular arrow:

As discussed in Chapter 13, RNA often has catalytic properties; such enzymatic RNAs are called **ribozymes.** Before the evolution of true cells, ribozymes may have catalyzed their own replication in the clays, shallow rock pools, or hydrothermal vents where life originated. When RNA strands are added to a test tube containing RNA nucleotides but no enzymes, the nucleotides combine to form short RNA molecules.

The occurrence of an RNA world early in the history of life can never be proven, but experiments with **in vitro evolution,** also called **directed evolution,** have shown that it is feasible. These experiments address an important question about the RNA world, namely, could RNA molecules have catalyzed the many different chemical reactions needed for life? In directed evolution a large pool of RNA molecules with different sequences is mixed, and molecules are selected for their ability to catalyze a single biologically important reaction (**FIG. 21-5**). Those molecules that have at least some catalytic ability are selected by researchers, who then amplify them into many copies. The researchers use certain chemicals to cause mutations and then expose the molecules to another round of selection. After this cycle is repeated several times, the RNA molecules at the end of the selection process function efficiently as catalysts for the reaction. In vitro evolution studies have shown that RNA has a large functional repertoire—that is, RNA can catalyze a variety of biologically important reactions.

Biologists hypothesize that in the RNA world, ribozymes initially catalyzed protein synthesis and other important biological reactions; only later did protein enzymes catalyze these reactions.

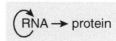

Interestingly, in test-tube experiments RNA molecules that direct protein synthesis by catalyzing peptide bond formation have evolved. Some single-stranded RNA molecules fold back on themselves as a result of interactions among the nucleotides composing the RNA strand. Sometimes the conformation (shape) of the folded RNA molecule is such that it weakly binds to an amino acid (see discussion of peptidyl transferase in Chapter 13). Amino acids held close to one another by RNA molecules may bond, forming a polypeptide.

Can in vitro natural selection result in chemical evolution of catalysts?

HYPOTHESIS: Self-replicating RNA molecules can undergo changes that make them more-efficient catalysts.

EXPERIMENT: RNA molecules are selected from a large pool, based on their ability to catalyze a specific reaction, and then amplified (*see figure*). Mutations occur as this process is repeated 7 to 20 additional times.

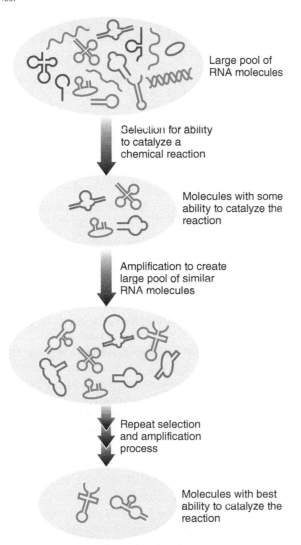

Large pool of RNA molecules

Selection for ability to catalyze a chemical reaction

Molecules with some ability to catalyze the reaction

Amplification to create large pool of similar RNA molecules

Repeat selection and amplification process

Molecules with best ability to catalyze the reaction

RESULTS AND CONCLUSION: The final group of RNA molecules is the most efficient at catalyzing the chemical reaction selected for. Scientists have developed more than two dozen synthetic RNA catalysts by in vitro evolution.

SOURCE: Wright, M.C., and G.F. Joyce, "Continuous in Vitro Evolution of Catalytic Function," *Science* 246: 614–617, 1997.

Figure 21-5 In vitro evolution of RNA molecules

PREDICT Would the same result have been obtained if no mutations had occurred during the amplification process?

© Cengage Learning

We have considered how the evolution of informational molecules may have given rise to RNA and later to proteins. If a self-replicating RNA capable of coding for proteins appeared prior to DNA, how did DNA, the universal molecule of heredity in cells, become involved? Perhaps RNA made double-stranded copies of itself that eventually evolved into DNA.

DNA ← RNA → protein

The incorporation of DNA into the information transfer system was advantageous because the double helix of DNA is more stable (less reactive) than the single strand of RNA. Such stability in a molecule that stores genetic information would have provided a decided advantage in the prebiotic world (as it does today).

Thus, in the DNA/RNA/protein world, DNA became the information storage molecule, RNA remained involved in protein synthesis and various regulatory activities, and protein enzymes catalyzed most cell reactions, including DNA replication and RNA synthesis.

DNA → RNA → protein

RNA is still a necessary component of the information transfer system because DNA is not catalytic. Thus, natural selection at the molecular level favored the DNA → RNA → protein information sequence. Once DNA was incorporated into this sequence, RNA molecules assumed their present role as an intermediary in the transfer of genetic information.

Several additional steps had to occur before a true living cell could evolve from macromolecular aggregations. For purposes of discussion, scientists have coined the acronym **LUCA** to refer to the hypothesized *last universal common ancestor*. The self-replicating genetic code that all known living organisms possess is certainly a legacy from LUCA, but how did this code originate? Also, how did an encapsulating membrane of lipid and protein evolve? These kinds of questions remain for scientists to address.

Biological evolution began with the first cells

No one knows exactly when or where the first cells appeared on Earth. Did they live at hydrothermal vents or at Earth's surface? Were they bacteria? We cannot answer these questions, in part because no fossils exist that trace the transition from nonlife to life. Nonfossil evidence—isotopic "fingerprints" of organic carbon in ancient rocks in Greenland—suggests to some researchers that life existed as early as 3.8 billion years ago (bya). However, other scientists vigorously debate this conclusion.

Microfossils, ancient remains of microscopic life, suggest that cells may have been thriving as long as 3.5 bya. Rich deposits of microfossils appear to exist in the Pilbara rocks of northwestern Australia and the Barberton rocks in South Africa; both of these deposits are about 3.3 billion to 3.5 billion years old. However, some scientists have challenged the interpretation of the oldest carbon-rich "squiggles" in ancient rocks as microfossils of prokaryotic organisms. They suggest that microfossils are not fossils at all but are formed by natural geologic processes.

(a) These living stromatolites at Hamlin Pool in Western Australia consist of mats of cyanobacteria (unicellular photosynthetic prokaryotes) and minerals such as calcium carbonate. They are several thousand years old.

(b) Cutaway view of a fossil stromatolite showing the layers of microorganisms and sediments that accumulated over time. This stromatolite, also from Western Australia, is about 3.5 billion years old.

Figure 21-6 Stromatolites

Evidence suggests that the earliest cells were prokaryotic. **Stromatolites,** another type of fossil evidence of the earliest cells, are rocklike columns composed of many minute layers of prokaryotic cells, that is, microbial biofilms (**FIG. 21-6**). Over time, sediment collects around the cells and mineralizes. Meanwhile, a new layer of living cells grows over the older, dead cells. Fossil stromatolite reefs are found in several places in the world, including Great Slave Lake in Canada and the Gunflint Iron Formations along Lake Superior in the United States. Some fossil stromatolites are extremely ancient. One group in Western Australia, for example, has been dated at more than 3 billion years. Living stromatolite reefs are rare but are found in certain hot springs and warm, shallow pools of fresh and salt water.

The first cells were probably heterotrophic

The earliest cells probably did not synthesize the organic molecules they needed but instead obtained them from the environment. These primitive **heterotrophs** may have consumed many types of organic molecules that had formed spontaneously, such as sugars, nucleotides, and amino acids. By fermenting these organic compounds, they obtained the energy they needed to support life. Of course, *fermentation,* discussed in Chapter 8, is an anaerobic process (performed in the absence of oxygen), and the first cells were almost certainly **anaerobes.**

When the supply of spontaneously generated organic molecules gradually declined, only certain organisms could survive. Mutations had probably already occurred that permitted some cells to obtain energy directly from sunlight, perhaps by using sunlight to make ATP. These cells, which did not require the energy-rich organic compounds that were now in short supply in the environment, had a distinct selective advantage.

Photosynthesis requires both light energy and a source of electrons, which are used to reduce CO_2 to form organic molecules such as glucose. (Recall the discussion of photosynthesis in Chapter 9.) Most likely, the first photosynthetic

autotrophs—organisms that produce their own food from simple raw materials—used the energy of sunlight to obtain electrons by splitting hydrogen-rich molecules such as H_2S, releasing elemental sulfur (not oxygen) in the process. Splitting H_2S is energetically much easier than splitting H_2O because sulfur is not electronegative like oxygen (see Chapter 9). Indeed, the green sulfur bacteria and the purple sulfur bacteria still use H_2S as a hydrogen (electron) source for photosynthesis. (Members of a third bacterial group, the purple nonsulfur bacteria, use other organic molecules or hydrogen gas as a hydrogen source.)

The first photosynthetic autotrophs to obtain hydrogen electrons by splitting *water* were the **cyanobacteria.** Water was quite abundant on early Earth, as it is today, and the selective advantage of splitting water allowed cyanobacteria to thrive. The process of splitting water released oxygen as a gas (O_2). Initially, the oxygen released during photosynthesis oxidized minerals in the ocean and in Earth's crust, and oxygen did not begin to accumulate in the atmosphere for a long time. Eventually, however, oxygen levels increased in the ocean and the atmosphere.

Scientists estimate the timing of the events just described on the basis of geologic and fossil evidence. Fossils from that period, which include rocks containing traces of chlorophyll as well as the fossil stromatolites discussed earlier, indicate that the first photosynthetic organisms may have appeared as early as 3.5 bya. This evidence suggests that heterotrophic forms may have existed even earlier.

Aerobes appeared after oxygen increased in the atmosphere

Based on sulfur isotope data from ancient rocks in South Africa, it appears that cyanobacteria had produced enough oxygen to begin significantly changing the composition of the atmosphere by 2.4 bya. This date may be changed as more data accumulate. Geoscientists at Pennsylvania State University have found strong isotopic evidence in Australia that oxygen was present in the oceans as early as 3.46 bya, and scientists are now looking for the same kind of evidence in other sedimentary layers known to be older than 2.4 bya.

The increase in atmospheric oxygen affected life profoundly. The oxygen poisoned *obligate anaerobes* (organisms that cannot use oxygen for cellular respiration), and many species undoubtedly perished. Some anaerobes, however, survived in environments where oxygen did not penetrate; adaptations evolved in others that neutralized the oxygen so that it could not harm them. In some organisms, called **aerobes,** a respiratory pathway that *used* oxygen to extract more energy from food evolved. Aerobic respiration (see Chapter 8) was joined with the existing anaerobic process of glycolysis.

The evolution of organisms that could use oxygen in their metabolism had several consequences. Organisms that respire aerobically gain much more energy from a single molecule of glucose than anaerobes gain by fermentation. (Recall the comparison of fermentation and aerobic respiration in Table 8-2.) As a result, the newly evolved aerobic organisms were more efficient and more competitive than anaerobes. Coupled with the poisonous nature of oxygen to many anaerobes, the efficiency of aerobes forced anaerobes into relatively minor roles. Today, the vast majority of organisms—including plants, animals, and most fungi, protists, archaea, and bacteria—use aerobic respiration; only a few archaea and bacteria and even fewer protists and fungi are anaerobic.

The evolution of aerobic respiration stabilized both oxygen and carbon dioxide levels in the biosphere. Photosynthetic organisms used carbon dioxide as a source of carbon for synthesizing organic compounds. This raw material would have been depleted from the atmosphere in a relatively brief period without the advent of aerobic respiration, which released carbon dioxide as a waste product from the complete breakdown of organic molecules. Carbon thus started cycling in the biosphere, moving from the nonliving physical environment to photosynthetic organisms to heterotrophs that ate the photosynthetic organisms (see Chapter 55). Aerobic respiration released carbon back into the physical environment as carbon dioxide, and the carbon cycle continued. In a similar manner, molecular oxygen was produced by photosynthesis and used during aerobic respiration.

Another significant consequence of photosynthesis occurred in the upper atmosphere, where molecular oxygen reacted to form **ozone (O_3)** (FIG. 21-7). A layer of ozone eventually blanketed Earth, preventing much of the sun's ultraviolet radiation from penetrating to the surface. With the ozone layer's protection from the mutagenic effect of ultraviolet radiation, organisms could live closer to the surface in aquatic environments and eventually move onto land. Because the energy in ultraviolet radiation may have been necessary to form organic molecules, however, their abiotic synthesis decreased.

Eukaryotic cells descended from prokaryotic cells

Eukaryotes may have appeared in the fossil record as early as 2.2 bya, and geochemical evidence suggests that eukaryotes were present much earlier. *Steranes,* molecules derived from steroids, have been discovered in Australian rocks dated at 2.7 billion

Ozone (O_3) forms in the upper atmosphere when ultraviolet radiation from the sun breaks the double bonds of oxygen molecules.

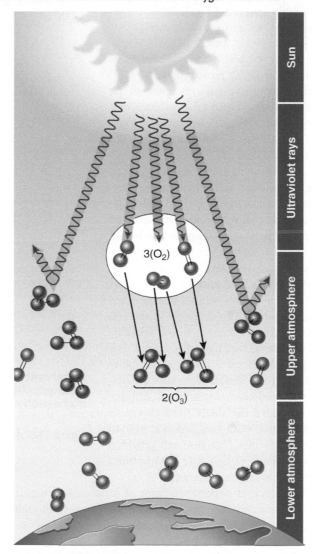

Figure 21-7 The formation of ozone

CONNECT As discussed in Chapter 57, certain human-produced chemicals rise to the stratosphere and react chemically with ozone. What consequences would you expect this reaction to have for organisms?

© Cengage Learning

years old. Because bacteria are not known to produce steroids, the steranes may be biomarkers for eukaryotes. These ancient rocks lack fossil traces of ancient organisms because the rocks have since been exposed to heat and pressure that would have destroyed any fossilized cells. Steranes, however, are very stable in the presence of heat and pressure.

Eukaryotes arose from prokaryotes. Recall from Chapter 4 that archaeal and bacterial cells lack nuclear envelopes as well as other membranous organelles such as mitochondria and chloroplasts. How did these organelles arise? According to the hypothesis of **serial endosymbiosis,** organelles such as mitochondria and chloroplasts may have originated from mutually advantageous symbiotic relationships between two prokaryotic organisms (FIG. 21-8). Chloroplasts apparently evolved from photosynthetic bacteria (cyanobacteria) that lived inside larger heterotrophic cells, whereas mitochondria presumably evolved from aerobic bacteria (perhaps ancient purple bacteria) that lived inside larger anaerobic cells. Thus, early eukaryotic cells were assemblages of formerly free-living prokaryotes.

How did these bacteria come to be **endosymbionts,** which are organisms that live symbiotically inside a host cell? They may originally have been ingested, but not digested, by a host cell. Once incorporated, they could have survived and reproduced along with the host cell so that future generations of the host also contained endosymbionts. A mutualistic relationship evolved between these two organisms in which each contributed something to the other. Eventually, the endosymbiont lost the ability to exist outside its host, and the host cell lost the ability to survive without its endosymbionts. This hypothesis stipulates that each of these partners brought to the relationship something that the other lacked. For example, mitochondria provided the ability to carry out the aerobic respiration lacking in the original anaerobic host cell. Chloroplasts provided the ability to use a simple carbon source (CO_2) to produce needed organic molecules. The host cell provided endosymbionts with a safe environment and raw materials or nutrients.

The principal evidence in favor of serial endosymbiosis is that mitochondria and chloroplasts possess some (although not all) of their own genetic material and translational components. They have their own DNA (as a circular molecule similar to that of archaea and bacteria; discussed in Chapter 25) and their own ribosomes (which resemble bacterial rather than eukaryotic ribosomes). Mitochondria and chloroplasts also possess some of the machinery for protein synthesis, including tRNA molecules, and conduct protein synthesis on a limited scale independent of the nucleus. Furthermore, it is possible to poison mitochondria and chloroplasts with an antibiotic that affects bacteria but not eukaryotic cells. As discussed in Chapter 4, double membranes envelope mitochondria and chloroplasts. The outer membrane apparently developed from the invagination (infolding) of the host cell's plasma membrane, whereas the inner membrane is derived from the endosymbiont's plasma membrane. (Serial endosymbiosis is discussed in greater detail in Chapter 26.)

Many endosymbiotic relationships exist today. Many corals have algae living as endosymbionts within their cells (see Fig. 54-12). Protozoa (*Myxotricha paradoxa*) live symbiotically in the gut of termites; in turn, several different endosymbionts, including spirochete bacteria, attach to the protozoa and function as whiplike flagella, allowing the protozoa to move.

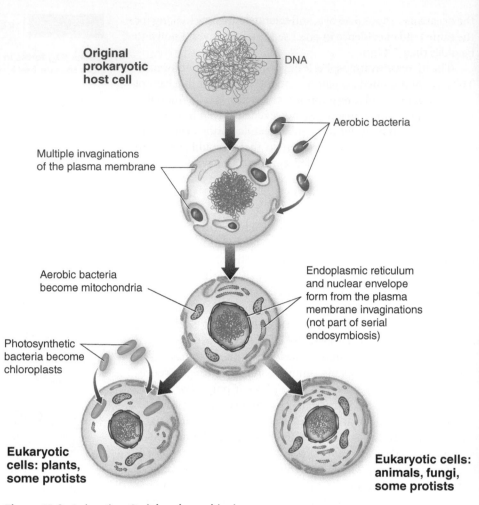

Figure 21-8 *Animation* **Serial endosymbiosis**
© Cengage Learning

Although much evidence supports serial endosymbiosis, it does not completely explain the evolution of eukaryotic cells from prokaryotes. For example, serial endosymbiosis does not currently explain how a double membranous envelope came to surround the genetic material in the nucleus.

CHECKPOINT 21.2

- *What major steps probably occurred in the origin of cells?*
- **CONNECT** *How did the presence of molecular oxygen in the atmosphere affect early life?*
- **VISUALIZE** *Draw a simple sketch illustrating the way in which aerobic bacteria are hypothesized to have become incorporated into an original prokaryotic host cell.*

21.3 THE HISTORY OF LIFE

LEARNING OBJECTIVE

6 Briefly describe the distinguishing organisms and major biological events of the Ediacaran period and the Paleozoic, Mesozoic, and Cenozoic eras.

The sequence of biological, climate, and geologic events that make up the history of life is recorded in rocks and fossils. The sediments of Earth's crust consist of five major rock strata (layers), each subdivided into minor strata, lying one on top of the other. Very few places on Earth show all layers, but the strata present typically occur in the correct order, with younger rocks on top of older ones. These sheets of rock formed from the accumulation of mud and sand at the bottoms of the ocean, seas, and lakes. Each layer contains certain characteristic **index fossils** that identify deposits made at about the same time in different parts of the world.

Geologists divide Earth's history into units of time based on major geologic, climate, and biological events. **Eons** are the largest divisions of the geologic time scale. Eons are divided into **eras;** where fossil evidence exists, these divisions are based primarily on organisms that characterized each era. Eras are subdivided into **periods,** which in turn are composed of **epochs.**

Relatively little is known about Earth from its beginnings approximately 4.6 bya up to 2.5 bya. Life originated on Earth during the **Archaean eon,** the period between 4.0 bya when Earth's crust formed and 2.5 bya (**TABLE 21-1**). Signs of life date as early as 3.5 bya. Not much physical evidence is available because the rocks of the Archaean eon, being extremely ancient, are deeply buried in most parts of the world. Ancient rocks are exposed in a few places, including the bottom of the Grand Canyon and along the shores of Lake Superior. Many Archaean rock formations have revealed what appear to be microfossils of cyanobacteria and other bacteria.

Rocks from the Ediacaran period contain fossils of cells and simple animals

That part of time from 2500 mya to 541 mya is known as the **Proterozoic eon.** This enormous span of time is easier to study than the preceding Archaean eon because the rocks are less altered by heat and pressure. Life at the beginning of the Proterozoic eon consisted of prokaryotes such as cyanobacteria. Stromatolites were abundant. About 2.2 bya, the first eukaryotic cells appeared. By the end of the Proterozoic eon, multicellularity was evident in the abundant fossils of small, soft-bodied, invertebrate animals.

The **Ediacaran period** (pronounced "ee-dee-ack'-uh-run"), from 635 mya to 541 mya, is the last (most recent) period of the Proterozoic eon. It is named for the fossil deposits in the Ediacara Hills in South Australia, although Ediacaran fossils are also found in Newfoundland, the Mackenzie Mountains of northwestern Canada, the Doushantuo Formation of China, and other locations. Currently, more than 270 Ediacaran species have been identified and described.

Ediacaran fossils are the oldest known fossils of multicellular animals (**FIG. 21-9**). Experts have not yet identified all the simple, soft-bodied animals found in the Ediacara Hills and at other sites. Some paleontologists interpret many of these fossils as early sponges, jellyfish, corals, and comb jellies; however, other scientists think that the Ediacaran animals were not ancestral to modern-day species but instead became extinct at the end of the Ediacaran period.

Figure 21-9 Reconstruction of life in an Ediacaran sea

The organisms shown here are based on fossils from the Ediacara Hills of South Australia, although similar associations have been found in Ediacaran rocks from every continent except Antarctica. Shown are organisms that some scientists have interpreted as jellyfish, flatworms, algae, and paddle-shaped organisms similar in appearance to soft corals.

A diversity of organisms evolved during the Paleozoic era

The **Paleozoic era** began approximately 541 mya and lasted about 289 million years. It is divided into six periods: Cambrian, Ordovician, Silurian, Devonian, Carboniferous, and Permian.

Rocks rich in fossils represent the oldest subdivision of the Paleozoic era, the **Cambrian period.** For about 40 million years, evolution was in such high gear, with the sudden appearance of many new animal body plans, that this period is called the **Cambrian radiation,** or more informally, **Cambrian explosion.** Fossils of all contemporary animal phyla are present, along with many bizarre, extinct phyla, in marine sediments. The seafloor was covered with sponges, corals, sea lilies, sea stars, snails, clamlike bivalves, primitive squidlike cephalopods, lampshells (brachiopods), and trilobites (see Fig. 31-26). In addition, small vertebrates—cartilaginous fishes—became established in the marine environment.

Scientists have not determined the factors responsible for the Cambrian radiation, a period unmatched in the evolutionary history of life. There is some evidence that oxygen concentrations, which had continued to gradually increase in the atmosphere, passed some critical threshold late in the Proterozoic eon. Scientists who advocate the *oxygen enrichment hypothesis* note that until late in the Proterozoic eon, Earth did not have enough oxygen to support larger animals. The most important fossil sites that document the Cambrian radiation are the *Chengjiang site* in China (for Early Cambrian fossils) and the *Burgess Shale* in British Columbia (for Middle Cambrian fossils) (**FIG. 21-10**).

According to geologists, seas gradually flooded the continents during the Cambrian period. In the **Ordovician period,** much land was covered by shallow seas, in which there was another burst of evolutionary diversification, although not as dramatic as the Cambrian radiation. The Ordovician seas were inhabited by giant cephalopods, squidlike animals with straight shells 5 to 7 m (16 to 23 ft) long and 30 cm (12 in.) in diameter.

TABLE 21-1 | Some Important Biological Events in Geologic Time

EON	ERA	PERIOD	EPOCH	TIME*	SOME IMPORTANT BIOLOGICAL EVENTS
Phanerozoic eon	Cenozoic era	Quaternary period	Holocene epoch	0.01 (10,000 years ago)	Decline of some woody plants; rise of herbaceous plants; age of *Homo sapiens*
			Pleistocene epoch	2.6 mya	Extinction of some plant species; extinction of many large mammals at end
		Neogene period	Pliocene epoch	5 mya	Expansion of grasslands and deserts; many grazing animals
			Miocene epoch	23 mya	Flowering plants continue to diversify; diversity of songbirds and grazing mammals
		Paleogene period	Oligocene epoch	34 mya	Spread of forests; apes appear; present mammalian families are represented
			Eocene epoch	56 mya	Flowering plants dominant; modern mammalian orders appear and diversify; modern bird orders appear
			Paleocene epoch	66 mya	Semitropical vegetation (flowering plants and conifers) widespread; primitive mammals diversify
	Mesozoic era	Cretaceous period		145 mya	Rise of flowering plants; dinosaurs reach peak, then become extinct at end; toothed birds become extinct
		Jurassic period		201 mya	Gymnosperms common; large dinosaurs; first toothed birds
		Triassic period		252 mya	Gymnosperms dominant; ferns common; first dinosaurs; first mammals
	Paleozoic era	Permian period		299 mya	Conifers diversify; cycads appear; modern insects appear; mammal-like reptiles; extinction of many invertebrates and vertebrates at end of Permian
		Carboniferous period		359 mya	Forests of ferns, club mosses, horsetails, and gymnosperms; many insect forms; spread of ancient amphibians; first reptiles
		Devonian period		419 mya	First forests; gymnosperms appear; many trilobites; wingless insects appear; fishes with jaws appear and diversify; amphibians appear
		Silurian period		444 mya	Vascular plants appear; coral reefs common; jawless fishes diversify; terrestrial arthropods
		Ordovician period		485 mya	Fossil spores of terrestrial plants (bryophytes?); invertebrates dominant; coral reefs appear; first fishes appear
		Cambrian period		541 mya	Bacteria and cyanobacteria; algae; fungi; age of marine invertebrates; first chordates
Proterozoic eon		Ediacaran period		635 mya	Algae and soft-bodied invertebrates diversify
		Early Proterozoic period		2500 mya	Eukaryotes evolve
Archaean eon				4000 mya	Oldest known rocks; prokaryotes evolve; atmospheric oxygen begins to increase

*Time from beginning of eon, period, or epoch to present (millions of years). Dates: Walker, J.D., Geissman, J.W, Bowring, S.A., and Babcock, L.E., compilers, 2012, Geologic Time Scale v.4:0: Geological Society of America.

(a) *Marrella splendens* was a small arthropod with 26 body segments. It is the most abundant fossil arthropod found in the Burgess Shale.

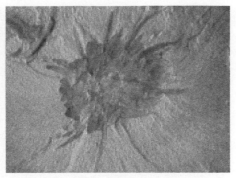

(b) *Wiwaxia* was a bristle-covered marine worm that was distantly related to earthworms. It had scaly armor and needlelike spines for protection.

Figure 21-10 Fossils from the Cambrian radiation
These fossils were discovered in the Burgess Shale in the Canadian Rockies of British Columbia.

Coral reefs first appeared during this period, as did small, jawless, bony-armored fishes called *ostracoderms* (FIG. 21-11). Lacking jaws, these fishes typically had round or slitlike mouth openings that may have sucked in small food particles from the water or scooped up organic debris from the bottom. Ordovician deposits also contain fossil spores of terrestrial (land-dwelling) plants, suggesting that the colonization of land had begun.

During the **Silurian period,** jawless fishes diversified considerably, and jawed fishes first appeared. Definitive evidence of two life-forms of great biological significance appeared in the Silurian period: terrestrial plants and air-breathing animals. The evolution of plants allowed animals to colonize the land because plants provided the first terrestrial animals with food and shelter. All air-breathing land animals discovered in Silurian rocks were arthropods: millipedes, spiderlike arthropods, and possibly centipedes. From an ecological perspective, the energy flow from plants to animals probably occurred via detritus, which is organic debris from decomposing organisms, rather than directly from living plant material. Millipedes eat plant detritus today, and spiders and centipedes prey on millipedes and other animals.

The **Devonian period** is frequently called the Age of Fishes. This period witnessed the explosive radiation of fishes with jaws, an adaptation that lets a vertebrate chew and bite. Armored *placoderms,* an extinct group of jawed fishes, diversified to exploit varied lifestyles (see Fig. 32-10). Appearing in Devonian deposits are sharks and the two predominant types of bony fishes: lobe-finned fishes and ray-finned fishes, which gave rise to the major orders of modern fishes (see Chapter 31).

Tiktaalik was a transitional form between fishes and *tetrapods,* which are vertebrates with four limbs (see Fig. 32-17). *Tiktaalik* is considered a fish because it had scales and fins. Like tetrapods, however,

Tiktaalik had a movable neck and ribs that enclosed lungs. Upper (more recent) Devonian sediments contain fossil remains of salamander-like amphibians (*labyrinthodonts*) that were often quite large, with short necks and heavy, muscular tails. Wingless insects also originated in the Late Devonian period.

The early vascular plants (plants with specialized tissue to conduct water and nutrients) diversified during the Devonian period in a burst of evolution that rivaled that of animals during the Cambrian radiation. With the exception of flowering plants, all major plant groups appeared during the Devonian period. Forests of ferns, club mosses, horsetails, and seed ferns (an extinct group of ancient plants that had fernlike foliage but reproduced by forming seeds) flourished.

The **Carboniferous period** is named for the great swamp forests whose remains persist today as major coal deposits. Much of the land during this time was covered with low swamps filled with horsetails, club mosses, ferns, seed ferns, and gymnosperms, which are seed-bearing plants such as conifers (FIG. 21-12). Amphibians, which underwent an **adaptive radiation** and exploited both aquatic and terrestrial ecosystems, were the dominant terrestrial carnivores of the Carboniferous period. Reptiles first appeared and diverged to form two major lines at this time. One line consisted of mostly small and midsized insectivorous (insect-eating) lizards; this line later led to lizards, snakes, crocodiles, dinosaurs, and birds. The other reptilian line led to a diverse group of Permian and Early Mesozoic mammal-like reptiles. Two groups of winged insects, cockroaches and dragonflies, appeared in the Carboniferous period.

Amphibians continued in importance during the **Permian period,** but they were no longer the dominant carnivores in

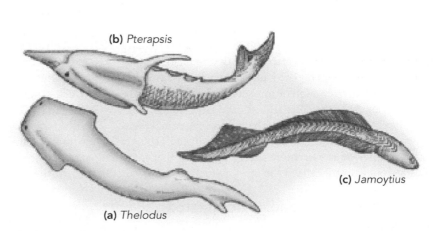

(b) *Pterapsis*

(c) *Jamoytius*

(a) *Thelodus*

Figure 21-11 Ostracoderms
Ostracoderms, primitive jawless fishes that lived in the Ordovician, Silurian, and Devonian periods, ranged from 10 to 50 cm (4 to 20 in.) in length.
© Cengage Learning

Figure 21-12 Reconstruction of a Carboniferous forest
Plants of this period included giant ferns, horsetails, club mosses, seed ferns, and early gymnosperms.

terrestrial ecosystems. During the Permian period, reptiles diversified and dominated both carnivorous and herbivorous terrestrial lifestyles. One important group of mammal-like reptiles, originating in the Permian and extending into the Mesozoic era, were the *therapsids,* a group that included the ancestor of mammals (see Fig. 32-24). During the Permian period, seed plants diversified and dominated most plant communities. Cone-bearing conifers were widespread, and cycads (plants with crowns of fernlike leaves and large, seed-containing cones) and ginkgoes (trees with fan-shaped leaves and exposed, fleshy seeds) appeared.

The greatest **mass extinction** of all time occurred at the end of the Paleozoic era, between the Permian and Triassic periods, 252 mya. More than 90% of all existing marine species became extinct at this time, as did more than 70% of the vertebrate genera living on land. There is also evidence of a major extinction of plants. Many causes for the Late Permian mass extinction have been suggested, from meteor impacts to global warming to changes in ocean chemistry. Regardless of cause, evidence suggests that the extinction occurred globally in a very compressed period, within a few hundred thousand years. In the geologic time scale, this period is extremely short, suggesting that some sort of catastrophic event caused the mass extinction.

Dinosaurs and other reptiles dominated the Mesozoic era

The **Mesozoic era** began about 252 mya and lasted some 186 million years. It is divided into the Triassic, Jurassic, and Cretaceous periods. Fossil deposits from the Mesozoic era occur worldwide.

Notable sites include the *Yixian Formation* in northeastern China, the Solnhofen Limestone in Germany, northwestern Patagonia in Argentina, the Sahara in central Niger, the Badlands in South Dakota, and other sites in western North America.

The outstanding feature of the Mesozoic era was the origin, differentiation, and ultimately the extinction of a large variety of reptiles. For this reason, the Mesozoic era is commonly called the Age of Reptiles. Most of the modern orders of insects appeared during the Mesozoic era. Snails and bivalves (clams and their relatives) increased in number and diversity, and sea urchins reached their peak diversity. From a botanical viewpoint, the Mesozoic era was dominated by gymnosperms until the Mid-Cretaceous period, when the flowering plants first diversified.

During the **Triassic period,** reptiles underwent an adaptive radiation leading to the formation of many groups. On land, the dominant Triassic groups were the mammal-like therapsids, which ranged from small-sized insectivores (insect-eating reptiles) to moderately large herbivores (plant-eating reptiles), and a diverse group of *thecodonts,* early "ruling reptiles," which were primarily carnivores. Thecodonts are the ancestral reptiles that gave rise to crocodilians, flying reptiles, dinosaurs, and birds.

In the ocean several important marine reptile groups, the plesiosaurs and ichthyosaurs, appeared in the Triassic period. *Plesiosaurs* had bodies up to 15 m (about 49 ft) long and paddle-like fins. *Ichthyosaurs* had body forms superficially resembling those of sharks or porpoises, with short necks, large dorsal fins, and shark-type tails (FIG. 21-13). Ichthyosaurs had very large eyes, which may have helped them see at diving depths of 500 m (1650 ft) or more.

Figure 21-13 Ichthyosaurs

Brachypterygius (also known by the genus *Grendelius*) was an ichthyosaur that superficially resembled a shark or porpoise. It had large teeth and strong jaws and was about 4 m (13 ft) long.

© John Sibbick

Figure 21-14 Pterosaurs

Shown are *Peteinosaurus* (*left*), with a wingspan of 60 cm (2 ft), and *Eudimorphodon* (*right foreground*), with a wingspan of 75 cm (2.5 ft). Both species had long, sharp teeth for catching insects or fishes while flying.

© John Sibbick

Pterosaurs, the first flying reptiles, appeared and underwent considerable diversification during the Mesozoic era (**FIG. 21-14**). This group produced some quite spectacular forms, most notably the giant *Quetzalcoatlus,* known from fragmentary Cretaceous fossils in Texas to have had a wingspan of 11 to 15 m (36 to 49 ft). Pterosaur wings were leathery membranes of skin that were supported by an elongated fourth finger bone. Claws extended from the other finger bones.

The first mammals to appear in the Triassic period were small insectivores that evolved from the mammal-like therapsids. Mammals diversified into a variety of mostly small, nocturnal insectivores during the remainder of the Mesozoic era, with marsupial and placental mammals appearing later in the Mesozoic.

During the **Jurassic** and **Cretaceous periods,** crocodiles, lizards, snakes, and birds appeared, and the dinosaurs diversified dramatically (**FIG. 21-15**). The *mosasaurs,* one group of lizards, were large, voracious marine predators during the Late Cretaceous period. The mosasaurs, which are now extinct, attained lengths of 10 m (33 ft) or more.

The evolutionary radiation of the dinosaurs expanded from one lineage to several dozen that ecologically filled a variety of adaptive zones. Dinosaurs are placed in two main groups based on their pelvic bone structure: the *saurischians* and the *ornithischians* (**FIG. 21-16**). Some saurischians

were fast, bipedal (walking on two feet) forms ranging from those the size of a dog to the ultimate representatives of this group, the gigantic carnivores of the Cretaceous period: *Tyrannosaurus, Giganotosaurus,* and *Carcharodontosaurus.* Other saurischians were huge, quadrupedal (walking on four feet) dinosaurs that ate plants. Some of these dinosaurs were the largest terrestrial animals that have ever lived, including *Argentinosaurus,* with an estimated length of 30 m (98 ft) and an estimated weight of 72 to 90 metric tons (80 to 100 tons).

The other group of dinosaurs, the ornithischians, was entirely herbivorous. Although some ornithischians were bipedal, most were quadrupedal. Some had no front teeth and possessed stout, horny, birdlike beaks. In some species these

© John Sibbick

Figure 21-15 Dinosaurs

Three *Deinonychus* dinosaurs attack a larger *Tenontosaurus.* The name *Deinonychus* means "terrible claw" and refers to the enlarged, sharp claw on the second digit of its hind feet. *Deinonychus* dinosaurs were small (3 m, or 10 ft in length) but fearsome predators that hunted in packs. *Tenontosaurus* adults were as long as 7.5 m (24 ft).

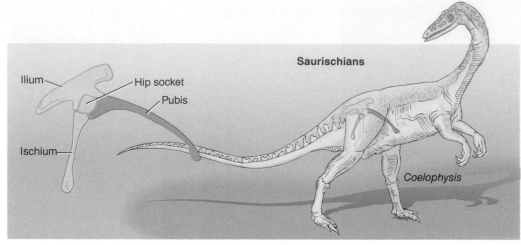

Saurischians

Ilium
Hip socket
Pubis
Ischium

Coelophysis

(a) The saurischian pelvis. Note the opening (hip socket), a trait possessed by no quadrupedal vertebrates other than dinosaurs.

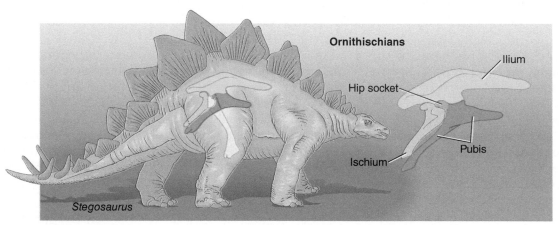

Ornithischians

Ilium
Hip socket
Ischium
Pubis

Stegosaurus

(b) The ornithischian pelvis. Note that it has the hole in the hip socket but differs from the saurischian pelvis in that it has a backward-directed extension of the pubis.

Figure 21-16 Saurischian and ornithischian dinosaurs
In each dinosaur figure, the pale yellow femur is shown relative to the pelvic bone.
© Cengage Learning

Archaeopteryx, the oldest known bird in the fossil record, lived about 150 mya (see Fig. 32-22b). It was about the size of a pigeon and had rather feeble wings that it used to glide rather than actively fly. Although *Archaeopteryx* is considered a bird, it had many reptilian features, including a mouthful of teeth and a long, bony tail.

Thousands of well-preserved bird fossils have been found in Early Cretaceous deposits in China. They include *Sinornis,* a 135-million-year-old sparrow-sized bird capable of perching; and the magpie-sized *Confuciusornis,* the earliest known bird with a toothless beak. *Confuciusornis* may date back as far as 142 mya.

At the end of the Cretaceous period, 66 mya, dinosaurs, pterosaurs, and many other animals abruptly became extinct. Many gymnosperms, with the exception of conifers, also perished. Evidence suggests that a catastrophic collision of a large extraterrestrial body with Earth dramatically changed the climate at the end of the Cretaceous period. Part of the evidence is a thin band of dark clay, with a high concentration of iridium, located between Mesozoic and Cenozoic sediments at more than two hundred sites around the world. Iridium is rare on Earth but abundant in meteorites. The force of the impact would have driven the iridium into the atmosphere, to be deposited later on the land by precipitation.

The Chicxulub crater, buried under the Yucatán Peninsula in Mexico, is the apparent site of this collision. The impact produced giant tsunamis (tidal waves) that deposited materials from the extraterrestrial body around the perimeter of the Gulf of Mexico, from Alabama to Guatemala. It may have caused global forest fires and giant smoke and dust clouds that lowered global temperatures for many years.

Although scientists widely accept that a collision with an extraterrestrial body occurred 66 mya, they have reached no consensus about the effects of such an impact on organisms. The extinction of many marine organisms at or immediately

beaks were broad and ducklike, hence the common name *duck-billed dinosaurs.* Other ornithischians had great armor plates, possibly as protection against carnivorous saurischians. *Ankylosaurus,* for example, had a broad, flat body covered with armor plates (actually bony scales embedded in the skin) and large, laterally projecting spikes.

Over the past few decades, scientists have reconsidered many traditional ideas about dinosaurs and no longer think that they were all cold-blooded, slow-moving monsters living in swamps. Recent evidence suggests that at least some dinosaurs were warm-blooded, agile, and able to move extremely fast. Many dinosaurs appear to have had complex social behaviors, including courtship rituals and parental nurturing of their young. Some species lived in social groups and hunted in packs.

Birds appeared by the Late Jurassic period, and fossil evidence indicates that they evolved directly from saurischian dinosaurs (see *Inquiring About: The Origin of Flight in Birds*).

Do we know how birds evolved? The evolution of birds is arguably one of the most interesting chapters in Earth's history of life. Given the substantial fossil evidence, most paleontologists have concluded that the ancestors of birds were dinosaurs, specifically the *dromaeosaurs,* a group of ground-dwelling, bipedal theropods (carnivorous saurischians). Beginning in 1997, paleontologists made several discoveries of fossil dinosaurs with feathers, indicating that feathers appeared before birds. Scientists think that feathers evolved as one or a series of evolutionary novelties, or **preadaptations** (see Chapter 20). The first feathers may have provided thermal insulation but were subsequently modified for flight.

Once dinosaurs and early birds had feathers, how did they fly? Did tree-dwelling animals glide as an intermediate step in bird flight, or did ground-dwelling animals flap their wings and run to provide thrust and lift for a takeoff? The question about how flight originated in birds has intrigued biologists for more than a century. In 1915, U.S. zoologist William Beebe hypothesized that the ancestors of birds were probably tree-dwelling gliders that had feathers on all four limbs.[1] Because no fossil evidence supported his suggestion, scientists did not consider it seriously at the time.

Almost a century later, in 2003, a group of Chinese paleontologists announced the discovery of two nearly complete fossils of the organisms that Beebe had hypothesized.[2] The fossils of a small, feathered dromaeosaur dinosaur

[1] Beebe, W.H. "A Tetrapteryx Stage in the Ancestry of Birds." *Zoologica,* Vol. 2, 1915.
[2] Xu, X., Z. Zhou, X. Wang, X. Kuang, F. Zhang, and X. Du. "Four Winged Dinosaurs from China." *Nature,* Vol. 421, Jan. 23, 2003.

were found in Liaoning Province in northeastern China. The dinosaur, *Microraptor gui,* had feathers on both forelimbs and hind limbs as well as on its long tail (see figure). It was small—77 cm (about 30 in.) in length, including the tail—and appeared to be adapted to life in the trees. The feathers on *M. gui* were similar to those of modern-day birds. Downy feathers covered the body, and each limb had about 12 "primary" flight feathers and about 18 shorter, "secondary" feathers. *Microraptor gui*'s flight feathers were asymmetrical, a characteristic associated with flight or gliding in modern birds. The primary and secondary feathers followed a similar pattern on both the forelimbs and hind limbs, and this pattern resembles that on modern birds. In part because *M. gui*'s breastbone was not structured to attach large flight muscles, the dinosaur probably glided rather than flapped its wings.

Microraptor gui, which is about 126 million years old, is not a direct ancestor of birds. Birds had already evolved when *M. gui* existed. The earliest known bird, *Archaeopteryx,* lived about 150 mya and therefore predates *M. gui* by about 25 million years. *Microraptor gui* is considered to have evolved from a *basal member*—that is, an earlier evolutionary branch—of the most recent ancestor of *Archaeopteryx* and other birds. Like *M. gui,* earlier feathered dinosaurs may have been four-winged organisms that lived and glided in the trees.

Portia Sloan/Getty Images

During the course of bird evolution, the feathered hind limbs may have become reduced and eventually lost. However, an alternative hypothesis is that feathered hind limbs may have been a failed evolutionary experiment restricted to dromaeosaurs and not important as an intermediate step in bird evolution. Further analysis of *M. gui* and future discoveries of earlier dromaeosaur fossils may shed some light on the importance of feathered hind limbs.

Microraptor gui has given paleontologists and biologists much to consider in the evolutionary transition from dinosaurs to birds. Scientists will continue to study and debate the evolution of flight in birds for many years.

---

after the time of the impact was probably the result of the environmental upheaval that the collision produced. However, many clam species associated with the mass extinction at the end of the Cretaceous period seem to have gone extinct *before* the impact, suggesting that other factors caused some of the massive extinctions occurring then.

The Cenozoic era is the age of mammals

With equal justice the Cenozoic era could be called the Age of Mammals, the Age of Birds, the Age of Insects, or the Age of Flowering Plants. This era is marked by the appearance of all these forms in great variety and numbers of species. The Cenozoic era extends from 66 mya to the present. It is subdivided into three periods: the **Paleogene period,** encompassing some 43 million years; the **Neogene period,** which was 20.4 million years in length; and the **Quaternary period,**

which covers the last 2.6 million years. The Paleogene period is subdivided into three epochs, named from earliest to latest: Paleocene, Eocene, and Oligocene. The Neogene period is subdivided into two epochs: the Miocene and Pliocene. The Quaternary period is subdivided into the Pleistocene and Holocene epochs.

Flowering plants, which arose during the Cretaceous period, continued to diversify during the Cenozoic era. During the Paleocene and Eocene epochs, fossils indicate that tropical and semitropical plant communities extended to relatively high latitudes. Palms, for example, are found in Eocene deposits in Wyoming. Later in the Cenozoic era, there is evidence of more open habitats. Grasslands and savannas spread throughout much of North America during the Miocene epoch, with deserts developing later in the Pliocene and Pleistocene epochs. During the Pleistocene epoch, plant communities changed dynamically in response to the fluctuating climates associated with the multiple advances and retreats of continental glaciers.

During the Paleocene epoch, an explosive radiation of primitive mammals occurred. Most of them were small forest dwellers that are not closely related to modern mammals. During the Eocene epoch, mammals continued to diverge, and all the modern orders first appeared. Again, many of the mammals were small, but there were also some larger herbivores.

During the Eocene epoch, there was an explosive radiation of birds, which acquired adaptations for different habitats. Paleontologists hypothesize that the jaws and beak of the flightless giant bird *Diatryma*, for example, may have been adapted primarily for crushing and slicing vegetation in Eocene forests, marshes, and grasslands. Other paleontologists hypothesize that these giant birds were carnivores that killed or scavenged mammals and other vertebrates (**FIG. 21-17**).

During the Oligocene epoch, many modern families of mammals evolved, including the first apes in Africa. Many lineages showed adaptations that suggest a more open type of habitat, such as grassland or savanna, than previously. Many mammals were larger than earlier mammals and had longer legs for running, specialized teeth for chewing coarse vegetation or for preying on animals, and increases in their relative brain sizes. The *indricotheres,* for example, are extinct relatives of the rhinoceros. These mammals, which lived on the grassless plains of Eurasia, became progressively larger during the Oligocene epoch (**FIG. 21-18**).

Human ancestors appeared in Africa during the Late Miocene and Early Pliocene epochs. *Homo,* the genus to

Figure 21-18 A mammal from the Oligocene epoch

Paraceratherium was an indricothere, a hornless relative of the rhinoceros. This huge land mammal was about 8 m (26 ft) long and weighed about 15 to 20 tons. It probably ate leaves and branches of deciduous trees, much as a modern-day giraffe does.

which humans belong, appeared approximately 2.5 mya. (Primate evolution, including human evolution, is discussed in Chapter 22.)

The Pliocene and Pleistocene epochs witnessed the introduction of spectacular North and South American large-mammal fauna, including mastodons, saber-toothed cats, camels, giant ground sloths, and giant armadillos. However, many of the large mammals became extinct at the end of the Pleistocene epoch. This extinction was possibly due to climate change—the Pleistocene epoch was marked by several ice ages—or to the influence of humans, which had spread from Africa to Europe and Asia, and later to North and South America by crossing a land bridge between Siberia and Alaska. Archaeological evidence indicates that this mass extinction event was concurrent with the appearance of human hunters.

CHECKPOINT 21.3

- **CONNECT** *What is the correct order of appearance in the fossil record, starting with the earliest: eukaryotic cells, multicellular organisms, prokaryotic cells?*

- **CONNECT** *What is the correct order of appearance in the fossil record, starting with the earliest: reptiles, mammals, amphibians, fishes?*

- **CONNECT** *What is the correct order of appearance in the fossil record, starting with the earliest: flowering plants, ferns, gymnosperms?*

Figure 21-17 A bird from the Eocene epoch

The flightless bird *Diatryma*, which stood 2.1 m (7 ft) tall and weighed about 175 kg (385 lb), may have been an herbivore or a formidable predator. In this picture *Diatryma* has captured a small, horselike perissodactyl.

21.1 Chemical Evolution on Early Earth (page 439)

1 Describe the conditions that scientists think existed on early Earth.

- Biologists generally agree that life originated from nonliving matter by **chemical evolution.** Hypotheses about chemical evolution are testable.
- Four requirements for chemical evolution are (1) the absence of oxygen, which would have reacted with and oxidized abiotically produced organic molecules; (2) energy to form organic molecules; (3) chemical building blocks, including water, minerals, and gases present in the atmosphere; and (4) sufficient time for molecules to accumulate and react.

2 Compare the prebiotic soup hypothesis with the iron–sulfur world hypothesis.

- During chemical evolution, small organic molecules formed spontaneously and accumulated. The **prebiotic soup hypothesis** proposes that organic molecules formed near Earth's surface in a "sea of organic soup" or on rock or clay surfaces. The **iron–sulfur world hypothesis** suggests that organic molecules were produced at **hydrothermal vents,** cracks in the deep-ocean floor.

21.2 The First Cells (page 441)

3 Outline the major steps hypothesized to have occurred in the origin of cells.

- After small organic molecules formed and accumulated, macromolecules assembled from the small organic molecules. Macromolecular assemblages called **protobionts** formed from macromolecules. Cells arose from the protobionts.
- According to a model known as the **RNA world,** RNA was the first informational molecule to evolve in the progression toward a self-sustaining, self-reproducing cell. Natural selection at the molecular level eventually resulted in the information sequence DNA → RNA → protein.

4 Explain how the evolution of photosynthetic autotrophs affected both the atmosphere and other organisms.

- The first cells were prokaryotic **heterotrophs** that obtained organic molecules from the environment. They were almost certainly **anaerobes.** Later, **autotrophs**—organisms that produce their own organic molecules by photosynthesis—evolved.
- The evolution of oxygen-generating photosynthesis ultimately changed early life. The accumulation of molecular oxygen in the atmosphere permitted the evolution of **aerobes,** organisms that could use oxygen for a more efficient type of cellular respiration.

5 Describe the hypothesis of serial endosymbiosis.

- Eukaryotic cells arose from prokaryotic cells. According to the hypothesis of **serial endosymbiosis,** certain eukaryotic organelles (mitochondria and chloroplasts) evolved from prokaryotic **endosymbionts** incorporated within larger prokaryotic hosts.

21.3 The History of Life (page 446)

6 Briefly describe the distinguishing organisms and major biological events of the Ediacaran period and the Paleozoic, Mesozoic, and Cenozoic eras.

- Life at the beginning of the **Proterozoic eon** (2500 mya to 541 mya) consisted of prokaryotes. About 2.2 bya, the first eukaryotic cells appeared. The **Ediacaran period,** from 635 mya to 541 mya, is the last period of the Proterozoic eon. Ediacaran fossils are the oldest known fossils of multicellular animals. Ediacaran fauna were small, soft-bodied invertebrates.
- During the **Paleozoic era,** which began about 541 mya and lasted approximately 289 million years, all major groups of plants, except flowering plants, and all animal phyla appeared. Fishes and amphibians flourished, and reptiles appeared. The greatest mass extinction of all time occurred at the end of the Paleozoic era, 252 mya. More than 90% of marine species and 70% of land-dwelling vertebrate genera as well as many plant species became extinct.
- The **Mesozoic era** began about 252 mya and lasted some 186 million years. Flowering plants appeared, and reptiles diversified. Dinosaurs, which descended from early reptiles, dominated. Insects flourished, and birds and early mammals appeared. At the end of the Cretaceous period, 66 mya, many species abruptly became extinct. A collision of a large extraterrestrial body with Earth may have resulted in dramatic climate changes that played a role in this mass extinction.

- In the **Cenozoic era,** which extends from 66 mya to the present, flowering plants, birds, insects, and mammals diversified greatly. Human ancestors appeared in Africa during the Late Miocene and Early Pliocene epochs.

Know and Comprehend

1. Energy, the absence of molecular oxygen, chemical building blocks, and time were the requirements for (a) chemical evolution (b) biological evolution (c) the Cambrian radiation (d) the mass extinction episode at the end of the Cretaceous period (e) directed evolution

2. Many scientists think that ___ was the first information molecule to evolve. (a) DNA (b) RNA (c) a protein (d) an amino acid (e) a lipid

3. The first cells were probably (a) heterotrophs (b) autotrophs (c) anaerobes (d) a and c (e) b and c

4. According to the hypothesis of serial endosymbiosis, (a) life originated from nonliving matter (b) the pace of evolution quickened at the start of the Cambrian period (c) chloroplasts, mitochondria, and possibly other organelles originated from intimate relationships among prokaryotic cells (d) banded iron formations reflect the buildup of sufficient oxygen in the atmosphere to oxidize iron at Earth's surface (e) the first photosynthetic organisms appeared 3.1 bya to 3.5 bya

5. During the Early ____, life consisted of prokaryotic cells, but by the end of this geologic time span, multicellular eukaryotic organisms had evolved. (a) Cenozoic era (b) Paleozoic era (c) Mesozoic era (d) Archaean eon (e) Proterozoic eon

6. Geologists divide the eons into (a) periods (b) epochs (c) eras (d) millennia (e) none of the preceding

7. Ediacaran fossils (a) are the oldest known fossils of multicellular animals (b) come from the Burgess Shale in British Columbia (c) contain remains of large salamander-like organisms (d) are the oldest fossils of early vascular plants (e) contain a high concentration of iridium

8. The time of greatest evolutionary diversification in the history of life occurred during the (a) Cambrian period (b) Ordovician period (c) Silurian period (d) Carboniferous period (e) Permian period

9. The greatest mass extinction episode in the history of life occurred at what boundary? (a) Pliocene–Pleistocene (b) Permian–Triassic (c) Mesozoic–Cenozoic (d) Cambrian–Ordovician (e) Triassic–Jurassic

10. The Age of Reptiles corresponds to the (a) Paleozoic era (b) Mesozoic era (c) Cenozoic era (d) Pleistocene epoch (e) Permian period

11. Evidence exists that a catastrophic collision between Earth and a large extraterrestrial body occurred 66 mya, resulting in the extinction of (a) worms, mollusks, and soft-bodied arthropods (b) jawless ostracoderms and jawed placoderms (c) dinosaurs, pterosaurs, and many gymnosperm species (d) mastodons, saber-toothed cats, and giant ground sloths (e) ferns, horsetails, and club mosses

12. Flowering plants and mammals diversified and became dominant during the (a) Paleozoic era (b) Mesozoic era (c) Cenozoic era (d) Devonian period (e) Cambrian period

Apply and Analyze

13. Which are thought to have evolved first, aerobic bacteria or photosynthetic bacteria? Explain.

Evaluate and Synthesize

14. **EVOLUTION LINK** If you were studying how protobionts evolved into cells and you developed a protobiont that was capable of self-replication, would you consider it a living cell? Why or why not?

15. **EVOLUTION LINK** If living cells were produced in a test tube from nonbiological components by chemical processes, would this accomplishment prove that life evolved in a similar manner billions of years ago? Explain your answer.

16. **EVOLUTION LINK** Why did the evolution of multicellular organisms such as plants and animals have to be preceded by the evolution of oxygen-producing photosynthesis?

17. **INTERPRET DATA** Evidence for the oldest cyanobacterial fossils (stromatolites) dates to about 2 billion years, but molecular evidence inferred from lipids in ancient rocks puts the date for living cyanobacteria and eukaryotes at 2.7 billion years. Develop two opposing hypotheses to explain the discrepancy between the dates.

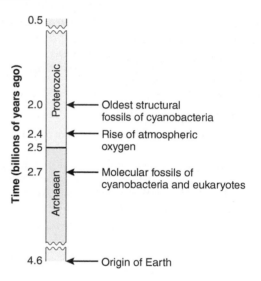

Viruses and Subviral Agents

During the late 1800s, botanists searched for the cause of tobacco mosaic disease, which stunts the growth of tobacco plants and gives the infected tobacco leaves a spotted, mosaic appearance. The investigators found that they could transmit this disease to healthy plants by daubing their leaves with the sap of diseased plants. In 1892, Dmitri Ivanowsky, a Russian botanist, showed that the sap was still infective after it had been passed through porcelain filters designed to filter out all known bacteria. A few years later, in 1898, Martinus Beijerinck, a Dutch microbiologist, provided evidence that the agent that caused tobacco mosaic disease had many characteristics of a living organism. However, it appeared that the infective agent could reproduce only within a living cell. Beijerinck named the infective agent "virus" (from the Latin word *virus,* which means "poison"). Tobacco mosaic virus was the first virus to be recognized.

Early in the 20th century, scientists discovered other infective agents, like those responsible for tobacco mosaic disease, that could cause disease in animals or kill bacteria. These pathogens were so small that they could not be seen with the light microscope. They also passed through filters that removed bacteria. Curiously, they could not be grown in laboratory cultures unless living cells were present. The development of the electron microscope in the 1930s made it possible to see viruses for the first time.

Most of the viruses that infect animals, plants, and bacteria were identified during the second half of the 20th century. Viruses cause many plant diseases and are responsible for billions of dollars in crop losses each year. You may recognize some of the many human viral diseases, such as rabies, influenza, herpes, and acquired human immunodeficiency syndrome (AIDS). You have probably received vaccinations for many common childhood viral diseases, including polio, rubella (German measles), mumps, and chickenpox.

Viruses make up a large component of Earth's biomass. Their huge numbers make up for their small size and weight. Viruses influence many ecological processes. For example, they kill large amounts of marine biomass each day, contributing significantly to the recycling of nutrients. Viruses adapt to their environments through evolution. They also influence the biodiversity of other organisms. Viruses can transfer their own genes into the genetic material of their hosts. They can also transfer eukaryotic genes from

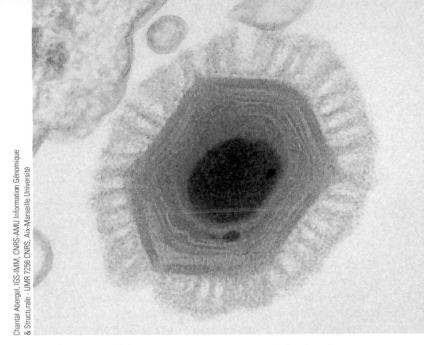

Chantal Abergel, IGS-IMM, CNRS-AMU Information Génomique & Structurale - UMR 7256 CNRS, Aix-Marseille Université

EM of *Megavirus chilensis*. Megavirus is a giant virus, the size of a very small bacterium (mycoplasma). The giant viruses discovered to date infect amoebas.

KEY CONCEPTS

24.1 A virus is a small particle consisting of a nucleic acid core surrounded by a protein coat; to reproduce, a virus must infect a living cell.

24.2 Viruses can be classified based on their host range, what type of nucleic acid they have, and whether the nucleic acid is single-stranded or double-stranded.

24.3 In a lytic reproductive cycle, a virus uses the host cell's molecular machinery to replicate itself, destroying the host cell in the process. In a lysogenic cycle, the viral genome becomes integrated into the host DNA and is then called a "provirus."

24.4 Viruses infect the cells of all kinds of organisms; they cause serious diseases in plants and animals.

24.5 Three different hypotheses suggest how viruses may have originated and evolved.

24.6 Subviral agents, which include satellites, viroids, and prions, are smaller and simpler than viruses.

one organism to another, crossing species boundaries. The discovery of giant viruses (see photograph) has raised new questions about the structure, genomes, origin, and phylogenetic relationships of viruses.

In this chapter we examine the characteristics and diversity of viruses as well as the smaller subviral agents, viroids and prions. We include viruses in the diversity unit of *Biology* because they have some characteristics of living things and because they impact all living organisms.

24.1 THE STATUS AND STRUCTURE OF VIRUSES

LEARNING OBJECTIVES

1 Contrast a virus with a cellular organism.
2 Describe the structure of a virus.

A **virus** is a very small infective agent that consists of a core of nucleic acid and is dependent on a living host. The study of viruses is called *virology,* and biologists who study viruses are *virologists.* Most biologists view viruses as nonliving particles because they are not composed of cells and they cannot carry on metabolic activities or reproduce on their own. They do not have the components necessary to carry on cellular respiration or to synthesize proteins and other molecules.

Viruses do contain the nucleic acids necessary to make copies of themselves. They replicate by invading living cells and commandeering their metabolic machinery. To multiply, a virus must *infect* a cell in which it can replicate. Thus, viruses are *obligate intracellular parasites;* they survive only by using the resources of a *host cell,* the cell the virus invades. Viruses infect all types of organisms, including bacteria, archaea, protists, plants, fungi, and animals. Some viruses even infect other viruses. Interestingly, viruses evolve by natural selection. For these reasons, most biologists view viruses as being at the edge of life, although a few argue that they are very simple life-forms.

Viruses are very small

Most known viruses are very small, ranging in size from 20 to 300 nm. (Recall that a nanometer is one-thousandth of a micrometer.) The poliovirus is about 30 nm in diameter (about the size of a ribosome). If we could line these viruses up end to end, it would take almost a million of them to span 1 inch! A poxvirus that causes smallpox can measure up to 300 nm long and 200 nm wide.

The paradigm that all viruses are very small and simple, with very small genomes, has been challenged by the discovery of *giant* viruses. *Mimivirus* was discovered in 2004, followed by *Megavirus* in 2011, and Pandoraviruses in 2013. One of the Pandoraviruses approaches 1 μm in length and is about 0.5 μm wide, larger than many bacteria and some eukaryotic cells. These giant viruses were discovered by French researchers in seawater off the coast of Chile and in a freshwater pond in Australia.

A virus consists of nucleic acid surrounded by a protein coat

The nucleic acid core of the virus is surrounded by a protein coat called a **capsid.** Microbiologists use the term *virion* to refer to the complete virus particle that is outside a host cell in a dormant state. The virion is the form in which the virus moves from the cell in which it was produced to a new host cell in which it can replicate its genome. However, here we will use the term *virus* in a broad sense, even when referring to virions.

A typical virus contains *either* deoxyribonucleic acid (DNA) or ribonucleic acid (RNA), not both. In 2012, however, researchers discovered an RNA–DNA hybrid virus in a high temperature acidic California lake. Further studies have found three other similar RNA–DNA hybrids in marine environments.

The nucleic acid of a virus can be single-stranded or double-stranded. Thus, a virus can have single-stranded (ss) DNA, double-stranded (ds) DNA, ssRNA, or dsRNA. As we will discuss, the type of nucleic acid is important in classifying viruses. The virus genome typically consists of 5000 to more than 100,000 bases or base pairs (depending on whether it is single-stranded or double-stranded). Again, the giant viruses are exceptions. *Megavirus* has seven transfer RNAs and some metabolic genes never before identified in any other virus. Researchers have sequenced the double-stranded DNA genomes of two species of *Pandoravirus* and reported that they range from 1.9 to 2.5 million base pairs. The species with the largest genome has 2556 proposed protein-coding genes (only 6% of which match known proteins).

The capsid is a protective protein coat

The capsid consists of protein subunits called *capsomers.* The capsomers determine the shape of the virus. Capsids generally are helical, polyhedral, or a combination of both shapes. Helical viruses, such as the tobacco mosaic virus (TMV), appear as long rods or threads (FIG. 24-1a). Its capsid is a hollow cylinder made up of proteins that form a groove into which the RNA fits.

Polyhedral viruses, such as the adenoviruses (which cause a number of human illnesses, including some respiratory infections), appear somewhat spherical (FIG. 24-1b). Its capsomers are organized in equilateral triangles. The capsid of a large virus can consist of several hundred capsomers. The most common polyhedral structure is an *icosahedron,* a structure with 20 identical surface faces (each face is a triangle). The human immunodeficiency virus (HIV) that causes AIDS is an enveloped virus (see next section) (FIG. 24-1c).

Some viruses have both helical and polyhedral components. Viruses that infect bacteria are called *bacteriophages,* or simply *phages* (FIG. 24-1d). The T4 phage that infects the bacterium *Escherichia coli* consists of a polyhedral "head" attached to a helical "tail." Many phages have this shape. Many phages also have tail fibers that attach to the host cell.

Some viruses are surrounded by an envelope

Some viruses, called *enveloped viruses,* have an outer membranous envelope that surrounds the capsid. Typically, the virus

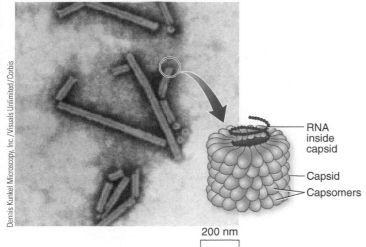

(a) TEM of tobacco mosaic virus. This rod-shaped virus has a helical arrangement of capsid proteins.

(b) Color-enhanced TEM of an adenovirus. The capsid is composed of 252 subunits (visible as tiny ovals) arranged into a 20-sided polyhedron. Twelve of the subunits have projecting glycoprotein spikes that permit the virus to recognize host cells.

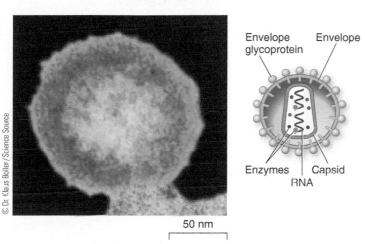

(c) Color-enhanced TEM of HIV, the virus that causes AIDS. The virus is leaving a host cell (*pink*). The virus is enclosed in an envelope (*green*) derived from the host's plasma membrane. Viral proteins project from the envelope. The capsid of the virus is shown in *yellow*.

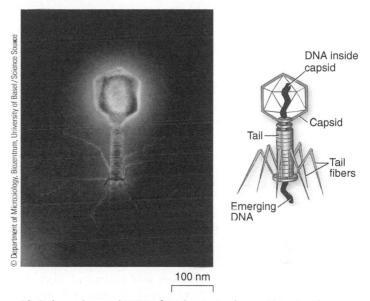

(d) Color-enhanced TEM of T4 bacteriophage. This virus has a polyhedral head and a helical tail. The virus attaches to the cell wall of the bacterial host by its tail fibers.

Figure 24-1 *Animation* **The structure of a virus**

A virus consists of a DNA or RNA core surrounded by a protein coat called a capsid. The capsid is made up of protein subunits called capsomers. Some viruses have an outer membranous envelope surrounding the capsid.

© Cengage Learning

acquires the envelope from the host cell's plasma membrane as it leaves the host cell (FIG. 24-2). Interestingly, while inside the host cell, the virus synthesizes certain proteins and inserts them into the host's plasma membrane. Thus, the viral envelope consists of phospholipids and proteins of the host's plasma membrane as well as distinctive proteins produced by the virus itself. Some viruses produce envelope glycoproteins that extend out from the envelope as spikes. As we will discuss, these glycoprotein spikes can be very important in the virus's interaction with the host cell.

CHECKPOINT 24.1

- CONNECT *What characteristics of a living organism are absent in a virus?*
- *What are the structural components of a virus?*

24.2 CLASSIFICATION OF VIRUSES

LEARNING OBJECTIVE

3 Identify three characteristics used to classify viruses.

Viruses present a taxonomic challenge to biologists because they do not have the characteristics that define living organisms (see Chapter 1). They are not cellular, they do not carry on metabolic activities, and they reproduce only by taking over the reproductive machinery of other cells. Viruses do not manufacture proteins and so do not have distinctive rRNA. For these reasons, viruses are not classified in any of the three domains.

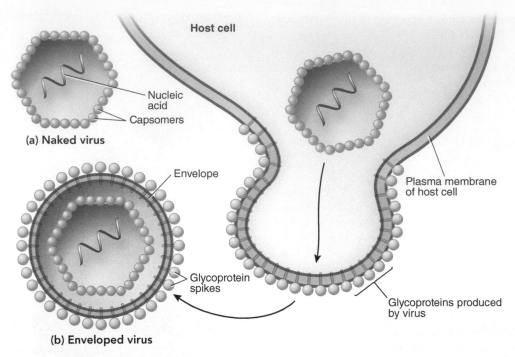

Host cell

Nucleic acid

Capsomers

(a) Naked virus

Envelope

Plasma membrane of host cell

Glycoprotein spikes

Glycoproteins produced by virus

(b) Enveloped virus

Figure 24-2 Comparison of naked and enveloped viruses
As the virus leaves the host cell, the host's plasma membrane wraps around the virus, forming the envelope. The envelope contains proteins produced by the virus.
© Cengage Learning

Viruses can be classified based on their **host range,** the types of host species a specific virus (or other type of infectious agent) can infect. They may be referred to as plant viruses, animal viruses, bacterial viruses, and so on. Viruses are more formally classified into taxa from species to orders. The International Committee on Taxonomy of Viruses (ICTV), a group of virologists, decides on specific criteria for classifying and naming viruses. Recently, based on host range and other characteristics, the ICTV classified viruses into 7 orders, 96 families, 420 genera, and more than 2600 species. Virus family names include the suffix *-viridae.* Note that this classification system is not a traditional Linnaean system; it does not assign viruses to domains, kingdoms, or phyla.

The Baltimore classification system classifies viruses based on the type of nucleic acid the virus contains, whether the nucleic acid is single-stranded or double-stranded, and how mRNA is produced. Other traits considered in viral classification are the size and shape of the virus, the presence of an envelope, and the method by which the virus is transmitted from host to host.

CHECKPOINT 24.2

- *What are three characteristics used to classify viruses?*

24.3 VIRAL REPLICATION

LEARNING OBJECTIVES

4   Characterize bacteriophages.
5   Contrast a lytic cycle with a lysogenic cycle.

As we have discussed, viruses reproduce, but only within the complex environment of the living host cells they infect. Viruses use their genetic information to force their host cells to replicate their viral nucleic acid and make the proteins they need. They take over the transcriptional and translational mechanisms of the host cell.

Bacteriophages infect bacteria

Much of our knowledge of viruses has come from studying **bacteriophages** ("bacteria eaters"), more simply referred to as **phages.** These viruses can be cultured easily within living bacteria in the laboratory. Microbiologists have identified more than 5000 phages. Bacteriophages are among the most complex viruses (see Fig. 24-1d). Their most common structure consists of a long nucleic acid molecule (usually dsDNA) coiled within a polyhedral head. Most have a tail, which may be contractile and may function in penetration of the host cell.

Phages have been clinically used to treat infection for close to a century. Although abandoned in Western countries after the discovery of sulfa drugs and antibiotics in the 1940s, they have continued to be commonly used in member countries of the former Soviet Union to treat patients. Antibiotics, which have long been more dependable and easier to use, are increasingly less effective than in the past due to the widespread and escalating problem of bacterial resistance. Phage therapy, alone and paired with antibiotics, is again a focus of research in the United States as well as in Eastern Europe. Phages are being engineered to specifically destroy particular bacteria due to their ability to target specific host species. Scientists are also genetically engineering phages so that bacteria will be slower to evolve resistance to them.

Phage therapy also has applications in dentistry, veterinary medicine, agriculture, and food science. For example, certain phages can kill deadly strains of *E. coli* in cattle. These bacteria do not appear to make cattle ill but can cause illness and death in people who eat contaminated, undercooked ground beef.

Viruses replicate inside host cells

Viruses infect bacterial, plant, and animal cells in basically similar ways. We will focus on phage infection of bacteria because this process is best understood. The reproductive cycle of viruses begins with a virus coming into contact with a host cell. The virus typically attaches to the surface of the host cell. The viral nucleic acid must enter the host cell and synthesize the components it needs to reproduce itself. Then viral components are assembled, and viruses are released from the cell, ready to invade other cells. Two types of viral reproductive cycles are lytic and lysogenic cycles.

Lytic reproductive cycles destroy host cells. In a **lytic cycle,** the virus lyses (destroys) the host cell. When the virus infects a susceptible host cell, it forces the host to use its metabolic machinery to replicate viral particles. Viruses that have only a lytic cycle are described as *virulent,* which means that they cause disease and often death.

Five steps are typical in lytic viral reproduction (FIG. 24-3):

1. **Attachment (or adsorption).** The virus attaches to specific receptors on the host cell. This process ensures that the virus infects only its specific host.
2. **Penetration.** The virus penetrates the host plasma membrane and moves into the cytoplasm. Many viruses that infect animal cells enter the host cell intact. Some phages inject only their nucleic acid into the cytoplasm of the host cell; the capsid remains on the outside.
3. **Replication and synthesis.** The viral genome contains all the information necessary to produce new viruses. Once inside a host cell, the virus degrades the host-cell nucleic acid. The virus then uses the molecular machinery of the host cell to replicate its own nucleic acid and produce viral proteins. Many antiviral drugs interfere with replication of viral nucleic acid.
4. **Assembly.** The newly synthesized viral components are assembled into new viruses.
5. **Release.** Assembled viruses are released from the cell. Generally, lytic enzymes, produced by the phage late in the replication process, destroy the host plasma membrane. Phage release typically occurs all at once and results in rapid cell lysis. In contrast, animal viruses are often released slowly or bud off from the plasma membrane.

Once released, the viruses infect other cells, and the process begins anew. The time required for viral reproduction, from attachment to the release of new viruses, varies from less than 20 minutes to more than 1 hour.

How do bacteria protect themselves from phage infection? You may recall from Chapter 15 that bacteria produce *restriction enzymes,* enzymes that cut up the foreign DNA of the phage. This action prevents the phage DNA from duplicating. The

Viruses reproduce by seizing control of the metabolic machinery of a host cell. In a lytic infection, the viruses destroy the host cell.

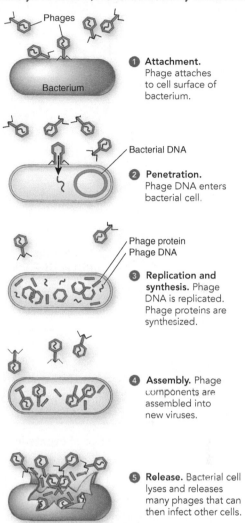

1 **Attachment.** Phage attaches to cell surface of bacterium.

2 **Penetration.** Phage DNA enters bacterial cell.

3 **Replication and synthesis.** Phage DNA is replicated. Phage proteins are synthesized.

4 **Assembly.** Phage components are assembled into new viruses.

5 **Release.** Bacterial cell lyses and releases many phages that can then infect other cells.

(a) The sequence of events in a lytic infection.

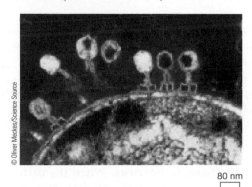

(b) Color-enhanced TEM of phages infecting a bacterium, *Escherichia coli*.

Figure 24-3 *Animation* The sequence of events in a lytic infection

Virulent bacteriophages kill their host cell during each cycle of infection.

PREDICT Would the phage components be able to infect other bacteria if they were released prior to assembly?

© Cengage Learning

In a lysogenic cycle, temperate phages integrate their nucleic acid into the host genome. The prophage replicates when the bacterial DNA replicates.

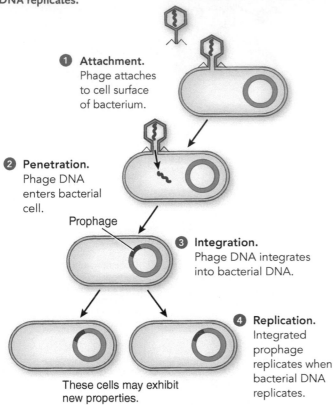

1 Attachment. Phage attaches to cell surface of bacterium.

2 Penetration. Phage DNA enters bacterial cell.

Prophage

3 Integration. Phage DNA integrates into bacterial DNA.

4 Replication. Integrated prophage replicates when bacterial DNA replicates.

These cells may exhibit new properties.

Figure 24-4 *Animation* **The sequence of events in a lysogenic cycle**

Temperate phages integrate their nucleic acid into the DNA of their bacterial host. The integrated viral DNA is called a prophage. The bacterium is called a lysogenic cell.

PREDICT How do temperate phages benefit from integrating into the bacterial DNA?

© Cengage Learning

bacterial cell protects its own DNA by slightly modifying it after replication so that the restriction enzyme does not recognize the sites it would cut.

In lysogenic cycles temperate viruses integrate into the host DNA

Temperate phages do not immediately destroy their hosts. These phages alternate between a lytic cycle and a lysogenic cycle. In a **lysogenic cycle,** the viral genome becomes integrated into the host bacterial DNA. The integrated virus is called a **prophage,** or **provirus.** When the bacterial DNA replicates, the prophage also replicates (FIG. 24-4). In this way, the prophage is passed on to new generations of the original infected cell. The viral genes that code for viral structural proteins may be repressed indefinitely. The temperate phage lambda (designated by the Greek letter λ) is a model organism used to study temperate viruses.

Certain external conditions (such as ultraviolet light and X-rays) cause temperate viruses to revert to a lytic cycle and then destroy their host. Sometimes temperate viruses become lytic spontaneously.

Bacterial cells carrying prophages are called *lysogenic cells.* Such bacterial cells may exhibit new properties. This type of change is called **lysogenic conversion.** An interesting example involves the bacterium *Corynebacterium diphtheriae,* which causes diphtheria. Two strains of this species exist, one that produces a toxin (and causes diphtheria) and one that does not. The only difference between these two strains is that the toxin-producing bacteria are infected by a specific temperate phage. The phage DNA codes for the powerful toxin that causes the symptoms of diphtheria. Similarly, the bacterium *Clostridium botulinum,* which causes botulism, a serious form of food poisoning, is harmless unless it contains certain prophage DNA that induces synthesis of the toxin.

CHECKPOINT 24.3

- **VISUALIZE** *What are the steps in a lytic cycle? Draw diagrams to illustrate your answer.*
- *How is a lysogenic cycle different from a lytic cycle?*

24.4 VIRAL DISEASES

LEARNING OBJECTIVES

6 Contrast viral infection of plants and animals, and identify specific diseases caused by viruses.

7 Describe the reproductive cycle of a retrovirus, such as human immunodeficiency virus (HIV).

Sir Peter Medawar, a winner of the 1960 Nobel Prize in Physiology or Medicine, defined a *virus* as "a piece of bad news wrapped in protein." Viruses that are **pathogens** are responsible for some very serious diseases, including Ebola hemorrhagic fever, rabies, influenza (flu), and AIDS. However, although viruses must infect cells to reproduce, most known viruses do *not* cause disease. Here we focus on viral infection of plants and animals.

Viruses cause serious plant diseases

Viruses cause many important plant diseases and are responsible for billions of dollars in agricultural losses and lower crop quality worldwide each year. Infected crops almost always produce lower yields than noninfected crops.

Viral infections do not usually kill plants, but they do stunt their growth; cause changes in the shape of the foliage; and may cause spots, streaks, or mottled patterns on leaves, flowers, or fruits (FIG. 24-5). Most plant viruses have capsids, but not envelopes. The genome of most plant viruses consists of ssRNA. Plant viruses are typically named according to the type of host plant they infect and their effects on the plant. Tobacco mosaic virus, described at the beginning of this chapter, was the first virus ever discovered.

Insects are important vectors of plant disease. As they feed on plant tissues, aphids, leaf-hoppers, and many other insects spread viral diseases among plants. Soil-borne nematodes and protozoa are vectors of viral infections in plant roots.

Because plants have thick cell walls, viruses cannot penetrate plant cells unless the cells are damaged. Plant viruses can be transmitted from one generation to the next through infected seeds or by asexual propagation (Fig. 24-5). Once a plant is infected, the virus spreads through the plant body by passing through *plasmodesmata,* cytoplasmic channels that connect adjacent plant cells.

There are no known cures for most viral diseases of plants, so infected plants are commonly burned. Many agricultural scientists are focusing their efforts on preventing viral disease by developing virus-resistant strains of important crop plants.

(a) Virus-streaked tulip. The virus that causes this relatively harmless disease affects pigment formation in the petals.

(b) Pepper leaves infected with tobacco mosaic virus. The leaf is characteristically mottled with light green areas.

Figure 24-5 Plant diseases caused by viruses

Viruses cause serious diseases in animals

Hundreds of different viruses infect animals, including humans. Animal viruses cause hog cholera, foot-and-mouth disease, canine distemper, and certain types of cancer (such as feline leukemia and cervical cancer). Viruses cause chickenpox, herpes simplex (one type causes genital herpes), mumps, rubella (German measles), rubeola (measles), rabies, warts, infectious mononucleosis, influenza, viral hepatitis, Ebola hemorrhagic fever, and AIDS (TABLE 24-1 and *Inquiring About: Influenza and Other Emerging Diseases*). Most humans suffer from two to six viral infections each year, including common colds and gastrointestinal disorders.

Norwalk virus is responsible for most worldwide viral gastroenteritis outbreaks and epidemics, affecting more than 200 million and killing more than 200,000 people each year. Norwalk virus is transmitted directly from person to person and indirectly by fecal contamination of water and food. The virus is also spread when infected people sneeze or cough, sending particles into the air; that is, virus particles become aerosolized. Infected individuals can shed viral particles for many weeks after symptoms abate. Norwalk virus infections are a serious concern, especially in closed communities, such as health care institutions, prisons, and cruise ships where people are in prolonged close contact. The genetically diverse strains of the Norwalk virus species make up the noroviruses.

Human activity, including social factors such as urbanization, global travel, and war, contributes to epidemics of infectious disease. Living conditions, including sanitation, nutrition, physical stress, level of health care, and sexual practices, are important factors in the spread of disease. In the United States and other highly developed countries, infectious disease accounts for about 4% to 8% of deaths compared with death rates of 30% to 50% in developing regions. Even at the level of our current knowledge about viruses and epidemiology, just how prepared are we to contain a particularly virulent virus? For example, how well are we containing HIV (the virus that causes AIDS), which continues to infect and kill millions of people worldwide every year?

Since the September 11, 2001, terrorist attacks in the United States, bioterrorism has become a critical concern worldwide. **Bioterrorism** is the intentional use of microorganisms or toxins derived from living organisms to cause death or disease in humans, animals, or plants on which humans depend. Terrorists could conceivably initiate epidemics of smallpox, anthrax, plague, yellow fever, Ebola hemorrhagic fever, and other potentially fatal diseases. (Note that anthrax and plague are caused by bacteria; see Table 25-5.) The quest for rapid identification and effective treatments and vaccines for these diseases has taken on new urgency.

Animal viruses have varied structure and life cycles

Most viruses cannot survive very long outside a living host cell, so their survival depends on their being transmitted from one animal to another. However, their host range may be quite limited because attachment to a host cell is very specific. The type of attachment proteins on the surface of a virus determines what type of cell it can infect. Receptors typically vary with each species and sometimes with each type of tissue. Thus, many human viruses can infect only humans because the viral attachment proteins combine only with receptor sites found on human cell membranes. The measles virus and poxviruses infect many types of human tissue because their attachment proteins combine with receptor sites on a variety of cells. In contrast, the poliovirus attaches to specific types of human cells, such as those that line the digestive tract and motor neurons of the brain and spinal cord.

Some viruses, such as the adenoviruses, have fibers that project from the capsid and adhere to complementary receptors

TABLE 24-1 | Some Viruses That Infect Vertebrates

GROUP	DISEASES CAUSED	CHARACTERISTICS
DNA VIRUSES WITH ENVELOPE		
Poxviruses	Smallpox, cowpox,* monkeypox, and economically important diseases of domestic fowl	**dsDNA;** large, complex viruses; replicate in the cytoplasm of the host cell
Herpesviruses	Cold sores (herpes simplex virus type 1); genital herpes, a sexually transmitted disease (herpes simplex virus type 2); chickenpox and shingles (herpes varicella–zoster virus); infectious mononucleosis and Burkitt's lymphoma (Epstein–Barr virus)	**dsDNA;** medium to large, enveloped viruses; replicate in the host nucleus[†]
DNA VIRUSES WITH NO ENVELOPE		
Adenoviruses	Respiratory tract disorders (e.g., sore throat, tonsillitis), conjunctivitis, and gastrointestinal disorders are caused by more than 40 types of adenoviruses in humans; other varieties infect other animals	**dsDNA;** replicate in the host nucleus
Papovaviruses	Human warts and some degenerative brain diseases; some cancers, including cervical cancer[‡‡]	**dsDNA**
Parvoviruses	Infections in dogs, swine, arthropods, rodents; gastroenteritis in humans (transmitted by consumption of infected shellfish)	**ssDNA;** some require a helper virus to multiply
RNA VIRUSES WITH ENVELOPE		
Togaviruses	Rubella (German measles)	**ssRNA** that can serve as mRNA; large diverse group of medium-sized enveloped viruses; many transmitted by arthropods
Orthomyxoviruses	Influenza (flu) in humans and other animals	**ssRNA** that serves as template for mRNA synthesis; medium-sized viruses that often exhibit projecting glycoprotein spikes
Paramyxoviruses	Rubeola (measles) and mumps in humans; distemper in dogs	**ssRNA;** resemble orthomyxoviruses but somewhat larger
Rhabdoviruses	Rabies	**ssRNA**
Coronaviruses	Upper respiratory infections; SARS	**ssRNA;** largest known RNA virus
Flaviviruses	Yellow fever; West Nile virus; hepatitis C (the most common reason for liver transplants in the United States)	**ssRNA**
Filoviruses	Hemorrhagic fever, including that caused by the Ebola virus	**ssRNA**
Bunyaviruses	St. Louis encephalitis; hantavirus pulmonary syndrome (caused by Sin Nombre virus, a hantavirus)	**ssRNA**
Retroviruses	AIDS; some types of cancer	**ssRNA** viruses that contain reverse transcriptase for transcribing the RNA genome into DNA; two identical molecules of ssRNA
RNA VIRUSES WITH NO ENVELOPE		
Picornaviruses	Polio (poliovirus); hepatitis A (hepatitis A virus); intestinal disorders (enteroviruses); common cold (rhinoviruses); aseptic meningitis (coxsackievirus, echovirus)	**ssRNA** that can serve as mRNA; diverse group of small viruses
Reoviruses	Vomiting and diarrhea; encephalitis	**dsRNA**
Noroviruses (This group made up of strains of Norwalk virus)	Most common cause of viral gastroenteritis in humans	**ssRNA**

*The vaccinia (cowpox) virus is used to produce genetically engineered vaccines.
[†]These viruses frequently cause latent infections; some cause tumors.
[‡‡]The virus SV40 has been used as a vector to transport genes into cells.

on the host cell. Other viruses, such as those that cause herpes and rabies, are surrounded by a lipoprotein envelope with projecting glycoprotein spikes that attach to a host cell. The influenza virus has rodlike, glycoprotein spikes that project from its envelope. These spikes bind with specific receptors present only on cells lining the respiratory tract of certain vertebrates, including wild and domestic birds, horses, swine, and humans. Influenza vaccine prevents attachment by stimulating the host's antibodies to cover the glycoprotein spikes projecting from the virus.

Viruses have several ways to penetrate animal cells (FIG. 24-6). After attachment to a host-cell receptor, some enveloped viruses fuse with the animal cell's plasma membrane. The entire virus, including the capsid and nucleic acid, is released into the animal cell. Other viruses enter the host cell by *endocytosis.* In this process the plasma membrane of the animal cell invaginates, forming a membrane-enclosed vesicle that contains the virus. Endocytosis is advantageous to the virus because the endocytotic vesicle delivers the virus deep into the cytosol.

How do new strains of the influenza virus re-emerge? **Emerging diseases,** those new to the human population—such as AIDS, severe acute respiratory syndrome (SARS), Ebola hemorrhagic fever, eastern equine encephalitis, and West Nile virus—often appear suddenly. Many new, continual, or re-emerging pathogens can strike globally.

Re-emerging diseases are those that have been almost eradicated and then suddenly recur, causing an epidemic, sometimes in a new geographic area. Many familiar diseases, such as influenza, malaria, tuberculosis, and bacterial pneumonias, continue to infect large numbers of people and increasingly reappear in forms that are resistant to drug therapy. Drug-resistant pathogens are a major challenge to public health and other health care professionals.

Historically, new viral strains have claimed many human lives. In 1918, for example, an influenza (flu) pandemic killed more than 20 million people throughout the world. Flu pandemics also occurred in 1957 and 1968. Each year new strains of influenza virus evolve and become infectious. If the new combination of viral genes is unfamiliar to the human immune system, the virus may spread easily, resulting in a pandemic. According to the Centers for Disease Control and Prevention, influenza kills about 36,000 individuals in the United States every year.

New strains of influenza are thought to infect one species, such as a species of birds. At first, they are not able to spread among mammals. However, because viruses can evolve, the avian strain can mutate and become virulent. The avian virus can also exchange RNA with a virus that has the genetic material necessary to spread among swine or other mammals. Swine can be susceptible to both avian and human strains of the virus. Inside a swine's body, the viruses can exchange bits of RNA and develop the ability to infect humans. When an animal disease crosses the species barrier and infects humans, it is called a **zoonotic disease.** (We discuss zoonosis further in Chapter 25.) Reassortment of genetic material can also occur inside a human host, producing a viral strain that can spread from person to person (see figure). H1N1 influenza evolved in this way.

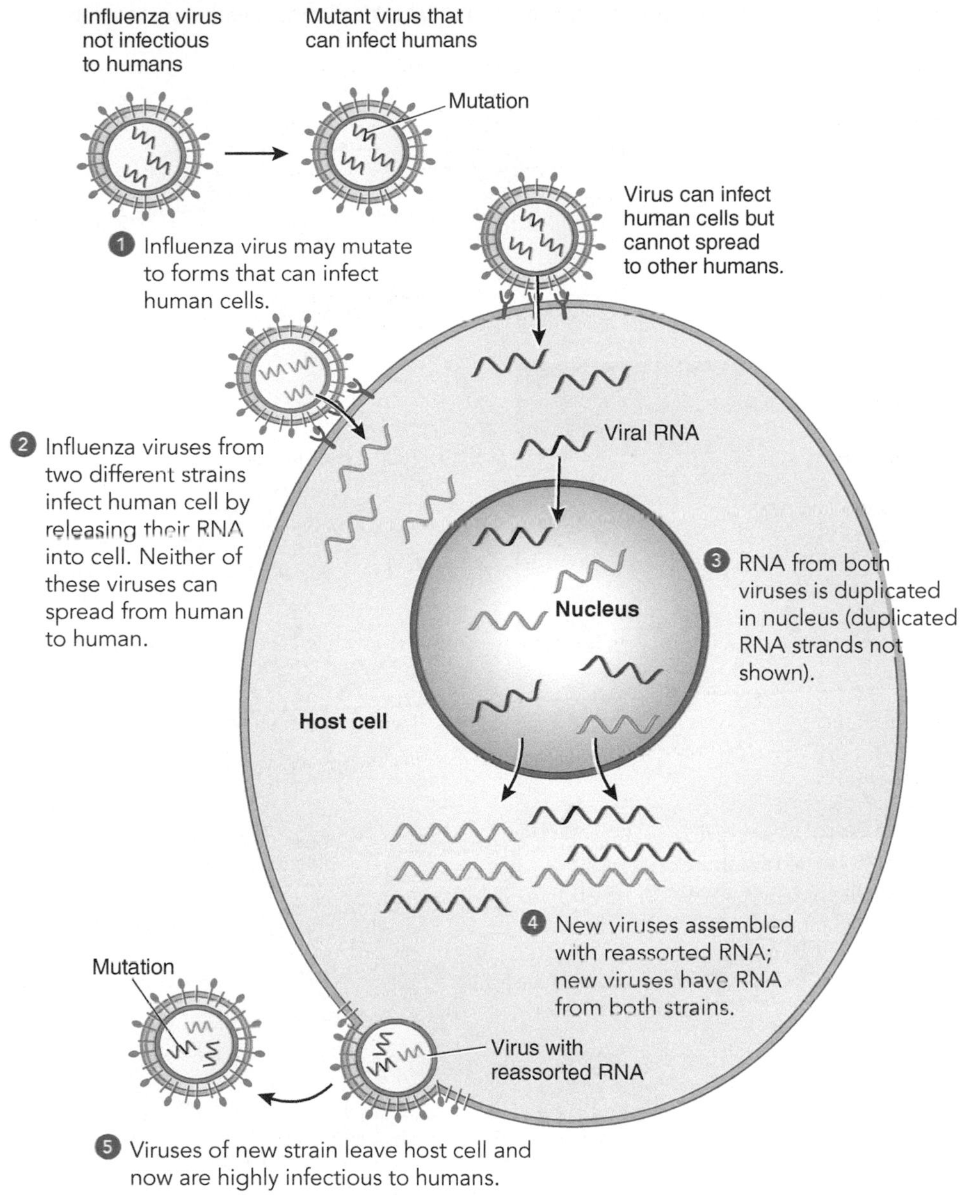

① Influenza virus may mutate to forms that can infect human cells.

② Influenza viruses from two different strains infect human cell by releasing their RNA into cell. Neither of these viruses can spread from human to human.

③ RNA from both viruses is duplicated in nucleus (duplicated RNA strands not shown).

④ New viruses assembled with reassorted RNA; new viruses have RNA from both strains.

⑤ Viruses of new strain leave host cell and now are highly infectious to humans.

An influenza virus such as H1N1 evolves as it mutates and its RNA reassorts in the bodies of birds, swine, and humans. Eventually, it becomes virulent.

© Cengage Learning

In DNA animal viruses, replication of viral DNA and protein synthesis are similar to the processes by which the host cell would normally carry out its own DNA replication and protein synthesis. In most RNA viruses, RNA synthesis takes place with the help of an RNA-dependent RNA polymerase.

Retroviruses are RNA viruses that have a DNA polymerase called **reverse transcriptase,** which transcribes the RNA genome into a DNA intermediate (FIG. 24-7). This DNA becomes integrated into the host DNA by an enzyme also carried by the virus. Copies of the viral RNA are synthesized as the incorporated DNA is transcribed by host RNA polymerases. The **human immunodeficiency virus (HIV)** that causes AIDS is a retrovirus. Some retroviruses can cause cancer directly or by interacting with other cancer-causing viruses.

After viral genes are transcribed, the viral structural proteins are synthesized. The capsid is produced, and then assembly of new virus particles takes place. Finally, release occurs.

Viruses bind to specific receptor proteins on the animal cell's plasma membrane. Enveloped viruses then enter the cell by membrane fusion.

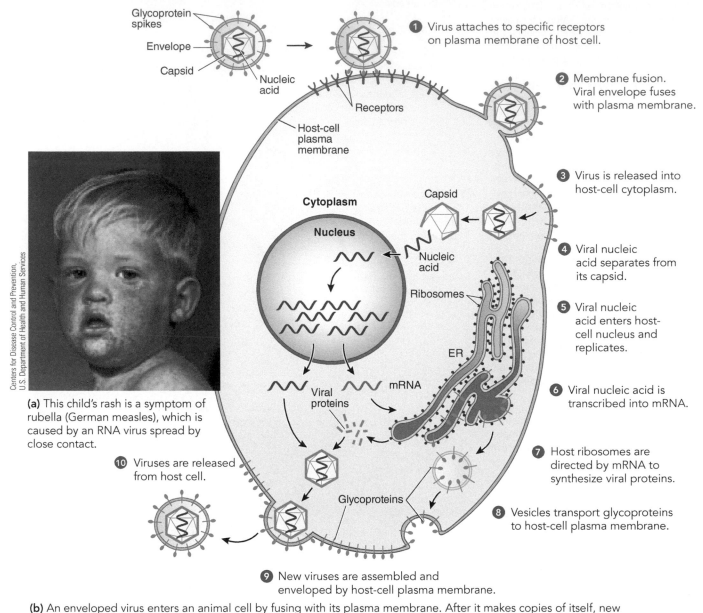

Glycoprotein spikes
Envelope
Capsid
Nucleic acid

Receptors

Host-cell plasma membrane

Cytoplasm

Nucleus

Capsid

Nucleic acid

Ribosomes

ER

Nucleic acid

mRNA

Viral proteins

Glycoproteins

1 Virus attaches to specific receptors on plasma membrane of host cell.

2 Membrane fusion. Viral envelope fuses with plasma membrane.

3 Virus is released into host-cell cytoplasm.

4 Viral nucleic acid separates from its capsid.

5 Viral nucleic acid enters host-cell nucleus and replicates.

6 Viral nucleic acid is transcribed into mRNA.

7 Host ribosomes are directed by mRNA to synthesize viral proteins.

8 Vesicles transport glycoproteins to host-cell plasma membrane.

9 New viruses are assembled and enveloped by host-cell plasma membrane.

10 Viruses are released from host cell.

(a) This child's rash is a symptom of rubella (German measles), which is caused by an RNA virus spread by close contact.

Centers for Disease Control and Prevention, U.S. Department of Health and Human Services

(b) An enveloped virus enters an animal cell by fusing with its plasma membrane. After it makes copies of itself, new viruses are released. A new envelope forms around each virus as it leaves the host cell.

Figure 24-6 *Animation* **Viral infection in animals**

CONNECT Why can't new viruses be completely assembled in the nucleus of the host?

© Cengage Learning

Viruses that do not have an outer envelope exit by cell lysis. The plasma membrane ruptures, releasing many new viral particles. Enveloped viruses obtain their lipoprotein envelopes by picking up a fragment of the host plasma membrane as they leave the infected cell (see Figs. 24-6b and 24-7).

Viral proteins damage the host cell in several ways. These proteins may alter the permeability of the plasma membrane or may inhibit synthesis of host nucleic acids or proteins. Viruses sometimes damage or kill their host cells by their sheer numbers. A poliovirus can produce 100,000 new viruses within a single host cell!

Viruses quickly become resistant to antiviral drugs
Antibiotics are specific for fighting bacteria; they do not kill viruses. Fortunately, researchers have developed antiviral drugs. These drugs inhibit the development, or replication, of many types of RNA and DNA viruses. Unfortunately, viruses rapidly develop resistance, making antiviral drug design and therapy a

Retroviruses use reverse transcriptase to transcribe their RNA into DNA; the viral DNA becomes part of the host DNA. When activated, viral DNA uses host enzymes to transcribe viral RNA.

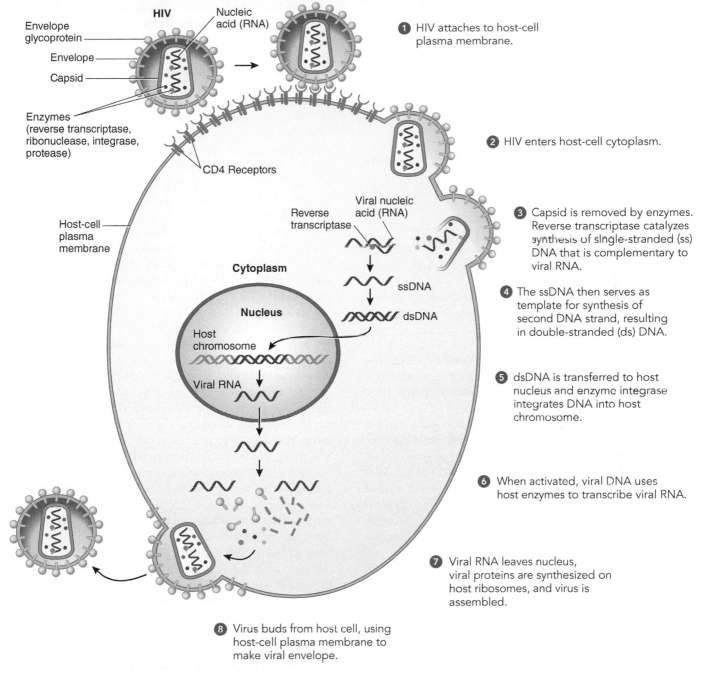

HIV

Envelope glycoprotein

Nucleic acid (RNA)

Envelope

Capsid

Enzymes (reverse transcriptase, ribonuclease, integrase, protease)

CD4 Receptors

Host-cell plasma membrane

Reverse transcriptase

Viral nucleic acid (RNA)

Cytoplasm

ssDNA

Nucleus

dsDNA

Host chromosome

Viral RNA

❶ HIV attaches to host-cell plasma membrane.

❷ HIV enters host-cell cytoplasm.

❸ Capsid is removed by enzymes. Reverse transcriptase catalyzes synthesis of single-stranded (ss) DNA that is complementary to viral RNA.

❹ The ssDNA then serves as template for synthesis of second DNA strand, resulting in double-stranded (ds) DNA.

❺ dsDNA is transferred to host nucleus and enzyme integrase integrates DNA into host chromosome.

❻ When activated, viral DNA uses host enzymes to transcribe viral RNA.

❼ Viral RNA leaves nucleus, viral proteins are synthesized on host ribosomes, and virus is assembled.

❽ Virus buds from host cell, using host-cell plasma membrane to make viral envelope.

Figure 24-7 *Animation* Life cycle of HIV, the retrovirus that causes AIDS

HIV infects T helper cells, specialized cells of the host's immune system. The virus attaches to protein receptors, known as CD4, on the plasma membrane of T helper cells. HIV has two identical single-stranded RNA molecules.

CONNECT What advantage does the retrovirus that causes AIDS have compared to an RNA virus?

© Cengage Learning

constantly changing, competitive endeavor. For example, amantadine, which inhibits penetration or uncoating of viral nucleic acids, has been effective in treating patients with influenza.

However, most strains of influenza virus have become resistant to amantadine, perhaps as a result of common use of the drug in poultry feed in certain areas of Asia, such as China.

Another type of antiviral drug (e.g., Tamiflu) inhibits a viral enzyme (neuraminidase) necessary for the virus to leave the host cell. Certain viral strains are becoming resistant to Tamiflu. A single mutation that occurs spontaneously is apparently responsible for this resistance. Many more antiviral drugs are being designed or are currently in clinical trials. Some inhibit viral attachment to host cells, and others interfere with replication of viral nucleic acid.

CHECKPOINT 24.4

- *How do viruses infect plant cells?*
- *What are the mechanisms by which viruses enter animal cells?*
- VISUALIZE *Draw a diagram illustrating how retroviruses, such as HIV, make copies of themselves.*

24.5 EVOLUTION OF VIRUSES

LEARNING OBJECTIVE

8 Trace the evolutionary origin of viruses according to current hypotheses and describe research regarding the evolution of polydnaviruses.

Scientists have been debating the origin of viruses ever since they were discovered. Currently, there are three main hypotheses: the progressive (or escape) hypothesis, the regressive (or reduction) hypothesis, and the virus-first hypothesis.

According to the *progressive hypothesis,* also known as the *escape hypothesis,* viruses may have originated as mobile genetic elements such as *transposons* (see Chapter 13) or *plasmids* (small, circular DNA fragments discussed in Chapters 15 and 25). Such fragments could have escaped from one cell and entered another cell through damaged cell membranes. According to this hypothesis, viruses may trace their origin to animal, plant, bacterial, or archaeal cells. Their multiple origins may explain why many viruses are species specific; perhaps they infect only those species that are closely related to the organisms from which they originated. This hypothesis is supported by the genetic similarity between some viruses and their host cells—a closer similarity than exists between one type of virus and another.

The *regressive hypothesis,* also called the *reduction hypothesis,* asserts that viruses are remnants of cellular organisms and evolved from small cells that were parasites in larger cells. Genes that they did not need, like those for protein synthesis, were gradually lost through evolution. This hypothesis is supported by certain bacteria (chlamydia and rickettsia) that are able to reproduce only inside the cells of their hosts (see Table 25-4).

The regressive hypothesis is also supported by the discovery that some giant viruses have genes that encode components for protein translation. Proponents of the regressive hypothesis suggest that these giant viruses evolved from a free-living, complex cellular ancestor. Later, they became parasitic and gradually lost some of the genes necessary for protein synthesis. This hypothesis explains how viruses could have existed before their present-day hosts evolved.

The *virus-first hypothesis* states that viruses predate or coevolved with their current cellular hosts even before the lifeforms assigned to the three domains diverged. One research team recently suggested that viruses initially existed in a precellular world as self-replicating units. Gradually, these small units became more organized and more complex. Eventually they evolved to produce enzymes for the synthesis of membranes and cell walls, leading to the origin of the first cells.

Evidence for this hypothesis comes from similarities found in the protein structures of some viral capsids and in genetic similarities between some viruses that infect archaea and some that infect bacteria. Molecular biologists studying this hypothesis consider it improbable that these similarities evolved independently. This evidence suggests that viruses diverged very early—before archaea, bacteria, or eukaryotes.

Recent studies on the origin of polydnaviruses contribute to our understanding of viral evolution. **Polydnaviruses** are particles that consist of multiple circles of dsDNA encased in capsid proteins and an envelope. Each circle of DNA contains part of the virus genome. These viruses are found in ovary cells of many species of parasitic wasps. The polydnaviruses are unusual in that their circular DNA does not have genes for making the proteins needed to replicate and produce new viruses. Genes needed for viral replication are found in the wasp genome; the viruses can replicate only in the wasp ovary cells.

The wasp injects polydnaviruses along with her eggs into certain caterpillars. The polydnaviruses express toxins that interfere with the caterpillar's immune defenses and development. The wasp eggs hatch and develop inside the caterpillar. The young wasps feed on the caterpillar.

Biologists wondered whether the polydnaviruses were really viruses. Were the polydnaviruses simply particles derived from wasp genes? An alternative hypothesis was that millions of years ago a particular virus infected wasps. The virus genome became integrated into the wasp genome and lost the capacity to enter virus particles. Instead, wasp DNA was incorporated into the particles. Read the Key Experiment, FIGURE 24-8, to learn which hypothesis is supported by the research of Jean-Michel Drezen, Annie Bézier, and their colleagues.

Today's viruses may have originated multiple times, through many mechanisms, or by a mechanism not yet discovered. No matter how viruses came to be and how they continue to evolve, they have important roles in evolution. They mutate constantly, producing many new alleles. They replicate rapidly, and some of their genes are incorporated into the genomes of host cells through horizontal gene transfer. In fact, viruses may provide a major source of new genes for their host cells.

CHECKPOINT 24.5

- CONNECT *How could viruses have evolved before their hosts? Explain your answer.*
- CONNECT *In what way are polydnaviruses mutualistic partners with certain wasps?*

What is the origin of polydnaviruses?

HYPOTHESIS: Polydnaviruses evolved from ancient viruses that infected wasps.

EXPERIMENT: Annie Bézier, Jean-Michel Drezen, and their colleagues searched for virus-related genes in the wasp genome. The team analyzed DNA from three different wasp species. They compared nucleotide sequences with sequences of public databases containing sequences of all organisms and viruses studied.

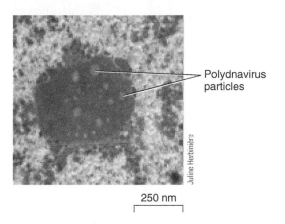

Polydnavirus particles

Juline Herbinière

250 nm

RESULTS AND CONCLUSION: The researchers identified 22 genes expressed in wasp ovaries where viral particles are produced. These genes are present in the wasp genome and resemble key genes of nudiviruses, a family of insect viruses. The investigators found that many of these genes code for proteins that are part of the polydnavirus particles. These genes have been conserved in several different wasp families that have polydnaviruses.

The research team concluded that the polydnavirus evolved from a nudivirus that infected wasps millions of years ago. In time, the virus genome became incorporated into the wasp genome. Proteins needed for viral replication are now part of the wasp's DNA, and the virus can replicate only in the wasp's ovaries.

At the same time, the wasps depend on the virus. The wasps inject their eggs into certain caterpillars along with polydnaviruses. The viruses depress the caterpillar's immune defenses, allowing the wasp larvae to develop in the caterpillar. Thus, a mutualistic relationship has evolved between the wasp and the polydnavirus.

The investigators suggested that the polydnavirus acts as a gene vector, transporting large chunks of DNA to the caterpillar. Might learning more about this mechanism have clinical applications?

SOURCE: Bézier, Annie, et al., "Polydnaviruses of Braconid Wasps Derive from an Ancestral Nudivirus." *Science*, Vol. 323, No. 5916, Feb. 13, 2009, pp. 926–930.

Figure 24-8 Exploring the evolution of polydnaviruses

This TEM shows polydnavirus particles in the nucleus of a cell in a wasp ovary. The polydnavirus particles are located at the periphery of an electron-dense region thought to be a "viral factory."

PREDICT What would happen if the polydnavirus mutated and no longer depressed the caterpillar's immune defenses?

24.6 SUBVIRAL AGENTS

LEARNING OBJECTIVE

9   Compare satellites, viroids, and prions.

Subviral agents are infective agents that are smaller and simpler than viruses. Subviral agents include satellites, viroids, and prions.

Satellites depend on helper viruses

Satellites are subviral agents that depend on co-infection of a host cell with a helper virus. The satellite, which consists of either DNA or RNA, cannot reproduce without the helper virus. The agent that causes hepatitis D is a satellite that can reproduce only when the hepatitis B virus is also present.

Sputnik is a satellite that infects Mimivirus, which in turn infects an amoeba. Sputnik is dependent on the replication and assembly machinery set up by Mimivirus. Some researchers now refer to Sputnik as a *virophage*, a word not yet completely defined by many virologists. The term implies that Sputnik, and perhaps other satellites, impairs the reproduction of Mimivirus, its helper virus.

Viroids are short, single strands of naked RNA

In 1971, Theodor Otto Diener, a plant pathologist, discovered an infective agent in potatoes that he named a **viroid**. Since then, about 30 species of viroids have been identified. Smaller than a virus, a viroid consists of a very short, circular, single strand of naked RNA (only 250 to 400 nucleotides). The viroid has no protective protein coat and no associated proteins to assist in duplication. Its RNA serves as a template that is copied by host RNA polymerases. Viroids are extremely hardy and are able to resist heat and ultraviolet radiation because of the condensed folding of their RNA.

Many viroids that cause plant diseases—including potato spindle tuber viroid, apple scar skin viroid, avocado sunblotch viroid, and tomato chlorotic dwarf viroid—have been identified. Viroids cause stunted or distorted growth and sometimes kill the plant. For example, cadang-cadang disease has killed more than 30 million coconut palm trees in the Philippines. Viroids are transmitted by infected pollen or seeds.

Viroids are generally found within the host-cell nucleus and appear to interfere with gene regulation. Molecular biologists have hypothesized that viroids mirror gene sequences in their hosts and silence critically important host genes. The viroid's ssRNA replicates, forming dsRNA. The plant's defense response cleaves this viroid RNA, producing small interfering RNAs (siRNAs), discussed in Chapters 13 and 14. However, the viroid siRNAs then cause host ribonucleases to selectively cleave host mRNAs with complementary base sequences. This action inactivates host mRNA and silences specific host genes. The viroids themselves are resistant to RNA silencing.

Prions are protein particles

Motivated by the death of a patient from Creutzfeldt–Jakob disease (CJD), a degenerative brain disease, Stanley Prusiner, professor of neurology and biochemistry at the University of California, San Francisco, began his studies of prions in the early 1970s. Prusiner discovered that the infective agent was not affected by radiation (which typically mutates nucleic acids), and he could not find DNA or RNA in the particles. In 1982, he named the infective agent **prion,** for "proteinaceous infectious particle."

Prusiner's hypothesis that an infectious agent could cause disease without nucleic acids was not readily accepted because there was no known mechanism by which this action could occur. However, Prusiner and other researchers continued to study prions and discovered how they can cause cells to malfunction. In 1997, Prusiner was awarded the Nobel Prize in Physiology or Medicine for his discovery of prions.

Prusiner and others have shown that animals have a gene that encodes a normally harmless protein known as PrP. Normal forms of the protein are found on the surfaces of brain cells and many other types of cells. The PrP protein, which consists of 208 amino acids, helps neurons transport copper and may play a role in the sense of smell in animals. Researchers have discovered that normal PrP interacts with the peptides associated with Alzheimer's disease.

Sometimes, the PrP protein folds into a different shape, an insoluble form that can cause disease. This misfolded protein is the prion. Mutations in the gene that encodes the PrP protein increase the risk that the protein will misfold and become a prion. The prion then somehow induces other PrP molecules to misfold into the pathogenic form (**FIG. 24-9**). Prions apparently can aggregate and accumulate in the brain and in certain other tissues and cause serious damage.

Prions are found in the brains of patients with *transmissible spongiform encephalopathies* (*TSEs*). This group of fatal degenerative brain diseases has been identified in birds and mammals. These diseases are called TSEs because when infected, the brain appears to develop holes and becomes somewhat spongelike. The TSEs are in some ways like viral illnesses. However, there is a long latency period (about 5 years in cows and up to 10 years in humans) between contracting the infection and developing symptoms of the illness. Also, the TSEs have proven very difficult to treat. Genetically engineered mice that lack the prion protein gene are immune to TSE infection.

The oldest known prion disease is *scrapie* in sheep and goats. When infected, animals lose coordination, become irritable, and itch so severely that they scrape off their wool or hair. Bovine spongiform encephalopathy (BSE) is a related prion disease popularly referred to as "mad cow disease" because some diseased cattle become aggressive. In the 1990s, BSE became epidemic in cattle in the United Kingdom.

More than 200 people have died from a human variety of BSE, providing evidence that the disease is transmissible from cow to human. The human disease is called vCJD because it is a variant of CJD, which is caused by the transformation of PrP proteins into prions. The infective agent of vCJD has

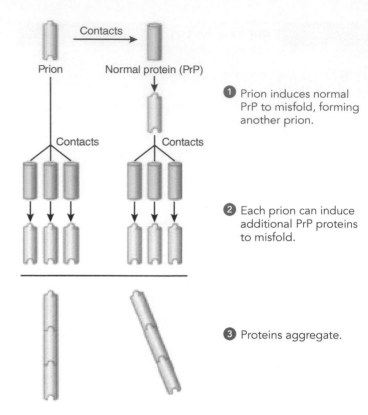

Figure 24-9 A model for how prion populations expand
Prions contact normal PrP proteins and induce them to misfold and become prions. Each new prion can then contact additional PrP molecules and induce them to misfold, thus expanding the prion population. Prions can form clumps by aggregating.
© Cengage Learning

been recovered from infected human neural tissue and appears similar to the prion that causes scrapie in sheep. New regulations have been instituted in many countries to safeguard the food supply. Human-to-human transmission of vCJD has been associated with tissue and organ transplants and with transfusion with contaminated blood.

Chronic wasting disease, an illness related to mad cow disease, has spread among deer and elk populations in North America. Studies are under way to determine whether chronic wasting disease can infect livestock or humans. Feline spongiform encephalopathy is a prion disease of domestic and captive felines. With this disease, large deposits of a misfolded protein accumulate in the liver and spleen.

Like viruses, prions exhibit variability. Different strains of prions may differ from one another in the conformation of their proteins, in their properties, and in the diseases they cause. Prions are different from viruses in that they can arise spontaneously, mostly as a result of mutation. Researchers are studying ways to block prions from forming. They are also looking for ways to stimulate cells to destroy prions. Early diagnosis is critical, and research for an assay, or test, to detect prion disease is ongoing.

CHECKPOINT 24.6

- **CONNECT** *What do viroids and prions have in common? How are they different?*

24.1 The Status and Structure of Viruses *(page 496)*

1 Contrast a virus with a cellular organism.

- A **virus** is a very small infective agent that consists of a core of nucleic acid and is dependent on a living host. Viruses contain the nucleic acids necessary to make copies of themselves, but to reproduce they must invade living cells and commandeer their metabolic machinery.

2 Describe the structure of a virus.

- A virus is a subcellular particle consisting of a DNA or RNA genome surrounded by a protein coat, called a **capsid.** In some viruses the capsid is surrounded by an outer envelope.

24.2 Classification of Viruses *(page 497)*

3 Identify three characteristics used to classify viruses.

- Viruses are classified based on **host range,** the types of host species they can infect; the type of nucleic acid they contain; and whether the nucleic acid is single-stranded or double-stranded. Other factors used to classify viruses include size and shape, presence of an envelope, and method of transmission from host to host.

24.3 Viral Replication *(page 498)*

4 Characterize bacteriophages.

- **Bacteriophages,** or **phages,** are complex viruses that infect bacteria. They typically consist of a long molecule of dsDNA coiled within a polyhedral head.

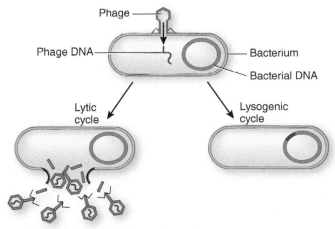

© Cengage Learning

5 Contrast a lytic cycle with a lysogenic cycle.

- In a **lytic cycle,** the virus destroys the host cell. The five steps in a lytic cycle are *attachment* to the host cell, *penetration* of viral nucleic acid into the host cell, *replication* of the viral nucleic acid, *assembly* of newly synthesized components into new viruses, and *release* from the host cell.
- The nucleic acid of some phages becomes integrated into the DNA of its bacterial host. The phage is then called a **prophage.** A **temperate virus** alternates between a lytic and a **lysogenic cycle.** In a lysogenic cycle, the genome of a temperate virus is replicated along with replication of the host's DNA without causing death of the host cell.

- Bacterial cells that carry prophages are lysogenic cells. In **lysogenic conversion** bacterial cells containing certain temperate viruses exhibit new properties.

24.4 Viral Diseases *(page 500)*

6 Contrast viral infection of plants and animals, and identify specific diseases caused by viruses.

- Most plant viruses are ssRNA viruses that do not have envelopes. Plant viruses penetrate plants through damaged cells and are also transmitted by infected seeds. Viruses can be spread among plants by insect vectors. Viruses spread through the plant via plasmodesmata.
- Viruses enter animal cells by membrane fusion or by endocytosis. Diseases caused by DNA viruses include herpes, respiratory infections, and gastrointestinal disorders. RNA viruses cause influenza, upper respiratory infections, AIDS, and some types of cancer.

7 Describe the reproductive cycle of a retrovirus, such as human immunodeficiency virus (HIV).

- **Retroviruses,** such as HIV, use **reverse transcriptase** to transcribe their RNA genome into a DNA intermediate that becomes integrated into the host DNA. Copies of the viral RNA are then synthesized.

24.5 Evolution of Viruses *(page 506)*

8 Trace the evolutionary origin of viruses according to current hypotheses and describe recent research regarding the evolution of polydnaviruses.

- According to the *progressive,* or *escape, hypothesis,* viruses may have originated as mobile genetic elements that could have escaped and moved from one cell and entered another through damaged cell membranes. Viruses may trace their origin to animal cells, plant cells, bacterial cells, or archaeal cells.
- The *regressive,* or *reduction, hypothesis* asserts that viruses are remnants of cellular organisms; they evolved from free-living, complex cellular ancestors. As they became parasitic, the viruses gradually lost some of the genes necessary for protein synthesis. Genes they no longer needed, like those for protein synthesis, were gradually lost through evolution.
- According to the *virus-first hypothesis,* viruses predate or coevolved with their current cellular hosts. Viruses may have initially existed as self-replicating units. As they evolved, viruses produced enzymes for the synthesis of membranes and cell walls, leading to the formation of the first cells.
- Evidence suggests that **polydnaviruses** evolved from viruses that infected wasps. They have become mutualistic partners with their wasp hosts.

24.6 Subviral Agents *(page 507)*

9 Compare satellites, viroids, and prions.

- Satellites, viroids, and prions are smaller than viruses. Satellites reproduce only with the help of a helper virus.
- A **viroid** consists of a short strand of RNA with no protein coat. Many viroids cause plant diseases. A **prion** consists only of protein. Prions cause fatal degenerative brain diseases, such as *transmissible spongiform encephalopathies (TSEs).*

Know and Comprehend

1. The genome of a virus consists of (a) DNA (b) RNA (c) prions (d) DNA and RNA (e) DNA or RNA

2. The capsid of a virus consists of (a) protein subunits (b) nucleic acid (c) helical lipids (d) a carbohydrate envelope (e) RNA and lipid

3. Viruses that kill host cells are (a) lysogenic (b) lytic (c) viroids (d) prophages (e) temperate

4. In lysogenic conversion (a) bacterial cells may exhibit new properties (b) the host cell dies (c) prions sometimes convert to viroids (d) reverse transcriptase transcribes DNA into RNA (e) lytic viruses become temperate

5. The types of host species a particular virus can infect are referred to as its (a) assembly (b) commensal cohort (c) host range (d) prophage factor (e) virulence factor

6. Plant viruses (a) typically cause rapid death of infected plants (b) are mainly retroviruses (c) can be killed with antibiotics (d) are transmitted throughout the plant body by insects (e) can be transmitted from one generation to the next through infected seeds

7. According to the progressive, or escape, hypothesis, viruses (a) appeared before the three domains diverged (b) came from mobile genetic elements and had multiple origins (c) evolved from early plant cells (d) are bits of nucleic acid that escaped from animal cells (e) evolved from cells that were parasites in larger cells

8. Prions (a) consist of RNA with no protein coat (b) are misfolded proteins (c) cause several important plant diseases (d) are the infective agents of several emerging diseases (e) consist of proteins that stimulate host RNA to produce DNA

Apply and Analyze

9. Arrange the following list into the correct sequence for viral reproduction:
   1. penetration 2. assembly 3. replication 4. attachment 5. release
   (a) 1, 2, 3, 4, 5 (b) 5, 2, 3, 4, 1 (c) 4, 1, 3, 2, 5 (d) 4, 1, 2, 3, 5 (e) 3, 1, 2, 4, 5

10. Arrange the following list into the correct sequence for part of the cycle of a retrovirus:
    1. dsDNA integrated into host DNA 2. viral proteins synthesized on host ribosomes 3. viral DNA uses host enzymes to transcribe viral RNA 4. reverse transcriptase catalyzes synthesis of ssDNA 5. synthesis of second DNA strand
    (a) 5, 2, 1, 3, 4 (b) 5, 2, 3, 4, 1 (c) 4, 5, 1, 3, 2 (d) 4, 1, 2, 3, 5 (e) 2, 1, 3, 4, 5

11. **VISUALIZE** What does this diagram illustrate? Complete the labels.

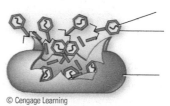

© Cengage Learning

12. **CONNECT** How are viral genomes different from those of plant or animal cells?

13. **CONNECT** How do viroids and prions differ from viruses?

Evaluate and Synthesize

14. **EVOLUTION LINK** Discuss the coevolution of polydnaviruses and their mutualistic partners. (See the discussion and Key Experiment on polydnaviruses.)

15. **EVOLUTION LINK** Based on what you have learned about viruses, present an argument for one of the three hypotheses of virus origin.

16. **SCIENCE, TECHNOLOGY, AND SOCIETY** What is the continuous challenge that the influenza virus presents to scientists and public health officials? How can they use technology and work together to meet this challenge?

aplia To access course materials, such as Aplia and other companion resources, please visit **www.cengagebrain.com.**

Bacteria and Archaea

In this chapter we examine the diversity and characteristics of the members of Domain Bacteria and Domain Archaea, two of the three main branches of the tree of life. These organisms, informally called prokaryotes, have inhabited our planet for more than 3.5 billion years, much longer than eukaryotes, which evolved at least 2.2 billion years ago. Although prokaryotes are microscopic, they are so numerous that they probably account for more than half of Earth's biomass, the mass of living material. Thus, the biomass of prokaryotes is greater than that of all the eukaryotes: fungi, plants, and animals. As scientists discover new prokaryotes and explore new niches and habitats, the percentage of bacteria and archaea in the Earth's total biomass continues to increase.

Anton van Leeuwenhoek, a Dutch microscopist, discovered bacteria and other microorganisms in 1674 when he looked at a drop of lake water through a glass lens. During the late 1800s, many microorganisms, including some bacteria, fungi, and protozoa, were identified as **pathogens,** agents that cause disease (see photograph). Bacteria cause many diseases, such as tuberculosis, tetanus, respiratory infections, and food poisoning in humans. However, only a small minority of bacterial species are pathogens. (No pathogenic archaea have been identified.)

Both bacteria and archaea play essential roles in the biosphere. As decomposers they break down organic molecules into their components. Along with fungi, prokaryotes are nature's chief recyclers. Without these microorganisms, elements such as carbon, nitrogen, phosphorus, and sulfur would remain locked up in the wastes and dead bodies of plants, animals, and other organisms and would be unavailable for the synthesis of new cells and organisms.

Some prokaryotes are producers that carry on photosynthesis. Others convert atmospheric nitrogen to ammonia and then to nitrates, forms that are used by plants (see Fig. 55-8). This conversion enables plants and animals (because they eat plants) to manufacture essential nitrogen-containing compounds such as proteins and nucleic acids.

We begin this chapter with a description of the structure of bacteria and archaea, and then we discuss prokaryote reproduction and evolution. We outline some of the nutritional and metabolic

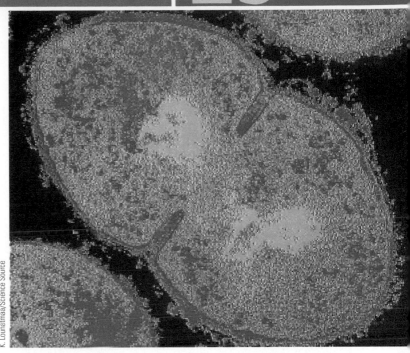

K. Lounatmaa/Science Source

Color-enhanced TEM of a bacterium (*Streptococcus pyogenes*) dividing by binary fission. This bacterium, a pathogen that inhabits the human nose and throat, can cause scarlet fever and inflammation of the heart tissue. The strain shown here is resistant to antibiotics, and infection can be fatal.

KEY CONCEPTS

25.1 Bacteria and archaea are single-celled organisms that, in contrast to eukaryotic cells, do not have membrane-enclosed organelles; most have a cell wall that surrounds the plasma membrane, and most have a single, circular DNA molecule.

25.2 Evolution occurs rapidly in prokaryotes; natural selection acts on the genetic variation provided by mutations and genetic recombination and is facilitated by rapid reproduction.

25.3 The great diversity that has evolved in their metabolism and mode of nutrition allows prokaryotes to thrive in all kinds of habitats.

25.4 Prokaryotes make up two of the three domains: Bacteria and Archaea.

25.5 Prokaryotes play critical roles in ecology, commerce, and technology.

25.6 The many adaptations that have evolved in pathogenic bacteria contribute to their great success.

adaptations of these organisms and describe the phylogeny of the two prokaryote domains. We then present an overview of the effect of prokaryotes on ecology, technology, and commerce, and end the chapter with a discussion of bacteria and disease.

25.1 THE STRUCTURE OF BACTERIA AND ARCHAEA

LEARNING OBJECTIVES

1. Describe the structure and common shapes of prokaryotic cells.
2. Compare the bacterial cell wall in gram-positive and gram-negative bacteria.
3. Describe movement in prokaryotes and describe the structure of the bacterial flagellum.

In contrast to viruses, viroids, and prions, which consist only of nucleic acid and/or protein, **prokaryotes,** assigned to domain Archaea or Bacteria, are cellular organisms. However, recall from Chapters 4 and 23 that the cell structure of prokaryotes is fundamentally different from that of the eukaryotic cells of other living organisms.

Most prokaryotic cells are very small. Typically, their diameter ranges from 0.5 to 1.0 μm, and their length ranges from 1.0 to 5.0 μm. Their cell volume is only about one-thousandth that of small eukaryotic cells, and their length is only about one-tenth. Most prokaryotes are unicellular, but some form colonies or filaments containing specialized cells.

Prokaryotes have several common shapes

Two basic prokaryote shapes are spherical and rod-shaped. Spherical prokaryotes, known as **cocci** (sing., *coccus*), occur singly in some species and in groups of independent cells in others (FIG. 25-1a). Cells may be grouped in twos (*diplococci*), in long chains (*streptococci*), or in irregular clumps that look like bunches of grapes (*staphylococci*). Rod-shaped prokaryotes, called **bacilli** (sing., *bacillus*), may occur as single rods or as long chains of rods (FIG. 25-1b). Some prokaryotes form spirals. If the spiral-shaped cell is flexible, it is a **spirochete;** if rigid, it is a **spirillum** (pl., *spirilla*) (FIG. 25-1c). A spirillum shaped like a comma is called a **vibrio.** Some archaea have unusual shapes, such as triangular or square-shaped cells.

Prokaryotic cells do not have membrane-enclosed organelles

In contrast to eukaryotic cells, prokaryotic cells do not have a nucleus or other membrane-enclosed organelles (FIG. 25-2; see Chapter 4). Although the prokaryotic cell does not have a membrane-enclosed nucleus, it does have a **nuclear area,** also referred to as the **nucleoid,** which contains DNA.

The dense cytoplasm of the prokaryotic cell contains ribosomes (smaller than those found in eukaryotic cells) and storage granules that hold glycogen, lipid, and phosphate compounds. Enzymes needed for metabolic activities may be located in the cytoplasm. Although the membranous organelles of eukaryotic cells are absent, in some prokaryotic cells the plasma membrane is extensively folded inward. Enzymes needed for cellular respiration and photosynthesis may be associated with the plasma membrane or its folds.

A cell wall protects most prokaryotes

Most prokaryotic cells have a **cell wall** surrounding the plasma membrane. The cell wall provides a rigid framework that supports the cell and maintains its shape. Bacterial cells have a high concentration of dissolved solutes. The cell wall keeps the cell from bursting under hypotonic conditions (see Chapter 5). Thus, most bacteria are adapted to hypotonic surroundings. When wall-less forms of bacteria are produced experimentally, they must be

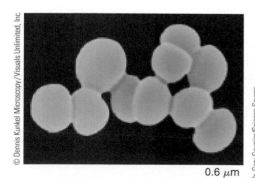

0.6 μm

(a) Cocci bacteria. Colorized SEM of *Staphylococcus aureus*. These cocci cause skin and wound infections, food poisoning, and toxic shock syndrome.

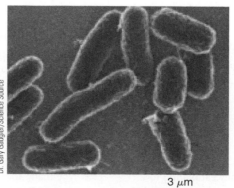

3 μm

(b) Bacilli bacteria. Colorized SEM of *Salmonella*. These bacilli cause food poisoning.

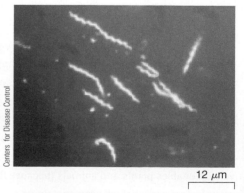

12 μm

(c) Spirochete bacteria. Colorized SEM of *Borrelia burgdorferi*. These spirochetes cause Lyme disease, transmitted by infected deer ticks.

Figure 25-1 Common shapes of prokaryotes

In contrast to eukaryotic cells, prokaryotic cells lack organelles enclosed by membranes; the DNA is not surrounded by a nuclear envelope.

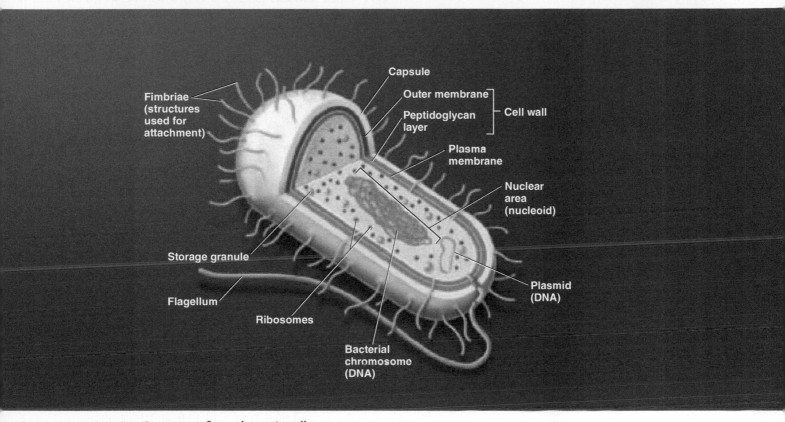

Fimbriae (structures used for attachment)

Capsule

Outer membrane
Peptidoglycan layer
Cell wall

Plasma membrane

Nuclear area (nucleoid)

Storage granule

Plasmid (DNA)

Flagellum

Ribosomes

Bacterial chromosome (DNA)

Figure 25-2 *Animation* **Structure of a prokaryotic cell**

This bacillus is a gram-negative bacterium (discussed in text). Prokaryotic cells typically have a nuclear area with a single, circular DNA molecule. They may also have one or more plasmids, small rings of DNA that replicate independently.

PREDICT Why might the absence of a nucleus be an advantage for prokaryotes?

© Cengage Learning

maintained in isotonic solutions to keep them from bursting. However, cell walls are of little help when a bacterium is in a hypertonic environment, as in food preserved by a high sugar or salt content. For this reason, most bacteria grow poorly in jellies, jams, salted fish, and other foods preserved in these ways.

The bacterial cell wall includes **peptidoglycan,** a complex polymer that consists of two unusual types of sugars (amino sugars) linked with short polypeptides. The sugars and polypeptides are cross-linked to form a crystalline lattice that surrounds the entire plasma membrane. Peptidoglycan is absent in the archaeon cell wall.

Differences in bacterial cell wall composition are of great interest to microbiologists and are important clinically. In 1888, Danish physician Christian Gram developed the Gram staining procedure. Bacteria that absorb and retain crystal violet stain in the laboratory are referred to as **gram-positive bacteria.** Bacteria that do not retain the stain when rinsed with alcohol are **gram-negative bacteria.** The cell walls of gram-positive bacteria are very thick and consist primarily of peptidoglycan. The cell walls of gram-negative bacteria have two layers: a thin

peptidoglycan layer and a thick outer membrane. The outer membrane resembles the plasma membrane but contains polysaccharides bonded to lipids (FIG. 25-3).

Distinguishing between gram-positive and gram-negative bacteria is important in treating certain diseases. For example, the antibiotic penicillin interferes with peptidoglycan synthesis, ultimately resulting in a fragile cell wall that cannot protect the cell (see Chapter 7 discussion of drugs that are enzyme inhibitors). Predictably, penicillin works most effectively against gram-positive bacteria.

Some bacteria produce capsules or slime layers

Many prokaryote species produce a **capsule** or **slime layer** that surrounds the cell wall. A slime layer is more loosely attached to the cell wall than a capsule. These outer layers are made of polysaccharide or protein.

In free-living species, the outer covering may provide the cell with added protection against phagocytosis (engulfment;

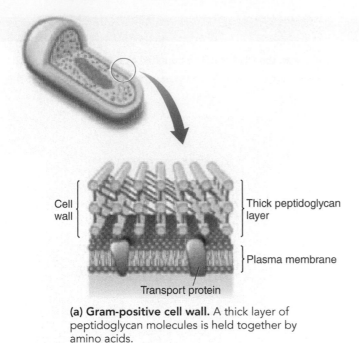

(a) Gram-positive cell wall. A thick layer of peptidoglycan molecules is held together by amino acids.

Cell wall — Thick peptidoglycan layer

Plasma membrane

Transport protein

(b) Gram-negative cell wall. A thin layer of peptidoglycan is covered by an outer membrane.

Polysaccharides

Lipoprotein

Cell wall — Outer membrane

Thin peptidoglycan layer

Plasma membrane

Transport protein

Figure 25-3 *Animation* Bacterial cell walls

If present, the capsule (shown only in the locater cells) is outside the cell wall.
© Cengage Learning

see Chapter 5) by other microorganisms. In disease-causing bacteria, a capsule or slime layer may protect against phagocytosis by the host's white blood cells. The ability of *Streptococcus pneumoniae* to cause bacterial pneumonia depends on its capsule. A strain of *S. pneumoniae* that lacks a capsule does not cause the disease. Bacteria also use their capsules to attach to surfaces such as rocks, plant roots, and human teeth (where they cause dental plaque).

Some prokaryotes have fimbriae or pili

Some prokaryotes have hundreds of hair-like appendages called **fimbriae** (sing., *fimbria*). Fimbriae, which are made of protein, are shorter than flagella. **Pili** (sing., *pilus*) are usually longer than fimbriae. There are typically fewer pili on the cell surface than fimbriae. Prokaryotes use fimbriae and pili to attach to cell surfaces and, in the case of pathogenic bacteria, to the surfaces of cells they infect. These protein structures also help bacteria adhere to one another. Some elongated pili, called *sex pili*, are important in transmitting DNA between bacteria.

Some bacteria survive unfavorable conditions by forming endospores

When the environment becomes unfavorable—for example, when nutrients are limited or the environment becomes very dry or hot—some types of bacteria become dormant. The cell loses water, shrinks slightly, and remains inactive until water is again available. Certain types of bacteria form dormant, extremely durable cells called **endospores.**

After an endospore forms, the cell wall of the original cell lyses, releasing the endospore. Formation of endospores is not a type of reproduction in bacteria; endospores are not comparable to the reproductive spores of fungi and plants. Only one endospore is formed per original cell, so the total number of individuals does not increase. Archaea do not form endospores; these prokaryotes produce unique enzymes on the cell surface that protect them from cold, heat, and desiccation.

Endospores survive in very dry, hot, or frozen environments or at times when food is scarce. Some endospores are so resistant that they can survive an hour or more of boiling or centuries of freezing. When environmental conditions are again suitable for growth, the endospore germinates, forming an active, growing bacterial cell.

Several types of bacteria that form endospores cause disease (**FIG. 25-4**). The endospore of *Bacillus anthracis,* the bacterium that causes anthrax, is so hardy that this pathogen has become a concern as an agent of biological warfare. The bacteria (*Clostridium tetani*) that cause tetanus and the bacteria (*C. perfringens*) that cause gas gangrene typically enter the body with soil when a person suffers a deep cut or puncture wound. Patients may also be exposed to these serious diseases when surgical instruments are not effectively sterilized, allowing endospores to survive.

Many types of prokaryotes are motile

Can you imagine trying to swim through molasses? Water has the same relative viscosity to prokaryotes that molasses has to humans. Most motile prokaryotes manage to move by means of rotating **flagella.** The number and location of flagella are important in classifying some bacterial species.

Unlike eukaryotic flagella, prokaryotic flagella do not consist of microtubules (see Chapter 4). A bacterial flagellum is a long, thin appendage consisting of three parts: a basal body, a hook, and a single filament (**FIG. 25-5**). The basal body is a complex

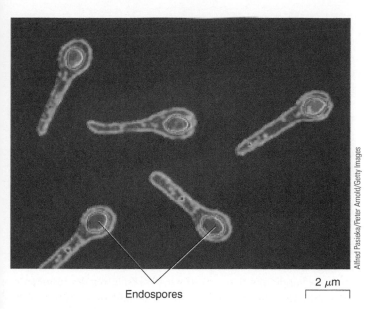

Endospores

2 μm

Alfred Pasieka/Peter Arnold/Getty Images

Figure 25-4 Endospores

Color-enhanced TEM of *Clostridium tetani*, the bacterium that causes tetanus. Each bacterial cell (*blue*) contains one endospore (*orange*), a resistant, dehydrated cell that develops within the original cell.

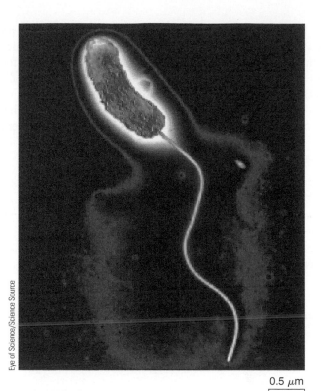

Eye of Science/Science Source

0.5 μm

(a) Color-enhanced TEM of *Vibrio cholerae*. This flagellate bacterium causes cholera in humans.

structure that anchors the flagellum into the cell wall by disc-shaped plates. The curved hook connects the basal body to the long, hollow filament that extends into the outside environment.

The basal body is a motor, somewhat like the propeller of a boat motor. The bacterium uses energy from ATP to pump protons out of the cell. Diffusion of these protons back into the cell powers the motor that spins the flagellum. The rotary motion produced pushes the cell much like a propeller pushes a boat through the water. The flagellum rotates counterclockwise, pushing the cell forward.

Archaea also have flagella. These flagella are thinner than those of bacteria and are more similar to a type of bacterial pili than to bacterial flagella. Biologists have determined that the structure of the motor and the assembly of the flagellum in archaea evolved differently from those of bacteria.

In addition to swimming, prokaryotic flagella perform other functions. Some prokaryotes use their flagella to swarm, to adhere to surfaces, and to participate in biofilm formation. Researchers have documented that bacteria use flagella to sense wetness. A recent study reported that some archaea can interact with one another by flagella, resulting in the formation of a biofilm composed of more than one species. Prokaryotes that lack flagella may move by gliding or twitching.

Scientists have recently discovered two extracellular structures that are unique to archaea: *cannulae* and *hami*. Cannulae are hollow glycoprotein tubes that extend from cells forming a network. Cannulae are extremely resistant to heat. They are produced by *Pyrodictium,* a genus of archaea that live in marine hydrothermal habitats. Hami are complex archaeal cell appendages that have been discovered entwined with bacterial filaments in sulfurous springs. Hami are helical, have barbs along the length of the filament, and have a three-part hook at the distal end, which facilitates attachment to surfaces. Cannulae and hami are adaptations to the extreme environments that many archaea inhabit.

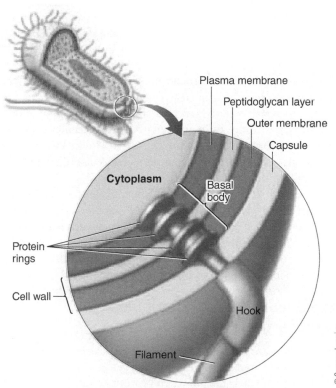

Plasma membrane

Peptidoglycan layer

Outer membrane

Capsule

Cytoplasm

Basal body

Protein rings

Cell wall

Hook

Filament

© Cengage Learning

(b) Structure of a bacterial flagellum. The basal body is the motor. It consists of a series of disc-shaped plates that anchor the flagellum to the cell wall and plasma membrane. These plates spin the hook and filament of the flagellum.

Figure 25-5 Bacterial flagella

Flagellated prokaryotes do not move aimlessly. Many prokaryotes exhibit *chemotaxis*, movement in response to chemicals in the environment. For example, prokaryotes move toward food and may also move toward one another using diverse signaling mechanisms. Some bacteria and archaea move away from certain harmful chemicals. In addition, many prokaryotes exhibit *phototaxis*, movement in response to light in the environment.

CHECKPOINT 25.1

- **CONNECT** *How do prokaryotic cells differ from eukaryotic cells? How do bacteria and archaea differ from each other?*

- **CONNECT** *How do gram-positive and gram-negative bacteria differ? Why is this difference important to humans?*

- **CONNECT** *How does a bacterial flagellum differ from a eukaryotic flagellum?*

25.2 PROKARYOTE REPRODUCTION AND EVOLUTION

LEARNING OBJECTIVES

4   Describe asexual reproduction in prokaryotes and summarize three mechanisms (transformation, transduction, and conjugation) that may lead to genetic recombination.

5   State specific factors that contribute to the rapid evolution of bacteria and archaea.

The genetic material of a prokaryote lies in the nuclear area but is not surrounded by a nuclear envelope. In most species the genetic material is contained in a single, circular DNA molecule. If stretched out to its full length, this molecule would be about 1000 times as long as the cell itself. Unlike the DNA in eukaryotic chromosomes, prokaryote DNA has little protein associated with it.

In addition to their genomic DNA, most bacteria and many archaea have one or more **plasmids,** smaller circular fragments of DNA. Bacterial plasmids often have genes that code for catabolic enzymes, for genetic exchange, or for resistance to antibiotics. Plasmids replicate independently of the genomic DNA or become integrated into it (see Chapter 15).

Rapid reproduction contributes to prokaryote success

Prokaryotes are extremely successful organisms in terms of their numbers and distribution. Their success is in large part due to their remarkable ability to reproduce rapidly. Prokaryotes reproduce asexually, generally by **binary fission,** a process in which one cell divides into two similar cells, as in the chapter-opening photograph (also see Fig. 10-12). First the circular DNA replicates, and then an ingrowth of both the plasma membrane and the cell wall forms a transverse wall.

Binary fission occurs with remarkable speed. Under ideal conditions, some bacterial species divide in less than 20 minutes.

At this rate, if nothing interfered, one bacterium could give rise to more than one billion bacteria within 10 hours! Prokaryotes cannot reproduce at this rate for very long, however, before lack of food or the accumulation of waste products slows their population expansion.

Bacteria and archaea also commonly reproduce by **budding.** In budding a cell develops a bulge, or bud, that enlarges, matures, and eventually separates from the mother cell. Some prokaryotes divide by **fragmentation.** In this process, walls develop within the cell, which then separates into several new cells.

Prokaryotes transfer genetic information

Although sexual reproduction involving the fusion of gametes does not occur in prokaryotes, genetic material can be exchanged among bacteria and among archaea and also between domains. Such exchange of genes, called *gene transfer*, results in genetic recombination. Transfer of genetic material from parent to offspring is called *vertical gene transfer*. **Horizontal gene transfer** occurs when an organism (or virus) transfers genetic material to another organism that is not its offspring. Gene transfer among prokaryotes takes place by three different mechanisms: transformation, transduction, and conjugation.

1.   When prokaryotes die, they release DNA that can be taken in by certain other prokaryotes. In **transformation** a prokaryotic cell takes up fragments of foreign DNA (or RNA) released by another prokaryotic cell. The foreign DNA must bind to DNA-binding proteins on the surface of the host cell. Once it enters the host cell, segments of the foreign DNA may be exchanged with homologous segments of the host DNA (reciprocal recombination) (FIG. 25-6). Recall

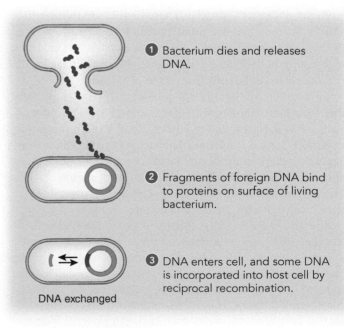

1 Bacterium dies and releases DNA.

2 Fragments of foreign DNA bind to proteins on surface of living bacterium.

DNA exchanged

3 DNA enters cell, and some DNA is incorporated into host cell by reciprocal recombination.

Figure 25-6   Transformation

In transformation a prokaryote takes in foreign DNA from its environment. The host cell exchanges some of its own DNA with homologous segments of the foreign DNA, resulting in a recombinant cell.

© Cengage Learning

from Chapter 12 that Oswald T. Avery and his colleagues identified DNA as the agent that transformed bacterial cells experimentally and showed that DNA is the chemical basis of heredity.

Foreign DNA can also be taken up as plasmids. When that occurs, DNA does not undergo recombination; instead, it remains as a plasmid separate from the prokaryotic chromosome.

2. In a different process of horizontal gene transfer, **transduction,** a phage carries bacterial or archaeal genes from one bacterial or archaeal cell into another (FIG. 25-7). Normally, a phage contains only its own DNA. However, sometimes a phage incorporates some of the DNA of its host. Then, when the phage infects another bacterium or archaeon, it transfers that DNA to its new host. The chromosome of this new host then becomes a recombination of its own original DNA and DNA from another bacterium or archaeon.

3. In **conjugation** two cells of different mating types come together, and genetic material is transferred from one to the other (FIG. 25-8). In contrast to transformation and transduction, conjugation involves contact between two cells.

Conjugation has been most extensively studied in the bacterium *Escherichia coli*. In the *E. coli* population, there are *donor cells,* or *F⁺ cells,* which have DNA that can be transmitted to *recipient cells,* or *F⁻ cells.* F⁺ cells have a DNA sequence known as the *F factor* (F stands for fertility) that is necessary for a bacterium to serve as a donor during conjugation. The F factor can be in the form of a plasmid, or it can be part of the DNA in the bacterial chromosome.

F genes encode enzymes essential for transferring DNA. Certain F genes encode **sex pili,** long, hair-like extensions that project from the cell surface. The sex pilus of an F⁺ cell recognizes and binds to the surface of an F⁻ cell, forming a cytoplasmic conjugation bridge between the two cells. The F plasmid replicates itself, and DNA is transferred from donor to recipient bacterium through the conjugation bridge. F plasmids may also have other types of genes, including those that determine resistance to antibiotics.

Evolution proceeds rapidly in bacterial populations

Because prokaryotes reproduce rapidly by binary fission, mutations are quickly passed on to new generations. Mutations that confer some advantage spread through the population, and the effects of natural selection are quickly evident.

Horizontal gene transfer greatly contributes to the rapid evolution that takes place in prokaryotes. Acquisition of new DNA and genetic recombination are important sources of the genetic variation required for diversification and adaptation. New DNA introduced into a prokaryote's genome represents raw material for evolution. New genes are subject to mutation and are acted on by the forces of natural selection. The changes in the genetic material are passed to succeeding generations by binary fission. Changes that result in adaptation

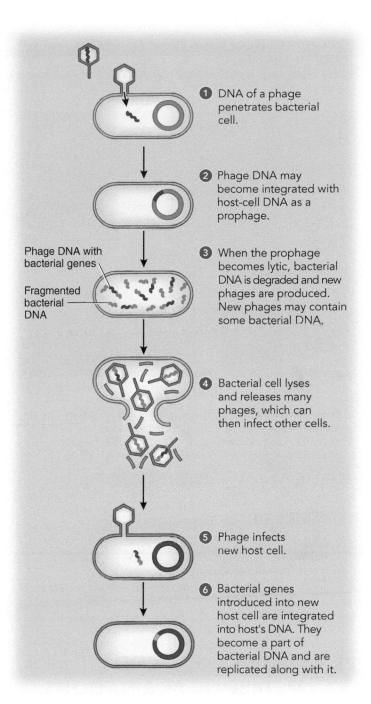

Figure 25-7 Transduction

In transduction a phage transfers bacterial DNA from one bacterium to another, resulting in genetic recombination. Transduction is an important means of horizontal gene transfer.

© Cengage Learning

can quickly spread through future bacterial and archaeal populations.

CHECKPOINT 25.2

- *How do prokaryotes reproduce? What mechanisms result in gene transfer?*
- **CONNECT** *How does transduction contribute to the rapid evolution of bacterial populations?*
- **VISUALIZE** *Draw the steps that take place during conjugation.*

During conjugation, horizontal gene transfer takes place resulting in genetic recombination.

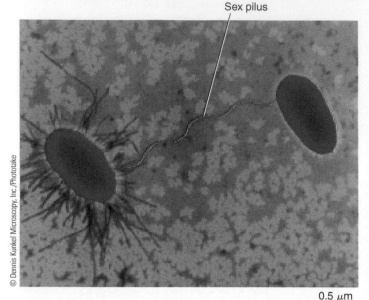

Sex pilus

(a) **Color-enhanced SEM of *E. coli* bacteria conjugating.** The bacteria are connected by a sex pilus. When stimulated by the contact, the cells pull close together and form a conjugation bridge between donor and recipient cells (*shown in* **b**).

0.5 μm

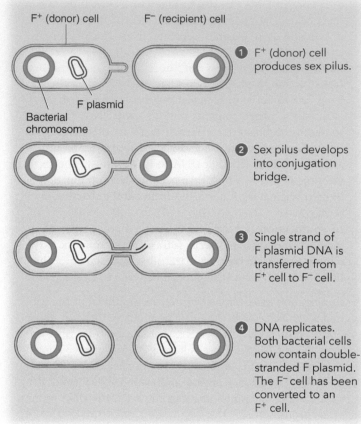

F⁺ (donor) cell   F⁻ (recipient) cell

Bacterial chromosome   F plasmid

1 F⁺ (donor) cell produces sex pilus.

2 Sex pilus develops into conjugation bridge.

3 Single strand of F plasmid DNA is transferred from F⁺ cell to F⁻ cell.

4 DNA replicates. Both bacterial cells now contain double-stranded F plasmid. The F⁻ cell has been converted to an F⁺ cell.

(b) **The process of conjugation.**

Figure 25-8 *Animation* **Conjugation**

In conjugation a donor bacterium transfers plasmid DNA to a recipient bacterium. Conjugation requires cell-to-cell contact.

CONNECT Why might it be advantageous for a bacterial cell to receive the F plasmid from another cell?

25.3 NUTRITIONAL AND METABOLIC ADAPTATIONS

LEARNING OBJECTIVE

6 Describe the principal modes by which prokaryotes carry on nutrition and energy capture, and compare their requirements for oxygen.

Some prokaryotes are *autotrophs* (*-troph* comes from a Greek word that means "nutrition"), and others are *heterotrophs*. **Autotrophs** are able to use inorganic compounds, such as carbon dioxide, as a source of carbon for manufacturing their organic molecules. Most prokaryotes are **heterotrophs** that obtain carbon atoms from the organic compounds of other organisms.

Based on *two principal ways of capturing energy,* an autotroph is classified as a chemotroph or a phototroph. **Chemotrophs** obtain their energy from chemical compounds. **Phototrophs**

capture energy from light. As early as 3.5 billion years ago the ability to use the sun as an energy source evolved in early prokaryotes. These early phototrophs used hydrogen sulfide to reduce carbon dioxide. They released sulfur as a waste product. About 2.7 billion years ago, the ability to use water rather than hydrogen sulfide to reduce carbon dioxide evolved in early cyanobacteria, and oxygen was released as a waste product. When we consider the source of carbon *and* the source of energy, we can classify prokaryotes into four main groups (TABLE 25-1):

1. **Photoautotrophs,** such as cyanobacteria, use the energy from sunlight to synthesize organic compounds from carbon dioxide and other inorganic compounds.

2. The majority of archaea and some bacteria are **chemoautotrophs,** which use carbon dioxide as a carbon source, but do not use sunlight as their energy source. Instead, they obtain energy by oxidizing inorganic chemical substances such as ammonia (NH_3) and hydrogen sulfide (H_2S).

3. **Photoheterotrophs,** such as the purple nonsulfur bacteria, obtain their carbon from other organisms but use

TABLE 25-1	Modes of Nutrition and Energy Capture		
MODE OF NUTRITION	**ENERGY SOURCE**	**CARBON SOURCE**	**EXAMPLES OF ORGANISMS**
AUTOTROPH			
Photoautotroph	Sunlight	CO_2	Cyanobacteria; purple sulfur bacteria
Chemoautotroph	Inorganic chemicals (e.g., NH_3, H_2S, Fe^{2+})	CO_2	Certain proteobacteria; most archaea (e.g., methanogens, extreme halophiles)
HETEROTROPH			
Photoheterotroph	Sunlight	Organic compounds	Purple and green nonsulfur bacteria
Chemoheterotroph	Organic compounds	Organic compounds	Free-living decomposers; most bacterial pathogens

© Cengage Learning

chlorophyll and other photosynthetic pigments to trap energy from sunlight.

4. The majority of bacteria are **chemoheterotrophs.** They depend on organic molecules for both their carbon and energy. Many prokaryote chemoheterotrophs are free-living **decomposers** that obtain their carbon and energy from dead organic matter. These organisms are sometimes called *saprotrophs.* Some bacterial chemoheterotrophs are pathogens, which obtain their nourishment from the organisms they infect. They harm their hosts by causing diseases. Other heterotrophic bacteria benefit their hosts. For example, some of the bacteria that inhabit the human large intestine produce vitamin K and certain B vitamins for their hosts.

Most prokaryotes require oxygen

Whether they are heterotrophs or autotrophs, most bacterial cells and many archaeal cells are **aerobic** and require oxygen for cellular respiration. Many are **facultative anaerobes** that use oxygen for cellular respiration if it is available but can carry on metabolism anaerobically when necessary. Other prokaryotes are **obligate anaerobes** that carry on anaerobic respiration; they respire with terminal electron acceptors other than oxygen, such as sulfate (SO_4^{2-}), nitrate (NO_3^-), or iron (Fe^{2+}). Some obligate anaerobes, including certain archaea, are actually killed by even low concentrations of oxygen.

Some prokaryotes fix and metabolize nitrogen

All organisms require nitrogen to manufacture amino acids and nucleic acids. Some bacteria (e.g., certain cyanobacteria) and archaea (e.g., methanogens) can reduce nitrogen in the atmosphere to ammonia. This process is called **nitrogen fixation.** Ammonia produced by nitrogen fixation is converted to ammonium ions (NH_4^+). Nitrogen-fixing prokaryotes can use these simple forms of nitrogen to produce organic compounds.

Certain prokaryotes convert ammonia or ammonium ions to nitrite (NO_2^-), and others convert nitrite to nitrate (NO_3^-). This process, called **nitrification,** converts nitrogen to a form that can be used by plants and fungi. Animals obtain nitrogen from organic compounds when they eat other organisms. As we will discuss in a later section, all other organisms ultimately depend on nitrogen fixation and nitrification by prokaryotes for their survival (discussed further in Chapter 55).

CHECKPOINT 25.3

- *How do chemoheterotrophs obtain energy?*
- **CONNECT** *How do facultative anaerobes differ from obligate anaerobes? How do they differ from aerobes?*
- *How do prokaryotes obtain nitrogen needed to produce amino acids and nucleic acids?*

25.4 THE PHYLOGENY OF THE TWO PROKARYOTE DOMAINS

LEARNING OBJECTIVES

7 Compare characteristics of the three domains: Archaea, Bacteria, and Eukarya.
8 Distinguish between the four main groups of archaea and identify specific types of archaea belonging to each group.
9 Describe the main groups of bacteria discussed in this chapter.

Under a microscope, most prokaryotes appear rather similar in size and form. However, using sequence analysis of small subunit 16S ribosomal RNA (SSU rRNA), Carl Woese and his co-workers demonstrated that there are two fundamentally different groups of prokaryotes (see Chapter 23). Each group has regions of SSU rRNA that have unique nucleotide sequences. The explanation is that after they diverged, prokaryote populations diversified, and mutations occurred that affect RNA sequences. Using such analyses, Woese hypothesized that ancient prokaryotes split into two lineages early in the history of life.

Based on Woese's work and on other recent data, systematists now classify the modern descendants of these two ancient lines in two domains: **Archaea** and **Bacteria** (FIG. 25-9). These groups are thought to have diverged from a common ancestor about four billion years ago. Archaea and bacteria were the only living organisms on our planet for about two billion years. Thus, archaea and bacteria have had a very long time to evolve and adapt to all types of environments. Their diversity is staggering. Horizontal gene transfer has contributed to the diversity of these organisms. As a result of gene transfer, sometimes from distantly related species, the genomes of archaea and bacteria are actually a mix of genes from many prokaryotes.

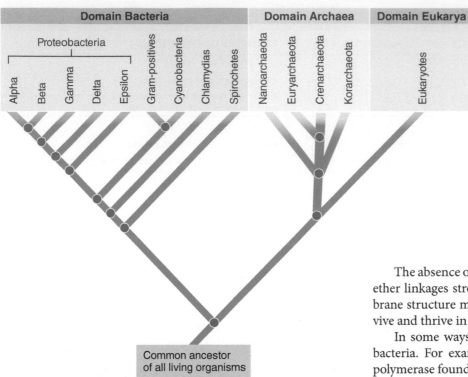

Figure 25-9 Three domains

This highly simplified diagram depicts some representative taxa of domain Bacteria and domain Archaea. The relationships illustrated are based on molecular data. As taxonomists consider additional data, these relationships will be modified.

© Cengage Learning

Key characters distinguish the three domains

Several key characters distinguish archaea from bacteria. In contrast to bacteria, archaea do not have peptidoglycan in their cell walls. Although their plasma membranes are structurally similar, they are chemically unique. In the plasma membranes of bacteria and eukaryotes, straight-chain fatty acids are linked to glycerol molecules by *ester linkages*. In contrast, fatty acid components are not found in archaea. Instead, branched-chain hydrocarbons (synthesized from isoprene units) are bonded to glycerol by *ether linkages* (TABLE 25-2).

Ester linkage   **Ether linkage**

The absence of a second electronegative oxygen atom makes ether linkages stronger than ester linkages. This unique membrane structure may contribute to the ability of archaea to survive and thrive in harsh environments.

In some ways, archaea are more like eukaryotes than like bacteria. For example, archaea do not have the simple RNA polymerase found in bacteria. Like eukaryotes, their translation process begins with methionine, whereas in bacteria, translation begins with formylmethionine (see Chapter 13). In addition, several antibiotics that affect bacteria do not affect archaea or eukaryotes.

Bacteria also share some characteristics (that are absent in archaea) with eukaryotes. For example, as stated above, bacteria and eukarya both have ester-linked membrane lipids, whereas archaea have ether-linked membrane lipids. Some microbiologists hypothesize that eukaryotes are a product of fusion between an archaeon, which contributed components for transcription and translation, and a bacterium, which contributed enzymes necessary for energy metabolism.

TABLE 25-2	Comparison of the Three Domains		
CHARACTERISTIC	**BACTERIA**	**ARCHAEA**	**EUKARYA**
Nuclear envelope	Absent	Absent	Present
Membrane-enclosed organelles	Absent	Absent	Present
Circular chromosome	Present (linear in some species)	Present	Absent
Number of chromosomes	Typically one (may also have plasmids)	Typically one (may also have plasmids)	Typically many
Histones associated with DNA	Absent	Present	Present
Peptidoglycan in cell wall	Present	Absent	Absent
Structure of lipids in plasma membrane	Straight-chain fatty acids bonded to glycerol by ester linkages	Branched-chain hydrocarbons linked to glycerol by ether linkages	Straight-chain fatty acids bonded to glycerol by ester linkages
Size of ribosomes	70S*	70S	80S except in mitochondria and chloroplasts
RNA polymerase	One relatively simple RNA polymerase	One relatively complex RNA polymerase	Several relatively complex RNA polymerases
Translation	Begins with formylmethionine	Begins with methionine	Begins with methionine
Growth above 70°C	Yes	Yes	No

*The numbers 70S and 80S refer to the sedimentation coefficient (a measure of relative size) when centrifuged.

© Cengage Learning

Taxonomy of archaea and bacteria continuously changes

Prokaryote taxonomy is based largely on molecular data, mainly RNA sequencing and more recently on sequencing entire genomes. Groups that branched off earlier had more time to accumulate mutations in their SSU rRNA. Their nucleotide sequences are less similar than those of groups that diverged more recently. Microbiologists who are developing phylogenetic trees based on sequencing entire genomes argue that there may be 1000 genes that code proteins for every 1 gene that codes an rRNA. These researchers prefer to consider the proportions of genes (or proteins) that genomes of various groups have in common. Taxonomy of archaea and bacteria continuously changes as systematists study new molecular data that provide new clues to the phylogeny of these groups.

Although prokaryotic taxonomy is controversial and continuously changing, about 10,000 species of prokaryotes have been classified. Many thousands of additional species are thought to exist. The editors of *Bergey's Manual of Systematic Bacteriology,* considered the definitive reference text by microbiologists, have divided archaea into 4 phyla and bacteria into more than 30 phyla based on 16S rRNA analyses.

Many archaea inhabit harsh environments

Domain Archaea consists of four major phyla: *Crenarchaeota, Euryarchaeota, Nanoarchaeota,* and *Korarchaeota.* This phylogeny is based on 16S rRNA and on sequencing of entire genomes. Based on continued detection of previously unidentified archaea and sequencing of archaeal genomes, systematists estimate that more than a dozen additional phyla may be added.

The **Crenarchaeota** include **extreme thermophiles,** archaea that require a very high temperature or very low temperature for growth. The optimum temperature for many is greater than 80°C (176°F) and some thrive at temperatures greater than 100°C. Some crenarcheotes have the highest growth temperatures known of any organisms. Some species inhabit acidic environments. One species is found in the hot sulfur springs of Yellowstone National Park at temperatures near 80°C and pH values of 1 to 2, the pH of concentrated sulfuric acid (**FIG. 25-10a**). Other crenarchaeotes inhabit volcanic areas under the sea. One species, found near deep-sea hydrothermal vents on the seafloor of the Pacific Ocean, lives at temperatures ranging from 80°C to 120°C. In contrast, some Crenarchaeota species live in very cold environments (1.8°C).

Studies have identified many diverse species of Crenarchaeota in soil and fresh water, demonstrating that members of this phylum are common to most environments. Crenarchaeotes are a main contributor to carbon fixation. They are also an important part of the plankton in cold, oxygen-rich seas. A few are photoheterotrophs.

The **Euryarchaeota** also include many archaea that inhabit extreme environments. This group includes methanogens, extreme aerobic and anaerobic thermophiles, acidophiles, and

(a) **Extreme thermophiles.** Orange and yellow colonies of extreme thermophiles thrive in the Grand Prismatic Spring in Yellowstone National Park in Wyoming.

(b) **Extreme halophiles.** These seawater salt-evaporation ponds are colored from the large number of extreme halophiles that inhabit them. The colors are from pigments in the cell membranes. These archaea are harmless, and the ponds are used to produce salt commercially.

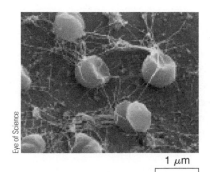

1 μm

(c) **SEM of *Pyrococcus furiosus,* an anaerobe that inhabits marine sediments.** This methanogen is highly resistant to heat; its optimum temperature is 100°C. *Pyrococcus* is classified as a euryarchaeote.

Figure 25-10 Archaea that inhabit extreme environments

halophiles (some extreme) (**FIG. 25-10b**). The **methanogens** (methane producers) are a large, diverse group that inhabit oxygen-free environments in sewage, swamps, and the digestive tracts of humans and other animals. They are obligate anaerobes that produce methane gas from simple carbon compounds. The methanogens are important in recycling components of organic products of organisms that inhabit swamps. Methanogens that inhabit the digestive tracts of cows and other grazing animals produce methane, which is belched out by the animals. Methanogens produce more than 80% of the methane (more than 2 billion tons each year) in Earth's atmosphere. Methanogens are also found in marine sediments (**FIG. 25-10c**). Methane is an important greenhouse gas (discussed in Chapter 57).

Extreme halophiles are heterotrophs that require large amounts of Na^+ for their growth. They live in saturated brine solutions such as salt ponds, the Dead Sea, and Great Salt Lake. The extreme halophiles use aerobic respiration to make ATP. However, they also carry out a form of the Calvin cycle (a part of photosynthesis) in which they capture the energy of sunlight using a purple pigment (*bacteriorhodopsin*). This pigment is very similar to the pigment rhodopsin involved in animal vision.

Korarchaeota is a phylum of Archaea that appears to have branched before the Crenarchaeota and Euryarchaeota branches separated. Korarchaeota have some characteristics of Crenarchaeota and some features of Euryarchaeota. Korarchaeotes have been found in terrestrial hot springs.

To date, only one genus of **Nanoarchaeota** has been identified. *Nanoarchaeum equitans* was discovered in a hydrothermal vent in 2002. This microbe is a very small (400 nm) anaerobic, extreme thermophile with a very small genome (less than 500,000 nucleotides). It lives attached to another archaeon, an autotroph, and depends on its host for many of its metabolic needs.

As more archaea have been discovered and studied, it has become evident that there are likely more archaea in marine and soil environments than in extreme habitats. The archaea are important in biogeochemical cycles and in marine food chains. Although archaea continue to be discovered on and in humans, no pathogenic archaea have been identified.

Bacteria are the most familiar prokaryotes

Bacteria have been known and studied much longer than the archaea. Bacteria are also widely distributed in the environment. Five major groups are considered here: proteobacteria (gram-negative), cyanobacteria (gram-negative), gram-positive bacteria, chlamydias (gram-negative), and spirochetes (gram-negative). These groups are summarized in **TABLE 25-3**.

CHECKPOINT 25.4

- *What types of environments are inhabited by the four phyla of archaea? Why are methanogens important?*
- **CONNECT** *How does each of the following groups of bacteria (described in Table 25-3) affect the biosphere: alpha proteobacteria, cyanobacteria, and chlamydias?*

25.5 IMPACT ON ECOLOGY, TECHNOLOGY, AND COMMERCE

LEARNING OBJECTIVES

10 Identify the critical ecological roles played by prokaryotes.
11 Describe some of the important roles played by prokaryotes in commerce and technology.

Prokaryotes inhabit virtually every environment on Earth and are vital members of the biosphere. They affect other organisms directly and by the ecological roles they play. Prokaryotes produce nitrogen in forms usable by other organisms, and they are a reservoir for nutrients. These microscopic organisms recycle nutrients and are key players in biogeochemical cycles.

Prokaryotes form intimate relationships with other organisms

Prokaryotes interact with other organisms in both beneficial and harmful ways. An intimate relationship between members of two or more species is called **symbiosis**. The partners in a symbiotic relationship are called **symbionts**. Symbiotic relationships arise by coevolution. Three forms of symbiosis are mutualism, commensalism, and parasitism.

Mutualism is a symbiotic relationship in which both partners benefit. Cows and other ruminants (cud-chewing animals) have mutualistic relationships with bacteria and archaea that inhabit their digestive tracts. Ruminants lack enzymes for digesting cellulose. They provide the prokaryotes with a nutrient-rich home, and the prokaryotes digest the cellulose for them.

Trillions of bacteria and some archaea inhabit the nutrient-rich human intestine. Some of them are mutualistic bacteria. For example, in exchange for nutrients and a place to live, *Bacteroides* break down indigestible complex carbohydrates into sugars that their human host can absorb. These bacteria also produce certain vitamins that their host absorbs and uses. In addition, *Bacteroides* promote proliferation of blood vessels that improve intestinal function. Investigators have reported that these bacteria can turn on specific genes in cells of the host's intestine; apparently, they can induce synthesis of a compound that may kill competing bacteria.

In **commensalism** one partner benefits, and the other is neither harmed nor helped. Many prokaryotes that inhabit the human intestine are commensals that live on unused food. In **parasitism** one partner lives on or in the other. The **parasite** benefits, and the **host** is harmed. Disease-causing bacteria are usually not considered obligate parasites because these *pathogens* typically can survive in other ways.

Some types of bacteria may influence evolution of other species The proteobacteria *Wolbachia* infect many invertebrates, including insects, spiders, crustaceans, and nematodes (roundworms). *Wolbachia* are transmitted from generation to generation in the eggs of their hosts, so male hosts are not useful to them. Consequently, these parasites limit or eradicate males from the population. In some insect species, infected males can reproduce only when they mate with infected females carrying the same *Wolbachia* strain. In some other species, these parasites convert male insects into females. In some wasp species, *Wolbachia* induces *parthenogenesis*, the development of unfertilized eggs into adult organisms. Because they affect reproduction in their hosts, *Wolbachia* and other reproductive parasites may influence evolutionary divergence and even extinction in some species. *Wolbachia* may also affect evolution by horizontal gene transfer.

Many prokaryotes form biofilms Many types of bacteria and archaea that inhabit watery environments form **biofilms,** dense communities of microorganisms that attach to solid surfaces. The prokaryotes secrete a slimy, gluelike substance rich in polysaccharides and become embedded in this matrix. A biofilm may consist of layers up to 200 μm thick. Biofilms are communities of many microorganisms and may consist of many species of bacteria, archaea, fungi, and protists. Scientists have found evidence of ancient biofilms in sediments from coastal marine environments 3.5 billion years old.

The dental plaque that forms on teeth is a familiar example of a biofilm (**FIG. 25-11**). Dental plaque consists of several hundred different types of bacteria and archaea. Biofilms also commonly form on the surfaces of contact lenses and catheters. They sometimes develop on surgical implants such as pacemakers and joint replacements. Biofilms, which form on and inside plants, cause considerable crop loss.

Prokaryotes play key ecological roles

Bacteria, especially actinomycetes and myxobacteria, are the most numerous inhabitants of soil. As described earlier in this chapter, many prokaryotes are essential decomposers, chemoheterotrophs that break down dead organic matter and wastes. They use the products of decomposition as an energy source. When prokaryotes break down organic compounds, many of their components, including nitrogen, oxygen, carbon, phosphorus, sulfur, and certain trace elements, are recycled. (The roles of bacteria and archaea in biogeochemical cycles, particularly the nitrogen cycle, are discussed in Chapter 55.)

Nitrogen is constantly removed from the soil by plants and other natural processes as well as by human activities such as agriculture. Plant growth depends on the availability of usable nitrogen, so it must be continually added to the soil. Several types of bacteria, including cyanobacteria, and some archaea transform atmospheric nitrogen to forms that can be used by plants (see Table 25-3). Marine archaea that carry on nitrification are important in the ocean nitrogen cycle.

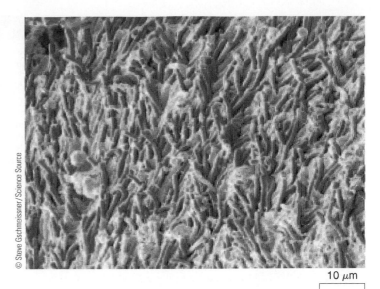

Figure 25-11 A familiar biofilm: dental plaque
Colorized SEM of dental plaque, which consists of a film of bacteria (*red*) embedded in a matrix of glycoprotein (*blue*). Bacteria in the plaque can produce acids that erode tooth enamel, leading to tooth decay.

Rhizobial prokaryotes, motile inhabitants of the soil, form mutualistic relationships with the roots of legumes, a large family of plants that includes important crops such as beans, peas, and peanuts. The infected plant cells form tumorlike nodules in which the microbes reside and fix nitrogen (see Fig. 55-9). The prokaryotes supply the plant with the nitrogen it requires, and the plant provides the prokaryotes with organic compounds, including sugar needed for cellular respiration. Because many soils are deficient in nitrogen, legumes that have formed mutualistic associations with rhizobial microbes have a decided advantage over other plants. When the legumes die and are decomposed, the fixed nitrogen is released and enriches the soil.

Many prokaryotes, such as cyanobacteria, carry on photosynthesis, using water as the electron source and generating oxygen. During this process they fix huge amounts of carbon dioxide into organic molecules.

Microbiologists are only beginning to unravel the mysteries of prokaryote ecology. For example, alpha proteobacteria in the SAR11 clade are among the most successful organisms on Earth. Although they are one of the most abundant organisms in the Atlantic Ocean, they were not successfully cultured until 2002, and very little is known about their ecological role. There is evidence that they are important in cycling carbon, nitrogen, and sulfur in the ocean.

Prokaryotes are important in many commercial processes and in technology

Some microorganisms produce *antibiotics*. These compounds limit competition for nutrients by inhibiting or destroying other microorganisms. By the 1950s, antibiotics had become

TABLE 25-3 | Major Groups of Bacteria

PROTEOBACTERIA (GRAM-NEGATIVE)

A large, very diverse clade of gram-negative bacteria. Based on rRNA sequences, the group is divided into five subgroups designated as alpha, beta, gamma, delta, and epsilon.

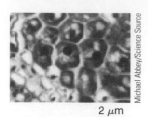

2 μm

Michael Abbey/Science Source

Rhizobia (*Rhizobium leguminosarum*) in root nodule
Rhizobia are nitrogen-fixing bacteria.

ALPHA PROTEOBACTERIA

Includes many symbionts of plants and animals, and some pathogens. *Rhizobium* species live symbiotically in root nodules of legumes (e.g., beans) and convert atmospheric nitrogen to a form usable by plants (nitrogen fixation). **Rickettsias** are very small, rod-shaped bacteria. A few species are pathogenic to humans and other animals; transmitted by arthropods through bites or through contact with their excretions. Rickettsias cause typhus (transmitted by fleas and lice) and Rocky Mountain spotted fever (transmitted by ticks). Members of the SAR11 clade are extremely abundant in the ocean.

1 μm

SPL/Science Source

SEM of bacteria (*Neisseria gonorrhoeae*) that cause gonorrhea
In this colorized SEM, these beta proteobacteria (*blue*) are infecting a human epithelial cell (*purple*).

BETA PROTEOBACTERIA

Several diverse groups, including *Nitrosomonas,* which oxidizes ammonia. Pathogenic bacteria in this group include *Neisseria gonorrhoeae,* which causes gonorrhea.

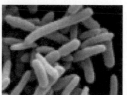

2 μm

SPL

SEM of *Escherichia coli* colony
E. coli are gamma proteobacteria.

GAMMA PROTEOBACTERIA

Includes the **enterobacteria,** decomposers that live on decaying plant matter, pathogens, and a variety of bacteria that inhabit humans. Although *Escherichia coli* is a normal inhabitant of the animal intestinal tract, certain strains can cause moderate to severe diarrhea. One species of *Salmonella* infects food and produces a toxin that causes a form of food poisoning; another species causes typhoid fever.

Vibrios are mainly marine; some are bioluminescent. *Vibrio cholerae* causes cholera.

Pseudomonads are heterotrophs that produce nonphotosynthetic pigments; cause disease in plants and animals, including humans.

Purple sulfur bacteria are photoautotrophs that do not produce oxygen.

DELTA PROTEOBACTERIA

Includes the **myxobacteria** (slime bacteria), which secrete slime and glide or creep along. When nutrients are exhausted, these bacteria aggregate into stalked, multicellular reproductive structures called fruiting bodies. Bacterial cells within the fruiting body enter a resting stage. When conditions are favorable, resting cells become active.

50 μm

© Phototake, Inc. / PhototakeUSA.com

SEM of fruiting body of the myxobacterium *Stigmatella aurantiaca*
Protective resting cells within the fruiting bodies are very resistant to heat and drying. Myxobacteria are delta proteobacteria.

EPSILON PROTEOBACTERIA

A small group of bacteria that inhabit the animal digestive tract. *Helicobacter* can cause peptic ulcers.

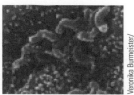

2 μm

Veronika Burmeister/ Visuals Limited

SEM of *Helicobacter pylori* attached to the epithelial lining of the stomach

Continued

TABLE 25-3 | Major Groups of Bacteria (*continued*)

GRAM-POSITIVE BACTERIA

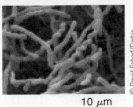

10 μm

SEM of *Actinomycetes naeslundi*, a soil-dwelling bacterium that forms filamentous colonies

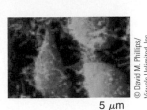

5 μm

SEM of *Mycoplasma* on fibroblast cells

Actinomycetes superficially resemble fungi. However, they have peptidoglycan in their cell walls, lack nuclear envelopes, and have other prokaryotic characteristics. Most actinomycetes are saprotrophs that decompose organic materials in soil. Some are anaerobic. Several species of the genus *Streptomyces* produce antibiotics such as streptomycin, erythromycin, chloramphenicol, and the tetracyclines. Some actinomycetes cause serious lung disease and other infections in humans and other animals.

Lactic acid bacteria ferment sugar, producing lactic acid as the main end product. Inhabit decomposing plant material, milk, and other dairy products; responsible for the characteristic taste of yogurt, pickles, sauerkraut, and green olives. Among the normal inhabitants of the human mouth and vagina.

Mycobacteria are slender, irregular rods; contain a waxy substance in their cell walls. One species causes tuberculosis; another causes leprosy.

Streptococci inhabit the mouth and digestive tract of humans and some other animals. Among the harmful species are those that cause "strep throat," dental caries, a form of pneumonia, scarlet fever, and rheumatic fever (see chapter-opening photograph).

Staphylococci normally live in the nose and on skin. Opportunistic pathogens that cause disease when the immunity of the host is lowered. *Staphylococcus aureus* causes boils and skin infections (some extremely serious); may infect wounds. Certain strains of *S. aureus* cause a form of food poisoning; other strains cause toxic shock syndrome (see Fig. 25-14).

Clostridia are anaerobic. One species causes tetanus; another causes gas gangrene. *Clostridium botulinum* can cause botulism, an often fatal type of food poisoning.

The **mycoplasmas** are a group of very small bacteria that lack cell walls. They may have evolved from bacteria with gram-positive cell walls. They inhabit soil and sewage; some are parasitic on plants or animals. Some inhabit human mucous membranes but do not generally cause disease; one species causes a mild type of bacterial pneumonia in humans.

CYANOBACTERIA (GRAM-NEGATIVE)

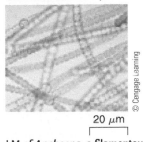

20 μm

LM of *Anabaena*, a filamentous cyanobacterium that fixes nitrogen
Nitrogen fixation takes place in the rounded cells, called *heterocysts*.

Cyanobacteria contain chlorophyll *a* and are the only prokaryotes that, like plants and algae, carry on photosynthesis that generates oxygen. Cyanobacteria were the first organisms that carried on oxygen-generating photosynthesis; very important in the evolution of life-forms because their photosynthesis changed the early reducing atmosphere on Earth to an oxidizing atmosphere. Chloroplasts are thought to have evolved from endosymbiotic cyanobacteria. Inhabit ponds, lakes, swimming pools, moist soil, dead logs, and tree bark. Some form filaments; other species are solitary. As primary producers, they are an important source of food for marine and freshwater organisms. Some species have special structures that fix nitrogen.

CHLAMYDIAS (GRAM-NEGATIVE)

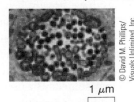

1 μm

TEM of *Chlamydia trachomatis* in human oviduct cell

Chlamydias lack peptidoglycan in their cell walls. They are energy parasites, completely dependent on their hosts for ATP. Infect almost every species of bird and mammal. A strain of *Chlamydia* causes trachoma, the leading cause of blindness in the world. Sexually transmitted chlamydias are the major cause of pelvic inflammatory disease in women.

SPIROCHETES (GRAM-NEGATIVE)

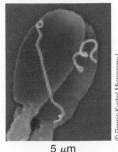

5 μm

LM of *Treponema pallidum*, the spirochete that causes syphilis

Spirochetes are spiral-shaped bacteria with flexible cell walls; move by means of unique internal flagella called *axial filaments*. Some species are free-living, whereas others form symbiotic associations; a few are parasitic. *Treponema pallidum* causes syphilis.

Figure 25-12 Bioremediation
As they feed on the gasoline and certain other waste products in contaminated soil, certain microorganisms convert hydrocarbons in these pollutants to carbon dioxide and water. Photographed at an oil refinery and chemical plant in the United Kingdom.

important clinical tools that transformed the treatment of infectious disease. Today, more than 100 clinically useful antibiotics are available, and literally tons of antibiotics are produced annually. Pharmaceutical companies obtain most antibiotics from three groups of microorganisms: a large group of gram-positive soil bacteria, the *actinomycetes;* gram-positive bacteria of the genus *Bacillus;* and molds (eukaryotes belonging to kingdom Fungi).

Because of their prolific reproduction rates, bacteria are ideal "factories" for the production of biomolecules. Microbiologists have genetically engineered bacteria to produce certain vaccines, human growth hormone, insulin, and many other clinically important compounds (see Chapter 15). Researchers are developing genetically engineered bacteria for production of many other medically and agriculturally useful products.

Microbial fermentation helps produce many foods and beverages. Lactic acid bacteria are used in producing acidophilus milk, yogurt, pickles, olives, and sauerkraut. Several types of bacteria are used in the production of cheese. Bacteria are involved in making fermented meats such as salami and in producing vinegar, soy sauce, chocolate, and certain B vitamins (B_{12} and riboflavin).

Bacteria are used in **bioremediation,** the process of using microorganisms (and sometimes other organisms) to detoxify or remove oil, gasoline, and other pollutants or toxic chemicals from the environment. Microorganisms break down certain toxins, leaving behind harmless metabolic byproducts such as carbon dioxide and chlorides (**FIG. 25-12**). More than 1000 different species of bacteria and fungi have been used to clean up various forms of pollution, and microbiologists are searching for others. For example, bacteria and other microorganisms are used in oil spills to break down oil, oxidizing it to CO_2. Microorganisms are also used in sewage treatment and to break down solid wastes in landfills.

Archaea are also economically important. Archaea that are adapted to high temperatures or extremely acidic conditions, for example, are a source of enzymes that can be used under these extreme conditions. Archaeal enzymes have been added to laundry and industrial detergents and to organic solvents to increase performance at higher temperatures and pH levels. Methanogens are important in the biogas production industry and in sewage treatment. Another archaeal enzyme has been useful in the food industry to convert cornstarch to dextrins (low molecular weight carbohydrates produced by hydrolysis of starch or glycogen).

Molecular biology and forensic biology have greatly benefited from heat-resistant DNA polymerase, derived from the archaeon *Pyrococcus furiosus* (see Fig. 25-10c). Like heat-resistant Taq polymerase, derived from a bacterium, it is used in the polymerase chain reaction (PCR) discussed in Chapter 15. Some archaea have antimicrobial properties and may someday be used in the production of new antibiotics. Acidophilic archaeons are promising as resources for extracting metal from ores and remediating toxic mining sites.

CHECKPOINT 25.5

- **CONNECT** *In what ways do bacteria form relationships with other organisms?*
- *Where would you expect to find biofilms? Name organisms you would expect to find in biofilms.*
- **CONNECT** *Describe how prokaryotes are ecologically important. Give specific examples.*
- *Describe the process of bioremediation.*

25.6 BACTERIA AND DISEASE

LEARNING OBJECTIVES

12 Describe the roles played by Louis Pasteur and Robert Koch in understanding infectious disease; list Koch's postulates.

13 Identify adaptations that have contributed to pathogen success.

Some prokaryote species have coevolved with eukaryotes and are interdependent with them. All plants and animals harbor a community of microorganisms referred to as **microbiota.** (This term is replacing a traditional designation, *microflora,* which is a misnomer because "flora" refers to plants.) An estimated 700 trillion symbiotic bacteria, archaea, and (a few) eukaryotic microorganisms normally inhabit the human body! This number greatly exceeds the number of the body's own cells (about 70 trillion).

Normal microbial populations have been shown to have multiple effects, including preventing harmful microorganisms from flourishing. The term **microbiome** refers to the community of these microorganisms, including their genomes and all of their interactions. Rapid DNA sequencing has greatly facilitated microbiome research because there are thousands of species of these organisms and many are difficult to grow in culture. Through the *Human Microbiome Project* supported by the National Institutes of Health since 2009, investigators are studying the **human microbiome.** Through their research, we are developing an ever-increasing understanding of the critical effects of these symbionts on health and disease.

A small percentage of bacterial species are important pathogens of plants and animals. Some of the normal bacterial inhabitants are opportunistic pathogens that cause disease only under certain conditions. For example, when the immune system is compromised, opportunistic bacteria increase in number and cause disease. Some important bacterial diseases and the pathogens that cause them are briefly described in **TABLE 25-4.**

Many scientists have contributed to our understanding of infectious disease

The idea that some unknown agent caused disease was debated long before Leeuwenhoek discovered microorganisms with his microscope in the late 1600s. However, not until much later did scientists develop the tools and methods needed to accurately understand the relationships between bacteria and disease. During the late 19th century, several physicians, microbiologists, and chemists working independently laid the foundations for the science of microbiology. French chemist Louis Pasteur disproved the prevailing views of spontaneous generation by demonstrating that sterilization of a sugar and protein culture prevented bacterial growth. Pasteur also developed a rabies vaccine, showing that people can be stimulated to develop immunity to disease.

German physician Robert Koch was the first to clearly demonstrate that bacteria cause infectious disease. In 1876, he showed that *Bacillus anthracis* caused anthrax. Using a microscope, Koch observed the bacteria in the blood and spleens of dead sheep. When he inoculated mice with the infected sheep blood, he was able to identify *B. anthracis* in the blood of the mice. He also cultured *B. anthracis* and showed that when he injected the bacteria into healthy mice they developed anthrax.

Koch proposed a set of guidelines, now known as **Koch's postulates,** that are still used to demonstrate that a specific pathogen causes specific disease symptoms: (1) the pathogen must be present in every individual with the disease, (2) a sample of the microorganism taken from the diseased host can be grown in pure culture, (3) a sample of the pure culture causes the same disease when injected into a healthy host, and (4) the microorganism can be recovered from the experimentally infected host. Sometimes these guidelines cannot be met, as, for example, when certain microorganisms cannot be grown in pure culture. In those situations, other criteria must be used.

Many adaptations contribute to pathogen success

Pathogenic microorganisms can enter the body in food, dust, or droplets or through wounds. Many diseases are transmitted by insect or animal bites. To cause disease, a pathogen must adhere to a specific cell type, multiply, and produce toxic substances. Adherence and multiplication occur only when the pathogen competes successfully with the normal microbiota and counteracts the host's defenses against invasion.

Helicobacter pylori, the most common cause of peptic ulcers (ulcers of the stomach and duodenum), is an extremely successful pathogen (FIG. 25-13). It is also associated with chronic gastritis (stomach inflammation) and with stomach cancer, the second most common type of cancer in the world. *Helicobacter pylori* inhabits the gastrointestinal tracts of an estimated 40% of adults in developed countries and 80% of adults in developing countries. Among its many adaptations is its ability to produce an alkaline shield around itself that protects it from stomach acid. Also contributing to its success are several powerful flagella used to propel the pathogen through the thick mucus lining the stomach.

Pathogens produce a variety of substances that increase their success. Some bacteria produce **exotoxins,** strong poisons that are either secreted from the cell or leak out when the bacterial cell is destroyed. The toxin, not the presence of the bacteria themselves, is responsible for the disease. Diphtheria is caused by a gram-positive bacillus (*Corynebacterium diphtheriae*) that produces a toxin only when lysogenized by a phage. The diphtheria toxin kills cells and causes inflammation.

Botulism, a type of food poisoning that can lead to paralysis and sometimes death, can result from eating improperly canned food. Botulism is caused by an exotoxin released by the

TABLE 25-4 | Important Bacterial Diseases and Their Causative Agents

DISEASE	PATHOGEN	EPIDEMIOLOGY/COMMENTS
Anthrax	*Bacillus anthracis*	Most commonly occurs in domestic animals such as cattle. Can be transmitted to humans from infected animals or animal products. Endospores can live in soil for many years. Anthrax is not spread from person to person. Infection can occur in three ways: cutaneous, by inhalation, and gastrointestinal.
Antibiotic-associated diarrhea; and inflammation of colon	*Clostridium difficile* (common name: *C. dif*)	Risk greatest for older people taking antibiotics, people with compromised immune systems, and patients in hospitals and health care facilities for extended periods
Botulism	*Clostridium botulinum*	Contracted by eating foods that contain the exotoxin or from infected wound. Infant botulism is caused by ingesting endospores. Causes muscle paralysis and can cause death from respiratory failure.
Chlamydia	*Chlamydia trachomatis*	One of the most frequently reported sexually transmitted infections in the U.S. About 75% of infected women and 50% of infected men have no symptoms. If untreated, infection spreads and can lead to infertility. *Chlamydia* can also infect eyes; cause millions of cases of blindness worldwide each year.
Cholera	*Vibrio cholerae*	Contracted by eating food or drinking water contaminated with the bacteria. Common in areas with inadequate sewage treatment and impure water. Infects intestine and can cause severe diarrhea. Rapid fluid loss can lead to dehydration and death.
Diphtheria	*Corynebacterium diphtheriae*	Transmitted from person to person by intimate respiratory and physical contact. Endemic in developing countries. Not common in U.S. since vaccine became available in 1920s. Infects the heart muscle and respiratory passageways.
Epidemic typhus	*Rickettsia prowazekii*	Transmitted by infected body lice. After an 8- to 12-day incubation period, symptoms include fever, severe headache, muscle aches, and chills. Several days later a rash appears. About 40% of untreated patients die.
Gonorrhea	*Neisseria gonorrhoeae*	Common sexually transmitted disease.
Hansen disease (leprosy)	*Mycobacterium leprae*	Thought to be spread from person to person in nasal secretions. Worldwide, this disease has disabled up to 2 million people.
Lyme disease	*Borrelia burgdorferi*	Transmitted to humans by bite of infected blacklegged ticks. Symptoms include skin rash, headache, fever, and fatigue. If untreated, infection can spread to joints, heart, and nervous system.
Peptic ulcer disease	*Helicobacter pylori*	Causes peptic ulcer, a lesion in the lining of the stomach or duodenum (upper part of small intestine).
Pertussis (whooping cough)	*Bordetella pertussis*	Highly communicable from person to person. Causes spasms of severe coughing. Vaccination available.
Plague	*Yersinia pestis*	Transmitted from wild rodents, squirrels, and cats to people by infected fleas. If untreated, can be fatal. Killed millions of people in Europe during the Middle Ages.
Pneumonia	*Streptococcus pneumoniae*	Transmitted from person to person. Strains of *S. pneumoniae* are resistant to some antibiotics. Incidence has decreased since introduction of a vaccine.
Salmonella (salmonellosis)	*Salmonella sp.*	Transmitted via contaminated chicken, eggs, or other food; also from feces of infected animals. Symptoms include fever, diarrhea, and stomach pain.
Syphilis	*Treponema pallidum*	Sexually transmitted disease passed through direct contact with a syphilis sore. If untreated, eventually damages brain, liver, bone, and spleen; can cause death.
Travelers' diarrhea	*Escherichia coli* is most common cause	Ingested in contaminated food and water. Affects 30% to 50% of travelers in high-risk areas (Central America, South America, Africa, Middle East, and most of Asia). Infecting bacteria produce toxins in gastrointestinal tract.
Tuberculosis	*Mycobacterium tuberculosis*	Transmitted from person to person through inhalation of air containing the pathogen. Symptoms include fatigue, cough, fever, and weight loss. Not common in U.S., but multidrug-resistant form is a growing threat.
Typhoid fever	*Salmonella typhi*	Transmitted from person to person in food or water contaminated with feces. Risk greatest for travelers in developing countries, but vaccine available. Symptoms include high fever, headache, and loss of appetite. Can cause death if not treated.

gram-positive, endospore-forming *Clostridium botulinum*. During the canning process, food must be heated sufficiently to kill any highly heat-resistant endospores that may be present. If not, the endospores can germinate. The resulting bacterial population grows and releases an exotoxin so powerful that 1 g could kill one million humans! Like many exotoxins, the one that causes botulism is inactivated by heating. (Food must be heated to 80°C for 10 minutes or boiled for 3 to 4 minutes to inactivate the exotoxin.)

The botulism exotoxin, marketed under the trade name Botox, is used in extremely tiny amounts to treat several medical conditions involving spasms (involuntary muscle contractions). Because Botox is a neurotoxin that works by paralyzing muscles, it can also relax facial wrinkles caused by contraction

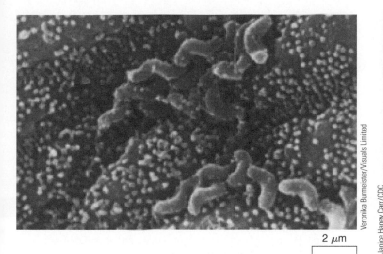

Figure 25-13 **SEM of *Helicobacter pylori* attached to the epithelial lining of the stomach**

Helicobacter pylori causes peptic ulcers.

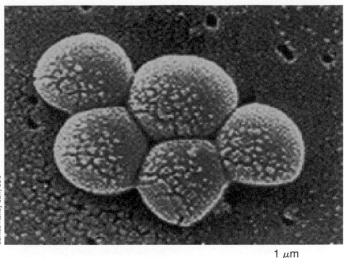

Figure 25-14 **Colorized SEM of methicillin-resistant *Staphylococcus aureus* (MRSA)**

These bacteria also show increased resistance to vancomycin.

of the underlying muscles. However, its effects last for only three to eight months.

Another gram-positive, endospore-forming bacterium, *Clostridium difficile,* is an anaerobe that produces two exotoxins. It is a common cause of antibiotic-associated diarrhea (AAD), accounting for 15% to 25% of all episodes of AAD. *C. difficile* has recently become more virulent and more resistant to antibiotics. It has been linked to more than 14,000 deaths in the United States each year (see Table 25-4).

Endotoxins are not secreted by pathogens but instead are components of the cell walls of most gram-negative bacteria. These compounds affect the host only when they are released from dead bacteria. Endotoxins bind to the host's macrophages (large phagocytic cells of the immune system) and stimulate them to release substances that cause fever and other symptoms of infection. Unlike exotoxins, which cause specific symptoms, endotoxins appear to affect the entire body. Endotoxins are not destroyed by heating.

Antibiotic resistance is a major public health problem

Bacteria mutate frequently and reproduce rapidly, often developing resistance to antibiotics. Many antibiotics target protein synthesis in bacteria. For example, streptomycin and related antibiotics block the initiation of protein synthesis. The tetracyclines block aminoacyl tRNA from binding to the A site on the ribosome.

Drug resistance may result from an accumulation of mutations in plasmid or chromosomal DNA. Plasmids that have genes for antibiotic resistance are called *R factors*. They have genes for resistance to a specific drug and for transferring the resistance to other bacteria. Some R factors have several genes for drug resistance, each encoding resistance to a different drug.

Methicillin-resistant *Staphylococcus aureus* (SA), referred to as *MRSA,* and vancomycin-resistant *Staphylococcus aureus,* or *VRSA,* have been directly linked to the horizontal transfer of antibiotic resistance genes by plasmids during conjugation. An estimated 1 in every 100 healthy people in the United States now carries MRSA (**FIG. 25-14**). This "superbug" can cause infection in individuals with compromised immune systems. The Centers for Disease Control estimates that MRSA causes more than 95,000 serious infections each year, resulting in more than 18,000 deaths annually.

Overuse of antibiotics is the principal contributing factor to drug resistance. In any bacterial population, there are likely at least a few bacteria that are genetically resistant to a particular antibiotic. The bacteria that are *not* resistant are killed by the antibiotic, leaving the resistant bacteria to multiply and produce a resistant population. Note that this process is a common, present-day example of natural selection.

The practice of feeding low-dose antibiotics to farm animals to promote growth has also resulted in many types of antibiotic-resistant bacteria that survive and multiply after susceptible bacteria are killed. Many countries have banned some antibiotics in animal feed. Antibiotic-resistance has significantly reduced the effectiveness of most common, inexpensive antibiotics. Scientists and pharmaceutical companies are challenged to rapidly develop new antibiotics to treat bacterial infections that were formerly easily cured.

Another type of drug resistance explains why some infections, such as urinary tract infections, are difficult to cure. When *E. coli* infect the bladder, the immune system launches a powerful defense. The bacteria subvert the attack by forming *biofilms* (discussed earlier in this chapter). Each biofilm is surrounded by a matrix rich in polysaccharides and by a protective shell. The bacteria in the biofilm are resistant to antibiotics as well as to host defenses. By one estimate, bacteria growing in a biofilm are up to 1000 times as resistant to antibiotics as are the same type of bacteria that have not formed a biofilm. Within biofilms differential gene expression and mutation lead to diverse bacterial colonies. The biofilm strategy also explains some other types of chronic or recurrent infections. A high percentage of infections acquired in hospitals involve biofilms.

CHECKPOINT 25.6

- **CONNECT** *Why is each of Koch's postulates important in determining whether a particular pathogen causes specific symptoms?*
- *Contrast endotoxins with exotoxins.*

SUMMARY: FOCUS ON LEARNING OBJECTIVES

25.1 The Structure of Bacteria and Archaea (page 512)

1 Describe the structure and common shapes of prokaryotic cells.

- Prokaryotic cells are very small and do not have membrane-enclosed organelles such as nuclei and mitochondria.
- Prokaryotic cells have several common shapes: spherical **(cocci)**, rod-shaped **(bacilli)**, and spiral. Spiral bacteria include the **spirillum,** which is a rigid helix, and **spirochete,** which is a flexible helix.

2 Compare the bacterial cell wall in gram-positive and gram-negative bacteria.

- Most bacteria have **cell walls** composed of **peptidoglycan.** The walls of **gram-positive** bacteria are very thick and consist mainly of peptidoglycan. The cell walls of **gram-negative** bacteria consist of a thin peptidoglycan layer and an outer membrane resembling the plasma membrane. Some species of bacteria produce a **capsule** or **slime layer** that surrounds the cell wall.
- Some prokaryotes have hairlike appendages called **fimbriae. Pili** also extend from the surface of some prokaryotes. Both fimbriae and pili help cells adhere to one another or to certain other surfaces, including cells they infect. *Cannulae* and *hami* are recently discovered hairlike appendages unique to archaea.

3 Describe movement in prokaryotes and describe the structure of the bacterial flagellum.

- Bacterial **flagella** are structurally different from eukaryotic flagella; each flagellum consists of a basal body, hook, and filament. They produce a rotary motion.

25.2 Prokaryote Reproduction and Evolution (page 516)

4 Describe asexual reproduction in prokaryotes and summarize three mechanisms (transformation, transduction, and conjugation) that may lead to genetic recombination.

- The genetic material of a bacterium typically consists of a circular DNA molecule and one or more **plasmids,** smaller circular fragments of DNA.
- Prokaryotes reproduce asexually by **binary fission** (the cell divides, forming two cells), **budding** (a bud forms and separates from the mother cell), or **fragmentation** (walls form inside the cell, which then separates into several cells).
- In prokaryotes genetic material can be exchanged by transformation, transduction, or conjugation. In **transformation** a prokaryotic cell takes in foreign DNA released by another cell. Homologous segments of foreign and host DNA are exchanged. In **transduction** a phage carries bacterial DNA from one bacterial cell into another. In **conjugation** a donor cell transfers plasmid DNA to a recipient cell.

© Cengage Learning

5 State specific factors that contribute to the rapid evolution of bacteria and archaea.

- Rapid reproduction ensures that mutations are rapidly passed to new generations. Horizontal gene transfer—by transformation, transduction, or conjugation—contributes to rapid evolution in prokaryotes.

25.3 Nutritional and Metabolic Adaptations (page 518)

6 Describe the principal modes by which prokaryotes carry on nutrition and energy capture, and compare their requirements for oxygen.

- Most prokaryotes are **heterotrophs** that obtain carbon from other organisms; some are **autotrophs** that make their own organic molecules from simple raw materials.
- **Chemotrophs** obtain energy from chemical compounds; **phototrophs** capture energy from light.
- Autotrophs may be **photoautotrophs,** which obtain energy from sunlight, or **chemoautotrophs,** which obtain energy by oxidizing inorganic chemicals such as ammonia.
- **Photoheterotrophs** obtain carbon from other organisms but use chlorophyll and other photosynthetic pigments to trap energy from sunlight. The majority of bacteria are **chemoheterotrophs.** They are mainly free-living **decomposers** that obtain both carbon and energy from dead organic matter.
- Most bacteria are **aerobic;** that is, they require oxygen for cellular respiration. Some prokaryotes are **facultative anaerobes** that metabolize anaerobically when necessary; others are **obligate anaerobes** that can carry on metabolism *only* anaerobically.
- Some bacteria and archaea carry on **nitrogen fixation;** that is, they reduce nitrogen in the atmosphere to ammonia. Other prokaryotes convert ammonia to nitrite or nitrate in a process called **nitrification.**

25.4 The Phylogeny of the Two Prokaryote Domains
(page 519)

7 Compare characteristics of the three domains: Archaea, Bacteria, and Eukarya.
- Prokaryotes are assigned to domain **Archaea** and domain **Bacteria.**
- Unlike those of bacteria, the cell walls of archaea do not have peptidoglycan. The translational mechanisms of eukaryotes more closely resemble those of archaea than those of bacteria.

8 Distinguish between the four main groups of archaea and identify specific types of archaea belonging to each group.
- The **Crenarchaeota** include many **extreme thermophiles,** archaea that can inhabit very hot, sometimes acidic, environments and archaea that are marine dwellers. **Euryarchaeota** include methanogens, extreme halophiles, and some extreme thermophiles. **Methanogens** are obligate anaerobes that produce methane gas from simple carbon compounds. **Extreme halophiles** inhabit saturated salt solutions. **Korarchaeota** have been found in terrestrial hot springs. **Nanoarchaeota** has only one member to date, *Nanoarchaeum equitans,* a very small, extreme thermophile discovered in a hydrothermal vent.

9 Describe the main groups of bacteria discussed in this chapter.
- Major groups of bacteria include proteobacteria, gram-positive bacteria, cyanobacteria, chlamydias, and spirochetes (see Table 25-3).

25.5 Impact on Ecology, Technology, and Commerce
(page 522)

10 Identify the critical ecological roles played by prokaryotes.
- Many bacteria are symbiotic with other organisms. **Mutualism** is a symbiotic relationship in which both partners benefit. In **commensalism** one partner benefits, and the other is neither harmed nor helped. In **parasitism** the **parasite** benefits, and the **host** is harmed. Bacterial **pathogens** cause disease, but are

usually not considered obligate parasites. **Biofilms** are dense communities of microorganisms, in which cells adhere to one another on a surface. Biofilms may include bacteria, archaea, protists, and fungi.
- Prokaryotes play essential ecological roles as decomposers and are important in recycling nitrogen and other nutrients. Some bacteria carry out photosynthesis.

11 Describe some of the important roles played by prokaryotes in commerce and technology.
- Some prokaryotes produce antibiotics. We have developed the technology for using certain bacteria to produce vaccines, insulin, and other important compounds. We use bacteria in the production of many foods, including cheese, yogurt, vinegar, and chocolate. We also use microbes in sewage treatment and in bioremediation.

25.6 Bacteria and Disease *(page 527)*

12 Describe the roles played by Louis Pasteur and Robert Koch in understanding infectious disease; list Koch's postulates.
- Louis Pasteur demonstrated that sterilization prevented bacterial growth. **Koch's postulates** are a set of guidelines developed by Robert Koch to demonstrate that a specific pathogen causes specific disease symptoms: (1) the pathogen must be present in every individual with the disease, (2) a sample of the microorganism taken from the diseased host can be grown in pure culture, (3) a sample of the pure culture causes the same disease when injected into a healthy host, and (4) the microorganism can be recovered from the experimentally infected host.

13 Identify adaptations that have contributed to pathogen success.
- Some pathogenic bacteria release strong poisons called **exotoxins;** others produce **endotoxins,** poisonous components of their cell walls that are released when bacteria die. Many bacteria have become resistant to antibiotics. Plasmids that have genes for antibiotic resistance are called *R factors.* See Table 25-4 for a description of some pathogenic bacteria.

TEST YOUR UNDERSTANDING

Know and Comprehend

1. Peptidoglycan is a chemical compound found in the cell walls of (a) most viroids (b) most archaea (c) all prokaryotes (d) most bacteria (e) most eukarya
2. Bacterial flagella (a) are homologous with eukaryotic flagella (b) exhibit a rotary motion (c) consist of a basal body and nine pairs of microtubules (d) are important in transduction (e) are characteristic of gram-positive bacteria
3. Endospores (a) are formed by some viruses (b) are extremely durable cells (c) are comparable to the reproductive spores of fungi and plants (d) cause fever and other symptoms in the host (e) are vulnerable to infection by archaea
4. In conjugation (a) two bacterial cells of different mating types come together, and genetic material is transferred from one to another (b) a bacterial cell develops a bulge that enlarges and eventually separates from the mother cell (c) fragments of DNA released by a broken cell are taken in by another bacterial cell (d) a phage carries bacterial genes from one bacterial cell into another (e) walls develop in the cell, which then divides into several new cells
5. The majority of heterotrophic bacteria are (a) free-living chemoheterotrophs (b) photoautotrophs (c) chemoautotrophs (d) facultative anaerobes (e) obligate anaerobes
6. Bacteria that are autotrophs (a) do not require atmospheric oxygen for cellular respiration (b) must obtain organic compounds from other organisms (c) manufacture their own organic molecules from simple raw materials (d) get their nourishment from dead organisms (e) produce endospores when oxygen levels are too low for active growth
7. Bacteria that thrive in puncture wounds are likely to be (a) aerobes (b) photoautotrophs (c) chemoautotrophs (d) endospores (e) obligate anaerobes

8. Which of the following do *not* belong to domain Archaea? (a) prokaryotes that produce methane from carbon dioxide and hydrogen (b) thermophiles (c) halophiles (d) bacteriophages (e) prokaryotes with cell walls that lack peptidoglycan

9. Rhizobial bacteria (a) are used in the production of yogurt (b) produce antibiotics (c) cause peptic ulcers (d) are the pathogens that cause syphilis (e) form mutualistic relationships with the roots of legumes and fix nitrogen

10. Robert Koch (a) proposed a set of guidelines to demonstrate that a specific pathogen causes specific disease symptoms (b) discovered *Helicobacter* (c) showed that biofilms consist of microorganisms (d) proposed a hypothesis for antibiotic resistance (e) demonstrated that people can be stimulated to develop immunity to disease

11. Which group of bacteria contains the gram-positive, anaerobic bacterium that causes botulism? (a) clostridia (b) actinomycetes (c) enterobacteria (d) spirochetes (e) streptococci

Apply and Analyze

12. **VISUALIZE** Label the diagram.

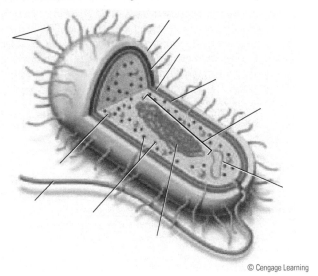

© Cengage Learning

13. Imagine that you discover a new microorganism. After careful study you determine that it should be classified in domain Archaea. What characteristics might lead you to this decision?

Evaluate and Synthesize

14. What would be the consequences for eukaryotes if all prokaryotes suddenly became extinct?

15. **EVOLUTION LINK** In what way does the use of antibiotics impose selective pressure on bacteria?

16. **SCIENCE, TECHNOLOGY, AND SOCIETY** The Centers for Disease Control considers antibiotic resistance to be one of the world's most pressing health problems. How can scientists help solve this problem? (Consider both technology and the general public.)

 To access course materials, such as Aplia and other companion resources, please visit **www.cengagebrain.com**.

Protists

Protists are an informal group of primarily aquatic eukaryotic organisms with diverse body forms, types of reproduction, modes of nutrition, and lifestyles. Protists, which include algae, water molds, slime molds, and protozoa, are unicellular, colonial, or simple multicellular organisms that have a eukaryotic cell organization (see photograph). The word *protist*, from the Greek for "the very first," reflects the idea that protists were the first eukaryotes to evolve.

Protists are members of domain Eukarya, the third domain on the tree of life. (Recall the three domains depicted in Figure 23-2.) Eukaryotic cells are characteristic of protists as well as of complex multicellular organisms belonging to the kingdoms Fungi, Animalia, and Plantae. However, having a eukaryotic cell structure clearly differentiates protists from members of the prokaryotic domains Bacteria and Archaea. Recall from Chapter 4 that unlike prokaryotic cells, eukaryotic cells have nuclei and other membrane-enclosed organelles such as mitochondria and plastids, 9 + 2 flagella, and multiple chromosomes in which DNA and proteins form a complex called chromatin. Sexual reproduction, meiosis, and mitosis are also characteristic of eukaryotes.

Until recently, all protists were classified as the kingdom Protista, but this classification was by default: protists included any eukaryotes that were not land plants, fungi, or animals. Based largely on recent molecular data that have clarified many evolutionary relationships among eukaryotes, kingdom Protista is no longer a recognized clade. Although we have made great progress in understanding the evolutionary relationships among protists, many relationships remain uncertain.

Biologists currently recognize dozens of protist taxa, which, along with other eukaryotes, are classified into five "supergroups." Consideration of all protist taxa is beyond the scope of this text, but we discuss several representative examples of each supergroup and provide insights into how such diverse eukaryotes may have evolved.

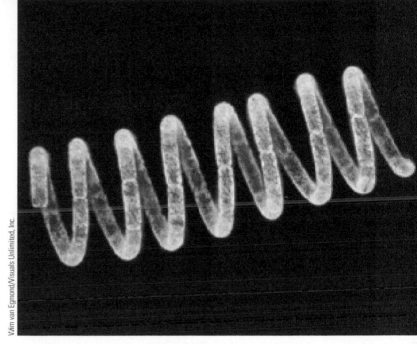

Vlim van Egmond/Visuals Unlimited, Inc.

Light micrograph (LM) of a marine diatom. The widely distributed diatom *Guinardia striata* forms colonies composed of spiraling chains of cells.

KEY CONCEPTS

26.1 Protists are a diverse group of eukaryotic organisms that vary in body plan (unicellular, colonial, coenocytic, multicellular), method of motility (pseudopodia, cilia, flagella), nutrition type (autotrophic, heterotrophic), and mode of reproduction (asexual, sexual).

26.2 Much uncertainty surrounds eukaryote evolution, but eukaryote organelles such as chloroplasts probably descended from engulfed cells that survived and became organelles. Current scientific evidence supports splitting the protists and other eukaryotes (land plants, fungi, and animals) into five informal "supergroups."

26.3 Excavates are a supergroup of unicellular protists with atypical, greatly modified mitochondria; they get their name because many have a deep, or excavated, oral groove.

26.4 Chromalveolates are a supergroup of diverse protists that may have originated as a result of secondary endosymbiosis in which an ancestral cell engulfed a red alga.

26.5 Rhizarians are a supergroup of amoeboid cells that often have tests (shells) through which cytoplasmic projections extend; forams, actinopods, and certain shell-less amoebas are rhizarians.

26.6 Archaeplastids are a supergroup that includes red algae, green algae, and land plants, all of which have plastids enclosed by two external membranes.

26.7 Unikonts are a supergroup that includes amoebozoa and choanoflagellates as well as fungi and animals.

26.1 DIVERSITY IN THE PROTISTS

LEARNING OBJECTIVE

1 Discuss in general terms the diversity inherent in protists, including means of locomotion, modes of nutrition, interactions with other organisms, habitats, and modes of reproduction.

Because of their huge numbers, protists are crucial to the natural balance of the living world. Protists are an important source of food for other organisms, and photosynthetic protists supply oxygen to aquatic and terrestrial ecosystems. Certain protists are economically important, and others cause devastating diseases such as malaria.

Body plan varies considerably among protists. Most protists are *unicellular,* with each cell forming a complete organism capable of performing all the functions characteristic of life. Some protists form **colonies,** loosely connected groups of cells; some are **coenocytes,** consisting of a multinucleate mass of cytoplasm; and some are *multicellular,* composed of many cells. Unlike animals, plants, and many fungi, most multicellular protists have relatively simple body forms without specialized tissues.

Size and structural complexity are not the only variable features of protists. During the course of the long evolutionary history of protists, diversity has evolved in their means of locomotion, ways of obtaining nutrients, interactions with other organisms, habitats, and modes of reproduction.

Protists, most of which are motile at some point in their life cycle, have various means of locomotion. Some move by pushing out cytoplasmic extensions (*pseudopodia*) along the leading edge and retracting the cytoplasm that trails behind, as an amoeba does. Other protists move by flexing individual cells; by gliding over surfaces; by waving *cilia,* short, hairlike organelles; or by lashing *flagella,* long, whiplike organelles. Some protists have two or more means of locomotion, such as both flagella and pseudopodia.

Methods of obtaining nutrients differ widely among protists. Most algae are autotrophic and photosynthesize as plants do (FIG. 26-1a). Some heterotrophic protists obtain their nutrients by absorption, as fungi do, whereas others resemble animals in that they ingest food. Some protists switch their modes of nutrition and are autotrophic at certain times and heterotrophic at others.

Although many protists are free-living, others form stable symbiotic associations with unrelated organisms. These intimate associations range from **mutualism,** a more or less equal partnership where both partners benefit; to **commensalism,** where one partner benefits and the other is unaffected; to **parasitism,** where one partner (the parasite) lives on or in another (the host) and metabolically depends on it (see Chapter 54). Some parasitic protists are important *pathogens* (disease-causing agents) of plants or animals. Throughout this chapter, we describe specific examples of symbiotic associations involving protists.

Most protists are aquatic and live in the ocean or in freshwater streams, lakes, and ponds (FIG. 26-1b). They make up most of the **plankton,** the floating, often microscopic organisms that inhabit surface waters and are the base of the food web in aquatic ecosystems. Other aquatic protists attach to rocks or other surfaces in the water. Even parasitic protists are aquatic because they live in the watery environments of other organisms' body fluids. Terrestrial protists are restricted to damp places such as soil, cracks in bark, and leaf litter.

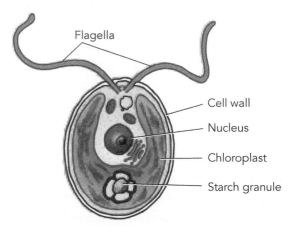

(a) *Chlamydomonas* is a photosynthetic organism with two flagella and a cup-shaped chloroplast.

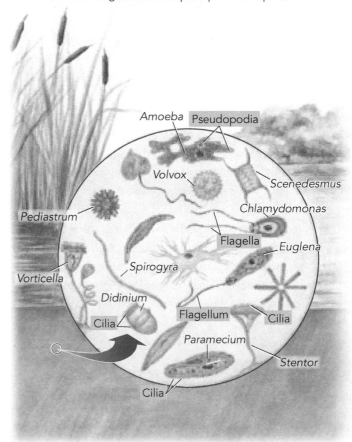

(b) Protists in a drop of pond water. Several modes of locomotion are shown.

Figure 26-1 Protists
© Cengage Learning

Reproduction is varied among protists. Almost all protists reproduce asexually, and many also reproduce sexually. However, most protists do not develop multicellular reproductive organs, nor do they form embryos the way more complex organisms do.

CHECKPOINT 26.1

- How do protists vary in their means of obtaining nutrients?
- What are some of the ways protists interact with other organisms?

26.2 HOW DID EUKARYOTES EVOLVE?

LEARNING OBJECTIVES

2 Discuss the hypothesis of serial endosymbiosis and briefly explain some of the evidence that supports it.
3 Describe the kinds of data biologists use to classify eukaryotes.

For many years biologists have hypothesized that protists were the first eukaryotic cells and that they evolved from ancestral prokaryotes. However, the more we study eukaryote origins, the more uncertain we are. One thing we can say with absolute certainty is that the evolution of eukaryotes was a complex process.

Eukaryotes may have appeared in the fossil record as early as 2.2 billion years ago. Other than a few protists with hard shells, such as diatoms and forams, most ancient protists did not leave many fossils because their bodies were too soft to leave permanent traces. Evolutionary studies of protists focus primarily on molecular and structural comparisons of present-day organisms, which contain many clues about their evolutionary history.

Mitochondria and chloroplasts probably originated from endosymbionts

Throughout evolutionary history, one organism has engulfed another to the mutual benefit of both. According to the hypothesis of **serial endosymbiosis,** certain eukaryotic organelles, particularly mitochondria and chloroplasts, arose from symbiotic relationships between larger cells and smaller bacteria that were incorporated and lived within them. (You might want to review serial endosymbiosis in Figure 21-8.) Cell biologists hypothesize that mitochondria originated from aerobic bacteria. Studies of mitochondrial DNA suggest that it is a remnant from the mitochondrion's past, when it was an independent organism. Ribosomal RNA (rRNA) sequences from mitochondria closely match rRNAs found in purple bacteria, suggesting that ancient purple bacteria were the ancestors of mitochondria.

Chloroplast evolution is more complex given that there were probably several endosymbiotic events (FIG. 26-2). Molecular evidence supports the view that incorporation of an ancient cyanobacterium within a host cell, known as *primary endosymbiosis,*

resulted in the chloroplasts in today's red algae, green algae, and land plants. (The host cell was eukaryotic because mitochondria almost certainly evolved before chloroplasts.) Biologists hypothesize that these chloroplasts, which are enclosed by two external membranes (known as the outer and inner chloroplast membranes; see Chapter 9), later provided other eukaryotes with their chloroplasts during *secondary endosymbiosis.*

Secondary endosymbiosis occurred frequently in eukaryote evolution, as evidenced by the presence of additional chloroplast membranes. For example, *three* membranes envelop the chloroplasts of euglenoids and dinoflagellates, and *four* membranes surround the chloroplasts of diatoms, golden algae, and brown algae. Understanding how these membranes originated is an essential aspect of serial endosymbiosis, and many researchers are studying the origin of chloroplasts in different organisms.

Even non-photosynthetic protists may contain chloroplast relics from secondary endosymbiotic events. Apicomplexans—protists such as *Plasmodium,* which causes malaria—have a non-photosynthetic chloroplast derived from a red alga, surrounded by four external membranes. Because this plastid carries out certain functions essential to the survival of the parasite, it has become a target of ongoing research focused on the development of antimalarial drugs.

A consensus in eukaryote classification is beginning to emerge

Scientists re-evaluate evolutionary relationships among the eukaryotes as additional evidence becomes available. Two types of modern research, molecular analysis and ultrastructural studies, have contributed substantially to scientific understanding of the phylogenetic relationships among protists. Molecular data were initially obtained for the gene that codes for small subunit ribosomal RNA in different eukaryotes (SSU rRNA; see Chapter 25). More recently, biologists have compared other nuclear genes, many of which code for proteins, in different protist taxa.

Ultrastructure is the fine details of cell structure revealed by electron microscopy. In many cases, ultrastructure data complement molecular data. Electron microscopy reveals similar structural patterns among those protist taxa that comparative molecular evidence suggests are **monophyletic;** that is, they evolved from a common ancestor (see Chapter 23). For example, molecular and ultrastructure data suggest that water molds, diatoms, golden algae, and brown algae—protist taxa that at first glance seem to share few characteristics—are a monophyletic group.

Given the diversity in protist ultrastructure and molecular data, biologists regard the protists as a **paraphyletic group;** that is, protists contain some, but not all, of the descendants of a common eukaryote ancestor. Molecular and ultrastructural analyses continue to help biologists clarify relationships among the various protist phyla and among protists and the other eukaryotic kingdoms.

Biologists use these data to develop various classification schemes. A current scheme that is used in this edition splits the protists and other eukaryotes (land plants, fungi, and animals)

Scientists hypothesize that plastids have evolved through both primary and secondary endosymbiosis.

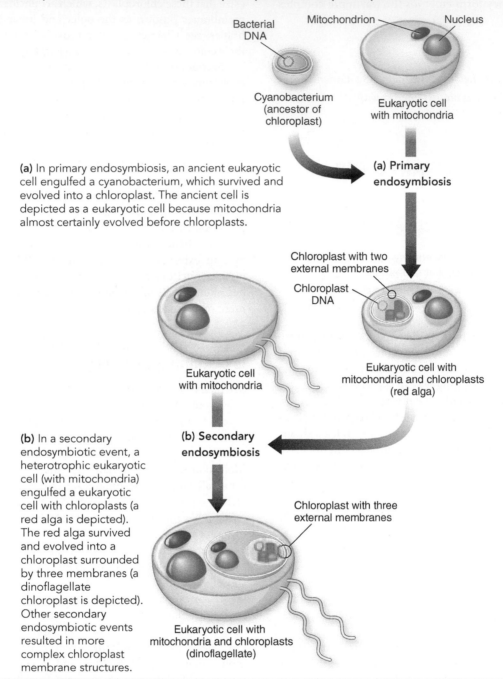

(a) In primary endosymbiosis, an ancient eukaryotic cell engulfed a cyanobacterium, which survived and evolved into a chloroplast. The ancient cell is depicted as a eukaryotic cell because mitochondria almost certainly evolved before chloroplasts.

(b) In a secondary endosymbiotic event, a heterotrophic eukaryotic cell (with mitochondria) engulfed a eukaryotic cell with chloroplasts (a red alga is depicted). The red alga survived and evolved into a chloroplast surrounded by three membranes (a dinoflagellate chloroplast is depicted). Other secondary endosymbiotic events resulted in more complex chloroplast membrane structures.

Figure 26-2 Chloroplast evolution by primary and secondary endosymbiosis

CONNECT How many external membranes are present in a land plant chloroplast? Use Figure 9-4b to check your answer.

© Cengage Learning

into five informal supergroups (**FIG. 26-3** and **TABLE 26-1**). This classification scheme will almost certainly be modified as new information becomes available.

Now that we have a basic understanding of evolution of the protists and other eukaryotes, let's examine representative protists within the five supergroups.

CHECKPOINT 26.2

- *How does serial endosymbiosis explain the origin of chloroplasts?*
- *What kinds of scientific evidence support the hypothesis that protists are a paraphyletic group?*

Unraveling phylogenetic relationships among the protists has been difficult, but progress is occurring. Many biologists currently classify eukaryotes into five major "supergroups."

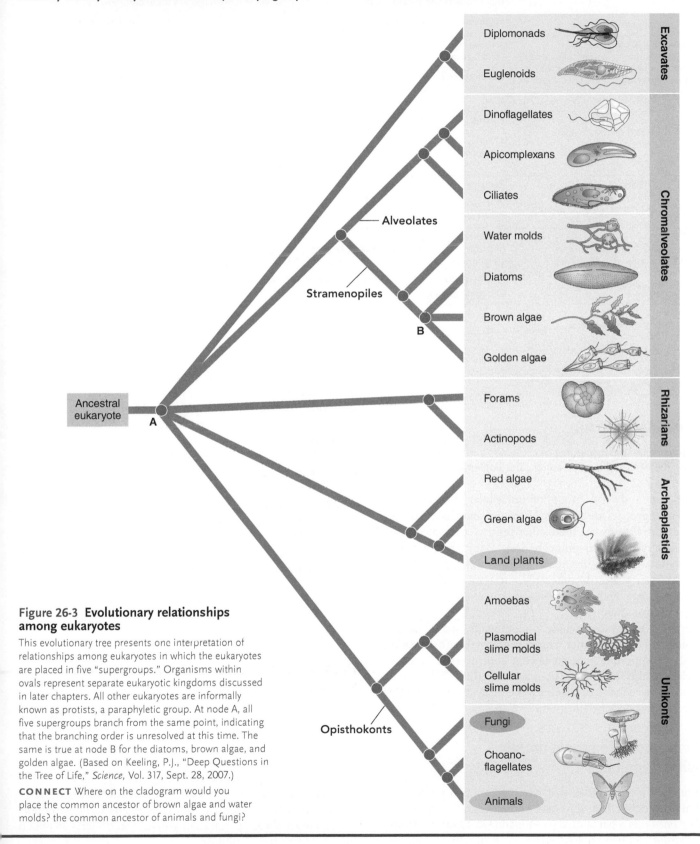

Figure 26-3 Evolutionary relationships among eukaryotes

This evolutionary tree presents one interpretation of relationships among eukaryotes in which the eukaryotes are placed in five "supergroups." Organisms within ovals represent separate eukaryotic kingdoms discussed in later chapters. All other eukaryotes are informally known as protists, a paraphyletic group. At node A, all five supergroups branch from the same point, indicating that the branching order is unresolved at this time. The same is true at node B for the diatoms, brown algae, and golden algae. (Based on Keeling, P.J., "Deep Questions in the Tree of Life," *Science*, Vol. 317, Sept. 28, 2007.)

CONNECT Where on the cladogram would you place the common ancestor of brown algae and water molds? the common ancestor of animals and fungi?

EUKARYOTE "SUPERGROUP"	REPRESENTATIVE "PROTIST" CLADES	KEY CHARACTERS
EXCAVATES Unicellular protists with atypical, greatly modified mitochondria; bikonts	**Diplomonads and parabasalids**	Two or more flagella; ventral oral (feeding) groove
	Euglenoids and trypanosomes	Some with plastids; crystalline rod in flagella
CHROMALVEOLATES Diverse protists that may have originated as a result of secondary endosymbiosis in which an ancestral cell engulfed a red alga; bikonts	**Alveolates** Dinoflagellates, ciliates, apicomplexans	Alveoli (flattened vesicles) just inside the plasma membrane
	Stramenopiles Water molds, diatoms, brown algae, golden algae	Most have two flagella, one with hairs; no flagella in some
RHIZARIANS Amoeboid cells that often have tests (shells); bikonts	**Forams**	Porous tests (hard shells) through which cytoplasmic projections (pseudopods) extend
	Actinopods	Endoskeletons (internal shells) through which axopods (filamentous pseudopods) extend
ARCHAEPLASTIDS Plastids bounded by outer and inner membranes; include land plants; bikonts	**Red algae**	Chloroplast pigments include phycoerythrin (red pigment) and phycocyanin (blue pigment)
	Green algae	Chloroplast pigments identical to those in land plants
UNIKONTS Cells that have a single flagellum or are amoebas with no flagella; have a triple-gene fusion that is lacking in other eukaryotes; include animals and fungi	**Amoebozoa** Amoebas, plasmodial slime molds, cellular slime molds	Naked amoebas (no tests) with lobelike pseudopods
	Opisthokonts Choanoflagellates	No flagella or single posterior flagellum on motile cells

© Cengage Learning

26.3 EXCAVATES

LEARNING OBJECTIVE

4 Summarize the basic features of excavates and distinguish among diplomonads, parabasilids, and euglenoids.

Excavates are a diverse group of unicellular protists with flagella. These protists are so named because many have a deep, or *excavated,* oral groove. Unlike other protists, excavates have atypical, greatly modified mitochondria. Many excavates are endosymbionts and live in anoxic (without oxygen) environments. These excavates do not carry out aerobic respiration; they obtain energy by the anaerobic pathway of glycolysis (presumably by fermentation).

Currently, excavates include diplomonads, parabasalids, euglenoids, and trypanosomes. The inclusion of these organisms into a single superfamily is somewhat controversial because their relationships to one another are uncertain. Additional studies will be needed to determine if the excavates as currently presented are a monophyletic group.

Diplomonads are small, mostly parasitic flagellates

Diplomonads are excavates that have one or two nuclei, no functional mitochondria, no Golgi complex, and up to eight flagella. *Giardia* is a parasitic diplomonad (FIG. 26-4a). Interestingly, *Giardia* has two haploid nuclei, each of which contains

a complete copy of *Giardia*'s genome. *Giardia* lacks functional mitochondria, although it contains certain genes that code for proteins associated with mitochondria in other organisms. *Giardia* also has reduced structures that somewhat resemble mitochondria. This information suggests to some biologists that an early eukaryotic ancestor of *Giardia* may have possessed mitochondria, which were somehow lost or reduced at a later time during its evolutionary history.

Giardia intestinalis is a major cause of water-borne diarrhea throughout the world. *Giardia* is eliminated as a resistant cyst in the feces of many vertebrate animals. These cysts are a common contaminant in untreated drinking water, even in environments considered relatively pristine, such as isolated mountain streams. In a heavy infection, much of the wall of the small intestine is coated with these flagellates, which interfere with the absorption of digested nutrients and cause weight loss, abdominal cramps, and diarrhea.

Parabasilids are anaerobic endosymbionts that live in animals

Parabasilids are anaerobic, flagellated excavates that often live in animals. Trichonymphs and trichomonads are examples of parabasilids. *Trichonymphs,* which have hundreds of flagella, live in the guts of termites and wood-eating cockroaches (FIG. 26-4b). Trichonymphs ingest wood chips from the wood that termites or roaches eat. The trichonymphs rely on endosymbiotic bacteria to digest cellulose in the wood. Thus, in an excellent example of mutualism, the insects, trichonymphs, and bacteria all obtain their nutrients from cellulose.

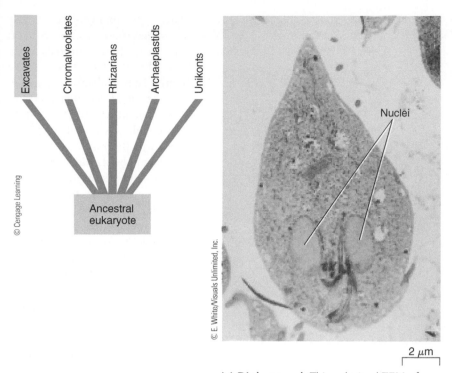

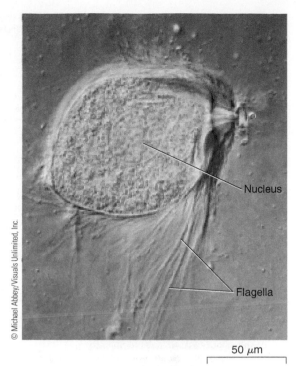

(a) **Diplomonad.** This colorized TEM of *Giardia intestinalis*, a parasitic diplomonad, reveals two nuclei.

(b) **Parabasalid.** LM of *Trichonympha*, a parabasalid that lives in the gut of wood-eating termites and cockroaches. *Trichonympha* has hundreds of flagella.

Figure 26-4 Diplomonads and parabasalids

The most well-known trichomonad is probably *Trichomonas vaginalis*, which causes trichomoniasis, a curable sexually transmitted disease (STD) in humans. Trichomoniasis affects both men and women, although the symptoms are more obvious in women. According to the Centers for Disease Control and Prevention, about 7.4 million new cases occur in the United States each year.

Euglenoids and trypanosomes include both free-living species and parasites

Euglenoids and *trypanosomes* are characterized by an unusual flagellum: in addition to the 9 + 2 arrangement of microtubules characteristic of all eukaryotic flagella, these excavates have a crystalline rod in their flagella; the function of this rod is unknown. Like other excavates, euglenoids and trypanosomes also have atypical mitochondria.

Most **euglenoids** are unicellular flagellates, and about one-third of them are photosynthetic (**FIGS. 26-5a** and **b**). They generally have two flagella: one long and whiplike and one that is often so short that it does not extend outside the cell. Some euglenoids, such as *Euglena*, change shape continually as they move through the water because their **pellicle,** or outer covering, is flexible.

Autotrophic euglenoids have chloroplasts with the same photosynthetic pigments that green algae and plants have. However, these chloroplasts were acquired by secondary endosymbiosis; euglenoids are not closely related to either

group, as shown in Figure 26-3. Some photosynthetic euglenoids lose their chlorophyll when grown in the dark, and they obtain their nutrients heterotrophically, by ingesting organic matter. Other euglenoids are always colorless and heterotrophic. Some heterotrophic species absorb organic compounds from the surrounding water, whereas others engulf bacteria and protists by **phagocytosis;** they digest the prey within food vacuoles.

Trypanosomes are excavates with a single mitochondrion that has an organized deposit of DNA called a **kinetoplastid.** Trypanosomes are colorless, and many are parasitic and cause disease. In vertebrates, including humans, trypanosomes live in the blood. For example, Trypanosoma *brucei* is a human parasite that causes African sleeping sickness (**FIG. 26-5c**). It is transmitted by the bite of infected tsetse flies. Early symptoms include recurring attacks of fever. Later, when the trypanosomes have invaded the central nervous system, infected people are lethargic, have difficulty speaking or walking, and may die if the disease is untreated. Control efforts are showing some success; the incidence of the disease dropped from at least 50,000 new cases in 2005 to an estimated 30,000 in 2010.

CHECKPOINT 26.3

- *What cell organelle is atypical in excavates?*
- *Give an example of a human disease caused by each of the following: diplomonads, parabasilids, and trypanosomes.*

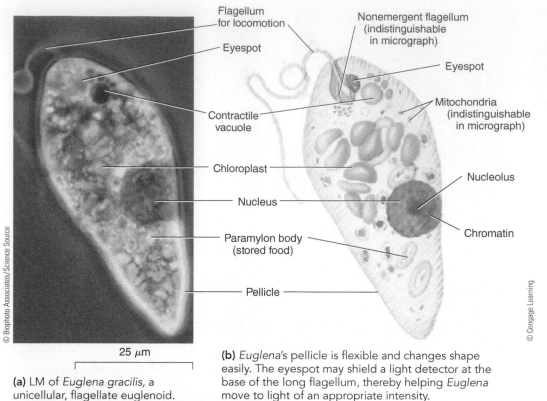

Flagellum for locomotion

Eyespot

Contractile vacuole

Chloroplast

Nucleus

Paramylon body (stored food)

Pellicle

Nonemergent flagellum (indistinguishable in micrograph)

Eyespot

Mitochondria (indistinguishable in micrograph)

Nucleolus

Chromatin

© Biophoto Associates/Science Source

© Cengage Learning

25 μm

(a) LM of *Euglena gracilis*, a unicellular, flagellate euglenoid.

(b) *Euglena*'s pellicle is flexible and changes shape easily. The eyespot may shield a light detector at the base of the long flagellum, thereby helping *Euglena* move to light of an appropriate intensity.

Red blood cells

Trypanosome with undulating membrane

Flagellum

© Eye of Science/Science Source

10 μm

(c) SEM of the flagellate *Trypanosoma brucei* among human red blood cells. *Trypanosoma brucei* causes African sleeping sickness in humans.

Figure 26-5 *Animation* **Euglenoids and trypanosomes**

26.4 CHROMALVEOLATES

◖EARNING OBJECTIVES

5 Contrast the two main groups of chromalveolates: alveolates and stramenopiles.

6 Distinguish among the alveolates: dinoflagellates, apicomplexans, and ciliates.

7 Distinguish among the stramenopiles: water molds, diatoms, golden algae, and brown algae.

The **chromalveolates** are a supergroup composed of extremely diverse protists with few shared characters. Chromalveolates probably originated as a result of secondary endosymbiosis in which an ancestral cell engulfed a red alga (which itself was the result of primary endosymbiosis). Most chromalveolates are photosynthetic, and evidence suggests that heterotrophic chromalveolates, such as the water molds and ciliates, descended from autotrophic ancestors. Classification of the chromalveolates as a monophyletic supergroup is controversial because some DNA sequence data have indicated that they are not monophyletic. The chromalveolates are divided into two main groups: alveolates and stramenopiles.

The unifying features of protists classified as **alveolates** include similar ribosomal DNA sequences and **alveoli** (sing., *alveolus*), flattened vesicles located just inside the plasma membrane. In some alveolates the vesicles contain plates of cellulose. Alveolates include the dinoflagellates, apicomplexans, and ciliates.

The **stramenopiles** include water molds, diatoms, golden algae, and brown algae. At first glance stramenopiles appear too diverse to classify together. However, most stramenopiles have motile cells with two flagella, one of which has tiny hairlike projections extending from the shaft. The word *stramenopile* comes from Latin words referring to "straw" (i.e., the shaft of the flagellum) and "hairs."

Most dinoflagellates are a part of marine plankton

Dinoflagellates are generally unicellular, although a few are colonial. Their alveoli contain interlocking cellulose plates impregnated with silicates. The typical dinoflagellate has two flagella. One flagellum wraps around a transverse groove in the center of the cell like a belt, and the other lies in a longitudinal groove (perpendicular to the transverse groove), projecting behind the cell (FIG. 26-6a). The undulation of these flagella propels the dinoflagellate through the water like a spinning top. Indeed, the name is derived from the Greek *dinos,* meaning "whirling." Many marine dinoflagellates are bioluminescent.

Many dinoflagellates are photosynthetic, but others are heterotrophic and ingest other microorganisms for food. Some dinoflagellates are endosymbionts that live in the bodies

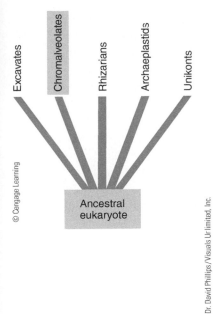

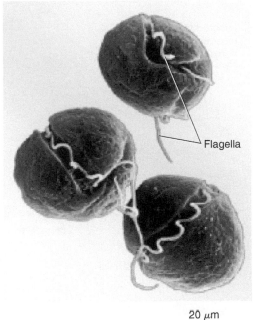

Flagella

20 μm

(a) SEM of *Gymnodinium*. Note the two flagella, which are located in grooves.

(b) Red tide in Mexico. Billions of dinoflagellates produce the orange cloudiness in the water.

Figure 26-6 Dinoflagellates

of marine invertebrates such as mollusks, jellyfish, and corals (see Fig. 54-12). These symbiotic dinoflagellates, called **zooxanthellae,** photosynthesize and provide carbohydrates for their invertebrate partners. Zooxanthellae contribute substantially to the productivity of coral reefs. Other dinoflagellates that are endosymbionts lack pigments and are parasites that live off their hosts.

Ecologically, dinoflagellates are important producers in marine ecosystems. A few dinoflagellates are known to have occasional population explosions, or blooms. These blooms, known as **red tides,** frequently color coastal waters orange, red, or brown (FIG. 26-6b). Dinoflagellate blooms are particularly common in warm, nutrient-enriched water. Some dinoflagellate species that form red tides produce a toxin that attacks the nervous systems of fishes, leading to fish kills. Birds sometimes die after eating contaminated fish. Research has also linked red tides to manatee and dolphin deaths in Florida.

Apicomplexans are spore-forming parasites of animals

Apicomplexans are a large group of parasitic, spore-forming alveolates, some of which cause serious diseases in humans. As discussed earlier in the chapter, they contain the unpigmented remnant of a chloroplast derived from a red alga. Apicomplexans lack specific structures for locomotion (cilia, flagella, or pseudopodia) and move by flexing.

Apicomplexans have an *apical complex* of microtubules that attaches the parasite to its host cell; the apical complex is visible only by using electron microscopy. They also have the ability to form a structure known as a *moving junction,* which enables them to form a vacuole that encloses and protects them as they invade a host cell. At some stage in their life cycle, apicomplexans produce **sporozoites,** small infective agents transmitted to the next host. Many apicomplexans spend part of their complex life cycle in one host species and part in a different host species.

Malaria is caused by an apicomplexan (FIG. 26-7). According to the World Health Organization, there were approximately 219 million cases of malaria worldwide in 2010; about 660,000 people, mostly children in developing countries, died from the disease. Although for centuries Chinese, Greek, Arabic, and Roman writings described the disease, its causative agent and mode of transmission by means of mosquitoes were not identified until the end of the 19th century. British scientist Ronald Ross received the Nobel Prize in Physiology or Medicine in 1902 for his role in elucidating the life cycle of *Plasmodium,* the apicomplexan that causes malaria.

Control measures that have lost effectiveness due to the evolution of chemotherapy resistance on the part of *Plasmodium* and pesticide resistance on the part of the mosquitoes are currently being replaced by newer methods, but the battle is ongoing. For example, chemotherapies that include the drug artemisinin in combination with other drugs have emerged as the standard of care, but there are signs that resistance of the parasite to artemisinin is beginning to evolve in some countries.

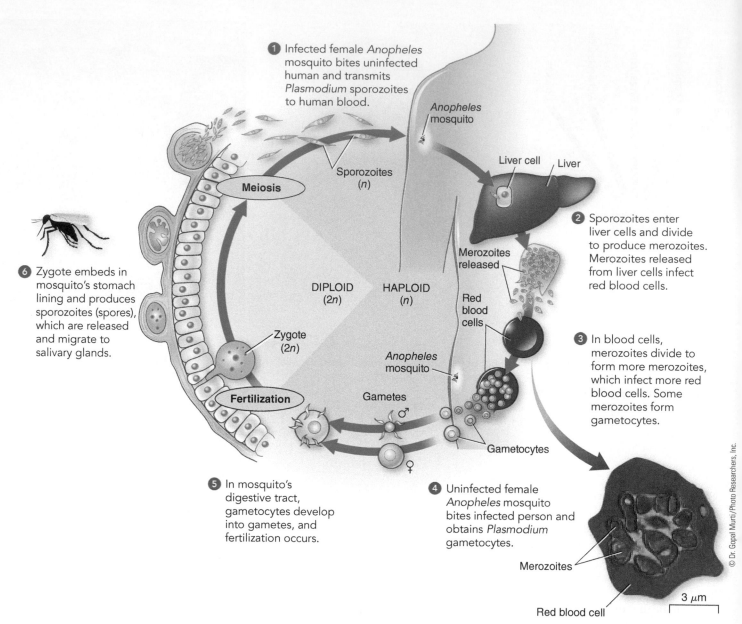

Figure 26-7 *Animation* **Life cycle of *Plasmodium,* the causative agent of malaria**

Plasmodium, an apicomplexan, lives in two hosts: mosquitoes and humans. The inset shows a TEM of a colorized human red blood cell filled with merozoites.

© Cengage Learning

1. Infected female *Anopheles* mosquito bites uninfected human and transmits *Plasmodium* sporozoites to human blood.

Sporozoites (*n*)

Meiosis

Anopheles mosquito

Liver cell Liver

2. Sporozoites enter liver cells and divide to produce merozoites. Merozoites released from liver cells infect red blood cells.

Merozoites released

DIPLOID (2*n*) HAPLOID (*n*)

Red blood cells

6. Zygote embeds in mosquito's stomach lining and produces sporozoites (spores), which are released and migrate to salivary glands.

Zygote (2*n*)

3. In blood cells, merozoites divide to form more merozoites, which infect more red blood cells. Some merozoites form gametocytes.

Fertilization

Anopheles mosquito

Gametes

Gametocytes

5. In mosquito's digestive tract, gametocytes develop into gametes, and fertilization occurs.

4. Uninfected female *Anopheles* mosquito bites infected person and obtains *Plasmodium* gametocytes.

Merozoites

Red blood cell

3 μm

© Dr. Gopal Murti/Photo Researchers, Inc.

Researchers are currently testing new antimalarial drugs and several possible vaccines against malaria. The sequencing of the genomes of *P. falciparum* and the *Anopheles* mosquito may lead to new diagnostics, drugs, and vaccines.

Ciliates use cilia for locomotion

Ciliates are among the most complex of eukaryotic cells. These unicellular alveolates have a pellicle that gives them a definite but changeable shape. In *Paramecium* the surface of the cell is covered with several thousand fine, short, hairlike **cilia** that extend through pores in the pellicle to facilitate movement (**FIGS. 26-8a** and b; also see Fig. 4-5c). The cilia beat with such precise coordination that the organism can back up and turn around as well as move forward.

Not all ciliates are motile. Some sessile forms have stalks, and others, although capable of some swimming, are more likely to remain attached to a rock or other surface at one spot. Their cilia set up water currents that draw food toward them.

Ciliates differ from other protists in having two kinds of nuclei: one or more small, diploid **micronuclei** that function in reproduction; and a larger, polyploid **macronucleus** that controls cell metabolism and growth. Most ciliates are capable of a sexual process called **conjugation,** in which two individuals come together and exchange genetic material (**FIG. 26-8c**). Conjugation results in two "new" cells that are genetically identical to each other but different from what they were before conjugation. Mitosis and cell division need not follow immediately after conjugation. Ciliates usually divide perpendicularly to their longitudinal axis.

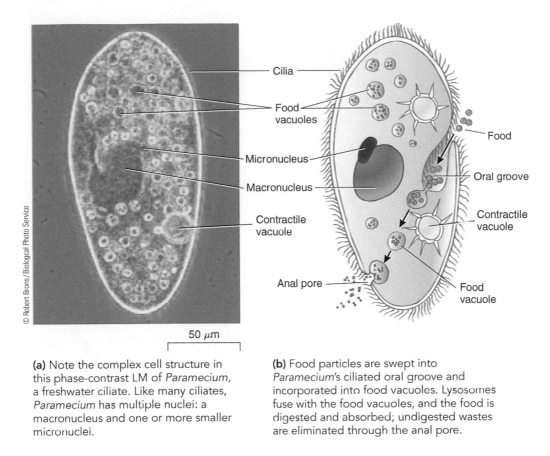

Cilia

Food vacuoles

Micronucleus

Macronucleus

Contractile vacuole

Anal pore

Food

Oral groove

Contractile vacuole

Food vacuole

© Robert Brons / Biological Photo Service

50 μm

(a) Note the complex cell structure in this phase-contrast LM of *Paramecium*, a freshwater ciliate. Like many ciliates, *Paramecium* has multiple nuclei: a macronucleus and one or more smaller micronuclei.

(b) Food particles are swept into *Paramecium*'s ciliated oral groove and incorporated into food vacuoles. Lysosomes fuse with the food vacuoles, and the food is digested and absorbed; undigested wastes are eliminated through the anal pore.

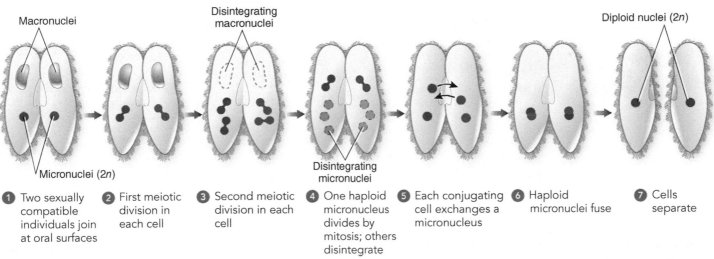

Macronuclei

Disintegrating macronuclei

Diploid nuclei (2*n*)

Micronuclei (2*n*)

Disintegrating micronuclei

1 Two sexually compatible individuals join at oral surfaces

2 First meiotic division in each cell

3 Second meiotic division in each cell

4 One haploid micronucleus divides by mitosis; others disintegrate

5 Each conjugating cell exchanges a micronucleus

6 Haploid micronuclei fuse

7 Cells separate

(c) Conjugation in *Paramecium caudatum*.

Figure 26-8 *Animation* **Ciliates**
© Cengage Learning

Water molds produce biflagellate reproductive cells

Water molds are stramenopiles that were once classified as fungi because of their superficial resemblance. Both water molds and fungi have a body, called a **mycelium,** that grows over organic material, digesting it and then absorbing the predigested nutrients (FIG. 26-9). The threadlike **hyphae** that make up the mycelium in water molds are *coenocytic,* meaning that there are no cross walls; the body consists of a single multinucleate cell. The cell walls of water molds are composed of cellulose (as in plants), chitin (as in fungi), or both.

When food is plentiful and environmental conditions are favorable, water molds reproduce asexually. A hyphal tip swells, and a cross wall is formed, separating the hyphal tip from the rest of the mycelium. Within this structure, called

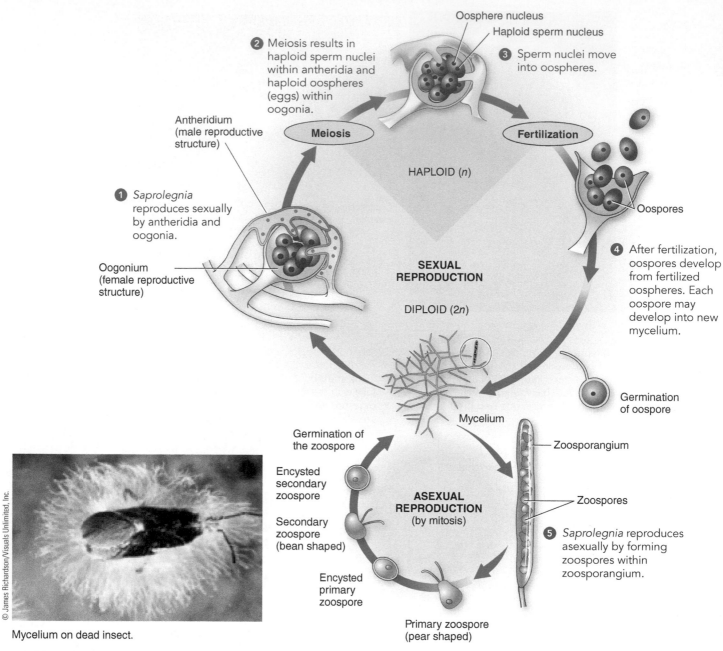

① *Saprolegnia* reproduces sexually by antheridia and oogonia.

② Meiosis results in haploid sperm nuclei within antheridia and haploid oospheres (eggs) within oogonia.

Oosphere nucleus
Haploid sperm nucleus

③ Sperm nuclei move into oospheres.

Antheridium (male reproductive structure)

Oogonium (female reproductive structure)

Meiosis

Fertilization

HAPLOID (*n*)

SEXUAL REPRODUCTION

DIPLOID (*2n*)

Oospores

④ After fertilization, oospores develop from fertilized oospheres. Each oospore may develop into new mycelium.

Germination of oospore

Mycelium

Zoosporangium

Germination of the zoospore

Encysted secondary zoospore

Secondary zoospore (bean shaped)

Encysted primary zoospore

ASEXUAL REPRODUCTION (by mitosis)

Zoospores

⑤ *Saprolegnia* reproduces asexually by forming zoospores within zoosporangium.

Primary zoospore (pear shaped)

Mycelium on dead insect.

Figure 26-9 Water molds

The life cycle of *Saprolegnia*, a water mold. *Inset:* A mycelium of *Saprolegnia* radiates from a dead insect.

© Cengage Learning

a **zoosporangium,** tiny biflagellate **zoospores** form, each of which swims about, lands and encysts, and eventually develops into a new mycelium. When environmental conditions worsen, water molds initiate sexual reproduction. After fusion of male and female nuclei, thick-walled **oospores** develop from the oospheres (female gametes). Water molds often spend the winter as oospores.

Some water molds have played a profound role in human history. For example, the Irish potato famine of the 19th century was precipitated by the water mold *Phytophthora infestans,* which causes late blight of potatoes. (The genus *Phytophthora* is named from Greek words meaning "plant destruction.") During several rainy, cool summers in Ireland in the 1840s, the water mold multiplied unchecked, causing potato tubers to rot in the fields. Because potatoes were the staple of the Irish peasants' diet, as many as one million people starved. The famine prompted a mass migration out of Ireland to the United States and other countries.

A close relative of the late blight water mold, *P. ramorum,* causes sudden oak death, which is killing oak forests in several western states. Plant pathologists are concerned that the disease may spread to midwestern and eastern forests. This particular water mold also attacks redwoods, Douglas firs, bay trees, maples, and several other plant species, but most have only twig and leaf infections, not the rapid death observed in oaks.

Diatoms are stramenopiles with shells composed of two parts

Most **diatoms** are unicellular, although a few exist as colonies (see chapter-opener figure). The cell wall of each diatom consists of two shells that overlap where they fit together, much like a petri dish. Silica is deposited in the shell, and this glasslike material is laid down in intricate patterns (FIG. 26-10a). There are two basic groups of diatoms: those with radial symmetry (wheel shaped) and those with bilateral symmetry (boat shaped or needle shaped). Although some diatoms are part of the floating **plankton,** others live on rocks and sediments, where they move by gliding. This gliding movement is facilitated by the secretion of a slimy material from a small groove along the shell.

Diatoms most often reproduce asexually by mitosis. When a diatom divides, the two halves of its shell separate, and each becomes the larger half of a new diatom shell (FIG. 26-10b). Because the glass shell cannot grow, some diatom cells get progressively smaller with each succeeding generation. When a diatom reaches a fraction of its original size, sexual reproduction occurs, with the production of shell-less gametes. Sexual reproduction restores the diatom to its original size because the resulting *zygote,* a 2n cell that results from the fusion of n gametes, grows substantially before producing a new shell.

Diatoms are common in fresh water but are especially abundant in relatively cool ocean water. They are ecologically significant as major producers in aquatic ecosystems. At least one species is toxic and linked to shellfish poisonings, marine mammal strandings, and the deaths of sea lions along the central California coast.

When diatoms die, their shells trickle to the ocean floor and accumulate in layers that eventually become sedimentary rock. After millions of years, geologic upheaval has exposed some of these deposits on land. Called *diatomaceous earth,* these deposits are mined and used as filtering, insulating, and soundproofing materials. As a filtering agent, diatomaceous earth is used to refine raw sugar and process vegetable oils. Because of its abrasive properties, diatomaceous earth is a common ingredient in scouring powders and metal polishes; it is no longer added to most toothpastes because it is too abrasive for tooth enamel. The intricately detailed diatom shells are often used to test microscope resolution down to 1 μm.

Brown algae are multicellular stramenopiles

Brown algae are the largest and most complex of all algae commonly called seaweeds. All brown algae are multicellular and range in size from a few centimeters (about an inch) to 75 m (about 260 ft). Their body forms are branched filaments; tufts; fleshy "ropes"; or thick, flattened branches. The largest brown algae, called *kelps,* are tough and leathery in appearance.

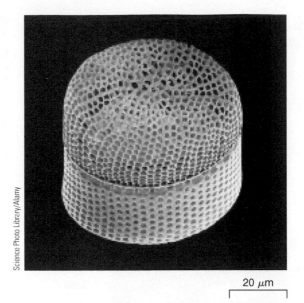

20 μm

(a) False color SEM of a unicellular diatom. Note the striking shell that contains silica.

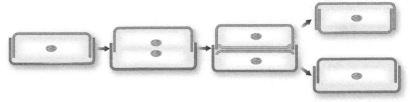

(b) Asexual reproduction in diatoms. After cell division, each new cell retains half of the original shell. The newly synthesized half of the shell always fits *inside* the original half. As a result, one of the new cells is slightly smaller than the other.

Figure 26-10 Diatoms
© Cengage Learning

Many kelps have leaflike **blades** in which most photosynthesis occurs, stemlike **stipes,** and rootlike anchoring **holdfasts** (FIG. 26-11a). They often have gas-filled *bladders* that provide buoyancy. (The blades, stipes, and holdfasts of brown algae are not homologous to the leaves, stems, and roots of plants. Brown algae and plants arose from different unicellular ancestors, as shown in Figure 26-3.)

Reproduction is varied and complex in the brown algae. Their reproductive cells, both asexual zoospores and sexual gametes, are usually biflagellate. Most have a life cycle that exhibits **alternation of generations,** in which they spend part of their life as multicellular haploid organisms and part as multicellular diploid organisms (see Fig. 10-19c).

Brown algae are commercially important for several reasons. Their cell walls contain a polysaccharide called *algin* that is harvested from kelps such as *Macrocystis* and used as a thickening and stabilizing agent in ice cream, toothpaste, shaving cream, hair spray, and hand lotion. Brown algae are an important human food, particularly in eastern Asia, and they are rich sources of certain vitamins and minerals such as iodine.

Blade

Stipe

Holdfast

© J. R. Waaland/Biological Photo Service

(a) *Laminaria* is widely distributed on rocky coastlines of temperate and polar seas. It grows to 2 m (6.5 ft).

© Gregory Ochock/Science Source

(b) A kelp (*Macrocystis pyrifera*) bed is ecologically important to aquatic organisms, including the sea lion shown here. Photographed off the coast of California.

Figure 26-11 Brown algae

Brown algae are common in cooler marine waters, especially along rocky coastlines, where they live mainly in the intertidal zone or relatively shallow offshore waters. Kelps form extensive underwater "forests," or kelp beds (FIG. 26-11b). They are essential in that ecosystem as important food producers, and they provide habitat for many marine invertebrates, fishes, and mammals. The diversity of life supported by kelp beds rivals that found in coral reefs.

of golden algae gives them a golden or golden brown color. A few species ingest bacteria and other particles of food. Ecologically, golden algae are important producers in marine environments. They compose a significant portion of the ocean's **nanoplankton,** extremely minute algae (2 to 10 μm) that are major producers because of their great abundance.

Most golden algae are unicellular biflagellates

Golden algae are found in both freshwater and marine environments. Most species are biflagellate, unicellular organisms, although some are colonial (FIG. 26-12a). A few of these stramenopiles lack flagella and are similar to amoebas in appearance except that golden algae contain chloroplasts. Tiny scales of either silica or calcium carbonate may cover the cells. Reproduction in golden algae is primarily asexual and involves the production of biflagellate, motile *zoospores.*

Most golden algae are photosynthetic, and the pigment composition

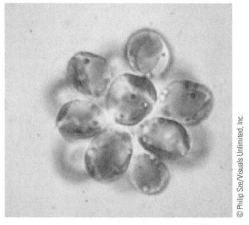

© Philip Sze/Visuals Unlimited, Inc.

10 μm

(a) LM of a colonial golden alga (*Synura*) found in freshwater lakes and ponds.

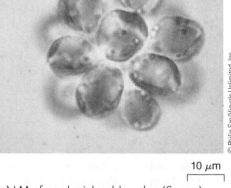

Dr. Elizabeth Venrick/Scripps Institution of Oceanography

1 μm

(b) SEM of a coccolithophorid (*Emiliania huxleyi*). Note the overlapping scales of calcium carbonate.

Figure 26-12 Golden algae

Classification of golden algae is controversial. Some biologists lump diatoms and golden algae in a single phylum, whereas others classify both groups as brown algae. At the other extreme, some biologists divide the golden algae into two phyla by placing many of the marine species, such as *coccolithophorids* (FIG. 26-12b), in a separate phylum.

CHECKPOINT 26.4

- *What are the two main groups of chromalveolates? What are their distinguishing characters?*
- *Why do some biologists think that the apicomplexans descended from dinoflagellates?*
- *Which water mold has influenced human history? Explain your answer.*
- *What is the ecological significance of the diatoms? the brown algae?*

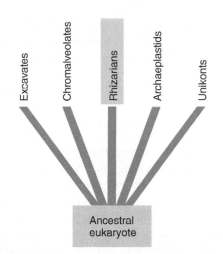

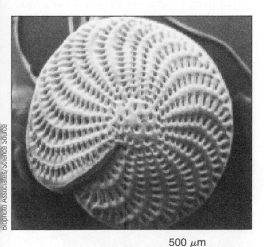

500 μm

(a) SEM of a foram test. Note the pores through which cytoplasm extrudes.

26.5 RHIZARIANS

LEARNING OBJECTIVE

8 Describe the forams and actinopods, and explain why many biologists classify them in the rhizarian supergroup.

Rhizarians are a diverse supergroup of amoeboid cells that often have hard outer shells, called **tests,** through which cytoplasmic projections extend. The threadlike cytoplasmic projections suggest the name *rhizarian,* from the Greek *rhiza,* meaning "root." Forams and actinopods are rhizarians, as are certain shell-less amoebas. Not all amoebas are rhizarians, however, and many amoeba species are more closely related to other eukaryotic clades. Current molecular evidence indicates that the rhizarian supergroup is monophyletic.

Forams extend cytoplasmic projections that form a threadlike, interconnected net

Almost all **foraminiferans (forams)** are marine rhizarians that produce elaborate tests (FIG. 26-13a). The ocean contains enormous numbers of forams, which secrete chalky, many-chambered tests with pores through which cytoplasmic projections are extended. (*Foraminifera* is derived from the Latin for "bearing openings.") The cytoplasmic projections form a sticky, interconnected net that entangles prey. Many forams contain unicellular algal endosymbionts (green algae, red algae, or diatoms) that provide food by photosynthesis. Many foram species live on the ocean floor, but others are part of the plankton.

100 μm

(b) LM of an unidentified living actinopod from the Red Sea. Many slender axopods project from the cell. The shell is not visible because it is an endoskeleton and cytoplasm covers it on all sides.

Dead forams settle on the bottom of the ocean, where their tests form a gray mud that is gradually transformed into chalk. With geologic uplifting, these chalk formations become part of the land, as in the White Cliffs of Dover in England. (The White Cliffs of Dover are the remains of a variety of carbonate organisms, not only forams.) Because foram tests often appear in rock layers covering oil deposits, geologists exploring for oil look for foram tests in rock strata. Forams are well preserved in the fossil record, and biologists use some as **index fossils,** markers to help identify ancient sedimentary rock layers (see Chapter 18).

Figure 26-13 Rhizarians

Actinopods project slender axopods

Actinopods are mostly marine plankton rhizarians with long, filamentous cytoplasmic projections called **axopods** that protrude through pores in their shells (FIG. 26-13b). A cluster of microtubules strengthens each axopod. Unicellular algae and other prey become entangled in these axopods and are engulfed outside the main body of the actinopod; cytoplasmic streaming carries the prey inside the body. Many actinopods contain algal endosymbionts that provide them with the products of photosynthesis.

Some actinopods, called **radiolarians,** secrete elaborate, beautiful glassy shells made of silica. Radiolarians are an important constituent of marine plankton. When radiolarians and other actinopods die, their shells settle and become an ooze (sediment) that may be several meters thick on the ocean floor.

CHECKPOINT 26.5

- *What character does the term* rhizarian *indicate about the forams and actinopods?*

26.6 ARCHAEPLASTIDS

LEARNING OBJECTIVE

9 Describe evidence supporting the hypothesis that red algae and green algae should be included in a monophyletic group with land plants.

In the classification scheme adopted in this text, the monophyletic group of **archaeplastids** includes red algae and green algae, which are discussed here, and land plants, which are in a separate kingdom (see Chapters 27 and 28). Biologists classify these groups together based on molecular data and on the presence of chloroplasts bounded by outer and inner membranes, suggesting that they developed directly from a cyanobacterial endosymbiont. All photosynthetic protists other than archaeplastids have plastids surrounded by three or four membranes.

Red algae do not produce motile cells

The vast majority of **red algae** are multicellular organisms, although there are a few unicellular species. The multicellular body form of red algae commonly consists of complex, interwoven filaments that are delicate and feathery (FIG. 26-14a); a few red algae are flattened sheets of cells. Most multicellular red algae attach to rocks or other substrates by a basal holdfast. Reproduction in the red algae is remarkably complex, with an alternation of sexual and asexual stages. No flagellate cells develop during the life cycle. Some unicellular red algae may exhibit unusual features. For example, in 2013 a team of scientists working in the United States, Germany, and France reported on the genome of a unicellular extremophilic red alga adapted to toxic hot sulfur springs. The genome includes at least 75 genes acquired from archaea and bacteria needed for this extreme lifestyle, providing a striking example of horizontal gene transfer involving a eukaryote. (See Chapter 23 and Figure 23-4a for a discussion of the evolutionary significance of horizontal gene transfer.)

Red algae primarily live in warm tropical ocean waters, although a few species occur in fresh water and in soil. Some red algae, known as *coralline algae,* incorporate calcium carbonate in their cell walls from the ocean water (FIG. 26-14b). The hard calcium carbonate may protect coralline algae from the rigors of wave action. These coralline red algae build "coral" reefs and are perhaps as crucial as coral animals in this process.

The cell walls of red algae often contain thick, sticky polysaccharides that have commercial value. For example, *agar* is a polysaccharide extracted from certain red algae used as a food thickener and culture medium, a substrate on which to grow microorganisms and propagate some plants, such as orchids.

Excavates
Chromalveolates
Rhizarians
Archaeplastids
Unikonts

Ancestral eukaryote

© Cengage Learning

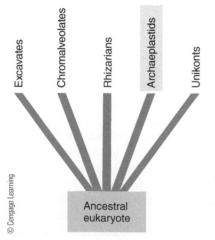

(a) *Polysiphonia*, which is widely distributed throughout the world, has a highly branched body of interwoven filaments.

© Philip Sze/Visuals Unlimited, Inc.

(b) *Bossiella* is a coralline red alga encrusted with calcium carbonate. It lives in the Pacific Ocean.

© D. Gotshall/Visuals Unlimited, Inc.

Figure 26-14 *Animation* **Red algae**

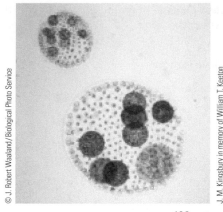

100 μm

(a) LM of two *Volvox* colonies, each composed of up to 50,000 cells. New colonies are inside the parental colonies, which eventually break apart.

(b) *Ulva's* thin, sheetlike form suggests its common name, sea lettuce.

(c) *Chara*, a green alga commonly called a stonewort, is closely related to land plants. *Chara* is widely distributed in fresh water.

Figure 26-15 Green algae

Another polysaccharide extracted from red algae, *carrageenan,* is a food additive used to stabilize chocolate milk; it also provides a thick, creamy texture to ice cream and other soft processed foods. Carrageenan is also used to stabilize paints and cosmetics. Red algae are a source of vitamins (particularly A and C) and minerals, especially in Japan and other eastern Asian countries where people eat red algae fresh, dried, or toasted in such traditional foods as sushi and nori.

Green algae share many similarities with land plants

Green algae have pigments, energy reserve products, and cell walls that are chemically identical to those of land plants. Green algae are photosynthetic, with chloroplasts of a wide variety of shapes. Most green algae have cell walls with cellulose, although some lack walls. Because of these and other similarities, biologists generally accept that land plants arose from ancestral green algae (see Fig. 26-3). Based on recent molecular and ultrastructure data, some biologists classify this diverse group in the plant kingdom.

Green algae exhibit a variety of body types, from single cells to colonial forms, to coenocytic algae (multinucleate), to multicellular filaments and sheets (FIG. 26-15). The multicellular forms do not have cells differentiated into tissues, a characteristic that separates them from land plants. Most green algae have, or produce, flagellate cells during their life cycle, although a few are totally nonmotile.

Reproduction in the green algae is as varied as their body forms, with both sexual and asexual reproduction. Many green algae have life cycles with an alternation of multicellular haploid and multicellular diploid generations. Asexual reproduction is by mitosis and cell division in single cells or by fragmentation in multicellular forms. Many green algae produce spores asexually by mitosis; if these spores have flagella

and are motile, they are called *zoospores* (FIG. 26-16). Sexual reproduction in the green algae involves gamete formation in unicellular **gametangia** (sing., *gametangium*), reproductive structures in which gametes are produced. Green algae are found in both aquatic and terrestrial environments. Aquatic green algae primarily inhabit fresh water, although there are many marine species. Terrestrial green algae are restricted to damp soil, cracks in tree bark, and other moist places. Many green algae are symbionts with other organisms; some live as endosymbionts in body cells of invertebrates, and a few grow together with fungi as "dual organisms" called *lichens* (discussed in Chapter 29). Regardless of where they live, green algae are ecologically important as producers.

CHECKPOINT 26.6

- *Why do many biologists classify red algae and green algae with land plants?*

26.7 UNIKONTS

LEARNING OBJECTIVE

10 Briefly describe and compare the following unikonts: amoebas, plasmodial slime molds, cellular slime molds, and choanoflagellates.

Unikonts are a supergroup composed of certain amoebas, plasmodial slime molds, cellular slime molds, choanoflagellates, fungi (discussed in Chapter 29), and animals (discussed in Chapters 30 through 32). Unikonts share a single posterior flagellum in flagellate cells such as sperm and motile spores, although some extant organisms in this supergroup have lost the flagellum. Many unikonts also have a single centriole. Examine

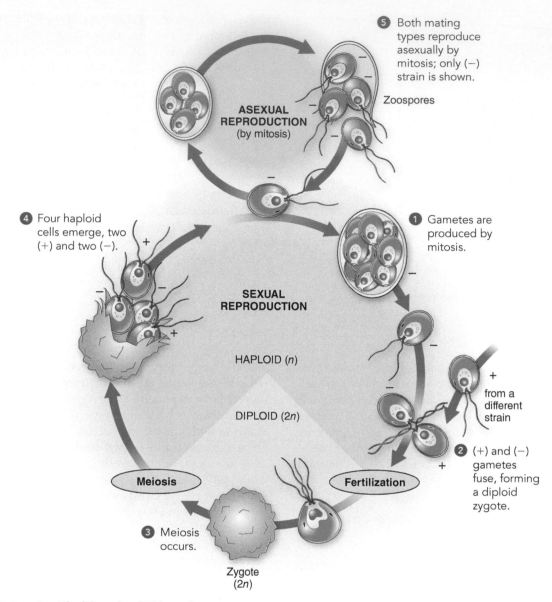

5 Both mating types reproduce asexually by mitosis; only (−) strain is shown.

Zoospores

ASEXUAL REPRODUCTION (by mitosis)

4 Four haploid cells emerge, two (+) and two (−).

SEXUAL REPRODUCTION

1 Gametes are produced by mitosis.

+ from a different strain

2 (+) and (−) gametes fuse, forming a diploid zygote.

HAPLOID (*n*)

DIPLOID (2*n*)

Meiosis

Fertilization

3 Meiosis occurs.

Zygote (2*n*)

Figure 26-16 *Animation* The life cycle of *Chlamydomonas*

Chlamydomonas is a unicellular, haploid green alga with two mating types, (+) and (−). The only diploid cell in the life cycle is the zygote.

© Cengage Learning

Figure 26-3 again and note that the unikonts are divided into two clades. One clade is the **opisthokonts,** which consist of fungi, choanoflagellates, and animals. You will learn more about the opisthokonts in Chapters 29 and 30.

Unikonts also have a **triple-gene fusion** that has major evolutionary significance. In a triple-gene fusion, three separate genes fused into a single unit early in the course of eukaryote evolution; the fused gene codes for a multi-enzyme protein. You may recall that Figure 26-3 showed all five supergroups branching from the same point, indicating that the branching order is unresolved. However, triple-gene fusion provides evidence of a bifurcation, or branch of the eukaryotes into two main clades, close to the root of the common ancestor of all eukaryotes (**FIG. 26-17**). The two branches consist of (1) unikonts, which had a common ancestor with

a single posterior flagellum; and (2) all other eukaryotes, collectively called **bikonts,** which had a common ancestor with two flagella.

Amoebozoa are unikonts with lobose pseudopodia

Most **amoebozoa** produce temporary cytoplasmic projections called **pseudopodia** (sing., *pseudopodium,* meaning "false foot") at some point in their life cycle. The pseudopodia of amoebozoa are *lobose*—that is, rounded and wide—as opposed to the slender cytoplasmic projections characteristic of rhizarians. Many biologists currently classify amoebas, plasmodial slime molds, and cellular slime molds as amoebozoa.

How do we deduce details of eukaryote evolution near the root of the evolutionary tree?

HYPOTHESIS: Derived gene fusions, which have occurred rarely during the course of evolution, can provide insights into eukaryote evolutionary relationships.

EXPERIMENT: Alexandra Stechmann and Thomas Cavalier-Smith of Oxford University sequenced a double-gene fusion that codes for two enzymes: dihydrofolate reductase (DHFR) and thymidylate synthase (TS). In a second experiment, they sequenced a triple-fused gene involved in the enzymatic synthesis of pyrimidine nucleotides. They tested for the presence of these two gene fusions in various eukaryote groups as well as in bacteria and archaea.

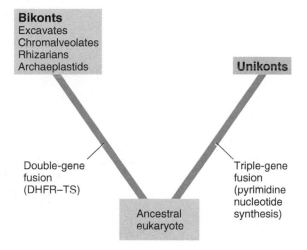

RESULTS AND CONCLUSION: The double-gene fusion is present in all eukaryotes examined except for unikonts; bacteria and archaea also lack the double-gene fusion. The unikonts have the triple-gene fusion that is lacking in all other eukaryotes, bacteria, and archaea. These gene fusions suggest a fundamental division of eukaryotes into two main clades, the unikonts and all other eukaryotes, which are collectively called bikonts.

SOURCE: Stechmann, A. and T. Cavalier-Smith. "The Root of the Eukaryote Tree Pinpointed." *Current Biology*, Vol. 13, Sept. 2, 2003.

Figure 26-17 Stechmann and Cavalier-Smith's research on evolution of the protists

CONNECT Are you a bikont or a unikont?

Amoebas move by forming pseudopodia

Amoebas are unicellular amoebozoa found in soil, fresh water, the ocean, and other organisms (as parasites). Because of the extreme flexibility of their outer plasma membrane, many members of this group have an asymmetrical body form and continually change shape as they move. (The word *amoeba* derives from a Greek word meaning "change.") An amoeba moves by pushing out lobose pseudopodia from the surface of the cell. More cytoplasm flows into the pseudopodia, enlarging them until all the cytoplasm has entered and the organism as a whole has

moved. Pseudopodia also capture and engulf food by surrounding and forming a vacuole around it (FIG. 26-18). Food particles are digested when the food vacuole fuses with a lysosome containing digestive enzymes. Digested materials are absorbed from the food vacuole, which gradually shrinks as it empties. Amoebas reproduce asexually, splitting into two equal parts after mitotic division of the nucleus; sexual reproduction has not been observed.

Parasitic amoebas include *Entamoeba histolytica,* which causes *amoebic dysentery,* a serious human intestinal disease characterized by severe diarrhea, bloody stools, and ulcers in the intestinal wall. In especially severe cases the organism spreads from the large intestine and causes abscesses in the liver, lungs, or brain. *Entamoeba histolytica* is transmitted as cysts in contaminated drinking water. A *cyst* is a thick-walled, resistant, resting stage in the life cycle of some protists. Other amoebas, such as *Acanthamoeba,* are usually free-living but produce opportunistic infections such as eye infections in wearers of contact lenses.

Plasmodial slime molds feed as multinucleate plasmodia

The feeding stage of a **plasmodial slime mold** is a **plasmodium,** a multinucleate mass of cytoplasm that can grow up to 30 cm (1 ft) in diameter (FIG. 26-19a). The slimy plasmodium streams over damp, decaying logs and leaf litter, often forming a network of channels that covers a large surface area. As it creeps along, it ingests bacteria, yeasts, spores, and decaying organic matter.

When the food supply dwindles or there is insufficient moisture, the plasmodium crawls to an exposed surface and starts reproducing. Stalked structures of intricate complexity and beauty usually form from the drying plasmodium (FIG. 26-19b). Within these structures, called **sporangia,** meiosis produces haploid spores that are extremely resistant to adverse environmental conditions.

When conditions become favorable, the spores germinate, and a haploid reproductive cell emerges from each. This haploid cell is either a biflagellate *swarm cell* or an amoeboid *myxamoeba,* depending on available moisture; flagellate cells form in wet conditions. Swarm cells and myxamoebas act as gametes, which fuse to form a zygote with a diploid nucleus. The resultant diploid nucleus divides many times by mitosis, but the cytoplasm does not divide, so the result is a multinucleate plasmodium.

The plasmodial slime mold *Physarum polycephalum* is a model organism that researchers use to study many fundamental biological processes, such as growth, cytoplasmic streaming, and the function of the cytoskeleton.

Cellular slime molds feed as individual amoeboid cells

The **cellular slime molds** are amoebozoa with close affinities to amoebas and plasmodial slime molds. During its feeding stage, each cellular slime mold is an individual amoeboid cell that behaves as a separate, solitary organism (FIG. 26-20). Each cell creeps over rotting logs and soil or swims in fresh water, ingesting bacteria and other particles of food as

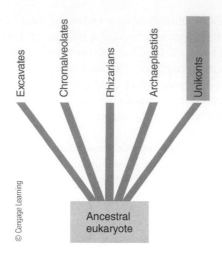

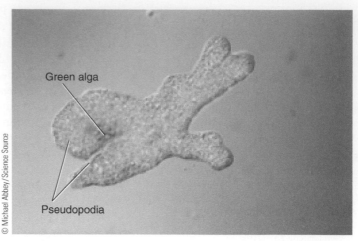

Green alga

Pseudopodia

100 μm

Figure 26-18 *Animation* **Amoeba**

LM of a giant amoeba (*Chaos carolinense*). This unicellular protist, which moves and feeds by pseudopodia, is surrounding and ingesting a colonial green alga. *Chaos* amoebas are generally scavengers that feed on debris in freshwater habitats, but they ingest living organisms when the opportunity arises.

it goes. Each amoeboid cell has a haploid nucleus and reproduces by mitosis, as a true amoeba does.

When moisture or food becomes inadequate, certain cells send out a chemical signal, cyclic adenosine monophosphate (cAMP; see Fig. 3-26), that causes them to aggregate by the hundreds or thousands. During this stage the cells creep about for short distances as a single multicellular aggregate, or slug. Each cell of the slug retains its plasma membrane and individual identity. Eventually, the slug settles and reorganizes, forming a stalked fruiting body containing spores. After being released each spore opens, and a single haploid amoeboid cell—the feeding stage—emerges. The spore-forming reproductive cycle is asexual, although sexual reproduction is observed occasionally. The life cycles of most cellular slime molds lack a flagellate stage.

The cellular slime mold *Dictyostelium discoideum* is a model organism for the study of cell differentiation, cell communication, and cell motility and adhesion. Its biology has been studied intensively, particularly as it relates to **cell signaling** molecules, such as cAMP, which are found in many organisms in addition to the cellular slime molds (see Chapter 6).

Choanoflagellates are opisthokonts closely related to animals

Choanoflagellates are collared flagellates in the opisthokont clade, which also includes fungi and animals. These small, inconspicuous unikonts are found globally in both freshwater and marine environments. Choanoflagellates include both free-swimming and **sessile** species that are permanently attached by a thin stalk to bacteria-rich debris. Their single flagellum is surrounded at the base by a delicate collar of microvilli that trap food (FIG. 26-21).

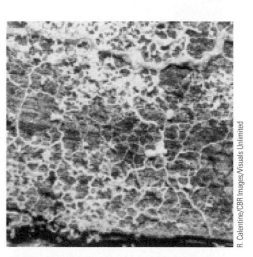

(a) The brightly pigmented plasmodium, shown on a dead log, feeds on bacteria and other microorganisms.

250 μm

(b) The reproductive structures are sporangia on stalks.

Figure 26-19 **The plasmodial slime mold *Physarum polycephalum***

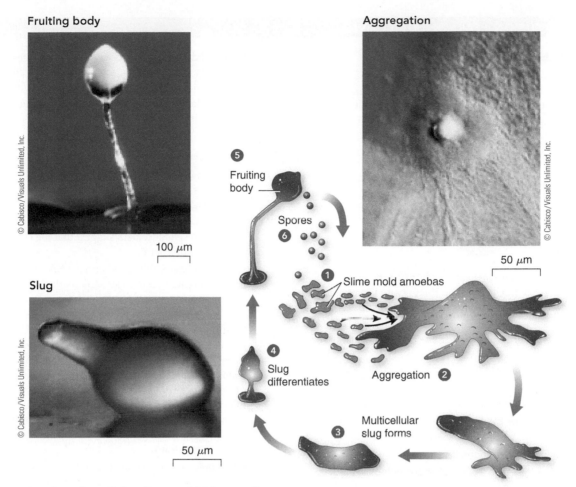

Fruiting body

Aggregation

5 Fruiting body

Spores 6

1 Slime mold amoebas

4 Slug differentiates

Aggregation 2

Multicellular slug forms 3

100 μm

Slug

50 μm

50 μm

© Cabisco/Visuals Unlimited, Inc.

Figure 26-20 *Animation* **The cellular slime mold** *Dictyostelium discoideum*

Slime mold amoebas ingest food, grow, and reproduce by cell division. After their food is depleted, hundreds of amoeboid cells stream together (*inset in upper right*) and form a migrating sluglike aggregate (*inset in lower left*). When it stops migrating, the aggregate forms a fruiting body on a stalk (*inset in upper left*). The fruiting body releases spores, each of which opens in a favorable environment to liberate an amoeboid cell.

© Cengage Learning

Choanoflagellates are of special interest because of their striking resemblance to collar cells in sponges (see Fig. 31-1b). Other animal phyla, such as cnidarians, flatworms, and echinoderms, also contain choanoflagellate-like cells, but no other group of protists has been observed to possess these cells. Evidence supporting the close relationship between choanoflagellates and animals includes comparative DNA sequence data of mitochondrial and nuclear genes. Given the similarities in structure and molecular genomics that has accumulated in recent years, many biologists hypothesize that choanoflagellates are the closest living nonanimal relative of animals. Thus, living choanoflagellates and animals probably share a common choanoflagellate-like ancestor.

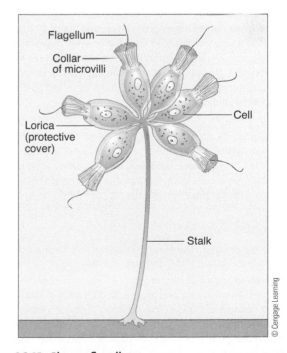

Flagellum

Collar of microvilli

Lorica (protective cover)

Cell

Stalk

© Cengage Learning

Figure 26-21 Choanoflagellates

Choanoflagellates are free-living flagellates that obtain food by waving their flagella, causing water currents to carry bacteria and other small particles of food into the collar of microvilli. A colonial form is shown. Each cell is 5 to 10 μm long, not including the flagellum.

CHECKPOINT 26.7

- *What features distinguish the amoebozoa from the rhizarians?*
- **CONNECT** *Which group of unikonts is structurally and genetically most similar to animals?*

26.1 Diversity in the Protists *(page 534)*

1 Discuss in general terms the diversity inherent in protists, including means of locomotion, modes of nutrition, interactions with other organisms, habitats, and modes of reproduction.

- Protists have various means of locomotion, including pseudopodia, flagella, and cilia; a few are nonmotile.

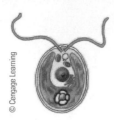

- Protists obtain their nutrients autotrophically or heterotrophically. Protists are free-living or symbiotic, with symbiotic relationships ranging from **mutualism** to **parasitism.**
- Most protists live in the ocean or in freshwater ponds, lakes, and streams. Parasitic protists live in the body fluids or cells of their hosts.
- Many protists reproduce both sexually and asexually; others reproduce only asexually.

26.2 How Did Eukaryotes Evolve? *(page 535)*

2 Discuss the hypothesis of serial endosymbiosis and briefly explain some of the evidence that supports it.

- According to the hypothesis of **serial endosymbiosis,** mitochondria and chloroplasts arose from symbiotic relationships between larger cells and the smaller bacteria that were incorporated and lived within them.
- Chloroplasts of red algae, green algae, and plants probably arose in a single primary endosymbiotic event in which a cyanobacterium was incorporated into a cell. Multiple secondary endosymbioses led to chloroplasts in euglenoids, dinoflagellates, diatoms, golden algae, and brown algae and to the nonfunctional chloroplasts in apicomplexans.

3 Describe the kinds of data biologists use to classify eukaryotes.

- Relationships among protists are determined largely by **ultrastructure,** which is the fine details of cell structure revealed by electron microscopy, and by comparative molecular data. Biologists have compared nuclear genes, many of which code for proteins, in different protist taxa.

26.3 Excavates *(page 538)*

4 Summarize the basic features of excavates and distinguish among diplomonads, parabasilids, and euglenoids.

- **Excavates** are a diverse group of unicellular protists with flagella, an excavated oral groove, and atypical, greatly modified mitochondria. The inclusion of diplomonads, parabasalids, and euglenoids in the excavate superfamily is controversial.
- **Diplomonads** are excavates with one or two nuclei, no functional mitochondria, no Golgi complex, and up to eight flagella.

- **Parabasilids** are anaerobic, flagellated excavates that often live in animals. Trichonymphs and trichomonads are examples of parabasilids.
- **Euglenoids** are unicellular and flagellate. Some euglenoids are photosynthetic.

26.4 Chromalveolates *(page 540)*

5 Contrast the two main groups of chromalveolates: alveolates and stramenopiles.

- **Chromalveolates** probably originated as a result of secondary endosymbiosis in which an ancestral cell engulfed a red alga. Some DNA sequence data suggest that the chromalveolates are not monophyletic.
- **Alveolates** have similar ribosomal DNA sequences and alveoli, flattened vesicles located just inside the plasma membrane. Most **stramenopiles** have motile cells with two flagella, one of which has tiny hairlike projections off the shaft.

6 Distinguish among the alveolates: dinoflagellates, apicomplexans, and ciliates.

- **Dinoflagellates** are mostly unicellular, biflagellate, photosynthetic alveolates of great ecological importance as producers in marine ecosystems. Their **alveoli,** flattened vesicles under the plasma membrane, often contain cellulose plates impregnated with silicates. Some dinoflagellates produce toxic blooms known as **red tides.**
- **Apicomplexans** are parasites that produce **sporozoites** and are nonmotile. An apical complex of microtubules attaches the apicomplexan to its host cell. The apicomplexan *Plasmodium* causes malaria.
- **Ciliates** are alveolates that move by hairlike **cilia,** have **micronuclei** (for sexual reproduction) and **macronuclei** (for controlling cell metabolism and growth), and undergo a sexual process called **conjugation.**

7 Distinguish among the stramenopiles: water molds, diatoms, golden algae, and brown algae.

- **Water molds** have a coenocytic **mycelium.** They reproduce asexually by forming biflagellate **zoospores** and sexually by forming **oospores.**
- **Diatoms** are mostly unicellular, with shells containing silica. Some diatoms are part of floating **plankton,** and others live on rocks and sediments where they move by gliding.
- **Brown algae** are multicellular stramenopiles that are ecologically important in cooler ocean waters. The largest brown algae (kelps) possess leaflike **blades,** stemlike **stipes,** anchoring **holdfasts,** and gas-filled bladders for buoyancy.
- **Golden algae** are mostly unicellular, biflagellate freshwater and marine stramenopiles that are of ecological importance as a component of the ocean's extremely minute **nanoplankton.**

26.5 Rhizarians *(page 547)*

8 Describe the forams and actinopods, and explain why many biologists classify them in the rhizarian supergroup.

- **Rhizarians** are amoeboid cells that often have hard outer shells, called **tests,** through which cytoplasmic projections extend; molecular evidence indicates that this group is monophyletic.
- **Forams** secrete many-chambered tests with pores through which cytoplasmic projections extend to move and obtain food.
- **Actinopods** are mostly marine plankton that obtain food by means of **axopods,** slender cytoplasmic projections that extend through pores in their shells.

26.6 Archaeplastids (page 548)

9 Describe evidence supporting the hypothesis that red algae and green algae should be included in a monophyletic group with land plants.
- Red algae, green algae, and land plants, collectively called **archaeplastids,** are considered a monophyletic group based on molecular data and on the presence of chloroplasts bounded by outer and inner membranes.
- **Red algae,** which are mostly multicellular seaweeds, are ecologically important in warm tropical ocean waters.

- **Green algae** exhibit a wide diversity in size, structural complexity, and reproduction. Botanists hypothesize that ancestral green algae gave rise to land plants.

26.7 Unikonts (page 549)

10 Briefly describe and compare the following unikonts: amoebas, plasmodial slime molds, cellular slime molds, and choanoflagellates.
- **Unikonts** have a single posterior flagellum in flagellate cells.
- **Amoebas** move and obtain food using cytoplasmic extensions called **pseudopodia.**
- The feeding stage of **plasmodial slime molds** is a multinucleate **plasmodium.** Reproduction is by haploid spores produced within **sporangia.**
- **Cellular slime molds** feed as individual amoeboid cells. They reproduce by aggregating into an aggregate (slug) and then forming asexual spores.
- **Choanoflagellates** are unikonts that are probably the closest living nonanimal relative of animals. A collar of microvilli surrounds their single flagellum at the base. Choanoflagellates are included with animals in the **opisthokont** clade, which also includes fungi.

TEST YOUR UNDERSTANDING

Know and Comprehend

1. Which of the following is *not* true of the protists? (a) they are unicellular, colonial, coenocytic, or simple multicellular organisms (b) their cilia and flagella have a 9 + 2 arrangement of microtubules (c) they are prokaryotic, as bacteria and archaea are (d) some are free-living, and some are endosymbionts (e) most are aquatic and live in the ocean or in freshwater ponds
2. Molecular evidence supports the view that all plastids evolved from an ancient (a) cyanobacterium (b) archaean (c) diplomonad (d) apicomplexan (e) unikont
3. Forams (a) are endosymbionts that live in many marine invertebrates (b) were responsible for the Irish potato famine in the 19th century (c) secrete many-chambered tests with pores through which cytoplasmic extensions project (d) have numerous axopods that may aid in trapping and holding prey (e) have numerous cilia to direct food into the oral groove
4. *Paramecium* and other ciliates often display a sexual phenomenon called (a) oogamy (b) conjugation (c) serial endosymbiosis (d) red tide (e) alternation of generations
5. Parasitic alveolates that form spores at some stage in their life belong to which group? (a) actinopods (b) ciliates (c) coccolithophorids (d) apicomplexans (e) dinoflagellates
6. Malaria (a) is transmitted by the bite of a female tsetse fly (b) is caused by a parasitic flagellate, *Giardia intestinalis* (c) is a serious form of amoebic dysentery caused by *Entamoeba histolytica* (d) is caused by an apicomplexan that spends part of its life cycle in the *Anopheles* mosquito and part in humans (e) is transmitted when people drink water tainted by a red tide

7. Photosynthetic protists with shells composed of two halves that fit together like a petri dish are (a) golden algae (b) diatoms (c) euglenoids (d) brown algae (e) forams
8. The pigments, energy reserve products, and cell walls found in land plants are also characteristic of (a) green algae (b) brown algae (c) golden algae (d) diatoms (e) euglenoids and diatoms
9. Kelps are ___ with multicellular bodies differentiated into blades, stipes, holdfasts, and gas-filled floats. (a) golden algae (b) diatoms (c) euglenoids (d) brown algae (e) red algae
10. Cellular slime molds (a) include *Physarum* and *Phytophthora* (b) are more closely related to bacteria than are any other protists (c) are responsible for late blight of potatoes, which led to starvation in Ireland in the 1840s (d) have double-gene fusion (e) form a slug when cells aggregate in response to cyclic AMP
11. Water molds reproduce asexually by forming ___ and sexually by forming ___. (a) oospores; holdfasts (b) zoospores; zooxanthellae (c) zoospores; oospores (d) holdfasts; oospores (e) oospores; zoospores

Apply and Analyze

12. **VISUALIZE** Draw simple sketches of a *Euglena* and a *Paramecium*. Choose the appropriate structures for each organism from the following list and label them in your drawings: flagellum, cilia, chloroplast, mitochondrion, nucleus, macronucleus, micronucleus, contractile vacuole, pellicle, food vacuole.

Evaluate and Synthesize

13. **EVOLUTION LINK** Why are the protists considered paraphyletic? Use Figure 26-3 to help explain your answer.

14. **INTERPRET DATA** In the corresponding darkfield LM of unicellular choanoflagellates, actin has been stained *red*, tubulin *green*, and DNA *blue*. Identify the cell parts that contain each of these chemical materials.

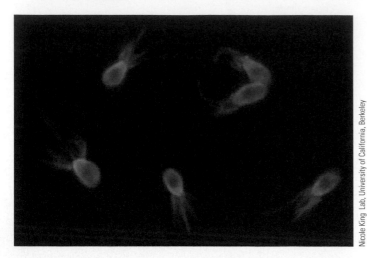

Nicole King Lab, University of California, Berkeley

15. **SCIENCE, TECHNOLOGY, AND SOCIETY** Use examples associated with the malaria parasite, *Plasmodium*, to illustrate why an understanding of evolution is indispensable to modern medical research. (*Hint:* Be sure to include serial endosymbiosis and drug resistance in your answer.)

 To access course materials, such as Aplia and other companion resources, please visit **www.cengagebrain.com.**

Seedless Plants

Land plants. Note the ferns and the moss-covered dead tree. Both mosses and ferns are seedless plants.

About 445 million years ago (mya), planet Earth would have seemed an inhospitable place because even though life abounded in the ocean, it did not yet exist in abundance on land. Occasionally, perhaps, an animal would crawl out of the water onto land, but it never stayed there permanently because there was little to eat on land: not a single blade of grass, no fruit, and no seeds.

During the next 30 million years, a time corresponding roughly to the Silurian period in geologic time (see Table 21-1), plants appeared in abundance and colonized the land. Where did they come from? Although plants living today exhibit great diversity in size, form, and habitat (see photograph), biologists hypothesize that they all evolved from a common ancestor that was an ancient green alga.

Modern green algae share many biochemical and metabolic traits with modern plants. Both green algae and plants contain the same photosynthetic pigments: chlorophylls *a* and *b* and carotenoids, including xanthophylls (yellow pigments) and carotenes (orange pigments). Both store excess carbohydrates as starch and have cellulose as a major component of their cell walls. In addition, plants and some green algae share certain details of cell division, including formation of a cell plate during cytokinesis (see Chapter 10).

What exactly is a plant? A **plant** is a complex multicellular eukaryote that has cellulose cell walls, chlorophylls *a* and *b* in plastids, and starch as a storage product and that may have cells with two anterior flagella. In addition, all plants develop from multicellular *embryos* that are enclosed in maternal tissues; this last character is one that distinguishes plants from green algae. Many botanists refer to land plants as *embryophytes* because of this character.

Plants range in size from minute, almost microscopic duckweeds and water-meal to massive giant sequoias, some of the largest organisms that have ever lived. Plants include hundreds of thousands of species that live in varied habitats, from frozen arctic tundra to lush tropical rain forests to harsh deserts to moist stream banks.

KEY CONCEPTS

27.1 Adaptations of land plants include a waxy cuticle to prevent water loss; multicellular gametangia; stomata; and for most plants, vascular tissues containing lignin. Plants undergo an alternation of generations between multicellular gametophyte and sporophyte generations.

27.2 Mosses and other bryophytes lack vascular tissues and do not form true roots, stems, or leaves.

27.3 In club mosses and ferns, lignin-hardened vascular tissues that transport water and dissolved substances throughout the plant body have evolved.

27.1 ADAPTATIONS OF PLANTS TO LIFE ON LAND

LEARNING OBJECTIVES

1 Discuss some environmental challenges of living on land and describe how several plant adaptations meet these challenges.
2 Name the green algal group from which plants are hypothesized to have descended and describe supporting evidence.

How were plants modified during the transition from life in the water to life on land? What are some features of plants that have let them colonize so many types of environments? One important difference between plants and algae is that a waxy **cuticle** covers the aerial portion of a plant. Essential for existence on land, the cuticle helps prevent desiccation, or drying out, of plant tissues by evaporation. Plants that are adapted to moister habitats may have a very thin layer of wax, whereas those adapted to drier environments often have a thick, crusty cuticle. (Many desert plants also have a reduced surface area, particularly of leaves, which minimizes water loss.)

Plants obtain the carbon they need for photosynthesis from the atmosphere as carbon dioxide (CO_2). To be fixed into organic molecules such as sugar, CO_2 must first diffuse into the chloroplasts that are inside green plant cells. Because a waxy cuticle covers the external surfaces of leaves and stems, however, gas exchange through the cuticle between the atmosphere and the interior of cells is negligible. Tiny pores called **stomata** (sing., *stoma*), which dot the surfaces of leaves and stems of almost all plants, facilitate gas exchange.

The sex organs, or **gametangia** (sing., *gametangium*), of most plants are multicellular, whereas the gametangia of algae are unicellular (FIG. 27-1). Each plant gametangium has a layer of sterile (nonreproductive) cells that surrounds and protects the delicate gametes (eggs and sperm cells). In plants the fertilized egg develops into a multicellular **embryo** (young plant) within the female gametangium. Thus, the embryo is protected during its development. In algae the fertilized egg develops away from its gametangium; in some algae the gametes are released before fertilization, whereas in others the fertilized egg is released.

The plant life cycle alternates between haploid and diploid generations

Plants have a clearly defined **alternation of generations** in which they spend part of their lives in a multicellular haploid stage and part in a multicellular diploid stage (FIG. 27-2).[1] The haploid portion of the life cycle is called the **gametophyte generation** because it gives rise to

haploid gametes by mitosis. When two gametes fuse, the diploid portion of the life cycle, called the **sporophyte generation,** begins. The sporophyte generation produces haploid spores by the process of meiosis; these spores represent the first stage in the gametophyte generation.

Let us examine alternation of generations more closely. The haploid gametophytes produce male gametangia, known as **antheridia** (sing., *antheridium*), in which sperm cells form (FIG. 27-3a). Gametophytes also produce female gametangia, known as **archegonia** (sing., *archegonium*), each bearing a single egg (FIG. 27-3b). Sperm cells reach the female gametangium in a variety of ways, and one sperm cell fertilizes the egg to form a **zygote,** or fertilized egg.

The diploid zygote is the first stage in the sporophyte generation. The zygote divides by mitosis and develops into a multicellular embryo, the young sporophyte plant. Embryo development takes place within the archegonium; thus, the embryo is protected as it develops. Eventually, the embryo grows into a mature sporophyte plant. The mature sporophyte has special cells called *sporogenous cells* (spore-producing cells, also called *spore mother cells*) that divide by meiosis to form haploid **spores.**

fertilization of egg by sperm cell ⟶ zygote ⟶ embryo ⟶ mature sporophyte plant ⟶ sporogenous cells ⟶ meiosis ⟶ spores

All plants produce spores by meiosis, in contrast with algae and fungi, which may produce spores by meiosis or mitosis. The spores represent the first stage in the gametophyte generation. Each spore divides by mitosis to produce a multicellular gametophyte, and the cycle continues. Plants therefore alternate between a haploid gametophyte generation and a diploid sporophyte generation.

spores ⟶ mature gametophyte plants ⟶ archegonia ⟶ eggs / antheridia ⟶ sperm cells

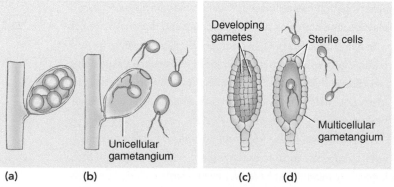

(a) **(b)** **(c)** **(d)**

Figure 27-1 Generalized reproductive structures of algae and plants

(a, b) In algae gametangia are generally unicellular. When the gametes are released, only the wall of the original cell remains. **(c, d)** In plants the gametangia are multicellular, but only the inner cells become gametes. The gametes are surrounded by a protective layer of sterile (nonreproductive) cells.

© Cengage Learning

---

[1] For convenience, we limit our discussion to plants that are not polyploid, although polyploidy is very common in land plants. We therefore use the terms *diploid* and *2n* (and *haploid* and *n*) interchangeably, but these terms are not actually synonymous.

Plants have an alternation of generations, spending part of the cycle in a haploid gametophyte stage and part in a diploid sporophyte stage.

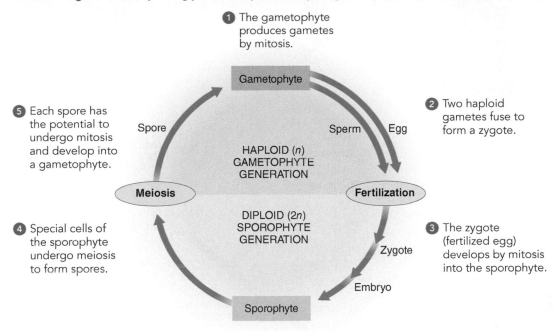

❶ The gametophyte produces gametes by mitosis.

❷ Two haploid gametes fuse to form a zygote.

❸ The zygote (fertilized egg) develops by mitosis into the sporophyte.

❹ Special cells of the sporophyte undergo meiosis to form spores.

❺ Each spore has the potential to undergo mitosis and develop into a gametophyte.

Gametophyte

Spore

Sperm   Egg

HAPLOID (*n*) GAMETOPHYTE GENERATION

Meiosis

Fertilization

DIPLOID (2*n*) SPOROPHYTE GENERATION

Zygote

Embryo

Sporophyte

Figure 27-2 *Animation* **The basic plant life cycle**

Depending on the plant group, the haploid or the diploid stage may be greatly enlarged or reduced; as you will learn, this fact has evolutionary significance.

CONNECT Do diploid cells undergo mitosis in this life cycle? haploid cells?

© Cengage Learning

Four major groups of plants exist today

Structural and molecular data indicate that land plants probably descended from a group of green algae called **charophytes** or *stoneworts* (see Figure 26-15c, which shows a charophyte). Recall from Chapter 26 that red algae, green algae, and land plants are collectively classified as **archaeplastids.** Molecular comparisons, particularly of DNA and RNA sequences, provide compelling evidence that green algae are closely allied to plants (**FIG. 27-4**). These comparisons among plants and various green algae include sequences of chloroplast DNA, certain nuclear genes, and ribosomal RNA. In each case, the closest match occurs between

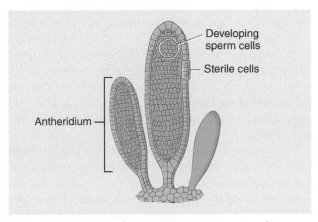

Developing sperm cells

Sterile cells

Antheridium

(a) Each antheridium, the male gametangium, produces numerous sperm cells.

Egg

Sterile cells

Archegonium

(b) Each archegonium, the female gametangium, produces a single egg.

Figure 27-3 Plant gametangia

Shown are generalized moss gametangia.

© Cengage Learning

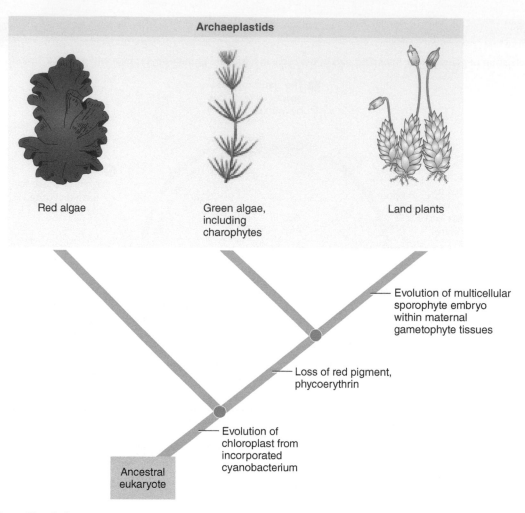

Archaeplastids

Red algae

Green algae, including charophytes

Land plants

Evolution of multicellular sporophyte embryo within maternal gametophyte tissues

Loss of red pigment, phycoerythrin

Evolution of chloroplast from incorporated cyanobacterium

Ancestral eukaryote

Figure 27-4 Evolution of land plants

Cladograms such as this one represent an emerging consensus that is open to change as new discoveries are made.
© Cengage Learning

charophytes and plants, indicating that modern charophytes and plants probably share a recent common ancestor.

Plants consist of four major groups: bryophytes; seedless vascular plants; and two groups of seeded vascular plants, the gymnosperms and angiosperms (flowering plants). Their relationships are illustrated in FIGURE 27-5; see also TABLE 27-1, which is an overview of the ten extant (living) plant phyla.

The mosses and other bryophytes are small nonvascular plants that lack a specialized vascular, or conducting, system to transport nutrients, water, and essential minerals (inorganic nutrients) throughout the plant body. In the absence of such a system, bryophytes rely on diffusion and osmosis to obtain needed materials. This reliance means that bryophytes are restricted in size; if they were much larger, some of their cells could not obtain enough necessary materials. Bryophytes do not form seeds, the reproductive structures discussed in Chapter 28. Bryophytes reproduce and disperse primarily via haploid spores. Recent molecular and fossil evidence, discussed later in this chapter, suggests that bryophytes may have been the earliest plants to colonize land.

The other three groups of plants—seedless vascular plants, gymnosperms, and flowering plants—have vascular tissues and

are thus known as vascular plants. The two vascular tissues are **xylem,** for conducting water and dissolved minerals, and **phloem,** for conducting dissolved organic molecules such as sugar. A key step in the evolution of vascular plants was the ability to produce **lignin,** a strengthening polymer in the walls of cells that function for support and conduction (see Chapter 33 for a discussion of plant cell wall chemistry, including lignin). The stiffening property of lignin enabled plants to grow tall, which let them maximize light interception. The successful occupation of the land by plants, in turn, made the evolution of terrestrial animals possible by providing them with both habitat and food.

Club mosses and ferns (which include whisk ferns and horsetails) are seedless vascular plants that, like the bryophytes, reproduce and disperse primarily via spores. Seedless vascular plants arose and diversified during the Silurian and Devonian periods of the Paleozoic era, between 444 mya and 359 mya. Club mosses and ferns extend back more than 420 million years and were of considerable importance as Earth's dominant plants in past ages. Fossil evidence indicates that many species of these plants were the size of immense trees. Most living representatives of club mosses and ferns are small.

Based on recent evidence, scientists are beginning to reach a consensus about the evolutionary relationships among living plants.

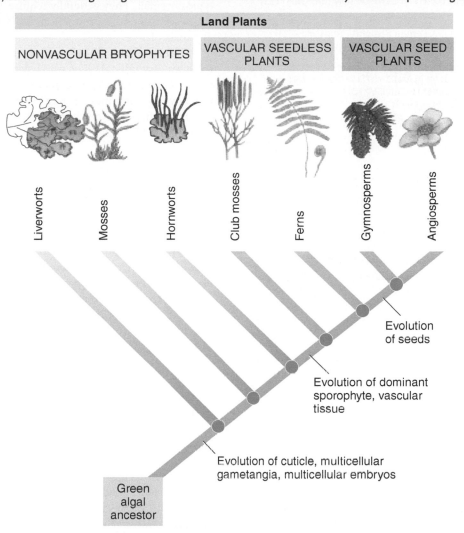

Figure 27-5 *Animation* **Plant evolution**

The four major groups of plants are bryophytes, seedless vascular plants, and two groups of seed plants: gymnosperms and angiosperms. The seed plants are covered in Chapter 28.

CONNECT How does the cladogram relate to many botanists referring to land plants as embryophytes?

© Cengage Learning

The gymnosperms are vascular plants that reproduce by forming seeds. Gymnosperms produce seeds borne exposed (unprotected) on a stem or in a cone. Plants with seeds as their primary means of reproduction and dispersal first appeared about 359 mya, at the end of the Devonian period. These early seed plants diversified into many varied species of gymnosperms.

The most recent plant group to appear is the flowering plants, or angiosperms, which arose during the early Cretaceous period of the Mesozoic era, about 130 mya. Like gymnosperms, flowering plants reproduce by forming seeds. Flowering plants, however, produce seeds enclosed within a fruit.

CHECKPOINT 27.1

- *What are the most important environmental challenges that plants face living on land?*
- *What adaptations do plants have to meet these environmental challenges?*
- *What types of evidence support the hypothesis that land plants descended from the group of green algae known as charophytes?*
- **VISUALIZE** *Draw a simple diagram illustrating alternation of generations in plants, including the sporophyte and gameto-phyte generations, spores, gametes (eggs and sperm), meiosis, and fertilization. Be sure to indicate whether each generation or kind of cell is haploid or diploid.*

TABLE 27-1	Ten Extant Plant Phyla

NONVASCULAR PLANTS WITH A DOMINANT GAMETOPHYTE GENERATION (BRYOPHYTES)

Phylum Hepatophyta (liverworts)

Phylum Bryophyta (mosses)

Phylum Anthocerophyta (hornworts)

VASCULAR PLANTS WITH A DOMINANT SPOROPHYTE GENERATION
Seedless plants

Phylum Lycopodiophyta (club mosses)

Phylum Pteridophyta (ferns and their allies, the whisk ferns and horsetails)

Seed plants
Plants with naked seeds (gymnosperms)

Phylum Coniferophyta (conifers)

Phylum Cycadophyta (cycads)

Phylum Ginkgophyta (ginkgoes)

Phylum Gnetophyta (gnetophytes)

Seeds enclosed within a fruit (angiosperms)

Phylum Anthophyta (angiosperms or flowering plants)

Class Eudicotyledones (eudicots)

Class Monocotyledones (monocots)

© Cengage Learning

27.2 BRYOPHYTES

LEARNING OBJECTIVES

3 Summarize the features that distinguish bryophytes from other plants.

4 Name and briefly describe the three phyla of bryophytes.

5 Describe the life cycle of mosses and compare their gametophyte and sporophyte generations.

The **bryophytes** (from the Greek words meaning "moss plant") consist of about 16,000 species of mosses, liverworts, and hornworts; bryophytes are the only living nonvascular plants (TABLE 27-2). Because they have no means for extensive internal transport of water, sugar, and essential minerals, bryophytes are typically small. They generally require a moist environment for active growth and reproduction, but some bryophytes tolerate dry areas.

The bryophytes are divided into three distinct phyla: mosses (phylum Bryophyta), liverworts (phylum Hepatophyta), and hornworts (phylum Anthocerophyta). These three groups differ in many ways and may or may not be closely related. They are usually studied together because they lack vascular tissues and have similar life cycles.

Moss gametophytes are differentiated into "leaves" and "stems"

Mosses (phylum Bryophyta), which include about 9900 species, usually live in dense colonies or beds (FIG. 27-6). Each individual gametophyte plant has tiny, hairlike absorptive structures called *rhizoids* and an upright, stemlike structure that bears leaflike blades, each normally consisting of a single layer of undifferentiated cells except at the midrib. Because mosses lack vascular tissues, they do not have true roots, stems, or leaves; the moss structures are not homologous to roots, stems, or leaves in vascular plants. Some moss species have water-conducting cells and sugar-conducting cells, although these cells are not lignified, nor are they as specialized or effective as the conducting cells of vascular plants.

Alternation of generations is clearly defined in the life cycle of mosses (FIG. 27-7). The green moss gametophyte often bears its gametangia at the top of the plant. Many moss species have separate sexes: male plants that bear antheridia and female plants that bear archegonia. Other mosses produce antheridia and archegonia on the same plant.

Fertilization occurs when one of the sperm cells fuses with the egg within the archegonium. Sperm cells, which have flagella, are transported from antheridium to archegonium by flowing water, such as splashing rain droplets. A raindrop lands on the top of a male gametophyte, and sperm cells are released into it from the antheridia. Another raindrop landing on the male plant may splash the sperm-laden droplet into the air and

TABLE 27-2	A Comparison of Major Groups of Seedless Plants	
PLANT GROUP	DOMINANT STAGE OF LIFE CYCLE	REPRESENTATIVE GENERA
NONVASCULAR; REPRODUCE BY SPORES (BRYOPHYTES)		
Liverworts (phylum Hepatophyta)	Gametophyte: thalloid or leafy plant	*Marchantia*
Mosses (phylum Bryophyta)	Gametophyte: leafy plant	*Polytrichum, Sphagnum, Physcomitrella*
Hornworts (phylum Anthocerophyta)	Gametophyte: thalloid plant	*Anthoceros*
VASCULAR; REPRODUCE BY SPORES		
Club mosses (phylum Lycopodiophyta)	Sporophyte: roots, rhizomes, erect stems, and leaves (microphylls)	*Lycopodium, Selaginella*
Ferns (phylum Pteridophyta)	Sporophyte: roots, rhizomes, and leaves (megaphylls)	*Pteridium, Polystichum, Azolla, Platycerium*
Whisk ferns (phylum Pteridophyta)	Sporophyte: rhizomes and erect stems; no true roots or leaves	*Psilotum*
Horsetails (phylum Pteridophyta)	Sporophyte: roots, rhizomes, erect stems, and leaves (reduced megaphylls)	*Equisetum*

© Cengage Learning

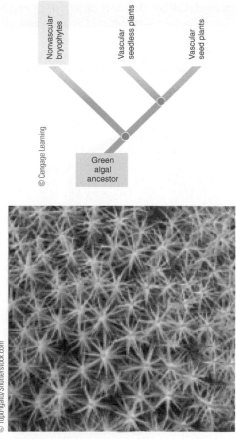

- Capsule

- Seta

- Foot

(a) Moss gametophytes. Close-up of haircap moss (*Polytrichum commune*) gametophytes. The haircap moss is a popular ground cover in rock gardens, particularly in Japan.

(b) Moss sporophytes. Each consisting of a foot, seta, and capsule, the haircap moss sporophytes grow out of the top of the gametophytes. Spores are produced within the capsule.

Figure 27-6 Bryophytes: mosses

onto the top of a nearby female plant. Alternatively, arthropods such as insects and mites may touch the sperm-laden fluid and inadvertently carry it for considerable distances. Once in a film of water on the female moss, a sperm cell swims into the archegonium, which secretes chemicals to attract and guide the sperm cells, and fuses with the egg.

The diploid zygote, formed by fertilization, grows by mitosis into a multicellular embryo that develops into a mature moss sporophyte. This sporophyte grows out of the top of the female gametophyte and remains attached and nutritionally dependent on the gametophyte throughout its existence (see Fig. 27-6b). Initially green and photosynthetic, the sporophyte becomes golden brown at maturity. It consists of three main parts: a *foot,* which anchors the sporophyte to the gametophyte and absorbs minerals and nutrients from it; a *seta,* or stalk; and a *capsule,* which contains sporogenous cells (spore mother cells). The capsule of some species is covered by a caplike structure, the *calyptra,* which is derived from the archegonium.

The sporogenous cells undergo meiosis to form haploid spores. When the spores are mature, the capsule opens and releases them, and they are then transported by wind or rain. If a moss spore lands in a suitable spot, it germinates and grows into a filament of cells called a **protonema.** The protonema, which superficially

resembles a filamentous green alga, forms buds, each of which grows into a green gametophyte, and the life cycle continues.

Biologists consider the haploid gametophyte generation the dominant generation in mosses because it lives independently of the diploid sporophyte. In contrast, the moss sporophyte is attached to and nutritionally dependent on the gametophyte.

Mosses make up an inconspicuous but significant part of their environment. They play an important role in forming soil. Mosses, which form mats that cover the rock, eventually die, forming a thin layer of organic matter in which grasses and other plants can grow. Because they grow tightly packed in dense colonies, mosses hold soil in place and help prevent erosion. At the same time, they retain moisture that they and other organisms need. Waxwings and other birds use moss, along with twigs and grass, as nesting material.

Commercially, the most important mosses are the peat mosses in the genus *Sphagnum.* One of the distinctive features of *Sphagnum* "leaves" is the presence of many large, empty cells that absorb and hold water. This feature makes peat moss a useful packing material for shipping live plants as well as a good soil conditioner. Added to sandy soils, for example, peat moss helps absorb and retain moisture.

The acidic and anaerobic conditions of a peat bog retard the growth of bacterial and fungal decomposers. As a result,

The dominant phase in the life cycle of mosses, like that of other bryophytes, is the gametophyte.

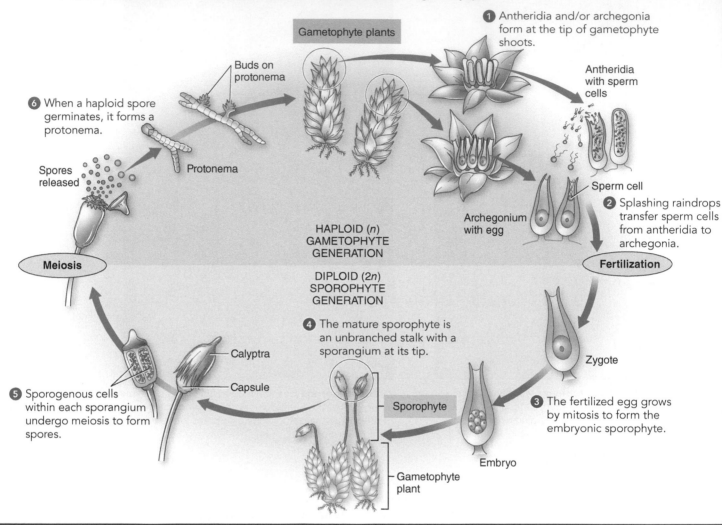

Gametophyte plants

Buds on protonema

1 Antheridia and/or archegonia form at the tip of gametophyte shoots.

Antheridia with sperm cells

6 When a haploid spore germinates, it forms a protonema.

Spores released

Protonema

Sperm cell

HAPLOID (n) GAMETOPHYTE GENERATION

Archegonium with egg

2 Splashing raindrops transfer sperm cells from antheridia to archegonia.

Fertilization

Meiosis

DIPLOID (2n) SPOROPHYTE GENERATION

4 The mature sporophyte is an unbranched stalk with a sporangium at its tip.

Zygote

Calyptra

Capsule

Sporophyte

3 The fertilized egg grows by mitosis to form the embryonic sporophyte.

5 Sporogenous cells within each sporangium undergo meiosis to form spores.

Gametophyte plant

Embryo

Gametophyte plant

Figure 27-7 Animation The life cycle of mosses

The gametophyte generation is dominant in the moss life cycle. After sexual reproduction, the sporophyte grows out of the gametophyte.

© Cengage Learning

VISUALIZE Sketch an embryo developing in an archegonium. Indicate to what generation each belongs and whether the tissue is haploid or diploid.

dead peat mosses accumulate as thick deposits—some several meters in depth—under the growing mat of living peat mosses. Over time, the organic material compresses to form *peat*. In some countries, such as Ireland and Scotland, people cut out blocks of peat that has accumulated for hundreds of years in peat bogs, dry them, and burn them for fuel. Occasionally, the remains of well-preserved humans have been uncovered during the excavations of old peat bogs in Ireland and other parts of Europe (**FIG. 27-8**).

Figure 27-8 Preserved human remains in a peat bog in Denmark

The clothing and features of the Tollund man, estimated to be about two thousand years old, are remarkably well preserved because the bog's acidic conditions inhibited decay.

© Robin Weaver/Alamy

The name *moss* is often misused to refer to plants that are not truly mosses. For example, reindeer "moss" is a lichen that is a dominant form of vegetation in the arctic tundra, Spanish "moss" is a flowering plant, and club "moss" (discussed later in this chapter) is a relative of ferns.

Liverwort gametophytes are either thalloid or leafy

Liverworts (phylum Hepatophyta) consist of about 6000 species of nonvascular plants with a dominant gametophyte generation, but the gametophytes of some liverworts are quite different from those of mosses. Their body form is often a flattened, lobed structure called a **thallus** (pl., *thalli*) that is not differentiated into leaves, stems, or roots. The common liverwort, *Marchantia polymorpha*, is thalloid (FIGS. 27-9a and b). Liverworts are so named because the lobes of their thalli superficially resemble the lobes of the human liver; *wort* is derived from the Old English word *wyrt*, meaning "plant." On the underside of the liverwort thallus are hairlike rhizoids that anchor the plant to the soil. Other liverworts, known as *leafy liverworts*, superficially resemble mosses, with leaflike blades, "stems," and rhizoids rather

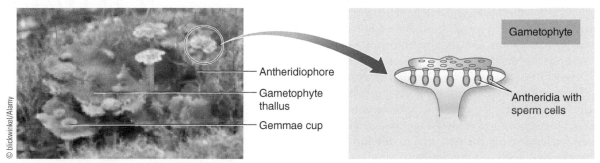

(a) Flattened, ribbon-like lobes characterize the gametophyte of the common liverwort (*Marchantia polymorpha*). This male gametophyte thallus has both asexual gemmae cups and sexual antheridiophores, which produce sperm-bearing antheridia.

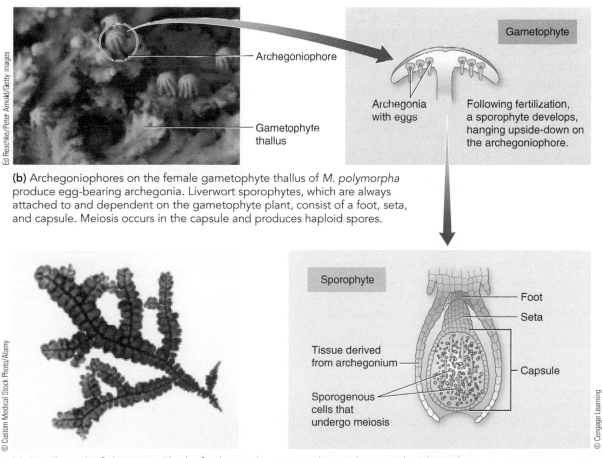

(b) Archegoniophores on the female gametophyte thallus of *M. polymorpha* produce egg-bearing archegonia. Liverwort sporophytes, which are always attached to and dependent on the gametophyte plant, consist of a foot, seta, and capsule. Meiosis occurs in the capsule and produces haploid spores.

(c) *Porella* is a leafy liverwort. The leafy plant is the gametophyte. It bears antheridia and archegonia on special branches that look quite similar to the nonreproductive branches. After fertilization, a small sporophyte develops that produces spores following meiosis.

Figure 27-9 *Animation* Bryophytes: liverworts

than a lobed thallus (FIG. 27-9c). As in the mosses, leafy liverwort "leaves" consist of a single layer of undifferentiated cells. Like other bryophytes, liverworts are small, generally inconspicuous plants that are largely restricted to damp environments. Unlike mosses, hornworts, and other plants, liverworts lack stomata, although some liverworts have surface pores thought to be analogous to stomata.

Liverworts reproduce both sexually and asexually (see Figs. 27-9a and b). Their sexual reproduction involves production of archegonia and antheridia on the haploid gametophyte. In some liverworts these gametangia are borne on stalked structures called *archegoniophores,* which bear archegonia, and *antheridiophores,* which bear antheridia. Their life cycle is basically the same as that of mosses, although some of the structures look quite different. Splashing raindrops transport sperm cells to the archegonia, where fertilization takes place. The resulting zygote develops into a multicellular embryo that becomes a mature sporophyte. The liverwort sporophyte is attached to the gametophyte, as in mosses. Sporogenous cells in the capsule of the sporophyte undergo meiosis, producing haploid spores. Each spore has the potential to develop into a green gametophyte, and the cycle continues.

Some liverworts reproduce asexually by forming tiny balls of tissue called **gemmae** (sing., *gemma*), which are borne in a saucer-shaped structure, the gemmae cup, directly on the liverwort thallus (see Fig. 27-9a). Splashing raindrops and small animals help disperse gemmae. When a gemma lands in a suitable place, it grows into a new liverwort thallus. Liverworts may also reproduce asexually by thallus branching and growth. The individual thallus lobes elongate, and each becomes a separate plant when the older part of the thallus that originally connected the individual lobes dies.

Hornwort gametophytes are inconspicuous thalloid plants

Hornworts (phylum Anthocerophyta) are a small group of about 100 species of bryophytes whose gametophytes superficially resemble those of the thalloid liverworts. Hornworts live in disturbed habitats such as fallow fields and roadsides.

Hornworts may or may not be closely related to other bryophytes. For example, their cell structure, particularly the presence of a single large chloroplast in each cell, resembles certain algal cells more than plant cells. In contrast, mosses, liverworts, and other plants have many disc-shaped chloroplasts per cell.

In the common hornwort (*Anthoceros natans*), archegonia and antheridia are embedded in the gametophyte thallus rather than on archegoniophores and antheridiophores. After fertilization and development, the needlelike sporophyte projects out of the gametophyte thallus, forming a spike or "horn," hence the name *hornwort.* A single gametophyte often produces multiple sporophytes (FIG. 27-10). Meiosis occurs, forming spores within each **sporangium** (pl., *sporangia*), or spore case. The sporangium splits open from the top to

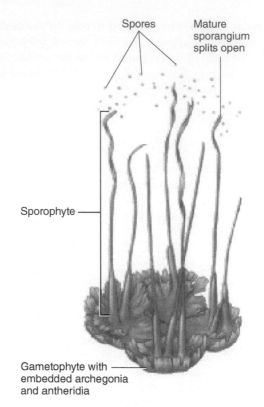

Figure 27-10 Bryophytes: hornworts

The gametophyte of the common hornwort (*Anthoceros natans*) is a small thallus with unicellular rhizoids on the lower (ventral) surface. After fertilization, sporophytes project up out of the gametophyte, forming "horns."
© Cengage Learning

release the spores; each spore can give rise to a new gametophyte thallus. A unique feature of hornworts is that the sporophytes, unlike those of mosses and liverworts, continue to grow from their bases for the remainder of the gametophyte's life, a characteristic known as **indeterminate growth.** Some botanists think that indeterminate growth may indicate that hornworts evolved from plants with larger, more complex sporophytes.

Bryophytes are used for experimental studies

Botanists use certain bryophytes as experimental models to study many fundamental aspects of plant biology, including genetics, growth and development, plant ecology, plant hormones, and *photoperiodism,* which is plant responses to varying periods of night and day length.

The moss *Physcomitrella patens* is a particularly important research organism for studying plant evolution because its features and genome can be compared with those of algae and flowering plants (FIG. 27-11). In this regard *Physcomitrella* is a plant equivalent of the fruit fly *Drosophila,* which is an important model organism for studies of animal inheritance, development, and evolution. As experimental organisms, *Physcomitrella*

Does the Physcomitrella *genome reveal any insights in plant evolution?*

HYPOTHESIS: Comparing the genome of the model organism *Physcomitrella* with genomes of other land plants as well as green algae will provide details of genes that were probably associated with the colonization of land.

EXPERIMENT: Several dozen scientists in Germany, the United States, Japan, the United Kingdom, Australia, Canada, and Belgium collaborated to produce the draft genome sequence for the model organism *Physcomitrella* (see photograph). This bryophyte was selected because researchers have used *Physcomitrella* in a wide variety of experiments and have a good understanding of its biology.

After sequencing the genome of *Physcomitrella*, it was compared with available genomes of green algae (*Ostreococcus* and *Chlamydomonas*) and land plants: the model flowering plant *Arabidopsis*, rice (*Oryza sativa*), and western balsam poplar (*Populus trichocarpa*).

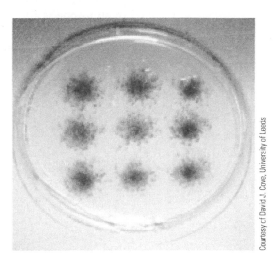

Courtesy of David J. Cove, University of Leeds

RESULTS AND CONCLUSION: Researchers found that *Physcomitrella* has lost some genes needed for life in the water and gained new genes needed for life on land. Every land plant has to meet the same environmental challenges, such as obtaining enough water and preventing excessive water loss, tolerating high and low temperatures, and adapting to increased levels of solar radiation. These challenges have resulted in many modifications in plant body plans and physiological processes.

Bryophytes and vascular plants living today represent remnants of the first plants that colonized land some 450 mya. Compared with green algae, *Physcomitrella* lacks the genes needed to survive in aquatic environments but has gained genes involving plant signaling molecules (auxin, abscisic acid, and cytokinins) needed to adapt to drought, extremes of temperature, and light reception. Compared with *Physcomitrella*, other land plants have gained additional signaling molecules (gibberellins, jasmonic acid, and brassinosteroids) that enable a more complex tolerance of environmental stressors.

Because of its intermediary position in evolution (i.e., between green algae and vascular land plants), *Physcomitrella*'s genome allows biologists to reconstruct which genes may have been acquired and lost during the colonization of land by the last common ancestor of all land plants.

SOURCE: Rensing, S.A., et al. "The *Physcomitrella* Genome Reveals Evolutionary Insights into the Conquest of Land by Plants." *Science*, Vol. 319, pp. 64–69, Jan. 4, 2008.

PREDICT Would you expect *Physcomitrella* to possess genes required to produce xylem or phloem?

Figure 27-11 **The moss *Physcomitrella*, the first bryophyte to have its genome sequenced**

---

and other bryophytes are easy to grow on artificial media and do not require much space because they are so small.

Recap: details of bryophyte evolution are based on fossils and on structural and molecular evidence

Plants are a **monophyletic group;** that is, all plants probably evolved from a common ancestral green alga. Fossil evidence indicates that bryophytes are ancient plants, probably the first group of plants to arise from the common plant ancestor. The fossil record of ancient bryophytes is incomplete, consisting mostly of spores and small tissue fragments, and can be interpreted in different ways. As a result, it does not provide a definite answer on bryophyte evolution.

The oldest known recognizable plant fossils are dated at about 425 million years old. These fossils resemble modern liverworts in many respects, but the spores are virtually identical to those in 470-million-year-old rocks. Fossil fragments of tiny liverwort-like plants associated with ancient spores have been discovered in Oman. This evidence suggests that liverwort-like plants may have been the earliest plants to colonize land.

CHECKPOINT 27.2

- *Which of the following are parts of the gametophyte generation in mosses: antheridia, zygote, embryo, capsule, archegonia, sperm cells, egg cell, spores, and protonema?*
- **CONNECT** *How are mosses, liverworts, and hornworts similar? How is each group distinctive?*

27.3 SEEDLESS VASCULAR PLANTS

LEARNING OBJECTIVES

6 Discuss the features that distinguish seedless vascular plants from algae and bryophytes.
7 Name and briefly describe the two phyla of seedless vascular plants.
8 Describe the life cycle of ferns and compare their sporophyte and gametophyte generations.
9 Compare the generalized life cycles of homosporous and heterosporous plants.

The most important adaptation found in seedless vascular plants, although absent in algae and bryophytes, is specialized vascular tissues—xylem and phloem—for support and conduction. This system of conduction lets vascular plants grow larger than bryophytes because water, minerals, and sugar are transported to all parts of the plant. Although seedless vascular plants in temperate environments are relatively small, tree ferns in the tropics may grow to heights of 18 m (60 ft). All seedless vascular plants have true stems with vascular tissues, and most also have true roots and leaves.

Botanists have extensively studied the evolution of the leaf as the main organ of photosynthesis. The two basic types of true leaves—microphylls and megaphylls—evolved independently of each other (FIG. 27-12). The **microphyll,** which is usually small and has a single vascular strand, probably evolved from small, projecting extensions of stem tissue (*enations*). Only one group of living plants, the club mosses, has microphylls.

In contrast, **megaphylls** probably evolved from stem branches that gradually filled in with additional tissue (*webbing*) to form most leaves as we know them today. Megaphylls have more than one vascular strand, as we would expect if they evolved from branch systems. Ferns (with the exception of whisk ferns, discussed later in this chapter), gymnosperms, and flowering plants have megaphylls.

Recent evidence suggests megaphylls evolved over a 40-million-year period in the Late Paleozoic era in response to a gradual decline in the level of atmospheric CO_2. As CO_2 declined, plants developed a flattened blade with more stomata for gas exchange. (More stomata allowed cells inside the leaf to get enough CO_2.)

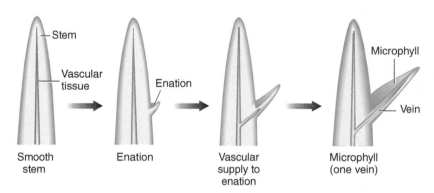

(a) Microphyll evolution. Microphylls probably originated as outgrowths (enations) of stem tissue that developed a single vascular strand later. Club mosses have microphylls.

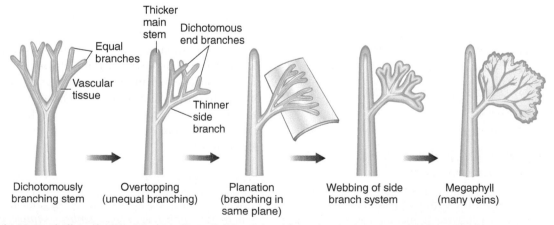

(b) Megaphyll evolution. Megaphylls probably evolved from the evolutionary modification of side branches. Webbing is the evolutionary process in which the spaces between close branches become filled with chlorophyll-containing cells. Ferns, horsetails, gymnosperms, and flowering plants have megaphylls.

Figure 27-12 Evolution of microphylls and megaphylls
© Cengage Learning

There are two main clades of seedless vascular plants: the club mosses and the ferns. Biologists originally considered horsetails and whisk ferns distinct enough to be classified in separate phyla. However, many kinds of evidence, such as DNA comparisons and similarities in sperm structure, have resulted in their being reclassified as ferns. As shown in FIGURE 27-13, ferns, including horsetails and whisk ferns, are a monophyletic group and the closest living relatives of seed plants (also see Table 27-2).

Club mosses are small plants with rhizomes and short, erect branches

Club mosses (phylum Lycopodiophyta) were important plants millions of years ago, when species that are now extinct often reached great size (FIG. 27-14a). These large, treelike plants were major contributors to our present-day coal deposits (see *Inquiring About: Ancient Plants and Coal Formation*).

The 1200 or so species of club mosses living today, such as *Lycopodium* (FIG. 27-14b), are small (less than 25 cm, or 10 in., tall), attractive plants common in temperate woodlands. They possess true roots, both rhizomes and erect aerial stems, and small, scalelike leaves (microphylls). Sporangia are borne on reproductive leaves that are either clustered in conelike strobili at the tips of stems or scattered in reproductive areas along the stem. Club mosses are evergreen and often fashioned into wreaths and other decorations. In some areas they are endangered by overharvesting.

That common names are sometimes misleading in biology is vividly evident in this group of plants. The most common names for the phylum Lycopodiophyta are "club mosses" and "ground pines," yet these plants are neither mosses, which are nonvascular, nor pines, which are seed plants.

Ferns are a diverse group of spore-forming vascular plants

Most of the 11,000 species of **ferns** (phylum Pteridophyta) are terrestrial, although a few have adapted to aquatic habitats. Ferns range from the tropics to the Arctic Circle, with most species living in tropical rain forests, where they perch high in the branches of trees. In temperate regions ferns commonly inhabit swamps, marshes, stream banks, and moist woodlands (FIG. 27-15a). Some species grow in fields, rocky crevices on cliffs or mountains, or even deserts.

The life cycle of ferns involves a clearly defined alternation of generations. The ferns grown as houseplants (e.g., Boston fern, maiden-hair fern, and staghorn fern) represent the larger, more conspicuous sporophyte generation.

The fern sporophyte consists of a horizontal underground stem, or *rhizome,* that bears leaves, called *fronds,* and true roots. As each young frond first emerges from the ground, it is tightly coiled and resembles the top of a violin, hence the name *fiddlehead* (FIG. 27-15b). As fiddleheads grow, they unroll and expand to form fronds. Fern fronds are usually compound (the blade is divided into leaflets), with the leaflets forming

Seedless vascular plants include lycophytes and ferns.

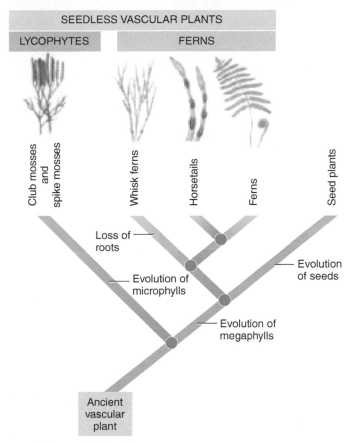

Figure 27-13 Evolutionary relationships among extant seedless vascular plants

These relationships are based on structural and molecular comparisons.

CONNECT According to the cladogram, which group, the lycophytes or the ferns, is most closely related to the seed plants?

© Cengage Learning

beautifully complex leaves. Fronds, roots, and rhizomes all contain vascular tissues.

Spore production usually occurs in certain areas on the fronds, which develop sporangia. Many species bear the sporangia in clusters, called **sori** (sing., *sorus*) (FIGS. 27-15c and d). Within sporangia, sporogenous cells (spore mother cells) undergo meiosis to form haploid spores. The sporangia burst open and discharge spores that may germinate and grow by mitosis into gametophytes.

The mature fern gametophyte, which bears no resemblance to the sporophyte, is a tiny (less than half the size of one of your fingernails), green, often heart-shaped structure that grows flat against the ground. Called a **prothallus** (pl., *prothalli*), the fern gametophyte lacks vascular tissues and has tiny, hairlike absorptive rhizoids to anchor it (FIG. 27-15e). The prothallus usually produces both archegonia and antheridia on its underside. Each archegonium contains a single egg, whereas numerous sperm cells are produced in each antheridium.

Ferns use water as a transport medium. The flagellate sperm cells swim, usually from a nearby prothallus, to the neck of an archegonium through a thin film of water on the ground underneath the prothallus. After one of the sperm cells fertilizes the egg, a diploid zygote grows by mitosis into a multicellular embryo (an immature sporophyte). At this stage the sporophyte embryo is attached to and dependent on the gametophyte, As the embryo matures, however, the prothallus withers and dies, and the sporophyte becomes free-living.

The fern life cycle alternates between the dominant, diploid sporophyte with its rhizome, roots, and fronds and the haploid gametophyte (prothallus) (FIG. 27-16). The sporophyte generation is dominant not only because it is larger than the gametophyte but also because it persists for an extended period (most fern sporophytes are perennials), whereas the gametophyte dies soon after reproducing.

Whisk ferns are classified as reduced ferns

Only about 12 species of **whisk ferns** (phylum Pteridophyta) exist today, and the fossil record contains several extinct species. Whisk ferns, which live mainly in the tropics and subtropics, are relatively simple in structure and lack true roots and leaves but have vascularized stems. *Psilotum nudum*, a representative whisk fern, has both a horizontal underground rhizome and vertical aerial stems (FIG. 27-17a). Whenever the stem forks, or branches, it always divides into two equal halves. Botanists call this forking **dichotomous branching.** In contrast, when most plant stems branch, one stem is more vigorous and becomes the main trunk.

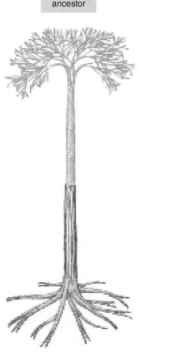

(a) Reconstruction of *Lepidodendron*, an ancient club moss the size of a large tree. Numerous fossils of *Lepidodendron* were preserved in coal deposits, particularly in Great Britain and the central United States. (Redrawn from Hirmer, M., *Handbuch der Paläobotanik*, R. Olderbourg, Munich, 1927.)

(b) The sporophyte of *Lycopodium*, a club moss, has small, scalelike, evergreen leaves (microphylls). Spores are produced in sporangia on reproductive leaves clustered in a conelike strobilus (*shown*) or, in other species, scattered along the stem.

Figure 27-14 **Seedless vascular plants: club mosses**

How did the coal that industrial society depends on for energy form? Coal, which is burned to produce electricity and to manufacture items of steel and iron, is one of the most important fossil fuels. Although mined, coal is not an inorganic mineral like gold or aluminum but rather is an organic material formed from the remains of ancient vascular plants, particularly those of the Carboniferous period, approximately 320 mya. Four main groups of plants contributed to coal formation. Two were seedless vascular plants: the club mosses and ferns (see figure), including horsetails. The other two were seed plants: seed ferns (now extinct) and early gymnosperms.

It is hard to imagine that relatives of the small, relatively inconspicuous club mosses, ferns, and horsetails of today were so significant in forming vast beds of coal. However, many members of these groups that existed during the Carboniferous period were giants compared with their modern counterparts and formed immense forests. (Figure 21-12 shows a reconstruction of a Carboniferous forest.)

The climate during the Carboniferous period was warm, moist, and mild. Plants in most locations could grow year-round because of the favorable conditions. Forests of these plants often grew in low-lying, swampy areas that periodically flooded when the sea level rose. As the sea level receded, these plants would re-establish.

When these large plants died or were blown over in storms, they decomposed incompletely because they were covered by swamp water. (The anaerobic conditions of the water prevented wood-rotting fungi from decomposing the plants, and anaerobic bacteria do not decompose wood rapidly.) Thus, over time the partially decomposed plant material accumulated and consolidated.

Layers of sediment formed over the plant material each time the water level rose and flooded the low-lying swamps. With time, heat and pressure built up in these accumulated layers and converted the plant material to coal and the sediment layers to sedimentary rock. Much later, geologic upheavals raised the layers of coal and sedimentary rock. Coal is usually found in seams, underground layers that vary in thickness from 2.5 cm (1 in.) to more than 30 m (100 ft).

© David Lyons/Alamy

This piece of Carboniferous coal contains a fossilized fern. The coal and fossil are about 300 million years old.

The various grades of coal (lignite, the lowest grade; subbituminous; bituminous; and anthracite, the highest grade) formed as a result of the different temperatures and pressures to which the layers were exposed. Coal exposed to high heat and pressure during its formation is drier, is more compact (and therefore harder), and has a higher heating value (i.e., a higher energy content) than coal exposed to lower heat and temperature conditions.

The upright stems of *Psilotum* are green and are the main organs of photosynthesis. Tiny, round sporangia, borne directly on the erect, aerial stems, contain sporogenous cells that undergo meiosis to form haploid spores. After dispersal, the spores germinate to form haploid prothalli. Because they grow underground, the prothalli of whisk ferns are difficult to study (FIG. 27-17b). They are nonphotosynthetic as a result of their subterranean location, and they apparently have a symbiotic relationship with mycorrhizal fungi that provides them with sugar and essential minerals (see Chapter 29).

Botanists have carefully studied whisk ferns in recent years. Molecular data, including comparisons of nucleotide sequences of ribosomal RNA, chloroplast DNA, and mitochondrial DNA in living species, support the hypothesis that the whisk ferns should be classified as reduced ferns rather than as surviving representatives of extinct vascular plants (see discussion of rhyniophytes later in this chapter).

Horsetails are an evolutionary line of ferns

About 300 mya, the **horsetails** (phylum Pteridophyta) were among the dominant plants and grew as large as modern trees (FIG. 27-18a). Because they contributed to Earth's vast coal deposits, these ancient horsetails, like ancient club mosses, are still significant today.

The few surviving horsetails, about 15 species in the genus *Equisetum*, grow mostly in wet, marshy habitats and are less than 1.3 m (4 ft) tall, but extremely distinctive (FIG. 27-18b). They are widely distributed on every continent except Australia. Traditionally classified in their own phylum, horsetails are now grouped with ferns. This reclassification is based on molecular similarities between horsetails and other ferns.

Horsetails have true roots, stems (both rhizomes and erect aerial stems), and small leaves. The hollow, jointed stems are impregnated with silica, which gives them a gritty texture. Small leaves, interpreted as reduced megaphylls, are fused in whorls at each node (the area on the stem where leaves attach). The green stem is the main organ of photosynthesis. Horsetails are so named because certain vegetative (nonreproductive) stems have whorls of branches that give the appearance of a bushy horse's tail. In the past, horsetails were called "scouring rushes" and were used to scrub pots and pans along stream banks.

Each reproductive branch of a horsetail bears a terminal conelike **strobilus** (pl., *strobili*). The strobilus consists of several stalked, umbrella-like structures, each of which bears five to ten sporangia in a circle around a common axis.

The horsetail life cycle is similar in many respects to the fern life cycle. In horsetails, as in ferns, the sporophyte is the conspicuous plant, whereas the gametophyte is a minute, lobed thallus ranging in width from the size of a pinhead to about 1 cm across. The sporophyte and gametophyte are both photosynthetic and nutritionally independent at maturity. Like ferns, horsetails require water as a medium for flagellate sperm cells to swim to the egg.

(a) **Fronds.** The Christmas fern (*Polystichum acrostichoides*), photographed in the Great Smoky Mountains in Tennessee, has fronds that grow to 0.6 m (2 ft) in length.

Ed Reschke/Getty Images

(b) **Fiddleheads.** Some fiddleheads are edible.

© Cengage Learning

(c) **Sori.** These round sori of rabbit's foot fern (*Polypodium aureum*) are arranged in two prominent rows on the leaf's underside.

John Arnaldi

(d) **Sporangia.** SEM of sporangia in a fern (*Dryopteris filix-mas*) sorus.

Ted Kinsman/Science Source

100 μm

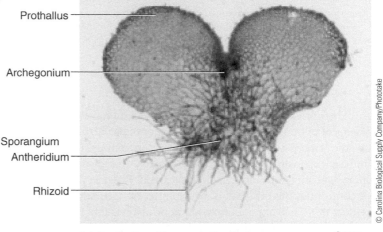

Prothallus

Archegonium

Sporangium
Antheridium

Rhizoid

(e) **Prothallus.** The prothallus is the gametophyte generation of a fern.

3 mm

© Carolina Biological Supply Company/Phototake

Figure 27-15 **Seedless vascular plants: ferns**

Some ferns and club mosses are heterosporous

In the life cycles examined thus far, plants produce only one type of spore as a result of meiosis. This condition, known as **homospory,** is characteristic of bryophytes, horsetails, whisk ferns, and most ferns and club mosses. However, certain ferns and club mosses (known as spike mosses) exhibit **heterospory,** in which they produce two types of spores: microspores and megaspores.

FIGURE 27-19 illustrates the generalized life cycle of a heterosporous plant. The sporophyte plant produces sporangia within a conelike strobilus. Each strobilus usually bears two kinds of sporangia: microsporangia and megasporangia. *Microsporangia* are sporangia that produce *microsporocytes* (also called *microspore mother cells*), which undergo meiosis to form microscopic, haploid **microspores.** Each microspore develops into a male gametophyte that produces sperm cells within antheridia.

Megasporangia produce *megasporocytes* (also called *megaspore mother cells*). When megasporocytes undergo meiosis, they form haploid **megaspores,** each of which develops into a female gametophyte that produces eggs in archegonia.

The development of male gametophytes from microspores and of female gametophytes from megaspores occurs within their respective spore walls, using stored food provided by the sporophyte. As a result, and unlike the gametophytes of other seedless vascular plants, the male and female gametophytes are not truly free-living. Fertilization is followed by the development of a new sporophyte.

Heterospory evolved several times during the history of land plants. It was a significant development in plant evolution because it was the forerunner of the evolution of seeds. Heterospory characterizes the two most successful groups of plants existing today, the gymnosperms and the flowering plants, both of which produce seeds.

The dominant phase in the life cycle of ferns, like that of all other vascular plants, is the sporophyte.

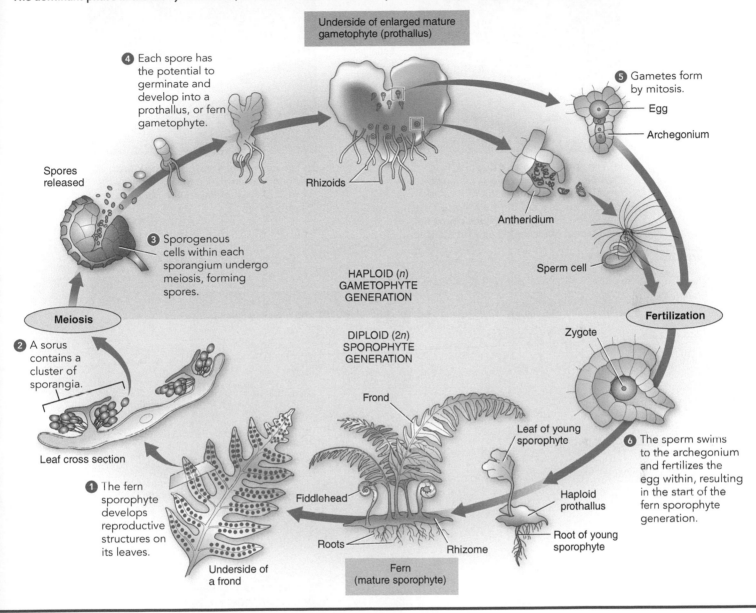

Figure 27-16 *Animation* **The life cycle of ferns**

Note the clearly defined alternation of generations between the gametophyte (prothallus) and sporophyte (leafy plant) generations.

CONNECT What is the most fundamental difference between the fern life cycle and that of mosses?

© Cengage Learning

Seedless vascular plants are used for experimental studies

Botanists use many seedless vascular plants as experimental models to study certain aspects of plant biology, such as physiology, growth, and development. Ferns and other seedless vascular plants are useful in studying how apical meristems give rise to plant tissues. An **apical meristem** is the area at the tip (apex) of a root or shoot where growth—cell division,

elongation, and differentiation—occurs. Ferns and other seedless vascular plants have a single large *apical cell* located at the center tip of the apical meristem. This apical cell is the source, by mitosis, of all the cells that eventually make up the root or shoot. The apical cell divides in an orderly fashion, and the smaller daughter cells produced by the apical cell, in turn, divide and give rise to different parts of the root or shoot. It is possible to trace mature cells in the root or shoot back to their origin from the single apical cell.

Sporangia

Aerial stem
with scalelike
outgrowths
(no leaves)

John Arnaldi

Antheridia

Archegonia

Rhizoids

© Cengage Learning

(a) The sporophyte of the whisk fern
Psilotum nudum. The stem is the main
organ of photosynthesis in this rootless,
leafless, vascular plant. Sporangia, which
turn yellow as they mature, are borne on
short lateral branches directly on the stems.

(b) The gametophyte of the whisk fern
Psilotum nudum. The gametophyte
(prothallus) lives underground, nourished by
mycorrhizal fungi.

Figure 27-17 Whisk ferns

Strobilus

Vegetative
shoots

Reproductive
shoots

Ed Reschke/Getty Images

(a) Reconstruction of *Calamites*, an
ancient horsetail that grew as tall as
many modern trees, to 20 m (about
65 ft). *Calamites* had an underground
rhizome where roots and aerial shoots
originated. (Redrawn from Emberger,
L., *Les Plantes Fossiles*, Masson et
Cie, Paris, 1968.)

(b) *Equisetum telematia*, a horsetail with a
wide distribution in Eurasia, Africa, and North
America, has unbranched reproductive shoots
bearing conelike strobili and separate, highly
branched vegetative (nonreproductive) shoots.
In some horsetail species, both reproductive
and vegetative shoots are unbranched.

Figure 27-18 Horsetails

Ferns are interesting research plants for studies in genetics
because they are **polyploids** and have multiple sets of chromosomes. (Many ferns have hundreds of chromosomes.) However,
gene expression in ferns is exactly what one would expect of a
diploid plant. Apparently, genes in the extra sets of chromosomes
are gradually silenced and therefore not expressed.

Seedless vascular plants arose more than 420 mya

Currently, the oldest known megafossils of early vascular plants
are from Silurian (420 mya) deposits in Europe. (Plant *megafossils*
are fossilized roots, stems, leaves, and reproductive structures.)

Heterospory—the production of two types of spores—was the forerunner of the evolution of seeds.

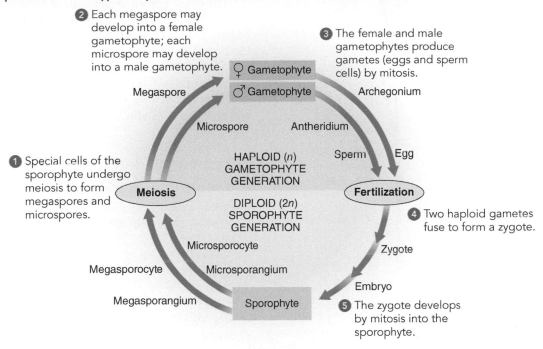

Figure 27-19 The basic life cycle of heterosporous plants

Two types of spores, microspores and megaspores, are produced during the life cycle of heterosporous plants.

CONNECT What fundamental similarities does a heterosporous life cycle share with the basic plant life cycle depicted in Figure 27-2?

© Cengage Learning

Megafossils of several kinds of small, seedless vascular plants also occur in Silurian deposits in Bolivia, Australia, and northwestern China. Microscopic spores of early vascular plants appear in the fossil record earlier than megafossils, suggesting that even older megafossils of simple vascular plants may be discovered.

Botanists assign the oldest vascular plants to phylum Rhyniophyta, which, according to the fossil record, arose some 420 mya and became extinct about 380 mya. The rhyniophytes are so named because many fossils of these extinct plants were found in fossil beds near Rhynie, Scotland. *Rhynia gwynne-vaughanii* is an example of an early vascular plant that superficially resembled whisk ferns in that it consisted of leafless upright stems that branched dichotomously from an underground rhizome (FIG. 27-20). *Rhynia* lacked roots, although it had absorptive rhizoids. Sporangia formed at the ends of short branches. The internal structure of its rhizome contained a central core of xylem cells for conducting water and minerals.

For many years, botanists considered *Rhynia major*, a plant that grew about 50 cm (20 in.) tall and probably lived in marshes, a classic example of a rhyniophyte. Fossils indicate that this plant had rhizoids, dichotomously branching rhizomes, and upright stems that terminated in sporangia. However, recent microscopic studies of fossil rhizomes indicate that the central core of tissue lacked the xylem cells characteristic

Figure 27-20 Reconstruction of *Rhynia gwynne-vaughanii*

This leafless plant, one of Earth's earliest vascular plants, is now extinct. It grew about 18 cm (7 in.) tall. (Redrawn from Edwards, D., "Evidence for the Sporophytic Status of the Lower Devonian Plant *Rhynia gwynne-vaughanii*," *Review of Palaeobotany and Palynology*, Vol. 29, 1980.)

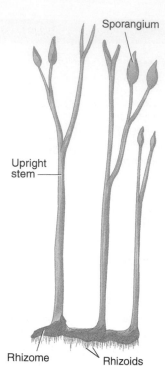

Figure 27-21 Reconstruction of *Aglaophyton major*

Recent evidence indicates that this plant, although superficially similar to other early vascular plants, lacked conducting tissues that are characteristic of vascular plants. For this reason, it has been reclassified into a new genus and is no longer considered a rhyniophyte. (Redrawn from Mauseth, J.D., *Botany: An Introduction to Plant Biology*, 2nd ed., Saunders College Publishing, Philadelphia, 1995.)

of vascular plants. For that reason, *R. major* was reclassified into a new genus, *Aglaophyton,* and is no longer considered a rhyniophyte (FIG. 27-21).

The oldest known megafossils of fernlike trees, discovered in New York, are dated at 380 million years old. These trees, which were about 8 m (26 ft) tall, had vascular tissues but no leaves and a minimal root system. They grew vertically and reproduced by forming spores. The trunks were discovered in the late 1800s (and named *Eospermatopteris*), but not until 2007 was a fossil of an entire tree pieced together. The treetops had previously been found separate from the trunks and named *Wattieza.*

CHECKPOINT 27.3

- *What adaptations do ferns have that both algae and bryophytes lack?*
- CONNECT *How does one distinguish between megaphylls and microphylls?*
- *Which of the following are parts of the sporophyte generation in ferns: frond, sperm cells, egg cell, roots, sorus, sporangium, spores, prothallus, rhizome, antheridium, archegonium, and zygote?*
- *Why are whisk ferns and horsetails now classified as ferns?*
- *How does heterospory modify the plant life cycle?*

SUMMARY: FOCUS ON LEARNING OBJECTIVES

27.1 Adaptations of Plants to Life on Land *(page 558)*

1 Discuss some environmental challenges of living on land and describe how several plant adaptations meet these challenges.

- The colonization of land by plants required the evolution of many anatomical, physiological, and reproductive adaptations. Plants have a waxy **cuticle** to protect against water loss and **stomata** for gas exchange needed for photosynthesis.
- Plant life cycles have an **alternation of generations** in which they spend part of their life cycle in a multicellular haploid **gametophyte generation** and part in a multicellular diploid **sporophyte generation.** The gametophyte plant produces gametes by mitosis. During fertilization these gametes fuse to form a **zygote,** the first stage of the sporophyte generation. The zygote develops into a multicellular **embryo** that the gametophyte protects and nourishes. The mature sporophyte plant develops from the embryo and produces sporogenous cells (spore mother cells). These cells undergo meiosis to form **spores,** the first stage in the gametophyte generation.
- Most plants have multicellular **gametangia** with a protective jacket of sterile cells surrounding the gametes. **Antheridia** are gametangia that produce sperm cells, and **archegonia** are gametangia that produce eggs.
- Ferns and other vascular plants have **xylem** to conduct water and dissolved minerals and **phloem** to conduct dissolved sugar.

2 Name the green algal group from which plants are hypothesized to have descended and describe supporting evidence.

- Plants probably arose from a group of green algae called **charophytes.** This conclusion is based in part on molecular comparisons of DNA and RNA sequences, which show the closest match between charophytes and plants.

27.2 Bryophytes *(page 562)*

3 Summarize the features that distinguish bryophytes from other plants.

- Unlike other land plants, **bryophytes** are nonvascular and lack xylem and phloem. Bryophytes are the only plants with a dominant gametophyte generation. Their sporophytes remain permanently attached and nutritionally dependent on the gametophytes.

4 Name and briefly describe the three phyla of bryophytes.

- **Mosses** (phylum Bryophyta) have gametophytes that are green plants that grow from a filamentous **protonema.**
- Many **liverworts** (phylum Hepatophyta) have gametophytes that are flattened, lobelike **thalli;** others are leafy.
- **Hornworts** (phylum Anthocerophyta) have thalloid gametophytes.

5 Describe the life cycle of mosses and compare their gametophyte and sporophyte generations.

- The green moss gametophyte bears archegonia, antheridia, or both at the top of the plant. During fertilization, a sperm cell fuses with an egg cell in the archegonium. The zygote grows into an embryo that develops into a moss sporophyte, which is attached to the gametophyte. Meiosis occurs within the capsule of the sporophyte to produce spores. When a spore germinates, it grows into a protonema that forms buds that develop into gametophytes.

27.3 Seedless Vascular Plants *(page 568)*

6 Discuss the features that distinguish seedless vascular plants from algae and bryophytes.

- Seedless vascular plants have several adaptations that algae and bryophytes lack, including vascular tissues and a dominant sporophyte generation. As in bryophytes, reproduction in seedless vascular plants depends on water as a transport medium for motile sperm cells.

7 Name and briefly describe the two phyla of seedless vascular plants.

- Sporophytes of **club mosses** (phylum Lycopodiophyta) consist of roots, rhizomes, erect branches, and leaves that are **microphylls.**
- **Ferns** (phylum Pteridophyta) are the largest and most diverse group of seedless vascular plants. The fern sporophyte consists of a rhizome that bears fronds and true roots. Phylum Pteridophyta also includes whisk ferns and horsetails. Sporophytes of **whisk ferns** have **dichotomously branching** rhizomes and

erect stems; they lack true roots and leaves. **Horsetail** sporophytes have roots, rhizomes, aerial stems that are hollow and jointed, and leaves that are reduced **megaphylls.**

8 Describe the life cycle of ferns and compare their sporophyte and gametophyte generations.

- Fern sporophytes have roots, rhizomes, and leaves that are megaphylls. Their leaves, or fronds, bear sporangia in clusters called **sori.** Meiosis in sporangia produces haploid spores. The fern gametophyte, called a **prothallus,** develops from a haploid spore and bears both archegonia and antheridia.

9 Compare the generalized life cycles of homosporous and heterosporous plants.

- **Homospory,** the production of one kind of spore, is characteristic of bryophytes, most club mosses, and most ferns, including whisk ferns and horsetails. In homospory spores give rise to gametophyte plants that produce both egg cells and sperm cells.
- **Heterospory,** the production of two kinds of spores (microspores and megaspores), occurs in certain club mosses, certain ferns, and all seed plants. **Microspores** give rise to male gametophytes that produce sperm cells. **Megaspores** give rise to female gametophytes that produce eggs. The evolution of heterospory was an essential step in the evolution of seeds.

Know and Comprehend

1. Plants probably descended from a group of green algae called (a) rhyniophytes (b) *Calamites* (c) epiphytes (d) charophytes (e) club mosses
2. Which of the following is *not* a characteristic of plants? (a) cuticle (b) unicellular gametangia (c) stomata (d) multicellular embryo (e) alternation of generations
3. In plant life cycles (a) the first products of meiosis are gametes (b) spores are part of the diploid sporophyte generation (c) the embryo gives rise to a zygote (d) the first stage in the diploid sporophyte generation is the zygote (e) the first stage in the haploid gametophyte generation is the prothallus
4. The bryophytes (a) include mosses, liverworts, and hornworts (b) include whisk ferns, horsetails, and club mosses (c) are small plants that lack a vascular system (d) a and c (e) b and c
5. The waxy layer that covers aerial parts of plants is the (a) cuticle (b) archegonium (c) protonema (d) stoma (e) thallus
6. A strengthening compound found in cell walls of vascular plants is (a) chitin (b) lignin (c) cutin (d) cellulose (e) carotenoid
7. Stomata (a) help prevent desiccation of plant tissues (b) transport water and minerals through plant tissues (c) allow gas exchange for photosynthesis (d) strengthen cell walls (e) produce male gametes
8. The green, gametangia-bearing moss plant (a) is the haploid gametophyte generation (b) is the diploid sporophyte generation (c) is called a protonema (d) contains cells with single large chloroplasts (e) b and c
9. _____ is a leaf that arose from a branch system. (a) An antheridium (b) A microphyll (c) A megaphyll (d) A sorus (e) A microspore
10. These plants have vascularized stems but lack true roots and leaves. (a) mosses (b) club mosses (c) horsetails (d) whisk ferns (e) hornworts

11. These plants have hollow, jointed stems that are impregnated with silica. (a) mosses (b) club mosses (c) horsetails (d) whisk ferns (e) hornworts
12. Which of the following statements about ferns is *not* true? (a) ferns have motile sperm cells that swim through water to the egg-containing archegonium (b) ferns are vascular plants (c) ferns are the most economically important group of bryophytes (d) the fern sporophyte consists of a rhizome, roots, and fronds (e) the diversity of ferns is greatest in the tropics

Apply and Analyze

13. **VISUALIZE** Draw a simple diagram illustrating a heterosporous life cycle. Include the sporophyte generation, megaspore, female gametophyte, egg, microspore, male gametophyte, sperm, meiosis, and fertilization. Be sure to indicate whether each generation or kind of cell is haploid or diploid.

Evaluate and Synthesize

14. **EVOLUTION LINK** How may the following trends in plant evolution be adaptive to living on land?
    a. dependence on water for fertilization → no need for water as a transport medium
    b. homospory → heterospory
15. **INTERPRET DATA** According to the cladogram in Figure 27-5, which plants evolved first: nonvascular bryophytes, seedless vascular plants, or seed plants?
16. **EVOLUTION LINK** Where would you position the rhyniophytes on Figure 27-13? Would the line for rhyniophytes extend to the tips of the rest of the cladogram? Why or why not?

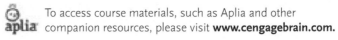

To access course materials, such as Aplia and other companion resources, please visit **www.cengagebrain.com.**

28 | Seed Plants

© Peggy Greb/Science Source

Hairy vetch seed pods. The seeds are developing within each pod. Hairy vetch (*Vicia villosa*) is native to Europe and Asia but has become naturalized in the United States.

KEY CONCEPTS

28.1 Seed plants, which produce young sporophytes enclosed within seeds, include gymnosperms and angiosperms.

28.2 Gymnosperms produce exposed ovules that, following fertilization, develop into seeds that are usually borne in cones on the sporophytes. Conifers are the most diverse and numerous of the four living gymnosperm phyla.

28.3 Angiosperms produce ovules enclosed within carpels; following fertilization, seeds develop from the ovules, and the ovaries of carpels become fruits. Angiosperms dominate the land and exhibit great diversity in both vegetative and reproductive structures.

28.4 Gymnosperms evolved from ancestral seedless vascular plants; angiosperms evolved from ancestral gymnosperms, possibly an ancient conifer.

C hapter 27 focused on plants that reproduce by means of *spores*, haploid cells that disperse and germinate to produce gametophytes. Although gymnosperms and angiosperms also produce spores, their primary means of reproduction and dispersal is by **seeds,** which represent an important adaptation for life on land (see photograph). Each seed consists of an embryonic sporophyte, nutritive tissue, and a protective coat. Seeds develop from the fertilized egg cell, the female gametophyte, and its associated tissues. The two groups of seed plants, gymnosperms and angiosperms (flowering plants), exhibit the greatest evolutionary complexity of land plants and are the dominant plants in most terrestrial environments.

Seeds are reproductively superior to spores for several reasons. First, a seed is further along in its development before it is released to survive on its own: a seed contains a multicellular young plant with embryonic root, stem, and one or more leaves already formed, whereas a spore is a single cell. Second, a seed contains an abundant food supply. After germination, food stored in the seed nourishes the plant embryo until it becomes self-sufficient. Because a spore is a single cell, few food reserves exist for the plant that develops from a spore. Third, a seed is protected by a multicellular **seed coat** that is very thick and hard in some plants, as, for example, in lima beans. Like spores, seeds live for extended periods at reduced rates of metabolism and germinate when conditions become favorable.

Seeds and seed plants are intimately connected with the development of human civilization. From prehistoric times, early humans collected and used seeds for food. Seeds often contain a concentrated source of proteins, oils, carbohydrates, and vitamins, which are nourishing for humans as well as for germinating plants. Seeds are easy to store (if kept dry), so humans can collect them during times of plenty to save for times of need. Few other foods are stored as conveniently or for as long. Although flowering plants produce most seeds that humans consume, the seeds of certain gymnosperms—the piñon pine, for example—are edible.

In this chapter we present the diversity in seed plants—both gymnosperms and angiosperms—followed by an examination of what we know about how seed plants evolved.

28.1 AN INTRODUCTION TO SEED PLANTS

LEARNING OBJECTIVE

1 Compare the features of gymnosperms and angiosperms.

Like the bryophytes and seedless vascular plants introduced in Chapter 27, seed plants have life cycles with an **alternation of generations;** they spend part of their lives in the multicellular diploid sporophyte stage and part in the multicellular haploid gametophyte stage. The sporophyte generation is the dominant stage in seed plants, and the gametophyte generation is significantly reduced in size and entirely dependent on the sporophyte generation. Unlike the bryophytes and ferns, seed plants do not have free-living gametophytes. Instead, the female gametophyte is attached to and nutritionally dependent on the sporophyte generation.

In Chapter 27 you learned that some seedless vascular plants are heterosporous. (Figure 27-19 shows a generalized life cycle for heterosporous plants.) However, *all* seed plants are heterosporous and produce two types of spores: microspores and megaspores. In fact, heterospory is a requirement of seed production.

Seed plants produce **ovules,** each of which is a *megasporangium* surrounded by **integuments,** layers of sporophyte tissue that enclose the megasporangium. After fertilization takes place, the ovule develops into a seed, and the integuments develop into the seed coat (**FIG. 28-1a**).

Botanists divide seed plants into two groups based on whether or not an ovary wall surrounds their ovules (an *ovary* is a structure that contains one or more ovules). The two groups of seed plants are the **gymnosperms** and the **angiosperms** (**TABLE 28-1**). The word *gymnosperm* is derived from the Greek for "naked seed." Gymnosperms produce seeds that are totally exposed or borne on the scales of cones (**FIG. 28-1b**). In other words, an ovary wall does not surround the ovules of gymnosperms. Pine, spruce, fir, hemlock, and ginkgo are examples of gymnosperms.

The term *angiosperm* is derived from the Greek expression that means "seed enclosed in a vessel or case." Angiosperms are flowering plants that produce their seeds within a *fruit* (a mature ovary) (**FIG. 28-1c**). Thus, the ovules of angiosperms are protected. Flowering plants, which are extremely diverse, include corn, oaks, water lilies, cacti, apples, grasses, palms, and buttercups.

Both gymnosperms and flowering plants have vascular tissues: **xylem,** for conducting water and dissolved minerals (inorganic nutrients), and **phloem,** for conducting dissolved sugar.

CHECKPOINT 28.1

- *What is an ovule?*
- *What kinds of seeds are surrounded by an ovary wall?*

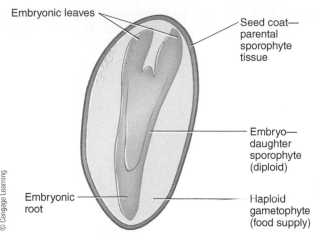

(a) **Gymnosperm seed.** Longitudinal section through a pine seed.

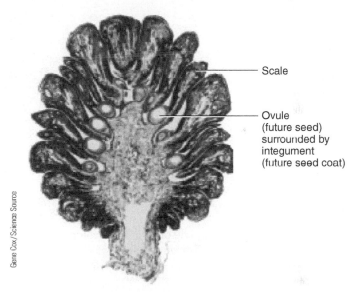

(b) **Gymnosperm cone.** Longitudinal section through a female pine cone, showing the ovules (which develop into seeds) borne on scales. Note the absence of an ovary wall.

(c) **Angiosperm fruit.** Longitudinal section through an avocado fruit, showing the seed surrounded by ovary tissue of the maternal sporophyte.

Figure 28-1 Seeds

TABLE 28-1	A Comparison of Gymnosperms and Angiosperms	
CHARACTERISTIC	GYMNOSPERMS	ANGIOSPERMS
Growth habit	Woody trees and shrubs	Woody or herbaceous
Conducting cells in xylem	Tracheids	Vessel elements and tracheids
Reproductive structures	Cones (usually)	Flowers
Pollen grain transfer	Wind (usually)	Animals or wind
Fertilization	Egg and sperm → zygote	Double fertilization: egg and sperm → zygote; two polar nuclei and sperm → endosperm
Seeds	Exposed or borne on scales of cones	Enclosed within fruit derived from ovary
Nutritive material	Female gametophyte	Endosperm
Number of species	About 840	More than 300,000
Geographic distribution	Worldwide	Worldwide

© Cengage Learning

28.2 GYMNOSPERMS

LEARNING OBJECTIVES

2   Trace the steps in the life cycle of a pine and compare its sporophyte and gametophyte generations.

3   Summarize the features that distinguish gymnosperms from bryophytes and ferns.

4   Name and briefly describe the four phyla of gymnosperms.

The gymnosperms include some of the most interesting plants. For example, a giant sequoia (*Sequoiadendron giganteum*) known as the General Sherman Tree, in Sequoia National Park in California, is one of the world's most massive organisms. It is 84.2 m (275 ft) tall and has a girth of 24.1 m (79 ft) measured 1.5 m (5 ft) above ground level. Another gymnosperm, a coast redwood (*Sequoia sempervirens*) nicknamed "Hyperion" after a giant in Greek mythology, is possibly the world's tallest tree, measuring 115.7 m (379 ft) in 2007. Botanists using tree-ring analysis determined that one of Earth's oldest living organisms, a bristlecone pine (*Pinus longaeva*) in the White Mountains of California, is about 5,000 years old.

Gymnosperms are usually classified into four phyla, which branch from a single evolutionary line (FIG. 28-2). Numbering 630 species, the largest phylum of gymnosperms is Coniferophyta, commonly called *conifers*. Two phyla of gymnosperms, Ginkgophyta (the ginkgoes) and Cycadophyta (the cycads), are evolutionary remnants of groups that were more significant in the past. The fourth phylum, Gnetophyta (gnetophytes), is a collection of some unusual plants that share certain traits not found in other gymnosperms; until recently, the gnetophytes were thought to be more closely related to flowering plants than were other gymnosperm clades. Current evidence, however, suggests that gnetophytes are probably most closely related to conifers (see Fig. 28-2).

Conifers are woody plants that produce seeds in cones

The **conifers** (phylum Coniferophyta), which include pines, spruces, hemlocks, and firs, are the most familiar group of gymnosperms (FIG. 28-3a). These 630 species of woody trees or shrubs produce annual additions of secondary tissues (wood and bark); there are no herbaceous (nonwoody) conifers. The wood (*secondary xylem*) consists of **tracheids,** which are long, tapering cells with pits through which water and dissolved minerals move from one cell to another.

Many conifers produce **resin,** a viscous, clear or translucent substance consisting of several organic compounds that may protect the plant from attack by fungi or insects. The resin collects in resin ducts, tubelike cavities that extend throughout the roots, stems, and leaves. Cells lining the resin ducts produce and secrete resin.

Conifers generally have leaves called *needles* that are long, narrow, tough, and leathery (FIG. 28-3b). Most pines bear clusters of two to five needles, depending on the species. In a few conifers, such as American arborvitae, the leaves are scalelike and cover the stem (FIG. 28-3c). Most conifers are evergreen and bear their leaves throughout the year. Only a few, such as the dawn redwood, larch, and bald cypress, are deciduous and shed their needles at the end of each growing season.

Most conifers are **monoecious:** they have separate male and female reproductive parts in different locations on the same plant. These reproductive parts are generally borne in *strobili* (commonly called *cones*), hence the name *conifer,* which means "cone-bearing."

Conifers occupy extensive areas, ranging from the Arctic to the tropics, and are the dominant vegetation in the forested regions of Alaska, Canada, northern Europe, and Siberia. In addition, they are important in the Southern Hemisphere, particularly in wet, mountainous areas of temperate and tropical regions in South America, Australia, New Zealand, and Malaysia. Southwestern China, with more than 60 species of conifers, has the greatest regional diversity of conifer species in the world. California, New Caledonia (an island east of Australia), southeastern China, and Japan also have considerable diversity of conifer species. Ecologically, conifers contribute food and shelter to animals and other organisms, and their roots hold the soil in place and help prevent soil erosion.

Humans use conifers for their wood (for building materials as well as paper products), medicinal value (such as the anticancer drug Taxol from the Pacific yew), turpentine, and resins.

Seed plants include four gymnosperm phyla and one phylum of flowering plants (angiosperms).

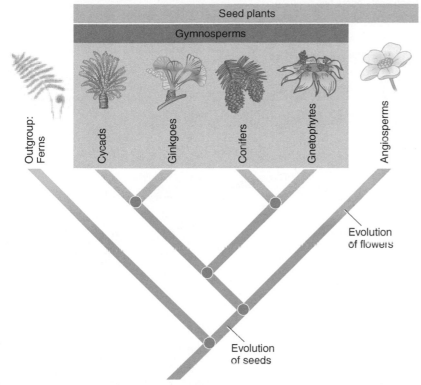

Figure 28-2 **Gymnosperm and angiosperm evolution**

This cladogram shows a current hypothesis of phylogenetic relationships among living seed plants, based on structural evidence, molecular comparisons, and fossils. Relationships among extant gymnosperm clades and angiosperms remain controversial. The arrangement of the phyla shown here may change as future analyses help clarify relationships.

CONNECT According to the cladogram, which group is most closely related to the conifers?

© Cengage Learning

(a) White fir (*Abies concolor*). Photographed in Milford, Pennsylvania, at the historic home of Gifford Pinchot, the first Chief Forester of the U.S. Forest Service (under T. R. Roosevelt).

(b) In white pine (*Pinus strobus*), leaves are long, slender needles that occur in clusters of five.

(c) In American arborvitae (*Thuja occidentalis*), leaves are small and scalelike.

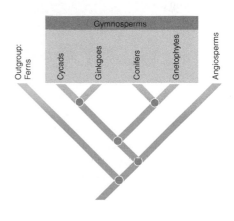

Figure 28-3 **Conifers**

© Cengage Learning

Gymnosperms, like all seed plants, are heterosporous.

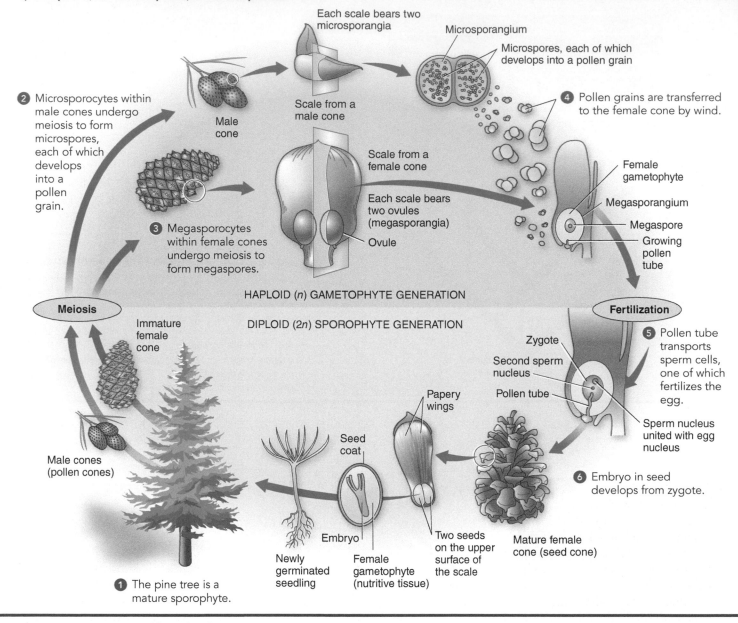

Each scale bears two microsporangia

Microsporangium

Microspores, each of which develops into a pollen grain

2 Microsporocytes within male cones undergo meiosis to form microspores, each of which develops into a pollen grain.

Male cone

Scale from a male cone

4 Pollen grains are transferred to the female cone by wind.

Scale from a female cone

Female gametophyte

Megasporangium

Megaspore

Growing pollen tube

3 Megasporocytes within female cones undergo meiosis to form megaspores.

Each scale bears two ovules (megasporangia)

Ovule

HAPLOID (*n*) GAMETOPHYTE GENERATION

Meiosis

DIPLOID (2*n*) SPOROPHYTE GENERATION

Fertilization

Immature female cone

Zygote

Second sperm nucleus

Pollen tube

5 Pollen tube transports sperm cells, one of which fertilizes the egg.

Sperm nucleus united with egg nucleus

Papery wings

Male cones (pollen cones)

Seed coat

Embryo

Newly germinated seedling

Female gametophyte (nutritive tissue)

Two seeds on the upper surface of the scale

Mature female cone (seed cone)

6 Embryo in seed develops from zygote.

1 The pine tree is a mature sporophyte.

Figure 28-4 *Animation* **Life cycle of pine**

One major advantage of gymnosperms over the seedless vascular plants is the production of wind-borne pollen grains.
© Cengage Learning

CONNECT Is a pine pollen grain haploid or diploid? Is it a gamete? Explain your answer.

Because of their attractive appearance, conifers such as firs, spruces, pines, and cedars are grown for landscape design and decorative holiday trees and wreaths.

Pines represent a typical conifer life cycle

The genus *Pinus*, by far the largest genus in the conifers, consists of about 100 species. A pine tree is a mature sporophyte (FIG. 28-4). Pine is heterosporous and therefore produces microspores and megaspores in separate cones. Male cones, usually 1 cm or less in length, are smaller than female cones

and are generally produced on the lower branches each spring (FIG. 28-5). The more familiar, woody female cones, which are on the tree year-round, are usually found on the upper branches of the tree and bear seeds after reproduction. Female cones vary considerably in size. The sugar pine (*P. lambertiana*) that grows in California produces the world's longest female cones, which reach lengths of 60 cm (2 ft).

Each male cone, also called a *pollen cone,* consists of **sporophylls,** leaflike scales that bear sporangia on the underside. At the base of each sporophyll are two **microsporangia,** which contain numerous **microsporocytes,** also called

Pollen grains (immature male gametophytes)

50 μm

Ed Reschke/Getty Images

Walt Anderson/Visuals Unlimited

Figure 28-5 Male and female cones in lodgepole pine (*Pinus contorta*)

Mature woody female cones (*top*) have opened to shed their seeds. Clusters of male cones (*bottom*) produce copious amounts of pollen grains in the spring. (*Inset*) Each pollen grain develops from a microspore.

microspore mother cells. In Figure 28-4, each microsporocyte undergoes meiosis to form four haploid microspores. **Microspores** then develop into extremely reduced male gametophytes. Each immature male gametophyte, also called a **pollen grain,** consists of four cells, two of which—a *generative cell* and a *tube cell*—are involved in reproduction. The other two cells soon degenerate. Two large air sacs on each pollen grain provide buoyancy for wind dissemination. Male cones shed pollen grains in great numbers, and wind currents carry some to the immature female cones.

Many botanists think that the female cones (also called *seed cones*) are modified branch systems. Each cone scale bears two **ovules,** or **megasporangia,** on its upper surface. Within each megasporangium, meiosis of a **megasporocyte,** or *megaspore mother cell,* produces four haploid **megaspores.** One of them divides mitotically, developing into the female gametophyte, which produces an egg within each of several archegonia. The other three megaspores are nonfunctional and soon degenerate.

When the ovule is ready to receive pollen, it produces a sticky droplet at the opening where the pollen grains land. **Pollination,** the transfer of pollen to the female cones, occurs in the spring for a week or ten days, after which the pollen cones wither and drop off the tree. One of the many pollen grains that adhere to the sticky female cone grows a **pollen tube,** an outgrowth that digests its way through the megasporangium to the egg within the archegonium. The germinated pollen grain with its pollen tube is the mature male gametophyte.

Ultimately, two nonmotile (nonflagellate) sperm cells form within the germinated pollen grain. When it reaches the female gametophyte, the pollen tube discharges the two sperm cells near the egg. One of these sperm cells fuses with the egg, in the

process of **fertilization,** to form a zygote, or fertilized egg, which subsequently grows into a young pine embryo in the seed. The other sperm cell degenerates.

The developing embryo consists of an embryonic root and an embryonic shoot with several cotyledons (embryonic leaves). Haploid female gametophyte tissue surrounds the embryo and becomes the nutritive tissue in the mature pine seed. A tough, protective seed coat derived from the integuments encloses the embryo and nutritive tissue. The seed coat forms a thin, papery wing at one end that enables dispersal by air currents. Some seeds remain within the female cones for several years before being shed.

In the pine life cycle, the sporophyte generation is dominant, and the gametophyte generation is restricted in size to microscopic structures in the cones. Although the female gametophyte produces archegonia, the male gametophyte is so reduced that it does not produce antheridia. The gametophyte generation in pines, as in all seed plants, depends totally on the sporophyte generation for nourishment.

A major adaptation in the pine life cycle is elimination of the need for external water as a sperm transport medium. Instead, air currents carry pine pollen grains to female cones, and nonflagellate sperm cells move through a pollen tube to the egg. Pine and other conifers are plants whose reproduction is totally adapted for life on land.

Cycads have seed cones and compound leaves

Cycads (phylum Cycadophyta) were very important during the Triassic period, which began about 251 million years ago (mya) and is sometimes referred to as the "Age of Cycads." Most cycad species are now extinct, and the few surviving ones, about 140 species, are tropical and subtropical plants with stout, trunklike stems and compound leaves that resemble those of palms or tree ferns (FIG. 28-6). Many cycads are endangered, primarily because they are popular as ornamentals and are gathered from the wild and sold to collectors. In the United States, cycads can be found in Florida, Texas, and California.

Cycad reproduction is similar to that in pines except that cycads are **dioecious** and therefore have seed cones on female plants and pollen cones on male plants. Their seed structure is most like that of the earliest seeds found in the fossil record. Cycads have also retained motile sperm cells, each of which has many hairlike flagella. Motile sperm cells are a vestige retained from the ancestors of cycads, in which sperm cells swam from antheridia to archegonia. In cycads specialized insects (almost exclusively beetles) carry pollen grains to the female plants and

Figure 28-6 Cycads

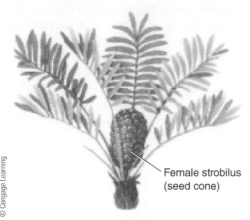

(a) A female Florida arrowroot (*Zamia integrifolia*) produces seed cones. This plant is the only cycad native to the United States. Like *Zamia*, most cycads are short plants, less than 2 m (6.5 ft) tall.

Female strobilus (seed cone)

© Cengage Learning

Martin Harvey/Getty Images

(b) This female cycad (*Encephalartos princeps*) native to South Africa bears three seed cones.

outer coverings give off a foul odor that smells like rancid butter. In China and Japan, where people eat the seeds, the female trees are more common.

Ginkgo has been an important medicinal plant for centuries and is still a common herbal remedy today. Extracts from the leaves may enhance neurological functioning by increasing blood flow to the brain, although several recent studies have concluded that ginkgo does not improve memory or prevent dementia in elderly people. In 2013 scientists from the National Toxicology Program of the National Institutes of Health reported the development of cancers in rats and mice fed high doses of *Gingko biloba* extract.

their cones. Following transfer to the female cone, the pollen grain germinates and grows a pollen tube. The sperm cells are released into this tube and swim to the egg.

Ginkgo biloba is the only living species in its phylum

Ginkgo (phylum Ginkgophyta) is represented by a single *extant* (living) species, the maidenhair tree, *Ginkgo biloba* (**FIG. 28-7**). This native of eastern China grew in the wild in only two locations, although people had cultivated it for its edible seeds in China and Japan for centuries. *Ginkgo* is the oldest genus (and species) of extant trees. Fossil ginkgoes 200 million years old have been discovered that are strikingly similar to the modern ginkgo.

People often plant ginkgo in North America and Europe today, particularly in parks and along city streets, because it is hardy and somewhat resistant to air pollution. Its leaves are deciduous and turn a beautiful yellow before being shed in the fall.

Like cycads, ginkgo is dioecious, with separate male and female trees. It has flagellate sperm cells, an evolutionary vestige that is not required because ginkgo produces airborne pollen grains. Ginkgo seeds are completely exposed rather than contained within cones. Male trees are usually planted because the female trees bear seeds whose fleshy

Gnetophytes include three unusual genera

The **gnetophytes** (nee′ toe phites) (phylum Gnetophyta) consist of about 70 species in three diverse and obscure genera (*Gnetum, Ephedra,* and *Welwitschia*). Gnetophytes share certain features that make them unique among the gymnosperms. For example, gnetophytes have more efficient water-conducting cells, called *vessel elements,* in their xylem (see Chapter 33). Flowering plants also have vessel elements in their xylem, but of the gymnosperms, only the gnetophytes do. In addition, the cone clusters that some gnetophytes produce resemble flower clusters, and certain details in their life cycles resemble those of flowering plants. Despite these similarities, most botanists now think that gnetophytes represent evolutionary diversity in gymnosperms and are not in a direct line to flowering plants (see Fig. 28-2).

Marion Lobstein

(a) Close-up of a branch from a female ginkgo, showing the exposed seeds and the distinctive, fan-shaped leaves.

Figure 28-7 Ginkgo, or maidenhair tree

Joseph Malcolm Smith/Science Source

(b) Ginkgo (*Ginkgo biloba*) tree in a formal garden in northern England.

The genus *Gnetum* contains tropical vines, shrubs, and trees with broad leaves (FIG. 28-8a). Species in the genus *Ephedra* include many shrubs and vines that grow in deserts and other dry temperate and tropical regions. Some *Ephedra* species resemble horsetails in that they have jointed green stems with tiny leaves (FIG. 28-8b). Commonly called *joint fir*, *Ephedra* has been used medicinally for centuries. An Asiatic *Ephedra* is the source of ephedrine, which stimulates the heart and raises blood pressure. At one time, ephedrine was commonly sold over the counter in weight-control medications and herbal energy boosters; several deaths were reported from chronic use or overdose of products containing ephedrine, so its use has been restricted.

The third gnetophyte genus, *Welwitschia*, contains a single species found in deserts of southwestern Africa (FIG.28-8c). Most of *Welwitschia*'s body—a long taproot—grows underground. Its short, wide stem forms a shallow disc, up to 0.9 m (3 ft) in diameter, from which two ribbon-like leaves extend. These two leaves continue to grow from the stem throughout the plant's life, but their ends are usually broken and torn by the wind, giving the appearance of numerous leaves. Each leaf grows to about 2 m (6.5 ft) in length. When *Welwitschia* reproduces, cones form around the edge of its disclike stem.

CHECKPOINT 28.2

- *What is the dominant generation in the pine life cycle? How does pollination occur in gymnosperms?*
- CONNECT *What features distinguish gymnosperms from seedless plants?*
- *What are the four groups of gymnosperms?*
- *What features distinguish cycads from ginkgo? from gnetophytes?*

(a) The leaves of *Gnetum gnemon* resemble those of flowering plants. Note the exposed seeds. The species is native to southern Asia and the Maldives.

(b) A male joint fir (*Ephedra*) has pollen cones clustered at the nodes. In the 19th century, European pioneers used species native to the American Southwest to make a beverage, Mormon tea.

(c) *Welwitschia mirabilis* is native to deserts in southwestern Africa. It survives on moisture-laden fogs that drift inland from the ocean. Photographed in the Namib Desert, Namibia.

Figure 28-8 Gnetophytes

28.3 FLOWERING PLANTS

LEARNING OBJECTIVES

5   Summarize the features that distinguish flowering plants from other plants.
6   Briefly explain the life cycle of a flowering plant and describe double fertilization.
7   Contrast monocots and eudicots, the two largest classes of flowering plants.
8   Discuss the evolutionary adaptations of flowering plants.

Flowering plants, or angiosperms (phylum Anthophyta), are the most successful plants today, surpassing even the gymnosperms in importance. They have adapted to almost every habitat and, with at least 300,000 species, are Earth's dominant plants. Flowering plants come in a wide variety of sizes and forms, from herbaceous violets to massive eucalyptus trees. Some flowering plants—tulips and roses, for example—have large, conspicuous flowers; others, such as grasses and oaks, produce small, inconspicuous flowers.

Flowering plants are vascular plants that reproduce sexually by forming flowers and, following a unique double fertilization process, seeds within fruits. The fruit protects the developing seeds and often aids in their dispersal (see Chapter 37). Flowering plants have efficient water-conducting cells called **vessel elements** in their xylem and efficient sugar-conducting cells called **sieve tube elements** in their phloem (see Chapter 33).

Flowering plants are extremely important to humans because our survival as a species literally depends on them. All our major food crops are flowering plants; examples include rice, wheat, corn, potatoes, tomatoes, beans, apples, and citrus fruits. Woody flowering plants such as oak, cherry, and walnut provide valuable lumber. Flowering plants give us fibers, such as cotton and linen, and medicines, such as digitalis and codeine. Products as diverse as rubber, tobacco, coffee, chocolate, wine, and aromatic oils for perfumes come from flowering plants. *Economic botany* is the subdiscipline of botany that deals with plants of economic importance.

TABLE 28-2	Distinguishing Features of Monocots and Eudicots	
FEATURE	**MONOCOTS**	**EUDICOTS**
Flower parts	Usually in threes	Usually in fours or fives
Pollen grains	One furrow or pore	Three furrows or pores
Leaf venation	Usually parallel	Usually netted
Vascular bundles in stem cross section	Usually scattered or more complex arrangement	Arranged in a circle (ring)
Roots	Fibrous root system	Taproot system
Seeds	Embryo with one cotyledon	Embryo with two cotyledons
Secondary growth (wood and bark)	Absent	Often present

© Cengage Learning

Monocots and eudicots are the two largest classes of flowering plants

Phylum Anthophyta is divided into several classes with only a few members each and two very large classes: the monocots (class Monocotyledones) and the eudicots (class Eudicotyledones). The smaller classes will be discussed later in this chapter in the context of their evolutionary significance. For now, we restrict our discussion of flowering plants to the monocots and eudicots, which collectively represent about 97% of all flowering plant species. Eudicots are more diverse and include many more species (at least 200,000) than the monocots (at least 90,000). **TABLE 28-2** provides a comparison of some of the general features of the two classes.

Monocots include palms, grasses, orchids, irises, onions, and lilies. Monocots are mostly herbaceous plants with long, narrow leaves that have parallel veins (the main leaf veins run parallel to one another). The parts of monocot flowers usually occur in threes (**FIG. 28-9a**). For example, a flower may have three sepals, three petals, six stamens, and a compound pistil consisting of three fused carpels (these flower parts are

discussed shortly). Monocot seeds have a single **cotyledon,** or embryonic seed leaf; **endosperm,** a nutritive tissue, is usually present in the mature seed.

Eudicots include oaks, roses, mustards, cacti, blueberries, and sunflowers. Eudicots are either herbaceous (such as a tomato plant) or woody (such as a hickory tree). Their leaves vary in shape but usually are broader than monocot leaves, with netted (finely branched) veins. Flower parts usually occur in fours or fives or multiples thereof (**FIG. 28-9b**). Two cotyledons are present in eudicot seeds, and endosperm is usually absent in the mature seed, having been absorbed by the two cotyledons during seed development.

Sexual reproduction takes place in flowers

Flowers are reproductive shoots usually composed of four parts—sepals, petals, stamens, and carpels—arranged in whorls (circles) on the end of a flower stalk, or **peduncle** (**FIG. 28-10**). The peduncle may terminate in a single flower or a cluster of flowers known as an **inflorescence.** The tip of the flower stalk that bears the flower parts is known as the **receptacle.**

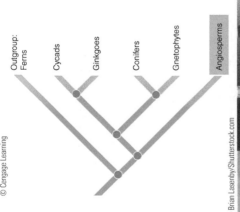

(a) Monocot. *Trillium erectum,* like most monocots, has floral parts in threes. Note the three green sepals, three red petals, six stamens, and three stigmas (the compound pistil consists of three fused carpels).

(b) Eudicot. Most eudicots, such as this *Tacitus,* have floral parts in fours or fives. Note the five petals, ten stamens, and five separate pistils. Five sepals are also present but barely visible against the background.

Figure 28-9 Flowering plants

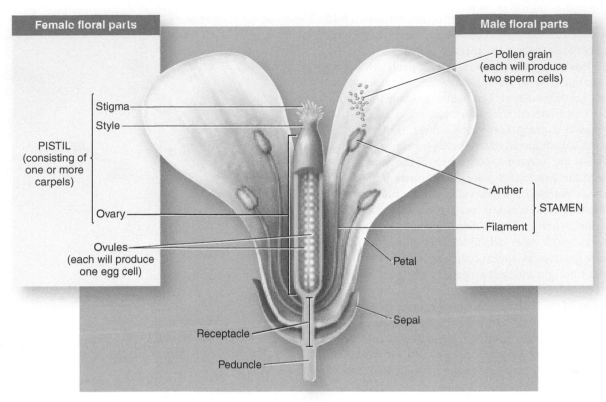

Female floral parts

Male floral parts

Stigma

Style

PISTIL
(consisting of
one or more
carpels)

Ovary

Ovules
(each will produce
one egg cell)

Pollen grain
(each will produce
two sperm cells)

Anther

STAMEN

Filament

Petal

Sepal

Receptacle

Peduncle

Figure 28-10 *Animation* **Floral structure**

This cutaway view of an *Arabidopsis* flower shows the details of basic floral structure. Each flower has four sepals (two are shown), four petals (two are shown), six stamens, and one long pistil. Four of the stamens are long, and two are short (two long and two short are shown). Pollen grains develop within sacs in the anthers. In *Arabidopsis,* the compound pistil consists of two carpels that each contain numerous ovules.
© Cengage Learning

All four floral parts are important in the reproductive process, but only the stamens (the "male" organs) and carpels (the "female" organs) produce gametes. A flower that has all four parts is a **complete flower,** whereas an **incomplete flower** lacks one or more of these four parts. A flower with both stamens and carpels is a **perfect flower,** whereas an **imperfect flower** has stamens or carpels, but not both.

Sepals, which make up the lowermost and outermost whorl on a floral shoot, are leaflike in appearance and often green (FIG. 28-11a). Sepals cover and protect the other flower parts

Petals   Sepals

James Mauseth/University of Texas

(a) The leaflike sepals of a rosebud (*Rosa*) enclose and protect the inner flower parts.

Stamen

Pistil

Marion Lobstein

(b) A twinleaf (*Jeffersonia diphylla*) flower has eight yellow stamens. Note the simple pistil with its green ovary in the center of the flower.

Figure 28-11 Parts of a flower

when the flower is a bud. As the flower opens, the sepals fold back to reveal the more conspicuous petals. The collective term for all the sepals of a flower is the **calyx.**

The whorl just above the sepals consists of **petals,** which are broad, flat, and thin (like sepals and leaves) but vary in shape and are frequently brightly colored. Petals attract animal pollinators to the flower (see Chapter 37). Sometimes petals are fused to form a tube (as in trumpet honeysuckle flowers) or other floral shape (as in snapdragons, whose petals form two lips). The petals of a flower are referred to collectively as the **corolla.**

Just inside the petals is a whorl of **stamens** (FIG. 28-11b). Each stamen is composed of a thin stalk, called a **filament,** and a saclike **anther,** where meiosis occurs to form microspores that develop into pollen grains. Each pollen grain produces two cells surrounded by a tough outer wall. One cell eventually divides to form two male gametes, or sperm cells, and the other produces a pollen tube through which the sperm cells travel to reach the ovule.

In the center of most flowers are one or more closed **carpels,** the "female" reproductive organs. Carpels bear ovules, which, as you may recall, are structures with the potential to develop into seeds. The carpels of a flower can be separate or fused into a single structure. The female part of the flower is also called a **pistil** (see Fig. 28-11b). A pistil may consist of a single carpel (a simple pistil) or a group of fused carpels (a compound pistil) (FIG. 28-12). Each pistil generally has three sections: a **stigma,** on which the pollen grain lands; a **style,** a necklike structure through which the pollen tube grows; and an **ovary,** an enlarged structure that contains one or more ovules. Each young ovule contains a female gametophyte that forms one female gamete (an egg), two *polar nuclei,* and several other haploid cells. After fertilization, the ovule develops into a seed, and the ovary develops into a fruit.

The life cycle of flowering plants includes double fertilization

Flowering plants undergo alternation of generations in which the sporophyte generation is larger and nutritionally independent (FIG. 28-13). The gametophyte generation in flowering plants is microscopic and nutritionally dependent on the sporophyte. Flowering plants, like gymnosperms and certain other vascular plants, are heterosporous and produce two kinds of spores: microspores and megaspores. Sexual reproduction occurs in the flower.

Each young ovule within an ovary contains a megasporocyte (megaspore mother cell) that undergoes meiosis to produce four haploid megaspores. Three of them usually disintegrate, and one divides mitotically and develops into a mature female gametophyte, also called an **embryo sac.**

Embryo sacs in the vast majority of angiosperms contain seven cells with eight haploid nuclei. Six of these cells, including the egg cell, contain a single nucleus each, and a central cell has two nuclei, called **polar nuclei.** The egg and the central cell with two polar nuclei are directly involved in fertilization; the other five cells in the embryo sac apparently have no direct role in

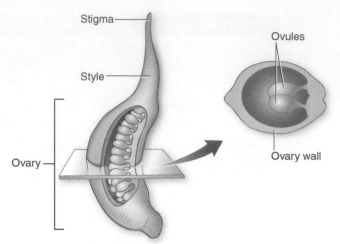

(a) Simple pistil. This simple pistil consists of a single carpel.

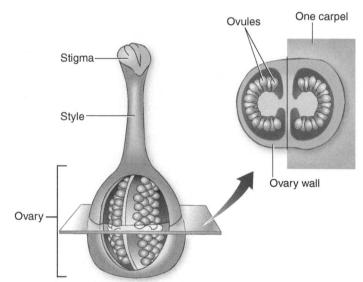

(b) Compound pistil. This compound pistil has two united carpels. In most flowers with single pistils, the pistils are compound, consisting of two or more fused carpels.

Figure 28-12 Simple and compound pistils
© Cengage Learning

the fertilization process and disintegrate. As the *synergids* (the two cells flanking the egg) disintegrate, however, they release chemicals that may affect the direction of pollen tube growth.

Each pollen sac, or microsporangium, of the anther contains numerous microsporocytes (microspore mother cells), each of which undergoes meiosis to form four haploid microspores. Every microspore develops into an immature male gametophyte, also called a *pollen grain.* Pollen grains are small, and each consists of two cells: the *tube cell* and the *generative cell.*

The anthers split open and begin to shed pollen. A variety of agents—including wind, water, insects, and other animal pollinators—transfer pollen grains to the stigma (see

A significant feature of the flowering plant life cycle is double fertilization, in which one sperm cell unites with the egg, forming a zygote; the other sperm cell unites with the two polar nuclei, forming a triploid cell that gives rise to endosperm.

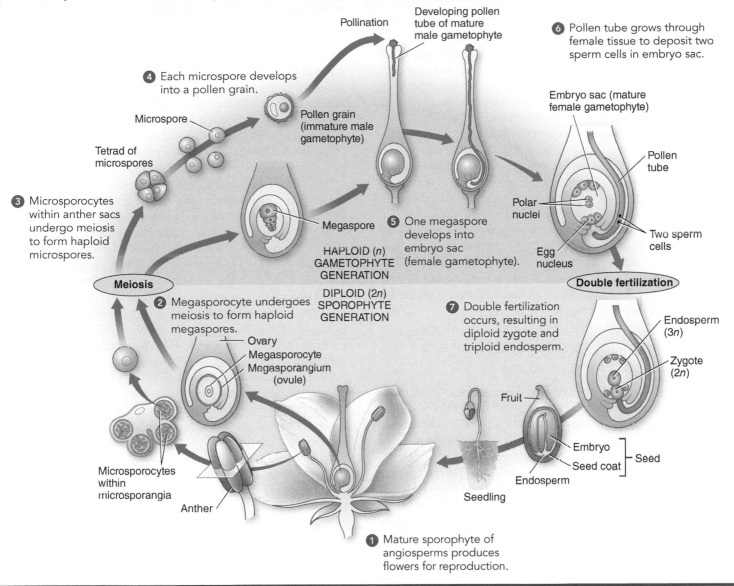

Figure 28-13 *Animation* **Life cycle of flowering plants**

CONNECT Are microspores and megaspores haploid or diploid? Are they gametes? Explain your answer.

© Cengage Learning

Chapter 37). If compatible with the stigma, the pollen grain germinates, and a pollen tube grows down the style and into the ovary. The germinated pollen grain with its pollen tube is the mature male gametophyte. Next, the generative cell divides to form two nonflagellate sperm cells. The sperm cells move down the pollen tube and are discharged into the embryo sac.

When the two sperm cells enter the embryo sac, *both* participate in fertilization. One sperm cell fuses with the egg, forming a zygote that divides by mitosis and develops into a multicellular embryo in the seed. The second sperm cell fuses with the two haploid polar nuclei of the central cell to form a triploid (3n) cell that divides by mitosis and develops into **endosperm,** a nutrient tissue rich in lipids, proteins, and carbohydrates that nourishes the growing embryo. This fertilization process, which involves two separate nuclear fusions, is called **double fertilization** and is, with two exceptions, unique to flowering plants. (Double fertilization has been reported in the gymnosperms *Ephedra nevadensis* and *Gnetum gnemon.* This process differs from double fertilization in flowering plants in that an additional zygote, rather than endosperm, is produced. The second zygote later disintegrates.)

Seeds and fruits develop after fertilization

As a result of double fertilization and subsequent growth and development, each seed contains a young plant embryo and nutritive tissue (the endosperm), both of which are surrounded by a protective seed coat. In monocots the endosperm persists and is the main source of food in the mature seed. In most eudicots the endosperm nourishes the developing embryo, which subsequently stores food in its cotyledons.

As a seed develops from an ovule following fertilization, the ovary wall surrounding it enlarges dramatically and develops into a **fruit.** In some instances, other tissues associated with the ovary also enlarge to form the fruit (see discussion of fruits in Chapter 37). Fruits serve two purposes: to protect the developing seeds from desiccation as they grow and mature and to aid in the dispersal of seeds. For example, dandelion fruits have feathery plumes that are lifted and carried by air currents. Animals often assist in dispersing seeds found in edible fruits (**FIG. 28-14**). Once a seed lands in a suitable place, it may germinate and develop into a mature sporophyte that produces flowers, and the life cycle continues as described.

Flowering plants have many adaptations that account for their success

The evolutionary adaptations of flowering plants account for their success in terms of their ecological dominance and their great number of species. Seed production as the primary means of reproduction and dispersal, an adaptation shared with the gymnosperms, is clearly significant and provides a definite advantage over seedless vascular plants. Closed carpels, which give rise to fruits surrounding the seeds, and the process of double fertilization with its resulting endosperm increase the likelihood of reproductive success. The evolution of a variety of interdependencies with many types of insects, birds, and bats, which disperse pollen from one flower to another of the same species, is another reason for angiosperm success. Pollen transfer results in cross-fertilization, which mixes the genetic material and promotes genetic variation among the offspring.

Several distinctive features have contributed to the success of flowering plants in addition to their highly successful reproduction involving flowers, fruits, and seeds. Recall that most flowering plants have very efficient water-conducting vessel elements in their xylem, as well as tracheids. In contrast, the xylem of almost all seedless vascular plants and gymnosperms consists exclusively of tracheids. Most flowering plants also have efficient carbohydrate-conducting sieve tube elements in their phloem. Vascular plants other than flowering plants and gnetophytes lack vessel elements and sieve tube elements.

The leaves of flowering plants, with their broad, expanded blades, are very efficient at absorbing light for photosynthesis. Abscission (shedding) of these leaves during cold or dry periods reduces water loss and has enabled some flowering plants to expand into habitats that would otherwise be too harsh for survival. The stems and roots of flowering plants are often modified for food or water storage, another feature that helps flowering plants survive in severe environments.

Probably most crucial to the evolutionary success of flowering plants, however, is the overall adaptability of the sporophyte generation. As a group, flowering plants readily adapt to new habitats and changing environments. This adaptability is evident in the great diversity of growth forms exhibited by the various species of flowering plants. For example, the cactus is remarkably well-adapted to desert environments. Its stem stores water; its leaves (spines) have a reduced surface area available for transpiration (loss of water vapor; see Chapter 34) and may also protect against thirsty herbivorous animals; and its thick, waxy cuticle reduces water loss. In contrast, the water lily is well-adapted for wet environments, in part because it has air channels that provide adequate oxygen to stems and roots living in oxygen-deficient water and mud.

Figure 28-14 Guava fruit and seeds
Animals eat fleshy fruits such as guava. The seeds are frequently swallowed whole and pass unharmed through the animals' digestive tracts.

Floral structure provides insights into the evolutionary process

In evolution new structures or organs often originate by modification of previously existing structures or organs. (See Chapter 20 discussion of preadaptations.) Much evidence supports the classical interpretation that the four organs of a flower—sepals, petals, stamens, and carpels—arose from highly modified leaves. This evidence includes comparisons of the arrangement of vascular tissues in both flowers and leafy stems and of the developmental stages of floral parts and leaves.

Sepals are the most leaflike of the four floral organs, and botanists generally agree that sepals are specialized leaves. Although petals of many flowering plant species are leaflike in appearance, botanists generally view petals as modified stamens that later became sterile and leaflike. Cultivated roses and camellias provide evidence supporting this hypothesis; in some varieties the stamens have been transformed into petals,

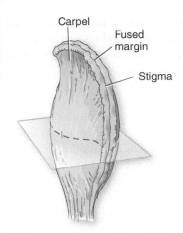

Carpel
Fused margin
Stigma

(a) The carpel resembles a folded leaf in which the ovules borne on its upper surface are enclosed.

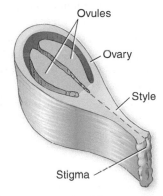

Ovules
Ovary
Style
Stigma

(b) A cross section of the carpel, cut along the dashed line in **(a)**.

Figure 28-15 Carpel of *Drimys piperita*
© Cengage Learning

forming showy flowers with large numbers of petals.

The remarkably leaflike stamens and carpels of certain tropical trees and other species support the origin of stamens and carpels from leaves or leaflike organs. Consider, for example, the carpel of *Drimys,* a genus of flowering trees and shrubs native to Southeast Asia, Australia, and South America. This carpel resembles a leaf that is folded inward along the midrib, thereby enclosing the ovules, and joined along the entire length of the leaf's margin (**FIG. 28-15**).

The fundamental question is whether these leaflike stamens and carpels are shared ancestral characters that were conserved (retained) during the course of evolution or instead are highly specialized organs (i.e., shared derived characters) that do not resemble early stamens and carpels. Many botanists who have studied this question have concluded that stamens and carpels are probably derived from leaves. Not all botanists accept the origin of stamens and carpels from highly modified leaves, however.

During the course of more than 130 million years of angiosperm evolution, floral structure diversified as floral organs fused or became reduced in size or number. These changes led to greater complexity in floral structure in some species and greater simplicity in other species. Interpreting the floral structures of so many different angiosperm species is sometimes difficult, but it is important because correct interpretations are essential to devising a phylogenetic classification scheme.

CHECKPOINT 28.3

- *How do nonreproductive adaptations of flowering plants differ from those of gymnosperms?*
- **CONNECT** *How does the flowering plant life cycle differ from that of the gymnosperms?*
- *What are the two major classes of flowering plants, and how can one distinguish between them?*
- **CONNECT** *How does fertilization differ in gymnosperms and flowering plants?*

28.4 THE EVOLUTION OF SEED PLANTS

LEARNING OBJECTIVE

9   Summarize the evolution of gymnosperms from seedless vascular plants and trace the evolution of flowering plants from gymnosperms.

One group that descended from ancestral seedless vascular plants was the **progymnosperms,** all of which are now extinct. Progymnosperms had two derived features: leaves with branching veins (*megaphylls*) and woody tissue (*secondary xylem*) similar to that of modern gymnosperms. Progymnosperms, however, reproduced by spores, not seeds. *Archaeopteris,* a progymnosperm that lived about 370 mya, is one of the earliest known trees with "modern" woody tissue (**FIG. 28-16a**).

Fossils of several progymnosperms with reproductive structures intermediate between those of spore plants and seed plants have been discovered. For example, the evolution of microspores into pollen grains and of megasporangia into ovules (seed-producing structures) can be traced in fossil progymnosperms. Plants producing seeds appeared during the late Devonian period, more than 359 mya. The fossil record indicates that different groups of seed plants apparently arose independently several times.

As mentioned previously, fossilized remains of ginkgo are found in 200-million-year-old rocks, and other groups of gymnosperms were well established by 160 mya to 100 mya. Although the gymnosperms are an ancient group, some questions persist about the exact pathways of gymnosperm evolution. The fossil record indicates that progymnosperms probably gave rise to conifers and to another group of extinct plants called **seed ferns,** which were seed-bearing woody plants with fernlike leaves (**FIG. 28-16b**). The seed ferns, in turn, probably gave rise to cycads and ginkgo as well as to several gymnosperm groups now extinct. The origin of gnetophytes remains unclear, although molecular data indicate that they are closely related to conifers.

Our understanding of the evolution of flowering plants has made great progress in recent years

Flowering plants are the most recent clade of plants to evolve. The fossil record, although incomplete, suggests that flowering plants descended from gymnosperms. By the middle of the Jurassic period, about 180 mya, several gymnosperm lines existed with some features resembling those of flowering plants. Among other traits, these derived gymnosperms possessed leaves with broad, expanded blades and the first modified seed-bearing leaves, which nearly enclose the ovules. Beetles were evidently visiting these plants, and biologists have suggested that perhaps this relationship was the beginning of **coevolution,** a mutual adaptation between plants and their animal pollinators (see Chapter 37).

One important task facing paleobotanists (biologists who study fossil plants) is determining which of the ancient

(a) Progymnosperm. *Archaeopteris,* which existed about 370 mya, had some features in common with modern seed plants but did not produce seeds.

(b) Seed fern. *Emplectopteris* produced seeds on fernlike leaves. Seed ferns existed from about 360 mya to 250 mya.

Figure 28-16 Evolution of seed plants

(**a,** Redrawn from Beck, C.B., "Reconstructions of *Archaeopteris* and Further Consideration of Its Phylogenetic Position," *American Journal of Botany,* Vol. 49, 1962. **b,** Redrawn from Andrews, H.N., *Ancient Plants and the World They Lived In,* Comstock, New York, 1947.)

gymnosperms are in the direct line of evolution leading to the flowering plants. Given the structural data, most botanists hypothesize that flowering plants arose only once; that is, they think that there is only one line of evolution from the gymnosperms to the flowering plants.

Based largely on structural data, many evolutionary botanists previously thought that the gnetophytes were the gymnosperm clade most closely related to flowering plants. However, new hypotheses of angiosperm origin have been proposed in recent years with advances in molecular comparisons, genetic studies (particularly as gene function relates to reproductive development), and additional fossil discoveries. Currently, many botanists think that the closest extant gymnosperms related to flowering plants are probably conifers, but this hypothesis is far from certain, and the origin and early evolution of flowering plants continue to challenge botanists.

The oldest definitive trace of flowering plants in the fossil record consists of ovules enclosed in tiny podlike fruits interpreted as carpels in Jurassic and Lower Cretaceous rocks some 125 million to 145 million years old (**FIG. 28-17a**). The oldest fossilized flowers are about 118 million to 120 million years old.

Carpel

Ovule

5 mm

(a) The oldest known fossil angiosperm. This fossil of *Archaefructus* shows a carpel-bearing stem. Discovered in northeastern China, it is about 125 million years old.

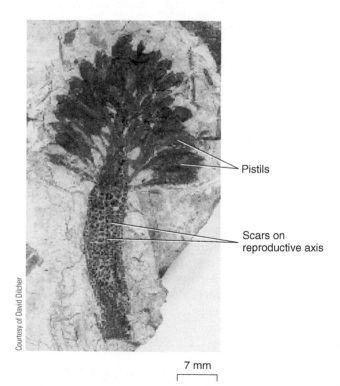

Pistils

Scars on reproductive axis

7 mm

(b) Fossil flower. The fossilized flower of the extinct plant *Archaeanthus linnenbergeri,* which lived about 100 mya. The scars on the reproductive axis (receptacle) may show where stamens, petals, and sepals were originally attached but abscised (fell off). Many spirally arranged pistils were still attached at the time this flower was fossilized.

Figure 28-17 Fossil angiosperms

Flowering plants evolved from ancient gymnosperms. Basal angiosperms are early diverging clades that still survive today.

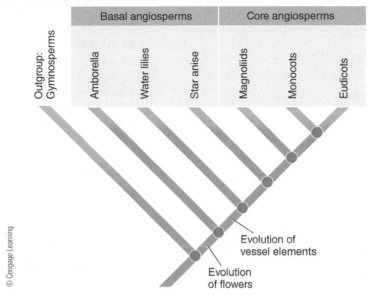

(a) One hypothesis of relationships among the flowering plants, based on fossil and molecular evidence. *Amborella*, water lilies, and star anise are living plants whose ancestors apparently branched off of the angiosperm family tree early. These early clades were followed by the magnoliids, the monocots, and the eudicots.

(b) *Amborella trichopoda*, a basal angiosperm.

(c) Water lily (*Nymphaea*), a basal angiosperm.

(d) Star anise (*Illicium verum*), a basal angiosperm.

(e) *Magnolia*, a core angiosperm.

Figure 28-18 Evolution of flowering plants

CONNECT According to the cladogram, do all basal angiosperms possess vessel elements?

By 90 mya, during the Cretaceous period, flowering plants had diversified and had begun to replace gymnosperms as Earth's dominant plants. Fossils of flowering plant leaves, stems, flowers, fruits, and seeds are numerous and diverse. They outnumber fossils of gymnosperms and ferns in Late Cretaceous deposits, indicating the rapid success of flowering plants once they appeared (FIG. 28-17b). Many angiosperm species apparently arose from changes in chromosome number. (See discussion of allopolyploidy and sympatric evolution in Chapter 20.)

The basal angiosperms comprise three clades

Beginning in 1999, a series of cladistic analyses of structural features and molecular comparisons have helped clarify relationships among the angiosperm classes. In the process many long-held assumptions about early angiosperm lineages have been discarded. The evidence indicates that several clades of basal (early-diverging) angiosperms evolved before the divergence of core angiosperms (FIG. 28-18a). The 170 species of

Plants commonly known as hydatellas were incorrectly classified as grasses until recent molecular evidence indicated that they are basal angiosperms closely related to water lilies. Do these plants have any reproductive features that may indicate that they are one of the most ancient surviving lineages of angiosperms?

EXPERIMENT: *Trithuria inconspicua* (formerly *Hydatella inconspicua*), a small aquatic plant, was collected at a lake in Northland, New Zealand, and its embryo sacs were carefully analyzed.

© Justin Goh, School of Biological Sciences, University of Auckland, Auckland, New Zealand

RESULTS AND CONCLUSION: As in gymnosperms, the mother plant turns over nutrients to the seed *before* fertilization has occurred. This gymnosperm-like reproductive feature may represent a shared ancestral character that was retained during the transition from gymnosperms to flowering plants, thus supporting the view that hydatellas are representative of an ancient angiosperm lineage. Alternatively, this feature may represent a shared derived character not found in earlier hydatella ancestors.

SOURCE: Friedman, W.E. "Hydatellaceae Are Water Lilies with Gymnospermous Tendencies." *Nature*, Vol. 453, May 1, 2008.

Figure 28-19 The basal angiosperm *Trithuria*

Trithuria inconspicua belongs to an ancient clade that consists of about 10 species native to Australia, New Zealand, and India.

CONNECT How is the nutritive tissue in the seeds of gymnosperms formed?

---

basal angiosperms represent groups thought to be ancestral to all other flowering plants.

The oldest surviving clade of basal angiosperms is represented by a single extant species, *Amborella trichopoda* (FIG. 28-18b). A shrub native to New Caledonia, an island in the South Pacific, *Amborella* may be the nearest living relative to the ancestor of all flowering plants. The water lilies and related families compose the second clade of basal angiosperms (FIG. 28-18c and FIG. 28-19). This clade, which contains about 70 species of aquatic or wetland herbs, may be the second-oldest surviving lineage. Star anise and relatives—the third clade of basal angiosperms—consist of about 100 species of vines, trees, and shrubs found mostly in warmer climates. Star anise is important economically because it is a source of spice used by confectioners and anise oil (FIG. 28-18d). Star anise is also used to make Tamiflu, a treatment for influenza.

The core angiosperms comprise magnoliids, monocots, and eudicots

Most angiosperm species belong to a clade of **core angiosperms,** which is divided into three subclades: magnoliids, monocots, and eudicots. **Magnoliids** include species in the magnolia, laurel, and black pepper families as well as several related families (FIG. 28-18e). Although magnoliids were traditionally classified with the eudicots as "dicots," molecular evidence such as DNA sequence comparisons indicates that the magnoliids are neither eudicots nor monocots. Native to tropical or warm temperate regions, magnoliids include several economically important plants, such as avocado, black pepper, nutmeg, and bay laurel.

CHECKPOINT 28.4

- *What features distinguish progymnosperms from seed ferns?*
- *Describe the significant features of the oldest known fossil angiosperm.*
- *Are monocots considered basal or core angiosperms? Explain your answer.*

SUMMARY: FOCUS ON LEARNING OBJECTIVES

28.1 An Introduction to Seed Plants *(page 579)*

1 Compare the features of gymnosperms and angiosperms.
- The two groups of seed plants are the **gymnosperms** and the **angiosperms.** Gymnosperms produce seeds that are totally exposed or borne on the scales of cones; an ovary wall does not surround the ovules of gymnosperms. Angiosperms are flowering plants that produce their seeds within a fruit (a mature ovary).

28.2 Gymnosperms *(page 580)*

2 Trace the steps in the life cycle of a pine and compare its sporophyte and gametophyte generations.
- A pine tree is a mature sporophyte; pine gametophytes are extremely small and nutritionally dependent on the sporophyte generation. Pine is heterosporous and produces microspores and megaspores in separate cones.

- Male cones produce **microspores** that develop into **pollen grains** (immature male gametophytes) that are carried by air currents to female cones.
- Female cones produce **megaspores.** One of each four megaspores produced by meiosis develops into a female gametophyte within an **ovule (megasporangium).**
- After **pollination,** the transfer of pollen to the female cones, a **pollen tube** grows through the megasporangium to the egg within the archegonium. After **fertilization,** the zygote develops into an embryo encased inside a seed adapted for wind dispersal.

3 Summarize the features that distinguish gymnosperms from bryophytes and ferns.
- Unlike bryophytes, gymnosperms are vascular plants. Unlike bryophytes and ferns, gymnosperms produce seeds. Gymnosperms also produce wind-borne pollen grains, a feature absent in ferns and other seedless vascular plants.

4 Name and briefly describe the four phyla of gymnosperms.
- **Conifers** (phylum Coniferophyta), the largest phylum of gymnosperms, are woody plants that bear *needles* (slender leaves that are usually evergreen) and produce seeds in cones. Most conifers are **monoecious** and have male and female reproductive parts in separate cones on the same plant.
- **Cycads** (phylum Cycadophyta) are palmlike or fernlike in appearance. They are **dioecious**—they have male and female reproductive structures on separate plants—but reproduce with pollen and seeds in conelike structures.
- *Ginkgo biloba*, the only surviving species in phylum Ginkgophyta, is a deciduous, dioecious tree. The female **ginkgo** produces fleshy seeds directly on branches.
- **Gnetophytes** (phylum Gnetophyta) are an obscure clade of gymnosperms that has a few traits associated with angiosperms.

28.3 Flowering Plants *(page 585)*

5 Summarize the features that distinguish flowering plants from other plants.
- **Flowering plants,** or angiosperms (phylum Anthophyta), constitute the phylum of vascular plants that produce flowers and seeds enclosed within a **fruit.** They are the most diverse and most successful group of plants.
- The flower, which may contain **sepals, petals, stamens,** and **carpels,** functions in sexual reproduction. Unlike those of gymnosperms, the ovules of flowering plants are enclosed within an **ovary.** After fertilization, the ovules become seeds, and the ovary develops into a fruit.

6 Briefly explain the life cycle of a flowering plant and describe double fertilization.
- The sporophyte generation is dominant in flowering plants; gametophytes are extremely reduced in size and nutritionally dependent on the sporophyte generation. Flowering plants are heterosporous and produce microspores and megaspores within the flower.
- Each microspore develops into a pollen grain (immature male gametophyte). One of each four megaspores produced by meiosis develops into an **embryo sac** (female gametophyte). Within the embryo sac, the egg cell and the central cell with two **polar nuclei** participate in fertilization.
- **Double fertilization,** which results in the formation of a diploid zygote and triploid **endosperm,** is characteristic of flowering plants.

7 Contrast monocots and eudicots, the two largest classes of flowering plants.
- Most **monocots** (class Monocotyledones) have floral parts in threes, and their seeds each contain one **cotyledon.** The nutritive tissue in their mature seeds is endosperm.
- **Eudicots** (class Eudicotyledones) usually have floral parts in fours or fives or multiples thereof, and their seeds each contain two cotyledons. The nutritive organs in their mature seeds are usually the cotyledons, which have absorbed the nutrients in the endosperm.

8 Discuss the evolutionary adaptations of flowering plants.
- Flowering plants reproduce sexually by forming flowers. After double fertilization, seeds form within fruits. Flowering plants have efficient water-conducting **vessel elements** in their xylem and efficient carbohydrate-conducting **sieve tube elements** in their phloem. Wind, water, insects, or other animals transfer pollen grains in various flowering plants.

28.4 The Evolution of Seed Plants *(page 591)*

9 Summarize the evolution of gymnosperms from seedless vascular plants and trace the evolution of flowering plants from gymnosperms.
- Seed plants arose from seedless vascular plants. **Progymnosperms** were seedless vascular plants that had megaphylls and "modern" woody tissue. Progymnosperms probably gave rise to conifers as well as to **seed ferns,** which in turn likely gave rise to cycads and ginkgo.
- The evolution of the gnetophytes is unclear, although molecular data indicate that they are closely related to conifers.
- Flowering plants probably descended from ancient gymnosperms that had specialized features, such as leaves with broad, expanded blades and closed carpels. Flowering plants likely arose only once; that is, there is only one line of evolution from the gymnosperms to the flowering plants.

TEST YOUR UNDERSTANDING

Know and Comprehend

1. Seed plants *lack* which of the following structure(s)? (a) ovules surrounded by integuments (b) microspores and megaspores (c) vascular tissues (d) a large, nutritionally independent sporophyte (e) a large, nutritionally independent gametophyte

2. Conifers, cycads, ginkgo, and gnetophytes are collectively called (a) club mosses (b) gymnosperms (c) angiosperms (d) eudicots (e) seedless vascular plants

3. The immature male gametophytes of pine are called (a) ovules (b) stamens (c) seed cones (d) pollen grains (e) polar nuclei

4. The transfer of pollen grains from the male to the female reproductive structure is known as (a) pollination (b) fertilization (c) embryo sac development (d) seed development (e) fruit development

5. Motile sperm cells are found as vestiges in these two gymnosperm groups: (a) monocots, eudicots (b) gnetophytes, conifers (c) gnetophytes, flowering plants (d) cycads, conifers (e) cycads, ginkgo

6. There are at least _____ species of flowering plants worldwide. (a) 300 (b) 3000 (c) 30,000 (d) 300,000 (e) 3,000,000

7. A simple pistil consists of a single (a) calyx (b) carpel (c) ovule (d) filament (e) petal

8. A flower that lacks stamens is both _____ and _____. (a) complete; imperfect (b) incomplete; perfect (c) complete; perfect (d) incomplete; imperfect

9. After fertilization, the _____ develop(s) into a fruit and the _____ develop(s) into a seed. (a) ovary; ovule (b) polar nuclei; ovule (c) ovary; endosperm (d) ovule; ovary (e) ovule; polar nuclei

10. The female gametophyte in flowering plants is also called the (a) polar nuclei (b) anther (c) embryo sac (d) endosperm (e) sporophyll

11. This flowering plant may be the nearest living relative to the ancestor of all flowering plants. (a) *Amborella* (b) *Archaeopteris* (c) *Gnetum* (d) water lily (e) magnolia

Apply and Analyze

12.  This cross section through an ovary reveals that the pistil is (a) simple, with one carpel (b) compound, with two fused carpels (c) compound, with three fused carpels (d) compound, with six separate carpels (e) compound, with six fused carpels

13. You are given a plant that you have never seen before (see figure). Is it a gymnosperm or angiosperm? A monocot or eudicot? What are the features that helped you make these determinations?

Carlyn Iverson

14. **VISUALIZE** Sketch a seed of a gymnosperm and of a monocot. Label the embryo, seed coat, and nutritive tissue (giving its specific name). Indicate the ploidy of each structure (haploid, diploid, or triploid).

15. **CONNECT** How do the life cycles of seedless plants (see Chapter 27) and seed plants differ? In what fundamental ways are they alike?

Evaluate and Synthesize

16. **EVOLUTION LINK** Most flowers contain both male and female reproductive structures, in contrast to the cones of gymnosperms, which are either male or female. Explain how bisexual flowers might be an advantageous evolutionary adaptation to the flowering plants that possess them.

17. **EVOLUTION LINK** Contrast the algae, mosses, ferns, gymnosperms, and angiosperms with respect to their dependence on water as a transport medium for reproductive cells. Suggest a hypothesis to explain how the differences might be adaptive to living on land.

18. **EVOLUTION LINK** Where would you place the progymnosperms on Figure 28-2? Explain your reasoning.

To access course materials, such as Aplia and other companion resources, please visit **www.cengagebrain.com**.

The Fungi

Mushrooms, morels, and truffles, delights of the gourmet, share a recent common ancestry with baker's yeast, the black mold that forms on stale bread, and the mildew that collects on damp shower curtains. The science of **mycology,** the study of fungi, is concerned with all these diverse life-forms. Mycologists have described about 100,000 species, most of which are terrestrial, but they estimate that there are more than 1.5 million species. Biologists who use the kingdom as a taxon group these organisms in kingdom Fungi, one of the eukaryotic kingdoms.

Fungi grow best in moist habitats, but they are found universally wherever organic material is available. They require moisture to grow, and they can obtain water from a humid atmosphere as well as from the medium on which they live. When the environment becomes dry, fungi survive by going into a resting stage or by producing spores (see photograph) that resist desiccation (drying out).

Some fungi grow to enormous size. In Washington State a fungal clone (*Armillaria ostoyae*) has been identified that covers more than 1500 acres. This giant fungus, which is mainly underground, developed from a single spore that germinated more than a thousand years ago. The fungus has fragmented and is no longer one continuous body.

Like prokaryotes, most fungi are decomposers that obtain nutrients and energy from dead organic matter. They are vital members of ecosystems because they break down the organic compounds found in dead organisms, leaves, garbage, sewage, and other waste. When they decompose organic compounds, carbon and other elements are released into the environment, where they are recycled.

Many fungi form vital symbiotic associations. For example, most terrestrial plants have fungal partners that live in close association with their roots. The fungi help the plants obtain phosphate ions and other needed minerals from the soil. In exchange, the plants provide the fungi with organic nutrients. Some fungi live symbiotically with algae and cyanobacteria as lichens. Others are parasites and pathogens that cause disease in animals or plants.

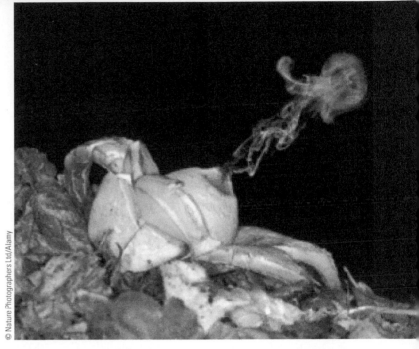

© Nature Photographers Ltd/Alamy

Fungal spores. The collared earthstar (*Geastrum triplex*) releases a puff of microscopic spores after the sac, which is about 1.3 cm (0.5 in.) wide, is hit by a raindrop. This fungus is common in leaf litter under trees throughout North America.

KEY CONCEPTS

29.1 Fungi are eukaryotic heterotrophs that absorb nutrients from their surroundings; most grow as multicellular filaments called hyphae that form a tangled mass called a mycelium.

29.2 Most fungi have complex life cycles and reproduce both asexually and sexually by means of spores.

29.3 According to current hypotheses, fungi evolved from a unicellular, flagellate protist and diverged into several groups.

29.4 Fungi are of major ecological importance; they are decomposers, and they form symbiotic relationships with other organisms.

29.5 Fungi are of major economic, biological, and medical importance.

29.1 CHARACTERISTICS OF FUNGI

1 Describe the distinguishing characteristics of fungi.
2 Describe the body plan of a fungus.

All **fungi** (sing., *fungus*) are eukaryotes; their cells contain membrane-enclosed nuclei, mitochondria, and other membranous organelles. Although they vary strikingly in size and shape, fungi share certain key characters, including their way of obtaining nutrition.

The optimum pH for most fungal species is about 5.6, but various fungi can tolerate and grow in environments where the pH ranges from 2 to 9. Many fungi are less sensitive to high osmotic pressures than are bacteria. As a result, they can grow in concentrated salt solutions or in sugar solutions such as jelly, which discourage or prevent bacterial growth. Fungi also thrive over a wide temperature range. Even refrigerated food may be invaded by fungi.

Fungi absorb food from the environment

Like animals, fungi are heterotrophs. For their nutritional and energy needs, they depend on preformed carbon molecules produced by other organisms. However, fungi do not ingest food and then digest it in the body as animals do. Instead, they infiltrate a food source and secrete digestive enzymes onto it. Digestion takes place outside the body. When complex molecules are broken down into smaller compounds, the fungus absorbs the predigested food into its body.

The fungus is very efficient at absorbing nutrients and growing. It rapidly converts nutrients into new cell material.

If excessive amounts of nutrients are available, fungi store them, usually as lipid droplets or glycogen.

Fungi have cell walls that contain chitin

Like the cells of bacteria, certain protists, and plants, fungal cells are enclosed by cell walls during at least some stage in their life cycle. Fungal cell walls, however, have a different chemical composition from cell walls of other organisms. In most fungi the cell wall consists of complex carbohydrates, including **chitin,** a polymer that consists of subunits of a nitrogen-containing sugar (see Fig. 3-11). Chitin is also a component of the external skeletons of insects and other arthropods. It is resistant to breakdown by most microorganisms.

Most fungi consist of a network of filaments

The simplest fungi are the **yeasts,** which are unicellular, with a round or oval shape. Yeasts are widely distributed in the soil; on leaves, fruits, and cured meats; and on and in our bodies. The importance of some yeasts in medicine, biological research, and the food industry is discussed later in this chapter.

Most fungi are multicellular. The body consists of long, branched, threadlike filaments called **hyphae** (sing., *hypha*) (**FIGS. 29-1a** and b). Hyphae consist of tubular cell walls surrounding the plasma membranes of the fungal cells. They are an adaptation to the fungal mode of nutrition. Growth occurs at the tips of the hyphae; as the hyphae elongate, the fungus grows into and infiltrates food sources. The fungus absorbs nutrients through its very large surface area.

As hyphae grow they form a tangled mass or tissuelike network, called a **mycelium** (pl., *mycelia*). Fungi that form mycelia are commonly called *molds.* The cobweblike mold sometimes seen on bread is the mycelium of a fungus. What is not seen is

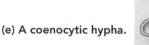
Hyphae

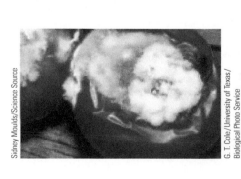

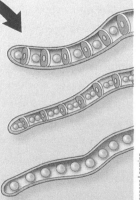

(c) **A hypha divided into cells by septa.** Each cell is monokaryotic (has one nucleus). In some taxa the septa are perforated, as shown.

(d) **A septate hypha.** In this hypha, each cell is dikaryotic (has two nuclei).

(e) **A coenocytic hypha.**

25 μm

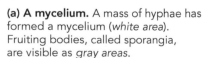

(a) **A mycelium.** A mass of hyphae has formed a mycelium (*white area*). Fruiting bodies, called sporangia, are visible as *gray areas.*

(b) **SEM of a mycelium.** The fungus *Blumeria graminis* growing on a leaf (darker area underneath the mycelium).

Figure 29-1 *Animation* **Fungus body plan**
Spores carried by the air settle on food. They germinate and produce a mass of threadlike filaments called hyphae. The hyphae penetrate the food to obtain nourishment and produce a mass of hyphae called the mycelium. Eventually, specialized hyphae grow from the mycelium, giving rise to erect stalks with fruiting bodies (sporangia) at their tops. When the walls of the sporangia rupture, new spores are released into the air.

the extensive mycelium that grows into the bread. Depending on environmental conditions, some fungi can alternate between a yeast phase and a phase in which they produce hyphae.

In most fungi hyphae are divided by cross walls, called **septa** (sing., *septum*), into individual cells containing one or more nuclei (FIGS. 29-1c and d). As we will discuss, the presence of septa is an important character in the two largest fungal phyla (which include the most complex fungi). The septa of many fungi are perforated by a pore that may be large enough to permit organelles to flow from cell to cell. Some fungi are **coenocytes,** which lack septa. In these species nuclear division is not followed by cytoplasmic division. As a result, a coenocytic fungus is one elongated, multinucleated, giant cell (FIG. 29-1e).

CHECKPOINT 29.1

- **CONNECT** *What characters distinguish fungi from other organisms?*
- *How does the body of a yeast differ from that of a mold?*

29.2 FUNGAL REPRODUCTION

LEARNING OBJECTIVE

3 Describe the life cycle of a typical fungus, including sexual and asexual reproduction.

Most fungi reproduce by means of microscopic **spores,** reproductive cells that can develop into new organisms. In most groups spores are nonmotile. They are dispersed by wind, water, or animals. The air we breathe is filled with hundreds of thousands of fungal spores. When a spore germinates, it gives rise to a hypha, which then develops into a mycelium (FIG. 29-2).

Fungi produce spores either sexually or asexually. With asexual reproduction new individuals are produced quickly, but there is little genetic variability. Sexual reproduction involves meiosis and generates new genotypes.

Spores are usually produced on specialized aerial hyphae or in fruiting structures. When positioned up above the ground, spores can be easily dispersed. Structures in which spores are produced are called **sporangia** (sing., *sporangium*). The aerial hyphae of some fungi produce spores in large, complex reproductive structures, referred to as **fruiting bodies.** The familiar part of a mushroom is a large fruiting body. We do not normally see the bulk of the fungus, a nearly invisible mycelium buried out of sight in the rotting material or soil on which it grows.

Many fungi reproduce asexually

Yeasts reproduce asexually, primarily by forming buds that pinch off from the parent cell (FIG. 29-3). Many species of multicellular fungi also reproduce asexually. Spores are produced by mitosis and then released into the air or water. **Conidiophores** (from the Greek, meaning "dust-bearers") are specialized hyphae that produce asexual spores called **conidia** (sing., *conidium*). The arrangement of conidia on conidiophores varies from species to species.

Most fungi reproduce sexually

Fungi are a diverse group with many variations in their life cycles. Most fungi (but not all) reproduce both asexually and sexually. FIGURE 29-4 illustrates a generalized life cycle. Many fungal species reproduce sexually when they come into contact with other mating types. In contrast to the majority of animal and plant cells, most fungal cells contain haploid nuclei. In sexual reproduction the hyphae of two genetically compatible mating types come together, and their cytoplasm fuses,

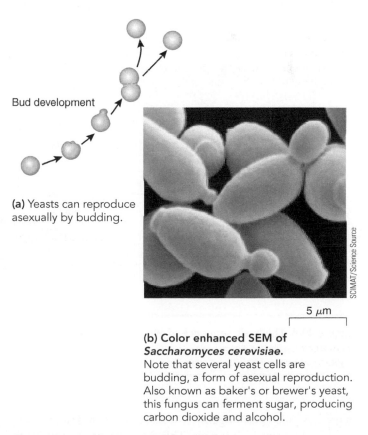

Bud development

(a) Yeasts can reproduce asexually by budding.

5 μm

SCIMAT/Science Source

(b) Color enhanced SEM of *Saccharomyces cerevisiae.* Note that several yeast cells are budding, a form of asexual reproduction. Also known as baker's or brewer's yeast, this fungus can ferment sugar, producing carbon dioxide and alcohol.

Figure 29-3 Yeasts are unicellular fungi
© Cengage Learning

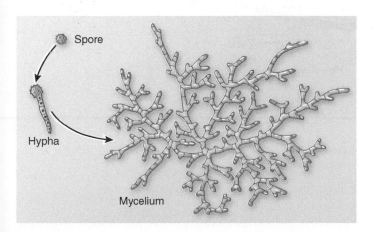

Spore

Hypha

Mycelium

Figure 29-2 Germination of a spore to form a mycelium
© Cengage Learning

Most fungi can reproduce both asexually (which allows rapid proliferation) and sexually (which produces new genotypes).

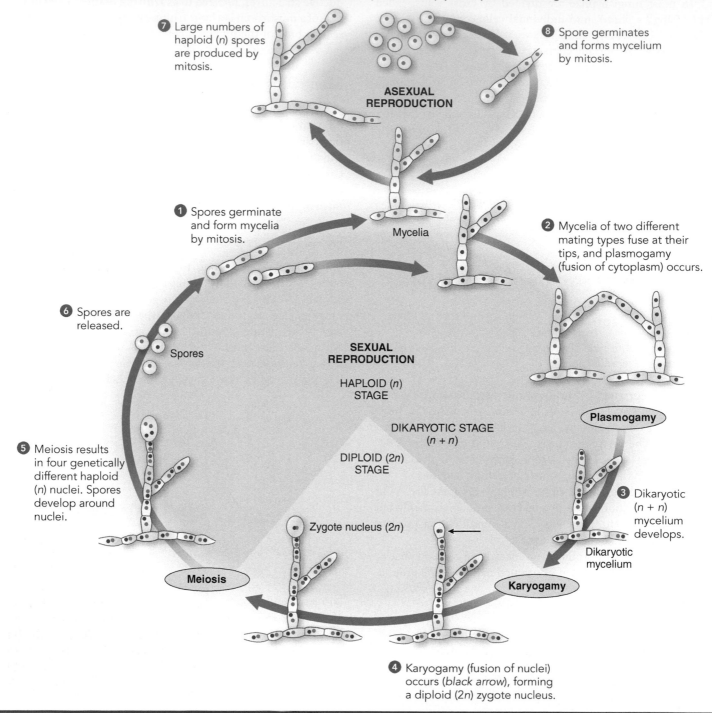

7 Large numbers of haploid (*n*) spores are produced by mitosis.

8 Spore germinates and forms mycelium by mitosis.

ASEXUAL REPRODUCTION

1 Spores germinate and form mycelia by mitosis.

Mycelia

2 Mycelia of two different mating types fuse at their tips, and plasmogamy (fusion of cytoplasm) occurs.

6 Spores are released.

Spores

SEXUAL REPRODUCTION

HAPLOID (*n*) STAGE

Plasmogamy

DIKARYOTIC STAGE (*n* + *n*)

DIPLOID (2*n*) STAGE

5 Meiosis results in four genetically different haploid (*n*) nuclei. Spores develop around nuclei.

3 Dikaryotic (*n* + *n*) mycelium develops.

Dikaryotic mycelium

Zygote nucleus (2*n*)

Meiosis

Karyogamy

4 Karyogamy (fusion of nuclei) occurs (*black arrow*), forming a diploid (2*n*) zygote nucleus.

Figure 29-4 The basic sequence of events in most fungal life cycles

CONNECT Beadle and Tatum used asexual spores of the fungus *Neurospora* in their experiments described in Figure 13-2. How did they obtain strains that differed in their nutritional requirements, given that asexual spores derived from the same parent are expected to be genetically identical?

© Cengage Learning

a process called **plasmogamy.** The resulting cell has two haploid nuclei, one from each fungus. This cell gives rise by mitosis to other cells with two nuclei. At some point the two haploid nuclei fuse. This process, called **karyogamy,** results in a cell containing

a diploid nucleus known as a *zygote nucleus.* In some groups the zygote nucleus is the only diploid nucleus.

In the two largest fungal phyla, the ascomycetes and basidiomycetes (discussed later in this chapter), plasmogamy occurs (hyphae fuse), but karyogamy (fusion of the two different nuclei) does not follow immediately. For a time, the nuclei remain separate within the fungal cytoplasm. Hyphae that contain two genetically distinct, sexually compatible nuclei within each cell are described as **dikaryotic** (see Fig. 29-1d). This condition is referred to as $n + n$ rather than $2n$ because there are two separate haploid nuclei. Hyphae that contain only one nucleus per cell are described as **monokaryotic.** The presence of a dikaryotic stage is an important defining character of the ascomycetes and basidiomycetes.

Fungi communicate chemically by secreting signaling molecules called **pheromones.** At least one pheromone has been identified in each major fungal group. The pheromone binds with a compatible receptor on a different mating type. For example, in the zygomycetes, a pheromone induces the formation of specialized aerial hyphae. Another pheromone causes the tips of aerial hyphae of opposite mating types to grow toward each other and fuse prior to sexual reproduction.

CHECKPOINT 29.2

- **CONNECT** *How is a diploid cell different from a dikaryotic cell?*
- **VISUALIZE** *Draw a generalized life cycle of a fungus. Include asexual and sexual reproduction as well as haploid, diploid, and dikaryotic stages.*

29.3 FUNGAL DIVERSITY

LEARNING OBJECTIVES

4 Give arguments to support the hypothesis that fungi are opisthokonts, more closely related to animals than to plants.

5 Give arguments to support the hypothesis that chytrids may have been the earliest fungal group to evolve from the most recent common ancestor of fungi.

6 List distinguishing characteristics, describe a typical life cycle, and give examples of each of the following fungal groups: chytridiomycetes, zygomycetes, glomeromycetes, ascomycetes, and basidiomycetes.

For centuries biologists classified fungi in the plant kingdom. Like plants, fungi have cell walls and vacuoles and are sessile; that is, they cannot move around from place to place. Also, like plants, many types of fungi inhabit the soil. However, systematists began to question this classification, and in 1969, R.H. Whittaker proposed that fungi be assigned to a separate kingdom, Fungi.

Unlike plants, fungal cell walls do not contain cellulose. Rather, they contain chitin, a polysaccharide found in insect skeletons. The fungal mode of nutrition is also very different from that of plants. Unlike plants, fungi cannot produce their own organic materials from a simple carbon source (carbon dioxide). Like animals, fungi are heterotrophs.

As with systematics for other kingdoms, fungal systematics is a challenging and continuously changing process. For example, slime molds and water molds were formerly classified as fungi but are now included among the protists (see Chapter 26).

Fungi are assigned to the opisthokont clade

Systematists hypothesize that the common ancestor of all plants, fungi, and animals was an ancient flagellate protist. As discussed in Chapter 26, amoebozoa (a group of amoebas), fungi, animals, and a few protists, including the choanoflagellates (a group of flagellate protists), form a monophyletic "supergroup," the **unikonts.** Within this supergroup, the clade **opisthokonts** includes the choanoflagellates, the animals, and the fungi. Both genetic and structural similarities support this grouping. Like animals, fungi have platelike cristae in their mitochondria. Another key character shared by members of this clade is that flagellate cells propel themselves with a single posterior flagellum. In other eukaryote groups, flagellate cells move by means of one or more anterior flagella. Based on structural characters and on molecular data, systematists now view fungi as more closely related to animals than to plants.

Diverse groups of fungi have evolved

Fossil evidence has not been very helpful to systematists studying evolutionary relationships among fungal groups. Most fossilized fungi recovered to date have been microscopic. For example, fossilized fungal spores have been found in amber more than 225 million years old, and fossils of hyphae associated with cyanobacteria or algae have been dated as more than 550 million years old. Few large fungal fossils, such as mushrooms, have been found.

Historically, fungi have been classified mainly on the characteristics of their sexual spores and fruiting bodies. More recently, molecular data, such as comparative DNA and RNA sequences, have helped clarify relationships among fungal groups. Currently, many mycologists assign fungi to five main groups: Chytridiomycota, Zygomycota, Glomeromycota, Ascomycota, and Basidiomycota (**FIG. 29-5** and **TABLE 29-1**). Some biologists consider each of these groups to be a phylum. However, some of these groups are not monophyletic (see Chapter 23), and mycologists are in the process of assigning fungi to additional clades.

In this edition of *Biology*, we will discuss fungi in the five phyla shown in Figure 29-5 and listed in Table 29-1. Microsporidia, a group of intracellular parasites, are classified in this text with the zygomycetes, although in the future they may be assigned to their own taxon. About 95% of all named fungi have been assigned to phyla Ascomycota and Basidiomycota. These phyla are considered *sister taxa* because they share a more recent common ancestor with each other than either does with any other group. Fungi of phyla Ascomycota and Basidiomycota have septate hyphae and a dikaryotic stage during the sexual part of their life cycle.

Until recently, mycologists had assigned about 25,000 species of fungi that did not fit into the major groups to a group called deuteromycetes (phylum Deuteromycota). It was a polyphyletic group (members did not share a recent common ancestor)

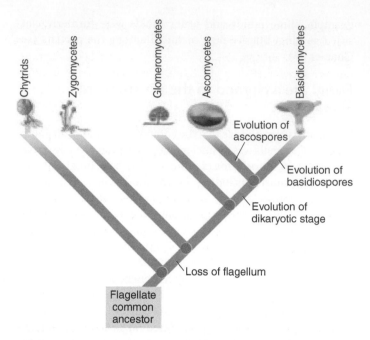

Figure 29-5 Cladogram of currently recognized groups of fungi

This cladogram shows phylogenetic relationships among living fungi, based on comparisons of ribosomal and nuclear gene sequence data for many species. The chytrids were the lineage that branched off first during fungal evolution. Note that ascomycetes and basidiomycetes are sister clades. Remember that the phylogeny of fungi is a work in process.

© Cengage Learning

lumped together simply as a matter of convenience. Mycologists classified fungi as deuteromycetes if no sexual stage had been observed for them at any point during their life cycle. Some of these fungi have lost the ability to reproduce sexually, whereas others reproduce sexually only rarely. Most fungi classified as deuteromycetes reproduce only by means of asexual spores, as ascomycetes do. Mycologists have identified relationships between deuteromycetes and their sexually reproducing relatives, based on DNA comparisons among various species. Most of the deuteromycetes have been reassigned to phylum Ascomycota, and a few have been reassigned to phylum Basidiomycota. (By convention, the asexual stage is still identified as a deuteromycete.)

Chytrids have flagellate spores

At one time, biologists considered the **chytrids,** also known as **chytridiomycetes** (phylum Chytridiomycota), to be funguslike protists, similar in many respects to the water molds. However, both structural and molecular characters indicate that the approximately 1000 species of chytridiomycetes are members of kingdom Fungi. Like fungi, their cell walls contain chitin, and molecular comparisons—particularly of DNA and RNA sequences—have provided compelling evidence that chytrids are indeed fungi. However, recent comparisons of rRNA sequences suggest that chytrids are not a monophyletic group, and they may be divided into four clades.

TABLE 29-1	Characteristics of Currently Recognized Phyla of Fungi			
	PHYLUM AND COMMON TYPES	**ASEXUAL REPRODUCTION**	**SEXUAL REPRODUCTION**	**OTHER KEY CHARACTERS**
	Chytridiomycota (chytrids or chytridiomycetes) *Allomyces*	Flagellate, diploid zoospores produced by mitosis in zoosporangia	Flagellate, haploid gametes in some species	Haploid zoospores produced in resting sporangia; form haploid thallus
	Zygomycota (zygomycetes) Black bread mold. Microsporidia are classified with the zygomycetes	Haploid spores produced in sporangia	Zygospores develop in zygosporangia	Important decomposers; some are insect parasites. Microsporidia are opportunistic pathogens that infect animals.
	Glomeromycota (glomeromycetes)	Large, multinucleate blastospores	Has not been observed	Form arbuscular mycorrhizae with plant roots
	Ascomycota (ascomycetes) Yeasts, powdery mildews, molds, morels, truffles	Conidia pinch off from conidiophores	Ascospores develop in asci	Have a dikaryotic stage; form important symbiotic relationships as lichens and mycorrhizae
	Basidiomycota (basidiomycetes or club fungi) Mushrooms, bracket fungi, puffballs, rusts, smuts	Uncommon	Basidiospores develop on club-shaped basidia	Have a dikaryotic stage; many form mycorrhizae with tree roots

© Cengage Learning

Chytrids are small, relatively simple fungi that inhabit ponds and damp soil. A few species have been found in salt water. Most chytrids are decomposers that degrade organic matter. However, a few species cause disease in plants and animals. A parasitic chytrid has been partly responsible for declining amphibian populations. Infected frogs have been identified in many parts of the world (see *Inquiring About: Declining Amphibian Populations,* in Chapter 57).

Most chytrids are unicellular or composed of a few cells that form a simple body, called a **thallus.** The term *thallus* describes the simple body plan of certain algae, fungi, and plants. The thallus may have slender extensions, called *rhizoids,* that anchor it to a food source and absorb food (**FIG. 29-6**). Chytrids are the only fungi that have flagellate cells. Their spores bear a single, posterior flagellum. Sexual reproduction has not been identified in most chytrids. Species that do reproduce sexually have flagellate gametes.

Some chytrids produce branched, coenocytic mycelia. *Allomyces,* a large, common chytrid, has an unusual life cycle compared with that of most fungi. It undergoes an **alternation of generations** (common in plants, but rare in fungi), spending part of its life as a multicellular haploid (*n*) thallus and part as a multicellular diploid (*2n*) thallus (**FIG. 29-7**). The haploid and diploid thalli are similar in appearance. At the tips of its branches, the haploid thallus bears two types of sporangia, structures in which gametes form by mitosis. Each sporangium produces a different type of flagellate gamete.

Each type of gamete secretes a pheromone that attracts the other type. The two gametes fuse, and plasmogamy and karyogamy occur, resulting in a motile zygote. Each zygote can develop into a diploid thallus. The thallus bears two kinds of spore cases: zoosporangia and resting sporangia. Zoosporangia produce flagellate diploid **zoospores** that develop into new diploid thalli. Meiosis occurs within resting sporangia, producing haploid zoospores. Each zoospore has the potential to develop into a haploid thallus.

Molecular evidence suggests that chytrids were probably the earliest fungal group to evolve. Chytrids produce flagellate cells at some stage in their life history, a character that systematists trace to the protist that was the common ancestor of all opisthokonts. No other fungal group has flagellate cells. At some point in their evolutionary history, other fungal groups apparently lost the ability to produce motile cells, perhaps during the transition from aquatic to terrestrial habitats.

Zygomycetes reproduce sexually by forming zygospores

Mycologists have named more than 1100 species of **zygomycetes** (phylum Zygomycota). Of all the fungi, members of this taxon appear most closely related to the chytrids. However, zygomycetes are not a monophyletic group, and as mycologists learn more about fungal relationships, they may divide this phylum into several taxa or reassign its members to other existing phyla.

Most zygomycetes are decomposers that live in the soil on decaying plant or animal matter (**FIG. 29-8**). Some zygomycetes form a type of symbiotic association (mycorrhizal relationship) with plant roots. (Recall that a symbiotic association is an intimate relationship between organisms of different species.) A few species cause disease in plants and animals, including humans.

During sexual reproduction, zygomycetes produce sexual spores, called **zygospores.** The zygospores are typically produced in spore sacs called **zygosporangia.** The hyphae in zygomycetes are coenocytic; that is, they lack regularly spaced septa. However, septa do form to separate the hyphae from reproductive structures.

Perhaps the most familiar zygomycete is the black bread mold, *Rhizopus stolonifer,* a decomposer that breaks down bread and other foods. If preservatives are not added, bread left at room temperature for a few days often becomes covered with a black, fuzzy growth. Bread becomes moldy when a spore falls on it and then germinates and grows into a mycelium (**FIG. 29-9** on page 606). Hyphae penetrate the bread and absorb nutrients. Eventually, certain hyphae grow upward and develop sporangia at their tips. Clusters of more than 50,000 black asexual spores can develop within each sporangium. The spores are released when the delicate sporangium ruptures. The spores give the black bread mold its characteristic color.

Sexual reproduction in the black bread mold occurs when the hyphae of two different mating types, designated plus (+) and minus (−), grow into contact with one another. The bread mold is **heterothallic,** meaning that an individual fungal hypha

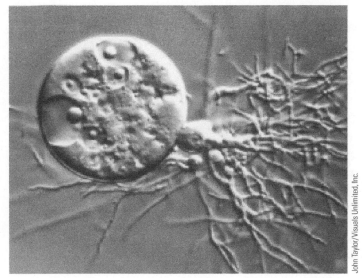

5 μm

John Taylor/Visuals Unlimited, Inc.

Figure 29-6 Chytrid

Nomarski differential interference micrograph of a common chytrid (*Chytridium convervae*). Many chytrids have a microscopic body form consisting of a rounded, coenocytic thallus and branched rhizoids that superficially resemble roots. The rhizoids may anchor the chytrid thallus and absorb predigested food.

Chytrids have flagellate reproductive cells.

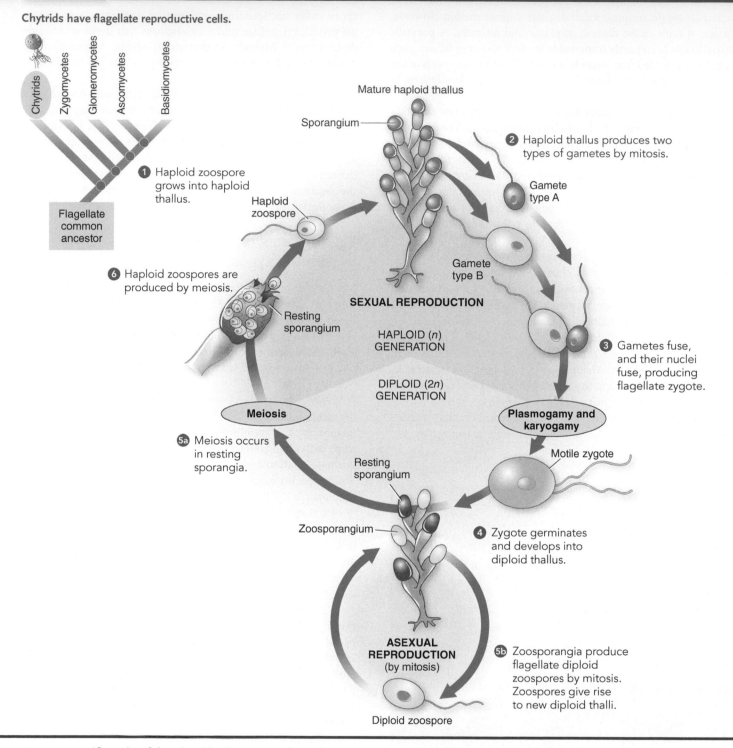

Figure 29-7 Life cycle of the chytrid _Allomyces arbuscula_

Allomyces alternates between multicellular haploid and multicellular diploid stages, which are similar in appearance.

CONNECT _Allomyces_ produces gametes by mitosis. By what type of cell division do animals produce gametes?

© Cengage Learning

mates only with a hypha of a different mating type. That is, sexual reproduction occurs only between a member of a (+) strain and one of a (−) strain, not between members of two (+) strains or members of two (−) strains. Because there are no physical differences between the two mating types, it is not appropriate to refer to them as "male" and "female."

When hyphae of opposite mating types grow in close proximity, they signal one another with pheromones. In response

Figure 29-8 *Pilobolus*, **a zygomycete that grows in animal dung**

Stalked sporangia of *Pilobolus* protruding from a pile of dung, which contains an extensive mycelium of the fungus. The stalked sporangia, which are 5 to 10 mm tall, act like shotguns and forcefully discharge sporangia (the black tips) away from the dung onto nearby grass. When animals such as cattle or horses eat the grass, the spores pass unharmed through the animal's digestive tract and are deposited in a fresh pile of dung.

to these chemical signals, the tips of the hyphae come together and form **gametangia,** which serve as gametes. Plasmogamy occurs as the gametangia fuse. Then karyogamy occurs as the (+) and (−) nuclei fuse to form the diploid zygote nucleus. The zygote develops into a zygospore. Zygospores are encased in a thick protective zygosporangium. The zygospore may lie dormant for several months. It can survive desiccation and extreme temperatures. Meiosis probably occurs at or just before germination of the zygospore.

When the zygospore germinates, an aerial hypha develops with a sporangium at the tip. Mitosis within the sporangium produces haploid spores. These spores may be all (+) spores, all (−) spores, or a mixture of (+) and (−) spores. When released, the spores germinate to form new hyphae. Only the zygote and zygospore of a black bread mold are diploid; all the hyphae and the asexual spores are haploid.

Microsporidia have been a taxonomic mystery

Microsporidia are small, unicellular parasites that infect eukaryotic cells. They are opportunistic pathogens that infect animals. For example, microsporidia infect people with compromised immune systems, such as HIV-infected individuals. Microsporidia cause a variety of diseases involving many organ systems, and some species cause lethal infections. Some species of microsporidia appear to be host-specific.

Microsporidia have two developmental stages inside their host: a feeding stage and a reproductive stage. Some microsporidian species divide into two cells by binary fission, and others divide into several cells. Some species undergo nuclear fusion and meiosis before producing spores. The spores, which have thick protective walls, can pass from cell to cell inside the host

or can be excreted in urine or through the skin. The spores, the only stage with distinct characters, are used to identify groups.

Each spore is equipped with a unique structure, a long, threadlike *polar tube.* When the spore enters the gut of a new host, it discharges its polar tube and penetrates the lining of the gut. Acting as a hypodermic needle, the polar tube injects the contents of the spore into the host cell (**FIG. 29-10**).

Microbiologists estimate that there may be more than one million species of microsporidia, but only about 1500 species have been named. Microsporidia were originally classified with yeasts and bacteria. In 1976, they were assigned to the protozoa. In the 1980s, biologists viewed microsporidia as the most primitive example of a eukaryote. They were the smallest and simplest known eukaryotes, and the genomes of some species are smaller than most bacterial genomes. Microsporidia lack mitochondria, flagella, and Golgi complexes. Their ribosomes resemble those of prokaryotes.

In 1998, British biologist Thomas Cavalier-Smith reassigned microsporidia to kingdom Fungi. Molecular studies show that microsporidia have gene sequences that indicate that they originally had mitochondria. Microbiologists now generally agree that these organisms have become simpler as they adapted to their parasitic way of life. Other molecular studies have provided additional evidence for their taxonomic relationship with fungi. Establishing that they are closely related to fungi is important in developing medications that will be effective in treating microsporidian infections. Recent genome studies suggest that microsporidia descended from a zygomycete ancestor. For now, we classify the microsporidia with the zygomycetes, but in the future they may be assigned to a separate taxon.

Glomeromycetes have a symbiotic relationship with plant roots

Glomeromycetes (phylum Glomeromycota) have coenocytic (no septa) hyphae. They reproduce asexually with large, multinucleate spores called *blastospores.* Sexual reproduction has not been documented. About 230 species of glomeromycetes have been described. Glomeromycetes were previously considered zygomycetes, but taxonomists using molecular data have determined that they form a separate monophyletic group.

Glomeromycetes are symbionts that form intracellular associations with the roots of most trees and herbaceous plants. These symbiotic associations between the hyphae of certain fungi and the roots of plants are called **mycorrhizae** (from Greek words meaning "fungus roots") (**FIG. 29-11**). Glomeromycetes extend their hyphae through the cell walls of root cells but often may not penetrate the plasma membrane. As each hypha pushes forward, the plasma membrane of the root cell surrounds it. Thus, the hyphae can be thought of as fingers pushing into a glove formed by the plasma membrane. Because they penetrate the cell wall, these fungi are referred to as **endomycorrhizal fungi.**

The most widespread endomycorrhizae are called *arbuscular mycorrhizae* because the hyphae inside the root cells form branched, tree-shaped structures known as **arbuscules** (see Fig. 29-11 and Fig. 36-11b). The arbuscules are the sites of

Like most fungi, most zygomycetes reproduce both asexually and sexually.

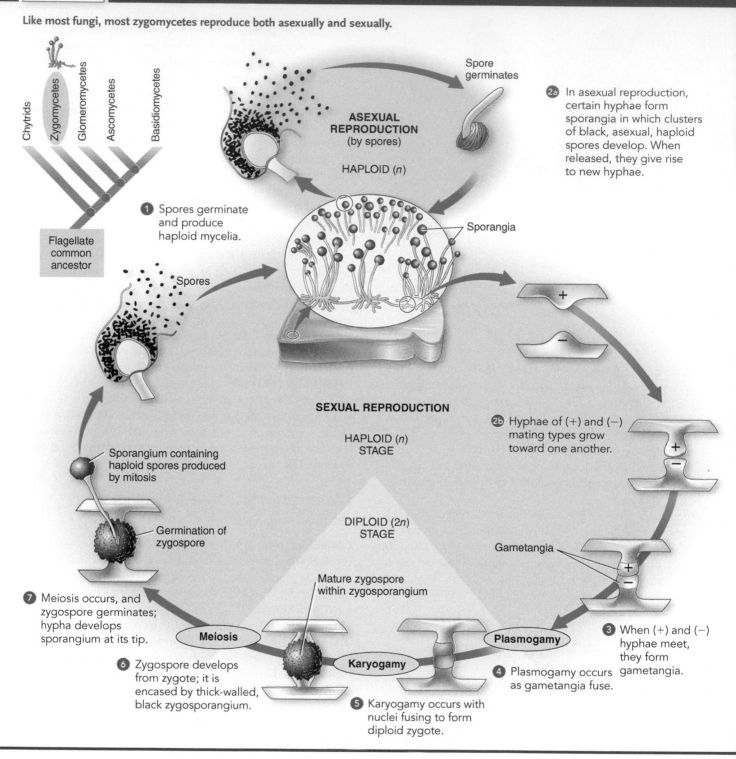

2a In asexual reproduction, certain hyphae form sporangia in which clusters of black, asexual, haploid spores develop. When released, they give rise to new hyphae.

ASEXUAL REPRODUCTION (by spores)

HAPLOID (*n*)

Spore germinates

1 Spores germinate and produce haploid mycelia.

Sporangia

Spores

SEXUAL REPRODUCTION

HAPLOID (*n*) STAGE

2b Hyphae of (+) and (−) mating types grow toward one another.

DIPLOID (2*n*) STAGE

Gametangia

Sporangium containing haploid spores produced by mitosis

Germination of zygospore

Mature zygospore within zygosporangium

Plasmogamy

3 When (+) and (−) hyphae meet, they form gametangia.

7 Meiosis occurs, and zygospore germinates; hypha develops sporangium at its tip.

Meiosis

Karyogamy

4 Plasmogamy occurs as gametangia fuse.

6 Zygospore develops from zygote; it is encased by thick-walled, black zygosporangium.

5 Karyogamy occurs with nuclei fusing to form diploid zygote.

Figure 29-9 *Animation* **Life cycle of a zygomycete, the black bread mold (*Rhizopus stolonifer*)**

CONNECT Identify the structures that function as the equivalent of gametes in the zygomycete life cycle. Are they haploid, diploid, or dikaryotic?
© Cengage Learning

nutrient exchange between the plant and the fungus. Arbuscular mycorrhizae live entirely underground.

In mycorrhizal relationships the roots supply the fungus with sugars, amino acids, and other organic substances. The

mycorrhizal fungus decomposes organic material in the soil and also benefits the plant by extending the reach of its roots. The slender mycelia are far thinner than roots and can extend into narrow spaces, absorbing nutrients that the plant could not

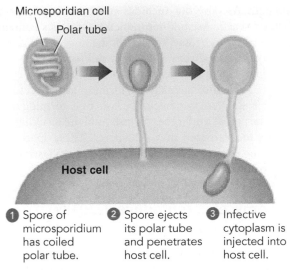

1 Spore of microsporidium has coiled polar tube.

2 Spore ejects its polar tube and penetrates host cell.

3 Infective cytoplasm is injected into host cell.

Figure 29-10 Infection by a microsporidium
© Cengage Learning

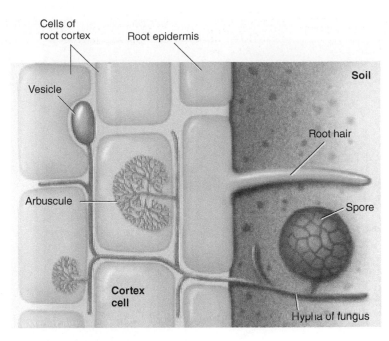

Figure 29-11 Arbuscular mycorrhizae

This mycelium has grown into a plant root. Its hyphae branch between the cells of the root. Hyphae have penetrated through the cell walls of two root cells and have branched extensively to form arbuscules. The tip of one hypha between root cells has enlarged and serves as a vesicle that stores food. The tip of a hypha in the soil has enlarged, forming a spore. The spaces between the root cells have been magnified for clarity.
© Cengage Learning

capture on its own. Thus, with the help of the mycorrhizal fungus, the plant can also take in more nutrient minerals such as phosphorus and nitrogen.

What we have just described is a mutualistic symbiotic association: both partners benefit. Studies show that if a plant grows in phosphate-deficient soil or has a limited root system, its growth is enhanced by having a fungal partner. However, a plant in a phosphate-rich soil with a well-developed root system may not need fungal partners. For these plants, the fungus may be a parasite.

Much remains to be learned about mycorrhizal associations. Other, yet unknown, benefits of the symbiosis may further define the association as mutualistic. For example, some fungi release alkaloids that protect the plants from herbivores and pathogens. Plants also exchange nutrients with one another through fungi that connect them.

Scientists have discovered mycorrhizal fungi within ancient plant fossils in rocks that are about 400 million years old. These findings suggest that when plants moved onto the land, their fungal partners moved with them. In fact, the fungal partners may have been critical for early vascular plants to colonize the land because the fungal hyphae may have provided plants with water and minerals before their own root systems evolved.

Ascomycetes reproduce sexually by forming ascospores

Ascomycetes (phylum Ascomycota) comprise a large group of fungi consisting of more than 32,000 described species. The diverse ascomycetes include most yeasts; the powdery mildews; most of the blue-green, pink, and brown molds that cause food to spoil; decomposer cup fungi; and the edible morels and truffles.

The ascomycetes, more than any other group of fungi, affect humans. As we will discuss in a later section, ascomycetes are used to flavor cheeses, to bake bread (yeast), and to ferment alcohol. Some are enjoyed as foods (morels and truffles). Ascomycetes are used to produce antibiotics. They have also served as valuable model organisms for biologists studying cellular processes, including protein synthesis. Many fungi in this group form mycorrhizae with tree roots, and about 40% join with green algae or cyanobacteria to form lichens. On the negative side, ascomycetes cause most fungal diseases of plants and animals, including humans. For example, ascomycetes cause serious plant diseases such as Dutch elm disease, ergot disease on rye, powdery mildew on fruits and ornamental plants, and chestnut blight.

Ascomycetes are sometimes referred to as *sac fungi* because their sexual spores are produced in microscopic sacs called **asci** (sing., *ascus*). Their hyphae usually have septa, but these cross walls have pores so that cytoplasm is continuous from one cell compartment to another.

In most ascomycetes asexual reproduction involves production of spores called **conidia,** which form at the tips of certain specialized hyphae known as *conidiophores* (FIG. 29-12). Production of these spores is a means of rapidly propagating new mycelia when environmental conditions are favorable. Conidia occur in various shapes, sizes, and colors in different species. The color of the conidia produces the characteristic blue-green, pink, brown, or other tints of many of these molds.

Some species of ascomycetes are heterothallic. (Recall that heterothallic means that an individual fungal hypha mates only with a hypha of a different mating type.) Others are **homothallic,** which means that they are self-fertile and

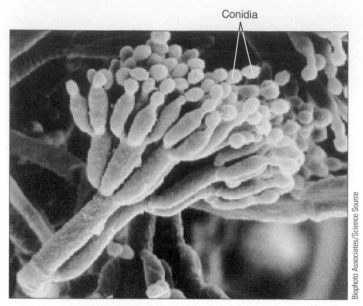

Conidia

10 μm

Biophoto Associates/Science Source

Figure 29-12 Conidia

SEM of *Penicillium* conidiophores, which resemble paintbrushes. Note the conidia pinching off from the tips of the "brushes." Conidia are asexual reproductive cells produced by ascomycetes and some basidiomycetes. Biologists use the arrangement of conidia on conidiophores to identify species of these fungi.

have the ability to mate with themselves. In both heterothallic and homothallic ascomycetes, sexual reproduction takes place after two gametangia come together and their cytoplasm mingles.

Let us examine the life cycle of a typical ascomycete (FIG. 29-13). In our example plasmogamy takes place as hyphae of two different mating types come together and fuse. Within this fused structure, pairs of haploid nuclei, one from each parent hypha, associate but do not fuse. New hyphae, with dikaryotic cells, develop from the fused structure. The hyphae branch repeatedly until the hyphal tips reach the site where asci will be produced. As the many sac-shaped asci develop, each containing two dissimilar nuclei (one from each parent), they are surrounded by intertwining haploid (monokaryotic) hyphae. These hyphae help make a fruiting body known as an **ascocarp** (FIG. 29-14a).

Karyogamy occurs in each ascus. The two nuclei fuse and form a diploid zygote nucleus. The zygote nucleus then undergoes meiosis to form four haploid nuclei with different genotypes. One mitotic division of each of the four nuclei usually follows, resulting in eight haploid nuclei. Each haploid nucleus becomes incorporated into a thick-walled **ascospore**; thus, there are typically eight haploid ascospores within the ascus (FIG. 29-14b). The ascospores are usually released through a pore, slit, or hinged lid at the tip of the ascus. Air currents carry individual ascospores, often for long distances. If one lands in a suitable location, it germinates and forms a new mycelium. The fungus can reproduce asexually by producing conidia that can develop into new mycelia.

Phylum Ascomycota includes more than 300 species of unicellular yeasts. Asexual reproduction of yeasts is mainly by **budding;** in this process a small protuberance (bud) grows and eventually separates from the parent cell (see Fig. 29-3). Each bud can grow into a new yeast cell.

Yeasts reproduce sexually by forming ascospores. During sexual reproduction, two haploid yeasts fuse, forming a diploid zygote. The zygote undergoes meiosis, and the resulting haploid nuclei are incorporated into ascospores. These spores remain enclosed for a time within the original cell wall, which corresponds to an ascus.

Basidiomycetes reproduce sexually by forming basidiospores

The more than 30,000 species of **basidiomycetes** (phylum Basidiomycota) include the largest and most familiar of the fungi: the mushrooms, bracket fungi, and puffballs (FIG. 29-15). Many basidiomycetes are decomposers that obtain nutrients by breaking down organic matter. Some species cause great economic loss because they cause dry rot in buildings. Certain basidiomycetes form mycorrhizae. Others, such as wheat rust and corn smut, infect important crops. A few basidiomycetes cause human disease.

Sometimes called *club fungi,* basidiomycetes derive their name from their microscopic club-shaped **basidia** (sing., *basidium*). Basidia are comparable in function to the asci of ascomycetes. Each basidium is an enlarged hyphal cell that undergoes meiosis to form four **basidiospores** (FIG. 29-16). Note that basidiospores develop on the *outside* of a basidium, whereas ascospores develop *within* an ascus.

Each individual fungus produces millions of basidiospores, and each basidiospore has the potential to give rise to a new **primary mycelium.** Hyphae of a primary mycelium consist of monokaryotic cells. The mycelium of a basidiomycete, such as the commonly cultivated mushroom *Agaricus brunnescens,* consists of a mass of white, branching, threadlike hyphae that live mostly underground. Septa divide the hyphae into cells, but as in ascomycetes, the septa are perforated and allow cytoplasmic streaming between cells.

Let us examine the life cycle of a typical basidiomycete. Asexual reproduction is less common in basidiomycetes than in other groups, so we will focus here on sexual reproduction. We begin with two compatible primary mycelia (FIG. 29-17 on page 612). When in the course of its growth a hypha of a primary mycelium encounters a compatible monokaryotic hypha, typically of a different mating type, the two hyphae fuse (plasmogamy). As in the ascomycetes, the two haploid nuclei remain separate within each cell. In this way a **secondary mycelium** with dikaryotic hyphae, in which each cell contains two haploid nuclei, is produced. The $n + n$ hyphae of the secondary mycelium grow rapidly and extensively.

When environmental conditions are favorable, the hyphae form compact masses, called *buttons,* along the mycelium. Each button grows into a fruiting body that we know as a mushroom. A mushroom is more formally referred to as a **basidiocarp.**

Ascomycetes produce asexual spores called conidia and sexual spores called ascospores.

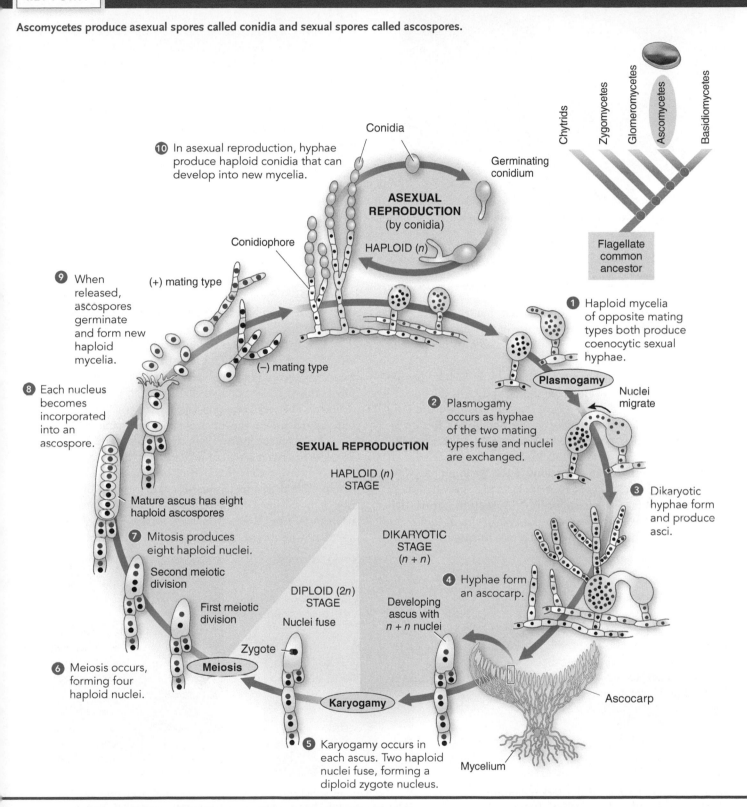

① In asexual reproduction, hyphae produce haploid conidia that can develop into new mycelia.

② Plasmogamy occurs as hyphae of the two mating types fuse and nuclei are exchanged.

③ Dikaryotic hyphae form and produce asci.

④ Hyphae form an ascocarp.

⑤ Karyogamy occurs in each ascus. Two haploid nuclei fuse, forming a diploid zygote nucleus.

⑥ Meiosis occurs, forming four haploid nuclei.

⑦ Mitosis produces eight haploid nuclei.

⑧ Each nucleus becomes incorporated into an ascospore.

⑨ When released, ascospores germinate and form new haploid mycelia.

① Haploid mycelia of opposite mating types both produce coenocytic sexual hyphae.

Conidia

Germinating conidium

ASEXUAL REPRODUCTION (by conidia)

HAPLOID (*n*)

Conidiophore

(+) mating type

(−) mating type

SEXUAL REPRODUCTION

HAPLOID (*n*) STAGE

DIKARYOTIC STAGE (*n* + *n*)

Mature ascus has eight haploid ascospores

Second meiotic division

First meiotic division

DIPLOID (2*n*) STAGE

Nuclei fuse

Zygote

Meiosis

Karyogamy

Developing ascus with *n* + *n* nuclei

Plasmogamy

Nuclei migrate

Ascocarp

Mycelium

Chytrids

Zygomycetes

Glomeromycetes

Ascomycetes

Basidiomycetes

Flagellate common ancestor

Figure 29-13 Life cycle of a typical heterothallic ascomycete

Sexual reproduction requires haploid mycelia of different mating types. Note the dikaryotic stage and the separation of plasmogamy and karyogamy. Steps 5 through 8 take place within an ascus in the ascocarp.

CONNECT Is each of the following haploid, diploid, or dikaryotic: conidium, ascocarp, ascospore, zygote?

© Cengage Learning

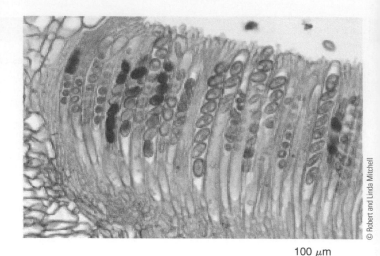

(a) The ascocarp (fruiting body) of the common brown cup (*Peziza badio-confusa*). This ascocarp is shaped like a saucer or bowl and is 3 to 10 cm (1 to 4 in.) wide. It is found on damp soil in woods throughout North America. Photographed in Muskegon, Michigan.

100 μm

(b) Asci. Each ascus contains eight ascospores. Asci line the inner portion of the ascocarp.

Figure 29-14 Sexual reproduction in the ascomycetes

Each basidiocarp consists of intertwined, matted hyphae and has a stalk and a cap. The lower surface of the cap usually consists of many thin, perpendicular plates called **gills** that radiate from the stalk to the edge of the cap.

Karyogamy takes place within the young basidia on the gills of the mushroom. The haploid nuclei fuse in the dikaryotic cells, forming diploid zygote nuclei. They are the only diploid cells that form during a basidiomycete's life cycle. Meiosis then takes place, forming four haploid nuclei with different genotypes. These nuclei move to the outer edge of the basidium. Fingerlike extensions of the basidium develop, into which the nuclei and some cytoplasm move; each of these extensions becomes a basidiospore. A septum forms that separates the basidiospore from the rest of the basidium by a delicate stalk that breaks when the basidiospore is forcibly

discharged. Each basidiospore can germinate and give rise to a primary mycelium.

Many basidiomycetes produce "fairy rings" in lawns and forests (FIG. 29-18 on page 613). A fairy ring may first appear as a dark green ring surrounding an inner brown circle. The size of the ring ranges from a few centimeters to more than 15 m (about 51 ft) in diameter. The green ring consists of grass, well nourished by the nutrients released as the fungi decompose organic material. Grass dies, producing the inner brown circle, because the mass of mycelia decreases the movement of water into the area. As the fungi grow outward, the circle widens. The rings grow a few centimeters to more than a meter per year. After rainfall or irrigation, a ring of mushrooms may appear just outside the green circle. The name "fairy ring" comes from a legend that a ring of mushrooms appeared where fairies had danced in a circle the night before.

(a) Basidia line the gills of the Jack-o'-lantern mushroom (*Omphalotus olearius*). The gills of this poisonous species produce a greenish glow in the dark. Each cap is about 15 cm (6 in.) wide. The Jack-o'-lantern occurs throughout eastern North America and California.

(b) The elegant stinkhorn (*Phallus ravenelii*) has a foul smell that attracts flies. The flies help disperse the slimy mass of basidiospores. Fruiting bodies of elegant stinkhorns grow to 18 cm (7 in.) tall. Photographed in Pennsylvania.

(c) Turkey-tail (*Trametes versicolor*) is a common bracket fungus. Bracket fungi grow on both dead and living trees and produce shelf-like fruiting bodies. Basidiospores are produced in pores located underneath each shelf.

Figure 29-15 Basidiomycete fruiting bodies

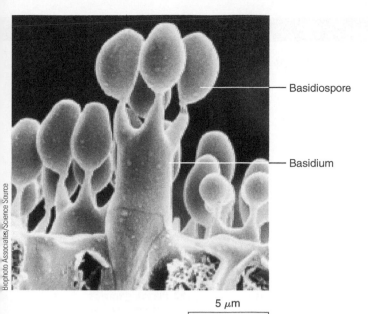

Basidiospore

Basidium

5 μm

Figure 29-16 SEM of a basidium
Each basidium produces four basidiospores.

CHECKPOINT 29.3

- *What evidence supports the hypothesis that chytrids were the earliest fungal group to evolve from the common ancestor of fungi?*

- *What are the distinguishing characteristics of each of the following fungal groups: zygomycetes, glomeromycetes, ascomycetes, and basidiomycetes?*

- **VISUALIZE** *Use simple diagrams to illustrate how the life cycle of a typical basidiomycete differs from that of a typical ascomycete.*

- *Distinguish among (1) ascocarp, ascus, and ascospore and among (2) basidiocarp, basidium, and basidiospore.*

29.4 ECOLOGICAL IMPORTANCE OF FUNGI

LEARNING OBJECTIVES

7   Summarize the ecological significance of fungi as decomposers.

8   Describe the important ecological role of mycorrhizae.

9   Characterize the unique nature of a lichen.

Fungi make vital contributions to the ecological balance of our planet. Like bacteria, most fungi are free-living decomposers, chemoheterotrophs that absorb nutrients from organic wastes and dead organisms. For example, many fungal decomposers degrade cellulose and lignin, the main components of plant cell walls. When fungi degrade wastes and dead organisms, they release water, carbon (as CO_2), and mineral components of organic compounds, and these elements are recycled (see biogeochemical

cycles in Chapter 55). Without this continuous decomposition, essential nutrients would remain locked up in huge mounds of animal carcasses, feces, branches, logs, and leaves. These nutrients would be unavailable for use by new generations of organisms, and life would eventually cease.

Fungi form important symbiotic relationships with animals, plants, bacteria, and protists. A three-way symbiotic relationship involving a fungus, a grass, and a virus has recently been reported. In the geothermal hot spots of Yellowstone National Park, a fungus infects the roots of the host grass. When infected with a specific virus, the fungus is heat tolerant and confers heat tolerance to the grass. When not infected by the virus, the fungus does not confer heat tolerance. The symbiotic relationships of fungi with other organisms have major effects on ecosystems.

Fungi form symbiotic relationships with some animals

Because animals do not have the enzymes necessary to digest cellulose and lignin, cattle and other grazing animals cannot, by themselves, obtain needed nutrients from the plant material they eat. Their survival depends on fungi that inhabit their guts because fungi, like many other microorganisms, do have the enzymes that break down these organic compounds. The fungi benefit by living in a nutrient-rich environment.

Fungi also form symbiotic associations with ants and termites. More than 200 species of ants farm fungi. Leaf-cutting ants bring leaves to their fungi and protect them from competitors and predators. The ants also disperse the fungi to new locations. In exchange, the fungi digest the leaves, providing nutrients for the ants. This symbiosis can involve other organisms. The farmed fungi can be infested by fungal parasites. In response, the ants culture bacteria (actinomycetes) that produce antibiotics to control these parasites. These symbiotic relationships, the most complex known, are the product of 50 million years of coevolution.

Mycorrhizae are symbiotic associations between fungi and plant roots

Mycorrhizae occur in about 80% of plants (and more than 90% of all plant families). As discussed in the section on glomeromycetes, mycorrhizal fungi decompose organic material in the soil and increase the surface area of a plant's roots so that the plant can absorb more water and mineral nutrients. In exchange, the roots supply the fungus with organic nutrients.

To establish and maintain a symbiotic relationship, cells of the fungi and cells of the plant roots must communicate. For example, signaling molecules from the plant root cells stimulate fungal cells to shift to a presymbiotic growth phase in which their energy metabolism increases and their hyphae branch. The fungal cells then signal the root cells, activating a signaling pathway that activates gene expression in the root cells.

The importance of mycorrhizae first became evident when horticulturalists observed that orchids do not grow unless an appropriate fungus lives with them. Similarly, many

Basidiomycetes produce sexual basidiospores on the gills of basidiocarps (fruiting bodies).

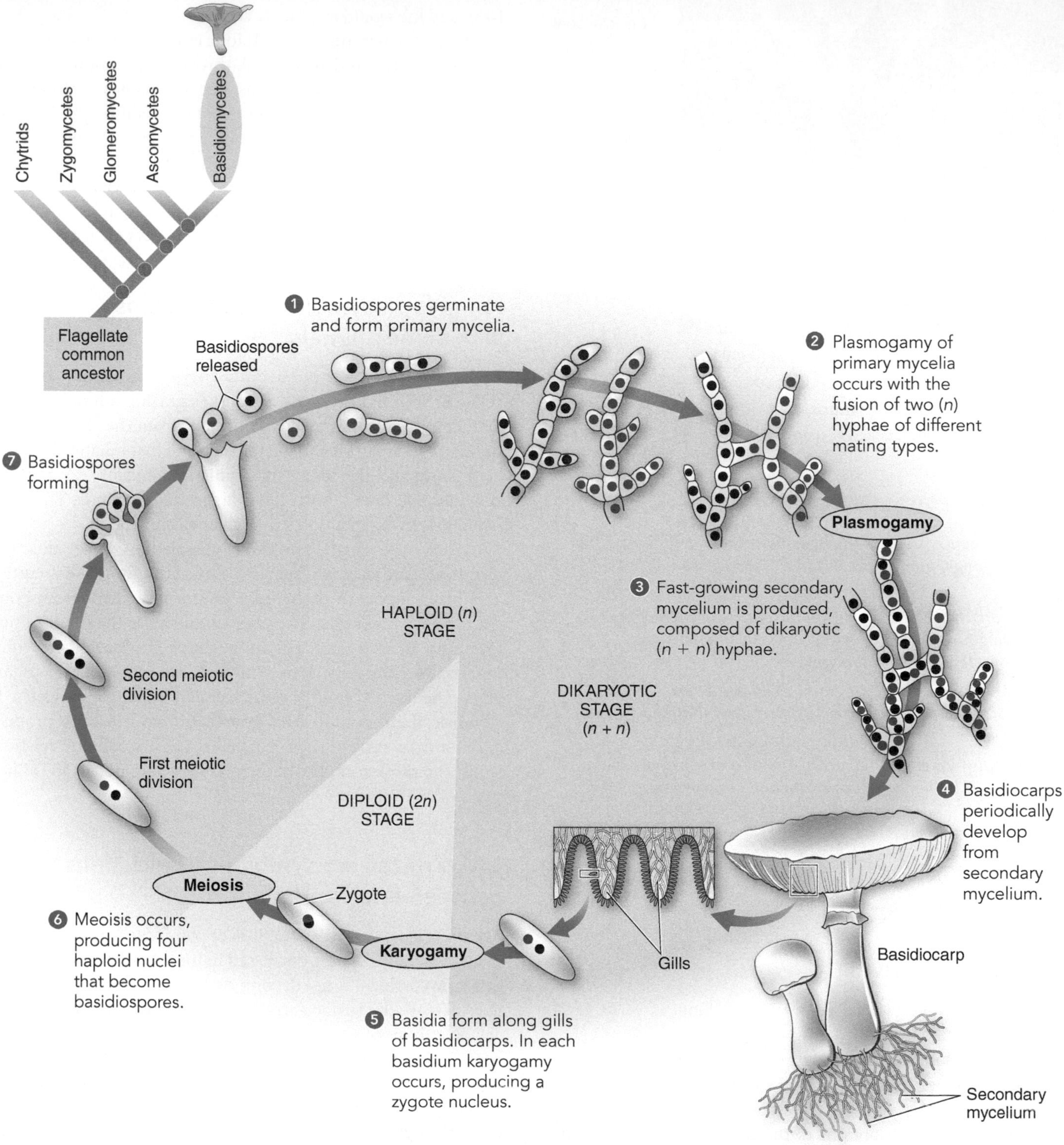

① Basidiospores germinate and form primary mycelia.

② Plasmogamy of primary mycelia occurs with the fusion of two (*n*) hyphae of different mating types.

Plasmogamy

③ Fast-growing secondary mycelium is produced, composed of dikaryotic (*n* + *n*) hyphae.

④ Basidiocarps periodically develop from secondary mycelium.

⑦ Basidiospores forming

Basidiospores released

HAPLOID (*n*)
STAGE

DIKARYOTIC
STAGE
(*n* + *n*)

Second meiotic division

First meiotic division

DIPLOID (2*n*)
STAGE

Meiosis

Zygote

⑥ Meoisis occurs, producing four haploid nuclei that become basidiospores.

Karyogamy

⑤ Basidia form along gills of basidiocarps. In each basidium karyogamy occurs, producing a zygote nucleus.

Gills

Basidiocarp

Secondary mycelium

Flagellate common ancestor

Chytrids
Zygomycetes
Glomeromycetes
Ascomycetes
Basidiomycetes

Figure 29-17 *Animation* **Life cycle of a typical basidiomycete**

Note the dikaryotic stage and the separation of plasmogamy and karyogamy. Steps 5 and 6 take place within the basidia of the basidiocarp. Asexual reproduction is uncommon in this group.

CONNECT Is each of the following haploid, diploid, or dikaryotic: basidiocarp, basidiospore, primary mycelium, zygote, secondary mycelium?

© Cengage Learning

Figure 29-18 A fairy ring

forest trees, such as pines, decline and eventually die from mineral deficiencies when transplanted to mineral-rich grassland soils that lack the appropriate mycorrhizal fungi. When forest soil containing the appropriate fungi or their spores is added to the soil around these trees, they quickly resume normal growth. Studies performed with various types of plants, including cedar, have confirmed the role of mycorrhizae in plant growth (FIG. 29-19).

As we have discussed, glomeromycetes form *endomycorrhizal* connections; they infiltrate the cells of plant roots. At least 5000 species of ascomycetes and basidiomycetes also form mycorrhizal connections, but their hyphae coat the plant root rather than penetrate its cells. These species are referred to as **ectomycorrhizal fungi.** Interestingly, researchers have shown that some mycorrhizal fungi harbor bacteria in their cytoplasm. Although the role of the bacteria is not yet clear, their presence suggests that they may be members of a three-way partnership: fungus, plant, and bacteria.

Mycorrhizal fungi connect plants, allowing nutrient transfer among them. Scientists have measured the movement of organic materials from one tree species to another through shared mycorrhizal connections. Mycorrhizal fungi also release chemicals that protect the plant against herbivores and pathogens.

Mycorrhizae improve the soil by decreasing water loss and erosion. Ecologists are studying the role of mycorrhizal fungi in reclaiming soils damaged by pollution. For example, mycorrhizae can modify toxic heavy metals, such as cadmium, so that plants cannot absorb them.

A lichen consists of two components: a fungus and a photoautotroph

Although a **lichen** looks like a single organism, it is actually a dual organism, a combination of a fungus and a *photoautotroph* (FIG. 29-20a). Almost one-fifth of all known fungal species form these symbiotic relationships. About 14,000 kinds of lichens have been described. Fossils suggest that fungi developed symbiotic partnerships with photoautotrophs before the evolution of vascular plants.

The photoautotrophic component of a lichen is a green alga, a cyanobacterium, or both. The fungus is most often an ascomycete, although a basidiomycete is the fungal partner in some tropical lichens. Most photoautotrophic organisms found in lichens also occur as free-living species in nature, but the fungal components are generally found only as a part of the lichen. Typically, the fungus forms most of the lichen thallus (body). The fungus surrounds hundreds of photosynthetic partners and holds them in place. Lichens are named for the fungal component.

In the laboratory researchers can isolate the fungal and photoautotrophic components of some lichens and grow them separately in appropriate culture media. The photoautotroph grows more rapidly when separated, whereas the fungus grows more slowly and requires many complex carbohydrates. Neither organism resembles a lichen in appearance when grown separately. The photoautotroph and fungus can be reassembled as a lichen thallus, but only if they are placed in a culture medium under conditions that cannot support either of them independently.

What is the nature of this partnership? The lichen was originally considered a definitive example of mutualism. The photoautotroph carries on photosynthesis, producing energy-rich carbon compounds for both members of the lichen. It is unclear how the photoautotroph benefits from the relationship. Some biologists have suggested that the photoautotroph obtains water and nutrient minerals from the fungus as well as protection against desiccation. More recently, researchers have suggested that the lichen partnership is not really a case of mutualism but one of controlled parasitism of the photoautotroph by the fungus.

Lichens typically exhibit one of three different growth forms (FIG. 29-20b). *Crustose lichens* are flat and grow tightly against their substrate (the surface they are growing on). *Foliose lichens* are also flat, but they have leaflike lobes and are not as tightly pressed to the substrate. *Fruticose lichens* grow erect and have many branches.

Able to tolerate extremes of temperature and moisture, lichens grow in almost all terrestrial environments except polluted cities. They exist farther north than any plants of the arctic region and are equally at home in the steaming equatorial rain forest. They grow on tree bark, leaves, and exposed rock surfaces, from solidified lava to tombstones. In fact, lichens are often the first organisms to inhabit rocky areas, and their growth in these areas is important in forming soil from rock. They secrete acid that gradually etches tiny cracks in the rock, releasing minerals. This process sets the stage for further disintegration of the rock by wind and rain. When the lichens themselves die and are decomposed, they become part of the soil.

Reindeer mosses of the arctic region, which serve as the main source of food for migrating herds of caribou, are actually lichens, not mosses. Some lichens produce colored pigments. One of them, orchil, is used to dye wool; another, litmus, is widely used in chemistry laboratories as an acid–base (pH) indicator.

Lichens vary greatly in size. Some are almost invisible, whereas others, such as the reindeer mosses, may cover many

Is plant growth affected by fungi in the soil?

HYPOTHESIS: In low-phosphorus soils, plants that form mycorrhizal associations with fungi exhibit enhanced growth.

EXPERIMENT: Western red cedar seedlings (*Thuja plicata*) were selected for this study. Control seedlings were grown in low-phosphorus soil in the absence of the fungus. Experimental seedlings of the same age as the control plants were grown under the same conditions as the controls except that their roots formed mycorrhizal associations.

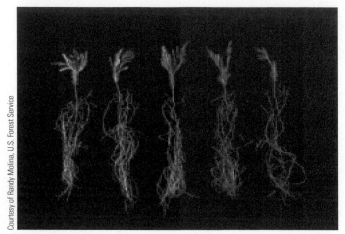

(a) No mycorrhizal associations. Control seedlings were grown in low-phosphorus soil in the absence of the fungus.

(b) Mycorrhizal associations. Experimental seedlings were grown under the same conditions as the controls, except that the fungus was present. The seedlings formed mycorrhizal associations with the fungus.

RESULTS AND CONCLUSION: Growth of the plants that formed mycorrhizal associations was significantly enhanced. Mycorrhizal associations enhance the growth of western red cedar plants. Many similar studies using other types of plants and other types of soil have confirmed the importance of mycorrhizal association to plant growth.

SOURCE: Kough, J.L., R. Molina, and R.G. Linderman. "Mycorrhizal Responsiveness of *Thuja, Calocedrus, Sequoia*, and *Sequoiadendron* Species of Western North America," *Canadian Journal of Forest Research*, Vol. 15 (1985): 1049–1054.

Figure 29-19 The effect of mycorrhizae on western red cedar (*Thuja plicata*) seedlings

CONNECT Biologists have discovered that many mycorrhizal fungi are sensitive to a low pH. What human-caused environmental problem may prove catastrophic for these fungi? How may this problem affect their plant partners? What measures could we take to decrease the problem?

---

square kilometers of land with an ankle-deep growth. Growth proceeds slowly; the radius of a lichen may increase by less than 1 mm each year. Some mature lichens are thought to be thousands of years old.

Lichens absorb minerals from the air, rainwater, and the surface on which they grow. They cannot excrete the elements they absorb, and perhaps for this reason they are extremely sensitive to toxic compounds. This sensitivity was first reported in 1866 by a Finnish biologist who observed that lichens growing on tree trunks in Paris were poorly developed or sterile. He deduced that lichens could be used to measure air purity. Today, reduction in lichen growth is used as a sensitive indicator of air pollution, particularly from sulfur dioxide. In one study investigators demonstrated a relationship between lung cancer and air pollution by comparing the locations of low lichen biodiversity (and therefore of air pollution) with the locations of lung cancer deaths in young males. The return of lichens to an area indicates an improvement in air quality.

Lichens reproduce mainly by asexual means, usually by fragmentation, a process in which special dispersal units of the lichen, called **soredia** (sing. *soredium*), break off and, if they land on a suitable surface, establish themselves as new lichens. Soredia contain cells of both partners. In some lichens the fungus produces ascospores, which may be dispersed by wind and find an appropriate algal partner only by chance.

CHECKPOINT 29.4

- **CONNECT** *What is the ecological importance of fungal decomposers?*

- *What are some ways in which the relationship between a plant root and a mycorrhizal fungus is mutualistic?*

- *Many biologists consider a lichen an example of controlled parasitism. In this view, which component is the likely parasite, and which is the likely host?*

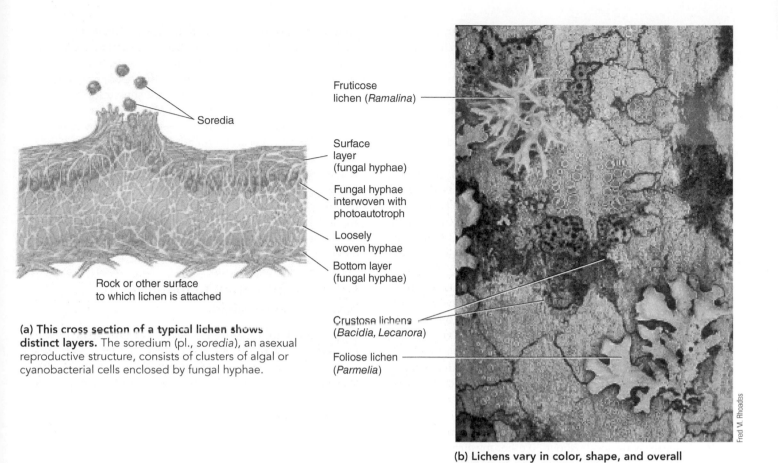

Soredia

Fruticose
lichen (*Ramalina*)

Surface
layer
(fungal hyphae)

Fungal hyphae
interwoven with
photoautotroph

Loosely
woven hyphae

Bottom layer
(fungal hyphae)

Rock or other surface
to which lichen is attached

Crustose lichens
(*Bacidia, Lecanora*)

Foliose lichen
(*Parmelia*)

Fred M. Rhoades

(a) This cross section of a typical lichen shows distinct layers. The soredium (pl., *soredia*), an asexual reproductive structure, consists of clusters of algal or cyanobacterial cells enclosed by fungal hyphae.

(b) Lichens vary in color, shape, and overall appearance. Three growth forms—crustose, foliose, and fruticose—are shown on a maple branch in Washington State.

Figure 29-20 Lichens

These organisms are a combination of a fungus and an alga or cyanobacterium.
© Cengage Learning

29.5 ECONOMIC, BIOLOGICAL, AND MEDICAL IMPACT OF FUNGI

LEARNING OBJECTIVES

10 Summarize some specific ways that fungi affect humans economically.
11 Summarize the importance of fungi to biology and medicine; describe how fungi infect plants and humans, describing at least one fungal animal disease and one fungal plant disease.

The same powerful digestive enzymes that fungi use to decompose wastes and dead organisms can also be used with great efficiency to reduce wood, fiber, and food to their basic components. Many species of basidiomycetes have enzymes that break down the lignin in wood. (Lignin is the second most abundant organic compound on Earth, second only to cellulose.) From the human perspective, various fungi cause incalculable damage to stored goods and building materials each year. Bracket fungi,

for example, cause enormous losses by decaying wood, both in living trees and in stored lumber.

Some fungi cause serious diseases in animals and plants, yet fungi also contribute to our quality of life. They are responsible for economic gains as well as losses. People eat them and grow them to make various medications, such as penicillin. We use them to make certain industrial chemicals and for bioremediation. Renewable fuel companies are actively searching for fungi and other microbes that can produce fuel. For example, a fungus has been discovered that synthesizes 55 hydrocarbons, perhaps to inhibit the growth of other organisms. Researchers may be able to use the genes of this fungus to engineer other microorganisms to produce fuel more efficiently.

Fungi provide beverages and food

Humans exploit the ability of yeasts to produce bread and alcoholic beverages. Yeasts produce ethyl alcohol and carbon dioxide from glucose and other sugars by fermentation (see Chapter 8).

Yeast species of the genus *Saccharomyces* (ascomycetes) are used to produce wine, beer, and other fermented beverages.

Wine is produced when yeasts ferment fruit sugar, and beer results when yeasts ferment sugar derived from starch in grains (usually barley).

Saccharomyces cerevisiae, referred to as baker's yeast, is used to bake bread, pizza, and other wheat products. During the process of making bread, carbon dioxide produced by yeast becomes trapped in dough as bubbles, causing the dough to rise and giving leavened bread its light quality. Both the carbon dioxide and the alcohol produced by the yeast escape during baking.

The unique flavor of cheeses such as Roquefort, Brie, Gorgonzola, and Camembert is produced by species of *Penicillium.* For example, *P. roquefortii,* found in caves near the French village of Roquefort, is used to make Roquefort cheese. By French law, only cheeses produced in this area can be called Roquefort cheese. (The blue spots in Roquefort and certain other cheeses are masses of conidia.)

Aspergillus tamarii and certain other fungi are used to produce traditional soy sauce by fermenting soybeans with the fungi for at least three months. Soy sauce enriches other foods with more than just its special flavor. It also adds vital amino acids from both the soybeans and the fungi themselves, which, in some parts of the world, supplement a low-protein rice diet.

Among the basidiomycetes, there are some 200 kinds of edible mushrooms and about 70 species of poisonous ones. Many edible mushrooms are cultivated commercially. The mushroom *Agaricus brunnescens* is the principal fungal species grown extensively for food. About 30 other mushroom species, such as oyster, shiitake, portobello, and straw mushrooms, are available in supermarkets. Morels, which superficially resemble mushrooms, and truffles, which produce underground fruiting bodies, are ascomycetes (FIG. 29-21). Truffles are now cultivated as mycorrhizal fungi on the roots of tree seedlings.

Edible and poisonous mushrooms can look very much alike and may even belong to the same genus. There is no simple way to tell them apart; an expert must identify them. Some of the most poisonous mushrooms belong to the genus *Amanita* (FIG. 29-22). Toxic species of this genus have been appropriately called such names as "destroying angel" (*A. virosa*) and "death cap" (*A. phalloides*). Eating a single mushroom of either species can be fatal.

Certain species of mushrooms cause intoxication and hallucinations. The sacred mushrooms of the Aztecs—*Conocybe* and *Psilocybe*—are still used in religious ceremonies by native peoples of Central America for their hallucinogenic properties. The chemical ingredient *psilocybin* is responsible for the trances and visions experienced by those who eat these mushrooms. Ingestion of psychoactive mushrooms is dangerous because negative reactions vary considerably, from mild indigestion, sweating, and heart palpitations, to death. In addition, the possession and use of such mushrooms are illegal in the United States and some other countries.

Fungi are important to modern biology and medicine

As discussed in Chapter 17, yeast *Saccharomyces cerevisiae* has served as a model eukaryotic cell (see Fig. 29-3). It was the first eukaryote whose genome was sequenced, and with its 6000 genes, it has the smallest genome of any eukaryotic model organism. Molecular biologists are in the process of determining the functions of the proteins encoded by its genes. Biologists have used *S. cerevisiae* to study molecular genetics, including how genes regulate cell division. Researchers continue to use this yeast to study such problems as genetic recombination and the correlation between cell age and cancer. *Saccharomyces cerevisiae* is also being used to study the mechanism of action of antifungal drugs and resistance to these drugs.

Biologists have used the ascomycete *Aspergillus nidulans,* an opportunistic pathogen of humans, to study mitosis and other cell processes. This fungus has provided valuable knowledge about the genetics of microtubules. Biologists are using

(a) The yellow morel (*Morchella esculenta*). This morel grows 6 to 10 cm (2.5 to 4 in.) tall. It is found throughout North America. Photographed in Michigan.

(b) The Oregon white truffle (*Tuber gibbosum*). This truffle, which is found underground near Douglas firs and possibly oak trees in British Columbia and northern California, is 1 to 5 cm (0.4 to 2 in.) wide. People find these subterranean ascocarps with the help of trained dogs or pigs. Here, truffles are shown whole and sectioned to show the conspicuous white, marbled tissue.

Figure 29-21 Edible ascomycetes

Figure 29-22 Poisonous mushrooms

The destroying angel (*Amanita virosa*) is an extremely poisonous mushroom that is distinguished, as are other amanitas, by the ring of tissue around its stalk and by the underground cup from which the stalk protrudes. About 50 g (2 oz) of this mushroom can kill an adult man. The destroying angel, which is 7.5 to 20 cm (3 to 8 in.) tall, is found in grass or near trees throughout North America.

recombinant DNA techniques to manipulate yeasts and certain filamentous fungi to produce important biological molecules, such as hormones. Among the many genes that have been cloned in yeast are those for insulin, human growth hormone, and molecules important in immune function. These procedures allow researchers to produce unlimited amounts of these compounds for study and eventual medical use.

Fungi produce useful drugs and chemicals. Discovered in 1928 by British bacteriologist Alexander Fleming, penicillin, produced by the mold *Penicillium notatum,* is still among the most widely used and effective antibiotics (see Chapter 1). Other drugs derived from fungi include the cephalosporin antibiotics (produced by *Cephalosporium*), statins (used to lower blood cholesterol levels), and cyclosporine (used to suppress immune responses in patients who receive organ transplants). Fumagillin, a chemical produced by the ascomycete *Aspergillus fumigatus,* inhibits the formation of new blood vessels. Because solid tumors need a rich blood supply, fumagillin shows promise as an anticancer agent. Fumagillin is also used to treat diseases caused by microsporidia. Researchers have identified several other promising compounds produced by fungi that are antiviral or that destroy cancer cells.

The ascomycete *Claviceps purpurea* infects the flowers of rye plants and other cereals. It produces a structure called an *ergot* where a seed would normally form in the grain head. When livestock eat this grain or when humans eat bread made from ergot-contaminated rye flour, they may be poisoned by the extremely toxic substances in the ergot. However, some ergot compounds are now used clinically in small quantities as drugs to induce labor, to stop uterine bleeding, to treat high blood pressure, and to relieve one type of migraine headache.

Fungi are used in bioremediation and to biologically control pests

Some fungi can biodegrade pesticides, herbicides, coal tars, and petroleum. Fungi convert these products into carbon dioxide and the basic elements of which they are composed. These fungi can be used along with certain bacteria to decontaminate farm land and to clean up oil spills.

Researchers are investigating fungi—for example, certain species of microsporidia—for the biological control of pathogens and insect pests. Some of these species are already being used to parasitize insect pests. In some cases, they interfere with reproduction in their insect host. It should be noted that some microsporidia may pose a threat to beneficial insects. For example, a microsporidian has been implicated as one factor in the die-off of honeybee colonies.

Some fungi cause diseases in humans and other animals

Certain ascomycetes cause superficial infections in which only the skin, hair, or nails are infected. Ringworm, athlete's foot, and jock itch are examples of superficial fungal infections. Because these fungi infect dead layers of skin that are not fed by capillaries, the immune system cannot launch an effective response.

Many pathogenic fungi are opportunists that cause infections only when the body's immune system is compromised, such as in patients infected with HIV. Cancer patients and organ transplant recipients who are given medication to suppress their immune systems are also at risk. *Candida* is an ascomycete that inhabits the human mouth and vagina. The immune system and the normal bacteria of these regions normally prevent this yeast from causing infection. However, when the immune system is compromised, *Candida* multiplies, causing thrush, a painful yeast infection of the mouth, throat, and vagina.

The ascomycete *Aspergillus fumigatus* is usually harmless but causes aspergillosis in people with lowered immune function. During the course of aspergillosis, the fungus can invade the lungs, heart, brain, kidneys, and other vital organs and cause death.

Other fungi also infect internal tissues and organs and may spread through many regions of the body. Histoplasmosis, for example, is a lung infection caused by inhaling spores of a fungus common in soil contaminated with bird feces. Most people in the eastern and midwestern parts of the United States have been exposed to this fungus at some time, and an estimated 40 million Americans have had mild infections. Fortunately, the infection is usually confined to the lungs and is of short duration, but if the infection spreads through the blood to the heart, brain, or other parts of the body, it can be serious and sometimes fatal.

Some fungi produce poisonous compounds collectively called **mycotoxins.** A few species of *Aspergillus,* for example, produce potent mycotoxins called *aflatoxins* that harm the liver and are known carcinogens. Foods on which aflatoxin-producing fungi commonly grow include peanuts, pecans, corn, and other grains. Other foods that may contain traces of aflatoxins include animal products such as milk, eggs, and meat (from animals that consumed feed contaminated by aflatoxin). Avoiding aflatoxin in the diet is impossible, but exposure should be minimized as much as possible. Any human food or animal forage product that has become moldy should be suspected of aflatoxin contamination and should be discarded.

Fungi contribute to sick-building syndrome, a situation in which occupants of a building experience acute adverse health effects linked to the time they spend in a given building. Mold-related insurance claims amount to hundreds of millions of dollars each year. When conditions are moist, molds can grow on carpets, leather, cloth, wood, insulation, and food. Mold spores, fragments, and aerosol mold products make their way into the air, and people are exposed through inhalation as well as by skin contact.

Exposure to molds and their toxins has been linked to depressed immune function, irritation of the throat and respiratory passageways, infection, and toxicity. The most common responses to mold exposure are reactions that range from mild to severe illnesses, including hay fever, sinusitis, asthma, and dermatitis.

Fungi cause many important plant diseases

Fungi are more destructive to plants than any other disease-causing organism. They are responsible for about 70% of all major crop diseases. Fungi cause serious epidemic diseases that spread rapidly and often result in complete crop failure. Fungal plant diseases costs billions of dollars in agricultural damage yearly.

All plants are apparently susceptible to some fungal infection. Damage may be localized in certain tissues or structures of the

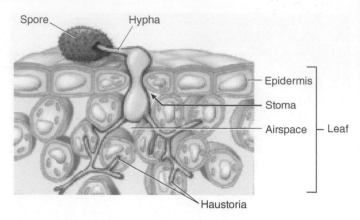

Figure 29-23 How a fungus parasitizes a plant

In this example, the hypha enters the leaf through a stoma. The hypha grows, branching extensively through the internal air spaces, and penetrates plant cells with specialized hyphal extensions called haustoria.

© Cengage Learning

plant, or the disease may be systemic and spread throughout the entire plant. Fungal infections may cause stunting of plant parts or of the plant and may cause wartlike growths or kill the plant.

A plant often becomes infected after hyphae enter through stomata (pores) in the leaf or stem or through wounds in the plant body (FIG. 29-23). Alternatively, the fungus may produce *cutinase*, an enzyme that dissolves the waxy cuticle that covers the surface of leaves and stems. After dissolving the cuticle, the fungus easily invades the plant tissues. As the mycelium grows, it may stay mainly between the plant cells, or it may penetrate the cells. Parasitic fungi often produce special hyphal branches called **haustoria** (sing., *haustorium*) that penetrate the host cells and obtain nourishment from the cytoplasm.

(a) Brown rot of peaches. This disease is caused by *Monilinia fruticola*, an ascomycete. Photographed in Oregon.

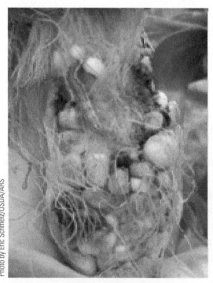

(b) Corn smut on an ear of sweet corn. This fungal disease is caused by *Ustilago maydis*, a basidiomycete.

(c) Black stem rust infection on wheat (*Triticum* sp.) stem. This plant disease is caused by *Puccinia graminis*, a basidiomycete.

Figure 29-24 Fungi that cause plant diseases

Ascomycetes cause serious plant diseases, including powdery mildew, chestnut blight, Dutch elm disease, apple scab, wilt on potatoes, and brown rot, which attacks cherries, peaches, plums, and apricots (FIG. 29-24a).

Basidiomycetes cause smuts and rusts that attack corn, wheat, oats, and other grains (FIGS. 29-24b and c). Some fungal parasites, such as the basidiomycete *Puccinia graminis*, which causes black stem rust of wheat, have complex life cycles that involve two or more different host plants and the production of several kinds of spores. Before the late 1950s, black stem rust outbreaks occurred every few years somewhere in the world, destroying entire wheat crops. By the early 1960s, Norman Borlaug, winner of the Nobel Peace Prize in 1970, and other researchers had developed rust-resistant varieties of wheat, heralding in the green revolution. However, new mutations have put *Puccinia* and wheat rust back in the news. The new strain has spread through parts of Africa and into the Middle East. Each fungus releases billions of spores, which the wind can blow for hundreds of miles, spreading the fungus to new regions of the world. Its spread may lead to widespread food shortages. The genomes of several *Puccinia* species have been sequenced, and researchers are developing methods to quickly diagnose the diseases they cause. They are also working to develop new varieties of disease-resistant wheat.

CHECKPOINT 29.5

- **CONNECT** *In what ways (both positive and negative) are fungi important in modern biology and medicine?*
- **CONNECT** *Can fungi be beneficial to plants? In what ways are they harmful?*

SUMMARY: FOCUS ON LEARNING OBJECTIVES

29.1 Characteristics of Fungi *(page 598)*

1 Describe the distinguishing characteristics of fungi.
- **Fungi** are eukaryotic heterotrophs that secrete digestive enzymes onto their food source and then absorb the predigested food. Fungi are characterized by cell walls that contain **chitin.**

2 Describe the body plan of a fungus.
- A fungus may be a unicellular **yeast** or a filamentous, multicellular *mold*. The body of most multicellular fungi consists of long, threadlike filaments called **hyphae** that branch and form a tangled mass called a **mycelium.**
- In most fungi perforated **septa**, or cross walls, divide the hyphae into individual cells. In some fungi the hyphae are **coenocytes** that form an elongated, multinuclear cell.

29.2 Fungal Reproduction *(page 599)*

3 Describe the life cycle of a typical fungus, including sexual and asexual reproduction.
- Most fungi reproduce both sexually and asexually by means of **spores.** Spores are produced on aerial hyphae. When fungal spores land in a suitable spot, they germinate.
- When fungi of two different mating types meet, their hyphae fuse, a process called **plasmogamy.** The cytoplasm fuses, but the nuclei remain separate. The fungi enter a **dikaryotic** $(n + n)$ stage in which each new cell formed has one nucleus of each type.
- **Karyogamy,** fusion of the nuclei, takes place in the hyphal tip and results in a diploid $(2n)$ *zygote nucleus.*
- Meiosis produces four genetically different haploid (n) nuclei. Each nucleus becomes part of a spore. When the spores germinate, they form new mycelia by mitosis.
- Genetically similar asexual spores are produced by mitosis. When these spores germinate, they also develop into mycelia.

29.3 Fungal Diversity *(page 601)*

4 Give arguments to support the hypothesis that fungi are opisthokonts, more closely related to animals than to plants.
- Like animals, some fungi have flagellate cells—for example, chytrid gametes and spores—and the flagellate cells propel themselves with a single posterior flagellum. Also like animal cells, fungal mitochondria have platelike cristae.
- Based on chemical and structural characters, fungi are classified, along with animals and choanoflagellates, as **opisthokonts.**

5 Give arguments to support the hypothesis that chytrids may have been the earliest fungal group to evolve from the most recent common ancestor of fungi.
- **Chytrids,** or **chytridiomycetes,** produce flagellate spores at some stage in their life cycle. No other fungi have flagella. Thus, chytrids probably were the earliest fungi to evolve; the most recent common ancestor of all fungi was a flagellate protist.

6 List distinguishing characteristics, describe a typical life cycle, and give examples of each of the following fungal groups: chytridiomycetes, zygomycetes, glomeromycetes, ascomycetes, and basidiomycetes.

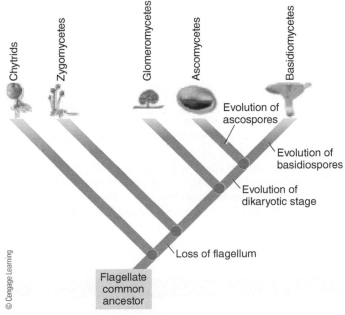

- Chytrids reproduce both asexually and sexually. Their gametes and zoospores are flagellate. *Allomyces,* a common chytrid, spends part of its life as a multicellular haploid **thallus** and part as a multicellular diploid thallus. The haploid thallus produces two types of flagellate gametes that fuse. Both plasmogamy and karyogamy occur, producing a flagellate zygote. The diploid thallus bears zoosporangia that produce diploid **zoospores** and resting sporangia in which haploid zoospores form by meiosis. The haploid zoospores form new haploid thalli.

- **Zygomycetes,** such as the black bread mold, *Rhizopus,* form a haploid thallus that produces both asexual spores and sexual spores. Asexual spores germinate and form new thalli. In sexual reproduction hyphae of two different haploid mating types form gametangia. Plasmogamy occurs as the gametangia fuse. Karyogamy occurs, and a diploid zygote is formed; the zygote develops into a **zygospore.** Meiosis produces recombinant haploid zygospores. When zygospores germinate, each hypha develops a sporangium at its tip. Spores are released and develop into new hyphae.

- **Microsporidia,** currently classified as zygomycetes, are opportunistic pathogens that penetrate and infect animal cells with their long, threadlike *polar tubes*.

- **Glomeromycetes** have coenocytic hyphae. They reproduce asexually with large, multinucleate spores called blastospores. Glomeromycetes are symbionts that form intracellular associations called **mycorrhizae** with the roots of plants. Because they extend their hyphae into root cells, glomeromycetes are **endomycorrhizal fungi.** The most common endomycorrhizae are called *arbuscular mycorrhizae* because the hyphae inside the root cells form branched, tree-shaped structures known as **arbuscules.**

- **Ascomycetes** include yeasts, cup fungi, morels, truffles, and blue-green, pink, and brown molds. Some ascomycetes form mycorrhizae; others form lichens. Ascomycetes produce asexual spores called **conidia;** they produce sexual spores called **ascospores** in saclike **asci.** The asci line a fruiting body called an **ascocarp.**

- In ascomycetes haploid mycelia of opposite mating types produce septate hyphae. Plasmogamy occurs, and nuclei are exchanged. A dikaryotic ($n + n$) stage occurs in which hyphae form and produce asci and an ascocarp. Karyogamy occurs, followed by meiosis. The recombinant nuclei divide by mitosis, producing eight haploid nuclei that develop into ascospores. When the ascospores germinate, they can form new mycelia.

- **Basidiomycetes** include mushrooms, puffballs, bracket fungi, rusts, and smuts.

- These fungi produce sexual spores called **basidiospores** on the outside of a **basidium.** Basidia develop on the surface of **gills** in mushrooms; mushrooms are a type of **basidiocarp** (a fruiting body).

- Hyphae in the basidiomycetes have septa. Plasmogamy occurs with the fusion of two hyphae of different mating types. A dikaryotic **secondary mycelium** forms. Then a basidiocarp develops, and basidia form. Karyogamy occurs, producing a diploid zygote nucleus. Meiosis produces four haploid nuclei

that become basidiospores. When basidiospores germinate, they form haploid **primary mycelia.**

29.4 Ecological Importance of Fungi *(page 611)*

7 Summarize the ecological significance of fungi as decomposers.
- Most fungi are decomposers that break down organic compounds in dead organisms, leaves, garbage, and wastes into simpler nutrients that can be recycled.

8 Describe the important ecological role of mycorrhizae.
- Mycorrhizae are mutualistic associations between fungi and the roots of plants. The fungus supplies water and nutrient minerals to the plant, and the fungus obtains organic compounds from the plant. Glomeromycetes form endomycorrhizae with roots. Some ascomycetes and basidiomycetes are **ectomycorrhizal fungi** that form mycorrhizae when their hyphae coat tree roots, but do not penetrate the root cells.

9 Characterize the unique nature of a lichen.
- A **lichen** is a combination of a fungus and a photoautotroph (an alga or cyanobacterium). In this symbiotic relationship, the photoautotroph provides the fungus with organic compounds. The fungus may provide the photoautotroph with shelter, water, and minerals. Lichens have three main forms: crustose, foliose, and fruticose.

29.5 Economic, Biological, and Medical Impact of Fungi *(page 615)*

10 Summarize some specific ways that fungi affect humans economically.
- Fungi cause huge economic losses by damaging food and crops. On the other hand, some fungi, like mushrooms, are foods; others, like yeasts, are used to produce beer, wine, and bread; and still others are used to produce cheeses or industrial chemicals.

11 Summarize the importance of fungi to biology and medicine; describe how fungi infect plants and humans, describing at least one fungal animal disease and one fungal plant disease.
- Biologists use the yeast *Saccharomyces cerevisiae* and other fungi as model organisms for research in molecular biology and genetics. Fungi are also being investigated for the biological control of insects.
- Fungi are used to make many medications, including penicillin and other antibiotics; they are used in bioremediation and to control pests biologically.
- Fungi are opportunistic pathogens in humans. They cause human diseases, such as histoplasmosis; some fungi produce **mycotoxins,** such as *aflatoxins,* which can cause liver damage and cancer.
- Fungal hyphae infect plants through stomata. Hyphal branches called **haustoria** penetrate plant cells and obtain nourishment from the cytoplasm. Fungi cause many important plant diseases, including brown rot, corn smut, and wheat rust.

TEST YOUR UNDERSTANDING

Know and Comprehend

1. Fungi are (a) eukaryotes and opisthokonts (b) prokaryotes and opisthokonts (c) flagellate and dikaryotic (d) autotrophic eukaryotes (e) heterotrophs with cellulose cell walls

2. Which of the following fungi does *not* have a mycelium? (a) black bread mold (b) yeast (c) decomposer cup fungus (d) cultivated mushroom (e) *Penicillium*

3. A cell described as *n* + *n* is (a) monokaryotic (b) diploid (c) haploid (d) coenocytic (e) dikaryotic

4. With the exception of chytridiomycetes, fungi are generally disseminated by (a) water currents (b) fragmentation of hyphae (c) soredia (d) airborne spores (e) flagellate zoospores

5. Which statement is *not* true of the chytrids? (a) they are simple aquatic fungi (b) they produce motile cells with single, posterior flagella (c) they undergo both sexual and asexual reproduction (d) their cells are dikaryotic (e) they were the earliest fungi to evolve

6. Which statement is *not* true of the zygomycetes? (a) many members of this group form endomycorrhizae with tree roots (b) their sexual spores are called zygospores (c) they undergo both sexual and asexual reproduction (d) plasmogamy and karyogamy occur (e) they have coenocytic hyphae

7. Glomeromycetes (a) reproduce mainly by sexual spores called glomerospores (b) are characterized by unique structures called polar tubes (c) associate with cyanobacteria to form lichens (d) include many opportunistic pathogens that cause human disease (e) form arbuscular endomycorrhizae with tree roots

8. The ascomycete life cycle typically includes (a) mainly diploid thalli (b) the formation of a thick zygosporangium (c) the production of eight haploid ascospores within an ascus (d) the production of microsporidia (e) the production of ascospores, zoospores, and conidia at different stages

9. Which statement is *not* true of the basidiomycetes? (a) they produce a secondary mycelium with *n* + *n* hyphae (b) their sexual spores are called basidiospores (c) they have a diploid thallus that produces zoospores (d) reproduction is mainly sexual (e) they have microscopic basidia

10. A combination organism consisting of a photoautotroph and a fungus is called (a) an arbuscular endomycorrhiza (b) an ectomycorrhiza (c) a lichen (d) a pathogenic agent (e) an aflatoxin

11. Mutualistic associations between fungi and the roots of plants are called (a) lichens (b) mycorrhizae (c) pathogenic associations (d) parasitic haustoria (e) mycotoxic symbioses

12. When a fungus infects a plant, it (a) infiltrates leaves with lichens (b) forms relationships by attaching mycorrhizae to stems (c) secretes powerful digestive juices onto the leaves (d) uses haustoria to dissolve roots (e) enters leaves or stems through stomata

Apply and Analyze

13. **VISUALIZE** The secondary mycelium of a basidiomycete is shown here. (a) How would you describe its cells? (b) What stage of its life cycle is it in? (c) Draw the next steps in this stage of its life cycle.

© Cengage Learning

14. Explain the statement "Mushrooms are like the tips of icebergs." If you do not see mushrooms in your lawn, can you conclude that no fungi live there? Why or why not?

Evaluate and Synthesize

15. **EVOLUTION LINK** Justify (a) classifying fungi as opisthokonts, (b) classifying microsporidia as fungi, and (c) grouping ascomycetes and basidiomycetes as sister clades.

16. **CONNECT** The development of safe and effective antifungal agents presents a daunting challenge to researchers. Explain. (*Hint:* Drugs that combat bacterial diseases typically target differences between bacterial cells and those of the host.)

17. **SCIENCE, TECHNOLOGY, AND SOCIETY** Develop an argument for or against the use of scientific resources, including the latest technology, to sequence the genomes of fungi.

 To access course materials, such as Aplia and other **aplia** companion resources, please visit **www.cengagebrain.com.**

30 | An Introduction to Animal Diversity

Daniela Dirscherl/Getty Images

The tube sponge (*Callyspongia vaginalis*). This animal, sometimes mistaken for a plant, ranges in color from purple to blue to gray. It is common on coral reefs in the Caribbean, from Florida to Mexico.

KEY CONCEPTS

30.1 Animals are multicellular, eukaryotic heterotrophs composed of cells specialized to perform specific functions. Most animals are diploid organisms that reproduce sexually, and most have a nervous system and a muscular system.

30.2 Animals evolved in marine environments, and members of most animal phyla still inhabit marine environments. However, many animals are adapted to life in fresh water and others to terrestrial habitats.

30.3 The common ancestors of animals are choanoflagellates; choanoflagellates, fungi, and animals are a monophyletic group known as opisthokonts.

30.4 Biologists classify animals based on many characteristics, including their morphology (structure), features of their early development, and molecular data; they generally agree that bilateral animals split into at least three major clades.

Although members of most animal species are readily recognizable as animals, the identity of some others is less obvious. Early naturalists thought sponges were plants because they did not move from place to place. Some people still mistake certain marine animals, such as sponges and corals, for plants (see photograph; also see the image of the sea anemone on the cover of your textbook). Locomotion is not a requirement for being classified as an animal.

Animal phylogeny is an exciting and rapidly changing field of study. Biologists have described and named more than 1.5 million species of animals, and 15,000 to 20,000 new species are named each year. Millions more probably remain to be discovered and classified. Interestingly, an estimated 99% of all animal species that ever inhabited our planet are extinct. Taxonomists have assigned the extant (living) animals to about 35 phyla. Molecular studies have confirmed that many of these groups are **monophyletic;** that is, they consist of *all* the descendants and *only* the descendants of a common ancestor. (Recall from Chapter 23 that a monophyletic group is called a **clade.**)

Animal groups that are not monophyletic have been split or reorganized, with some members of the groups being reassigned to other taxa. It is important to remember that the classification of animals and the relative positions of animal groups are a work in progress. As they consider new data, systematists redraw the tree of animal life.

In this chapter we discuss the characteristics of animals and their habitats. We then explore animal origins and some of the criteria biologists use to determine evolutionary relationships and to classify animals. Finally, we introduce the major animal groups, including the three major clades of bilateral animals.

30.1 ANIMAL CHARACTERISTICS

LEARNING OBJECTIVE

1   Describe several characteristics common to most animals.

Animals are so diverse that for almost any definition we can find exceptions. We can best describe animals by the characteristics they share:

1. Animals are multicellular eukaryotes. In contrast to plants, algae, and fungi, animal cells lack cell walls. Instead, structural support depends on an **extracellular matrix,** which the cells secrete (see Chapter 4). Collagen, the main structural protein in the extracellular matrix, forms very tough fibers. Collagen is an important *shared derived character* in animals (see Chapter 23).
2. Animals are **heterotrophs.** As consumers, they depend on producers for their raw materials and energy. In contrast to the fungi, most animals ingest their food first and then digest it inside the body, usually within a digestive system.
3. Cells that make up the animal body are specialized to perform specific functions. In all but the simplest animals, cells are organized to form tissues, and tissues are organized to form organs. In small animals with simple body plans, life processes such as gas exchange, circulation of materials, and waste disposal can take place by diffusion of gases and other substances directly to and from the environment. In larger animals, specialized organ systems perform these functions.
4. Animals have diverse body plans. The term *body plan* refers to the basic structure and functional design of the body. An animal's body plan and lifestyle are adapted to its methods of obtaining food and reproducing.
5. Most animals are capable of locomotion at some time during their life cycle. Some animals (such as sponges and corals) move about as larvae (immature forms) but are **sessile** (firmly attached to the ground or some other surface) as adults (see chapter-opening photograph).
6. Most animals have nervous systems and muscle systems that enable them to respond rapidly to stimuli in their environment.
7. Most animals are diploid organisms that reproduce sexually, with large, nonmotile eggs and small, flagellate sperm. A haploid sperm unites with a haploid egg, forming a diploid **zygote** (fertilized egg).
8. Animals go through a period of embryonic development. The zygote undergoes **cleavage,** a series of mitotic cell divisions. During cleavage the zygote develops into a hollow ball of cells called a **blastula.** Although some animals develop directly into adults, the majority first develop into a **larva,** a sexually immature form that may look very different from the adult (FIG. 30-1). The larva differs from the adult in many ways, including where it lives (its habitat), how it moves, and what it eats. Larvae typically go through **metamorphosis,** a developmental process that converts the immature animal into a juvenile form that can then grow into an adult.

CHECKPOINT 30.1

*   **CONNECT** *For centuries, scientists classified sponges as plants, but now they are classified as animals. What characteristics do sponges share with other animals?*

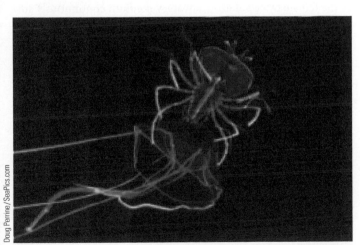

(a) Spiny lobster larva. This larva is hitching a ride on a jellyfish. Over a period of months, the larva passes through several stages before becoming an adult. Photographed in open ocean at night, Hawaii.

(b) Adult spiny lobster. The adult has two long antennae used to sense movement. Spiny lobsters lack large claws. The spines on their back help protect them. In this image you can see the two large spines above the animal's eyes. Spiny lobsters leave their hiding places at night to hunt.

Figure 30-1 Larva and adult spiny lobster (*Panulirus* sp.)
Most animals go through a larva stage before developing into an adult. The larva usually differs from the adult in size, appearance, and lifestyle.

30.2 ADAPTATIONS TO OCEAN, FRESHWATER, AND TERRESTRIAL HABITATS

LEARNING OBJECTIVE

2 Compare the advantages and disadvantages of life in the ocean, in fresh water, and on land.

Fossil evidence suggests that animals first evolved in shallow, marine environments during the Proterozoic eon, at least 600 million years ago (mya; see Chapter 21). Although animals are now distributed in virtually every environment, at least some members of most animal phyla still inhabit marine environments.

Marine habitats offer many advantages

The buoyancy of sea water provides support, and its large volume keeps the water temperature relatively stable. The body fluids of most invertebrates have about the same osmotic concentration as sea water, so fluid and salt balance are more easily maintained there than in fresh water. **Plankton,** which consists of the mainly microscopic animals and protists that are suspended in water and float with its movement, provides a ready source of food for many aquatic animals.

Life in the ocean also presents some challenges. Although the continuous motion of water brings nutrients to animals and washes their wastes away, animals must be able to cope with the water's movements and the currents that could sweep them away. Squids, fishes, and marine mammals have evolved as strong swimmers, usually able to direct their movements and maintain their location. However, most invertebrates and young vertebrates cannot swim strongly, and they have adapted in various ways to the tides and currents.

Some sessile animals attach permanently to a stable structure such as a rock. Others burrow in the sand and silt that cover the sea bottom. Many invertebrates have adapted by maintaining a small body size and becoming part of the plankton. As they are tossed about, their food supply continues to surround them.

Some animals are adapted to freshwater habitats

Far fewer kinds of animals make their homes in fresh water than in the ocean because living in this habitat is more difficult. Fresh water is hypotonic to the tissue fluids of animals, so water tends to move into the animal by osmosis. To survive in this habitat, freshwater species must have mechanisms for removing excess water while retaining salts. This *osmoregulation* requires an expenditure of energy.

Fresh water offers a much less constant environment than sea water. Animals that inhabit fresh water must have adaptations for surviving variations in oxygen content, temperature,

turbidity (because of sediments suspended in the water), and even water volume. In addition, fresh water generally contains less food than the sea.

Terrestrial living requires major adaptations

Living on land is even more difficult than living in fresh water, and the evolution of terrestrial animals involved major adaptations. Analyzing the fossil record, many biologists hypothesize that the first air-breathing terrestrial animals were scorpionlike arthropods that came ashore in the Silurian period about 444 mya. The first vertebrates to inhabit terrestrial environments, the amphibians, did not appear until the Devonian period, about 30 million years later.

The chief problem facing all terrestrial organisms is desiccation (drying out). Water is constantly lost by evaporation and is often difficult to replace. A body covering adapted to minimize fluid loss helps solve this problem in many terrestrial animals (FIG. 30-2). Location of the respiratory surface deep within the animal also helps prevent fluid loss. Thus, the gills of aquatic animals are typically located externally, but lungs and tracheal tubes of terrestrial animals are typically found deep within the body.

Reproduction on land also poses challenges to protecting gametes and the developing offspring from desiccation. Aquatic animals typically shed their gametes in the water, where fertilization occurs. Some land animals, including most amphibians, return to the water for reproduction, and their larval forms develop in the water.

The evolution of internal fertilization has permitted many terrestrial animals, including land planarians, earthworms, land snails, insects, reptiles (including birds), and mammals, to meet the desiccation challenge. Because these terrestrial animals transfer sperm from the body of the male directly into the body of the female by copulation, a watery medium continuously surrounds the sperm. Another important adaptation to reproduction on land is the tough, protective shell that surrounds the eggs of many species (see Fig. 30-2). Secreted by the female, this

Figure 30-2 Adaptations to terrestrial life

The tough, horny skin of the green iguana (*Iguana iguana*) has scales and is water resistant. Leathery eggs protect the embryos from drying out.

E.R. Degginger/Science Source

shell protects the developing embryo from drying out. An alternative adaptation for terrestrial reproduction is development of the embryo within the moist body of the mother.

Water has buoyancy that helps support animals that inhabit aquatic environments. Air is less dense than water, and to inhabit the land, animals must have structures, such as a skeletal system and muscles, that support the body. The temperature extremes of terrestrial habitats also present challenges. In later chapters we discuss behavioral and physiological adaptations for maintaining body temperature.

CHECKPOINT 30.2

- *What are some advantages of marine environments over freshwater and terrestrial habitats?*
- **CONNECT** *What are some animal adaptations to the terrestrial environment?*

30.3 ANIMAL EVOLUTION

LEARNING OBJECTIVE

3 Use current hypotheses to trace the early evolution of animals.

Biologists generally agree that animals share a common ancestor with a group of protists known as *choanoflagellates* (see Fig. 26-21). The cells of these colonial flagellates became specialized to perform specific functions, such as movement, feeding, or reproduction. As this division of labor evolved, a colony of flagellates reached the level of cooperation and coordination that qualified it to be considered a single organism, the first animal. The choanoflagellates, fungi, and animals are a monophyletic group known as **opisthokonts.** Recall from Chapter 26 that opisthokonts are characterized by a posterior flagellum on motile cells.

Historically, biologists depended on fossils, on similarities in body plan (i.e., structure), and on patterns of development to determine evolutionary relationships among various groups of animals. **Molecular systematics,** the science that focuses on molecular structure to clarify evolutionary relationships, has provided additional data that are critical in answering questions about phylogeny. In many cases, molecular data have confirmed hypotheses that were based on morphology (structure).

Complex genomes were apparently present early during animal evolution. Molecular studies suggest that the ancestor of animals had more than 1500 genes not found in other eukaryotes. Some of these genes may be traced to horizontal gene transfer from other domains, followed by modification of the genes. Complex genomes have been described in the sea anemone and in other animals that are relatively simple morphologically.

Molecular analyses indicate that the structure of genes that control development, RNA molecules, and many other molecules are very similar among all animal groups that have been studied. According to the *principle of parsimony,* such complex molecules are unlikely to have evolved multiple times

(see Chapter 23). Thus, these data support the hypothesis that animals evolved only once. Animals are a monophyletic group.

Molecular systematics helps biologists interpret the fossil record

Because early animals were soft-bodied forms that left few fossils, the evolutionary history of animals has been vigorously debated. The scarcity of fossils has made it difficult to determine the age, rate of divergence, and number of branches of animal groups. In 2009, a research team found fossil traces in an oil field on the Arabian Peninsula that are thought to date back more than 635 million years. The fossil traces are steroids found only in the skeletal structures of certain sponges (demosponges). Before this discovery, the earliest known animal fossils were the *Ediacaran biota* from the **Ediacaran period** (635 mya to 541 mya). These fossils of small, simple animals suggest that sponges, jellyfish, and comb jellies were present during this period (see Fig. 21-9).

Paleontologists have discovered many large, complex animal fossils in Chengjiang, an Early Cambrian (542 mya to 520 mya) fossil site in China, and in the Burgess Shale in British Columbia, a Middle Cambrian fossil site (520 mya to 515 mya). Fossils of most extant phyla (and also many extinct animals) have been found at these sites. The rapid appearance of an amazing variety of body plans during this time is known as the **Cambrian radiation,** or less formally as the **Cambrian explosion** (see Fig. 21-10). According to the Cambrian radiation hypothesis, which is based on the fossil record, major modifications in body plan that occurred during this time account for many branches of the animal tree.

Studies of large molecular data sets suggest that most animal clades actually diverged over a very long period during the Proterozoic eon (2.5 bya to 541 mya). Thus, the animal phyla that first left fossils during the Cambrian radiation may have evolved several hundred million years *before* they appear in the fossil record. Biologists estimate that certain groups are about twice as old as the oldest fossils found to date. According to this view, the Cambrian radiation was a rapid evolution of new animal body plans among clades that already existed. Perhaps fossils of these early animals remain to be discovered in Proterozoic rocks. Another hypothesis holds that a change in environmental conditions that occurred prior to the Cambrian radiation allowed fossils to form.

Biologists develop hypotheses about the evolution of development

Changes in animal body plans are linked to changes in patterns of embryonic development. Biologists have long used similarities and differences in embryonic development to hypothesize how animal groups are related. Traditionally, biologists depended mainly on structural changes to compare the process of development in various groups.

Today, researchers are focusing on the molecular basis of developmental processes. They have identified the genes that direct the early development of the body plan and have discovered that many of these genes have been conserved during animal evolution. The same basic set of genes controls early development in all animal groups. Furthermore, the same genes are used in the same ways to regulate development.

Evolutionary developmental biology, sometimes referred to as **Evo Devo,** has become an important approach to studying animal relationships. Biologists compare molecular events, such as gene regulation during development, in various animal groups.

Recall from Chapter 17 that *Hox* **genes** are a group of regulatory genes that specify the anterior–posterior axis during development (see Fig. 17-13). The presence and number of *Hox* genes provide insights about evolutionary relationships. These genes have been identified in all the bilateral animal groups that have been studied, suggesting that the last common ancestor of all bilateral animals had similar *Hox* genes. These genes have been identified in a sea anemone (*Nematostella vectensis*), which is a cnidarian. Cnidarians are marine animals, for example, jellyfish, with radial symmetry. This finding suggests that the cnidarians share a common ancestor with the bilateral animals.

Investigators think that all the *Hox* gene groups had evolved by the beginning of the Cambrian period. Mutations in *Hox* genes could have resulted in rapid changes in animal body plans. For example, regulation by *Hox* gene groups has been linked with the development of wings or legs. Similarities in molecular development among different animal groups suggest that they had a common ancestor.

CHECKPOINT 30.3

- *What was the Cambrian radiation?*
- *According to the current hypothesis, when did most major groups of animals evolve?*
- CONNECT *How has the discovery of* Hox *genes helped biologists understand animal evolution?*

30.4 RECONSTRUCTING ANIMAL PHYLOGENY

LEARNING OBJECTIVES

4   Describe how biologists use morphology (including variations in body symmetry, number of tissue layers, and type of body cavity) and patterns of early development to infer relationships among animal phyla.

5   Cite specific examples of how data from molecular systematics have confirmed or modified traditional animal phylogeny and identify the three major clades of bilateral animals.

Because some animal body plans have been highly conserved throughout evolutionary history, variations in body plans can provide clues to animal relationships. For example, biologists compare variations in body symmetry, number of tissue layers,

types of body cavity, and pattern of development. Biologists also use similarities and differences in embryonic development to infer evolutionary relationships among animal groups. In addition to these traditional methods, researchers now have molecular tools to enhance our understanding of animal phylogeny. Because of technological improvements over the last few decades, comparisons of nucleic acid (DNA and RNA) and protein structure provide critical data for biologists seeking to interpret and reconstruct animal phylogeny.

Animals exhibit two main types of body symmetry

Symmetry refers to the arrangement of body structures in relation to the body axis. Most sponges are not symmetrical, so when a sponge is cut in half, the two halves are not similar to each other. Most other animals exhibit either radial or bilateral body symmetry.

Cnidarians (jellyfish, sea anemones, and their relatives) and adult echinoderms (sea stars and their relatives) have **radial symmetry.** The body has the general form of a wheel or cylinder, and similar structures are regularly arranged as spokes from a central axis (FIG. 30-3a). Multiple planes can be drawn through the central axis, each dividing the organism into two mirror images. An animal with radial symmetry receives stimuli equally from all directions in the environment. Some animals have modified radial symmetry. For example, sea anemones and ctenophores (comb jellies) have *biradial symmetry,* in which parts of the body have become specialized so that only two planes can divide the body into similar halves.

Most animals exhibit **bilateral symmetry,** at least in their larval stages. A bilaterally symmetrical animal can be divided through only one plane (which passes through the midline of the body) to produce roughly equivalent right and left halves that are mirror images (FIG. 30-3b).

As bilateral symmetry evolved, natural selection led to **cephalization,** the development of a head where sensory structures are concentrated. In these groups, concentrations of nerve cells in the head form a brain, and one or two nerve cords extend from the brain toward the rear end of the animal. Bilateral symmetry and cephalization are adaptations for locomotion. The head end of the animal meets its environment first and is best equipped to capture food or respond to danger.

Some definitions of basic terms and directions will help in locating body structures in bilaterally symmetrical animals. The back surface of an animal is its **dorsal** surface; the underside (belly) is its **ventral** surface. **Anterior** (or *cephalic*) means toward the head end of the animal; **posterior,** or *caudal,* means toward the tail end. A structure is said to be *medial* if it is located toward the midline of the body, and it is *lateral* if it is toward one side of the body; for example, the human ear is lateral to the nose. In human anatomy the term *superior* refers to a structure located above some point of reference, or toward the head end of the body. The term *inferior* is used in human anatomy to mean located below some point of reference, or toward the feet.

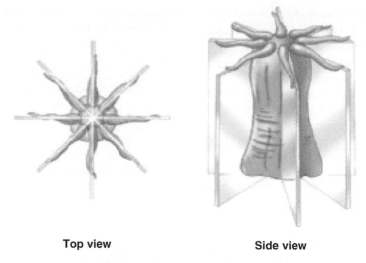

Top view   **Side view**

(a) Radial symmetry. Multiple planes can be drawn through the central axis; each divides the animal into two mirror images.

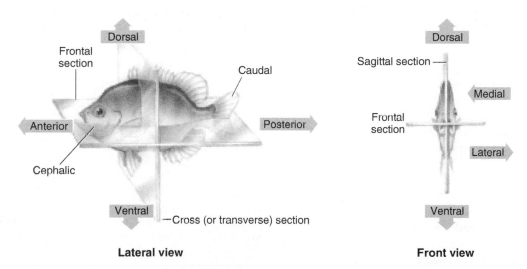

Lateral view   **Front view**

(b) Bilateral symmetry. The head of the animal is its anterior end, and the opposite end is its posterior end. The back of the animal is its dorsal surface, and the belly is its ventral surface. The diagrams illustrate various ways the body can be sectioned (cut) to study its internal structure. A sagittal section (lengthwise vertical cut) divides the animal into right and left parts. A frontal, or longitudinal, cut (lengthwise horizontal) divides the body into dorsal and ventral parts.

Figure 30-3 *Animation* **Radial and bilateral symmetry**

Sections of animals are used in illustrations throughout this book to show the structure and arrangement of tissues and organs.

© Cengage Learning

A bilaterally symmetrical animal has three axes, each at right angles to the other two: an anterior–posterior axis extending from head to tail, a dorsal–ventral axis extending from back to belly, and a left–right axis extending from side to side. We can distinguish three planes or sections that divide the body into specific parts. A *sagittal plane* divides the body into right and left parts. A sagittal plane passes from anterior to posterior and from dorsal to ventral. A *frontal plane* divides a bilateral body into dorsal and ventral parts. A *transverse section,* or *cross section,* cuts at right angles to the body axis and separates anterior and posterior parts.

Animal body plans are linked to the level of tissue development

Sponges have several types of cells, but their cells are not organized into **tissues,** which are groups of closely associated, similar cells that work together to carry out specific functions.

In the early development of all animals except sponges, cells form layers, called **germ layers.** The outer germ layer, or **ectoderm,** gives rise to the tissues that form the outer covering of the body as well as to nervous tissue. The inner layer, or **endoderm,** forms the lining of the digestive tube and other digestive structures. These layers develop into specific types of tissues.

Biologists describe cnidarians and ctenophores as **diploblastic** because they have only two germ layers. Other animals are **triploblastic.** They have a third germ layer, the **mesoderm,** which gives rise to most other body structures, including muscles, skeletal structures, and circulatory system (when present).

Most bilateral animals have a body cavity lined with mesoderm

The vast majority of bilateral animals have a fluid-filled body cavity, or **coelom** (pronounced "see´-lum"), between the outer wall of the body and the digestive tube (FIG. 30-4). The flatworms and ribbon worms are exceptions. They are bilateral and triploblastic but have a solid body; that is, they have no body cavity. They are referred to as **acoelomates** (*a-*, "without"; and *coelom,* "cavity").

Most animals have a body cavity that is completely lined with mesoderm. Such a body cavity is a *true* coelom. An animal with a true coelom is referred to as a **coelomate.** The coelom was one of the most important early animal adaptations. Evolution of the coelom was a critical step in the evolution of larger, more complex animals.

With the evolution of the coelom came a new body design, the *tube-within-a-tube* body plan. The coelom is a space that separates the body wall, the outer tube, from the digestive tube (gut), which is the inner tube. The digestive tube is attached to the body wall at its ends. Typically, the digestive tube has a mouth at one end for taking in food and an anus at the other end for eliminating wastes. Because the coelom separates the muscles of the body wall from those in the wall of the digestive tract, the digestive tube can move food along independently of body movements.

Because it is an enclosed compartment (or series of compartments) of fluid under pressure, the coelom can serve as a **hydrostatic skeleton** in which contracting muscles push against a tube of fluid. The hydrostatic skeleton also shapes the body of soft animals. The evolution of various shapes and divisions of the coelom provided the opportunity for animals to become

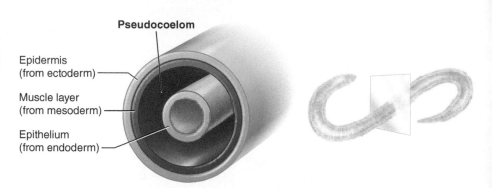

(a) Acoelomate: flatworm (planarian worm). Acoelomate animals have no body cavity.

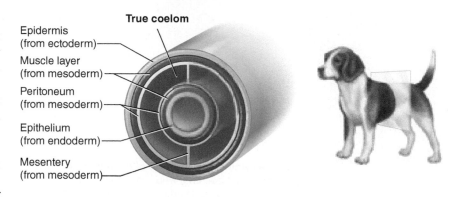

(b) Pseudocoelomate: nematode. Pseudocoelomate animals have a body cavity that is not completely lined with mesoderm.

(c) True coelomate: vertebrate. Coelomate animals have a coelom, a body cavity completely lined with tissue that develops from mesoderm. Many internal organs are located in the coelom.

Figure 30-4 *Animation* **Three basic body plans in triploblastic animals**
The germ layer from which each tissue was derived is indicated in parentheses. Ectoderm is shown in *blue,* mesoderm in *red,* and endoderm in *yellow.*
© Cengage Learning

specialized in swimming, crawling, or walking. Animals that can move quickly to capture food or avoid predators are more likely than slower-moving animals to survive.

Evolution of the coelom provided a space where internal organs could develop and function. For example, the pumping action of the heart is possible because of the surrounding space the coelom provides. The fluid-filled coelom also protects internal organs by cushioning them. (Other functions of the coelom will be discussed in Chapter 31.)

Some (typically, small) animals have a body cavity that is not completely lined with mesoderm. This type of body cavity is called a **pseudocoelom** ("false coelom"). Animals with a pseudocoelom, such as nematodes (roundworms) and rotifers, are called **pseudocoelomates.** Because the pseudocoelom appears to have evolved independently in different animal taxa, the presence of a pseudocoelom is not considered a useful characteristic for determining phylogeny. Instead, it is an example of homoplasy.

Bilateral animals form two main clades based on differences in development

Embryonic development begins as the zygote undergoes cleavage, the first several cell divisions of the embryo. During cleavage, the embryo develops into a hollow ball of cells, the blastula. Cells of the blastula undergo **gastrulation,** a process that forms and segregates the three germ layers.

Basic differences in the pattern of early development distinguish two main evolutionary lines of bilateral animals: **protostomes** (pro´-tuh-stomes), assigned to the clade *Protostomia,* and **deuterostomes** (doo´-ter-uh-stomes), assigned to the clade *Deuterostomia.* The protostomes include mollusks (e.g., snails, clams, squids), annelids (e.g., earthworms), arthropods (e.g., crabs, insects), and several other groups. Deuterostomes include the echinoderms (such as sea stars and sea urchins) and chordates (which include the vertebrates).

One important difference in the development of protostomes and deuterostomes is the pattern of cleavage. In many protostomes the early cell divisions are diagonal to the polar axis (the long axis of the embryo), resulting in a somewhat spiral arrangement of cells; any one cell lies between the two cells above or below it (FIG. 30-5a). This pattern of division is known as **spiral cleavage.** In **radial cleavage,** characteristic of the deuterostomes, the early divisions are either parallel or at right angles to the polar axis. The resulting cells lie directly above or below one another (FIG. 30-5b).

In the protostomes the developmental fate of each embryonic cell is typically fixed very early. For example, if the first four cells of an annelid embryo are separated, each cell develops into only a fixed quarter of the larva; this pattern of cleavage is called **determinate cleavage.** In contrast, deuterostomes typically undergo **indeterminate cleavage.** During early cleavage, each cell has the potential of developing into a complete embryo.

For example, if the first four cells of a sea star embryo are separated, each cell can form a complete, although small, larva. If a few cells are removed from a blastula undergoing indeterminate cleavage, other cells compensate, and the embryo develops normally. In contrast, if a few cells are removed from the blastula of an embryo undergoing determinate cleavage, some structure, such as a limb, does not develop.

During gastrulation, a group of cells moves inward, forming a sac that becomes the embryonic gut. The opening to the outside is called the **blastopore.** In most protostomes the blastopore develops into the mouth. The word *protostome* comes from Greek words meaning "first" and "the mouth." In deuterostomes the blastopore does not give rise to the mouth but generally develops into the anus. A second opening that forms later in development gives rise to the mouth. The word *deuterostome* derives from words meaning "second" and "the mouth."

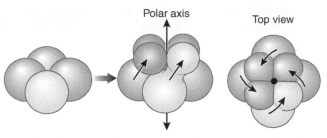

(a) Spiral cleavage is characteristic of protostomes. Note the spiral arrangement, with the upper cells centered between the lower cells.

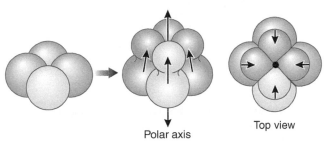

(b) Radial cleavage is characteristic of deuterostomes. The early divisions are either parallel to the polar axis or at right angles to it. The cells are stacked, with the upper cells centered directly above the lower cells.

Figure 30-5 Spiral and radial cleavage

The pattern of cleavage can be appreciated by comparing the positions of the *purple cells* in **(a)** and **(b).**

© Cengage Learning

Biologists have identified major animal clades based on structure, development, and molecular data

Biologists have long inferred evolutionary relationships among animals based on the structural variations and patterns of development we have just discussed. The development of sophisticated new technology, such as new types of microscopy and cell labeling, has helped systematists in their work. As discussed earlier, techniques for determining nucleotide sequences in DNA and RNA and other molecular tools have helped systematists clarify evolutionary relationships among animal groups. Molecular data have also challenged some traditional conclusions, such as *when* various animal groups diverged in relation to other groups. Such questions continue to be the topic of much debate.

Animals are referred to as *metazoa.* Animals with two or three germ layers (diploblastic or triploblastic) make up the *eumetazoa.* As we have described, some animals exhibit asymmetry (sponges), radial symmetry (cnidarians), or biradial symmetry (ctenophores). The *Bilateria,* the lineage of animals with bilateral symmetry, are triploblastic. (They have three germ layers: ectoderm, endoderm, and mesoderm.) As explained in the last section, biologists classify bilateral animals into protostome and deuterostome clades.

Molecular data show that the protostomes split into two major clades: **Lophotrochozoa** (pronounced "lo-fah-tro-kah-zo´-ah") and **Ecdysozoa** (pronounced "ek-dah-so-zo´-ah") (TABLE 30-1 and FIG. 30-6). Animals assigned to the *Lophotrochozoa*

TABLE 30-1 | Overview of the Animal Kingdom

MAJOR GROUPS AND SUBGROUPS	SOME KEY CHARACTERS/COMMENTS
Poriferans (sponges)	Collar cells, flagellated cells that trap food; cells loosely associated and do not form true tissues; sponge larvae have flagella and can swim about; poriferans are probably not a monophyletic group

Cnidarians
  Hydrozoans: hydras
  Scyphozoans: jellyfish
  Cubozoans: box jellyfish
  Anthozoans: corals, sea anemones
	Radial symmetry; cnidocytes (stinging cells); polyp and medusa body forms; tentacles surround mouth; mainly marine

Ctenophores (comb jellies)	Biradial symmetry; eight rows of cilia that resemble combs; tentacles with adhesive glue cells; marine predators

PROTOSTOMES: LOPHOTROCHOZOAN BRANCH

	Bilateral symmetry; triploblastic

Flatworms (platyhelminths)
  Turbellarians: planarians
  Trematodes and monogeneans: flukes
  Cestodes: tapeworms
	Gastrovascular cavity with one opening; no coelom; cephalization

Nemerteans (ribbon worms)	Proboscis (long, muscular tube that can be everted to capture prey); complete digestive tube; mainly marine carnivores

Mollusks
  Chitons
  Gastropods: snails, slugs, nudibranchs
  Bivalves: clams, oysters
  Cephalopods: squids, octopods
	Soft body usually covered by dorsal shell; muscular foot; mantle covers visceral mass; most have radula (belt of teeth)

Annelids
  Polychaetes: sandworms, tubeworms
  Oligochaetes: earthworms, freshwater worms
  Hirudinids: leeches
	Segmented body; most have bristles, called setae, that provide traction during crawling

Lophophorates
  Brachiopods
  Phoronids
  Bryozoans (ectoprocts)
	Lophophore (ring of ciliated tentacles around mouth); mainly sessile, marine

Rotifera (wheel animals)	Crown of cilia at anterior end; microscopic; freshwater and marine

Continued

are characterized by (1) a *lophophore*, a ciliated ring of tentacles surrounding the mouth that serves as a feeding organ; or (2) a type of larva called a *trochophore larva*. The Lophotrochozoa include the flatworms, ribbon worms, mollusks, annelids, and three groups sometimes referred to as the lophophorate phyla.

The name *Ecdysozoa* is derived from the animals in this group molting, a process called *ecdysis*. The Ecdysozoa include the nematodes and arthropods. Note that the phylogeny we have described assigns bilateral animals to three major clades: Lophotrochozoa, Ecdysozoa, and Deuterostomia.

TABLE 30-1	Overview of the Animal Kingdom *(continued)*
MAJOR GROUPS AND SUBGROUPS	**SOME KEY CHARACTERS/COMMENTS**
PROTOSTOMES: ECDYSOZOAN BRANCH	Protostomes with cuticle that is molted and replaced as animal grows
Nematodes (roundworms)	Fluid-filled pseudocoelom serves as hydrostatic skeleton; important decomposers; many are predators
Onycophorans (velvet worms)	Unjointed, paired appendages; sister group of arthropods?
Tardigrades ("water bears")	Unjointed, clawed legs; sister group of arthropods?
Arthropods	Segmented; exoskeleton of chitin; paired, jointed appendages; insects and many crustaceans have compound eyes
Myriapods (centipedes, millipedes)	
Chelicerates (horseshoe crabs, arachnids)	
Crustaceans (lobsters, crabs, barnacles, copepods)	
Hexapods (insects)	
DEUTEROSTOMES	Radial, indeterminate cleavage; pharyngeal slits
Echinoderms	Water vascular system; tube feet; endoskeleton with spines; larvae bilateral, ciliated; adult, pentaradial symmetry; marine
Crinoids (sea lilies, feather stars)	
Asteroids (sea stars)	
Ophiuroids (basket stars, brittle stars)	
Echinoids (sea urchins, sand dollars)	
Holothuroids (sea cucumbers)	
Hemichordates (acorn worms)	Proboscis, collar, and trunk
Chordates	Notochord; dorsal, tubular nerve cord; postanal tail; endostyle; segmented body
Cephalochordates (lancelets)	Notochord extends from anterior to posterior tip
Urochordates (tunicates)	Larvae have chordate characters
Vertebrates (hagfishes, lampreys, cartilaginous fishes, ray-finned fishes, coelacanths, lungfishes, amphibians, reptiles [including birds], mammals)	Vertebral column, cranium, neural crest cells; endoskeleton

© Cengage Learning

Segmentation apparently evolved three times

Over millions of years, evolutionary forces acting on the basic animal body plan have produced changes resulting in a remarkable diversity of body forms. One very important innovation has been *segmentation,* a body plan in which certain structures are repeated, producing a series of body structures and compartments. In some cases, each compartment can be regulated somewhat independently of the others, which allows various parts of the body to become specialized to perform specific functions.

Perhaps the most obvious example of segmentation can be found in earthworms. However, as will be discussed in the following chapters, arthropods and vertebrates also have segmented body plans. Thus, segmented animals are found within each of the three major clades of bilateral animals. Molecular data suggest that segmentation evolved independently three times and is therefore another example of homoplasy. This view is reflected in the cladogram in Figure 30-6. In each independent origin of segmentation, natural selection apparently acted on many of the same genes (e.g., *Hox* genes).

In this chapter we have briefly discussed characteristics common to animals and the early evolution of animals. We described animal body plans and examined some of the criteria

that biologists use to reconstruct phylogenetic relationships. The cladogram shown in Figure 30-6 depicts some of the current hypotheses regarding the relationships among major animals groups, and Table 30-1 summarizes these relationships. In the next two chapters, we survey these animal groups.

In Chapter 31 we describe three groups—sponges, cnidarians, and ctenophores—traditionally viewed as diverging early in the evolutionary history of animals. We then discuss one of the major clades of animals: the protostomes. Then, in Chapter 32, we discuss the deuterostomes, which include the echinoderms and chordates, the clade to which we humans belong. Many hypotheses are presented in these chapters, and we will discuss many examples of how systematists revise the relationships of the branches of the animal phylogenetic tree in response to new data.

CHECKPOINT 30.4

- *How are animals classified based on type of symmetry?*
- *What are some differences between protostomes and deuterostomes?*
- **VISUALIZE** *Draw a simple cladogram illustrating the evolutionary relationships among the three main clades of bilateral animals. How do they differ from one another?*

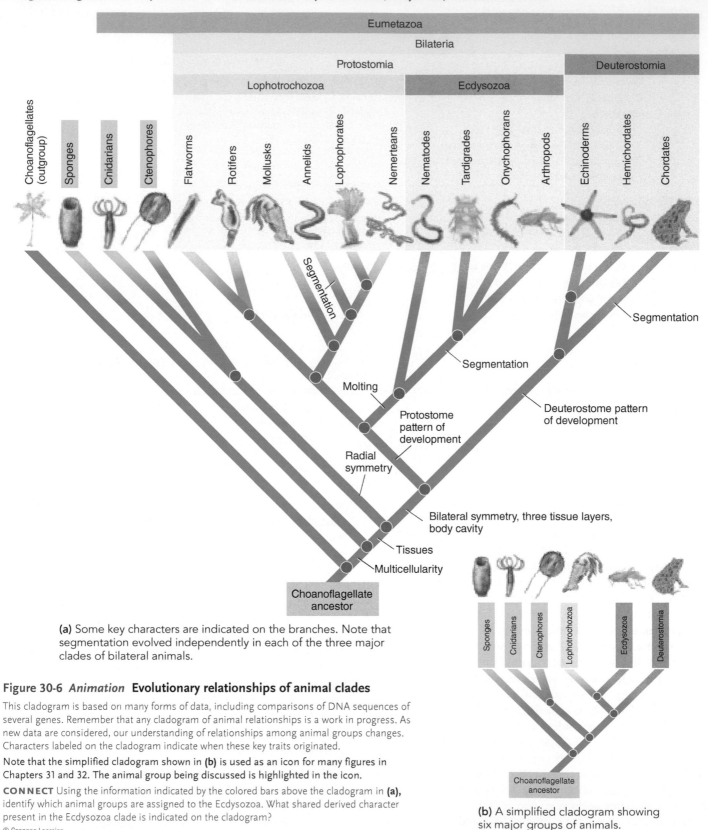

Biologists recognize three major clades of bilateral animals: Lophotrochozoa, Ecdysozoa, and Deuterostomia.

(a) Some key characters are indicated on the branches. Note that segmentation evolved independently in each of the three major clades of bilateral animals.

Figure 30-6 *Animation* Evolutionary relationships of animal clades

This cladogram is based on many forms of data, including comparisons of DNA sequences of several genes. Remember that any cladogram of animal relationships is a work in progress. As new data are considered, our understanding of relationships among animal groups changes. Characters labeled on the cladogram indicate when these key traits originated.

Note that the simplified cladogram shown in (b) is used as an icon for many figures in Chapters 31 and 32. The animal group being discussed is highlighted in the icon.

CONNECT Using the information indicated by the colored bars above the cladogram in (a), identify which animal groups are assigned to the Ecdysozoa. What shared derived character present in the Ecdysozoa clade is indicated on the cladogram?

© Cengage Learning

(b) A simplified cladogram showing six major groups of animals.

30.1 Animal Characteristics *(page 623)*

1 Describe several characteristics common to most animals.

- Animals are eukaryotic, multicellular, heterotrophic organisms with cells specialized to perform specific functions. Animals have diverse body plans. The *body plan* is the basic structure and functional design of the body.

- Most animals are capable of locomotion at some time during their life cycle, can respond adaptively to external stimuli, and can reproduce sexually.

- In sexual reproduction sperm and egg unite to form a **zygote.** The zygote undergoes **cleavage,** a series of cell divisions that produce a hollow ball of cells called a **blastula.** Most animals develop into a **larva,** a sexually immature form that may appear and behave differently from the adult. Larvae typically go through **metamorphosis,** a developmental process that converts the immature animal into a juvenile form that grows into an adult.

30.2 Adaptations to Ocean, Freshwater, and Terrestrial Habitats *(page 624)*

2 Compare the advantages and disadvantages of life in the ocean, in fresh water, and on land.

- Marine environments have relatively stable temperatures, provide buoyancy, and provide readily available food. Fluid and salt balance are more easily maintained in sea water than in fresh water. Currents and other water movements can be a disadvantage.

- Fresh water offers a less constant environment and less food than sea water. Because fresh water is hypotonic to tissue fluid, animals must osmoregulate.

- Terrestrial animals must have adaptations that protect them from drying out and from temperature changes, and that protect their gametes and embryos.

30.3 Animal Evolution *(page 625)*

3 Use current hypotheses to trace the early evolution of animals.

- Based on molecular data, biologists hypothesize that most animal clades actually diverged over a long period during the Proterozoic eon. During the **Cambrian radiation,** new animal body plans rapidly evolved among clades that already existed.

- *Hox* **genes** control early development in animal groups. These genes had evolved by the beginning of the Cambrian period, and mutations in these genes could have resulted in rapid changes in animal body plans.

30.4 Reconstructing Animal Phylogeny *(page 626)*

4 Describe how biologists use morphology (including variations in body symmetry, number of tissue layers, and type of body cavity) and patterns of early development to infer relationships among animal phyla.

- Biologists hypothesize that cnidarians (which have radial symmetry) and ctenophores (which have biradial symmetry) are more closely related to each other than to animals that exhibit bilateral symmetry. **Cephalization,** the development of a head, evolved along with bilateral symmetry.

- Biologists have also inferred relationships based on level of tissue development and type of body cavity. Embryonic tissues, called **germ layers,** include the outer layer, **ectoderm,** which gives rise to the body covering and the nervous system; the inner layer, **endoderm,** which lines the gut and other digestive organs; and a middle layer, **mesoderm,** which gives rise to muscle, skeletal structures, and most other body structures.

- In bilateral animals the type of body cavity has been used to classify animals. **Acoelomate** animals have no body cavity, and **coelomate** animals have a *true* coelom, a body cavity completely lined with mesoderm. Some animals have a **pseudocoelom** (literally, a "false cavity"), a body cavity that is not completely lined with mesoderm.

Pseudocoelom   True coelom

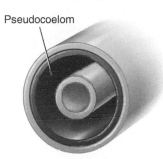
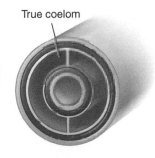

© Cengage Learning

- Two major evolutionary branches of bilateral animals are **protostomes** (mollusks, annelids, and arthropods) and **deuterostomes** (echinoderms and chordates).

- Protostomes undergo **spiral cleavage,** in which early cell divisions are diagonal to the polar axis. Deuterostomes undergo **radial cleavage,** in which the early cell divisions are either parallel or at right angles to the polar axis, so the cells lie directly above or below one another.

- Protostomes undergo **determinate cleavage,** in which the fate of each embryonic cell is fixed very early. Deuterostomes undergo **indeterminate cleavage,** in which early in development each cell has the potential to develop into a complete organism.

- In protostomes the **blastopore,** the opening from the embryonic gut to the outside, develops into the mouth; in deuterostomes the blastopore typically becomes the anus.

5 Cite specific examples of how data from molecular systematics have confirmed or modified traditional animal phylogeny and identify the three major clades of bilateral animals.

- Molecular systematics has confirmed much of animal phylogeny that was originally based on structural characters, including the axiom that animal body plans usually evolved from simple to complex. However, molecular systematics has also provided evidence for exceptions.

- Based on molecular data, biologists now subdivide the protostomes into two clades: **Lophotrochozoa** and **Ecdysozoa.** The Lophotrochozoa include the flatworms, ribbon worms, mollusks, annelids, rotifers, and animals that have a lophophore, a ciliated ring of tentacles surrounding the mouth. The Ecdysozoa, animals that molt, include the nematodes and arthropods. The third clade of animals, Deuterostomia, includes the echinoderms, hemichordates, and chordates. These animals have radial, indeterminate cleavage and pharyngeal slits.

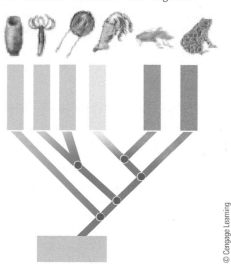

TEST YOUR UNDERSTANDING

Know and Comprehend

1. Which of the following is *not* a characteristic of all animals? (a) heterotrophic (b) multicellular (c) eukaryotic (d) presence of a coelom (e) formation of a zygote that undergoes cleavage
2. Which of the following is *not* an adaptation to terrestrial living? (a) internal fertilization (b) shell surrounding egg (c) adaptations for maintaining body temperature (d) surface for gas exchange deep in body (e) ability to maintain location
3. The Cambrian radiation (a) occurred during the late Cambrian period (b) was a rapid evolution of new animal body plans during the middle Cambrian (c) was a result of prokaryotic and eukaryotic migration to many new regions (d) is supported by the great variety of Ediacaran fossils (e) b and c
4. The germ layer that gives rise to the outer covering of the body and the nervous system is the (a) blastula (b) ectoderm (c) gastrula (d) endoderm (e) mesoderm
5. Radial symmetry is characteristic of (a) protostomes (b) chordates (c) mollusks (d) cnidarians (e) sponges
6. A coelom is a body cavity completely lined with (a) epithelium (b) ectoderm (c) mesoderm (d) endoderm (e) epidermis
7. Protostomes are characterized by (a) spiral cleavage (b) indeterminate cleavage (c) an acoelomate body plan (d) radial symmetry (e) a and c
8. The evolution of animals (a) followed an orderly progression from simple to complex (b) will be better understood as biologists continue to collect molecular and other types of data (c) has been determined by studying classification (d) began with the cnidarians (e) began with their common ancestor, a protostome
9. Which of the following is an example of a deuterostome? (a) lophotrochozoan (b) coral (c) chordate (d) planarian flatworm (e) insect

Apply and Analyze

10. **VISUALIZE** Label the branches of the diagram.

11. Imagine that you discover a new organism in a lake. How would you decide whether it is an animal? What are some characteristics that might contribute to your decision?
12. **EVOLUTION LINK** Examine the cladogram in Figure 30-6a. Based on the discussion in this chapter, what were some of the types of data that biologists used to determine these phylogenetic relationships?

Evaluate and Synthesize

13. **EVOLUTION LINK** Suggest and support a hypothesis for the view that segmentation evolved in three different animal clades.
14. **INTERPRET DATA** Imagine that a biologist discovers evidence that a newly discovered animal evolved from a very early protostome. Where would you place the branch (clade) for that animal on Figure 30-6a?

aplia To access course materials, such as Aplia and other companion resources, please visit **www.cengagebrain.com.**

Sponges, Cnidarians, Ctenophores, and Protostomes

31

In Chapter 30 we introduced the animal kingdom and explored animal phylogeny. We examined how systematists use fossils, morphology, developmental patterns, and molecular data to determine animal relationships. In this chapter we begin with an introduction to the sponges, cnidarians, and ctenophores, groups characterized by asymmetry, radial symmetry, and biradial symmetry, respectively. The phylogeny of these animals is the focus of much current research. Although sponges, cnidarians, and ctenophores are mainly small animals with simple body structures, they are of great ecological importance. They are important members of marine food chains, many provide shelter for other organisms, and some form symbiotic relationships with other animals. Corals that produce reefs are among the most ecologically important animals in the world.

Following our discussion of the sponges, cnidarians, and ctenophores, we begin our survey of the bilateral animals, the most familiar and by far the most numerous animals on Earth. More than 99% of animal species belong to the Bilateria. These diverse forms have adapted to life in almost every imaginable habitat in the ocean and in freshwater and terrestrial environments. The bearded fireworm shown in the photograph is an example of the diverse animals found among the Bilateria.

The remarkable success of the bilateral animals can be attributed to the evolution of adaptations that facilitated food capture, escape from predators, and reproduction. Among their key adaptations are cephalization (formation of a head), a central nervous system, muscles, a coelom, and compartmentalization of the body. Large animals developed body systems for gas exchange, waste disposal, and internal transport of nutrients, respiratory gases, wastes, and other materials.

Recall that based on molecular data, pattern of early development, and other data, biologists divide the bilateral animals into two main groups: protostomes and deuterostomes. The protostomes form two clades: Lophotrochozoa and Ecdysozoa. In this chapter we focus on the innovations in body plans, phylogenetic relationships, and life histories of several phyla of these two clades.

Marty Snyderman/Visuals Unlimited, Inc.

A bearded fireworm (*Hermodice carunculata*). The fireworm is a segmented worm (an annelid) that can grow up to 31 cm (11.8 in.) long. It lives in shallow marine waters: in coral reefs, in beds of turtle grass, or under rocks. Fireworm bristles, which are filled with venom, can break off in the skin and cause irritation.

KEY CONCEPTS

31.1 Animals with asymmetry, radial symmetry, or biradial symmetry include sponges, cnidarians (hydras, jellyfish, sea anemones), and ctenophores (comb jellies). Sponges are characterized by collar cells and by loosely associated cells that do not form true tissues; cnidarians are characterized by radial symmetry, two tissue layers, and cells that contain stinging organelles; and ctenophores have biradial symmetry, two tissue layers, eight rows of cilia, and tentacles with adhesive glue cells.

31.2 Protostomes are a large monophyletic group that includes two major clades: Lophotrochozoa and Ecdysozoa. The lophotrochozoans include the annelids (segmented worms), mollusks, and several smaller groups.

31.3 The ecdysozoans include the nematodes (roundworms) and arthropods (horseshoe crabs, spiders, crustaceans, insects). The remarkable biological success of the arthropods can be attributed to the evolution of complex body plans and life cycles, including their exoskeleton, segmentation, specialized jointed appendages, ability to fly (among insects), and metamorphosis.

31.1 SPONGES, CNIDARIANS, AND CTENOPHORES

1 Identify important characteristics of poriferans.
2 Identify distinguishing characteristics of cnidarians, describe four groups, and give examples of animals that belong to each group.
3 Identify characteristics of ctenophores.

Recall from Chapter 30 that based on available evidence, animals and choanoflagellates (a group of unicellular and colonial protists) share a common choanoflagellate ancestor. Many biologists assign sponges to a basal group, *Parazoa* (*para*, "alongside"; and *zoa*, "animals"). This classification is based on the asymmetry and simple body plan of sponges. The cells of sponges are loosely associated and do not form true tissues. Other animals have true tissues and are classified as **Eumetazoa** (*eu*, "true"; *meta*, "later"; and *zoa*, "animals"). Thus, these biologists divide the animal kingdom into two major animal groups: Parazoa and Eumetazoa.

According to this view, sponges are a monophyletic group. Based on molecular data, some biologists hypothesize that sponges are a polyphyletic group. There is some evidence that at least one group of sponges (calcareous sponges) became simplified as they evolved from animals with more complex body plans.

Systematists also debate about which animal group is the oldest. Some systematists have proposed that comb jellies (marine animals that swim by means of cilia), rather than sponges, are the oldest group of animals. Systematists continue to search for new clues that will settle the controversies over which branch of animals is the oldest and over the exact pattern of relationships among the major animal groups.

Sponges have collar cells and other specialized cells

Sponges, or **poriferans,** are aquatic, mainly marine animals that are most abundant in warm waters. Their phylum name, *Porifera* (paw-rif′-er-ah), means "to have pores." This name aptly describes these animals, whose bodies are perforated by tiny holes. Biologists have identified about 10,000 species of sponges. They range in size from a few millimeters to more than a meter in height and diameter (loggerhead sponges). Many sponges are asymmetrical, but they vary in shape from flat, encrusting growths to balls, cups, fans, or vases. Living sponges may be brightly colored—green, orange, red, yellow, blue, or purple—or they may be white or drab (FIG. 31-1). Some species are inhabited by symbiotic bacteria or algae that give them color.

Although they are multicellular and can be large, sponges function much like choanoflagellates. These protists are characterized by a single flagellum surrounded by a collar of microvilli (see Fig. 26-21). Sponges have flagellate cells called **collar cells,** or **choanocytes** (ko-an′-uh-sites), which are strikingly similar to choanoflagellates.

Sponge larvae have flagella and can swim about. Adult sponges attach to some solid object and have long been described as sessile. However, biologists have observed adults of several species moving slowly (about 4 mm per day), perhaps by the cumulative movement of cells along the sponge's lower surface.

Although sponges are multicellular, their cells are loosely associated and do not form true tissues. However, a division of labor exists among the several types of cells that make up the sponge, with certain cells specializing in nutrition, support, contraction, or reproduction. Many sponge cells are extremely versatile and can change form and function.

Collar cells make up the inner layer of certain sponges. Each cell is equipped with a tiny collar surrounding the base of the flagellum. The collar is an extension of the plasma membrane and consists of microvilli. Collar cells create the water current that brings food and oxygen to the cells and carries away carbon dioxide and other wastes. Collar cells also trap and phagocytize food particles. Together, the collar cells of some sponges can pump a volume of water equal to the volume of the sponge each minute!

Sponges have three types of canal systems through which water circulates. In the simple *asconoid* canal system, the beating flagella of collar cells create a current that pulls water through hundreds of tiny pores, called *ostia.* Specialized tubelike cells, called *porocytes,* form the pores. These cells regulate the diameter of the pores by contracting. Water passes into the central cavity, or **spongocoel** (spon′-jo-seel) (not a digestive cavity), and then flows out through the sponge's open end, the **osculum** (os′ kyuh-lum). The asconoid system is illustrated in Figure 31-1.

In the *syconoid* system, water enters through canals lined by collar cells. Most types of sponges have a *leuconoid* system. The body wall is extensively folded, and complex systems of canals provide increased surface area for food capture. *Epidermal cells* form the outer layer of the sponge and line the canals. The canals lead into small chambers that are lined with collar cells.

The skeletal framework of a sponge can be both rigid and fibrous. Between the outer and inner cell layers, the sponge body has a gelatin-like layer, the *mesohyl,* which is supported by slender skeletal spikes, or **spicules** (spik′-yuls). *Amoeboid cells,* which wander about in the mesohyl, secrete the spicules. The spicules are made of calcium carbonate or of silica. The fibrous part of the sponge skeleton consists of *spongin,* a form of collagen.

Sponges are *suspension feeders,* adapted for trapping and eating whatever food is suspended in the water. As water circulates through the body, bacteria, algae, and other organic particles are trapped along the sticky collars of the collar cells. Thus, the collars *filter* the suspended food particles out of the water. Suspension feeders that filter the suspended food are known as *filter feeders.* Food particles are either digested within the collar cell or transferred to an amoeboid cell for digestion. The amoeboid cell transports nutrients to epidermal cells. Undigested food passes out through the osculum and is simply eliminated into the water.

Gas exchange and excretion of wastes depend on diffusion into and out of individual cells. Although cells of the sponge can react to stimuli, sponges do not have specialized nerve cells and

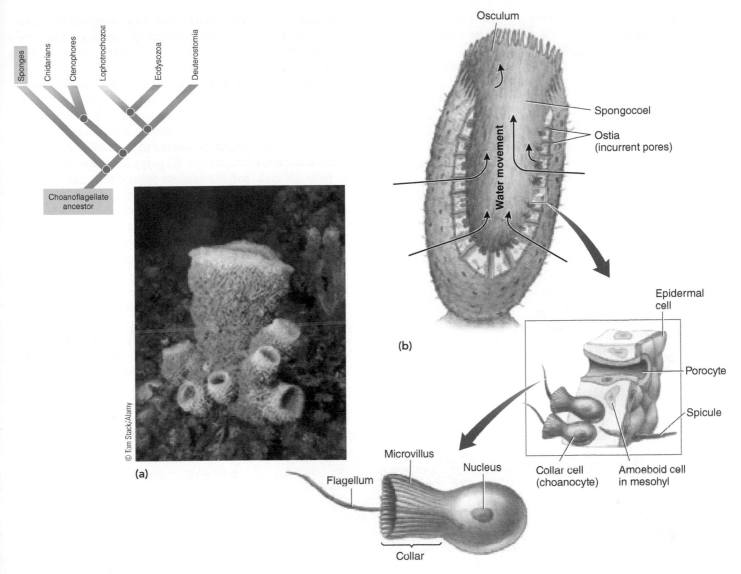

Figure 31-1 *Animation* **Sponge structure**

(a) Tube sponges (*Spinosella plicifera*) from the Caribbean attached to the coral reef substrate. **(b)** Sponge cut to expose its organization. This sponge has an asconoid type of canal system.

© Cengage Learning

so cannot react as a whole. However, electrical signals have been identified in certain glass sponges. Behavior appears limited to basic metabolic necessities such as capturing food and regulating the flow of water through the body.

Sponges reproduce both asexually and sexually. In asexual reproduction, a small fragment or bud may break free from the parent sponge and give rise to a new sponge. Such fragments may attach to the parent sponge, forming, or becoming part of, a colony. Most sponges are **hermaphrodites,** meaning that the same individual can produce both eggs and sperm. Some of the amoeboid cells develop into sperm cells and others into egg cells. However, hermaphroditic sponges usually produce eggs and sperm at different times, and they cross-fertilize with other sponges. They release mature sperm into the water, which are taken in by other sponges of the same species.

Fertilization and early development take place within the jellylike mesohyl. Zygotes develop into flagellate larvae that leave the parent along with the stream of outflowing water. After swimming for a while, a larva finds a solid object, attaches to it, and settles down to a sessile life.

Sponges have a remarkable ability to repair themselves when injured and to regenerate lost parts. When the cells of a sponge are separated experimentally, they recognize one another and their place in the whole and aggregate to re-form a complete sponge.

There are three main groups of sponges: the *calcareous sponges* have spicules composed of calcium carbonate, whereas the *glass sponges* and the *demosponges* have spicules of silicon. About 95% of living sponges are demosponges. In some of the demosponges, spicules are bound together by spongin. Some demosponges do not have spicules. These soft sponges have been used for thousands of years as bath sponges and for cleaning. Unfortunately, as a result of overfishing, bath sponges are now in short supply.

Sponges play significant roles in marine habitats. Larger species are important structural components in both shallow and deep water, providing homes to many species of annelids, crustaceans, and echinoderms. Sponges also serve as food for some invertebrates, fish, and sea turtles.

Cnidarians have unique stinging cells

More than 10,000 species of **cnidarians** (ni-dah′-ree-ans; phylum Cnidaria) have been described. Most are marine.

The radially symmetrical cnidarian body is organized as a hollow sac with the mouth and surrounding tentacles located at one end. Some cnidarians live a solitary existence, whereas many others, such as corals, form colonies.

Cnidarians have two body shapes: polyp and medusa (FIG. 31-2). The **polyp** form, represented by *Hydra*, typically has a dorsal mouth surrounded by tentacles. In the **medusa** (pl., *medusae*), or jellyfish form, the mouth is located in the lower concave, or *oral*, surface; the convex upper surface is the *aboral* surface. Some cnidarians have the polyp shape during one stage of their life cycle and the medusa form during another stage. The Portuguese man-of-war and some other cnidarians consist of colonies of many individuals, some of which are polyps and others medusae.

Cnidarians get their name from specialized cells, called **cnidocytes** (from a Greek word meaning "nettle cells"), that contain stinging organelles. Cnidocytes are located mainly in the epidermis, especially on the tentacles. The cnidocytes contain stinging "thread capsules," called **nematocysts** (FIG. 31-3). Each cnidocyte has a small, projecting trigger (*cnidocil*) on its outer surface and a coiled, hollow thread inside. We can compare the cnidocyte to a loaded gun, ready to fire. When stimulated by touch or certain chemicals dissolved in the water, the

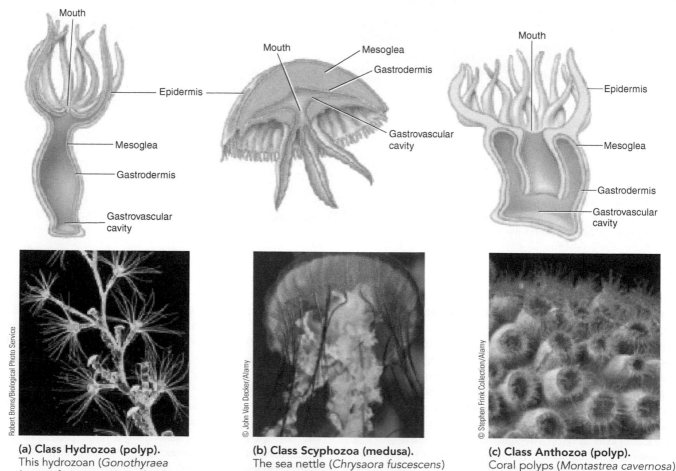

(a) Class Hydrozoa (polyp).
This hydrozoan (*Gonothyraea loveni*) forms a colony of polyps. The drawing illustrates a single polyp.

(b) Class Scyphozoa (medusa).
The sea nettle (*Chrysaora fuscescens*) uses its tentacles equipped with cnidocytes to capture small animals (zooplankton) suspended in the water.

(c) Class Anthozoa (polyp).
Coral polyps (*Montastrea cavernosa*) extended for feeding.

Figure 31-2 *Animation* Polyp and medusa body forms of cnidarians
© Cengage Learning

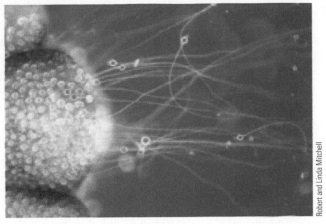

250 μm

(a) LM of discharged nematocysts of a Portuguese man-of-war (*Physalia physalis*). Photographed in the Gulf of Mexico.

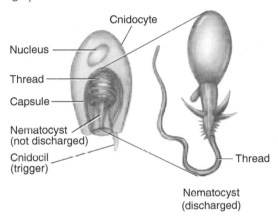

Cnidocyte

Nucleus

Thread

Capsule

Nematocyst (not discharged)

Cnidocil (trigger)

Thread

Nematocyst (discharged)

(b) Undischarged and discharged nematocyst. The cnidocil, or trigger, is a mechanoreceptor that discharges the nematocyst when it senses contact with an object.

Figure 31-3 *Animation* **Nematocysts**

When cnidarian stinging cells (cnidocytes) are stimulated, the nematocyst discharges, ejecting a thread that may entangle or penetrate the prey. Some nematocysts secrete a toxic substance that immobilizes the prey.

© Cengage Learning

nematocyst fires its thread. Some types of nematocyst threads are sticky. Others are long and coil around prey. A third type bears barbs or spines that can inject a protein toxin. This toxin paralyzes prey animals, such as small crustaceans.

Cnidarians use their tentacles to capture prey and push it into the mouth. The mouth leads into the **gastrovascular cavity,** where digestion takes place. The mouth is the only opening into the gastrovascular cavity and so must serve for both ingestion of food and expulsion of undigested material. Gas exchange and excretion occur by diffusion. The body wall is thin enough that no cell is far from the surface.

More highly organized than sponges, cnidarians are diploblastic; that is, they have two definite tissue layers. The ectoderm gives rise to the outer epidermis, a protective layer covering the body. The endoderm gives rise to the inner *gastrodermis*, which

lines the gastrovascular cavity and functions in digestion. These thin layers are separated by a thick, jellylike **mesoglea,** which is mainly acellular.

The nerve cells of a cnidarian form a **nerve net** that connects sensory cells in the body wall to contractile cells and gland cells. An impulse set up by one sensory cell passes in all directions more or less equally. Nerve cells are not organized to form a brain or nerve cord. In some types of medusae, sense organs are positioned around the edge of the body. The sense organs include simple "eyes," called eyespots; organs of balance (statocysts); and chemoreceptors (cells that sense certain chemicals).

Both the epidermis and gastrodermis have cells specialized to contract. (However, they are not true muscle cells). Contractile fibers in the epidermal cells are arranged lengthwise, and those in the gastrodermis are arranged in a circular pattern. These two sets of contractile cells act on the water-filled gastrovascular cavity, forming a **hydrostatic skeleton.** This skeleton supports the body and allows movement. By contracting one set of contractile cells or the other, the hydra can shorten, lengthen, or bend its body (see Fig. 40-2). We consider four groups of cnidarians: hydrozoans, scyphozoans, cubozoans, and anthozoans (TABLE 31-1).

Most hydrozoans form colonies Hydrozoans include hydras and *hydroids,* such as *Obelia* and the Portuguese man-of-war. Although not really typical, the solitary *Hydra* is the cnidarian that beginning biology students most often study (FIG. 31-4). To the naked eye, *Hydra* looks like a bit of frayed string. This tiny hydrozoan is found in freshwater ponds. Because it has a remarkable ability to regenerate, biologists named *Hydra* after the multiheaded monster of Greek mythology that could grow two new heads for each head cut off. When *Hydra* is cut into several pieces, each piece can regenerate all the missing parts and become a whole animal.

Hydra lives in fresh water and typically attaches to a rock, aquatic plant, or detritus by a disc of cells at its base. Hydras

TABLE 31-1	Major Classes of Phylum Cnidaria
CLASS AND REPRESENTATIVE ANIMALS	**CHARACTERISTICS**
HYDROZOA *Hydra, Obelia,* Portuguese man-of-war	Mainly marine, but some freshwater species; alternation of polyp and medusa stages in most species (polyp form only in *Hydra*); some form colonies
SCYPHOZOA Jellyfish	Mainly marine; typically inhabit coastal water, free-swimming medusa most prominent form; polyp stage often reduced
CUBOZOA "Box jellyfish"	Inhabit tropical and subtropical waters; have polyp stage, but medusa form most prominent; square shape when viewed from above; actively hunt prey; complex eyes form blurred images
ANTHOZOA Sea anemones, corals, sea fans	Marine; solitary or colonial polyps; no medusa stage in most; gastrovascular cavity divided by partitions into chambers, increasing area for digestion

© Cengage Learning

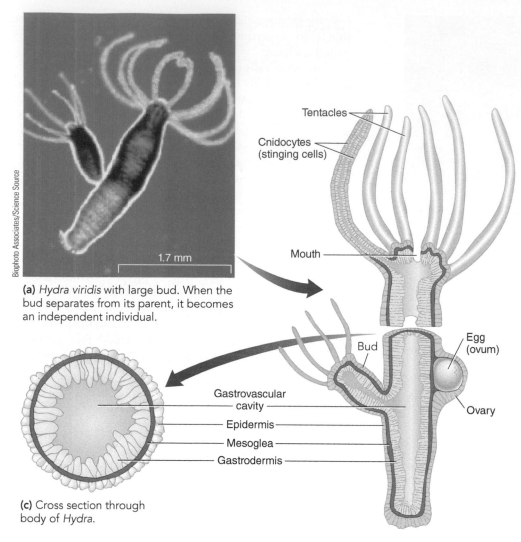

(a) *Hydra viridis* with large bud. When the bud separates from its parent, it becomes an independent individual.

Biophoto Associates/Science Source

1.7 mm

Tentacles

Cnidocytes (stinging cells)

Mouth

Bud

Egg (ovum)

Ovary

Gastrovascular cavity

Epidermis

Mesoglea

Gastrodermis

(c) Cross section through body of *Hydra*.

(b) *Hydra* cut longitudinally to show internal structure. Asexual reproduction by budding is represented on *left*; sexual reproduction is represented by ovary on *right*. Male hydras develop testes that produce sperm.

Figure 31-4 *Hydra*, a freshwater hydrozoan
© Cengage Learning

and medusa stages (FIG. 31-5). In *Obelia* polyps reproduce asexually by budding, whereas the medusae reproduce sexually, using meiosis to produce gametes. Both polyp and medusa are diploid; only sperm and eggs are haploid.

Scyphozoans are the "true" jellyfish In *scyphozoans* the medusa is the dominant body form. Jellyfish medusae are generally larger than hydrozoan medusae, and they have a thick, viscous mesoglea that gives firmness to the body. In scyphozoans the polyp stage is small and inconspicuous or may even be absent. The largest jellyfish, *Cyanea*, may be more than 2 m (6.5 ft) in diameter and have tentacles 30 m (98 ft) long. These orange and blue "monsters," among the largest invertebrates, can cause painful stings to swimmers in the North Atlantic and Pacific Oceans.

Cubozoans include the "box jellyfish" When viewed from above, *cubozoans* have a square shape. They have four tentacles, or groups of tentacles. These fast-swimming jellyfish have complex eyes that form blurred images, and they actively hunt for prey. Found in waters off the northern Australian coast, the sea wasp (*Chironex fleckeri*) has long tentacles that can extend more than 3 m (10 ft). The sea wasp produces one of the deadliest venoms in the animal kingdom. Its venom contains toxins that can stun or kill fish and other prey. These toxins can also cause respiratory failure and cardiac arrest in humans. Fatalities are mainly associated with severe stings caused by contact with tentacles over a large area of the body. Interestingly, sea turtles feed on box jellyfish, apparently unaffected by their venom.

Anthozoans are polyps *Anthozoans*, which include the sea anemones and corals, are either individual or colonial polyps. There is no free-swimming medusa stage. The polyp produces eggs and sperm, and the fertilized egg develops into a small, ciliated **planula larva.** This larval form may swim to a new location before attaching to develop into a polyp.

Anthozoans differ from hydrozoans in that a series of vertical partitions partially divides the gastrovascular cavity into

reproduce asexually by budding during periods when environmental conditions are optimal. However, they differentiate as males and females and reproduce sexually in the fall or when pond water becomes stagnant. The zygote may become covered with a shell that protects it through the winter or until conditions become more favorable.

Many hydrozoans form colonies consisting of hundreds or thousands of individuals. A colony begins with a single polyp that reproduces asexually by budding. However, instead of separating from the parent, the bud remains attached and eventually forms additional buds. Several types of individuals may develop in the same colony, some specialized for feeding, some for reproduction, and others for defense.

Some marine hydrozoans are remarkable for their alternation of sessile polyp and motile medusa stages. The life cycle of the colonial marine hydrozoan *Obelia* illustrates alternation of polyp

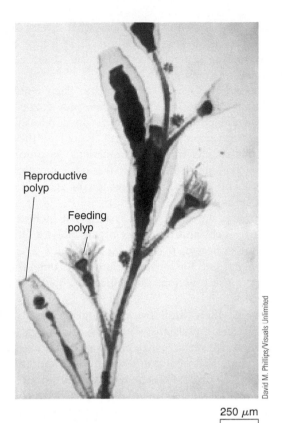

Reproductive polyp

Feeding polyp

David M. Phillips/Visuals Unlimited

250 μm

(a) LM of *Obelia*. Some polyps have tentacles and are specialized for feeding, whereas others are specialized for reproduction.

connected chambers. The partitions increase the surface area for digestion, enabling an anemone to digest an animal as large as a crab. Although corals can capture prey, many tropical species depend for nutrition on photosynthetic algae (*zooxanthellae*) that live within cells lining the coral's digestive cavity (see Chapter 26 and Fig. 54-12). The relationship between coral and zooxanthellae is symbiotic and mutually beneficial. The coral supplies the algae with waste products such as ammonia from which the algae make nitrogen compounds for both partners. In exchange, the algae provide the coral with oxygen and with carbon and nitrogen compounds. In warm, shallow seas, much of the bottom is covered with coral or anemones, most of them brightly colored. Coral reefs consist of colonies of millions of corals and of certain algae (mainly coralline red algae). Living colonies occur only in the uppermost regions of such reefs, adding their own skeletons to the forming rock. Coral reefs are among the most productive of all ecosystems, rivaling tropical rain forests in species diversity (see Fig. 56-21). A single reef can serve as home for more than 3000 species of fishes and other marine organisms, and an estimated one-fourth of all marine species depend on coral reefs.

Many species of reef-building corals are considered endangered or threatened and are at increased risk for extinction. Human activities are responsible for much of this damage. In 2012, the National Oceanic and Atmospheric Administration reported that the three major threats to coral reefs are rising ocean temperatures (due to global climate change), acidification of the ocean (caused by increase in carbon dioxide in the

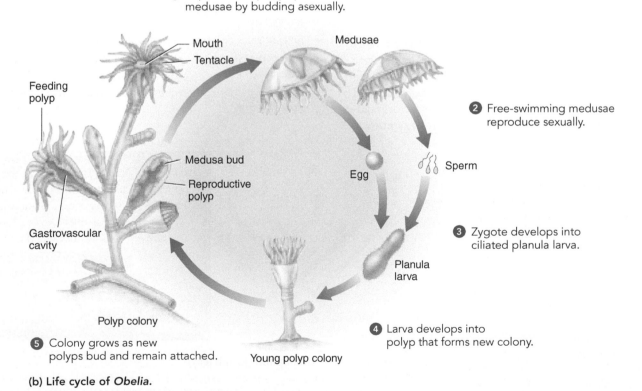

❶ Reproductive polyps produce medusae by budding asexually.

Mouth

Tentacle

Medusae

❷ Free-swimming medusae reproduce sexually.

Feeding polyp

Medusa bud

Reproductive polyp

Egg

Sperm

Gastrovascular cavity

❸ Zygote develops into ciliated planula larva.

Planula larva

Polyp colony

❹ Larva develops into polyp that forms new colony.

❺ Colony grows as new polyps bud and remain attached.

Young polyp colony

(b) Life cycle of *Obelia*.

Figure 31-5 *Animation* *Obelia*, a marine colonial hydrozoan
© Cengage Learning

Figure 31-6 Bleached staghorn coral

This staghorn coral (*Acropora*) was photographed off Heron Island on the Great Barrier Reef off the coast of Australia.

atmosphere), and disease. The stress caused by these factors can result in the coral expelling the colorful symbiotic algae that inhabit their cells. This process is called **coral bleaching** (FIG. 31-6). Without their algae, coral become malnourished and may die if conditions do not improve. Other factors leading to the decline of coral reefs include pollution, smothering coral with the silt washed downstream from clear-cut forests, and overfishing.

Comb jellies have adhesive glue cells that trap prey

The fragile, luminescent *comb jellies* are marine animals known as **ctenophores** (ten'-oh-forz). They are assigned to phylum *Ctenophora* (teh-nof'-er-uh). Approximately 150 species of ctenophores have been described. Some are as small as a pea; others are larger than a tomato. The outer surface of a ctenophore bears eight rows of cilia that resemble combs (FIG. 31-7). Ctenophores are biradially symmetrical, meaning you could obtain equal halves by cutting through the body axis in two different

ways. The ctenophore body plan is somewhat similar to that of a cnidarian medusa in that ctenophores have a type of radial symmetry, feeding tentacles, and two cell layers separated by a thick, jellylike mesoglea.

Some ctenophores have two tentacles. Their tentacles are equipped with adhesive glue cells. When prey comes in contact with the tentacle, the glue cells burst open, releasing sticky threads that trap the prey. Ctenophores do not have the stinging nematocysts characteristic of the cnidarians. Also unlike cnidarians, the ctenophore digestive system has a mouth for food intake at one end and two anal pores for the egestion of water and wastes at the other end.

Ctenophores have a nervous system that includes a network of nerve cells and a sensory organ called a "statocyst" that coordinates beating of the cilia in the combs. The coordinated beating of the cilia moves the animal through the water. The statocyst also functions in balance and helps the animal orient itself.

Because of their similarities, biologists classify ctenophores near the cnidarians. However, their development is different, and their digestive cavity has openings at both ends. The similarities between ctenophores and cnidarians may be a result of convergent evolution from living in a similar environment, the ocean. Where, then, do the ctenophores belong on our cladogram? As systematists gather new data, the position of the ctenophores on the animal tree will become clearer.

CHECKPOINT 31.1

- **CONNECT** *What is the significance of choanocytes in terms of the evolution of sponges? Explain their function in sponges.*

- *In what ways do cnidarians differ from sponges?*

- **VISUALIZE** *Sketch the major events of the life cycle of Obelia.*

- *In what ways are ctenophores like cnidarians? In what ways are they different?*

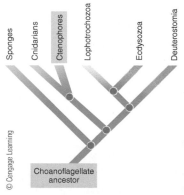

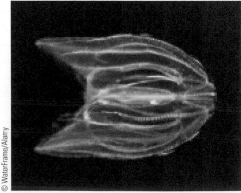

Figure 31-7 *Animation* Ctenophore (comb jelly)

Ctenophores are free-swimming, bioluminescent hermaphrodites capable of self-fertilization. The warty comb jelly (*Mnemiopsis leidyi*; also known as the sea walnut) refracts light so that it appears to have colors running down the track of its cilia. *Mnemiopsis* is also bioluminescent, and flashes when disturbed. This animal is a predator that consumes crustaceans, eggs and larvae of fishes, and zooplankton.

31.2 THE LOPHOTROCHOZOA

4 Summarize what is known about the phylogeny of the lophotrochozoans and cite the adaptive advantages of having a coelom and of cephalization.

5 Identify distinguishing characteristics of flatworms and nemerteans, and describe the main groups of flatworms, giving examples of animals that belong to each class.

6 Describe the main characteristics of mollusks and of the four main groups of mollusks discussed, giving examples of each group.

7 Describe the principal characteristics of annelids and of the three main groups of annelids discussed, giving examples of each group.

8 Describe the distinguishing characteristics of the lophophorates and of the rotifers.

We begin our discussion of the bilateral animals with the **Lophotrochozoa,** one of the two major clades of protostomes. The Lophotrochozoa includes the flatworms (platyhelminths), rotifers (wheel animals), nemerteans (ribbon worms), mollusks, annelids (segmented worms), and the lophophorate phyla (see Fig. 30-6). Recall from Chapter 30 that the name *Lophotrochozoa* comes from two important characters of some animals in this clade: (1) the *lophophore,* a ciliated ring of tentacles surrounding the mouth in three small groups of animals; and (2) the *trochophore larva,* a type of larva that characterizes two major groups: the mollusks and annelids. Some systematists argue that flatworms and rotifers should be assigned to a separate group, the *platyzoa.* Here, we include them with the lophotrochozoa.

Most lophotrochozoans have **bilateral symmetry,** at least in their larval stages. They are **triploblastic;** that is, they have three definite tissue layers. In addition to the outer epidermis derived from ectoderm and an inner endodermis derived from endoderm, lophotrochozoans have a middle tissue layer that develops from mesoderm.

Most lophotrochozoans have a true **coelom** and a *tube-within-a-tube body plan* (see Chapter 30). Most coelomate animals have well-developed circulatory, excretory, and nervous systems. Many internal organs are suspended within folds of the tissue lining the coelom and can move independently of the outer body wall. In addition, the coelom provides space for the gonads to develop. During the breeding season of many animals, such as birds, the gonads enlarge within the coelom as they fill with ripe gametes.

In some animals fluid within the coelom helps transport materials such as food, oxygen, and wastes. Cells bathed by the coelomic fluid can exchange materials with it. The cells receive nutrients and oxygen from the coelomic fluid and excrete wastes into it. Some coelomates have excretory structures that remove wastes directly from the coelomic fluid.

Animals that move about typically have an elongated body with definite anterior and posterior ends. They exhibit **cephalization,** the evolution of a head with a concentration of sense organs at the anterior end. A simple brain and paired sense organs are concentrated in the "head" region. An animal with a front end generally moves forward. With a concentration of sense organs in the part of the body that first meets its environment, the animal can actively search for food, shelter, and mates or can detect enemies quickly.

Flatworms are bilateral acoelomates

Platyhelminths (plat-ee-hel′-minths), or *flatworms,* (phylum *Platyhelminthes* are soft-bodied animals that left few fossils to provide clues to their evolutionary history. Their flat, elongated bodies are solid; that is, they are **acoelomate** (have no body cavity). Historically, biologists considered flatworms to be the simplest bilaterally symmetrical, triploblastic animals. However, it is unclear whether the Platyhelminthes evolved from ancestors that possessed a body cavity. A group of flatworm-like animals, the Acoelomorpha, were once considered a part of the phylum Platyhelminthes, but modern evidence, specifically DNA and RNA sequences, suggests that they form a separate lineage branching from the beginnings of the bilateral animals.

Based on our current understanding of the evidence, the 20,000 or so species within the Platyhelminthes fall within four classes. Class *Turbellaria* consists of the free-living flatworms, including planarians and their relatives. Classes *Trematoda* and *Monogenea* include the flukes, which are either internal or external parasites. Class *Cestoda* includes the tapeworms, which as adults are intestinal parasites of vertebrates (TABLE 31-2).

Flatworms typically have a simple **nervous system.** The brain consists of two masses of nervous tissue, called **ganglia,** in the head region. In many species the ganglia connect to two nerve cords that extend the length of the body. This nervous system is sometimes referred to as a "ladder-type nervous system" because a series of nerves connects the cords like the rungs of a ladder (see Fig. 42-2). Sense organs include simple "eyes," called eyespots, organs of balance (statocysts), and numerous chemoreceptors over their bodies for locating food and mates.

TABLE 31-2	Classes of Phylum Platyhelminthes
CLASS AND REPRESENTATIVE ANIMALS	**CHARACTERISTICS**
TURBELLARIA* Planarians	Mainly free-living; marine, freshwater, and terrestrial; body covered by ciliated epidermis; typically predatory on other invertebrates
TREMATODA AND MONOGENEA Flukes	Parasites with a wide range of vertebrate and invertebrate hosts; may require intermediate hosts; adults have suckers for attachment to host
CESTODA Tapeworms	Parasites of vertebrates; complex life cycle usually with one or two intermediate hosts; larval host may be invertebrate; typically have suckers and sometimes hooks for attachment to host; eggs produced within proglottids, which are shed; no digestive or nervous systems

*Systematists view Turbellaria as a paraphyletic group that will probably be divided into at least three groups.

© Cengage Learning

Flatworms have no organs for circulation or gas exchange. Gas exchange depends largely on diffusion through the body wall. The activities of some organs are coordinated and form simple organ systems, such as the digestive and nervous systems. As in the cnidarians, the digestive system is a gastrovascular cavity with only one opening, a mouth. The gastrovascular cavity is often extensively branched.

Parasitic flatworms—flukes and tapeworms—are highly adapted to and modified for their parasitic lifestyle. They have suckers or hooks for holding on to their hosts. The bodies of those that live in digestive tracts resist the digestive enzymes secreted by their hosts. Many have complicated life cycles and produce large numbers of eggs. Other adaptations include the loss of certain structures such as sense organs. Tapeworms have also lost the digestive system.

Turbellarians are free-living flatworms Most members of class Turbellaria are free-living flatworms. They inhabit marine, freshwater, and terrestrial habitats. Turbellarian flatworms typically have a muscular pharynx that takes in food and is connected with a branching gastrovascular cavity. They have a simple brain, multiple eyespots, and other sensory organs in the head; **protonephridia,** structures that function in osmoregulation (fluid balance) and metabolic waste disposal (excretion); and reproductive organs.

Planarians are turbellarian flatworms found in ponds, quiet streams, and moist terrestrial habitats throughout the world. One common genus of American planarians, *Dugesia*, contains aquatic worms that reach about 15 mm (0.6 in.) in length. They have what appear to be crossed "eyes" and flapping lateral projections called *auricles* (FIG. 31-8). The auricles actually serve as organs of chemoreception, which is important in locating food.

Most planarians are predators, capable of capturing and killing small animals. Their digestive system consists of a single opening (the mouth); a tubelike, muscular **pharynx** (the first portion of the digestive tube) and a branched gastrovascular cavity. Many planarians evert (turn inside out) their pharynx out of their mouth and release digestive enzymes onto their captured prey. The liquefied tissues of the prey are then swept by ciliary action into the gastrovascular cavity. The branches of the gastrovascular cavity distribute the nutrients throughout the body of the flatworm. Because planarians lack an anus, digestive wastes leave the body through the mouth.

Some metabolic wastes leave the body by diffusion. Other metabolic wastes are excreted by the protonephridia, blind tubules that end in **flame cells.** The flame cells are collecting cells equipped with cilia. The beating of the cilia channels waste through the system of tubules and eventually out of the body through excretory pores. Osmoregulation and protonephridia are discussed further in Chapter 48 (see Fig. 48-2).

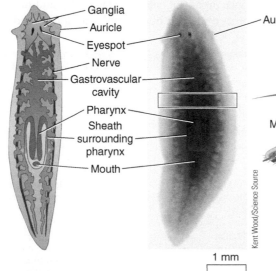

(a) Internal structure.

(b) LM of a living planarian (*Dugesia dorotocephala*). Note the auricles, used to locate food.

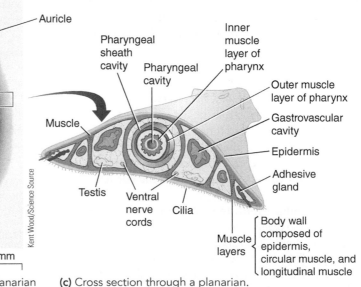

(c) Cross section through a planarian.

Figure 31-8 *Animation* **The common planarian,** *Dugesia*
© Cengage Learning

Planarians reproduce either asexually or sexually. In asexual reproduction an individual constricts its body and divides into two planarians. Each regenerates its missing parts. Sexually, these animals are hermaphrodites. During the warm months of the year, each is equipped with a complete set of male organs and female organs. Two planarians come together in copulation and exchange sperm cells so that their eggs are cross-fertilized.

Flukes parasitize other animals Although their body plan generally resembles that of the free-living flatworms, the *flukes,* members of classes Trematoda and Monogenea, have structures, such as hooks and suckers, for attachment to their host. Flukes also have extremely prolific reproductive organs.

Flukes that are parasitic in humans include blood flukes, which are widespread in tropical areas of the world, and liver flukes, which are common in Asia, particularly in areas where humans use their own feces for fertilizing crops. Blood flukes of the genus *Schistosoma* cause the human disease schistosomiasis,

the second most debilitating parasitic disease in the world. (Malaria is the first.) An estimated 200 million people are infected, most of them children. The worms live in blood vessels for many years and can damage the liver and kidneys.

Both blood flukes and liver flukes go through complicated life cycles involving several different forms. There is an alternation of sexual and asexual stages as well as parasitism on one or more intermediate hosts, such as snails and fishes (FIG. 31-9). The aquatic snails that serve as intermediate hosts thrive in ponds, rice paddies, and the marshy areas that develop when dams are built.

Tapeworms inhabit the intestine of vertebrates Adult members of the more than 5000 species of class Cestoda live as parasites in the intestine of probably every kind of vertebrate, including humans. Tapeworms are long, flat, ribbonlike animals strikingly specialized for their parasitic mode of life. The body consists of a *scolex* for attachment to a host and a long chain of segments called *proglottids.* The scolex is equipped

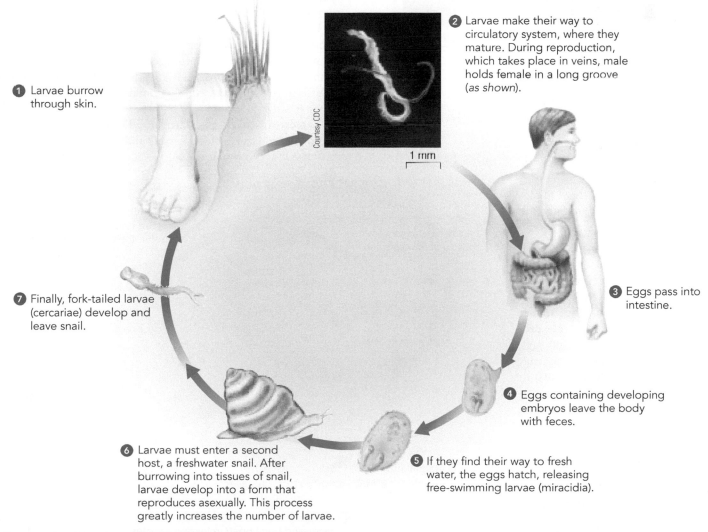

1 Larvae burrow through skin.

2 Larvae make their way to circulatory system, where they mature. During reproduction, which takes place in veins, male holds female in a long groove (*as shown*).

3 Eggs pass into intestine.

4 Eggs containing developing embryos leave the body with feces.

5 If they find their way to fresh water, the eggs hatch, releasing free-swimming larvae (miracidia).

6 Larvae must enter a second host, a freshwater snail. After burrowing into tissues of snail, larvae develop into a form that reproduces asexually. This process greatly increases the number of larvae.

7 Finally, fork-tailed larvae (cercariae) develop and leave snail.

1 mm

Courtesy CDC

Figure 31-9 *Animation* **Life cycle of the blood fluke (*Schistosoma*)**

The LM shows an adult male enfolding a smaller female.

© Cengage Learning

Figure 31-10 Scolex of a tapeworm

The small tapeworm (*Acanthrocirrus retrisrostris*) reaches maturity in the intestine of wading birds that eat barnacles. The color-enhanced SEM shows the pistonlike cluster of hooks that can be withdrawn into the head or thrust out and buried in the host's tissue. You can see two of the four powerful suckers beneath the hooks.

SPL/Science Library/Science Source

250 µm

organs. Some tapeworms have complex life cycles, spending their larval stage within the body of an intermediate host and their adult life within the body of a different, final host. FIGURE 31-11 illustrates the life cycle of the beef tapeworm, which can infect humans when they eat undercooked beef containing the larvae.

Nemerteans are characterized by their proboscis

The **nemerteans** (neh-mur′-tee-uns; phylum *Nemertea*) include the ribbon worms, a relatively small group of about 1200 species of free-living animals (FIG. 31-12). Most burrow in marine sediments, but a few species inhabit deep sea water, fresh water, or damp soil. Many nemerteans are predators, feeding on crustaceans and annelids. Nemerteans have long, narrow bodies, either cylindrical or flattened, ranging in length from 1 mm to more than 30 m (100 ft). Some are a vivid orange, red, or green, with black or colored stripes.

Their most remarkable organ, the *proboscis,* is a long, hollow, muscular tube that can be rapidly everted from the anterior end of the body. Used to capture prey, the sticky proboscis can be wrapped around a small animal. In some species the proboscis is sharp, and in various species it secretes toxic fluid that immobilizes prey. The proboscis is a *derived character* that distinguishes nemerteans from all other invertebrate groups. Because of this character, these animals are sometimes called *proboscis worms.*

Nemerteans have no heart; blood is circulated by contractions of muscular blood vessels and by movements of the

with suckers, and sometimes hooks, that enable the parasite to attach to the host's intestine (FIG. 31-10).

The reproductive adaptations and abilities of tapeworms are extraordinary. Each proglottid is an entire reproductive machine equipped with both male and female reproductive organs. A single proglottid contains up to 100,000 eggs. Because an adult tapeworm may have as many as 2000 segments, its reproductive potential is staggering. A single tapeworm can produce 600 million eggs per year! Proglottids farthest from the scolex contain the ripest eggs; these segments are shed from the host's body along with the feces.

A tapeworm has no mouth or digestive system. Digested food from the host is absorbed across the worm's body wall. Tapeworms also lack well-developed sense

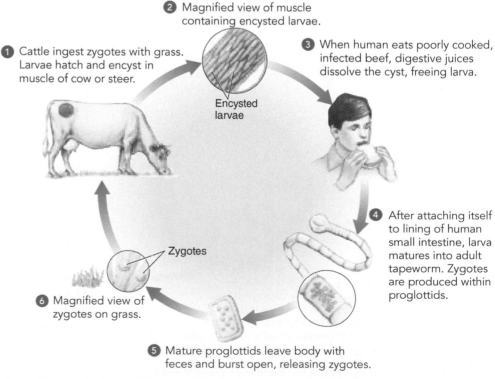

❶ Cattle ingest zygotes with grass. Larvae hatch and encyst in muscle of cow or steer.

❷ Magnified view of muscle containing encysted larvae.

Encysted larvae

❸ When human eats poorly cooked, infected beef, digestive juices dissolve the cyst, freeing larva.

❹ After attaching itself to lining of human small intestine, larva matures into adult tapeworm. Zygotes are produced within proglottids.

❺ Mature proglottids leave body with feces and burst open, releasing zygotes.

❻ Magnified view of zygotes on grass.

Zygotes

Figure 31-11 *Animation* Life cycle of the beef tapeworm, *Taenia saginata*
© Cengage Learning

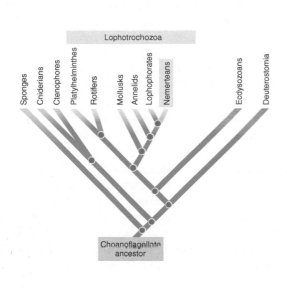

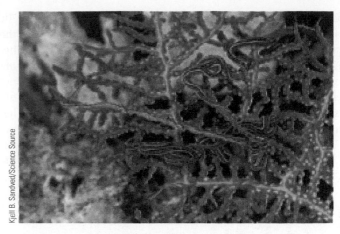

(a) Ribbon worm (*Lineus*) from the Pacific coast of Panama.

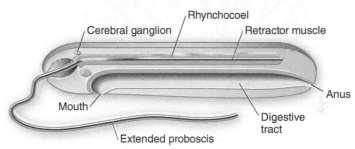

(b) Lateral view of a typical nemertean. Note the complete digestive tract that extends from mouth to anus.

Figure 31-12 Nemerteans (ribbon worms)
© Cengage Learning

body. The chamber surrounding the proboscis is a coelomic space known as a *rhynchocoel*. It develops in the embryo as the coelom does in coelomate protostomes (see Chapter 30). However, it differs in position and function from the coelom of other animals. Biologists view the rhynchocoel as a remnant of the coelom of a coelomate ancestor. Because of its presence and recent molecular evidence, biologists classify nemerteans with the lophotrochozoans. Like the flatworms, nemerteans evolved from coelomate animals and became simpler over time.

Mollusks have a muscular foot, visceral mass, and mantle

The **mollusks** (phylum *Mollusca*) include clams, oysters, snails, slugs, octopuses, and the largest of all the invertebrates, the giant squid, which averages 9 to 16 m (about 30 to 53 ft) in length, including its tentacles. More than 80,000 living species and 35,000 fossil species (second only to the arthropods in number) have been described. Here we discuss four of eight recognized classes. We illustrate representatives of these classes in **FIGURE 31-13** and describe them in **TABLE 31-3**.

Although most mollusks are marine, many snails and clams live in fresh water, and some species of snails and slugs inhabit the land. Mollusks probably evolved early in the history of the protostome clade, soon after the evolution of the coelom but

before the origin of the segmented body that is characteristic of annelids. Although mollusks vary widely in outward appearance, most share six basic characteristics:

1. A soft body, usually covered by a dorsal shell composed mainly of calcium carbonate.
2. A broad, flat, muscular foot, located ventrally, which is used for locomotion.
3. The body organs (viscera) are concentrated as a **visceral mass** located above the foot.
4. The dorsal body wall forms a pair of folds called the **mantle.** The mantle is a thin sheet of tissue that generally overhangs the visceral mass, forming a mantle cavity. The mantle may contain glands that secrete a shell. The mantle cavity contains gills or a lung.
5. A rasplike structure called a **radula,** which is a belt of teeth in the mouth region. (The radula is not present in clams or their relatives, which are filter feeders.)
6. A coelom, generally reduced to small compartments around certain organs, including the heart and excretory organs (*metanephridia*). The main body cavity is typically a **hemocoel,** a space containing blood (see the following discussion of open circulatory systems). The hemocoel is not a coelom.

Mollusks have all the organ systems typical of complex animals. The digestive system is a tube, often coiled, consisting of a mouth, buccal cavity (mouth cavity), esophagus, stomach, intestine, and anus. The mollusk radula, located within the buccal cavity, projects out of the mouth and shows variation in structure among species related to feeding behaviors. In herbivorous species the radula is used to scrape algae from the surface of rocks or to remove tissue from live plants. The radulas of predatory mollusks may be used to inject toxins into prey, drill holes in the shells of prey animals, or rip apart flesh held in the beaks of cephalopods.

Most mollusks have an **open circulatory system** in which the blood, called **hemolymph**, bathes the tissues directly. The heart pumps blood into a single blood vessel, the aorta, which may branch into other vessels. Eventually, blood flows into a network of large spaces called *sinuses,* bringing the blood into direct contact with the tissues. This network makes up the hemocoel, or blood cavity. From the sinuses, blood drains into vessels that conduct it to the gills, where it is recharged with oxygen. After passing through the gills, the blood returns to the heart. Thus, blood flow in a mollusk follows this pattern:

heart ⟶ aorta ⟶ smaller blood vessels ⟶ blood sinuses (hemocoel) ⟶ blood vessels to gills ⟶ heart

In open circulatory systems, blood pressure tends to be low, and tissues are not very efficiently oxygenated. Because most mollusks are slow-moving animals with low metabolic rates, this type of circulatory system is adequate. The active cephalopods (the class that includes the squids and octopuses) have a **closed circulatory system** in which blood flows through a complete circuit of blood vessels.

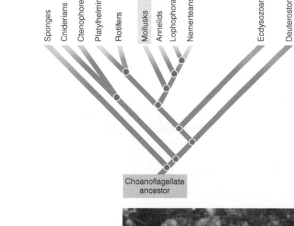

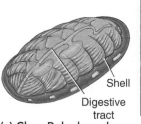

(a) **Class Polyplacophora**

Chitons are sluggish marine animals with shells composed of eight overlapping plates. This sea cradle chiton (*Tonicella lineata*), which reaches about 5 cm (2 in.) in length, inhabits rocks in coastal waters off the U.S. Pacific Northwest.

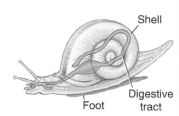

(b) **Class Gastropoda**

The broad, flat foot of the gastropod is an adaptation to its mobile lifestyle. The mystery snail (*Pomacea bridgesi*) inhabits fresh water and can be found burrowing in the mud.

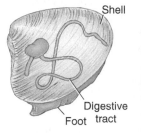

(c) **Class Bivalvia**

The compressed body of the horse-neck clam (*Tresus capax*) is adapted for burrowing in the North Pacific mud. Its shell grows to about 20 cm (8 in.) in length.

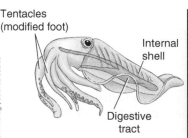

(d) **Class Cephalopoda**

The squid body is streamlined for swimming. To avoid being seen by potential predators, a squid can change color to blend with its background. This northern short-fin squid (*Illex illecebrosus*), which grows to a mantle length of up to about 31 cm (about 1 ft), inhabits the North Atlantic Ocean.

Figure 31-13 *Animation* **The mollusk body plan**
© Cengage Learning

TABLE 31-3 | Major Classes of Phylum Mollusca

CLASS AND REPRESENTATIVE ANIMALS	CHARACTERISTICS
POLYPLACOPHORA Chitons	Marine; dorsal shell consisting of eight separate transverse plates; head reduced; broad foot used for locomotion; uses radula to scrape algae and other small organisms off rocks
GASTROPODA Snails, slugs, nudibranchs	Marine, freshwater, or terrestrial; coiled shell in many species; torsion of visceral mass; well-developed head with tentacles and eyes; predators, herbivores, and detritus feeders
BIVALVIA Clams, oysters, mussels	Marine or freshwater; body laterally compressed; two-part shell hinged dorsally; hatchet-shaped foot; filter feeders
CEPHALOPODA Squids, octopuses	Marine; foot modified into tentacles, usually bearing suckers; well-developed eyes; closed circulatory system; predatory

© Cengage Learning

Most marine mollusks pass through one or more larval stages. The first stage is typically a **trochophore larva,** a free-swimming, top-shaped larva with two bands of cilia around its middle (FIG. 31-14). In many mollusks (gastropods such as snails and bivalves such as clams) the trochophore larva develops into a **veliger larva,** which has a shell, foot, and mantle. The veliger larva is unique to the mollusks.

Chitons may be similar to ancestral mollusks
Polyplacophorans (pol-ee-plah-kof'-o-rans; meaning "many plates") are *chitons,* marine animals with flattened bodies (see Fig. 31-13a). Their most distinctive feature is a shell composed of eight separate but overlapping dorsal plates. The head is reduced, and there are no eyes or tentacles.

Chitons inhabit rocky intertidal zones, using a broad, flat foot to move and to hold on firmly to rocks. By pressing its mantle against the substratum and lifting the inner edge of the mantle, a chiton can produce a partial vacuum. The resulting suction lets the animal adhere powerfully to its perch. Using the radula for grazing, chitons scrape algae and other small organisms off rocks and shells.

Gastropods are the largest group of mollusks
The *gastropods*—the snails, slugs, conchs, sea slugs, and their relatives—are the largest and most diverse group of mollusks (see Fig. 31-13b). In fact, with more than 70,000 extant species, gastropods constitute the second-largest class in the animal kingdom, second only to insects. Most gastropods inhabit marine waters, but others make their homes in brackish or fresh water or on land. We think of snails as having a single, spirally coiled shell into which they can withdraw the body, and many do. However, other gastropods, such as limpets, have shells like flattened dunce caps. Still others, such as garden slugs and the beautiful marine slugs known as *nudibranchs,* have no shell at all (FIG. 31-15).

Many gastropods have a well-developed head with tentacles. Two simple eyes may be located on stalks that extend from the head. The gastropod uses its broad, flat foot for creeping. Most land snails do not have gills. Instead, the mantle is highly vascularized and functions as a lung. Biologists describe these garden snails and slugs as *pulmonate* ("having a lung").

Torsion, a twisting of the visceral mass, is a unique feature of gastropods. This twisting is unrelated to the coiling of the shell. As the bilateral larva develops, one side of the visceral mass grows more rapidly than the other side. This uneven growth rotates the visceral mass. The visceral mass and mantle twist permanently

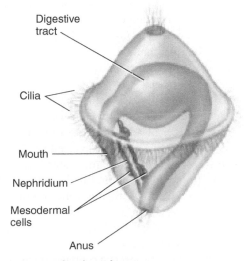

Figure 31-14 A trochophore larva

Digestive tract
Cilia
Mouth
Nephridium
Mesodermal cells
Anus

The first larval stage of a marine mollusk, the trochophore larva, is also characteristic of annelids. Just above the mouth a band of ciliated cells functions as a swimming organ and, in some species, collects suspended food particles.
© Cengage Learning

Joao Pedro Silva/Getty Images

Figure 31-15 Nudibranch (*Felimare tricolor*)

Nudibranchs (known as sea slugs) are a group of gastropods that have no shell. They feed on sponges and other small marine animals. The species shown here is small, about 25 mm, but other nudibranchs grow to about 600 mm (24 in.).

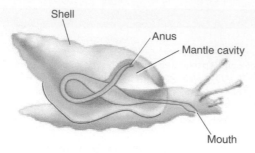

Figure 31-16 *Animation* Torsion in a gastropod

As the bilateral larva develops, the visceral mass twists 180 degrees relative to the head. The digestive tube coils, and the anus becomes relocated near the mouth.

© Cengage Learning

up to 180 degrees relative to the head. As a result, the digestive tract becomes somewhat U-shaped, and the anus comes to lie above the head and gill (**FIG. 31-16**). Subsequent growth is dorsal and usually in a spiral coil. Torsion limits space in the body, and typically the gill, excretory organ (metanephridium), and gonads are absent on one side. Some biologists hypothesize that torsion is an adaptation that protects the head by allowing it to enter the shell first during withdrawal from potential predators. Without torsion, the foot would be withdrawn first.

Most bivalves are filter feeders The *bivalves* include clams, oysters, mussels, scallops, and their relatives (see Fig. 31-13c). Typically, the soft body is laterally compressed and completely enclosed by a two-part shell that hinges dorsally and opens ventrally (**FIG. 31-17**). This arrangement allows the hatchet-shaped foot to protrude ventrally for locomotion and for burrowing in mud. The two parts, or *valves,* of the shell are connected by an elastic ligament. Stretching of the ligament opens the shell. Large, strong adductor muscles attached to the shell permit the animal to close its shell.

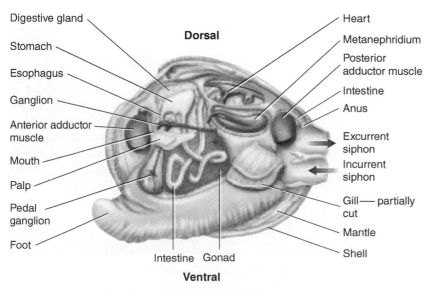

Figure 31-17 *Animation* Internal anatomy of a clam

The two shells of a bivalve hinge dorsally and open ventrally.

© Cengage Learning

The inner, pearly layer of the bivalve shell is made of calcium carbonate secreted in thin sheets by the epithelial cells of the mantle. Known as *mother-of-pearl,* this material is valued for making jewelry and buttons. Should a bit of foreign matter lodge between the shell and the mantle, the epithelial cells covering the mantle secrete concentric layers of calcium carbonate around the intruding particle. Many species of oysters and clams form pearls in this way.

Some bivalves, such as oysters, attach permanently to the substrate. Others burrow slowly through rock or wood, seeking protected dwellings. The shipworm, *Teredo,* a clam that damages dock pilings and other marine installations, is just looking for a home. A few bivalves, such as scallops, swim rapidly by clapping their two shells together with the contraction of a large adductor muscle (the part of the scallop that humans eat).

Clams and oysters are filter feeders that trap food particles suspended in sea water. They take water in through an extension of the mantle called the *incurrent siphon.* As the water passes over the gills, mucus secreted by the gills traps food particles in the stream of water. Cilia move the food to the mouth. Water and digestive wastes leave by way of an *excurrent siphon.* An oyster can filter more than 30 L (about 32 qt) of water per hour! As filter feeders, bivalves have no need for a radula, and indeed they are the only group of mollusks that lack this structure.

Cephalopods are active predators In contrast with most other mollusks, members of class *Cephalopoda* (meaning "head-foot") are fast-swimming predators (see Fig. 31-13d). The mouth of cephalopods is surrounded by tentacles, or arms: 8 in octopuses, 10 in squids, and as many as 90 in the chambered nautilus. The large cephalopod head has well-developed eyes that form images. Although they develop differently, their complex eyes are structurally similar to vertebrate eyes and function in much the same way. Octopuses have no shell, and the shells of squid, located inside the body, are greatly reduced.

Nautilus has a coiled shell consisting of many chambers built up over time. Each year, the animal lives in the newest and largest chamber of the series. *Nautilus* secretes a mixture of gases similar to air into the other chambers. By regulating the amount of gas in the chambers, the animal controls its buoyancy in the ocean.

The tentacles of squids, octopuses, and cuttlefish are covered with suckers for seizing and holding prey. In addition to a radula, the mouth has two strong, horny beaks used to kill prey and tear it to bits. The thick, muscular mantle is fitted with a funnel-like *siphon.* By filling the cavity with water and ejecting it through the siphon, cephalopods achieve forceful jet propulsion. Squids and cuttlefish have streamlined bodies adapted for efficient swimming.

In addition to speed, a cephalopod has two other adaptations that facilitate escape from its predators, which include certain whales, seals, large fish, and other cephalopods. It can confuse the enemy by rapidly changing colors. By expanding and contracting *chromatophores,* cells in the skin that contain pigment granules, a cephalopod can display an impressive variety of mottled colors. Another defense mechanism is its *ink sac,* which produces a thick, black liquid the animal releases in a dark cloud when alarmed. While its enemy pauses, temporarily blinded and confused, the cephalopod escapes. The ink inactivates the chemical receptors of some predators, making them incapable of detecting their prey.

Octopuses feed on crabs and other arthropods, catching and killing them with a poisonous secretion of their salivary glands. During the day, an octopus usually hides among the rocks; in the evening, it emerges to hunt for food. Its motion is incredibly fluid, giving little hint of the considerable strength in its eight arms.

Small octopuses survive well in aquariums and have been studied extensively. Because octopuses are relatively intelligent and can make associations among stimuli, researchers have used them as models for studying learning and memory. Their highly adaptable behavior more closely resembles that of the vertebrates than the more stereotypic patterns of behavior observed in other invertebrates (see Chapter 52).

Annelids are segmented worms

Annelids (an′-eh-lids; phylum *Annelida*) are segmented worms with bilateral symmetry and a tubular body that may be partitioned into more than 100 ringlike segments. This phylum, composed of about 15,000 species, includes three main groups: the polychaetes, a group of mainly marine worms; the earthworms and their relatives; and the leeches (TABLE 31-4 and FIG. 31-18).

The term *Annelida* (from a Latin word meaning "little rings") refers to the series of rings, or segments, that make up the annelid body. Both the body wall and many of the internal organs are segmented. Some structures, such as the digestive tract and certain nerves, extend the length of the body, passing through successive segments. Other structures, such as excretory organs, are repeated in each segment. In polychaetes and earthworms, segments are separated from one another internally by transverse partitions called **septa** (sing., *septum*).

An important advantage of **segmentation** is that it facilitates locomotion. The coelom is divided into segments, and

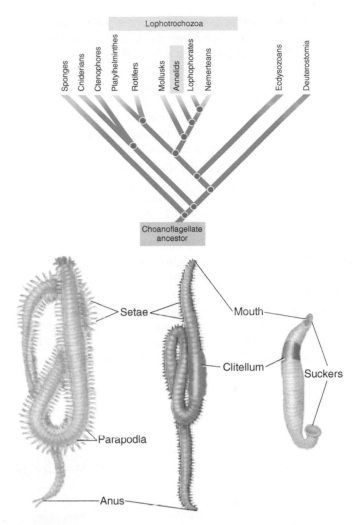

(a) Class Polychaeta. Polychaetes are marine worms with paddle-shaped parapodia.

(b) Class Oligochaeta. Oligochaetes, which include the earthworms, inhabit fresh water and moist terrestrial areas.

(c) Class Hirudinida. Many leeches are parasites that feed on blood.

Figure 31-18 Three major groups of annelids
© Cengage Learning

TABLE 31-4	Major Classes of Phylum Annelida
CLASS AND REPRESENTATIVE ANIMALS	**CHARACTERISTICS**
POLYCHAETA Sandworms, tubeworms	Mainly marine; each segment bears a pair of parapodia with many setae; well-developed head; separate sexes; trochophore larva
OLIGOCHAETA Earthworms	Terrestrial and freshwater worms; few setae per segment; lack well-developed head; hermaphroditic
HIRUDINIDA Leeches	Most are blood-sucking parasites that inhabit fresh water; appendages and setae absent; prominent muscular suckers

© Cengage Learning

each segment has its own muscles. This arrangement allows the animal to elongate one part of its body while shortening another part. The annelid's hydrostatic skeleton is important in movement. Polychaetes and earthworms have bristlelike structures called **setae** (sing., *seta*) located on each segment. Setae provide traction as the worm moves along by alternating contraction of its longitudinal and circular muscles. In earthworms setae consist mainly of chitin.

The annelid nervous system typically consists of a ventral nerve cord and a simple brain consisting of a pair of ganglia. Each segment has a pair of ganglia and lateral nerves. Annelids have a large, well-developed coelom; a closed circulatory system; and a complete digestive tract extending from mouth to anus. Respiration is *cutaneous*—that is, through the skin—or by gills. Typically, a pair of excretory tubules called **metanephridia** is located in each segment (described in Chapter 48).

Most polychaetes are marine worms with parapodia

Most *polychaetes* are marine worms, and many swim freely in the sea. Some polychaetes are part of the plankton and are important in marine food chains. Others burrow in the mud near the shore or in crevices of rocks or coral reefs. Still others live in tubes they secrete or make by cementing bits of shell and sand together with mucus. Giant tube worms have been found in deep vents in the floor of the Pacific Ocean (see *Inquiring About: Life without the Sun* in Chapter 55).

Each body segment typically bears a pair of paddle-shaped appendages called **parapodia** (sing., *parapodium*) that function in locomotion and in gas exchange. These fleshy structures bear many stiff setae (the term *polychaete* means "many bristles"; see the fireworm in the chapter-opening photograph). Most polychaetes have a well-developed head with eyes and antennae. The head may also be equipped with sensory tentacles and palps (feelers). Polychaetes develop from free-swimming trochophore larvae similar to those of mollusks.

Behavioral patterns that ensure fertilization have evolved in many polychaete species. By responding to certain rhythmic variations, or cycles, in the environment, nearly all the females and males of a given species release their gametes into the water at the same time. For example, more than 90% of reef-dwelling *Palolo* worms of the South Pacific shed their eggs and sperm within a 2-hour period on the same night of the year. The posterior portion of the *Palolo* worm, loaded with eggs or sperm, breaks off from the rest of the body. It comes to the surface and bursts, releasing its gametes. This mass reproductive event occurs in October or November at the beginning of the last lunar quarter. Local islanders gather great numbers of the swarming polychaetes, which they bake or eat raw.

Earthworms help maintain fertile soil

The approximately 3100 species of *oligochaetes* live almost exclusively in fresh water and in moist terrestrial habitats. These worms lack parapodia, have only a few bristles per segment (the term *oligochaete* means "few bristles"), and lack a well-developed head. All oligochaetes are hermaphroditic.

Lumbricus terrestris, a common earthworm, can reach 20 cm (8 in.) or more in length. Its body has more than 100 segments, separated externally by grooves that indicate the internal position of the septa (**FIG. 31-19**). The earthworm's body is somewhat protected from drying by a thin, transparent **cuticle** secreted by the cells of the epidermis. Mucus secreted by gland cells of the epidermis forms an additional protective layer over the body surface. The body wall has an outer layer of circular muscles and an inner layer of longitudinal muscles.

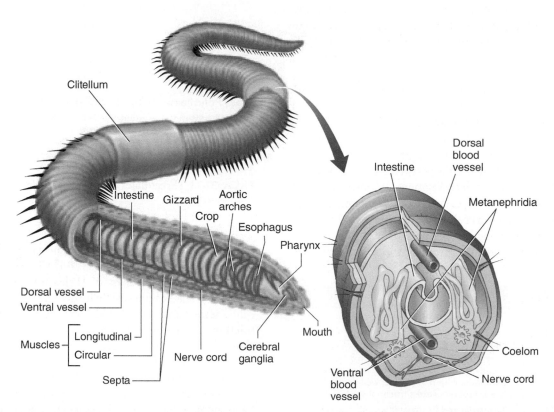

(a) The internal structure has been exposed at the anterior end of an earthworm.

(b) Cross section of an earthworm.

Figure 31-19 *Animation* **Body plan of an earthworm**

(Reproductive structures are not shown.)

© Cengage Learning

Earthworms eat living and dead plant material; some species feed mainly above the soil surface and other species feed within the ground, consuming mineral soil particles and organic matter. Burrowing and feeding activity by earthworms moves nutrients through the soil and creates pathways for oxygen and water movement, greatly influencing suitability of the soil for plant growth.

Earthworms process their meals in complex digestive systems. Food is swallowed through the muscular **pharynx** and passes through the **esophagus,** which is modified to form a thin-walled *crop* where food is stored, and a thick-walled, muscular *gizzard*. In the gizzard food is ground to bits by sand grains consumed along with the meal. The rest of the digestive system is a long, straight *intestine* that chemically digests food and absorbs nutrients. Wastes pass out of the intestine to the exterior through the **anus.**

The efficient closed circulatory system consists of two main blood vessels that extend longitudinally. The dorsal blood vessel, just above the digestive tract, collects blood from vessels in the segments. The dorsal vessel functions as a heart; it contracts to pump blood anteriorly. In the region of the esophagus, five pairs of circumesophageal blood vessels, referred to as *aortic arches,* conduct blood from the dorsal to the ventral blood vessel. The ventral blood vessel receives blood from the aortic arches. Small vessels branch from it and deliver blood to the various structures in each segment and to the body wall. Within these structures, blood flows through tiny capillaries before returning to the dorsal blood vessel.

Gas exchange takes place through the moist skin. Oxygen is transported by *hemoglobin,* a respiratory pigment in the blood. The excretory system consists of paired metanephridia, repeated in almost every segment of the body, that remove nitrogenous wastes from the coelomic fluid.

The nervous system consists of a pair of *cerebral ganglia* (a simple brain) just above the pharynx and a subpharyngeal ganglion just below the pharynx. A ring of nerve fibers connects these ganglia. From the lower ganglion, a ventral nerve cord extends beneath the digestive tract to the posterior end of the body. A pair of fused ganglia is present in each segment along the nerve cord. Nerves extend laterally from the ganglia to the muscles and other structures of that segment. The ganglia coordinate muscle contractions of the body wall, allowing the worm to creep along.

Like most annelids, earthworms are hermaphroditic. During copulation, two worms, headed in opposite directions, press their ventral surfaces together. These surfaces become glued together by the thick mucous secretions of each worm's *clitellum,* a thickened ring of epidermis. Sperm are then exchanged and stored in the *seminal receptacles* (small sacs) of the other worm. A few days later, each clitellum secretes a membranous cocoon containing a sticky fluid. As the cocoon is slipped forward, eggs are laid in it. Sperm are added as the cocoon passes over the openings of the seminal receptacles. As the cocoon slips free over the worm's head, its openings constrict so that a spindle-shaped capsule is formed. The fertilized eggs develop into tiny worms within this capsule. This reproductive pattern is an adaptation to terrestrial life; the cocoon protects the delicate gametes and young worms from drying out.

Many leeches are blood-sucking parasites Leeches are members of a group called *Hirudinida*. Most leeches inhabit fresh water, but some live in the sea or in moist areas on land. Some leeches are nonparasitic predators that capture small invertebrates such as earthworms and snails. However, about 75% of the known species of leeches are blood-sucking parasites. Leeches differ from other annelids in having neither setae nor parapodia.

Leeches have muscular suckers at both the anterior and posterior ends of their body. Most parasitic leeches attach themselves to a vertebrate host, bite through the skin, and suck out a quantity of blood, which is stored in pouches in the digestive tract. *Hirudin,* an anticoagulant secreted by glands in the crop, ensures leeches a full meal of blood. In 31 minutes, a leech can suck out as much as 10 times its own weight in blood! Some leeches feed only about twice each year because they digest their food slowly over several months.

Leeches have been used since ancient times for drawing blood from areas swollen by poisonous stings and bites. During the 19th century, they were widely used to remove "bad blood," thought to be the cause of many diseases. Leeches are sometimes used in modern medicine to remove excess fluid and blood that accumulate within body tissues as a result of injury, disease, or surgery (FIG. 31-20). The leech attaches its sucker near the site of injury, makes an incision, and secretes hirudin. The hirudin prevents the blood from clotting and dissolves clots that already exist.

The lophophorates are distinguished by a ciliated ring of tentacles

With a few exceptions, **lophophorates** are marine animals adapted for life on the ocean floor. These coelomates are distinguished by their *lophophore,* a ring of ciliated tentacles that surrounds the mouth. The lophophore is an adaptation for capturing suspended particles in the water. Lophophorates do not have a distinct head.

The three lophophorate groups are Brachiopoda, Phoronida, and Bryozoa (also known as Ectoprocta). *Brachiopods,* or lampshells, are solitary marine animals that inhabit cold water. Until the mid-19th century, they were thought to be mollusks because they are suspension feeders that superficially resemble clams and other bivalve mollusks. Their body is enclosed between two shells and has a mantle and mantle cavity (FIG. 31-21a). However, brachiopods differ from bivalve mollusks in that the shells are dorsal and ventral rather than lateral; each shell is symmetrical about the midline, and the two shell valves are typically of unequal size.

Brachiopods attach to the substrate by a long stalk. The action of cilia on the lophophore brings water with suspended food into the slightly opened shell. Although there are now only about 325 living species, brachiopods were abundant and diversified during the Paleozoic era. Paleobiologists have described about 12,000 fossil species.

Only about 20 extant species of *phoronids* are known. They are wormlike, sessile animals found in coastal marine sediments.

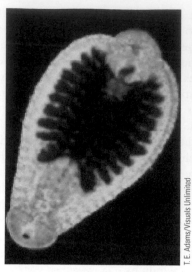

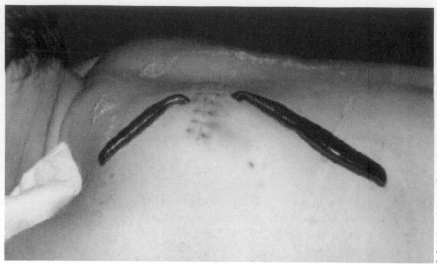

500 μm

(a) LM of a blood-sucking leech (*Helobdella stagnalis*) that feeds on mammals. The digestive tract (*dark area*) of its swollen body is filled with ingested blood.

(b) Medicinal leeches (*Hirudo medicinalis*) are used here to treat hematoma, an accumulation of blood within tissues that results from injury or disease.

Figure 31-20 Leeches

Adult phoronids secrete chitinous tubes in which they live (FIG. 31-21b). They extend their lophophores from their tubes for feeding. Phoronids vary in length from 2 cm to more than 20 cm (less than 1 in. to about 8 in.), but they are only 1 to 3 mm in diameter.

Bryozoans, also known as *ectoprocts* or "moss animals," are microscopic aquatic animals that form sessile colonies by asexual budding (FIG. 31-21c). Each colony can consist of millions of individuals and can extend in length up to about 31 cm (about 1 ft). The colonies typically appear plantlike, but some have the appearance of coral. Approximately 4500 living species are known.

Biologists are still debating the evolutionary position of the lophophorates. They were traditionally considered a monophyletic group and, based on certain structural similarities, a sister group to the deuterostomes. However, the lophophorate groups also have several morphological characters that suggest a relationship with the lophotrochozoans.

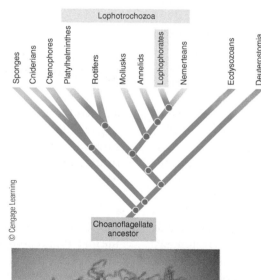

(a) Brachiopods. Like other brachiopods, these northern lampshells (*Terebratulina septentrionalis*) superficially resemble clams.

(b) Phoronids. A single lophophore of a phoronid (*Phoronopsis viridis*). This animal is about 20 cm (8 in.) long, but only 1–3 mm in diameter.

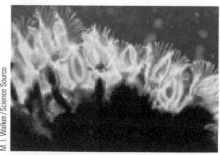

(c) Bryozoans. Like many bryozoans, this freshwater species (*Cristatella mucedo*) forms colonies by asexual budding.

Figure 31-21 Representative lophophorates

Based on molecular data (18S rDNA nucleotide sequences), the lophophorate phyla are currently classified as Lophotrochozoa, although their phylogeny is still being debated.

Rotifers have a crown of cilia

Rotifers (phylum *Rotifera*), or "wheel animals," are among the less familiar invertebrates. Although no larger than many protozoa, these aquatic, microscopic animals are multicellular with complex organ systems. Most of the 2000 described species inhabit fresh water, but some live in marine environments or damp soil. Rotifers are important in cycling nutrients in aquatic ecosystems. These animals do not have a true coelom and were formerly classified as pseudocoelomates. Current evidence suggests that rotifers evolved from animals with a true coelom, and we classify them as lophotrochozoans.

Rotifers have a characteristic crown of cilia on their anterior end. The cilia beat rapidly during swimming and feeding, giving the appearance of a spinning wheel (FIG. 31-22; also see Fig. 20-1). Rotifers feed on tiny organisms suspended in the stream of water drawn into the mouth by the cilia. A muscular organ posterior to the mouth grinds the food. The complete digestive tract ends in an anus through which wastes are eliminated.

Rotifers have a nervous system with a "brain" and sense organs, including eyespots. Protonephridia with flame cells remove excess water from the body and may also excrete metabolic wastes.

Biologists have discovered that rotifers, like some other animals with a pseudocoelom, are "cell constant," meaning that each member of a given species has exactly the same number of cells. Indeed, each part of the body has a precisely fixed number of cells arranged in a characteristic pattern. Cell division does not take place after embryonic development, and mitosis cannot be induced. Growth results from an increase in cell size. Do you think that rotifers could develop cancer? One of the challenging research problems of our time is to discover the difference between such nondividing cells and the dividing cells of other animals.

Another interesting characteristic of rotifers is their ability to survive very dry conditions and temperature extremes. These animals can remain in a dormant state for months or years. When conditions become favorable, they recover and become active once again.

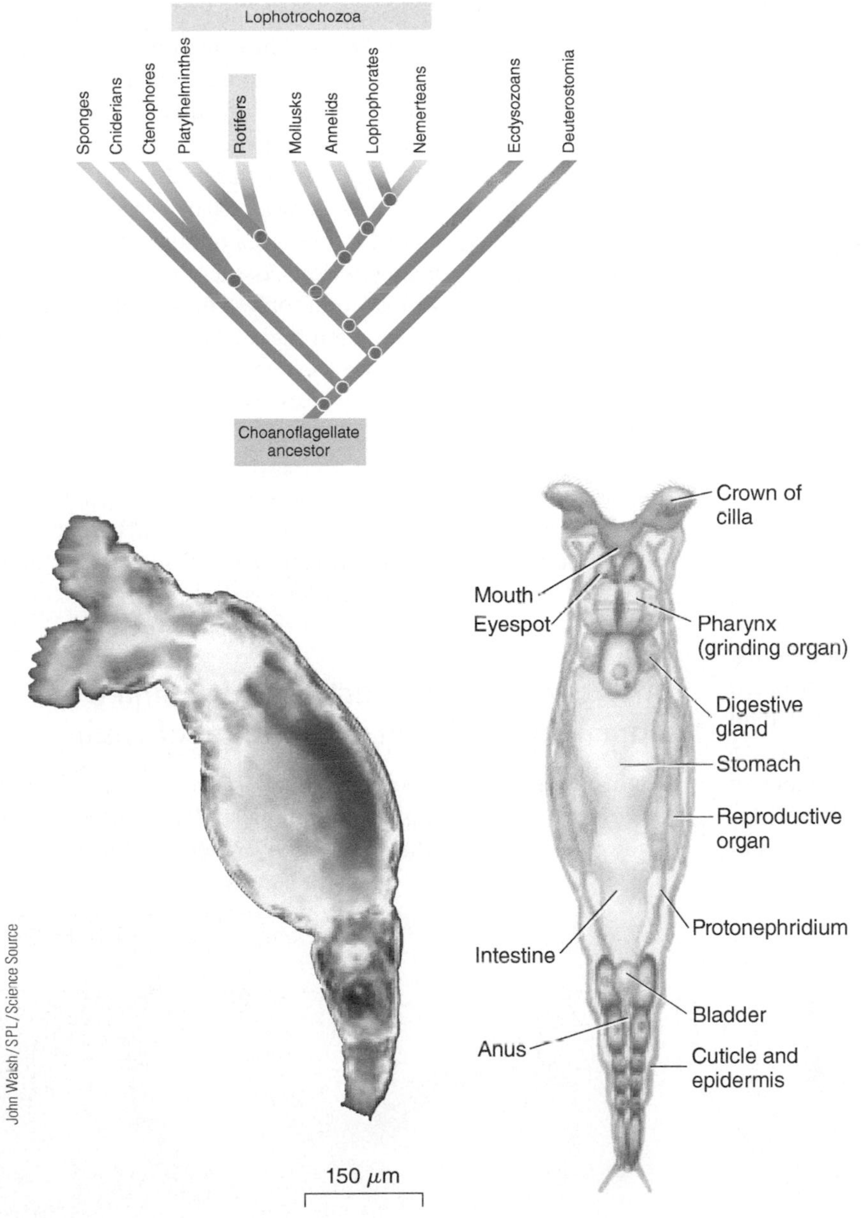

CHECKPOINT 31.2

- *What are some advantages of cephalization and a coelom?*
- CONNECT *On what basis have biologists classified nemerteans as lophotrochozoans?*
- CONNECT *How does the lifestyle of a gastropod differ from that of a cephalopod? Identify adaptations that have evolved in each for its particular lifestyle.*
- *What are two distinguishing characteristics for each of the following: flatworms, mollusks, and annelids?*

(a) LM of an Antarctic rotifer (*Philodina gregaria*) that survives the winter by forming a cyst. It reproduces in great numbers, sometimes coloring the water red.

(b) Longitudinal section showing rotifer anatomy. The motion of its cilia draws particles of food such as algae into the mouth.

150 μm

John Wash/SPL/Science Source

Figure 31-22 Rotifers (wheel animals)
© Cengage Learning

31.3 THE ECDYSOZOA

LEARNING OBJECTIVES

9 Summarize what is known about the phylogeny of the ecdysozoans.

10 Describe characteristics of nematodes and identify four parasitic nematodes.

11 Describe six key characteristics of arthropods, summarize proposed phylogeny of arthropods, and distinguish among arthropod subphyla and classes; give examples of animals that belong to each group.

12 Identify adaptations that have contributed to the biological success of insects.

The **Ecdysozoa** include the nematodes (roundworms) and arthropods, animals characterized by a **cuticle**, a noncellular body covering secreted by the epidermis. The name *Ecdysozoa* refers to the process of **ecdysis**, or **molting**, characteristic of animals in this group. During ecdysis, an animal sheds its outer covering (e.g., cuticle, exoskeleton, or skin), which is then replaced by the growth of a new one. The taxonomic validity of the Ecdysozoa has been supported by many types of data, including molecular data.

Roundworms are of great ecological importance

Nematodes (nem′-uh-todes; phylum *Nematoda*), or *roundworms*, play key ecological roles as decomposers, parasites, and predators of smaller organisms. Many soil nematodes eat bacteria. Nematodes are numerous and are widely distributed in soil and in marine and freshwater sediments. More than 25,000 species have been described, and many more remain to be discovered. The nematodes rival the insects in number of individuals. A spadeful of soil may contain thousands of these mainly microscopic worms, which thrash around, coiling and uncoiling. Greater understanding of soil nematode diversity and ecology will contribute to solving some important agricultural problems. *Caenorhabditis elegans*, a free-living soil nematode, is an important model research organism for biologists studying the genetic control of development (see Chapter 17).

The elongated, cylindrical, threadlike nematode body is pointed at both ends and covered with a tough, flexible cuticle (**FIG. 31-23**). Secreted by the underlying epidermis, the thick cuticle gives the nematode body shape and offers some protection. The epidermis is unusual in that it does not consist of distinct cells.

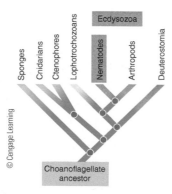

Nematodes have a fluid-filled pseudocoelom that serves as a hydrostatic skeleton. It transmits the force of muscle contraction to the enclosed fluid. Movement of fluid in the pseudocoelom is also important in transporting nutrients and wastes. Like ribbon worms, nematodes exhibit bilateral symmetry, a complete digestive tract, three definite tissue layers, and definite organ systems; however, they lack specific circulatory structures. The sexes are usually separate, and the male is generally smaller than the female.

Although most nematodes are free-living, others are important parasites in plants and animals. More than 50 species of roundworms are human parasites, including *Ascaris*, hookworms, pinworms, and the trichina worm. The common intestinal parasite *Ascaris* spends its adult life in the human intestine, where it ingests partly digested food (**FIG. 31-24**). *Ascaris* is a white worm up to 25 cm (10 in.) long. Like most parasites, it has remarkable reproductive adaptations that ensure survival within hosts. A mature female may produce as many as 200,000 eggs per day!

Hookworms attach to the lining of the intestine and suck blood, potentially causing serious tissue damage and blood loss. *Pinworms* are the most common worms found in children. The tiny pinworm eggs are often ingested by eating with hands contaminated with them. The *trichina worm* lives inside a variety of animals, including pigs, rats, and bears. Humans typically become infected by eating undercooked, infected meat. Larvae encyst in skeletal muscle and nervous tissue. Filarial nematodes are small, threadlike parasitic worms that are spread among hosts by the bites of insects. Members of this group cause elephantiasis in humans. The dog heartworm infects cats, dogs, and their relatives.

Arthropods are characterized by jointed appendages and an exoskeleton of chitin

Arthropods (ar′-thro-pods; phylum *Arthropoda*) are the most biologically successful group of animals. More than 80% of all known animals are arthropods! They are more diverse and live

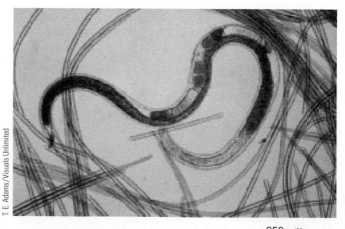

Figure 31-23 LM of a free-living nematode
This unidentified aquatic nematode is shown among the cyanobacterium *Oscillatoria*, which it eats.

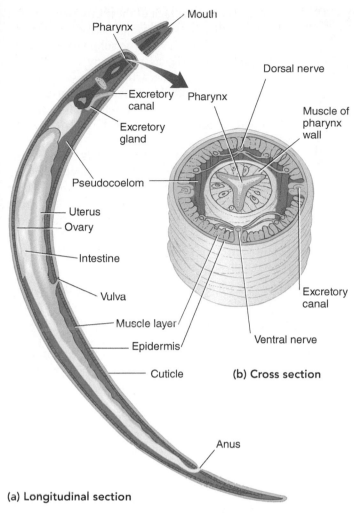

Pharynx
Mouth
Excretory
canal
Excretory
gland
Pseudocoelom
Uterus
Ovary
Intestine
Vulva
Muscle layer
Epidermis
Cuticle

Dorsal nerve
Pharynx
Muscle of
pharynx
wall
Excretory
canal
Ventral nerve

(b) Cross section

Anus

(a) Longitudinal section

Figure 31-24 *Animation* The roundworm *Ascaris*

(a) Note the complete digestive tract that extends from mouth to anus.
(b) This cross section through *Ascaris* shows the tube-within-a-tube body plan. The protective cuticle that covers the body helps this parasite resist host defenses.

© Cengage Learning

in a greater range of habitats than the members of any other animal phylum. More than one million species have been described, and biologists predict millions more will be identified. The following adaptations have greatly contributed to their success:

1. The arthropod body, like that of the annelid, is segmented. *Segmentation* is important from an evolutionary perspective because it provides the opportunity for specialization of body regions. In arthropods groups of segments are specialized to perform particular functions. Segments differ in shape, muscles, or the appendages they bear.

2. A hard **exoskeleton,** composed of chitin and protein, covers the entire body and appendages. The exoskeleton serves as a coat of armor that protects against predators and helps prevent excessive loss of moisture. It also supports the underlying soft tissues. Arthropods move effectively because distinct muscles attach to the inner surface of the exoskeleton and operate the joints of the body and appendages.

A disadvantage of the exoskeleton is that it is nonliving, and the arthropod periodically outgrows it. Recall that *molting* is the process of shedding an old exoskeleton, which is then replaced by a larger one. The shed exoskeleton represents a net metabolic loss, and molting also leaves the arthropod temporarily vulnerable to predators.

3. *Paired, jointed appendages,* from which this group gets its name (*arthropod* means "jointed foot"), are modified for many functions. They serve as swimming paddles, walking legs, mouthparts for capturing and manipulating food, sensory structures, or organs for transferring sperm.

4. The nervous system, which resembles that of the annelids, consists of a "brain" (cerebral ganglia) and a ventral nerve cord with ganglia. In some arthropods successive ganglia may fuse. Arthropods have a variety of very effective sense organs. Many have organs of hearing and **antennae** that sense taste and touch. Most insects and many crustaceans have **compound eyes** composed of many light-sensitive units called **ommatidia** (see Fig. 43-17). The compound eye can form an image and is especially adapted for detecting movement.

Arthropods have an *open circulatory system*. A dorsal, tubular heart pumps **hemolymph** into a dorsal artery, which may branch into smaller arteries. From the arteries, hemolymph flows into large spaces that collectively make up the hemocoel. Eventually, hemolymph re-enters the heart through openings, called *ostia,* in its walls.

The exoskeleton presents a barrier to diffusion of oxygen and carbon dioxide through the body wall, necessitating the evolution of specialized respiratory systems for gas exchange. Most aquatic arthropods have gills that function in gas exchange, whereas many terrestrial forms have a system of internal branching air tubes called **tracheae,** or **tracheal tubes** (see Fig. 46-1b). Other terrestrial arthropods have platelike *book lungs* (see Fig. 46-1d).

The arthropod digestive system is a tube similar to that of earthworms. Excretory structures vary somewhat among groups. The coelom is small and filled chiefly by the organs of the reproductive system.

Arthropod evolution and classification are controversial

Two groups of animals thought to be closely related to arthropods are the onychophorans and the tardigrades (FIG. 31-25). These three groups make up clade *Panarthropoda.* Like arthropods, onychophorans and tardigrades have a thick cuticle and must molt to grow. The body is segmented in all three groups, and all have legs, claws, and a ventral nervous system. Panarthropods have an open circulatory system, and the coelom is reduced to a hemocoel.

The caterpillar-like *onychophorans,* known as velvet worms, probably branched early from the arthropod line. They have paired appendages, but these are not jointed. As in arthropods, their jaws are derived from appendages. Some biologists place the *tardigrades,* known as "water bears," as the sister taxon of the arthropods. These tiny animals (typically less than 1 mm in length) have short, unjointed, clawed legs (see Fig. 2-12).

(a) Onychophoran. Note the soft segmented body and series of non-jointed legs. Extant onychophorans live in humid forests, but many extinct species inhabited the ocean.

(b) Tardigrades. Commonly known as water bears, tardigrades normally live in moist habitats, such as thin films of water on mosses. Most are less than 1 mm long.

Figure 31-25 Onychophorans and tardigrades
These animals are thought to be close relatives of arthropods.

Arthropod fossils have been identified dating back to the Proterozoic eon. Early in their evolutionary history, more than 540 million years ago (mya), arthropods diverged into several groups. Arthropods evolved rapidly during the Cambrian radiation, as evidenced by many diverse fossils in the Burgess Shale and other ancient sites.

We discuss five main arthropod groups, based on molecular and other data: the extinct trilobites and the extant Myriapoda, Chelicerata, Crustacea, and Hexapoda (TABLE 31-5). Some

systematists consider each of these groups a phylum; others view them as subphyla or classes. In this edition we classify these groups as subphyla of phylum Arthropoda. However, as you study the following sections, bear in mind that arthropod systematics is a work in progress. Both the relationship of arthropods to other protostomes and the relationships among arthropods continue to be topics of lively debate.

Trilobites were early arthropods Among the earliest arthropods to evolve, *trilobites* inhabited shallow Paleozoic seas more than 500 mya. These arthropods, which have been extinct for about 250 million years, lived on the sea bottom and filtered mud to obtain food. Most ranged from 3 to 10 cm (about 1 to 4 in.), but a few reached almost 1 m (39 in.) in length.

Covered by a hard, segmented exoskeleton, the trilobite body was a flattened oval divided into three parts: an anterior head bearing a pair of antennae and a pair of compound eyes, a thorax, and a posterior abdomen (FIG. 31-26). At right angles to these divisions, two dorsal grooves extended the length of the animal, dividing the body into a median lobe and two lateral lobes. (The name *trilobite* derives from this division of the body into three longitudinal parts.) Each segment had a pair of segmented **biramous appendages,** that had two jointed branches extending from their base. In trilobites each appendage consisted of an inner walking leg and an outer branch with gills.

TABLE 31-5	Extant Arthropod Subphyla					
SUBPHYLUM AND SELECTED GROUPS	**BODY DIVISIONS**	**APPENDAGES: ANTENNAE, MOUTHPARTS**	**APPENDAGES: LEGS**	**GAS EXCHANGE**	**DEVELOPMENT**	**MAIN HABITAT**
MYRIAPODA Chilopoda (centipedes) Diplopoda (millipedes)	Head with segmented body	Uniramous. Antennae: one pair Mouthparts: mandibles, maxillae	Chilopods: one pair/segment Diplopods: usually two pairs/ segment	Tracheae	Direct	Terrestrial
CHELICERATA Merostoma (horseshoe crabs) Arachnida (spiders, scorpions, ticks, mites)	Cephalothorax and abdomen	Uniramous. Antennae: none Mouthparts: chelicerae, pedipalps	Merostomes: four pairs of walking legs Arachnids: four pairs on cephalothorax	Merostomes: gills Arachnids: book lungs or tracheae	Direct, except mites and ticks	Merostomes: marine Arachnids: mainly terrestrial
CRUSTACEA Malacostraca (lobsters, crabs, shrimp, isopods) Cirripedia (barnacles) Copepoda (copepods)	Head, thorax, and segmented abdomen	Biramous. Antennae: two pairs Mouthparts: mandibles, two pairs of maxillae (for handling food)	Typically one pair/segment	Gills	Usually larval stages (nauplius larva)	Marine or freshwater; a few are terrestrial
HEXAPODA Insecta (bees, ants, grasshoppers, roaches, flies, beetles)	Head, thorax, and abdomen (some multi-segmented)	Uniramous. Antennae: one pair Mouthparts: mandibles, maxillae	Three pairs on thorax	Tracheae; gills in aquatic species	Typically, larval stages; most with complete metamorphosis	Mainly terrestrial

© Cengage Learning

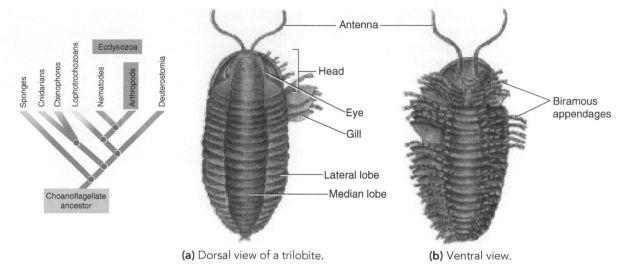

(a) Dorsal view of a trilobite.

(b) Ventral view.

Figure 31-26 Fossil trilobites

These extinct arthropods (*Phacops rana*) were about 3 cm (1.2 in.) long. Note the large, well-developed eyes visible on either side of the head region. Biologists consider these extinct marine arthropods the most primitive members of phylum Arthropoda. Trilobites flourished in the ocean during the Paleozoic era.
© Cengage Learning

Subphylum Myriapoda includes the centipedes and millipedes Members of subphylum *Myriapoda* are characterized by unbranched appendages called **uniramous appendages,** jawlike mandibles, and a single pair of antennae. Centipedes (*Chilopoda*) and millipedes (*Diplopoda*) are terrestrial and are typically found beneath stones or wood in the soil in both temperate and tropical regions. Both centipedes and millipedes have a head and an elongated trunk with many segments, each bearing uniramous legs (FIG. 31-27).

Centipedes ("hundred-legged") have one pair of legs on each segment behind the head. Most centipedes do not have enough legs to merit their name; typically, they have approximately 30, although a few species have 100 or more. Because centipedes have long legs, they are able to run rapidly. They are predators that feed on other animals, mostly insects. Larger centipedes eat snakes, mice, and frogs. Using their poison claws located just behind the head on the first trunk segment, centipedes capture and kill their prey.

Millipedes ("thousand-legged") have two pairs of legs on most body segments. They are not as agile as chilopods, and most species can crawl only slowly over the ground. However, they can powerfully force their way through earth and rotting wood. Millipedes are generally herbivorous and feed on both living and dead vegetation.

Chelicerates do not have antennae Subphylum *Chelicerata* includes the merostomes (horseshoe crabs) and the arachnids. The chelicerate body consists of a *cephalothorax* (fused head and thorax) and an abdomen. Chelicerates are the only arthropods without antennae. They have no chewing mandibles. Instead, the first appendages, located immediately anterior to the mouth, are a pair of **chelicerae** (sing., *chelicera*), fanglike feeding

(a) Centipede (*Lithobius*), a member of class Chilopoda. Centipedes have one pair of uniramous appendages per segment.

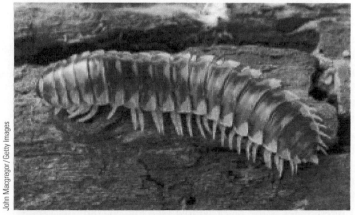

(b) Millipede (*Diplopoda pachydesmus*), a member of class Diplopoda. Note the two pairs of uniramous appendages per segment.

Figure 31-27 *Animation* **Myriapods**

appendages. Most chelicerates suck fluid food from their prey. The second appendages are the *pedipalps*. The chelicerae and pedipalps are modified to perform different functions in various groups, including manipulation of food, locomotion, defense, and copulation. The four pairs of legs on the cephalothorax are specialized for walking.

Almost all the *merostomes* are extinct. Only the horseshoe crabs have survived, essentially unchanged for more than 350 million years. *Limulus polyphemus,* the species common along the Atlantic shore of North America, is horseshoe-shaped (FIG. 31-28a). Its long, spikelike tail is used in locomotion, not for defense or offense. Horseshoe crabs feed at night, capturing mollusks, worms, and other invertebrates that they find on the sandy ocean floor.

Arachnids include spiders, scorpions, ticks, harvestmen (daddy longlegs), and mites (FIGS. 31-28b and c). Most of the approximately 80,000 named species are predators that feed on insects and other small arthropods. Most arachnids have six pairs of jointed appendages. In spiders the first appendages, the chelicerae, are used to penetrate prey; some species use the chelicerae to inject venom into their prey. Spiders use the second pair of appendages, the pedipalps, to manipulate food. Many arachnid species have pedipalps modified as sense organs for tasting food or for reproduction (for sperm transfer and courtship displays). Scorpions use their very large pedipalps as pincers for capturing prey. Chelicerates use the remaining four pairs of appendages for walking.

Typically, spiders have eight eyes arranged in two rows of four each along the anterior dorsal edge of the cephalothorax. The eyes detect movement, locate objects, and in some species form a relatively sharp image.

Gas exchange in arachnids takes place by tracheal tubes, book lungs, or both. A *book lung* consists of 15 to 20 parallel plates (like pages of a book) that contain tiny blood vessels. Air enters the body through abdominal slits and circulates between the plates. As air passes over the blood vessels in the plates, oxygen diffuses into the blood and carbon dioxide diffuses out of the blood into the air. As many as four pairs of book lungs provide an extensive surface area for gas exchange.

Spiders have unique glands in the abdomen that secrete silk, an elastic protein that is spun into fibers by organs called *spinnerets.* The silk is liquid as it emerges from the spinnerets but hardens after it leaves the body. Spiders use silk to build nests, to encase their eggs in a cocoon, and in some species to trap prey in a web. Many spiders lay down a silken dragline that serves both as a safety line and a means of communication between members of a species. From the type of dragline, another spider can determine the sex and maturity level of the spinner.

Although all spiders (and scorpions) have poison glands useful in capturing prey, only a few produce poison toxic to humans. The most widely distributed venomous spider in the United States is the black widow (see Fig. 31-28b). Its venom is a neurotoxin that interferes with transmission of messages from nerves to muscles. The shiny black female is about 3.8 cm (1.5 in.) long with a red or orange hourglass-shaped marking on the underside of its abdomen. Adult male black widow spiders

(a) Horseshoe crabs (*Limulus polyphemus*). The only living merostomes are a few closely related species of horseshoe crabs. Seasonally, horseshoe crabs return to beaches for mating.

(b) A female black widow spider (*Latrodectus mactans*) rests on her web. The venom of the black widow spider is a neurotoxin.

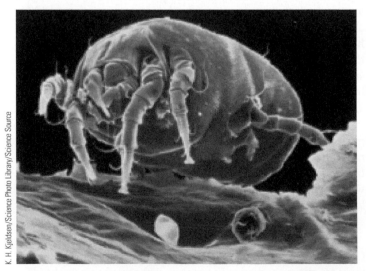

100 µm

(c) The house dust mite *Dermatophagoides*. This mite, a common inhabitant of homes, is associated with house dust allergies (color-enhanced SEM).

Figure 31-28 Chelicerates

are smaller and are harmless. After mating, the female sometimes kills and eats the male.

The brown recluse spider (*Loxosceles reclusa*) is more slender than the black widow and has a violin-shaped stripe on its dorsal cephalothorax. Its venom destroys the tissues surrounding the bite. Although painful, spider bites cause fewer than three fatalities per year in the United States.

Mites are incredibly abundant, but are rarely noticed because of their small size. Although some mites contribute to soil fertility by breaking down organic matter, many are serious nuisances. They eat crops, infest livestock and pets, and are external parasites. Some species have modified body shapes and reduced appendages, adaptations for their parasitic lifestyles. Chiggers (red bugs), the larval form of some red mite species, attach themselves to the skin and secrete an irritating digestive fluid that may cause itchy red welts. Certain mites cause mange in dogs and other domestic animals.

Larger than mites, ticks are parasites on dogs, deer, and many other animals. They transmit the bacteria that cause diseases such as Rocky Mountain spotted fever and Lyme disease (see Fig. 54-2).

Crustaceans are vital members of marine food webs

Crustaceans, members of Subphylum **Crustacea,** include lobsters, crabs, shrimp, and barnacles plus tens of thousands of smaller species with great diversity (FIG. 31-29). Many crustaceans are primary consumers of algae and detritus. Countless billions of microscopic crustaceans are part of marine zooplankton, the free-floating, mainly microscopic organisms in the upper layers of the oceans. These crustaceans are food for many fishes and other marine animals, such as certain baleen whales. Paleobiologists have dated crustacean fossils to the Cambrian period (more than 505 mya).

A distinctive feature of many crustaceans is the *nauplius larva*, which is often the first stage after hatching. This larva has only the most anterior three pairs of appendages. Crustaceans are also characterized by mandibles, biramous appendages, and two pairs of **antennae**. Their antennae, which are the first and second pairs of appendages, serve as sensory organs for touch and taste. Most adult crustaceans have compound eyes, and many crustaceans have **statocysts**, sense organs that detect gravity (see Fig. 43-6).

The hard **mandibles,** used for biting and grinding food, are the third pair of appendages; they lie on each side of the ventral mouth. Crustaceans show great diversity in the number of appendages posterior to the mandibles. Some species have several pairs of appendages near the mouth, called **maxillae** and maxillipeds, that manipulate and hold food. More posteriorly along the thorax and along the segmented abdomen, other appendages are modified for swimming, walking, defense, sensation, mating, or carrying eggs or young.

Crustaceans are primarily aquatic; not surprisingly, they typically have gills for gas exchange. Two large glands located in the head excrete metabolic wastes and regulate salt balance. Most crustaceans have separate sexes. During copulation, the male uses specialized appendages to transfer sperm into the female. Many crustaceans hatch into a nauplius larva

(a) Goose barnacles (*Lepas* sp.) filter feeding. These stalked barnacles are found in large numbers on intertidal rocks.

(b) Sponge crab (*Criptodromia octodenta*) wearing a sponge on its back. The sponge provides camouflage and shelter. The sponge crab uses its claws to cut out a fragment from a sponge and then trims the sponge to conform to its own shape. The last two pairs of the crab's legs bend upward over the crab's body and hold the sponge in place. The sponge grows along with the crab.

Figure 31-29 Crustaceans

and then molt through a series of larval stages before developing the adult body form. However, some species resemble small adults immediately upon hatching. Newly hatched animals may resemble adults, or they may undergo successive molts as they pass through a series of larval stages before developing an adult body.

Barnacles, the only sessile crustaceans, differ markedly in external anatomy from other members of the subphylum. They are marine suspension feeders that secrete limestone cups within which they live (see Fig. 31-29a). The larvae of barnacles are free-swimming forms that go through several molts. They eventually become sessile and develop into the adult form. Louis Agassiz, a 19th-century naturalist, described the barnacle as "nothing more than a little shrimplike animal standing on its head in a limestone house and kicking food into its mouth."

The bane of marine boaters, barnacles can proliferate on ship bottoms in great numbers. Barnacles can reduce the speed of a ship by more than 10% and increase fuel consumption by as much as 40%. The U.S. Office of Naval Research has been testing an underwater robot that cleans barnacles and other marine life from the hulls of ships when they are in port.

Isopods are mainly tiny (5 to 15 mm in length) marine crustaceans that inhabit the ocean floor. However, this group also includes some terrestrial animals: pill bugs and sow bugs. The most abundant crustaceans are the *copepods*, which are typically microscopic. Marine copepods are the most numerous component of zooplankton.

The largest and most familiar order of crustaceans, Decapoda, contains more than 10,000 species of lobsters, crayfish, crabs, and shrimp. Most **decapods** are marine, but a few, such as crayfish, certain shrimp, and a few crabs, live in fresh water. The crustaceans in general and the decapods in particular show striking specialization and differentiation of parts in the various regions of the animal. For example, the appendages in the different parts of the body differ markedly in form and function (FIG. 31-30).

In the lobster the five segments of the head and the eight segments of its thorax are fused into a cephalothorax, which is covered on the top and sides by a shield, the *carapace,* composed of chitin impregnated with calcium salts. The two pairs of antennae serve as chemoreceptors and tactile sense organs. The mandibles are short and heavy, with opposing surfaces used in grinding and biting food. Behind the mandibles are two pairs of accessory feeding appendages: the first and second maxillae.

The appendages of the first three segments of the thorax are the maxillipeds, which aid in chopping up food and passing it to the mouth. The fourth segment of the thorax has a pair of large *chelipeds,* or pinching claws. The last four thoracic segments bear walking legs. Gills for respiration branch dorsally from each of the thoracic appendages.

The appendages of the first abdominal segment are part of the reproductive system and are used by the male to transfer sperm. The following four abdominal segments bear paired *swimmerets,* small paddlelike structures used by some decapods for swimming and by the females of all species for holding eggs. Each branch of the sixth abdominal appendages consists of a large flattened structure. Together with the flattened posterior end of the abdomen, they form a tail fan used for swimming backward.

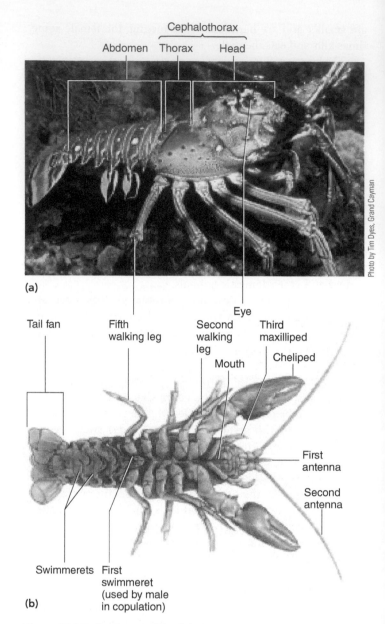

(a)

(b)

Figure 31-30 Anatomy of the lobster

(a) Like other decapods, the spiny lobster (*Panulirus argus*) has five pairs of walking legs. The first pair of walking legs is modified as chelipeds (*large claws*). Photographed in Grand Cayman. **(b)** Ventral view of a lobster. Note the variety of specialized appendages.
© Cengage Learning

Insects are articulated, tracheated hexapods With more than one million described species (and perhaps millions more not yet identified), *Insecta* of subphylum *Hexapoda* is the most successful group of animals on our planet in terms of number of individuals, number of species, diversity, and geographic distribution (TABLE 31-6). What they lack in size, insects make up in sheer numbers. If we could weigh all the insects in the world, their weight would exceed that of all the remaining terrestrial animals. Although primarily terrestrial, some insect species live in fresh water, a few are truly marine, and others inhabit the shore between the tides.

TABLE 31-6 | Some Orders of Insects

ORDER, NUMBER OF SPECIES, SOME CHARACTERISTICS	REPRESENTATIVE ADULT

HOMOPTERA (43,000)*

Leafhoppers, scale insects
Typically, two pairs of membranous wings; piercing–sucking mouthparts form beak; parasites of plants; vectors of plant diseases; incomplete metamorphosis

Buffalo treehopper
Stictocephala bubalus

ODONATA (6000)

Dragonflies, damselflies
Two pairs of long membranous wings; chewing mouthparts; large, compound eyes; active predators; larvae very different from adult; incomplete metamorphosis

Damselfly
Ischnura

ORTHOPTERA (20,000)

Grasshoppers, crickets
Forewings leathery, hindwings membranous; chewing mouthparts; most herbivorous, some cause crop damage; some predatory; incomplete metamorphosis

Fork-tailed bush katydid
Scudderia furcata

BLATTODEA (4000)

Cockroaches
When wings present, forewings leathery, hindwings membranous; chewing mouthparts; legs adapted for running; incomplete metamorphosis

American cockroach
Periplaneta americana

ISOPTERA (2500)

Termites
Two pairs of wings, or none; wings shed by sexual forms after mating; chewing mouthparts; social insects, form large colonies; eat wood; incomplete metamorphosis

Eastern subterranean termite
Reticulitermes flavipes

PHTHIRAPTERA (3000)

Lice, sucking lice
No wings; piercing–sucking mouthparts; ectoparasites of mammals; head and body louse and crab louse are human parasites; vectors of typhus fever; incomplete metamorphosis

Human head and body louse
Pediculus humanus

HEMIPTERA (75,000)

Chinch bugs, bedbugs, water striders; cicadas and aphids are now assigned to this order
Hindwings membranous; forewings smaller; piercing–sucking mouthparts form beak; most herbivorous; some parasitic; incomplete metamorphosis

Chinch bug
Blissus leucopterus

ORDER, NUMBER OF SPECIES, SOME CHARACTERISTICS	REPRESENTATIVE ADULT

LEPIDOPTERA (160,000)

Moths, butterflies
Usually two pairs of membranous, colorful, scaled wings; larvae are wormlike caterpillars with chewing mouthparts for eating plants; adult mouthparts adapted for sucking nectar; complete metamorphosis

Luna moth
Aetias luna

DIPTERA (150,000)

Houseflies, mosquitoes, fruit flies
Only forewings functional in flying; hindwings reduced to small, knob-like balancing organs (halteres); mouthparts usually adapted for sucking (and piercing in some); larvae are maggots that damage domestic animals or food; adults transmit diseases such as sleeping sickness, yellow fever, and malaria; complete metamorphosis

Deerfly
Chrysops vittatus

SIPHONAPTERA (2000)

Fleas
No wings; piercing–sucking mouthparts; legs adapted for clinging and jumping; parasites on birds and mammals; vectors of bubonic plague and typhus; complete metamorphosis

Dog flea
Ctenocephalides canis

COLEOPTERA (360,000)

Beetles, weevil
Forewings modified as protective coverings for membranous hindwings (which are sometimes absent); chewing mouthparts; largest order of insects; most herbivorous; some aquatic; many larvae are grubs; complete metamorphosis

Colorado potato beetle
Leptinotarsa decemlineata

HYMENOPTERA (more than 100,000)

Ants, bees, wasps
Usually two pairs of membranous wings; mouthparts may be modified for sucking or lapping nectar; many are social insects; some sting; important pollinators; complete metamorphosis

Bald-faced hornet
Vespula maculata

THYSANURA (600)

Silverfish
No wings; biting–chewing mouthparts; two to three "tails" extend from posterior tip of abdomen; inhabit dead leaves; eat starch in books; direct development

Silverfish
Lepisma saccharina

*The number of species listed for each order is approximate. Estimates vary widely.

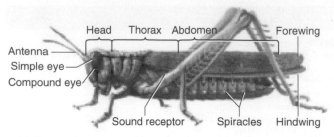

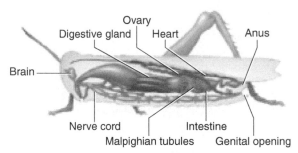

(a) External structure. Note the three pairs of segmented legs.

(b) Internal anatomy.

Figure 31-31 Anatomy of the grasshopper

Insects, the most successful of all animals, are articulated, tracheated hexapods.

© Cengage Learning

The earliest fossil insects—primitive, wingless species—date to the Devonian period more than 360 mya. Insect fossils from the Carboniferous period more than 310 mya include both wingless and primitive winged species. Cockroaches, mayflies, and cicadas are among the insects that have survived relatively unchanged from the Carboniferous period to the present day.

Molecular and developmental studies suggest that hexapods are a monophyletic group that evolved from within the crustaceans. Many biologists today classify crustaceans along with hexapods in clade *Pancrustacea*. We describe an insect as an *articulated* (jointed), *tracheated* (having tracheal tubes for gas exchange) *hexapod* (having six feet). The insect body consists of three distinct parts: head, thorax, and abdomen (**FIG. 31-31**). An insect's uniramous (unbranched) appendages include three pairs of legs that extend from the adult thorax and, in many orders, one or two pairs of wings. One pair of antennae protrudes from the head, and the sense organs include both simple and compound eyes. The complex mouthparts, which include mandibles and maxillae, are adapted for piercing, chewing, sucking, or lapping.

The tracheal system of insects has made an important contribution to their diversity. Air enters the tracheal tubes, or tracheae, through **spiracles,** tiny openings in the body wall. Oxygen passes directly to the internal organs via the tubes branching throughout the body. This effective oxygen delivery system permits insects to have the high metabolic rate necessary for activities such as flight, even though they have an open circulatory system.

Excretion is accomplished by two or more **Malpighian tubules,** which receive metabolic wastes from the blood, concentrate the wastes, and discharge them into the intestine. Unique to terrestrial arthropods, Malpighian tubules also perform the extremely important function of conserving water (see Fig. 48-4).

The sexes are separate, and fertilization takes place internally. Several molts occur during development. The immature stages between molts are called *instars*. Primitive insects with no wings, such as silverfish, have direct, or simple, development: the young hatch as juveniles that resemble the adult form. Other insects, such as grasshoppers and cockroaches, undergo **incomplete metamorphosis** in which the egg gives rise to a larva that resembles the adult in many ways but lacks functional wings and reproductive structures. The larva goes through a series of molts during which it becomes more and more like the adult.

Most insects, including bees, butterflies, and fleas, undergo **complete metamorphosis** with four distinct stages in the life cycle: *egg, larva, pupa,* and *adult* (**FIG. 31-32**). The wormlike larva does not look at all like the adult. For example, caterpillars have a body form entirely different from that of butterflies. Typically, an insect spends most of its life as a larva, which has chewing mouthparts. Eventually, the larva stops feeding, molts, and enters a pupal stage, usually within a protective cocoon or underground burrow. The **pupa** does not feed and typically cannot defend itself. Energy reserves stored during the larval stage are spent remodeling its body. When it emerges as an adult, it is equipped with functional wings and reproductive organs.

Certain species of bees, ants, and termites live as colonies or societies made up of several different types of individuals, each adapted for some particular function. The members of some insect societies communicate with one another by "dances" and by means of **pheromones,** substances secreted to the external environment. Social insects and their communication are discussed in Chapter 52.

Adaptations that contribute to the biological success of insects What are the secrets of insect success? The tough exoskeleton protects insects from predators and helps reduce water loss. Segmentation allows mobility and flexibility and permits regional specialization of the body. For example, cephalization and highly developed sense organs are important in both offense and defense.

The insect body plan has been modified and specialized in so many ways that insects are adapted to a remarkable number of lifestyles. The jointed appendages are specialized for various types of feeding, sensory functions, and different types of locomotion (walking, jumping, swimming). For example, grasshopper mouthparts are adapted for biting and chewing leaves. Moth and butterfly mouthparts are adapted for sucking nectar from flowers, and mosquito mouthparts are adapted for sucking blood. Aphids and leafhoppers have mouthparts specialized to pierce plants and feed on plant juices.

Another adaptation that contributes to insect success is the ability to fly. Unlike other terrestrial invertebrates, which creep slowly along on or under the ground, many insects fly rapidly through the air. Their wings and small size facilitate their wide

Complete metamorphosis reduces competition among insects within the same species; larval forms do not compete with adults for food or habitats.

Matt Meadows/Getty Images

(b) Caterpillar feeding on sweet gum leaf.

Adam Jones/Science Source

James H. Robinson/Science Source

(a) Polyphemus moth caterpillars hatching from eggs.

Millard H. Sharp/Science Source

(c) Cocoon cut open to show developing pupa.

(d) Adult on tree. Note eyespots.

Figure 31-32 **Complete metamorphosis in a Polyphemus moth**

Insects, the most successful of all animals, are articulated, tracheated hexapods. This moth (*Antheraea polyphemus*) belongs to the family of giant silk moths.

CONNECT Which of the following stages is haploid? Diploid? Embryo developing in egg, larva, pupa, adult?

distribution and, in many instances, their immediate survival. For example, when a pond dries up, adult aquatic insects can fly to another habitat.

The reproductive capacity of insects is remarkable. Under ideal conditions, the fruit fly *Drosophila* can produce 25 generations in a single year! Insect eggs are protected by a thick membrane. In addition, several eggs may be enclosed in a protective egg case. By dividing the insect life cycle into different stages, complete metamorphosis reduces competition among members of the same species (intraspecific competition). For example, larval forms have different lifestyles, so they do not compete with adults for food or habitats.

Insects have many interesting adaptations for offense and defense (see Fig. 7-8). We all are familiar with the stingers of bees and wasps, which are specialized egg-laying structures (ovipositors). Many insects have **cryptic coloration,** which allows them to blend into the background of their habitat; some look like dead twigs or leaves. Others mimic poisonous insects, deriving protection from this resemblance. Still others "play dead" by remaining motionless.

Insects communicate by tactile, auditory, visual, or chemical signals. For example, certain ant species use pheromones to mark trails and to warn of danger. Many insects use pheromones to attract mates.

Impact of insects on humans Not all insects compete with humans for food or cause us to scratch, swell up, or recoil from their presence. Bees, wasps, beetles, and many other insects pollinate the flowers of crops and fruit trees. Some insects destroy other insects that are harmful to humans. For example, dragonflies eat mosquitoes. And many organic farmers and home gardeners buy ladybird beetles, which are adept at ridding plants of aphids and other insect pests. Insects are important members of many food webs. Many birds, mammals, amphibians, reptiles, and some fishes depend on insects for food. Some beetles and the larvae (maggots) of flies are detritus feeders: they break down dead plants and animals and their wastes, permitting nutrients to be recycled.

Various insect products are useful to humans. Bees produce honey as well as beeswax, which we use to make candles, lubricants, and other products. Shellac is made from lac, a substance given off by certain scale insects that feed on the sap of trees. And the labor of silkworms provides us with beautiful fabric.

On the negative side, each year insects destroy crops worth billions of dollars. Fire ants not only inflict painful stings but cause farmers serious economic loss because of their large mounds, which damage mowers and other farm equipment. Moths damage clothing, and termites destroy buildings. Bloodsucking flies, screwworms, lice, fleas, and other insects annoy and transmit disease to humans and domestic animals. Mosquitoes are vectors of yellow fever and malaria (see Fig. 26-7). Fleas and lice transmit the rickettsia that cause typhus, and houseflies sometimes transmit typhoid fever and dysentery. Tsetse flies transmit African sleeping sickness, and fleas may be vectors of bubonic plague.

In this chapter we have surveyed the major groups of protostomes. TABLE 31-7 summarizes these groups. Chapter 32 focuses on the deuterostomes, which include the echinoderms and chordates.

CHECKPOINT 31.3

- CONNECT What characteristics distinguish nematodes from flatworms?
- CONNECT Describe four key arthropod characteristics, and explain how each contributes to arthropod success.
- How do crustaceans differ from chelicerates?
- CONNECT Describe four adaptations that have contributed to insect success.

TABLE 31-7	Overview of Sponges, Cnidarians, Ctenophores, and Protostomes	
MAJOR GROUPS	**BODY PLAN**	**SOME KEY CHARACTERISTICS**
Poriferans (sponges)	Asymmetrical; cells loosely arranged and do not form true tissues; body is sac with pores, central cavity, and osculum	Collar cells (choanocytes); aquatic, mainly marine
Cnidarians (hydras, jellyfish, corals)	Radial symmetry; diploblastic; gastrovascular cavity with one opening	Tentacles with cnidocytes (stinging cells) that discharge nematocysts; two body forms: polyp and medusa; some form colonies; mainly marine
Ctenophores (comb jellies)	Biradial symmetry; diploblastic; digestive system with mouth and anal pores	Eight rows of cilia that resemble combs; tentacles with adhesive glue cells; marine predators
PROTOSTOMES: LOPHOTROCHOZOAN CLADE		
Flatworms (planarians, tapeworms, flukes)	Bilateral symmetry; triploblastic; simple organ systems; gastrovascular cavity with one opening	No body cavity; some cephalization; some are free-living predators; many are parasites
Nemerteans (ribbon worms)	Bilateral symmetry; triploblastic; organ systems; complete digestive tube*	Proboscis (long, muscular tube that can be everted to capture prey); true coelom reduced; mainly marine predators
Mollusks (clams, snails, squids)	Bilateral symmetry; triploblastic; organ systems; complete digestive tube; true coelom	Soft body usually covered by dorsal shell; flat, muscular foot; mantle covers visceral mass; most have a radula (belt of teeth)
Annelids (some marine worms, earthworms, leeches)	Bilateral symmetry; triploblastic; organ systems; complete digestive tube; true coelom	Segmented body; most have setae, bristles that provide traction during crawling
Lophophorates (brachiopods, phoronids, bryozoans)	Bilateral symmetry; triploblastic; organ systems; complete digestive tube; true coelom	Lophophore (ciliated ring of tentacles) surrounds mouth, captures suspended particles in water; mainly sessile, marine animals
Rotifers (wheel animals)	Bilateral symmetry; triploblastic; organ systems; complete digestive tube; pseudocoelom	Crown of cilia at anterior end; cell number constant; microscopic, aquatic animals
PROTOSTOMES: ECDYSOZOAN CLADE		
Nematodes (roundworms, e.g., *Ascaris*, hookworms, trichina worms)	Bilateral symmetry; triploblastic; organ systems; complete digestive tube; pseudocoelom	Cylindrical, threadlike body; widely distributed in soil and aquatic sediments; important as decomposers; many are predators; some are parasites
Arthropods (centipedes, spiders, crabs, lobsters, insects)	Bilateral symmetry; triploblastic; organ systems; complete digestive tube; true coelom	Segmented body; exoskeleton; paired, jointed appendages; insects and many crustaceans have compound eyes; insects have tracheal tubes for gas exchange; wings

*A complete digestive tube has a mouth for food intake and an opening (anus) for elimination of wastes.

© Cengage Learning

31.1 Sponges, Cnidarians, and Ctenophores *(page 636)*

1 Identify important characteristics of poriferans.

- The **poriferans,** or sponges, are characterized by flagellate **collar cells (choanocytes),** which generate a water current that brings food and oxygen to the cells. Collar cells also trap and phagocytize food particles. The sponge body is a sac with tiny openings through which water enters; a central cavity, or **spongocoel;** and an open end, or **osculum,** through which water exits. The cells of sponges are loosely associated; they do not form true tissues.

2 Identify distinguishing characteristics of cnidarians, describe four groups, and give examples of animals that belong to each group.

- **Cnidarians** are characterized by radial symmetry, two tissue layers, and **cnidocytes,** cells containing stinging organelles called **nematocysts.** The **gastrovascular cavity** has a single opening that serves as both mouth and anus. Nerve cells form irregular, nondirectional **nerve nets** that connect sensory cells with contractile and gland cells.

- The life cycle of many cnidarians includes a sessile **polyp** stage (a form with a dorsal mouth surrounded by tentacles) and a free-swimming **medusa** (jellyfish) stage.

- Phylum Cnidaria includes four groups. *Hydrozoa* (hydras, hydroids, and the Portuguese man-of-war) are typically polyps and may be solitary or colonial. *Scyphozoa* (jellyfish) are generally medusae. *Cubozoa,* the "box jellyfish," have complex eyes that form blurred images. *Anthozoa* (sea anemones and corals) are polyps and may be solitary or colonial; anthozoans differ from hydrozoans in the organization of the gastrovascular cavity.

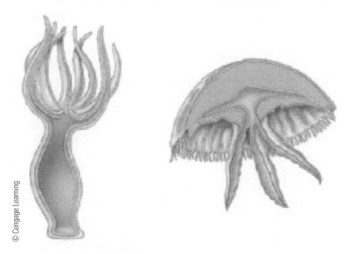
© Cengage Learning

3 Identify characteristics of ctenophores.

- **Ctenophores,** or *comb jellies,* are fragile, luminescent marine predators with biradial symmetry. Ctenophores have eight rows of cilia that resemble combs. They are diploblastic and have tentacles with adhesive glue cells.

31.2 The Lophotrochozoa *(page 643)*

4 Summarize what is known about the phylogeny of the lophotrochozoans and cite the adaptive advantages of having a coelom and of cephalization.

- The **Lophotrochozoa** make up a clade that includes some of the flatworms, nemerteans, mollusks, annelids, the lophophorate phyla, and rotifers.

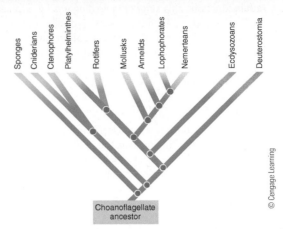
© Cengage Learning

- The true **coelom** is a fluid-filled body cavity completely lined by mesoderm that lies between the digestive tube and the outer body wall. The coelom brings about the *tube-within-a-tube body plan.* The body wall is the outer tube. The inner tube is the digestive tube. The coelom can serve as a **hydrostatic skeleton** in which contracting muscles push against a tube of fluid. The coelom is a space in which internal organs, including gonads, can develop; it helps transport materials and protects internal organs.

- **Cephalization,** the evolution of a head with the concentration of sense organs and nerve cells at the anterior end, increases the effectiveness of a bilateral animal to actively find food, shelter, and mates and to detect enemies.

5 Identify distinguishing characteristics of flatworms and nemerteans, and describe the main groups of flatworms, giving examples of animals that belong to each class.

- The *flatworms* are **acoelomate** (have no coelom) animals with bilateral symmetry, cephalization, three definite tissue layers, and well-developed organs. Many flatworms are **hermaphrodites:** a single animal produces both sperm and eggs. Flatworms have a ladder-type nervous system, typically consisting of sense organs and a simple brain composed of two **ganglia.** The ganglia are connected to two nerve cords that extend the length of the body. **Protonephridia** function in osmoregulation and disposal of metabolic wastes.

- Four groups of flatworms are recognized: class *Turbellaria* comprises free-living flatworms, including planarians; classes *Trematoda* and *Monogenea* include the parasitic *flukes;* and class *Cestoda* includes the parasitic tapeworms. The parasitic flukes and tapeworms typically have suckers or hooks for holding on to their hosts; they have complicated life cycles with intermediate hosts and produce large numbers of eggs.

- **Nemerteans** (ribbon worms) are characterized by the *proboscis,* a muscular tube used in capturing food and in defense. Nemerteans have a complete digestive tract with mouth and anus, and a circulatory system. The coelom is reduced.

6 Describe the main characteristics of mollusks and of the four main groups of mollusks discussed, giving examples of each group.

- **Mollusks** are soft-bodied animals typically covered by a shell. They have a ventral *foot* for locomotion and a pair of folds called the **mantle** that covers the **visceral mass,** a concentration of body organs.

- Mollusks have an **open circulatory system** except for cephalopods, which have a **closed circulatory system.** A rasplike **radula** functions as a scraper in feeding in all groups except the bivalves, which are filter feeders. Typically, marine mollusks have a free-swimming, ciliated **trochophore larva.**
- *Polyplacophorans* are chitons, mollusks with shells consisting of eight overlapping dorsal plates. The *gastropods,* which include the snails, slugs, and their relatives, have a well-developed head with tentacles. The body undergoes **torsion,** a twisting of the visceral mass.
- *Bivalves* are aquatic clams, scallops, and oysters. A two-part shell, hinged dorsally, encloses the bodies of these filter feeders. *Cephalopods* include the squids, octopuses, and *Nautilus.* These active, predatory swimmers have tentacles surrounding the mouth, which is located in the large head.

7 Describe the principal characteristics of annelids and of the three main groups of annelids discussed, giving examples of each group.

- The **annelids,** the segmented worms, include many aquatic worms, earthworms, and leeches. Annelids have long bodies with **segmentation** both internally and externally; their large, compartmentalized coelom serves as a hydrostatic skeleton.
- *Polychaetes* are marine annelids characterized by **parapodia,** appendages used for locomotion and gas exchange. The parapodia bear many bristlelike structures called **setae.** Polychaetes also differ from other annelids in having a well-defined head with sense organs.
- *Oligochaetes,* the group that includes the earthworms, are characterized by a few short setae per segment. The body is divided into more than one hundred segments separated internally by **septa.**
- Leeches belong to the group *Hirudinida.* Setae and appendages are absent. Parasitic leeches are equipped with suckers for holding on to their host.

8 Describe the distinguishing characteristics of the lophophorates and of the rotifers.

- The **lophophorates,** marine animals that have a lophophore, include the *brachiopods, phoronids,* and *bryozoans.* The *lophophore,* a ciliated ring of tentacles surrounding the mouth, is specialized for capturing suspended particles in the water.
- *Rotifers* are pseudocoelomates that are thought to have evolved from animals with a true coelom. They have a crown of cilia at their anterior end.

31.3 The Ecdysozoa *(page 656)*

9 Summarize what is known about the phylogeny of the ecdysozoans.

- **Ecdysozoa** is one of the three major animal clades; its validity is based on many types of evidence, including molecular data. Members of this group go through the process of **ecdysis,** or **molting,** during which an animal sheds its outer covering; the covering is then replaced by the growth of a new one.

10 Describe characteristics of nematodes and identify four parasitic nematodes.

- **Nematodes,** or *roundworms,* have a pseudocoelom. The body is covered by a tough **cuticle** that helps prevent desiccation. Parasitic nematodes that infect humans include *Ascaris, hookworms, trichina worms,* and *pinworms.*

11 Describe six key characteristics of arthropods, summarize proposed phylogeny of arthropods, and distinguish among arthropod subphyla and classes; give examples of animals that belong to each group.

- **Arthropods** are segmented animals with *paired, jointed appendages* and an armorlike **exoskeleton** of chitin. Molting is necessary for the arthropod to grow. Arthropods have an open circulatory system with a dorsal heart that pumps **hemolymph.** Aquatic forms have gills for gas exchange; terrestrial forms have either **tracheae** or *book lungs.*
- The arthropods along with the *onychophorans* (velvet worms) and *tardigrades* (water bears) make up the clade *Panarthropoda.* Based on molecular and other data, arthropods are currently assigned to five main groups: extinct trilobites and extant Myriapoda, Chelicerata, Crustacea, and Hexapoda.
- The *trilobites* are extinct marine arthropods covered by a hard, segmented shell. Each segment had a pair of **biramous appendages,** appendages with two jointed branches: an inner walking leg and an outer gill branch.
- Subphylum *Myriapoda* includes *Chilopoda,* the centipedes, and *Diplopoda,* the millipedes. Members of this subphylum have **uniramous appendages,** that is unbranched appendages, and a single pair of antennae.
- Subphylum *Chelicerata* includes the *merostomes* (horseshoe crabs) and the **arachnids** (spiders, mites, and their relatives). The chelicerate body consists of a cephalothorax and abdomen; there are six pairs of uniramous, jointed appendages, of which four pairs serve as legs. The first appendages are **chelicerae,** and the second are *pedipalps.* These appendages are adapted for manipulation of food, locomotion, defense, or copulation. Chelicerates have no antennae and no mandibles.
- **Crustaceans** include lobsters, crabs, shrimp, pill bugs, and barnacles, and their many relatives. The body typically consists of a cephalothorax and abdomen. Crustaceans vary greatly in the appearance and in the number of biramous appendages. Crustaceans have two pairs of **antennae** that sense taste and touch, and a pair of **mandibles** used for chewing. Two pairs of **maxillae,** posterior to the mandibles, manipulate and hold food. The decapod crustaceans typically have five pairs of walking legs.
- Subphylum *Hexapoda* includes *Insecta.* An insect is an *articulated, tracheated hexapod;* its body consists of head, thorax, and abdomen. Insects have uniramous appendages, a single pair of antennae, tracheae for gas exchange, and **Malpighian tubules** for excretion.

12 Identify adaptations that have contributed to the biological success of insects.

- The biological success of the insects can be attributed to their many adaptations, including a versatile exoskeleton, segmentation, specialized jointed appendages, highly developed sense organs, and ability to fly. **Complete metamorphosis,** transition during the life cycle from one developmental stage to another, includes egg, larva, pupa, and adult stages. Complete metamorphosis reduces competition within the same species.

Effective reproductive strategies, effective mechanisms for defense and offense, and the ability to communicate have evolved in insects.

Know and Comprehend

1. Collar cells (choanocytes) are characteristic of (a) poriferans (b) cnidarians (c) most coelomates (d) lophotrochozoans (e) ecdysozoans
2. Cnidocytes (a) are characteristic of sponges (b) are found among cells lining the gastrovascular cavity (c) contain stinging organelles (d) are lined with mesoderm (e) have two main shapes
3. Which of the following is associated with the evolution of the coelom? (a) radial symmetry (b) tube-within-a-tube body plan (c) incomplete metamorphosis (d) bilateral symmetry (e) development of ganglia
4. Trochophore larvae are characteristic of (a) arthropods (b) cnidarians (c) flatworms (d) mollusks (e) crustaceans
5. Which of the following is *not* an adaptation to parasitic life? (a) production of a few well-protected eggs (b) hooks (c) suckers (d) reduced digestive system (e) intermediate host
6. An open circulatory system (a) is characteristic of squids and other active mollusks (b) permits contracting muscles to recover quickly (c) has no blood vessels (d) is a unique characteristic of annelids (e) has hemolymph, which bathes tissues directly
7. Which of the following characteristics is associated with mollusks? (a) mandibles (b) mantle (c) pedipalps (d) chelipeds (e) setae
8. Trilobites (a) were early mollusks (b) are onychophorans (c) are characterized by parapodia and setae (d) were early arthropods (e) are an evolutionary link between annelids and arthropods
9. Which of the following is *not* characteristic of arthropods? (a) exoskeleton (b) pseudocoelom (c) paired, jointed appendages (d) chitin (e) segmentation
10. Which of the following is characteristic of insects? (a) biramous appendages (b) two pairs of antennae (c) chelicerae (d) eight legs (e) mandibles

Apply and Analyze

11. The correct sequence of complete metamorphosis of an insect is
    (a) egg ⟶ immature form ⟶ adult
    (b) egg ⟶ trochophore larva ⟶ adult
    (c) egg ⟶ pupa ⟶ larva ⟶ adult
    (d) egg ⟶ larva ⟶ pupa ⟶ adult
    (e) adult ⟶ larva ⟶ egg ⟶ pupa
12. **VISUALIZE** Draw a cross section through a hydra. Label the epidermis, gastrodermis, gastrovascular cavity, and mesoglea.

13. **EVOLUTION LINK** Discuss important adaptations made possible by the development of the coelom.
14. **EVOLUTION LINK** Discuss the idea that every evolutionary adaptation has both advantages and disadvantages, using each of the following as an example: (a) cephalization, (b) the arthropod exoskeleton, and (c) segmentation with specialization.

Evaluate and Synthesize

15. **INTERPRET DATA** Imagine that you discover a new animal in a rain forest. It has an elongated, segmented body with bristles, and it has no obvious head. Where would you place this animal in the accompanying cladogram? Support your decision. Look at the more detailed cladogram in Figure 30-6a (in Chapter 30). What additional characteristics would help you place your animal in this cladogram? Explain your decision-making process.

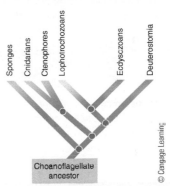

16. **EVOLUTION LINK** Why have biologists stopped using type of body cavity as a major criterion for inferring relationships among animal groups?
17. **EVOLUTION LINK** Animal body plans have generally evolved from simple to more complex. How can we explain the exceptions?
18. **EVOLUTION LINK** Insects that undergo complete metamorphosis outnumber those that do not by more than 10 to 1. Hypothesize an explanation.
19. **SCIENCE, TECHNOLOGY, AND SOCIETY** Several international monitoring projects are gathering data to help us understand coral reef destruction. In your opinion, why is it important to take action to protect coral reefs? What role might technology play?

 To access course materials, such as Aplia and other companion resources, please visit **www.cengagebrain.com**.

32 | The Deuterostomes

© David Fleetham/Alamy

Representative deuterostomes. This marine habitat was photographed in Hawaii above a coral reef. Echinoderms are represented by the pencil sea urchins (*Heterocentrotus mammilatus*). Chordates are represented by the fish, a Moorish idol (*Zanchus cornutus*).

KEY CONCEPTS

32.1 Echinoderms and chordates are the two most successful deuterostome lineages in terms of diversity, number of species, and number of individuals.

32.2 Echinoderms are characterized by radial symmetry in adults, a water vascular system, tube feet, and spiny skin.

32.3 At some time in its life, a chordate has a notochord; a dorsal, tubular nerve cord; a muscular postanal tail; and an endostyle (or thyroid gland).

32.4 Invertebrate chordates include tunicates and lancelets.

32.5 Shared derived characters of vertebrates include a vertebral column, a cranium, neural crest cells, and an endoskeleton of cartilage or bone.

32.6 Among the earliest vertebrates, ostracoderms were armored, jawless fishes. The extant hagfishes and lampreys have neither jaws nor paired fins.

32.7 Jaws and fins were key adaptations that contributed to the success of jawed fishes; and the evolution of limbs was important in the transition to terrestrial life.

32.8 The evolution of the amniotic egg allowed animals to become fully terrestrial; the amniotic egg was the key adaptation leading to the evolution of reptiles and, later, to birds and mammals.

What does a sea star have in common with a fish, frog, hawk, or human? You may think it strange to group the echinoderms—the sea stars, sea urchins, and sand dollars—with the chordates, the phylum to which we humans and other animals with a backbone belong. However, even though these animals look and behave very differently from one another, fossil evidence and morphological, developmental, and molecular data suggest that chordates and echinoderms share a common ancestor and are closely related.

In Chapter 31 we discussed the two major protostome branches of the animal kingdom: the lophotrochozoans and the ecdysozoans. In this chapter we focus on the third major branch of the animal kingdom, the deuterostomes. Some biologists speculate that the last common ancestor of the deuterostomes was an animal that obtained food by filtering ocean water. The two major groups (phyla) of living animals assigned to the deuterostomes are the echinoderms and chordates. The largest chordate subphylum is Vertebrata, which includes the animals with which we are most familiar: fishes, amphibians, reptiles (including birds), and mammals. Echinoderms are represented in the photograph by the pencil urchins, and chordates are represented by the fish.

We begin this chapter with an introduction to the deuterostomes and a survey of the echinoderms. We then turn our attention to the chordates. We describe the key chordate characteristics and discuss the invertebrate chordates. After an introduction to the vertebrates, we discuss jawless fishes and the evolution of jaws, and later the origin of limbed vertebrates. We discuss evolution of the adaptations that made the transition to life on land possible. We then describe the evolution of amniotes, which encompasses reptiles (including birds) and mammals.

32.1 WHAT ARE DEUTEROSTOMES?

LEARNING OBJECTIVE

1   Identify shared derived characters of deuterostomes and briefly describe the hemichordates.

The **deuterostomes** (clade Deuterostomia) make up the third major branch of the animal kingdom. Deuterostomes include the *echinoderms*—the sea stars, sea urchins, and sand dollars—and the *chordates,* the phylum to which we humans and other *vertebrates* (animals with a backbone) belong. Biologists also classify the **hemichordates,** a small group of wormlike marine animals, as deuterostomes. Hemichordates have a three-part body made up of a proboscis, collar, and trunk. These animals also have a characteristic ring of cilia surrounding the mouth. The most familiar of the hemichordates are the *acorn worms,* animals that live buried in mud or sand.

Deuterostomes evolved from a common ancestor during the Proterozoic eon more than 550 million years ago (mya). The major groups were present during the Early Cambrian period. Deuterostomes are characterized by several **shared derived characters** (synapomorphic characters), evolutionary novelties present in their most recent common ancestor (see Chapter 23). Evidence for the relatedness of the chordates, hemichordates, and echinoderms comes from molecular data and patterns of embryonic development. For example, deuterostomes are characterized by radial, rather than spiral, cleavage (see Chapter 30). Their cleavage is indeterminate, which means that the fate of their cells is fixed later in development than is the case in protostomes. In deuterostomes the mouth does not develop from the blastopore as in protostomes. The blastopore of deuterostomes becomes the anus (or is located near the future site of the anus), and the mouth develops from a second opening at the anterior end of the embryo, thus the name *deuterostome,* which is derived from the Greek words for "second mouth."

At some time in their life cycle, most deuterostomes develop *pharyngeal slits,* openings that connect the pharynx with the outside environment. Although there is evidence that some early echinoderms had pharyngeal slits, the extant (living) echinoderms have lost this character. *Basal deuterostomes* (members of the earliest deuterostome group to evolve) have a type of larva with a loop-shaped band of cilia used for locomotion. Deuterostomes have a true coelom.

CHECKPOINT 32.1

- *What are three shared derived characters of deuterostomes?*

32.2 ECHINODERMS

LEARNING OBJECTIVE

2   Identify three shared derived characters of echinoderms and describe the main classes of echinoderms.

The **echinoderms** (phylum *Echinodermata*) have one of the most highly derived body plans in the animal kingdom. With their unusual symmetry, spiny skins, water vascular system, and tube feet, echinoderms are one of the most unique animal groups. Echinoderm larvae are bilaterally symmetrical, ciliated, and free-swimming. However, during development the body reorganizes, and the adult exhibits *pentaradial symmetry,* in which the body is arranged in five parts around a central axis. Biologists have hypothesized that early echinoderms were sessile and that radial symmetry evolved as an adaptation to that lifestyle. Their radial symmetry allows these animals to respond effectively in every direction of their surrounding environment.

The most unique derived character of echinoderms is the **water vascular system,** a network of fluid-filled canals and chambers. In the sea star, for example, sea water enters through small pores in the *madreporite,* a sievelike structure on the body surface. Cilia lining the canals of the system move the water along. Branches of the water vascular system lead to numerous tiny **tube feet** that extend when filled with fluid. Each tube foot receives fluid from the main system of canals. A rounded muscular sac, or **ampulla,** at the base of the foot stores fluid and is used to operate the tube foot. A valve separates each tube foot from other parts of the system. When the valve shuts, the ampulla contracts, forcing fluid into the tube foot. The fluid causes the tube foot to extend. At the bottom of the foot, a suction-type structure presses against and adheres to whatever surface the tube foot is on. The water vascular system functions in feeding and gas exchange, and it serves as a hydrostatic skeleton important in locomotion.

Another unique echinoderm character is the **endoskeleton,** an internal skeleton, covered by a thin, ciliated epidermis. The endoskeleton consists of calcium carbonate ($CaCO_3$) plates and spines. The name *Echinodermata,* derived from words meaning "spiny skinned," was inspired by the spines that project outward from the endoskeleton. Some groups have pincerlike, modified spines called *pedicellariae* on the body surface. These structures, found only among the echinoderms, keep the surface of the animal free of debris.

Echinoderms have a well-developed coelom, containing coelomic fluid that transports materials. Although its structure varies in different groups, the complete digestive system is the most prominent body system. A variety of respiratory structures are found in the various classes. No excretory organs are present. The nervous system is simple, generally consisting of a nerve ring with nerves that extend out from it. Echinoderms have no brain. The sexes are usually separate, and eggs and sperm are generally released into the water, where fertilization takes place.

The fossil evidence suggests that echinoderms evolved from bilaterally symmetrical ancestors, probably during the Early Cambrian period. They achieved maximum diversity by the middle of the Paleozoic era, about 400 mya. By the beginning of the Mesozoic era 252 mya, they had declined, leaving five main groups that have survived to the present day. Biologists have identified about 7000 living and more than 13,000 extinct species. All echinoderms inhabit marine environments. They are found in the ocean at all depths. We consider the five extant groups: class Crinoidea, sea lilies and feather stars; class Asteroidea, sea stars; class Ophiuroidea, basket stars and brittle stars;

TABLE 32-1 Classes of Echinoderms

CLASS AND REPRESENTATIVE ANIMALS		CHARACTERISTICS
CRINOIDEA Feather stars, sea lilies		Feather stars motile; sea lilies, sessile, attach to ocean floor by stalk; oral surface on upper side of disc; tube feet along feathery arms trap microscopic organisms
ASTEROIDEA Sea stars		Arms (rays) extend from central disc; tube feet on undersurface of each arm; mouth in center of underside of disc; carnivorous predators and scavengers
OPHIUROIDEA Basket stars, brittle stars		Resemble sea stars, but arms long, slender, and more set off from central disc; tube feet used to collect and handle food
ECHINOIDEA Sea urchins, sand dollars		Skeletal plates flattened and fused to form a test; sand dollars burrow in sand and feed on organic particles; sea urchins graze on algae
HOLOTHUROIDEA Sea cucumbers		Body is elongated, muscular sac; mouth surrounded by tentacles that are modified tube feet; sluggish animals that live on sea bottom; many species eject organs when conditions are poor; for defense, can eject tubules out of anus

© Cengage Learning

class Echinoidea, sea urchins and sand dollars; and class Holothuroidea, sea cucumbers (TABLE 32-1 and FIG. 32-1).

Feather stars and sea lilies are suspension feeders

Feather stars and sea lilies (class *Crinoidea*) are the oldest living echinoderms (see Fig. 32-1a). Although many extinct crinoids are known, relatively few living species have been identified. The feather stars are motile, although they often remain in the same location for long periods. Sea lilies are sessile and remain attached to the ocean floor by a stalk.

Crinoids remove suspended food from the water. Several branched, feathery arms extend upward. Numerous tube feet shaped like small tentacles are located along the feathery arms. These tube feet are coated with mucus that traps microscopic organisms. The *oral surface* (location of the mouth) is on the upper side of the disc. In all other echinoderms, the mouth is located on the underside of the disc toward the substratum.

Many sea stars capture prey

Sea stars (commonly called starfish) are asteroids (class *Asteroidea*; see Fig. 32-1b). Their bodies consist of a central disc from which extend 5 to more than 20 arms, or rays (FIG. 32-2). The undersurface of each arm has hundreds of pairs of tube feet. The endoskeleton consists of a series of calcareous plates that permit some movement of the arms. Delicate dermal gills, small extensions of the body wall, carry on gas exchange. The mouth lies in the center of the underside of the disc.

Most sea stars are predators and scavengers that feed on cnidarians, crustaceans, mollusks, annelids, and even other echinoderms. A few species may catch small fish. The sea star's water vascular system does not permit rapid movement, so its prey usually consists of stationary or slow-moving animals, such as clams.

To attack a clam or other bivalve mollusk, the sea star mounts it and assumes a humped position as it straddles the edge opposite the hinge. Then, holding itself in position with its tube feet, the sea star slides its thin, flexible stomach out through its mouth and between the closed, or slightly gaping, valves (shell parts) of the clam. While the clam is still in its own shell, the sea star secretes enzymes that digest the soft parts of the clam to the consistency of a thick soup. When the partly digested meal is taken into the sea star body, it is further digested by enzymes secreted by digestive glands located in each arm.

The circulatory system in sea stars is poorly developed and probably of little help in transporting materials. Instead, the coelomic fluid, which fills the large coelom and bathes the internal tissues, assumes this function. Metabolic wastes pass to the outside by diffusion across the tube feet and dermal gills. The nervous system consists of a ring of nervous tissue encircling the mouth and a nerve extending from this ring into each arm.

Sea daisies are a curious group of asteroids characterized by small, disc-shaped, flat bodies (less than 1 cm in diameter) with no arms or mouth. They inhabit bacteria-rich wood sunk in deep water and apparently absorb bacteria through their body surface.

Basket stars and brittle stars make up the largest group of echinoderms

Basket stars and brittle stars (serpent stars) make up the largest group of echinoderms (class *Ophiuroidea*) both in number of species and individuals (see Fig. 32-1c). These animals resemble

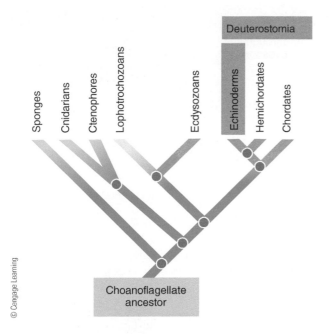

(a) Class Crinoidea. Feather stars use their slender, jointed appendages to cling to the surface of a rock or coral reef. They can creep away to escape predators.

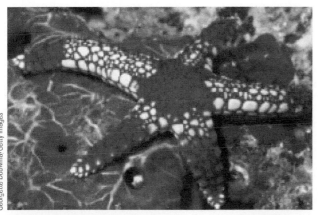

(b) Class Asteroidea. Orange and red sea star (*Fromia monilis*) on a colonial tunicate.

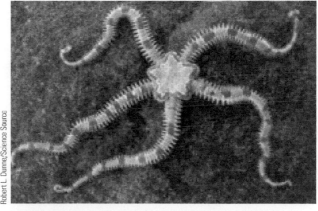

(c) Class Ophiuroidea. Daisy brittle star (*Ophiopholis aculeata*), photographed in Muscongus Bay, Maine.

(d) Class Echinoidea. With its flattened, circular body, the sand dollar (*Dendraster excentricus*) is adapted for burrowing on the ocean floor.

(e) Class Holothuroidea. A sea cucumber (*Thelonota*) raises its body to spawn.

Figure 32-1 Representative echinoderms

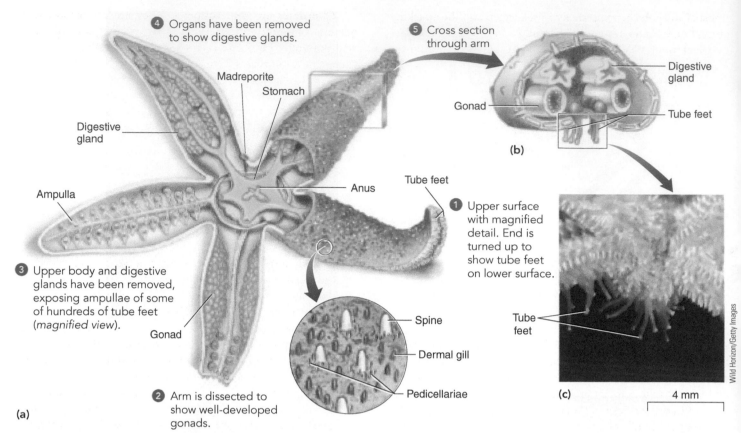

④ Organs have been removed to show digestive glands.

⑤ Cross section through arm

Madreporite

Stomach

Digestive gland

Digestive gland

Gonad

Tube feet

Ampulla

Anus

Tube feet

(b)

① Upper surface with magnified detail. End is turned up to show tube feet on lower surface.

③ Upper body and digestive glands have been removed, exposing ampullae of some of hundreds of tube feet (*magnified view*).

Gonad

Spine

Dermal gill

Pedicellariae

Tube feet

(c)

4 mm

② Arm is dissected to show well-developed gonads.

(a)

Wild Horizon/Getty Images

Figure 32-2 Body plan of a sea star

(a) A sea star viewed from above, with its arms in various stages of dissection. Similar structures are present in each arm, but some organs are not shown so as to highlight certain other structures. The two-part stomach is in the central disc with the anus on the aboral (*upper*) surface and the mouth beneath on the oral surface. **(b)** Cross section through arm and tube feet. **(c)** LM of underside of a sea star, showing its tube feet.

© Cengage Learning

sea stars in that their bodies consist of a central disc with arms. However, the arms are long and slender and more sharply set off from the central disc than those of sea stars. Some brittle stars use their arms for locomotion, making rowing movements. Their tube feet lack suckers; they may be used to collect and handle food and may also serve a sensory function, perhaps that of taste.

Sea urchins and sand dollars have movable spines

Sea urchins and sand dollars (class *Echinoidea*) have no arms (see Fig. 32-1d and chapter-opening photograph). Their skeletal plates are flattened and fused to form a solid shell called a test. The flattened body of the sand dollar is adapted for burrowing in the sand, where it feeds on tiny organic particles. Sand dollars have smaller spines than sea urchins.

Many sea urchins graze on algae, scraping the sea floor with their calcareous teeth. Sea urchins use their tube feet for locomotion. They also push themselves along with their movable spines. In some species the spines covering the body can penetrate flesh and are difficult to remove. So threatening are these spines that swimmers on tropical beaches are often cautioned to wear shoes when venturing offshore, where these living pincushions may dwell in abundance.

Sea cucumbers are elongated, sluggish animals

Sea cucumbers (class *Holothuroidea*) are appropriately named, for some species are about the size and shape of a cucumber. The elongated body is a flexible, muscular sac (see Fig. 32-1e). The mouth is usually surrounded by a circle of tentacles that are modified tube feet. The endoskeleton consists of microscopic plates embedded in the body wall. The circulatory system, which is more highly developed than in other echinoderms, functions to transport oxygen and perhaps nutrients.

Sea cucumbers are sluggish animals that usually live on the bottom of the sea, sometimes burrowing in the mud. Some graze with their tentacles, whereas others stretch their branched tentacles out in the water and wait for dinner to float by. Algae and other morsels are trapped in mucus along the tentacles.

An interesting habit of some sea cucumbers is evisceration, in which the digestive tract, respiratory structures, and gonads are ejected from the body, usually when environmental conditions are unfavorable. When conditions improve, the lost parts are regenerated. Even more curious, when certain sea cucumbers are irritated or attacked, they direct their rear end toward the enemy and shoot red tubules out of their anus! These unusual weapons become sticky in sea water, and the attacking animal may become hopelessly entangled in the spaghetti-like tangle of tubules. Some of the tubules release a toxic substance.

CHECKPOINT 32.2

- *What are three derived characters of echinoderms? Describe each.*
- CONNECT *How do sea stars differ from crinoids? from sea urchins?*

32.3 THE CHORDATES: MAJOR CHARACTERISTICS

LEARNING OBJECTIVE

3 Describe characteristics of chordates, including four shared derived characters.

Biologists currently assign the chordates (phylum Chordata) to three groups, or subphyla: urochordates, marine animals called *tunicates*; cephalochordates, marine animals called *lancelets*; and vertebrates, animals with backbones. Although the structures of living species may suggest otherwise, recent molecular data support that urochordates, and not cephalochordates, are the sister group to the vertebrates (FIG. 32-3).

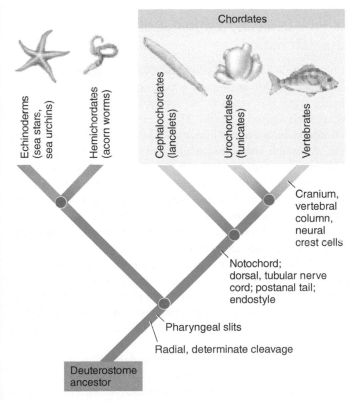

Figure 32-3 Evolutionary relationships of the chordates
This cladogram shows hypothesized phylogenetic relationships among deuterostomes based on structural and DNA data.
© Cengage Learning

Chordates are deuterostomes. They are coelomates with bilateral symmetry, a tube-within-a-tube body plan, and three well-developed germ layers. Four shared derived characters distinguish the chordates from all other groups of animals. These characters, which evolved in connection with their evolving methods of locomotion and obtaining food, are the notochord; the dorsal, tubular nerve cord; a postanal tail; and an endostyle or thyroid gland (FIG. 32-4).

1. All chordates have a **notochord** during some time in their life cycle. The notochord is a dorsal, longitudinal rod composed of spongy connective tissue cells surrounded by a tough fibrous sheath. The notochord is firm but flexible, and it supports the body. It also plays an important role in embryonic development of the vertebrates.
2. At some time in their life cycle, chordates have a **dorsal, tubular nerve cord.** The chordate nerve cord differs from the nerve cord of most other animals in that it is located dorsally rather than ventrally, is hollow rather than solid, and is single rather than double.
3. Chordates have a larva or embryo with a muscular **postanal tail,** an appendage that extends posterior to the anus.
4. The **endostyle** is a groove in the floor of the pharynx that secretes mucus and traps food particles in the sea water passing through the pharynx. The endostyle is present in the urochordates, cephalochordates, and lamprey larvae. The thyroid gland evolved from the endostyle and is present in all other chordates.

Pharyngeal slits are another important characteristic of chordates. During chordate embryonic development, a series of grooves develop in the body wall in the region of the pharynx (the part of the digestive tract just posterior to the mouth). A series of outpocketings from the lateral sides of the pharynx (pharyngeal pouches) extend to the grooves. In aquatic chordates the tissue between the grooves and pharyngeal pouches breaks through and forms **pharyngeal slits,** passageways that connect the inside of the pharynx with the surrounding environment.

The perforated pharynx first evolved as an adaptation for filtering food. As water flowed through the mouth and passed out of the pharynx through the pharyngeal slits, suspended food particles were trapped in mucus. Later, modifications evolved, including highly vascularized gills in the passageways. These additions adapted the pharyngeal slits for gas exchange in fishes and some other aquatic vertebrates. Early in vertebrate evolution, anterior pharyngeal arches (supporting tissue between the pharyngeal pouches) evolved into jaws. Although pharyngeal slits are found in all chordates, they are not considered a derived character of chordates because they are also present in hemichordates.

Typically, chordates have an endoskeleton and a closed circulatory system with a ventral heart. Chordates have segmented bodies, but specialization is so pronounced that the basic segmentation of the body plan may not be apparent. The segmentation is most obvious in the serially repeated body muscles and skeletal structures (like vertebrae), and in the nerves, which supply these tissues.

The shared derived characters of chordates include a notochord; dorsal, tubular nerve cord; postanal tail; and endostyle, a groove in the floor of the pharynx that traps food particles in sea water.

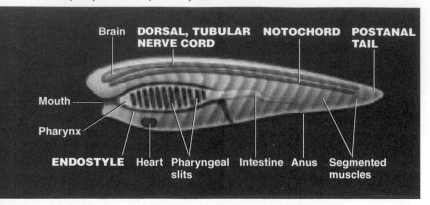

Brain **DORSAL, TUBULAR NERVE CORD** **NOTOCHORD** **POSTANAL TAIL**

Mouth

Pharynx

ENDOSTYLE Heart Pharyngeal slits Intestine Anus Segmented muscles

Figure 32-4 *Animation* **Generalized chordate body plan**

Identify the shared derived characters: notochord; dorsal, tubular nerve cord; postanal tail; and endostyle. Other key characteristics include pharyngeal slits and segmented muscles.

PREDICT What structures do you think the dorsal, tubular nerve cord gives rise to during the development of vertebrate chordates?

© Cengage Learning

CHECKPOINT 32.3

- *What are four shared derived characters of chordates?*
- **CONNECT** *How is the chordate nerve cord different from the nerve cord of most other animals?*
- **CONNECT** *What is the relationship between your jaws and the pharyngeal slits of early chordates?*

32.4 INVERTEBRATE CHORDATES

LEARNING OBJECTIVE

4 Compare tunicates and lancelets, and summarize the phylogeny of chordates.

Some chordates are not vertebrates. The invertebrate chordates include tunicates (urochordates) and lancelets (cephalochordates).

Tunicates are common marine animals

The **tunicates,** or **urochordates** (subphylum Urochordata), include the sea squirts and their relatives (**FIG. 32-5**). Larval tunicates have typical chordate characteristics and superficially resemble tadpoles. The expanded body has a pharynx with slits, and the long muscular tail contains a notochord and a dorsal, tubular nerve cord. Some tunicates (*appendicularians*) retain their chordate features and ability to swim. These animals are common members of the zooplankton.

Most tunicates are *ascidians,* commonly known as sea squirts (class Ascidiacea). A sea squirt larva swims for a time and then attaches itself to a rock, a piling, or the sea bottom.

It loses its tail, notochord, and much of its nervous system. Adult sea squirts are barrel-shaped, sessile marine animals unlike other chordates. Indeed, they are often mistaken for sponges or cnidarians. Only the pharyngeal slits, endostyle, and the structure of its larva indicate that the sea squirt is a chordate.

Adult tunicates develop a protective covering, or **tunic,** that may be soft and transparent or quite leathery. Curiously, the tunic consists of a carbohydrate much like cellulose. The tunic has two openings: the incurrent siphon, through which water and food enter; and the excurrent siphon, through which water, waste products, and gametes pass to the outside. Sea squirts get their name from their practice of forcefully expelling a stream of water from the excurrent siphon when irritated.

Tunicates are filter feeders that remove plankton suspended in the stream of water passing through the pharynx. Food particles are trapped in mucus secreted by cells of the endostyle, a groove that extends the length of the pharynx. Ciliated cells of the pharynx move the stream of food-laden mucus into the esophagus. Much of the water entering the pharynx passes out through the pharyngeal slits into an *atrium* (a chamber) and is discharged through the excurrent siphon.

Some species of tunicates form large colonies in which members share a common tunic and excurrent siphon. Colonial forms often reproduce asexually by budding. Sexual forms are usually hermaphroditic.

Lancelets clearly exhibit chordate characteristics

Most **cephalochordates** (subphylum **Cephalochordata**) belong to the genus *Branchiostoma,* which consists of animals commonly known as *lancelets,* or *amphioxus.* Lancelets are translucent, fish-shaped animals, 3 to 8 cm (1.3 to 3.2 in.) long and pointed at both ends. They are widely distributed in shallow seas. Although larvae and adults can swim freely, adults typically burrow in the sand in shallow water near the shore. In some parts of the world, lancelets are an important source of food. One Chinese fishery reports an annual catch of 35 tons (about one billion lancelets).

Chordate characteristics are highly developed in lancelets. The notochord extends from the anterior tip ("head"; hence the name *Cephalochordata*) to the posterior tip. A dorsal, tubular nerve cord also extends the entire length of the animal, and many pairs of pharyngeal slits are evident in the large pharyngeal region (**FIG. 32-6**). Although superficially similar to fishes, lancelets have a far simpler body plan. They do not have paired fins, jaws, sense organs, a heart, or a well-defined head or brain.

Like tunicates, lancelets are filter feeders. Cilia in the mouth and pharynx draw a current of water into the mouth. Microscopic organisms in the water are trapped in mucus secreted by the endostyle and are then moved back to the intestine by beating cilia.

Water passes through the pharyngeal slits into the atrium, a chamber with a ventral opening (the *atriopore*) located anterior to the anus. Metabolic wastes are excreted by segmentally

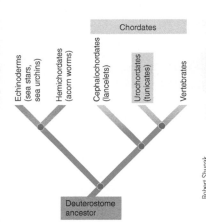

Chordates

Echinoderms (sea stars, sea urchins)
Hemichordates (acorn worms)
Cephalochordates (lancelets)
Urochordates (tunicates)
Vertebrates

Deuterostome ancestor

Robert Shupak

(a) Note the incurrent (*top*) and excurrent (*side*) siphons of this sea peach (*Halocynthia aurantium*), a solitary tunicate.

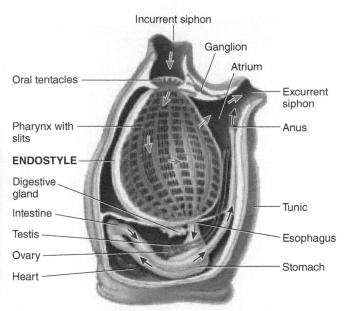

Incurrent siphon
Ganglion
Atrium
Oral tentacles
Excurrent siphon
Pharynx with slits
Anus
ENDOSTYLE
Digestive gland
Tunic
Intestine
Testis
Esophagus
Ovary
Stomach
Heart

(b) Lateral view of an adult tunicate. The *blue arrows* represent the flow of water, and the *red arrows* represent the path of food.

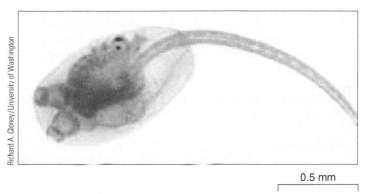

Richard A. Cloney / University of Washington

0.5 mm

(c) Swimming larval stage of a colonial species, *Distaplia occidentalis*.

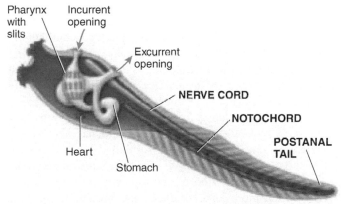

Pharynx with slits
Incurrent opening
Excurrent opening
NERVE CORD
NOTOCHORD
POSTANAL TAIL
Heart
Stomach

(d) Internal structure of a larval tunicate (*lateral view*).

Figure 32-5 *Animation* **Tunicate body plan**
© Cengage Learning

arranged, ciliated *protonephridia* that open into the atrium. Unlike circulation in other invertebrates, the blood flows anteriorly in the ventral vessel and posteriorly in the dorsal vessel in lancelets. This circulatory pattern is similar to that of fishes.

Systematists debate chordate phylogeny

Fossils of early chordates contribute to our understanding of chordate phylogeny. Invertebrate chordates are soft-bodied and did not leave many fossils. However, some well-preserved, key fossils that date back to the Middle Cambrian have been found in the Burgess Shale of British Columbia, Canada. Early Cambrian fossil sites have been discovered in Chengjiang and Haikou, China. At Chengjiang, fine-grained rocks about 530 million years old have preserved soft-bodied animals, including *Haikouella*, in some detail. *Haikouella* was about 2 to 3 cm (approximately 1 in.) long and had a nerve cord, a notochord, pharyngeal slits,

muscle segments, and a brain. Many biologists view *Haikouella* as an early chordate. Some investigators hypothesize that this fossil represents a transitional form between the earliest chordates and the first vertebrates.

Pikaia, a lancelet-like fossil discovered in the Burgess Shale, had a primitive notochord with muscles attached to it that allowed for locomotion. About 4 cm (1.5 in.) in length, *Pikaia* had a tail fin and probably filtered food from the water. *Pikaia* is also considered an early chordate, possibly sharing many similarities with modern cephalochordates.

Are cephalochordates or urochordates the sister group of the vertebrates? Although structural similarities implicated cephalochordates, rather than urochordates, as the sister group to the vertebrates, the predominance of recent molecular data supports that urochordates are the closest relatives of the vertebrates. The molecular data combined with information gathered from the available fossils suggest that cephalochordates, urochordates,

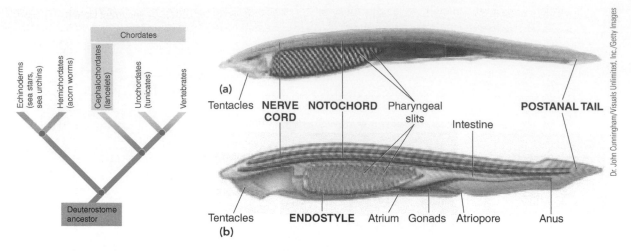

Figure 32-6 *Animation* **Cephalochordate body plan**

(a) Photograph of a lancelet, *Branchiostoma* (amphioxus). Note the prominent pharyngeal slits. **(b)** Longitudinal section showing derived characters and other internal structures.
© Cengage Learning

and vertebrates all evolved from early chordates that had elongated bodies. Some of these very early chordates retained the same general body form and gave rise to the cephalochordates. In others, an adult that was sessile, rather than swimming, gave rise to the urochordates. A third lineage added a number of specialized features while giving rise to the vertebrates.

The tunicate *Ciona intestinalis* is an excellent model organism for studying chordate genetics and development because its genome consists of only about 16,000 protein-coding genes, the basic set of genes found in chordates. Interestingly, about 80% of *Ciona*'s genes are found in vertebrates. In fact, *Ciona* has most vertebrate gene families, but in simplified form. For example, *Ciona* has only a single copy of each gene family involved in cell signaling and regulation of development, whereas vertebrates have two or more copies of these gene families. (A gene family is a group of genes that evolved over time from a single ancestral gene through duplication and divergence.) Some of the "extra" copies probably evolved to code for new structures or functions. *Ciona* also has genes for some vertebrate structures and processes, even though it does not express these genes.

CHECKPOINT 32.4

- **CONNECT** *How are the main derived chordate characters evident in a tunicate larva and in an adult tunicate?*
- **CONNECT** *If you found a small fishlike animal along the shoreline, how would you determine whether or not it was a lancelet?*

32.5 INTRODUCING THE VERTEBRATES

LEARNING OBJECTIVES

5 Describe four shared derived characters of vertebrates.
6 Describe the major taxa of extant vertebrates.

Numbering about 50,000 described species, the **vertebrates** (subphylum Vertebrata) are less diverse and much less numerous than the insects. However, vertebrates rival the insects in their adaptations to an enormous variety of lifestyles (FIG. 32-7). In addition to the basic chordate characteristics, vertebrates have a number of shared derived characters not found in other groups.

The vertebral column is a derived vertebrate character

The vertebrates are distinguished from other chordates in having a **vertebral column** that forms the skeletal axis of the body. Although sometimes called the "backbone," the vertebral column actually consists of a series of separate skeletal elements, the *vertebrae,* which are made of cartilage or bone. This flexible support develops around the notochord, and in most species it largely replaces the notochord during embryonic development. Dorsal projections of the vertebrae enclose the nerve cord along its length. Anterior to the vertebral column, a cartilaginous or bony **cranium,** or braincase, encloses and protects the brain, the enlarged anterior end of the nerve cord.

The cranium and vertebral column are part of the *endoskeleton.* In contrast with the nonliving exoskeleton of many invertebrates, the vertebrate endoskeleton is a living tissue that grows with the animal. Some vertebrates (jawless and cartilaginous fishes) have skeletons made of cartilage. However, in most vertebrates the skeleton is mainly bone, a tissue that contains fibers made of the protein collagen. The hard matrix of bone consists of the compound hydroxyapatite, composed mainly of calcium phosphate. Muscles are attached to the endoskeleton.

Many characters common to vertebrates have been derived from a group of embryonic cells called **neural crest cells.** These cells, found only in vertebrates, appear early in development and migrate to various parts of the embryo. Neural crest cells give rise to or influence the development of many structures, including nerves, head muscles, cranium, and jaws.

This cladogram provides a framework for understanding the evolution of vertebrate diversity and adaptations to aquatic and terrestrial environments.

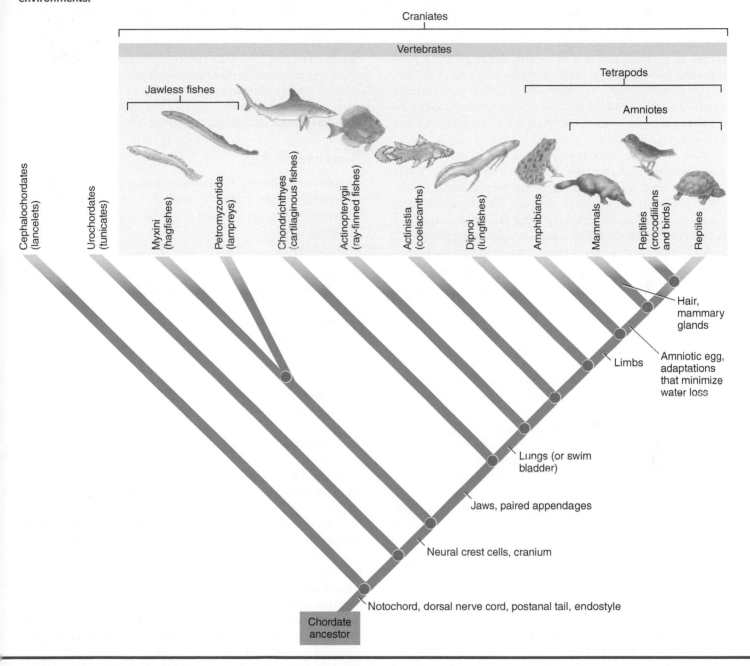

Figure 32-7 *Animation* Evolutionary relationships of extant vertebrates

This cladogram represents one phylogenetic interpretation of vertebrate phylogeny. The evolution of certain key characters is indicated. As new data are collected and considered, details of the cladogram will likely change. Amniote relationships are shown in more detail in Figure 32-20.
© Cengage Learning

CONNECT What are some advantages of the pronounced cephalization that occurred as vertebrates evolved from jawless fish to tetrapods?

Recall that *Hox* genes are important in determining pattern development in embryos (see Chapter 17). Specifically, *Hox* genes determine the fate of cells in the anterior–posterior axis. These genes occur in clusters on specific chromosomes. All invertebrates and non-vertebrate chordates that have been studied have one *Hox* gene cluster; vertebrates have four duplicated clusters. Other gene clusters, including some encoding transcription factors and others coding globin proteins for transporting oxygen, were also duplicated during the evolution of the early vertebrates. The significance of these genetic changes is the focus of current investigation, but it is reasonable to hypothesize that the increase in genetic complexity contributed to the development of more complex and varied bodies.

Recall that some invertebrate groups show an evolutionary trend toward **cephalization,** the concentration of nerve cells and sense organs in a definite head. The vertebrates are characterized by *pronounced* cephalization. The brain has become larger and more elaborate, and its various regions have specialized to perform different functions. Either 10 or 12 pairs of **cranial nerves** emerge from the brain and extend to various organs of the body. Vertebrates have well-developed sense organs concentrated in the head: eyes; ears that serve as organs of balance and, in some vertebrates, for hearing as well; and organs of smell and taste.

Most vertebrates have two pairs of appendages. The fins of fishes are appendages that stabilize and/or help propel the fish in the water. Paired pectoral and pelvic fins are also used in steering. Based on structural, molecular, and fossil data, biologists hypothesize that jointed appendages that facilitated locomotion on land (i.e., legs) evolved from the lobed fins of lungfishes.

Vertebrates have a closed circulatory system with a ventral heart and blood containing hemoglobin. The complete digestive tract has specialized regions and large digestive glands (the liver and pancreas). Several *endocrine glands,* which are ductless glands, secrete hormones. Paired kidneys regulate fluid balance. The sexes are typically separate.

Early vertebrates were probably marine animals. In contrast to the tunicates and lancelets, which use cilia to beat a stream of water into the mouth and filter particles of food from the water, vertebrates use muscles for feeding. Some vertebrates use muscles to draw in a current of water from which both food and oxygen can be extracted. Muscles in the wall of the digestive tube are more powerful than cilia and probably contributed to an increase in both size and activity of early vertebrates. A muscular pharynx with firm skeletal elements for support may have permitted animals to crush small prey after capture. The evolution of more effective sensory systems, a more complex brain, and organs that could support increased activity was important in the shift from filter-feeding to a more active lifestyle.

Vertebrate taxonomy is a work in progress

The study of evolutionary relationships of vertebrates is an important focus of research. The earliest vertebrate fossils include *Haikouichthys,* conodonts, and a group known as *ostracoderms* (discussed in the next section). *Haikouichthys* was a fishlike animal about 2.5 cm (1 in.) long. It had several characters found in vertebrates, and some researchers think it was an early jawless fish.

Conodonts were simple fishlike chordates with gill arches (tissues that support the gills), muscular segments, and fins. They had large eyes and complex tooth-like hooks that were probably used in capturing prey. Conodonts were abundant from the Precambrian to the Late Triassic period; they have been identified in several fossil beds around the world. Cladistic analyses suggest that conodonts were early vertebrates.

By the Late Cambrian, the chordates included a number of different taxa with skeletal elements (a rudimentary braincase,

or cranium) protecting the brain. Some of these animals also showed evidence of vertebrae. These earliest vertebrates lacked jaws and are sometimes referred to as **agnathans** (*a,* "without"; and *gnathos,* "jaw").

The extant vertebrates can be assigned to nine classes: six classes of fishes and three of **tetrapods** (four-limbed vertebrates) (**TABLE 32-2**; see also Fig. 32-7). Most modern biologists classify the tetrapods as *Tetrapoda* (including amphibians and amniotes) and *Amniota* (including the animals traditionally called reptiles, birds, and mammals). The extant Amphibia includes frogs, toads, salamanders, newts, and caecilians; the extant Reptilia includes lizards, snakes, turtles, alligators, and birds.

CHECKPOINT 32.5

- **CONNECT** *What shared derived characters distinguish the vertebrates from the rest of the chordates?*
- *What are the main classes of fishes? the main groups of tetrapods?*

32.6 JAWLESS FISHES

LEARNING OBJECTIVE

7 Distinguish among the major groups of jawless fishes.

Some of the earliest known vertebrates, collectively referred to as *ostracoderms,* consisted of several groups of small, armored, jawless fishes that lived on the bottom and strained their food from the water (see Fig. 21-11). Thick bony plates protected their heads from predators, and thick scales covered their trunks and tails. Most ostracoderms lacked paired fins. Fragments of ostracoderm scales have been found in rocks from the Cambrian period, but most ostracoderm fossils are from the Ordovician and Silurian periods. They became extinct by the end of the Devonian period.

Like ostracoderms, present-day hagfishes and lampreys have neither jaws nor paired fins. They are eel-shaped animals, up to 1 m (about 3 ft) long. Their smooth skin lacks scales, and they are supported by a cartilaginous skeleton and well-developed notochord.

Hagfishes, assigned to class *Myxini* (mik-sin′-y), are marine scavengers (**FIG. 32-8**). They burrow for worms and other invertebrates or prey on dead and disabled fishes. Hagfishes use toothlike projections from their tongue to pull off flesh from prey. For leverage, a hagfish can tie itself into a knot. As a defense mechanism, hagfishes secrete large amounts of fluid that forms sticky slime in sea water. The hagfish becomes so slippery that predators cannot grasp it.

Some systematists have argued that the hagfishes do not quite qualify as vertebrates. Although they have many vertebrate characteristics, including a cranium, hagfishes have no trace of vertebrae. The notochord is their only axial support. Some biologists use the term *Craniata,* based on the presence of a cranium, to designate a clade that includes the vertebrates plus the hagfishes. They view the Myxini as the sister group of all other living craniates. Molecular analyses, however, now support

TABLE 32-2 | **Extant Vertebrate Classes**

CLASS		EXAMPLES	CHARACTERISTICS
MYXINI		Hagfishes	Jawless, marine fishes that lack paired appendages; the notochord is their only axial support; lack vertebrae
PETROMYZONTIDA		Lampreys	Jawless, freshwater and marine fishes with skeleton of cartilage; complete cranium and rudimentary vertebrae; gills; specialized sense organs
CHONDRICHTHYES		Sharks, rays, skates, chimaeras	Jawed marine and freshwater fishes with skeleton of cartilage; vertebrae present; gills; placoid scales; two pairs of fins; oviparous, ovoviparous, or viviparous (a few species); well-developed sense organs
ACTINOPTERYGII (ray-finned fishes)		Perch, salmon, tuna, trout	Bony, marine and freshwater fishes; gills; swim bladder; generally oviparous
ACTINISTIA (fleshy-finned fishes)		Coelacanths	Bony fishes; marine, nocturnal predators on fish; lobed fins
DIPNOI (fleshy-finned fishes)		Lungfishes	Bony freshwater fishes; have both functional gills and lungs
AMPHIBIA		Salamanders, frogs and toads, caecilians	Aquatic larva typically undergoes metamorphosis into terrestrial adult; gas exchange through lungs and/or moist skin; two atria and single ventricle; systemic and pulmonary circulation
REPTILIA		Turtles, lizards, snakes	Amniotes with horny scales; adapted for reproduction on land (internal fertilization, leathery shell, amnion); lungs; ventricles of heart partly divided
		Crocodilians and birds	Amniotes with two complete ventricles; care for their young. Birds have feathers; anterior limbs modified as wings; compact, endothermic; vocal calls and complex songs
MAMMALIA		Monotremes (Protheria), marsupials (Metatheria), Eutheria (mammals with well-developed placentas)	Amniotes with hair; females nourish young with mammary glands; differentiation of teeth; three middle-ear bones; diaphragm; heart with two separate atria and two separate ventricles; endothermic; highly developed nervous system

© Cengage Learning

classifying hagfishes as vertebrates. Hagfishes may have evolved from vertebrates that had vertebrae but lost them during the course of their evolution.

Lampreys are jawless vertebrates assigned to class Petromyzontida (pet-tro-my-zon'-tih-da) (from the Greek *petros,* "stone," and *myzon,* "sucking"; lampreys hold onto stones by their mouths to prevent being washed away by the currents). Some lampreys spend their adult lives in the ocean and return to fresh water to reproduce. Many species of adult lampreys are parasites on other fishes (FIG. 32-9). Adult parasitic lampreys have a circular sucking disc around the mouth, which lies on the ventral side of the anterior end of the body. Using this disc to attach to a fish, the lamprey bores through the skin of its host

with horny teeth (made of keratin) on the disc and tongue. Then the lamprey injects an anticoagulant into its host and sucks out blood and soft tissues.

As in hagfish, the notochord persists throughout life and is not replaced by a vertebral column. However, lampreys have rudiments of vertebrae, cartilaginous segments that extend dorsally around the spinal cord.

CHECKPOINT 32.6

- **CONNECT** *How do lampreys and hagfishes resemble ostracoderms?*

- **CONNECT** *In what ways do hagfishes differ from other fishes?*

Figure 32-8 Pacific hagfish (*Eptatretus stoutii*)
The hagfish has a flexible body, which it can tie into knots. It knots its tail and then slides the knot toward its head. Being knotted gives it leverage when tearing flesh from its prey. Knotting itself also helps the hagfish remove excess slime from its body.

32.7 EVOLUTION OF JAWS AND LIMBS: JAWED FISHES AND TETRAPODS

LEARNING OBJECTIVE

8 Trace the evolution of jawed fishes and early tetrapods, and describe modern amphibians.

Imagine trying to hunt for food and then eat without jaws or limbs. Such was the challenge for early vertebrates, which helps explain why the jawless fishes are mainly scavengers and parasites. The evolution of jaws from a portion of the gill arch skeleton and the development of fins allowed fishes to become active predators. With jaws an animal can grasp and hold on to live prey while eating it. The evolution of fins allowed fishes to swim faster and with more control. Fishes with jaws and fins had many new opportunities for capturing food.

Fossil evidence suggests that jaws and paired fins evolved during the Late Silurian and Devonian periods. Two early groups of jawed fishes, now extinct, were the **acanthodians,** armored fishes with paired spines and pectoral and pelvic fins, and **placoderms,** armored fishes with paired fins (FIG. 32-10). Vertebrates with jaws are referred to as **gnathostomes** (nath'-o-stomes). The success of the jawed vertebrates probably contributed to the extinction of the ostracoderms.

When the fins of certain fishes evolved into limbs about 370 mya, a different type of locomotion was possible. These limbed vertebrates (early tetrapods) were able to move about in shallow waters and wetlands in search of food. Some of these early tetrapods were able to move on land and gained access to new food and habitats.

Most cartilaginous fishes inhabit marine environments

The cartilaginous fishes, members of class **Chondrichthyes** (kon-drik'-thee-eez), appeared as successful marine forms in the Devonian period. Chondrichthyes are a monophyletic group that includes the sharks, rays, skates, and ratfishes (FIG. 32-11). Most species are ocean dwellers, but a few have invaded fresh water. With the exception of whales, the sharks are the largest living vertebrates. Some whale sharks (*Rhincodon*) exceed 15 m (49 ft) in length.

Most rays and skates are flattened creatures that live partly buried in the sand. Their enormous pectoral fins propel them along the bottom, where they feed on mussels and clams. The

(a) Three lampreys attached to a carp by their suction-cup mouths. Note the absence of jaws and paired fins.

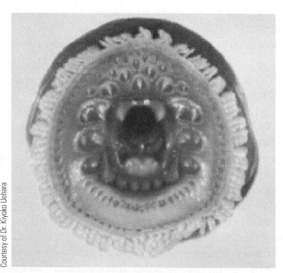

(b) Suction-cup mouth of adult lamprey (*Entosphenus japonicus*). Note the rasplike teeth.

Figure 32-9 Lampreys
Parasitic lampreys attach to fish and suck out body fluids. They leave wounds in the fish that may be fatal.

(a) An acanthodian. *Climatius* was a spiny-skinned acanthodian with large fin spines and five pairs of accessory fins between the pectoral and pelvic pairs. *Climatius* was a small fish that reached a length of 8 cm (3 in.).

(b) A placoderm. *Dunkleosteus* was a giant placoderm that grew to a length of 8 m (26 ft). [Most placoderms were only about 20 cm (8 in.) long.] Its head and thorax were covered by bony armor, but the rest of the body and tail were naked.

Figure 32-10 *Animation* **Early jawed fishes**

Acanthodians and placoderms flourished in the Devonian period.

© Cengage Learning

Jeffrey L. Rotman/Getty Images

(a) Blue-spotted stingray (*Taeniura lymma*). Stingrays typically feed on shellfish and bottom-dwelling fishes.

© Mike Parry/Minden Images

(b) The great white shark (*Carcharodon carcharias*). Photographed in Australia, this shark is considered the most dangerous shark to humans. It is actually white only on its ventral aspect; the rest of the body is brownish gray or bluish gray.

Figure 32-11 Cartilaginous fishes

stingray has a whiplike tail with a barbed spine at its base that can inflict a painful wound. The electric ray has electric organs on either side of the head. These modified muscles can discharge enough electric current (up to 200 volts) to stun fairly large fishes as well as human swimmers.

Chondrichthyes retain their cartilaginous embryonic skeleton. Although this skeleton is not replaced by bone, in many species calcium salts are added to the cartilage for strength. All chondrichthyes have jaws and two pairs of fins. The skin contains **placoid scales,** which are toothlike structures (FIG. 32-12). The lining of the mouth contains larger, but essentially similar, scales that serve as teeth. The teeth of other vertebrates are homologous with these scales. Shark teeth are embedded in the flesh and not attached to the jawbones; new teeth develop continuously in rows behind the functional teeth and migrate forward to replace any that are lost.

The streamlined shark body is adapted for rapid swimming. Lift is provided by body shape and fins. The shark stores a great deal of oil in its large liver (which may account for up to 30% of its body weight). Fats and oils decrease the overall density of fishes and contribute to buoyancy. Even so, the shark body is denser than water, so sharks tend to sink unless they are actively swimming.

Most sharks are predators that swim actively and prey on other fishes as well as on crustaceans and mollusks. The largest sharks and rays, like the largest whales, are filter feeders that strain plankton from the water. They gulp water through the mouth. As the water passes through the pharynx and out the gill slits, food particles are trapped in a sievelike structure.

Predatory sharks are attracted to blood, so a wounded swimmer or a skin diver towing speared fish is a target. However, despite the common portrayal of sharks in books and films as monstrous enemies, most do not go out of their way to attack humans. In fact, of the approximately 350 known shark species, fewer than 30 are known to attack humans.

Sharks have a complex brain and a spinal cord that is protected by vertebrae. Their well-developed sense organs effectively locate prey in the water. Sharks may detect other animals electrically in addition to sensing them by sight or smell. **Electroreceptors** on the shark's head sense weak electric currents generated by the muscle activity of animals. The **lateral line organ,** found in all fishes and many amphibians, is a groove along each side of the body with many tiny openings to the outside. Sensory cells in the lateral line organ detect vibrations caused by waves and other movement in the water, including movements by predators or prey (see Fig. 43-7).

Cartilaginous fishes have no lungs. Gas exchange takes place through their five to seven pairs of gills. A current of water enters the mouth and passes over the gills and out the pharyngeal slits, constantly providing the fish with a fresh supply of dissolved oxygen. Sharks that actively swim depend on their motion to enhance gas exchange. Rays, skates, and sharks that spend time on the ocean floor use muscles of the jaw and pharynx to pump water over their gills.

The digestive tract of sharks consists of the mouth cavity; a long pharynx leading to the stomach; a short, straight intestine; and a **cloaca,** which opens on the underside of the body and is characteristic of many vertebrates (see Fig. 32-12). The liver and pancreas discharge digestive juices into the intestine. The cloaca

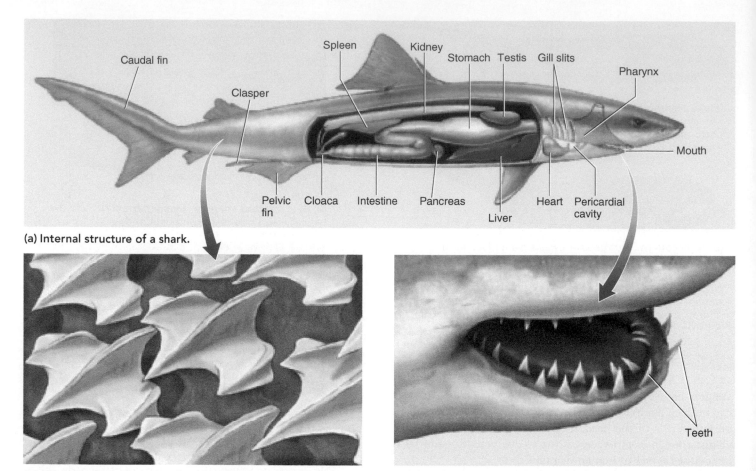

(a) Internal structure of a shark.

(b) Placoid scales. These tough scales protect the shark against predators. The base of each placoid scale is embedded in the skin. Placoid scales are toothlike structures. They are covered with hard enamel.

(c) Teeth. Placoid scales are embedded in the flesh along the inner surface of the jaw cartilage where they function as teeth. Sharks have several rows of teeth. Old teeth are shed and quickly replaced.

Figure 32-12 *Animation* **Anatomy of a shark**
© Cengage Learning

receives digestive wastes as well as metabolic wastes from the urinary system. In females the cloaca also serves as a reproductive organ.

The sexes are separate, and fertilization is internal. In the mature male, each pelvic fin has a slender, grooved section, known as a *clasper,* used to transfer sperm into the female's cloaca. The eggs are fertilized in the upper part of the female's oviducts. Part of the oviduct is modified as a shell gland, which secretes a protective coat around each egg.

Skates and some species of sharks are **oviparous;** that is, they lay eggs. Many species of sharks, however, are **ovoviviparous,** meaning that their young are enclosed in eggs and incubated within the mother's body. During development, the young depend on stored yolk for their nourishment rather than on transfer of materials from the mother. The young are born after hatching from the eggs.

A few species of sharks are **viviparous.** Not only do the embryos develop within the uterus, but much of their nourishment is delivered to them by the mother's blood. Nutrients are transferred between the blood vessels in the lining of the uterus and the yolk sac surrounding each embryo.

The ray-finned fishes gave rise to modern bony fishes

Although bony fishes appear earlier in the fossil record than cartilaginous fishes, both groups may have evolved about the same time, during the Late Silurian or Early Devonian period. The two groups share many characteristics (such as continuous tooth replacement), but they also differ in important ways.

Most bony fishes are characterized by a bony skeleton with many vertebrae. Bone has advantages over cartilage because it provides excellent support and effectively stores calcium. Most species have flexible median and paired fins supported by long rays made of cartilage or bone. Overlapping, bony dermal scales cover the body. A lateral bony flap, the **operculum,** extends posteriorly from the head and protects the gills.

Most bony fishes are oviparous. Most species lay an impressive number of eggs and fertilize them externally. The ocean sunfish, for example, lays more than 300 million eggs! Of course, most of the eggs and young become food for other animals. The probability of survival is increased by certain behavioral adaptations. For example, many species of fishes build nests for their eggs and protect them. Other species have internal fertilization and give birth to live young.

During the Devonian period, the bony fishes diverged into two major groups: the fleshy-finned fishes, *Sarcopterygii*; and the **ray-finned fishes,** class *Actinopterygii*. Fossils of the earliest sarcopterygians date back to the Devonian period, about 400 mya. Lungs and fleshy, *lobed fins* characterized these fishes. The flexible fins were supported by thin, bony rays radiating out from a thick base of multiple bones and muscles. Lobed fins may have evolved as an adaptation for pushing along the bottom of any body of water.

Early sarcopterygians evolved along three separate lines: the *lungfishes* (class *Dipnoi*), the *coelacanths* (class *Actinistia*), and the *Tetrapodomorpha*, a clade consisting of tetrapods and their most recent ancestors. All three lineages had fins with fleshy bases of muscle and bone. Surviving from these groups today are three genera of lungfishes, two species of *coelacanths,* and the many thousands of species of tetrapods (amphibians and amniotes) in habitats worldwide.

Although the earliest ray-finned fishes also had both lungs and gills, they differed from the sarcopterygians in having more flexible fins with less bone and muscle at the base. The ray-finned fishes (actinopterygians) underwent two important adaptive radiations. The first gave rise during the Late Paleozoic era to a group of fishes that are now mostly extinct. The second radiation began during the Early Mesozoic era and gave rise to the very successful modern bony fishes.

In addition to gills, the common ancestor of the bony fishes had primitive lungs that could exchange gases in air. Lungs for gas exchange were retained by the tetrapods and lungfishes. In the modern ray-finned fishes, the lungs became modified as a **swim bladder,** an air sac that helps regulate buoyancy (FIG. 32-13). Bones and muscles are heavier than water, and without the swim bladder the fish would sink. By regulating gas exchange between its blood and swim bladder, a fish can control the amount of gas in the swim bladder and thus change the overall density of its body. This ability allows a bony fish, in contrast to a shark, to hover at a given depth of water without much muscular effort.

There are more species of bony fishes than of any other vertebrate group. Biologists have identified tens of thousands of living species of freshwater and saltwater bony fishes, of many shapes and colors (FIG. 32-14). Bony fishes range in size from that of *Paedocypris progenetica,* which has been measured at less than 8 mm (about 0.3 in) long, to that of the ocean sunfish (or *Mola;* see Fig. 20-16c), which may reach 4 m (13 ft) and weigh about 1500 kg (about 3300 lb). *Paedocypris progenetica,* native to Indonesia, is the smallest known vertebrate.

The diversity of bony fishes may have resulted from the action of *Hox* genes. During the radiation of ray-finned fishes, entire chromosomes duplicated, resulting in one or more additional clusters of *Hox* genes. The zebrafish (see Fig. 17-6d) has seven *Hox* clusters. These additional genes could have provided the genetic material for the evolution of the diverse species of ray-finned fishes.

Tetrapods evolved from sarcopterygian ancestors

Biologists thought that the **coelacanths** were extinct by the end of the Paleozoic era, so in 1938 the scientific community was very excited when a commercial fisherman caught one off the coast of South Africa. Since that time, more than 200 specimens of these giant "living fossils" have been found in the deep waters off the southeastern coast of Africa, the Comores Islands, Madagascar, and Indonesia (FIG. 32-15). These coelacanths, which measure nearly 2 m (about 6 ft) in length, are nocturnal predators on other fishes.

The relationships among the three living groups of sarcopterygians (coelacanths, lungfishes, and tetrapods) have been investigated for many years. Although it was known that the tetrapods evolved from the fleshy-finned fishes, it was not known whether the lungfishes or the coelacanths were the

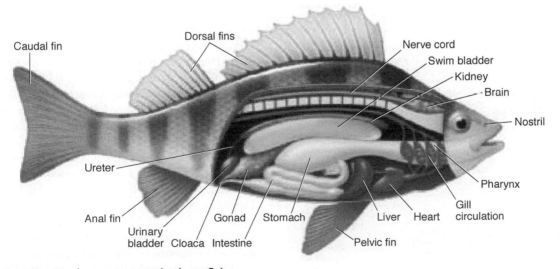

Figure 32-13 *Animation* **Perch, a representative bony fish**
The swim bladder is a hydrostatic organ that enables the fish to change the density of its body and remain stationary at a given depth. Pectoral fins (*not shown*) and pelvic fins are paired.
© Cengage Learning

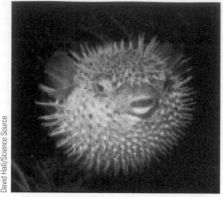

(a) The porcupine fish (*Diodon hystrix*). This fish swallows air or water to inflate its body, a strategy that discourages potential predators. Photographed in the Virgin Islands.

(b) The parrotfish (*Scarus gibbus*). The parrotfish feeds on coral, grinds it in its digestive tract, and extracts the coralline algae. The fish eliminates a fine white sand. These fishes contribute to white sand beaches in many parts of the world. Parrotfish begin life as females and later become males.

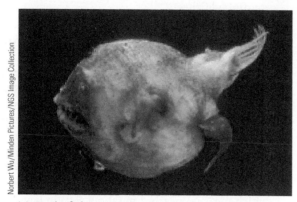

(c) Anglerfishes. In some clades of anglerfishes, the much smaller male attaches himself to a female with his sharp teeth and becomes a lifelong parasitic mate. Most species have at least one long spine projecting from the middle of the head. This "lure" is used as bait to attract prey.

(d) The leafy sea dragon (*Phycodurus eques*). The leafy sea dragon inhabits kelp-covered rocky reefs and seaweed beds in the waters off the southern and western coast of Australia. This fish is a striking example of camouflage.

Figure 32-14 Modern bony fishes

Figure 32-15 Coelacanth

Although they were more diverse and widespread during their early history, the coelacanths, like this *Latimeria chalumnae*, are restricted today to certain deep sea environments.

nearest relatives of this group. Fossil evidence and DNA analyses now support the lungfishes as the sister group to the tetrapods (FIG. 32-16).

Molecular data support the structural evidence that the limbs of tetrapods evolved from the lobed fins of fishes. Proteins encoded by certain regulatory genes, including *Hox* genes, have been found at the same developmental times and in the same locations in both limbs and fins. These findings indicate that limb and fin development are governed by the same genes.

What drove the evolution of tetrapod limbs? One hypothesis suggests that during the frequent seasonal droughts of the Devonian period, swamps became stagnant or dried up completely. Fishes with lobed fins had a tremendous advantage for survival under those conditions. They were strikingly preadapted for moving onto the land. They had lungs for breathing air, and their sturdy, fleshy fins allowed them to "walk" along in shallow water. These fins could support the fish's weight, so it could emerge onto dry land and make its way to another pond or stream.

Figure 32-16 South American lungfish (*Lepidosiren paradoxus*)
Lungfishes were common in Devonian and Carboniferous times (400 mya to 300 mya). South American lungfish have paired lungs on either side of the throat and can survive for long periods if the river they inhabit dries up.

A more recent hypothesis holds that limbs evolved in a fully aquatic environment. Animals with more-developed limbs could move along in shallow water or creep through dense aquatic vegetation more efficiently than their lobe-finned ancestors. *Tiktaalik* was a transitional form between fishes and tetrapods (FIG. 32-17). Biologists consider *Tiktaalik*, which lived about 375 mya (during the Devonian period), a fish because it had scales and fins. However, *Tiktaalik* also had tetrapod features such as a movable neck and ribs that supported lungs.

Acanthostega was one of the earliest known tetrapods. Fossils from the Devonian period show that this animal had four legs with well-formed digits. However, because its limbs were not properly positioned for walking effectively on land and because it possessed gills and a tail fin, *Acanthostega* was a fully aquatic tetrapod. The ichthyostegids, tetrapods known from somewhat later in the Devonian, had more robust limbs and girdles, suggesting that they could move more easily on land.

Figure 32-17 *Tiktaalik*
This extinct fish, which grew to 2.75 m (9 ft), had limblike fins and other tetrapod features.

However, the evidence suggests that these early tetrapods were also very aquatic.

Those early tetrapods that could explore shallow wetlands and make their way onto dry land had access to new food sources. Terrestrial plants were already established, and terrestrial insects and arachnids were rapidly evolving. A vertebrate that could survive on land had less competition for food than one that was solely aquatic. However, success on land required the evolution of several major adaptations in addition to legs.

As already discussed, the early sarcopterygians had lungs for gas exchange in addition to gills. Lungs were important because gills cannot function in air. Life on land also required changes in the muscles and skeleton to support the body's weight in air. Body coverings and other mechanisms were needed to protect animals against the drying effect of air.

Evolution of ears that could hear sound transmitted through air and olfactory mechanisms for detecting airborne odors contributed to the ability to find food and mates, and to avoid predators. It is likely that early tetrapods needed to return to the water for reproduction, but eventually adaptations evolved that allowed some animals to reproduce in terrestrial environments. The early tetrapods were very successful and eventually gave rise to the amphibians and the amniotes (including reptiles, birds, and mammals).

Amphibians were the first successful land vertebrates

Biologists classify modern **amphibians** (class *Amphibia*) in three orders. Order Caudata ("with tail") includes salamanders, mud puppies, and newts, all animals with long tails; order *Anura* ("no tail") is made up of frogs and toads, most with legs adapted for hopping; and order *Gymnophiona* contains the limbless caecilians (FIG. 32-18). Although some adult amphibians are quite successful as land animals and live in dry environments, most must return to the water to reproduce. Eggs and sperm are typically released in the water.

Many amphibians undergo **metamorphosis,** a transition from larva to adult. The embryos of most frogs and toads develop into larvae called *tadpoles.* These larvae have tails and gills, and most feed on aquatic plants. After a time, the tadpole undergoes metamorphosis, which is regulated by hormones secreted by the *thyroid gland.* During metamorphosis, gills and gill slits disappear, the tail is resorbed, and limbs emerge. The digestive tract shortens, and food preference shifts from plant material to a carnivorous diet; the mouth widens; a tongue develops; the tympanic membrane (eardrum) and eyelids appear; and the eye lens changes shape. Many biochemical changes accompany the transformation from a completely aquatic life to a semiterrestrial one.

Several salamanders, such as the mudpuppy *Necturus,* do not undergo complete metamorphosis; they retain many larval characteristics even when sexually mature adults. Recall from Chapter 20 that this retention of juvenile features is called **paedomorphosis** (see Fig. 20-17). This type of development

(a) Red dart frog (*Dendrobates histrionicus*). Poison dart frogs, native to Central America and South America, are active during the day. Most are brightly colored. Many secrete toxins through their skin as a chemical defense against predators.

(b) Fire salamander (*Salamandra salamandra*). Fire salamanders are well known in Europe. Their poison glands release neurotoxins.

Figure 32-18 Modern amphibians

permits these salamanders to remain aquatic rather than having to compete on land.

The coloration of amphibians may conceal them in their habitat or may be very bright and striking. Many of the brightly colored species are poisonous (see Fig. 32-18). Their distinctive colors warn predators that they are not encountering an ordinary amphibian. Some frogs camouflage themselves by changing color.

Adult amphibians do not depend solely on their primitive lungs for the exchange of respiratory gases. Their moist, glandular skin, which lacks scales and is plentifully supplied with blood vessels, also serves as a respiratory surface. The numerous mucous glands within the skin help keep the body surface moist, which is important in gas exchange. The mucus also makes the animal slippery, facilitating its escape from predators. Most amphibians have glands in their skin that secrete toxic and/or foul-tasting substances that repel predators.

The amphibian heart contains two **atria** (sing. *atrium*), receiving blood, and a single **ventricle,** pumping blood into the arteries. A double circuit of blood vessels keeps oxygen-rich and oxygen-poor blood partially separate. Blood passes through the **systemic circulation** to the various tissues and organs of the

body. Then, after returning to the heart, it is directed through the **pulmonary circulation** to the lungs and skin, where it is recharged with oxygen. The oxygen-rich blood returns to the heart to be pumped out into the systemic circulation again. We discuss the comparative anatomy of the heart and circulation of various vertebrate classes in Chapter 44.

CHECKPOINT 32.7

- **CONNECT** *From an evolutionary perspective, what is the significance of each of the following: (1) placoderms, (2) lungfishes, (3) ray-finned fishes, and (4) Tiktaalik?*
- *What changes allow amphibians to move from aquatic life as a tadpole to terrestrial life as an adult?*

32.8 AMNIOTES: TERRESTRIAL VERTEBRATES

LEARNING OBJECTIVES

9 Describe three vertebrate adaptations to terrestrial life.
10 Describe the reptiles (including the birds) and argue for including the birds in the reptile clade.
11 Describe five key characters of mammals and contrast protherian (monotremes), metatherian (marsupials), and eutherian mammals, giving examples of animals that belong to each group.

The evolution of **reptiles** from ancestral amphibians required many adaptations that allowed them to become completely terrestrial. Evolution of the **amniotic egg** was an extremely important event because it allowed terrestrial vertebrates to complete their life cycles on land. The amniotic egg contains an **amnion,** a membrane that forms a fluid-filled sac around the embryo. The amnion provides the embryo with its own private "pond," permitting independence from a watery external environment. In addition to keeping the embryo moist, the amniotic fluid serves as a shock absorber that cushions the developing embryo.

The evolution of the amniotic egg is so important to the success of terrestrial vertebrates—reptiles (including birds) and mammals—that biologists refer to these animals as **amniotes**. Amniotes are a monophyletic group because they have a recent common ancestor that was itself an amniote.

In addition to the amnion, the amniotic egg has three other extraembryonic (not part of the developing body itself) membranes: *yolk sac, chorion,* and *allantois* (**FIG. 32-19**). These membranes protect the developing embryo, store nutrients (*yolk sac*), carry on gas exchange (chorion, allantois, and yolk sac), and store wastes (allantois). We discuss development of the extraembryonic membranes in Chapter 51. Although most extant mammals do not lay eggs, their embryos have an amnion and other extraembryonic membranes.

Another important adaptation to terrestrial life is a body covering that minimizes water loss. The amniote body covering is typically thick and contains **keratin,** a water-insoluble

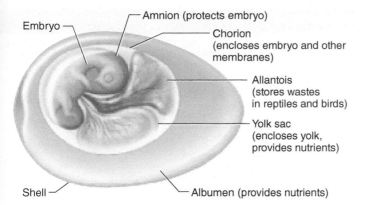

Figure 32-19 *Animation* **An amniotic egg**

The amnion, a fluid-filled sac surrounding the embryo, keeps the embryo moist and protects it from mechanical shock. Other extraembryonic membranes include the yolk sac, which functions in nutrition; the allantois, which stores metabolic wastes; and the chorion, which along with the allantois, functions in gas exchange.

© Cengage Learning

protein that helps protect the animal from injury. Keratin is found in the epidermis and in derivatives of the epidermis, such as scales, nails, feathers, hair, and horns. A body covering containing keratin presents another challenge: it severely decreases gas exchange across the body surface. This challenge has been met by the evolution of efficient lungs and circulatory systems for exchange of oxygen and carbon dioxide. Amniotes also have physiological mechanisms for conserving water. For example, much of the water filtered from the blood by the kidneys is reabsorbed in the kidney tubules to decrease fluid loss during excretion of metabolic wastes.

Our understanding of amniote phylogeny is changing

Biology instructors once taught that the three classes of amniotes were Reptilia, Aves (birds), and Mammalia. However, cladistic analysis determined that class Reptilia was not a monophyletic group without the birds. Because it included some, but not all, of its descendants, it was paraphyletic (see Fig. 23-7). For this reason, most biologists now classify the birds as a group of reptiles.

Biologists hypothesize that the earliest amniotes resembled lizards. By the Late Carboniferous period, about 290 mya, amniotes had undergone an impressive adaptive radiation and had diverged into two main branches: **diapsids** and **synapsids** (FIG. 32-20 and TABLE 32-3). The term *diapsid* refers to the two pairs of openings in the temporal bones that characterize the skulls of these animals. Synapsid skulls have one pair of temporal openings. The diapsids comprise all extant reptilian groups, including the birds and most extinct reptiles. The synapsids include the extinct **therapsids** and the mammals.

A second great adaptive radiation of amniotes occurred during the Mesozoic era, which ended about 66 mya. During

that time reptiles were the dominant terrestrial vertebrates (see Chapter 21). In fact, the Mesozoic era is known as the "Age of Reptiles." These animals had radiated into an impressive variety of ecological lifestyles (see Figs. 21-13, 21-14, and 21-15). Some could fly, others became marine, and many filled terrestrial habitats. Among the major groups were the *pterosaurs* (ter′-uh-sawr), the flying reptiles; the *saurischian dinosaurs* (saw-ris′-kee-un), a group that included *Tyrannosaurus* and *Diplodocus*; and the *ornithischian dinosaurs* (awr-nuh-this′-kee-un), including *Triceratops*.

Some of the dinosaurs were among the largest land animals to ever walk on Earth. Some dinosaurs apparently traveled in social groups and took care of their young. Fossil evidence supports the hypothesis that at least some dinosaurs may have been **endotherms,** meaning that they used metabolic energy to maintain a constant body temperature despite changes in the temperature of the environment. An advantage of endothermy is that it allows animals to be more active. The natural history and evolution of dinosaurs and other early reptiles are discussed in more detail in Chapter 21.

The reptiles were the dominant land vertebrates for almost 200 million years. Then, toward the end of the Mesozoic era, many reptiles, including all the dinosaurs and pterosaurs, disappeared from the fossil record. In fact, more than half of all animal species became extinct at that time (see Chapter 21).

Reptiles have many terrestrial adaptations

Many reptilian characters are adaptations to terrestrial life. The female reptile secretes a protective leathery shell around the egg, which helps prevent the developing embryo from drying out. The shell presents a challenge for reproduction because sperm cannot penetrate it. Fertilization must take place within the body of the female before the shell is added. In this process, the male uses a copulatory organ (penis) to transfer sperm into the female reproductive tract. An amnion surrounds the embryo as it develops within the protective shell.

The hard, dry, keratin scales that are part of the reptile's skin retard drying in yet another adaptation to life on land, This scaly protective armor, which also protects the reptile from predators, is shed periodically. The dry reptilian skin does not allow effective gas exchange. Reptilian lungs are better developed than the saclike lungs of amphibians. Divided into many chambers, the reptilian lung provides an increased surface area for gas exchange.

The hearts of amniotes contain two atria. The ventricle of reptiles is either partially or completely divided. The division into right and left ventricles enhances the separation of oxygen-rich and oxygen-poor blood. The more efficient circulatory and respiratory systems of reptiles are critical for animals with a keratinized epidermis.

Like fishes and amphibians, many extant reptiles lack metabolic mechanisms for regulating body temperature. They are **ectotherms,** meaning that their body temperature fluctuates with the temperature of the surrounding environment. Some reptiles have behavioral adaptations that help them maintain a body temperature higher than that of their environment. For

The diapsid reptiles gave rise to the birds, and the synapsids gave rise to the mammals. Note the five main branches of extant diapsids.

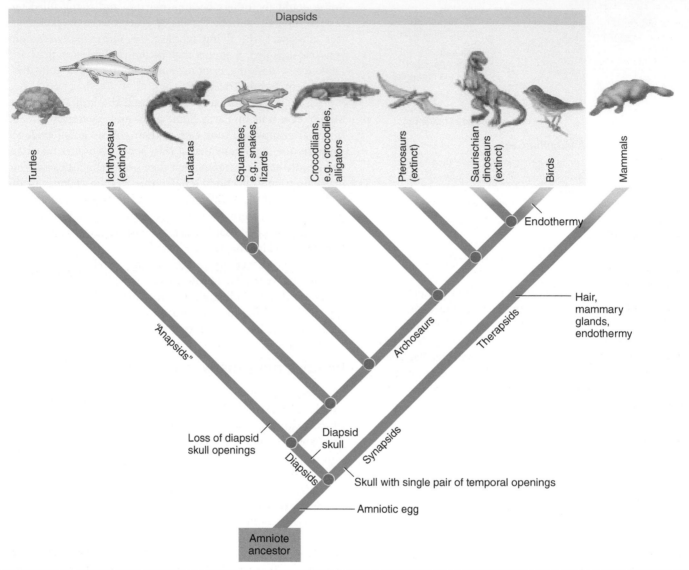

Figure 32-20 Evolutionary relationships of some amniotes

This cladogram shows proposed evolutionary relationships among reptiles, birds, and mammals. Systematists continue to study these relationships and may reinterpret some of them. Identify five main branches of extant diapsids on the cladogram. (*Hint:* Recall that turtles are diapsids even though they have "lost" their temporal openings during their evolution.)

CONNECT Are birds more closely related to extinct branches of reptiles or to mammals?

© Cengage Learning

example, you may have observed a lizard basking in the sun, which raises its body temperature and so increases its metabolic rate. This increased rate permits the lizard to hunt actively for food. When the body of a reptile is cold, its metabolic rate is low and the animal tends to be sluggish. Ectothermy helps explain why lizards, snakes, and turtles are more successful in warm than in cold climates.

Many reptiles are predators. Their paired limbs, usually with five toes, are well adapted for running and climbing in search of

prey. In addition, their well-developed sense organs enable them to locate prey.

Biologists assign reptiles to several major clades

Order Testudines includes the turtles, terrapins, and tortoises (see Table 32-3). The **lepidosaurs** make up a superorder of diapsid vertebrates. This clade includes order Squamata—snakes,

TABLE 32-3	Some Major Groups of Amniotes	
CLADES		**IMPORTANT CHARACTERS**
SUBCLASS DIAPSIDA		**Skull with two pairs of temporal openings**
Order Testudines (Chelonia) Turtles, terrapins, tortoises		Enclosed in bony shell; beak of keratin instead of teeth; some can withdraw head and legs into shell; temporal openings lost ("anapsids")
SUPERORDER LEPIDOSAURIA		Overlapping scales; a very successful group of modern reptiles
Order Squamata Snakes, lizards, amphisbaenians (worm lizards)		Flexible armor of overlapping, horny scales, which are shed Snakes: elongated body with no limbs; flexible, loosely jointed jaw; forked tongue protrusible Lizards: slender body, typically with four legs; some with no legs
Order Sphenodonta Tuataras		Vertebrae concave at both ends; only two extant species
SUPERORDER ICHTHYOSAURIA (extinct) Marine reptiles of Mesozoic		Body shaped like that of modern dolphins; large eyes; vertical tails
SUPERORDER ARCHOSAURIA		Mainly terrestrial; some specialized for flight; ventricle completely divided in living forms
Order Crocodilia Crocodiles, alligators, caimans, gavials		Heart with two atria and two ventricles; closest extant relative to birds
Pterosauria (extinct) Flying reptiles of Mesozoic		Membranous wings
Saurischia (extinct) Mesozoic dinosaurs (*Tyrannosaurus, Diplodocus*) **Birds descended from this lineage**		Some were two-legged carnivores; others were four-legged herbivores; some had feathers
Ornithischia (extinct) Mesozoic dinosaurs (*Triceratops*)		Bipedal and quadrupedal herbivores; social behavior and parental care in many
SUBCLASS SYNAPSIDA		**Skull with one pair of temporal openings**
Therapsida (extinct) **Mammals descended from this lineage**		Many mammal-like characters; became dominant land animals during Middle Permian

© Cengage Learning

lizards, and amphisbaenians (worm lizards)—and order Sphenodonta, which includes the tuataras, lizardlike animals that live in burrows. **Archosaurs** make up another superorder of diapsid vertebrates. Archosaurs include the extinct **pterosaurs**—the flying reptiles and dinosaurs—and the extant crocodiles, alligators, caimans, and gavials (order Crocodilia) and birds (order Aves). (FIG. 32-21).

Turtles have protective shells

Members of order Testudines (te-stood′-n-eez) are enclosed in a protective shell made of bony plates overlaid by keratin scales. Some terrestrial species can withdraw their heads and legs completely into their shells. Their keratin beak covers the jaws. Turtles do not have teeth. Turtles are diapsid reptiles. However, they are referred to as "anapsids" because during the course of evolution, they have "lost" the temporal openings.

The size of adult turtles ranges in length from about 8 cm (3 in.) to more than 2 m (6.5 ft) in leatherback turtles, which are the largest marine species. The weight of a leatherback turtle can exceed 500 kg (more than 1000 lb). The forelimbs of marine turtles are modified into flippers. Sea turtles migrate hundreds of miles from the beaches where they hatch to feeding grounds. Females return to the same beaches where they hatched to mate and nest. Most species of sea turtles are endangered as a result of human activities.

Lizards and snakes are common modern reptiles

Lizards and snakes are assigned to order Squamata (squa-ma′-tah). These animals have rows of scales that overlap like shingles on a roof, forming a continuous, flexible armor that is shed periodically. Lizards range in size from certain geckos, which weigh as little as 1 g (less than 0.1 oz), to the Komodo dragon of Indonesia, which may weigh 100 kg (220 lb). Their body sizes and shapes vary greatly. Some lizards—for example, the "worm lizards" and the glass lizards—are legless.

Carlyn Iverson

(a) **Green turtle (*Chelonia mydas*).** The paddlelike appendages are adapted for swimming.

Pete Oxford/Minden Pictures

(b) **The emerald tree boa (*Corallus canina*).** This boa inhabits tropical South American forests. It rarely leaves the trees to go to the ground. Emerald boas use their heat-sensitive pit organs to locate prey.

Betty and Nathan Cohen/Visuals Unlimited

(c) **Tuatara (*Sphenodon punctatus*).** These nocturnal predators reach a length of 60 cm (more than 2 ft) or longer. There are two species of tuataras. Both are classified as endangered.

Figure 32-21 Representative extant reptiles

© Trevor Kelly/Shutterstock.com

(d) **Nile crocodiles (*Crocodilus niloticus*) hatching from their eggs.** Both parents guard the leathery eggs. When the hatchlings emerge, the mother leads them to the water. She may carry them in her mouth.

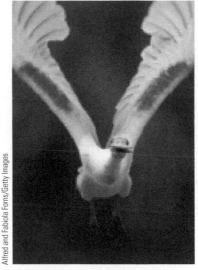

Alfred and Fabiola Forns/Getty Images

(e) **Roseate spoonbill (*Ajaia ajaja*) in its full breeding colors.** The roseate spoonbill is a long-legged wading bird nearly three feet tall with a wingspan of more than four feet. This bird is taking off for flight in the Alafia river banks in central Florida. The future of spoonbills in Florida depends on protection of their habitats—coastal marshes, estuaries, and mangrove areas.

Snakes are characterized by a flexible, loosely jointed jaw structure that lets them swallow animals larger than the diameter of their own jaws. These reptiles have elongated bodies with no legs, although pythons have vestigial hind-limb bones (see Fig. 18-17). Remember that although not all the tetrapods have four limbs, all evolved from four-limbed ancestors. Snake eyes are covered by a transparent scale. They do not have movable eyelids. Also absent are an external ear opening, a tympanic membrane (eardrum), and a middle-ear cavity.

Snakes use their forked tongues as accessory sensory organs for touch and smell. Chemicals from the ground or air adhere to the tongue. Snakes rub the tips of their tongues across the opening of a sense organ in the roof of the mouth that detects odors. Pit vipers and some boas also have *pit organs* that detect heat from endothermic prey (see Fig. 43-3). These snakes use their pit organs to locate and capture birds and small nocturnal mammals.

Some snakes, such as king snakes, pythons, and boa constrictors, kill their prey by rapidly wrapping themselves around the animal and squeezing so it cannot breathe. Others have fangs, which are hollow teeth connected to venom glands. When the snake bites, it pumps venom through the fangs into the prey. Some snake venoms cause the breakdown of red blood cells; others, such as that of the coral snake, are neurotoxins, which interfere with nerve function. Venomous snakes of the United States include rattlesnakes, copperheads, cottonmouths, and coral snakes. Except for the coral snakes, all are pit vipers.

Amphisbaenians (am-fus-bee'-nee-uns), or worm lizards, are considered an additional group of modified lizards. They are well adapted for their burrowing lifestyle. They have elongated bodies with either no legs or a single pair of legs. In many species the eyes are hidden under the skin. Most are less than 15 cm (6 in.) long. Most species of amphisbaenians inhabit South America and southern Africa. Only one species (known as the Florida worm lizard) is found in the United States.

Tuataras superficially resemble lizards

Tuataras look somewhat like iguanas but have certain distinct characters. For example, they are the only amniotes with vertebrae that are concave at both ends; such vertebrae are characteristic of fish and some amphibians. The two extant species of tuataras inhabit New Zealand and several small islands off its coast. Tuataras have long been considered endangered species. When humans brought rats, cats, and dogs to New Zealand, these non-native animals decimated the population of tuataras by eating their eggs. Tuataras became extinct on the New Zealand mainland. In 2005, these animals were reintroduced into a sanctuary in New Zealand, and they are now protected.

Crocodilians have an elongated skull

The extant members of order Crocodilia (crok-uh-dil'-ee-uh), along with the birds, are the surviving reptiles of the archosaur lineage. This lineage gave rise to the **pterosaurs** (flying reptiles) and the dinosaurs that dominated the Mesozoic era. Modern crocodilians include three groups: (1) the crocodiles of Africa, Asia, and the Americas; (2) the alligators of the southern United States and China, plus the caimans of Central America; and (3) the gavials of South Asia. Most species live in swamps, in rivers, or along seacoasts, feeding on various kinds of animals.

Crocodiles are the largest living reptiles; some exceed 7 m (23 ft) in length. The cranial skeleton is adapted for aquatic life. In the Americas, crocodiles can be distinguished from alligators or caimans by their more tapered snouts and by the large fourth tooth on the lower jaw that is visible when the mouth is closed.

How do we know that birds are really dinosaurs?

Cladistic analyses indicate that birds evolved from the lineage of saurischian dinosaurs, specifically from the **theropods** (theer'-uh-pods), a group of bipedal, saurischian dinosaurs that included *Tyrannosaurus* and *Deinonychus* (see Fig. 21-15). This view is supported by the remarkable array of Cretaceous and late Jurassic fossils discovered in the Yixian Formation and in other parts of China as well as in Europe.

Some dinosaurs had feathers Paleontologists have identified many theropod dinosaur fossils that demonstrate the evolution of feathers from very simple, tubular structures to complex modern forms. *Caudipteryx*, a feathered dinosaur discovered in the Yixian Formation, was about the size of a turkey. Fossils of *Caudipteryx* exhibit both dinosaur and bird characteristics. The bones in the foot and the shape and orientation of the pelvis were similar to those of dinosaurs. However, the fossils have well-preserved impressions of complex feathers on the tail and forelimbs. *Caudipteryx* had only a few teeth in the front of its upper jaw, and its bones show many birdlike characteristics. Although some investigators have argued that *Caudipteryx* was a flightless bird, the most recent consensus view is that this animal was a feathered dinosaur. Analyzing fossil evidence and molecular data, many paleontologists have hypothesized that feather evolution took place in terrestrial, bipedal dinosaurs *before* the evolution of birds or flight.

Modern birds use asymmetrical feathers for flight. In 2003, paleontologists reported finding a new species of feathered dinosaur, *Microraptor gui*. *Microraptor* had asymmetrical feathers on both its forelimbs and hind limbs, and also on its tail. (See the figure in *Inquiring About: The Origin of Flight in Birds*, in Chapter 21.) However, their small size and body structure support the hypothesis that flying evolved from gliding; that is, *Microraptor* climbed trees and used its feathered limbs for gliding. These small dinosaurs, which lived about 126 mya, coexisted with early birds.

Biologists have debated why feathers may have evolved in dinosaurs. Were feathers important in courtship rituals or in camouflage? Were feathers an adaptation that conserved body heat? Insulating feathers could have contributed to the evolution of endothermy (the ability to maintain a constant body temperature), permitting animals to be more active.

In 2010, paleontologists described a nearly complete skeleton of a basal theropod discovered in northwestern China. This new fossil, named *Haplocheirus sollers,* had organelles containing pigment that colored its feathers, suggesting that feathers may have first evolved for color displays in courtship rituals. The presence of feathers and the bone structure of *Haplocheirus* indicate that striking evolutionary convergence occurred between feathered dinosaurs and birds. In 2013 the fossil of a new bird-like theropod from the Jurassic period was discovered. This theropod was named *Eosinopteryx*.

Early birds were transitional forms Many extinct theropods were long-tailed animals that moved about on two feet and had forelimbs with three clawed fingers. Although the bones of birds are fragile and disintegrate quickly, paleobiologists have found a few fossils of early birds. The first birds looked very much like dinosaurs. They had teeth (which modern birds lack), a long tail, and bones with thick walls. Like certain extinct theropods, modern birds have feet with three digits and thin-walled, hollow bones. Both have a *furcula,* or wishbone, which is formed by the two clavicles (collarbones) fusing in the midline. Many biologists classify modern birds as theropods.

Archaeopteryx (meaning "ancient wing") was an early bird that was about the size of a pigeon. More than ten specimens of this genus have been found in Bavaria in Jurassic limestone, which was laid down about 150 mya. Unlike those of extant birds, the jawbones of *Archaeopteryx* were armed with teeth, and its long, reptilian tail was covered with feathers (**FIG. 32-22a**). Each of its short, broad wings had three claw-bearing, functional digits. Like modern birds, *Archaeopteryx* had wings, feathers, and a furcula. Its feathers were very similar to those of modern birds.

Using computer tomography and computerized 3-D reconstruction, researchers examined the inside of the *Archaeopteryx* skull. They found that *Archaeopteryx* had a birdlike brain with comparatively larger cerebral lobes than those of other reptiles. It had enlarged visual centers and highly developed inner ear canals similar to those of modern birds. These structures would support the coordination and agility needed for flight.

A complete fossil of an early bird from China was described in 2013. This fossil, named *Aurornis xui,* predates *Archaeopteryx* by about 10 million years. Like *Archaeopteryx, Aurornis xui* has a furcula, feathers, and teeth (**FIG. 32-22b**). The *Aurornis* fossil preserved traces of downy feathers. However, it shows no evidence of larger feathers, suggesting that this early bird was not able to fly.

Cretaceous rocks have yielded fossils of other early birds. *Hesperornis,* which lived in North America, was a toothed, aquatic diving bird with small wings and broad, lobed feet for swimming. *Ichthyornis* was a toothed, flying bird about the size of a small tern. Based on fossils, structural similarities, and molecular data, most biologists now view birds as living dinosaurs.

Modern birds are adapted for flight

By the end of the Cretaceous period, the major clades of present-day birds—palaeognaths and neognaths—had evolved. (Some biologists assign birds to class Aves and consider palaeognathae and neognathae as superorders.) *Palaeognaths* (from Greek *palaios,* "ancient," and *gnathos,* "jaw") include flightless birds such as the ostriches, kiwis, cassowaries, and emus. These birds are called **ratites.** Their sternum (breastbone) is flat and does not have a ridge for attachment of wing muscles. They have

(a) Reconstruction of *Archaeopteryx*, an early bird. This reconstruction represents the view that *Archaeopteryx* was a climbing animal that had at least some ability to use its wings and feathers for gliding.

(b) Fossil of *Aurornis xui*, a very early bird. *Aurornis xui,* about the size of a pheasant, lived during the Middle–Late Jurassic period about 160 million years ago.

Figure 32-22 Fossil evidence supports the evolution of birds from the dinosaur lineage

only vestigial wings, but they have well-developed legs used for running.

Most modern birds are *neognaths* (from Greek *neos,* "new," and *gnathos,* "jaw"). These birds have powerful flight muscles attached to their keeled (ridged) sternum, and most neognaths fly. The penguins are an exception. They use their strong pectoral muscles and small, flipperlike wings to swim.

Biologists have described more than 9000 species of extant birds and classified them into about 23 monophyletic taxa. Birds are a diverse group (**FIG. 32-23**). They have become adapted to a variety of environments, and various species have different types of beaks, feet, wings, tails, and behavioral patterns. They can be

(a) Southern cassowary (*Casuarius casuarius*), a ratite. The flightless southern cassowary, native to Australia, is the third largest bird in the world, after the ostrich and emu. This is the only bird known to have protective armor, including a hard crest that serves as a helmet atop its head.

(b) Peacock (*Pavo cristatus*). The Indian peacock displays his colorful, fully fanned tail feathers to get a female's attention. Peafowl (peacocks and peahens) belong to the pheasant family.

(c) Atlantic puffin (*Fratercula arctica*). This puffin has caught several fish. The puffin's beak becomes brightly colored during the breeding season.

Figure 32-23 Modern birds
Although they are diverse, most birds are highly adapted for flight, and their basic structure is similar.

found on all continents, most islands, and even the open sea. The largest living birds are the ostriches of Africa, which may be up to 2 m (6.5 ft) tall and weigh 136 kg (300 lb). The great condors of the Americas have wingspans of up to 3 m (10 ft). The smallest known bird is the bee hummingbird of Cuba, with a length of less than 6 cm (about 2 in.) and a weight of less than 2 g (about 0.06 oz).

Like their reptilian ancestors, modern birds lay eggs and have reptilian-type scales on their legs. Birds have evolved remarkable specializations for flight. They are the only extant animals with feathers. Their feathers are an amazing example of biological engineering. They are very light, yet flexible and strong, and present a flat surface to the air. Feathers also protect the body and decrease water and heat loss. The anterior limbs of birds are wings, usually adapted for flight. The posterior limbs are modified for walking, swimming, or perching.

Other adaptations for flight include the compact, streamlined body and the fusion of many bones, which provides the rigidity needed for flying. The bones are strong but very light. Many are hollow, containing large air spaces. The avian jaw is light, and instead of teeth, birds have a lightweight beak of bone and keratin. The breastbone is broad and keeled for the attachment of the large flight muscles.

Birds have lungs with *air sacs,* thin-walled extensions that occupy spaces between the internal organs and within certain bones. The unique "one-way" flow of air through their respiratory system is metabolically efficient because their lungs can extract great amounts of oxygen from the air. (This respiratory system is described in more detail in Chapter 46.) Birds have a four-chambered heart and a double circuit of blood flow. One circuit delivers oxygen-rich blood to the body tissues and returns low-oxygen blood to the heart; the other circuit takes blood to and from the lungs where it is oxygenated. The very effective respiratory and circulatory systems provide the cells with enough oxygen to permit a high metabolic rate, which is necessary for the strenuous muscular activity that flying requires. Some of the heat a bird generates by metabolic activities helps it maintain a constant body temperature. Because they are endotherms, birds can remain active in cold climates.

Birds excrete nitrogenous wastes mainly as semisolid uric acid. Because birds typically do not have a urinary bladder, these solid wastes are delivered into the cloaca. They leave the body with the feces, which are dropped frequently. This adaptive mechanism helps maintain a light body weight.

Bills are specifically adapted for the type of food the bird eats (see Fig. 1-13). Birds must eat frequently because they have a high metabolic rate and typically do not store much fat. Although the choice of food varies widely among species, most birds eat energy-rich foods such as seeds, fruits, worms, mollusks, or arthropods. Warblers and some other species eat mainly insects. Owls and hawks eat small mammals and other birds. Some hawks catch snakes and lizards. Vultures feed on dead animals. Pelicans, gulls, terns, and kingfishers catch fish.

An interesting feature of the bird digestive system is the *crop,* an expanded, saclike portion of the digestive tract below the esophagus in which food is temporarily stored. The stomach is divided into a *proventriculus*, which secretes gastric juices; and a thick, muscular *gizzard*, which grinds food. The bird swallows small bits of gravel that act as "teeth" in the gizzard to mechanically break down food.

Birds have a well-developed nervous system, with a brain that is proportionately larger than that of other reptiles. Birds rely heavily on vision, and their eyes are relatively larger than those of other vertebrates. Hearing is also well developed.

In striking contrast with the relatively silent non-avian reptiles, birds are very vocal. Most have short, simple *calls* that signal danger or influence feeding, flocking, or interaction between parent and young. *Songs* are usually more complex than calls and are performed mainly by males. Birds sing songs to attract and keep a mate and to claim and defend a territory.

One of the most fascinating aspects of bird behavior is the annual migration made by many species. Some birds, such as the golden plover and Arctic tern, fly from Alaska to Patagonia, South America, and back each year, covering perhaps 40,250 km (25,000 mi) en route. Migration and navigation are discussed in Chapter 52.

Many birds have beautiful, striking colors. The colors are due partly to pigments deposited during the development of the feathers and partly to reflection and refraction of light of certain wavelengths. Many birds, especially females, are protectively colored by their plumage. During the breeding season, the male often assumes brighter colors, which help attract a mate.

Mammals have hair and mammary glands

Hair is a key derived character of **mammals** (class Mammalia). All mammals have at least a few hairs at some time in their life, and no other organism has true hair. Hair insulates the body, helping maintain the high constant body temperature required for endothermy. The benefit of endothermy is a high metabolic rate, which allows a high level of activity even in low winter temperatures.

Other derived characters of mammals are **mammary glands,** which produce milk for the young; one pair of temporal openings in the skull; *differentiation of teeth* into incisors, canines, premolars, and molars; and three *middle-ear bones* (malleus, incus, and stapes) that transmit vibrations from the tympanic membrane (eardrum) to the inner ear. The other tetrapods have only a single bone, the stapes, in the middle ear. The evolution of the **cochlea,** the organ of hearing in the inner ear, gives mammals an excellent sense of hearing.

Contributing significantly to the success of the mammals, the nervous system is more highly developed than in any other group of animals. The cerebrum is especially large and complex, with an outer gray region, the **cerebral cortex.** In mammals the highly specialized cerebral cortex, called the *neocortex,* has six layers of neurons. Specific regions in the neocortex are specialized for functions such as vision, hearing, touch, movement, emotional response, and higher cognitive functions.

Fertilization in mammals is internal, and with the exception of the monotremes that lay eggs, mammals are viviparous.

Most mammals develop a **placenta,** an organ of exchange between developing embryo and mother. As the mother's blood passes through blood vessels in the placenta, it delivers nourishment and oxygen to the embryo and carries off wastes. By carrying their developing young internally, mammals avoid the hazards of having their eggs consumed by predators. By nourishing the young and caring for them, the parents offer both protection and an "education" on how to obtain food and avoid being eaten.

A muscular **diaphragm** helps move air into and out of the lungs. Like birds, mammals are endotherms, but mammals appear to have evolved endothermy independently of birds. Some of the adaptations that allow mammals to maintain a constant body temperature include the covering of insulating hair, very efficient lungs with alveoli (air sacs through which gas exchange with the blood takes place), a fully divided ventricle, and complete separation of pulmonary and systemic circulations. Red blood cells without nuclei serve as efficient oxygen transporters.

The limbs of mammals are variously adapted for walking, running, climbing, swimming, burrowing, or flying. In most terrestrial mammals, the limbs are more directly under the body than they are in extant reptiles, which contributes to speed and agility.

New fossil discoveries are changing our understanding of the early evolution of mammals

Mammals descended from **therapsids,** a group of synapsid amniotes, during the Triassic period more than 200 mya. The therapsids were somewhat doglike carnivores with differentiated teeth and legs adapted for running (FIG. 32-24). Until

Painting by John C. Germann, Department of Library Services, American Museum of Natural History

Figure 32-24 Therapsid (*Lycaenops*)
The therapsids were synapsid amniotes. *Lycaenops*, a predator about the size of a coyote, lived in South Africa during the Late Permian period.

recently, early mammals were thought to be small, about the size of a mouse or shrew. However, fossil evidence indicates that mammals diversified earlier than previously thought. Some early mammals were fairly large, with limbs adapted for swimming or burrowing. Some had fur, and some were probably endothermic.

How did mammals manage to coexist with the abundant archosaurs during the approximately 160 million years that reptiles ruled Earth? Many adaptations permitted early mammals to compete for a place on this planet. Perhaps one of the most important was their skill at being inconspicuous. Many were **arboreal** (tree dwelling) and nocturnal (active at night), searching for food (mainly insects and plant material, and perhaps reptile eggs) at night while the reptiles were inactive. Although their eyes may have been small, early mammals had well-developed sense organs for hearing and smell.

As many reptiles became extinct, mammals adapted to the niches (lifestyles) that reptiles abandoned. During this time, the flowering plants, including many trees, underwent an adaptive radiation, providing new habitats, sources of food, and protection from predators. Numerous new varieties of mammals evolved. During the Early Cenozoic era (more than 55 mya), the mammals underwent an adaptive radiation; they became widely distributed and adapted to an impressive variety of ecological lifestyles.

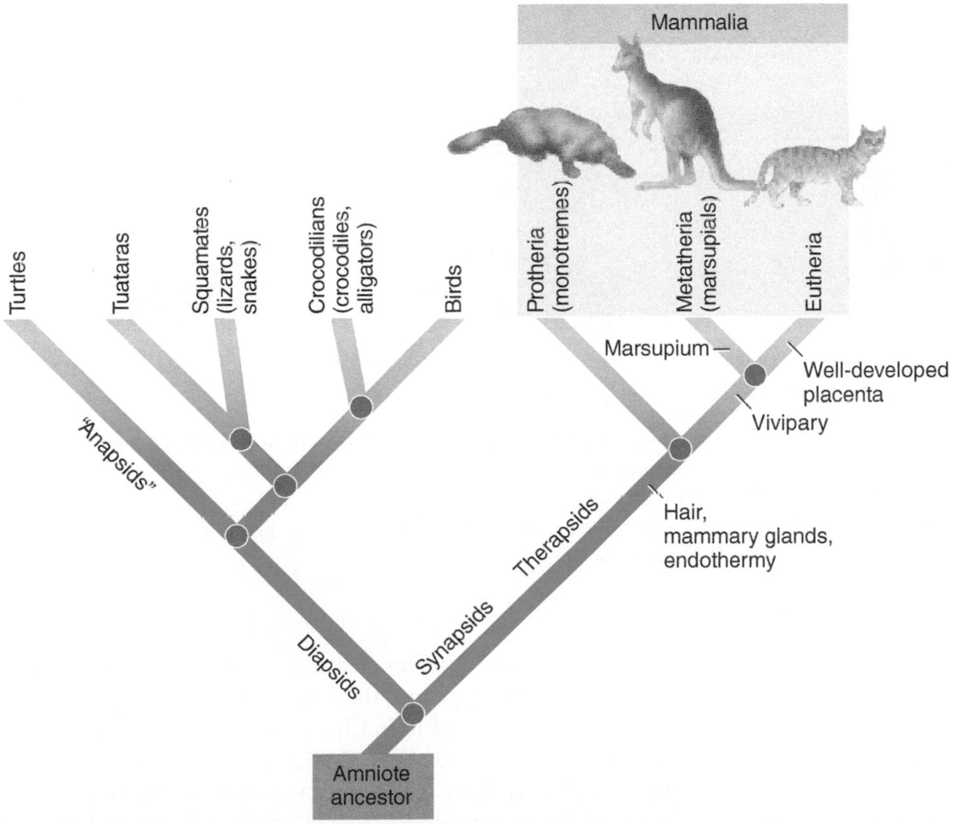

Modern mammals are assigned to three subclasses

By the end of the Cretaceous period, three main groups of mammals had evolved (FIG. 32-25). Today, mammals inhabit virtually every corner of Earth; they live on land, in fresh water and salt water, and in the air. They range in size from the tiny pygmy shrew, weighing about 2.5 g (less than 0.1 oz), to the blue whale, which may weigh up to 136,000 kg (150 tons) and which is probably one of the largest animals that has ever lived.

Modern mammals are classified in two main clades: Protheria, which includes the egg-laying mammals, or **monotremes;** and Theria, which includes the mammals that bear their young alive. The therian clade is further divided into two groups: Metatheria, the **marsupials** (pouched mammals); and Eutheria, mammals that are more developed at birth than the marsupials. **Eutherians** are often referred to as placental mammals because they have well-developed placentas. However, some marsupials do have simple placentas.

One group of protherians includes the duck-billed platypus and a second, the spiny echidnas (FIG. 32-26). These animals live in Australia and Tasmania; two species of spiny echidnas inhabit New Guinea. Female protherians lay eggs that they carry in a pouch on the abdomen or keep warm in a nest. When the young hatch, they lap up milk secreted by their mother's mammary glands. Unlike other mammals, monotremes do not have nipples. With their long beaks and long, sticky tongues, spiny echidnas capture ants and termites. The duck-billed platypus, which lives in burrows along river banks, preys on freshwater invertebrates. It has webbed feet and a flat, beaverlike tail, which help it swim.

Marsupials include pouched mammals such as kangaroos and opossums (FIG. 32-27a). Embryos begin their development in the mother's uterus, where they are nourished by fluid and yolk. After a brief gestation, the young are

Figure 32-25 Evolution of mammals

This cladogram shows the current interpretation of the evolution of mammals.
© Cengage Learning

Figure 32-26 Short-beaked echidna (*Tachyglossus aculeatus*)

Female protherians lay eggs. They have mammary glands, but do not have nipples.

(a) Eastern gray kangaroo (*Macropus giganteus*) with young, known as a joey. The kangaroo is native to Australia.

(b) A kangaroo soon after birth. Marsupials are born in an embryonic state and continue to develop in the safety of the mother's marsupium (pouch).

Figure 32-27 Marsupials

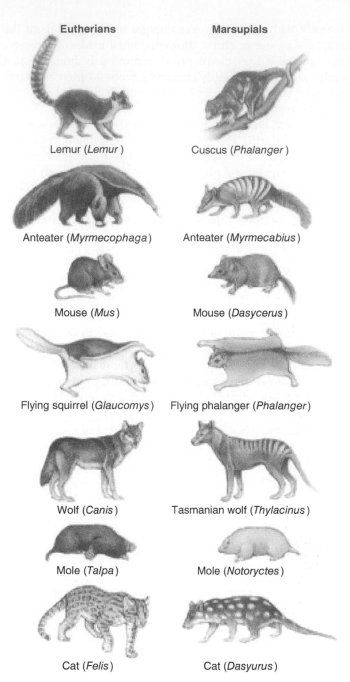

Eutherians	Marsupials
Lemur (*Lemur*)	Cuscus (*Phalanger*)
Anteater (*Myrmecophaga*)	Anteater (*Myrmecabius*)
Mouse (*Mus*)	Mouse (*Dasycerus*)
Flying squirrel (*Glaucomys*)	Flying phalanger (*Phalanger*)
Wolf (*Canis*)	Tasmanian wolf (*Thylacinus*)
Mole (*Talpa*)	Mole (*Notoryctes*)
Cat (*Felis*)	Cat (*Dasyurus*)

Figure 32-28 Convergent evolution in eutherian and marsupial mammals

For each mammal in one group, a counterpart has evolved in the other group. Their similarities include both lifestyles and structural features.

© Cengage Learning

born in an undeveloped stage. The young make their way to the *marsupium* (pouch), where they attach to a nipple. Nourished by the mother's milk, they complete their development (**FIG. 32-27b**).

At one time, marsupials probably inhabited much of the world, but placental mammals largely outcompeted them. Now marsupials live mainly in Australia, Central America, and South America. The only marsupial species that ranges into the United States is the Virginia opossum. Australia became geographically isolated from

the rest of the world before placental mammals migrated there, and the marsupials remained the dominant mammals (see the discussion of continental drift in Chapter 18). Australian marsupials underwent adaptive radiation, paralleling the evolution of placental mammals elsewhere. Thus, marsupials that live in Australia and adjacent islands independently evolved body forms and natural histories similar to North American placental wolves, bears, rats, moles, flying squirrels, and even cats (**FIG. 32-28**).

(a) **Wildebeest (*Connochaetes taurinus*), photographed in Tanzania.** The dominant plains antelope in many areas of eastern and southern Africa, wildebeest migrate long distances during the dry season in search of food and water.

(b) **Humpback whales (*Megaptera novaeangliae*) exhibiting a rare double breach.**

(c) **Wolverine (*Gulo gulo*), a tough, powerful animal.** Wolverines are fierce predators that sometimes take down large prey, such as caribou. The wolverine population has declined due to trapping, fragmentation of their habitat, and reduction of their range. Their habitat is also being reduced by climate change. They are protected by the Endangered Species Act.

(d) **Egyptian fruit bat (*Rousettus aegyptiacus*).** Often called "flying foxes," these small bats cluster in large colonies. They often hang by one foot from the cave ceiling.

Figure 32-29 Eutherian mammals

Most familiar to us are the eutherian mammals, which are born at a more mature stage than marsupials (FIG. 32-29). Indeed, among some species the young can walk and begin to interact with other members of the group within a few minutes after birth. Eutherians have a well-developed **placenta.** The placenta develops from both embryonic membranes and the maternal uterine wall. In the placenta blood vessels of the embryo come very close to the blood vessels of the mother, so materials can be exchanged by diffusion. (The two circulations do not normally mix.) The placenta allows the young to remain within the mother's body until embryonic development is complete.

Biologists assign extant placental mammals to about 19 orders. TABLE 32-4 gives a brief summary of some of these orders.

Remember that aquatic mammals, such as dolphins, whales, and seals, evolved from terrestrial ancestors (see Fig. 18-9). Also refer to TABLE 32-5, which reviews the three main deuterostome groups.

CHECKPOINT 32.8

- CONNECT *Describe three adaptations that have allowed amniotes to become completely terrestrial.*
- CONNECT *Which amniotes are endothermic? What are some advantages of endothermy?*
- *Argue for classifying birds and reptiles in a single clade.*
- *Contrast the three main clades of mammals.*

TABLE 32-4	Some Orders of Extant Eutherian Mammals

ORDER, REPRESENTATIVE MEMBERS, AND SOME CHARACTERISTICS

INSECTIVORA (moles, hedgehogs, shrews)

Nocturnal; eat insects. Shrew is smallest living mammal; some weigh less than 5 g (about 0.2 ounces).

African hedgehog
Atelerix albiventris

ARTIODACTYLA (cattle, sheep, pigs, deer, giraffes)

Hoofed with even numbers of digits per foot; most have two toes, some have four. Most have antlers or horns. Herbivores; most are ruminants, chew a cud, and have a series of stomachs inhabited by bacteria that digest cellulose.

American elk
Cervus elaphus

CHIROPTERA (bats)

Adapted for flying; fold of skin extends from elongated fingers to body and legs, forming wing. Guided in flight by type of biological sonar; emit high-frequency squeaks and are guided by echoes from obstructions. Eat insects and fruit or suck blood of other animals.

Bat
Eptesicus fuscus

XENARTHRA (sloths, anteaters, armadillos)

Teeth reduced or no teeth. Sloths are sluggish animals that hang upside down from branches; often protectively colored by green algae that grow on their hair. Armadillos are protected by bony plates; eat insects and small invertebrates.

Nine-banded armadillo
Dasypus bellus

CARNIVORA (cats, dogs, wolves, foxes, bears, otters, mink, weasels, skunks, seals, sea lions, walruses)

Predators with sharp, pointed canine teeth and molars for shearing; keen sense of smell; complex social interactions; among fastest, strongest, and smartest animals. Seals, sea lions, and walruses are large marine predators with limbs adapted as flippers for swimming.

Wolf
Canis lupus

RODENTIA (squirrels, beavers, rats, mice, hamsters, porcupines, guinea pigs)

Gnawing animals with chisel-like incisors. As they gnaw, teeth are worn down and so must grow continually. Most numerous mammals both in numbers and species.

Flying squirrel
Glaucomys volans

PERISSODACTYLA (horses, zebras, tapirs, rhinoceroses)

Herbivores; hoofed with odd number of digits per foot; one or three toes; teeth adapted for chewing; usually large animals with long legs.

Tapir
Tapirus sp.

PROBOSCIDEA (elephants)

Largest land animals; weigh up to 7 tons; large head; broad ears; long, muscular, flexible trunk (proboscis); thick loose skin is characteristic; two upper incisors are elongated as tusks. Includes extinct mastodons and woolly mammoths.

African elephant
Loxodonta africana

LAGOMORPHA (rabbits, hares, pikas)

Like rodents, have chisel-like incisors; typically have long hind legs adapted for jumping; many have long ears.

Pika
Ochontona sp.

SIRENIA (sea cows, manatees)

Herbivorous, aquatic mammals with fin-like forelimbs and no hind limbs. They are probably the basis for most tales about mermaids. Evolved from Proboscidean ancestors.

Manatee
Trichechus manatus

PRIMATES (lemurs, monkeys, apes, humans)

Highly developed brain and eyes; nails instead of claws; opposable thumb; eyes directed forward; omnivores; most species arboreal. (Primate evolution discussed in Chapter 22.)

Ring-tailed lemur
Lemur catta

CETACEA (whales, dolphins, porpoises)

Adapted for aquatic life with fish-shaped body and broad, paddlelike forelimbs (flippers); posterior limbs absent; many have thick layer of blubber under skin; some are filter feeders; mate and bear young in the water; very intelligent. Evolved from Artiodactylian ancestors.

Humpback whale
Megaptera noveangliae

© Cengage Learning

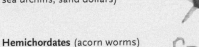

TABLE 32-5	Overview of the Deuterostomes		
MAJOR GROUPS		BODY PLAN	KEY CHARACTERISTICS
Echinoderms (sea stars, sea urchins, sand dollars)		Larva bilateral, ciliated; adult pentaradial; triploblastic; organ systems; complete digestive tube	Endoskeleton with spines; water vascular system functions in locomotion, feeding, and gas exchange; tube feet; marine
Hemichordates (acorn worms)		Bilateral symmetry; triploblastic; organ systems; complete digestive tube	Ring of cilia surrounds mouth; three-part body: proboscis, collar, and trunk; pharyngeal slits; wormlike marine animals
Chordates (tunicates, lancelets, vertebrates)		Bilateral symmetry; triploblastic; organ systems; complete digestive tube	Notochord; dorsal, tubular nerve cord; endostyle; postanal tail; pharyngeal slits during some time in life cycle; segmented muscles

© Cengage Learning

SUMMARY: FOCUS ON LEARNING OBJECTIVES

32.1 What Are Deuterostomes? (page 671)

1 Identify shared derived characters of deuterostomes and briefly describe the hemichordates.

- The **deuterostomes** include echinoderms, hemichordates, and chordates. Shared derived characters include: radial, indeterminate cleavage; the blastopore becomes (or is near the future site of) the anus; and pharyngeal slits at some time in the life cycle. Basal deuterostomes have a larva with a loop-shaped ciliated band used for locomotion.

- **Hemichordates** (acorn worms) are marine deuterostomes with a three-part body, including proboscis, collar, and trunk.

32.2 Echinoderms (page 671)

2 Identify three shared derived characters of echinoderms and describe the main classes of echinoderms.

- **Echinoderms** (phylum Echinodermata) are marine animals with a spiny "skin," **water vascular system, tube feet,** and **endoskeleton.** The larvae exhibit bilateral symmetry; most of the adults exhibit *pentaradial symmetry.*

- Class Crinoidea includes sea lilies and feather stars. The *oral surface* of crinoids is turned upward; some crinoids are sessile.

- Class Asteroidea consists of the sea stars. They have a central disc with five or more arms, and they use tube feet for locomotion.

- Class Ophiuroidea includes the brittle stars, which resemble sea stars but have longer, more slender arms that are set off more distinctly from the central disc. They use their arms for locomotion. Their tube feet lack suckers and are not used in locomotion.

- Class Echinoidea includes the sea urchins and sand dollars. Echinoids lack arms; they have a solid shell and are covered with spines.

- Class Holothuroidea consists of sea cucumbers, animals with elongated flexible bodies. The mouth is surrounded by a circle of modified tube feet that serve as tentacles.

32.3 The Chordates: Major Characteristics (page 675)

3 Describe characteristics of chordates, including four shared derived characters.

- The **chordates** (Phylum Chordata) include three subphyla: Urochordata, Cephalochordata, and Vertebrata. At some time in its life cycle, a chordate has a flexible, supporting **notochord;** a **dorsal, tubular nerve cord;** a muscular **postanal tail;** and an **endostyle,** or thyroid gland; they are also characterized by **pharyngeal slits,** but that is a derived character of deuterostomes.

32.4 Invertebrate Chordates (page 676)

4 Compare tunicates and lancelets, and summarize the phylogeny of chordates.

- The **tunicates,** which are **urochordates,** are suspension-feeding marine animals with tunics. Larvae have typical chordate characteristics and are free-swimming. Adults of most groups are sessile suspension feeders.

- The *lancelets* are **cephalochordates,** small, segmented, fishlike animals; their chordate characteristics are highly developed.

- The available evidence suggests that urochordates are the sister group of the vertebrates.

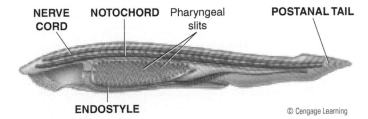

NERVE CORD   NOTOCHORD   Pharyngeal slits   POSTANAL TAIL

ENDOSTYLE   © Cengage Learning

32.5 Introducing the Vertebrates (page 678)

5 Describe four shared derived characters of vertebrates.

- The vertebrates have a *vertebral column* composed of *vertebrae* that forms the chief skeletal axis of the body and a braincase, or **cranium. Neural crest cells** are embryonic cells important in the development of many structures, including the cranium and jaws. Vertebrates have pronounced cephalization, a complex brain, a muscular pharynx, and muscles attached to the endoskeleton.

6 Describe the major taxa of extant vertebrates.

- Vertebrates can be assigned to nine classes. The hagfishes, which make up the *Myxini*, and the lampreys, which make up the *Petromyzontida*, have neither jaws nor paired fins. The *Chondrichthyes* comprise the sharks, rays, and skates; they are jawed fishes with skeletons of cartilage. The extant (living) bony fishes can be assigned to three classes: *Actinopterygii*, ray-finned fishes; *Actinistia*, coelacanths; and *Dipnoi*, lungfishes.

- The **tetrapods** (Tetrapoda) include the amphibians (class Amphibia; salamanders, frogs, and caecilians), many of which have aquatic larvae that undergo metamorphosis, and the amniotes (Amniota), which include reptiles and mammals. **Reptiles** (class Reptilia) include turtles, lizards, snakes, alligators, and birds. Reptiles are amniotes with keratin scales or feathers and reproduction adapted for terrestrial life; mammals (class Mammalia) include monotremes, marsupials, and placental mammals. Mammals are amniotes with hair and mammary glands. (See Table 32-2 for a more detailed review.)

32.6 Jawless Fishes *(page 680)*

7 Distinguish among the major groups of jawless fishes.

- The extant jawless fishes are the hagfishes (Myxini) and the lampreys (Petromyzontida). Jaws and paired fins are absent in both hagfishes and lampreys. Hagfishes are marine scavengers that secrete slime as a defense mechanism. Many lampreys are parasites on other fishes.

32.7 Evolution of Jaws and Limbs: Jawed Fishes and Tetrapods *(page 682)*

8 Trace the evolution of jawed fishes and early tetrapods, and describe modern amphibians.

- Chondrichthyes, the cartilaginous fishes (sharks, rays, and skates), evolved during the Devonian period. They have jaws, two pairs of fins, and **placoid scales.**

- During the Devonian period, bony fishes gave rise to two evolutionary lines: the Actinopterygii, or **ray-finned fishes,** and the *Sarcopterygii,* or *lobe-finned fishes.* The ray-finned fishes gave rise to the modern bony fishes. Their lungs have been modified as a **swim bladder,** an air sac for regulating buoyancy.

- The Sarcopterygii includes the Tetrapodomorpha, the *lungfishes* (Dipnoi), and the **coelacanths** (Actinistia). Evidence suggests that the Tetropodomorpha gave rise to the **tetrapods,** the land vertebrates. *Tiktaalik* was a transitional form between fishes and tetrapods.

- Early tetrapods were mainly aquatic animals that ventured onto the land to find food or escape predators. These early tetrapods had limbs strong enough to support the weight of their bodies on land.

- Modern **amphibians** (Amphibia) include salamanders and newts, frogs and toads, and caecilians. Most amphibians return to the water to reproduce. Frog embryos develop into tadpoles, which undergo **metamorphosis** to become adults. Amphibians use their moist skin as well as lungs for gas exchange. They have systemic and pulmonary circulations as well as hearts with two atria and one ventricle.

32.8 Amniotes: Terrestrial Vertebrates *(page 688)*

9 Describe three vertebrate adaptations to terrestrial life.

- Terrestrial vertebrates, or **amniotes,** include reptiles (including birds) and mammals. Adaptations for life on land include

(1) the evolution of the **amniotic egg** with its shell and **amnion,** a membrane that forms a fluid-filled sac around the embryo; (2) internal fertilization; and (3) a body covering that retards water loss and physiological mechanisms that conserve water.

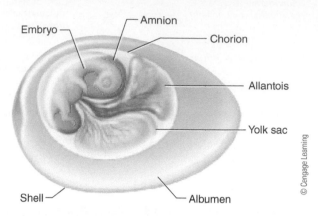

10 Describe the reptiles (including the birds) and argue for including the birds in the reptile clade.

- Biologists classify amniotes in two main groups: diapsids and synapsids. **Diapsids** include the turtles, squamates (snakes and lizards), tuataras, extinct ichthyosaurs, crocodiles, the extinct pterosaurs, the extinct ornisthischian dinosaurs, the extinct saurischian dinosaurs, and birds. The **synapsids** include the **therapsids,** which gave rise to the mammals. (See Table 32-3.)

- Extant **reptiles** (including birds) can be classified in five clades: (1) turtles, terrapins, and tortoises; (2) lizards, snakes, and amphisbaenians; (3) tuataras; (4) crocodiles, alligators, caimans, and gavials; and (5) birds (avian reptiles).

- Most non-avian reptiles have dry skin with horny scales, lungs with many chambers, and a heart with two completely separated atria and two ventricles that are incompletely separated. (In the crocodiles the two ventricles are completely partitioned.) Birds have many adaptations for powered flight, including feathers; wings; and light, hollow bones containing air spaces. They have completely divided ventricles and very efficient lungs, and they excrete solid metabolic wastes (uric acid). They are **endotherms;** that is, they maintain a constant body temperature. Birds have a well-developed nervous system with excellent vision and hearing.

- Based on fossil evidence and molecular data, feather evolution took place in terrestrial, bipedal dinosaurs before the evolution of birds or flight. Birds are considered feathered reptiles that evolved from the lineage of saurischian dinosaurs, specifically from the **theropods,** a group of bipedal, saurischian dinosaurs. Like theropods, modern birds have feet with three digits; thin-walled, hollow bones; and a *furcula*, or wishbone.

11 Describe five key characters of mammals and contrast protherian (monotremes), metatherian (marsupials), and eutherian mammals, giving examples of animals that belong to each group.

- **Mammals** have *hair,* **mammary glands,** *differentiated teeth,* lungs with alveoli, completely divided ventricles, and three *middle-ear bones.* They are endotherms and have a highly developed nervous system and a muscular **diaphragm.**

- *Protherians,* the **monotremes,** include the duck-billed platypus and spiny anteaters. Monotremes lay eggs.

- *Metatherians,* the **marsupials,** include pouched mammals, such as kangaroos and opossums. The young, born at an immature stage, complete their development in their mother's marsupium, where they are nourished with milk from mammary glands.

- **Eutherians** are more developed at birth than marsupials; they are characterized by a well-developed **placenta,** an organ of exchange that develops between the embryo and the mother.

TEST YOUR UNDERSTANDING

Know and Comprehend

1. Which of the following is *not* a shared derived character of echinoderms? (a) water vascular system (b) notochord (c) tube feet (d) pentaradial symmetry in adult (e) endoskeleton of calcium carbonate plates and spines
2. Which of the following is/are found in tunicates? (a) dorsal, tubular nerve cord (b) tube feet (c) anal gill slits (d) two pairs of appendages (e) vertebral column
3. A shark is characterized by (a) amnion (b) bony skeleton (c) water vascular system (d) placoid scales (e) endothermy *and* amnion
4. Which of the following characteristics is/are associated with amphibians? (a) amnion (b) placoid scales (c) heart with two complete ventricles (d) swim bladder (e) metamorphosis
5. Reptiles (a) are all endotherms (b) are amniotes (c) have a great deal of keratin in their epidermis (d) have external fertilization (e) b and c are both correct
6. Which of the following is *not* characteristic of birds? (a) hollow bones (b) amnion (c) ectothermy (d) high metabolic rate (e) reptilian-like scales on legs
7. Which of the following is true of mammals? (a) they evolved from saurischian dinosaurs (b) they are exotherms (c) they have hair and three middle ear bones (d) mammalian embryos do not have an amnion (e) they all bear their young alive (do not lay eggs).

Apply and Analyze

8. **VISUALIZE** Draw a simple cladogram illustrating the evolutionary relationships among extant mammals (marsupials,

eutherians, and monotremes). Include the following characters in your cladogram: well-developed placenta, vivipary, endothermy, marsupium, hair.
9. **EVOLUTION LINK** Sea urchins have radial symmetry. Explain why they are not classified as cnidarians.
10. **EVOLUTION LINK** Most biologists consider birds as living dinosaurs. Justify this position.
11. **EVOLUTION LINK** Discuss the relationships among the echinoderms and chordates, describing shared derived characters that support grouping these animals as deuterostomes.

Evaluate and Synthesize

12. **INTERPRET DATA** Imagine that you discover an interesting new animal. You examine it and gather the following data. It has a dorsal, tubular nerve cord; a cranium; skin with scales; and a heart with two atria and two ventricles. How would you classify the animal? Explain each step in your decision. Where would you place this animal on the cladogram shown in Figure 32-20?
13. **SCIENCE, TECHNOLOGY, AND SOCIETY** Every year hundreds of sea turtles are injured and killed as a result of human activities. All seven species of marine turtles are listed under the Endangered Species Act. What measures would you propose to protect sea turtles?

 To access course materials, such as Aplia and other companion resources, please visit **www.cengagebrain.com.**

Animal Structure and Function: An Introduction

39

© Francois Gagnon/Shutterstock.com

Larger body size does not mean bigger cells. The cells of the adult elephant, the young elephant, and the bird on the adult's head are all about the same size. The adult elephant is larger than the bird on its head because its genes specify that its body consists of a larger number of cells. The cells of the young elephant will continue to multiply until it reaches adult size.

Animal groups are dramatically diverse, with radically different body structures. For example, consider how different the elephant and the bird are, not only in size but also in body form and lifestyle (see photograph). Despite their differences, animal groups share many characteristics, including their relatively large size.

Why are most animals larger than bacteria, archaea, protists, and fungi? The answer may be related to *ecological niches,* which are the functional roles of a species within a community. By the time animals evolved, other organisms already occupied most available ecological niches. For new species to succeed, they had to displace others from a niche or adapt to a new one. Success in a new niche required a new body plan, and new body plans often required and accommodated larger size. Increased size also provided more opportunity for capturing food. Predators are typically larger than their prey.

To grow larger than their bacterial and protist competitors, animals had to be multicellular. Recall that the size of a single cell is limited by the ratio of its surface area (plasma membrane) to its volume (see Chapter 4). The plasma membrane needs to be large enough relative to the cell's volume to permit passage of materials into and out of the cell so that the conditions necessary for life can be maintained. In a multicellular animal, each cell has a large enough ratio of surface area to volume to effectively regulate its internal environment. Individual cells live and die, and they are replaced while the organism continues to maintain itself and thrive. The number of cells, not their individual sizes, is mainly responsible for the size of an animal.

In unicellular organisms such as bacteria and many protists, the single cell carries on all the activities necessary for life. Recall that unicellular and small, flat organisms depend on diffusion for many life processes, including gas exchange and disposal of metabolic wastes. One reason they can be small is that they do not require complex organ systems.

In this chapter we focus on the basic form and function of the animal body. **Anatomy** is the study of an organism's structure. **Physiology** is the study of how the body functions. Remember that in biological systems, structures are adapted to function at every level of organization. As we describe the types and

KEY CONCEPTS

39.1 Cells make up tissues, various types of tissues make up organs, and tissues and organs working together make up organ systems. The main types of tissues found in animals are epithelial, connective, muscle, and nervous tissues.

39.2 Homeostatic mechanisms are mainly negative feedback systems that maintain a relatively stable internal environment.

39.3 Thermoregulation is the process of maintaining homeostasis of body temperature despite changes in surrounding (or internal) temperature.

functions of tissues and the principal organ systems of animals, note the many examples of this basic principle. In this chapter we also discuss the important concept of *homeostasis,* using regulation of body temperature as an example. In the following chapters, we discuss how organ systems work together to maintain homeostasis as the animal carries out its many life processes.

39.1 TISSUES, ORGANS, AND ORGAN SYSTEMS

LEARNING OBJECTIVES

1   Compare the structure and function of the four main kinds of animal tissues: epithelial, connective, muscle, and nervous tissues.
2   Compare the main types of epithelial tissue and describe their functions.
3   Compare the main types of connective tissue and describe their functions.
4   Contrast the three types of muscle tissue and describe their functions.
5   Relate the structure of the neuron to its function.
6   Briefly describe the organ systems of a mammal and summarize the functions of each organ system.

In a multicellular organism, cells specialize to perform specific tasks. Recall from Chapter 1 that cells organize to form *tissues,* and tissues associate to form *organs* such as the heart or stomach. Groups of tissues and organs make up the *organ systems* of a complex *organism.* Billions of cells organize to form the tissues, organs, and organ systems of a butterfly, a crocodile, or an elephant.

A **tissue** consists of a group of closely associated, similar cells that carry out specific functions. Biologists classify animal tissues as epithelial, connective, muscle, or nervous tissue. Classification of tissues depends on their structure and origin. Each kind of tissue is composed of cells with characteristic sizes, shapes, and arrangements, and each type of tissue is specialized to perform a specific function or group of functions. For example, some tissues are specialized to transport materials, whereas others contract, enabling the animal to move. Still others secrete hormones that regulate metabolic processes. Structure and function are closely linked at every level of organization. As we discuss each tissue type, notice the relationship between its form and its function. Notice also how biological systems continuously interact.

Epithelial tissues cover the body and line its cavities

Epithelial tissue (also called *epithelium*) consists of cells fitted tightly together to form a continuous layer, or sheet, of cells. One surface of the sheet is typically exposed because it covers the body (outer layer of the skin) or lines a cavity, such as the *lumen* (the cavity in a hollow organ) of the intestine. The other surface of an epithelial layer attaches to the underlying tissue by a noncellular **basement membrane** consisting of tiny *fibers* and nonliving polysaccharide material that the epithelial cells produce.

Epithelial tissue forms the outer layer of the skin and the linings of the digestive, respiratory, excretory, and reproductive tracts. As a result, everything that enters or leaves the body must cross at least one layer of epithelium. Food taken into the mouth and swallowed is not really "inside" the body until it is absorbed through the epithelium of the digestive tract and enters the blood. To a large extent, the permeabilities of the various epithelial tissues regulate the exchange of substances between the different parts of the body as well as between the animal and the external environment.

Epithelial tissues perform many functions, including protection, absorption, secretion, and sensation. The epithelial layer of the skin, the **epidermis,** covers the entire body and protects it from mechanical injury, chemicals, bacteria, and fluid loss. The epithelial tissue lining the digestive tract absorbs nutrients and water into the body. Some epithelial cells form **glands** that secrete cell products such as hormones, enzymes, or sweat. Other epithelial cells are sensory receptors that receive information from the environment. For example, epithelial cells in taste buds and in the nose specialize as chemical receptors.

TABLE 39-1 illustrates the main types of epithelial tissue, indicates their locations in the body, and describes their functions (pages 818–819). We can distinguish three types of epithelial cells on the basis of shape. *Squamous* epithelial cells are thin, flat cells shaped like flagstones. *Simple squamous epithelium* lines the blood vessels and the air sacs in the lungs. *Cuboidal* epithelial cells are short cylinders that from the side appear cube-shaped, like dice. Actually, each cuboidal cell is typically hexagonal in cross section, making it an eight-sided polyhedron. *Simple cuboidal epithelium* lines the kidney tubules.

When viewed from the side, *columnar* epithelial cells look like columns or cylinders. The nucleus is usually located near the base of the cell. Viewed from above or in cross section, these cells often appear hexagonal. On its free surface, a columnar epithelial cell may have cilia that beat in a coordinated way, moving materials over the tissue surface. Most of the upper respiratory tract is lined with ciliated *columnar epithelium* that moves particles of dust and other foreign material away from the lungs.

Epithelial tissue is also classified by number of layers. *Simple epithelium* is composed of one layer of cells. It is usually located where substances are secreted, excreted, or absorbed, or where materials diffuse between compartments. For example, simple squamous epithelium lines the air sacs in the lungs. The structure of this thin tissue allows diffusion of gases in and out of air sacs.

Stratified epithelium, which has two or more layers, protects underlying tissues. For example, stratified squamous epithelium, which makes up the outer layer of your skin, is continuously sloughed off during normal wear and tear. It must also continuously regenerate. The cells of *pseudostratified epithelium* appear layered, but they are not. Although all its cells rest on a basement membrane, not every cell extends to the exposed surface of the tissue. This arrangement gives the impression of two or more cell layers. Some of the respiratory passageways are lined with pseudostratified epithelium equipped with cilia.

The lining of blood and lymph vessels is called endothelium. Endothelial cells have a different embryonic origin from "true" epithelium. However, these cells are structurally similar to squamous epithelial cells and can be included in that category.

Glands are made of epithelial cells

A **gland** consists of one or more epithelial cells specialized to produce and secrete a product such as sweat, milk, mucus, wax, saliva, hormones, or enzymes (FIG. 39-1). Epithelial tissue lining the cavities and passageways of the body typically has some specialized mucus-secreting cells called **goblet cells.** The mucus lubricates these surfaces, offers protection, and facilitates the movement of materials.

Glands are classified as exocrine or endocrine. **Exocrine glands,** like goblet cells and sweat glands, secrete their products onto a free epithelial surface, typically through a duct (tube). **Endocrine glands** lack ducts. These glands release their products, called **hormones,** into the **interstitial fluid** (tissue fluid) or blood. Hormones are typically transported by the cardiovascular system. (Endocrine glands are discussed in Chapter 49.)

Epithelial cells form membranes

An *epithelial membrane* consists of a sheet of epithelial tissue and a layer of underlying connective tissue. Types of epithelial membranes include mucous membranes and serous membranes. A **mucous membrane,** or *mucosa,* lines a body cavity that opens to the outside of the body, such as the digestive tract or respiratory tract. Goblet cells in the epithelial layer secrete mucus that lubricates the tissue and protects it from drying.

A **serous membrane** lines a body cavity that does not open to the outside of the body. It consists of simple squamous epithelium over a thin layer of loose connective tissue. This type of membrane secretes fluid into the cavity it lines. Examples of serous membranes are the pleural membranes lining the pleural cavities around the lungs and the pericardial membranes lining the pericardial cavity around the heart.

Connective tissues support other body structures

Almost every organ in the body has a framework of **connective tissue** that supports and cushions it. Compared with epithelial tissues, connective tissues contain relatively few cells. Its cells are embedded in an extensive **intercellular substance** consisting of threadlike, microscopic **fibers** scattered throughout a **matrix,** a thin gel of polysaccharides that the cells secrete. The structure and properties of the intercellular substance help determine the nature and function of each kind of connective tissue.

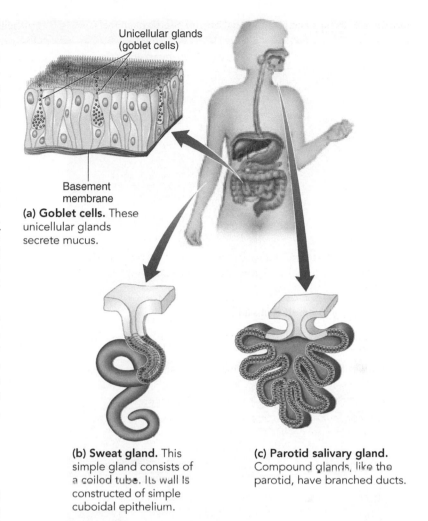

(a) Goblet cells. These unicellular glands secrete mucus.

(b) Sweat gland. This simple gland consists of a coiled tube. Its wall is constructed of simple cuboidal epithelium.

(c) Parotid salivary gland. Compound glands, like the parotid, have branched ducts.

Figure 39-1 Glands
A gland consists of one or more epithelial cells.
© Cengage Learning

Connective tissue typically contains three types of fibers: collagen, elastic, and reticular. *Collagen fibers,* the most numerous type, are made of **collagens,** a group of fibrous proteins found in all animals (see Fig. 3-23b). Collagens are the most abundant proteins in mammals, accounting for about 25% of their total protein mass. Collagen is very tough (meat is tough because of its collagen content). The tensile strength (ability to stretch without tearing) of collagen fibers is comparable to that of steel. Collagen fibers are wavy and flexible, allowing them to remain intact when tissue is stretched.

Elastic fibers branch and fuse to form networks. They can be stretched by a force and then (like a stretched rubber band) return to their original size and shape when the force is removed. Elastic fibers, composed of the protein elastin, are an important component of structures that must stretch.

Reticular fibers are very thin, branched fibers that form delicate networks joining connective tissues to neighboring tissues. Reticular fibers consist of collagen and some glycoprotein.

The cells of various kinds of connective tissues differ in their shapes and structures and in the kinds of fibers and matrices they

TABLE 39-1 | Epithelial Tissues

Nuclei of squamous epithelial cells

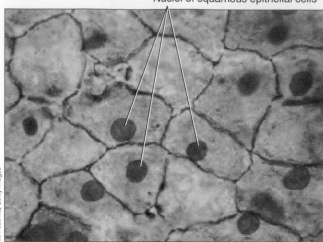

LM of simple squamous epithelium.

25 μm

Simple Squamous Epithelium

Main Locations
Air sacs of lungs; lining of blood vessels

Functions
Passage of materials where little or no protection is needed and where diffusion is major form of transport

Description and Comments
Cells are flat and arranged as single layer

Nuclei of cuboidal epithelial cells   Lumen of tubule

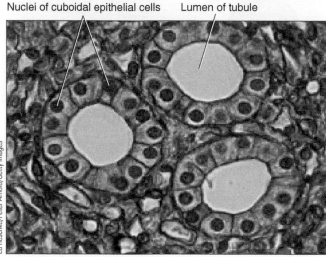

LM of simple cuboidal epithelium.

25 μm

Simple Cuboidal Epithelium

Main Locations
Linings of kidney tubules; gland ducts

Functions
Secretion and absorption

Description and Comments
Single layer of cells; LM shows cross section through tubules; from the side each cell looks like a short cylinder; some have microvilli for absorption

Goblet cell   Nuclei of columnar cells

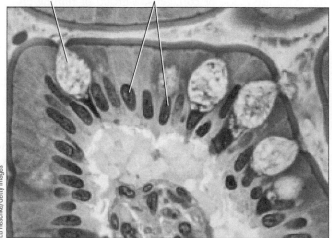

LM of simple columnar epithelium.

25 μm

Simple Columnar Epithelium

Main Locations
Linings of much of digestive tract and upper part of respiratory tract

Functions
Secretion, especially of mucus; absorption; protection; moves layer of mucus

Description and Comments
Single layer of columnar cells; highly developed Golgi complex; often ciliated; goblet cells secrete mucus

Continued

TABLE 39-1 | Epithelial Tissues (*continued*)

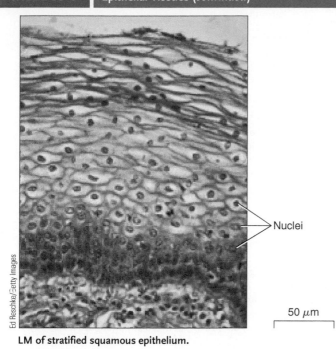

LM of stratified squamous epithelium.

Nuclei

50 μm

Ed Reschke/Getty Images

Stratified Squamous Epithelium

Main Locations
Skin; mouth lining; vaginal lining

Functions
Protection only; little or no absorption or transit of materials; outer layer continuously sloughed off and replaced from below

Description and Comments
Several layers of cells, with only the lower ones columnar and metabolically active; division of lower cells causes older ones to be pushed upward toward surface, becoming flatter as they move

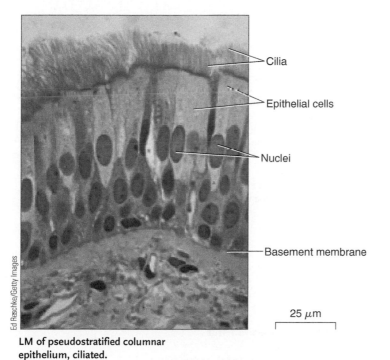

LM of pseudostratified columnar epithelium, ciliated.

Cilia

Epithelial cells

Nuclei

Basement membrane

25 μm

Ed Reschke/Getty Images

Pseudostratified Epithelium

Main Locations
Some respiratory passages; ducts of many glands

Functions
Secretion; protection; moves layer of mucus

Description and Comments
Ciliated, mucus-secreting, or with microvilli; comparable in many ways to columnar epithelium except that not all cells are the same height; so, although all cells contact the same basement membrane, the tissue appears stratified

© Cengage Learning

secrete. **Fibroblasts** are connective tissue cells that produce the fibers, as well as the protein and carbohydrate complexes, of the matrix. Fibroblasts release protein components that become arranged to form the characteristic fibers. These cells are especially active in developing tissues and are important in healing wounds. As tissues mature, the number of fibroblasts decreases, and they become less active. **Macrophages,** the body's scavenger cells, commonly wander through connective tissues, cleaning up cell debris and phagocytosing foreign matter, including bacteria.

Some of the main types of connective tissue are (1) loose and dense connective tissues; (2) elastic connective tissue; (3) reticular connective tissue; (4) adipose tissue; (5) cartilage; (6) bone; and (7) blood, lymph, and tissues that produce blood cells. These tissues vary widely in their structural details and in the functions they perform (TABLE 39-2).

TABLE 39-2 | Connective Tissues

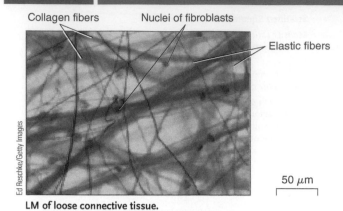

Collagen fibers   Nuclei of fibroblasts

Elastic fibers

50 μm

Ed Reschke/Getty Images

LM of loose connective tissue.

Loose Connective Tissue

Main Locations
Everywhere that support must be combined with elasticity, such as subcutaneous tissue (the layer of tissue beneath the dermis of the skin)

Functions
Support; reservoir for fluid and salts

Description and Comments
Fibers produced by fibroblast cells embedded in semifluid matrix; other types of cells, e.g., macrophages, present

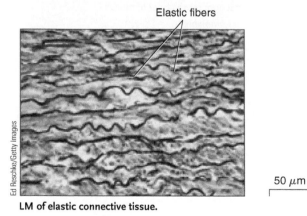

Nucleus of fibroblast

Collagen fibers

25 μm

Ed Reschke/Getty Images

LM of dense connective tissue.

Dense Connective Tissue

Main Locations
Tendons; many ligaments; dermis of skin

Functions
Support; transmits mechanical forces

Description and Comments
Collagen fibers may be regularly or irregularly arranged

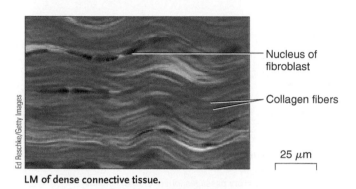

Elastic fibers

50 μm

Ed Reschke/Getty Images

LM of elastic connective tissue.

Elastic Connective Tissue

Main Locations
Structures that must both expand and return to their original size, such as lung tissue and large arteries

Function
Confers elasticity

Description and Comments
Branching elastic fibers interspersed with fibroblasts

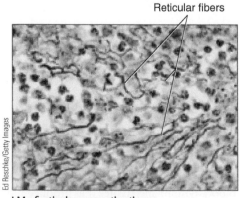

Reticular fibers

50 μm

Ed Reschke/Getty Images

LM of reticular connective tissue.

Reticular Connective Tissue

Main Locations
Framework of liver; lymph nodes; spleen

Function
Support

Description and Comments
Consists of interlacing reticular fibers

Continued

TABLE 39-2 | Connective Tissues (*continued*)

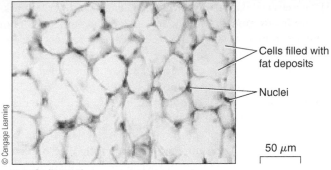

Cells filled with fat deposits

Nuclei

50 μm

© Cengage Learning

LM of adipose tissue.

Adipose Tissue

Main Locations
Subcutaneous layer; forms protective pads around certain internal organs

Functions
Stores fat; insulation; supports organs such as mammary glands, kidneys

Description and Comments
Fat cells are star shaped at first; fat droplets accumulate until typical ring-shaped cells are produced

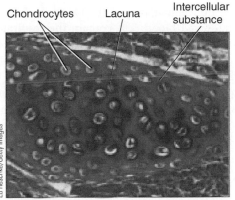

Chondrocytes   Lacuna   Intercellular substance

50 μm

Ed Reschke/Getty Images

LM of cartilage.

Cartilage

Main Locations
Supporting skeletons in sharks and rays; ends of bones in mammals and some other vertebrates; supporting rings in wall of trachea; tip of nose; external ear

Function
Flexible support

Description and Comments
Cells (chondrocytes) separated from one another by intercellular substance; cells occupy lacunae

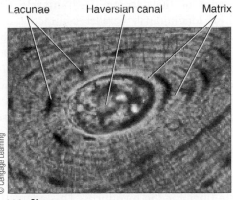

Lacunae   Haversian canal   Matrix

50 μm

© Cengage Learning

LM of bone.

Bone

Main Locations
Forms skeletal structure in most vertebrates

Functions
Supports and protects internal organs; calcium reservoir; skeletal muscles attach to bones

Description and Comments
Cells (osteocytes) in lacunae; in compact bone lacunae embedded in lamellae, concentric circles of matrix surrounding Haversian canals

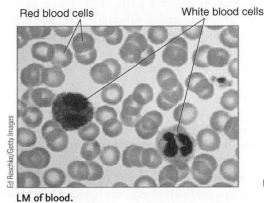

Red blood cells   White blood cells

25 μm

Ed Reschke/Getty Images

LM of blood.

Blood

Main Locations
Within heart and blood vessels of circulatory system

Functions
Transports oxygen, nutrients, wastes, and other materials; white blood cells defend against disease organisms

Description and Comments
Consists of red blood cells, white blood cells, and platelets dispersed in fluid matrix (plasma)

Loose connective tissue is the most widely distributed connective tissue in the vertebrate body. Together with adipose tissue, loose connective tissue forms the subcutaneous (below the skin) layer that attaches skin to the muscles and other structures beneath. Nerves, blood vessels, and muscles are wrapped in loose connective tissue. This tissue also forms a thin filling between body parts and serves as a reservoir for fluid and salts. Loose connective tissue consists of fibers running in all directions through a semifluid matrix. Its flexibility permits the parts it connects to move.

Dense connective tissue, found in the dermis (lower layer) of the skin, is very strong, but is somewhat less flexible than loose connective tissue. Collagen fibers predominate. **Tendons,** the cords that connect muscles to bones, and **ligaments,** the cables that connect bones to one another, consist of dense connective tissue in which collagen bundles are arranged in a definite pattern.

Elastic connective tissue consists mainly of bundles of parallel elastic fibers. This tissue is found in structures that must expand and then return to their original size, such as lung tissue and the walls of large arteries.

Reticular connective tissue is composed mainly of interlacing reticular fibers. It forms a supporting internal framework in many organs, including the liver, spleen, and lymph nodes.

The cells of **adipose tissue** store fat and release it when fuel is needed for cellular respiration. Adipose tissue is found in the subcutaneous layer and in tissue that cushions internal organs.

The supporting skeleton of a vertebrate is made of cartilage or of both cartilage and bone. **Cartilage** is the supporting skeleton in the embryonic stages of all vertebrates. In most vertebrates bone replaces cartilage during development. However, cartilage remains in some supporting structures. In humans, for example, cartilage is found in the external ear, the supporting rings in the walls of the respiratory passageways, the tip of the nose, the ends of some bones, and the discs that serve as cushions between the vertebrae.

Cartilage is firm yet elastic. Its cells, called **chondrocytes,** secrete a hard, rubbery matrix that surrounds them. They also secrete collagen fibers, which become embedded in the matrix and strengthen it. Chondrocytes eventually come to lie, singly or in groups of two or four, in small cavities in the matrix called *lacunae.* These cells remain alive and are nourished by nutrients and oxygen that diffuse through the matrix. Cartilage tissue lacks nerves, lymph vessels, and blood vessels.

Bone, the main vertebrate skeletal tissue, is like cartilage in that it consists mostly of matrix material. The bone cells, called **osteocytes,** are contained within lacunae. Osteocytes secrete and maintain the matrix (FIG. 39-2). Unlike cartilage, however, bone is a highly vascular tissue, with a substantial blood supply. Osteocytes communicate with one another and with capillaries by tiny channels (*canaliculi*) that contain long cytoplasmic extensions of the osteocytes.

A typical bone has an outer layer of **compact bone** surrounding a filling of *spongy bone.* Compact bone consists of spindle-shaped units called **osteons.** Within each osteon, osteocytes are arranged in concentric layers of matrix called *lamellae.* In turn, the lamellae surround central microscopic channels known as **Haversian canals,** through which capillaries and nerves pass.

Bones are amazingly light and strong. Calcium salts of bone render the matrix very hard, and collagen prevents the bony matrix from being overly brittle. Most bones have a large, central *marrow cavity* that contains a spongy tissue called *marrow.* Yellow marrow consists mainly of fat. Red marrow is the connective tissue in which blood cells are produced. We discuss bone in more detail in Chapter 40.

Blood and **lymph** are circulating tissues that help other parts of the body communicate and interact. Like other connective tissues, they consist of specialized cells dispersed in an intercellular substance. In mammals blood consists of **red blood cells, white blood cells,** and **platelets,** all suspended within **plasma,** the liquid, noncellular part of the blood. In humans and other vertebrates, red blood cells contain the respiratory pigment that transports oxygen. White blood cells defend the body against disease-causing microorganisms (see Chapter 45). Platelets, small fragments broken off from large cells in the bone marrow, play a key role in blood clotting. Plasma consists of water, proteins, salts, and a variety of soluble chemical messengers such as hormones that it transports from one part of the body to another. We discuss blood in Chapter 44.

Muscle tissue is specialized to contract

Most animals move by contracting the long, cylindrical or spindle-shaped cells of **muscle** tissue. Muscle cells are called muscle fibers because of their length. Each **muscle fiber** contains many thin, longitudinal, parallel contractile units called **myofibrils.** Two proteins, **myosin** and **actin,** are the chief components of myofibrils. Myosin and actin play a key role in contraction of muscle fibers.

Many invertebrates have skeletal and smooth muscle. Vertebrates have three types of muscle tissue: skeletal, cardiac, and smooth (TABLE 39-3 on page 824). **Skeletal muscle** makes up the large muscle masses attached to the bones of the body. Skeletal muscle fibers are very long, and each fiber has many nuclei. The nuclei of skeletal muscle fibers lie just under the plasma membrane, which frees the entire central part of the skeletal muscle fiber for the myofibrils. This adaptation appears to increase the efficiency of contraction. When skeletal muscles contract, they move parts of the body. Skeletal muscle fibers are generally under voluntary control. In contrast, you do not normally contract your cardiac and smooth muscle fibers at will.

Light microscopy shows that both skeletal and cardiac fibers have alternating light and dark transverse stripes, or *striations*, that change their relative sizes during contraction. Striated muscle fibers contract rapidly but cannot remain contracted for a long period. They must relax and rest momentarily before contracting again. (Muscle contraction is discussed in Chapter 40.)

Cardiac muscle is the main tissue of the heart. When cardiac muscle contracts, the heart pumps the blood. The fibers of

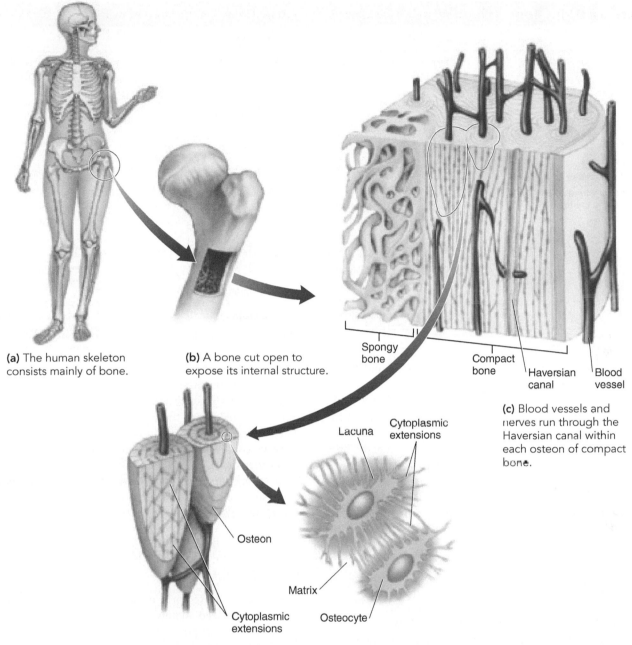

(a) The human skeleton consists mainly of bone.

(b) A bone cut open to expose its internal structure.

Spongy bone

Compact bone

Haversian canal

Blood vessel

(c) Blood vessels and nerves run through the Haversian canal within each osteon of compact bone.

Lacuna

Cytoplasmic extensions

Osteon

Matrix

Cytoplasmic extensions

Osteocyte

(d) The bone matrix is rigid and hard. Osteocytes become trapped within lacunae but communicate with one another by way of cytoplasmic extensions that extend through tiny canals.

Figure 39-2 *Animation* **Bone**
© Cengage Learning

cardiac muscle join end to end, and they branch and rejoin to form complex networks. One or two nuclei lie within each fiber. A characteristic feature of cardiac muscle tissue is the presence of *intercalated discs,* specialized junctions where the fibers join.

Smooth muscle occurs in the walls of the digestive tract, uterus, blood vessels, and many other internal organs. Contraction of smooth muscle is necessary for these organs to perform certain functions. For example, smooth muscle contraction in the wall of the digestive tract moves food through the digestive tract. When smooth muscle in the walls of arterioles (small arteries) contracts, the blood vessels constrict, raising blood pressure. Each spindle-shaped smooth muscle fiber contains a single, central nucleus.

Nervous tissue controls muscles and glands

Nervous tissue consists of neurons and glial cells. **Neurons** are specialized for receiving and transmitting signals. **Glial cells**

TABLE 39-3 | Muscle Tissues

	SKELETAL	CARDIAC	SMOOTH
Location	Attached to skeleton	Walls of heart	Walls of stomach, intestines, blood vessels, uterus
Type of control	Voluntary	Involuntary	Involuntary
Shape of fibers	Elongated, cylindrical, blunt ends	Elongated, cylindrical, fibers that branch and fuse	Elongated, spindle shaped, pointed ends
Striations	Present	Present	Absent
Number of nuclei per fiber	Many	One or two	One
Position of nuclei	Peripheral	Central	Central
Speed of contraction	Most rapid	Intermediate (varies)	Slowest
Resistance to fatigue (with repetitive contraction)	Least	Intermediate	Greatest

Skeletal muscle fibers — Nuclei, Striations

Cardiac muscle fibers — Nuclei, Intercalated discs

Smooth muscle fibers — Nuclei

© Cengage Learning

support and nourish the neurons, destroy pathogens, and modulate transmission of impulses (FIG. 39-3).

A typical neuron has a **cell body** containing the nucleus as well as two types of cytoplasmic extensions (discussed in Chapter 41). **Dendrites** are cytoplasmic extensions specialized for receiving signals and transmitting them to the cell body. The single **axon** transmits signals, called *nerve impulses,* away from the cell body. Axons range in length from 1 or 2 mm to more than a meter. Those extending from the spinal cord down the arm or leg in a human, for example, may be a meter or more in length.

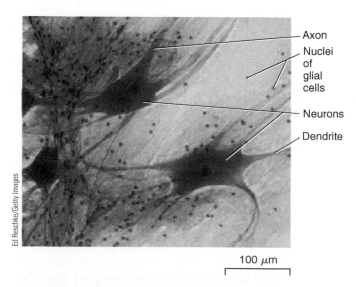

Figure 39-3 **LM of nervous tissue**

Neurons transmit information in the form of electrochemical signals. Glial cells support, protect, and nourish neurons. They also communicate and help regulate neural function.

Certain neurons receive signals from the external or internal environment and transmit them to the spinal cord and brain. Other neurons relay, process, or store information. Still others transmit signals from the brain and spinal cord to the muscles and glands. Neurons communicate at junctions called **synapses.** A **nerve** consists of a great many neurons bound together by connective tissue.

In this chapter we have focused on normal tissues. For a discussion of some abnormal tissues, see *Inquiring About: Unwelcome Tissues: Cancers.*

Tissues and organs make up the organ systems of the body

Tissues associate to form **organs.** Although an animal organ may be composed mainly of one type of tissue, other types are needed to support, protect, provide a blood supply, and transmit information. For example, the heart is mainly cardiac muscle tissue, but its chambers are lined with endothelium, and its walls contain blood vessels made of endothelium, smooth muscle, and connective tissue. The heart also has nerves that transmit information and help regulate the rate and strength of its contractions.

An organized group of tissues and organs that together perform a specialized set of functions make up an **organ system.** Working together in a very coordinated way, organ systems perform the functions required by the **organism.** We can identify 11 major organ systems that work together to carry out the physiological processes of a mammal: **integumentary system, skeletal system, muscular system, nervous system, endocrine system, cardiovascular system, lymphatic system,** which functions as the **immune system, respiratory system, digestive system, urinary system,** and **reproductive system.** FIGURE 39-4 summarizes the principal organs and functions of each organ system.

A **neoplasm** ("new growth"), or **tumor,** is an abnormal growth of cells. A neoplasm may be benign ("kind") or malignant (cancerous). A benign neoplasm tends to grow slowly, and its cells stay together. Because benign tumors form masses with distinct borders, they can usually be removed surgically. A **malignant** ("wicked") **neoplasm,** or **cancer,** typically grows much more rapidly and invasively than a benign tumor.

In Chapter 17 you learned that cancer results from abnormal expression of specific genes critical for cell division (see Fig. 17-20). Most cancer cells divide in an uncontrolled way. Unlike normal cells, which respect one another's boundaries and form tissues in an orderly, organized manner, cancer cells grow helter-skelter and infiltrate normal tissues. They apparently no longer receive or respond appropriately to signals from surrounding cells; communication is lacking (see figure).

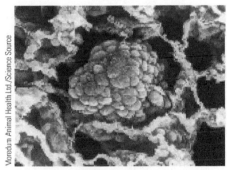

When cancer cells multiply, they invade normal tissues and interfere with their functions. This SEM shows a mass of malignant cells (*pink*) in the air sac in the center. Cancer cells that have separated from the main tumor can be seen in other air sacs. Microvilli on the surface of the cancer cells give them a fuzzy appearance.

When a cancer cell multiplies, all the cells derived from it are also abnormal. Unlike the cells of benign neoplasms, cancer cells do not retain normal structural features. Most human cancers originate in epithelial tissue and are

50 μm

called *carcinomas.* This group includes breast, prostate, colon, lung cancer, and most ovarian cancers. Cancers that develop from connective tissues or muscle are referred to as *sarcomas.*

Death from cancer typically results from **metastasis,** migration of cancer cells through blood or lymph channels to other parts of the body. Once there, cancer cells multiply, forming new malignant neoplasms that interfere with the normal functions of the tissues being invaded. Cancer often spreads so rapidly and extensively that surgeons cannot locate or remove all the malignant masses.

Solid tumors, which account for more than 85% of cancer deaths, require blood vessels to ensure delivery of nourishment and oxygen. Some tumors grow to several millimeters in diameter and then enter a dormant stage, which may last for months or even years. Eventually, cancer cells release a chemical substance that stimulates nearby blood vessels to develop new capillaries. These blood vessels grow into the abnormal mass of cells. Nourished by its new blood supply, the neoplasm may grow rapidly. Newly formed blood vessels have leaky walls that provide a route for metastasis. Malignant cells enter the blood through these walls and are transported to new sites.

Worldwide, cancer causes more than seven million deaths each year. In the United States, cancer is the second leading cause of death. One in three people in the United States develops cancer at some time in his or her life. Currently, the key to survival is early diagnosis and treatment with some combination of surgery, hormonal treatment, radiation therapy, chemotherapy, inhibitors that suppress development of new blood vessels, immunotherapy, and targeted therapies. Many treatments are under investigation, including new agents that inhibit the development of new blood vessels. Immunotherapy for cancer will be discussed in Chapter 45. Cancer is a large family of closely related diseases (there are hundreds of distinct varieties), and treatment must be tailored to the particular type of cancer.

Most cancers are thought to be triggered by **carcinogens,** cancer-producing agents, in the environment, and by diet and lifestyle. Alleles of some genes appear to affect an individual's level of tolerance to carcinogens. You can decrease your risk of developing cancer by following these recommendations:

1. Do not smoke or use tobacco. Smoking is responsible for more than 80% of lung cancer cases, and it increases the risk for many other cancers.

2. Avoid prolonged exposure to the sun. When in the sun, use sunscreen or sunblock. Exposure to the sun is responsible for almost all of the more than two million cases of skin cancer reported each year in the United States alone.

3. Eat a healthy diet, including fresh, unprocessed fruits, vegetables, and grains. Limit intake of red meat. Avoid smoked, salt-cured, and nitrite-cured foods. Limit intake of alcoholic beverages. Reduce intake of foods and drinks that contribute to weight gain. Obesity increases the risk of cancer.

4. Exercise. Physical inactivity has been linked with increased risk of colon, breast, and other cancers.

5. Avoid unnecessary exposure to X-rays.

6. Self-examination and screening can lead to early diagnosis. Beginning at age 50, both men and women should be screened for colorectal cancer. Detection and removal of polyps (benign growths that can become malignant) can prevent cancer.

7. Self-examination and screening for women includes examining their breasts each month and having regular mammograms after age 40. Cervical cancer can be prevented with regular screening tests, such as the Papanicolaou (Pap) and human papilloma virus (HPV) tests. Certain HPV strains cause cervical cancer; vaccines are available.

8. Men over age 55 should discuss with their doctor the benefits of screening for prostate cancer with the prostate-specific antigen (PSA) blood test.

9. Consider genetic testing. If you have a family history of certain cancers, you may be at higher risk genetically for cancer. Genetic tests are now available to determine if you have mutations in the *BRCA1* or *BRCA2* genes, which increase risk for breast, ovarian, and pancreatic cancers. Mutations in several other genes indicate increased risk for colon, uterine, stomach, and urinary tract cancer. If you are at increased risk for cancer, a genetic counselor can advise you of measures you can take to reduce that risk.

Voredum Animal Health Ltd./Science Source

CHECKPOINT 39.1

- **CONNECT** *What are the main differences in structure and function between epithelial tissue and connective tissue?*
- *What type of tissue lines the air sacs of the lungs? How is its structure adapted to its function?*
- *What are some differences between the three types of muscle tissue? How is the structure of each type adapted for its function?*
- *What are the main functions of each of the following organ systems: (1) respiratory, (2) urinary, and (3) endocrine? (Consult Figure 39-4 for help.)*

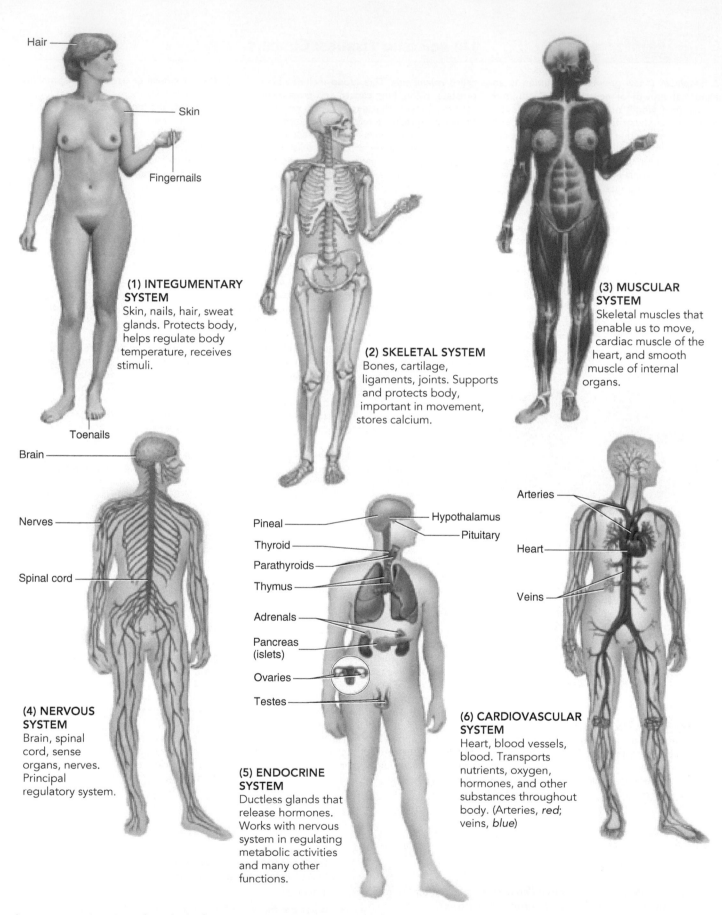

(1) INTEGUMENTARY SYSTEM
Skin, nails, hair, sweat glands. Protects body, helps regulate body temperature, receives stimuli.

Hair

Skin

Fingernails

Toenails

(2) SKELETAL SYSTEM
Bones, cartilage, ligaments, joints. Supports and protects body, important in movement, stores calcium.

(3) MUSCULAR SYSTEM
Skeletal muscles that enable us to move, cardiac muscle of the heart, and smooth muscle of internal organs.

(4) NERVOUS SYSTEM
Brain, spinal cord, sense organs, nerves. Principal regulatory system.

Brain

Nerves

Spinal cord

(5) ENDOCRINE SYSTEM
Ductless glands that release hormones. Works with nervous system in regulating metabolic activities and many other functions.

Pineal

Thyroid

Parathyroids

Thymus

Adrenals

Pancreas (islets)

Ovaries

Testes

Hypothalamus

Pituitary

(6) CARDIOVASCULAR SYSTEM
Heart, blood vessels, blood. Transports nutrients, oxygen, hormones, and other substances throughout body. (Arteries, *red*; veins, *blue*)

Arteries

Heart

Veins

Figure 39-4 *Animation* **The principal organ systems of the human body**

© Cengage Learning

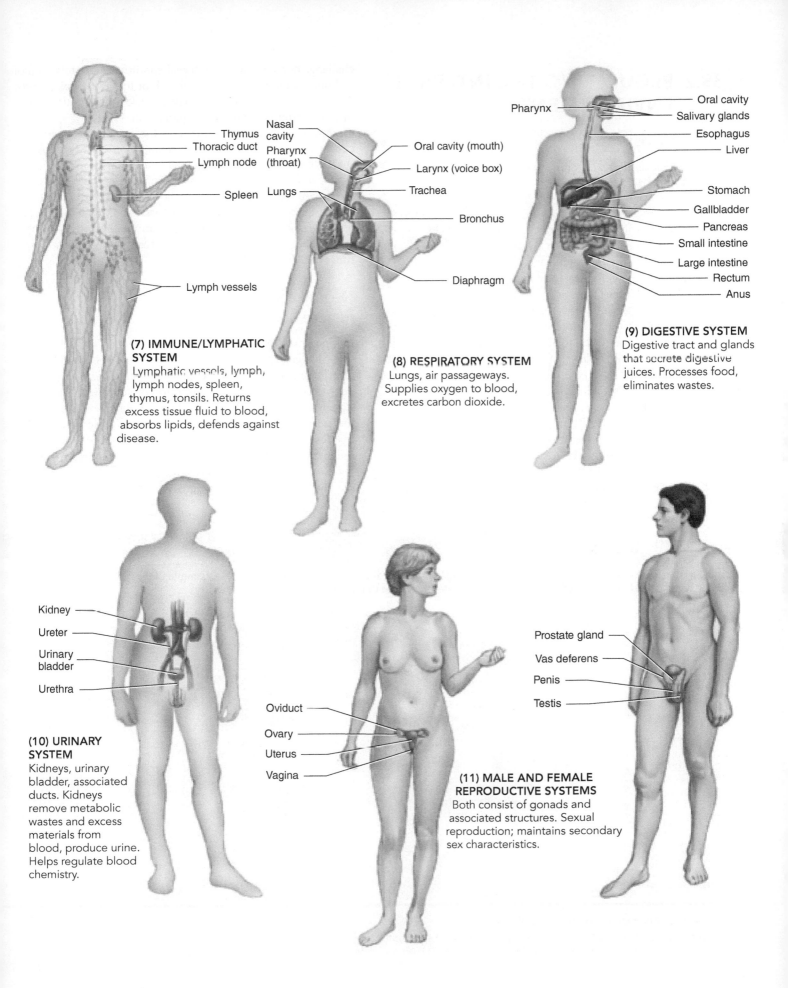

Thymus

Thoracic duct

Lymph node

Spleen

Lymph vessels

(7) IMMUNE/LYMPHATIC SYSTEM
Lymphatic vessels, lymph, lymph nodes, spleen, thymus, tonsils. Returns excess tissue fluid to blood, absorbs lipids, defends against disease.

Nasal cavity

Pharynx (throat)

Lungs

Oral cavity (mouth)

Larynx (voice box)

Trachea

Bronchus

Diaphragm

(8) RESPIRATORY SYSTEM
Lungs, air passageways. Supplies oxygen to blood, excretes carbon dioxide.

Pharynx

Oral cavity

Salivary glands

Esophagus

Liver

Stomach

Gallbladder

Pancreas

Small intestine

Large intestine

Rectum

Anus

(9) DIGESTIVE SYSTEM
Digestive tract and glands that secrete digestive juices. Processes food, eliminates wastes.

Kidney

Ureter

Urinary bladder

Urethra

(10) URINARY SYSTEM
Kidneys, urinary bladder, associated ducts. Kidneys remove metabolic wastes and excess materials from blood, produce urine. Helps regulate blood chemistry.

Oviduct

Ovary

Uterus

Vagina

Prostate gland

Vas deferens

Penis

Testis

(11) MALE AND FEMALE REPRODUCTIVE SYSTEMS
Both consist of gonads and associated structures. Sexual reproduction; maintains secondary sex characteristics.

39.2 REGULATING THE INTERNAL ENVIRONMENT

LEARNING OBJECTIVE

7 Define *homeostasis* and contrast negative and positive feedback systems.

To survive and function, animals must regulate the composition of the fluids that bathe their cells. They must maintain pH and internal temperature within relatively narrow limits. The body must also maintain the appropriate concentration of nutrients, oxygen, and other gases, ions, and compounds needed for metabolism at all times.

Cells, tissues, organs, and organ systems work together to maintain appropriate conditions in the body. The balanced internal environment is referred to as **homeostasis.** Homeostasis is a basic concept in physiology. First coined by U.S. physiologist Walter Cannon, the word *homeostasis* is derived from the Greek *homoios,* meaning "same," and *stasis,* "standing." Although the internal environment never really stays the same, it is a dynamic equilibrium in which conditions are maintained within narrow limits, which we call a **steady state.** The control processes that maintain these conditions are **homeostatic mechanisms.**

Stressors, changes in the internal or external environment that affect normal conditions within the body, continuously challenge homeostasis. An internal condition that moves out of its homeostatic range (either too high or too low) causes **stress.** An organism functions effectively because homeostatic mechanisms continuously operate to manage stress.

Many animals are **conformers** for certain environmental conditions. Some of their internal states vary with changes in their surroundings. For example, most marine invertebrates conform to the salinity of the surrounding sea water. Mammals are superb **regulators.** They have complex homeostatic mechanisms that maintain relatively constant internal conditions despite changes in the outside environment. How do homeostatic mechanisms work? Many are **feedback systems,** sometimes called "biofeedback systems."

Negative feedback systems restore homeostasis

In a **negative feedback system,** a change in some steady state (e.g., normal body temperature) triggers a response that counteracts, or reverses, the change. A **sensor** detects a change, a deviation from the normal condition or **set point.** The sensor signals an **integrator,** or control center. Based on the input of the sensor, the integrator activates homeostatic mechanisms that restore the steady state (**FIG. 39-5**). The response counteracts the inappropriate change, thereby restoring the steady state.

Note that in a negative feedback system, the response of the integrator is *opposite* (negative) to the output of the sensor.

KEY POINT

In a negative feedback system, the response of the integrator is opposite to the input of the sensor; for example, if the glucose concentration in the blood is too low, alpha cells in the pancreas secrete a hormone that increases glucose concentration.

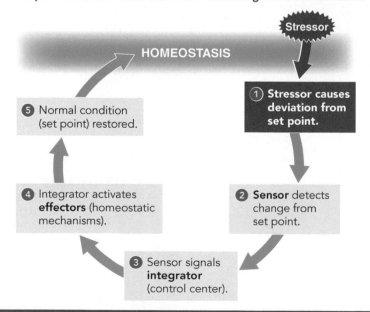

Figure 39-5 *Animation* **Negative feedback**

PREDICT If you drank a soda (high in carbohydrates), what would happen to the glucose concentration in your blood? How do you think your body would respond?

© Cengage Learning

When some condition varies too far from the steady state (either too high or too low), a control system using negative feedback brings the condition back to the steady state. For example, when the glucose concentration in the blood *decreases* below its homeostatic level, negative feedback systems *increase* its concentration. Most homeostatic mechanisms in the body are negative feedback systems.

Let us discuss heat regulation, a specific example of a negative feedback system. The temperature-regulating system in the human body is somewhat similar to how you regulate temperature in your home. You might set a particular room temperature on your thermostat. If the temperature in the room falls, the thermometer in the thermostat acts as a sensor that detects a change, or deviation, from the set point (FIG. 39-6a). The thermometer sends a signal to the thermostat, which then acts as an integrator, or control center. The thermostat compares the sensor's input with the set point. The thermostat then signals the furnace, which is the **effector** in this system. An effector is the device, organ, or process that helps restore the steady state. The furnace increases its heat output, a corrective response that brings the room temperature back to the set point. The thermometer no longer detects a change from the set point, so the thermostat and furnace are switched off.

As shown in FIGURE 39-6b, the negative feedback system that regulates body temperature works like a home thermostat. When body temperature decreases below normal limits, specialized nerve cells (sensors) signal the temperature-regulating center in the hypothalamus of the brain (the integrator). The integrator activates effectors that bring the temperature back to the set point. The return to normal temperature signals the

sensors, and the temperature-regulating center switches off the effectors.

A few positive feedback systems operate in the body

In a **positive feedback system,** a change in some steady state sets off a response that intensifies (rather than reverses) the changing condition. Although some positive feedback mechanisms are beneficial, they do not maintain homeostasis. For example, a positive feedback cycle operates during the birth of a baby. As the baby's head pushes against the cervix (lower part of uterus), a reflex action causes the uterus to contract. The contraction forces the head against the cervix again, stimulating another contraction, and the positive feedback cycle repeats again and again until the baby is born. Some positive feedback sequences, such as those that deepen circulatory shock following severe hemorrhage, can disrupt steady states and lead to death. A simplified example is shown in FIGURE 39-7.

Homeostatic mechanisms maintain the internal environment within the physiological limits that support life. As you continue your study of animal processes, you will learn many ways in which organ systems interact to maintain the steady state of the organism. Although the nervous and endocrine systems play major roles, all organ systems participate in these regulatory processes. In the next section, we discuss some specific homeostatic mechanisms that help regulate body temperature.

CHECKPOINT 39.2

- *Contrast negative and positive feedback systems.*

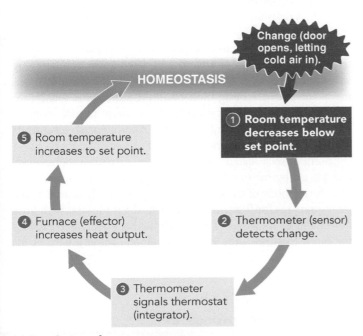

(a) Regulation of room temperature.

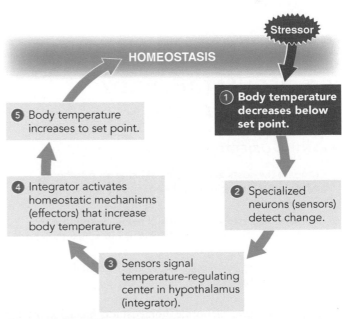

(b) Regulation of body temperature.

Figure 39-6 Negative feedback in temperature regulation

Note that the diagram in **(b)** is highly simplified. Figure 39-9 shows greater detail.

© Cengage Learning

Positive feedback intensifies the change taking place, moving conditions farther away from homeostasis; in some situations such as hemorrhage, the results can be fatal.

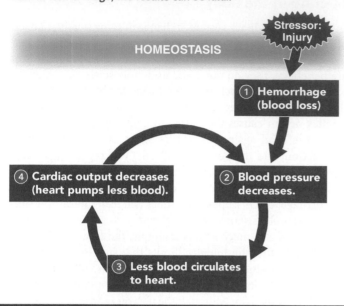

Figure 39-7 Positive feedback

In positive feedback the changes that occur increase the deviation from the set point. Conditions move away from the normal range. Loss of blood decreases blood pressure. Less blood reaches the heart, so heart function decreases. The resulting decrease in cardiac output further decreases blood pressure, bringing conditions farther from homeostasis.

PREDICT What might happen if you could convert this positive feedback system to a negative feedback system?

© Cengage Learning

39.3 REGULATING BODY TEMPERATURE

LEARNING OBJECTIVES

8 Compare the costs and benefits of being an ectotherm; and describe strategies ectotherms use to adjust their body temperature.

9 Compare the costs and benefits of being an endotherm; and describe strategies endotherms use to adjust their body temperature.

10 Describe strategies animals use to adjust to challenging temperature changes.

Many animals have elaborate homeostatic mechanisms for regulating body temperature. Some are physiological, and others are structural or behavioral. **Thermoregulation** is the process of maintaining body temperature within certain limits despite changes in the surrounding temperature. Animals produce heat as a byproduct of metabolic activities. Body temperature is determined by the rate at which heat is produced and the rate at which heat is lost to, or gained from, the outside environment.

The strategies for maintaining body temperature that are available to an animal may restrict the type of environment it can inhabit. Each species has an optimal environmental temperature range. Some animals, such as snowshoe hares, snowy owls, and weasels, can survive in cold arctic regions. Others, such as the Cape ground squirrel, which inhabits South Africa, are adapted to hot tropical climates. Although some animals can survive at temperature extremes, most survive only within moderate temperature ranges.

Ectotherms absorb heat from their surroundings

Ectotherms are animals that depend on the environment for their body heat. Their body temperature is determined mainly by the changing temperature of their surroundings. Most of the heat for their thermoregulation comes from the sun. In contrast, **endotherms** have homeostatic mechanisms that maintain body temperature despite changes in the external temperature. You may be surprised to learn that most animals are ectotherms.

An ectotherm's metabolic rate tends to change with the weather. These animals have a far lower daily energy expenditure than endotherms because they do not maintain a high metabolic rate. They therefore survive on less food and convert more of the energy in their food to growth and reproduction than do endotherms. Ectothermy also has costs. One disadvantage is that daily and seasonal temperature conditions may limit their activity.

Many ectotherms use behavioral strategies to adjust body temperature. For example, lizards may keep warm by burrowing in the soil at night. During the day, lizards take in heat by basking in the sun, orienting their bodies to expose the maximum surface area to the sun's rays (FIG. 39-8a). Many animals migrate to warmer climates during the winter. Another behavioral strategy for regulating temperature is *hibernation*.

Some insects use a combination of structural, behavioral, and physiological mechanisms to regulate body temperature. The "furry" body of the moth helps conserve body heat. When a moth prepares for flight, it contracts its flight muscles with little movement of its wings. The metabolic heat generated enables the moth to sustain the intense metabolic activity needed for flight.

Endotherms derive heat from metabolic processes

Birds and mammals, as well as some species of fish (e.g., tuna and some sharks) and some insects, are endotherms. The most important benefit of endothermy is the high metabolic rate, which can be as much as six times higher than that of ecto-therms. The constant body temperature of endotherms allows a higher rate of enzyme activity than is possible for ectotherms living in the same habitat. Endotherms also can respond more rapidly to internal and external stimuli than ectotherms. They can be active even in low winter temperatures, but these animals

must pay the high energy cost of thermoregulation even during times when they are inactive. You must maintain your body temperature even when you are asleep.

Endotherms have structural adaptations for maintaining body temperature. For example, the insulating feathers of birds, hair of mammals, and insulating layers of fat in birds and mammals reduce heat loss from the body. Birds and mammals also have behavioral adaptations for maintaining body temperature. The Cape ground squirrel positions its tail to shade its body from the direct rays of the sun. Elephants spray themselves with cool water.

Endotherms have a variety of physiological mechanisms for maintaining temperature homeostasis. They regulate heat production and regulate heat exchange with the environment. Most of their body heat comes from their own metabolic processes (see *Inquiring About: Electron Transport and Heat*, in Chapter 8).

In mammals receptors located in the hypothalamus of the brain and in the spinal cord regulate temperature. Heat from metabolic activities can be increased directly or can be increased indirectly by the action of hormones (such as thyroid hormones) that increase metabolic rate. Heat production is increased by contracting muscles, and in cold weather many animals shiver.

When body temperature rises, birds and many mammals pant, and some mammals sweat (FIG. 39-8b). These processes provide fluid for evaporation: the conversion of a liquid, such as sweat, to water vapor. (Recall from Chapter 2 that when molecules enter the vapor phase, they take their heat energy with them.) Heat transfers from the body to the surroundings, resulting in evaporative cooling.

In the human body, about 2.5 million sweat glands secrete sweat. As sweat evaporates from the skin surface, body temperature decreases. Constriction and dilation of capillaries in the skin are also homeostatic mechanisms for regulating body temperature.

In humans, when body temperature increases above normal, specialized nerve cells signal the temperature-regulating center in the hypothalamus (FIG. 39-9). This center sends messages by way of nerves to the sweat glands, which increase sweat secretion. At the same time, the hypothalamus sends messages to smooth muscle in the walls of blood vessels in the skin that cause them to dilate. More blood circulates through the skin, bringing heat to the body surface. The skin acts as a heat radiator that allows heat to radiate from the body surface into the environment. These homeostatic mechanisms help return body temperature to normal.

When body temperature decreases below normal, the hypothalamus signals the anterior pituitary gland to release a hormone that signals the thyroid gland. Secretion of thyroid hormones increases, which raises metabolic rate. Body tissues increase heat production. The hypothalamus also sends neural signals that cause blood vessels in the skin to constrict. As a result, less heat is brought to the body surface. In addition, nerves signal muscles to shiver or let you move muscles voluntarily to increase body temperature.

(a) Ectotherm. The rainbow agama (*Agama agama*) increases its body temperature by sunning itself. This insect-eating lizard was photographed in Serengeti National Park, Tanzania.

(b) Endotherm. This young emperor penguin (*Aptenodytes forsteri*) is panting to stay cool. Body temperature decreases as heat leaves the body through its open mouth.

Figure 39-8 Behavioral adaptations for thermoregulation

Figure 39-9 *Animation* **Regulation of temperature in the human body**

The hypothalamus is the integrator that maintains homeostasis of body temperature by activating mechanisms that **(a)** cool or **(b)** warm the body in response to stressors.

© Cengage Learning

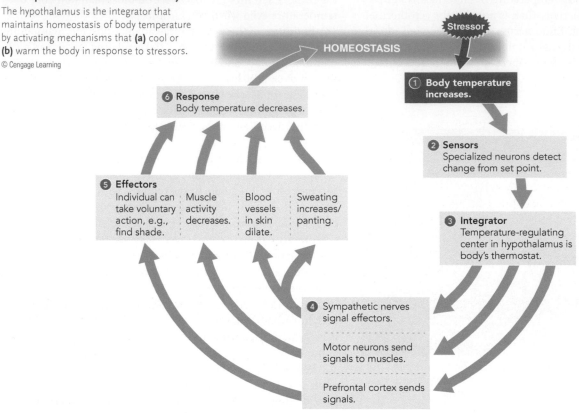

(a) **When body temperature increases.** Sensors detect any increase in body temperature above its homeostatic range. They send signals to the hypothalamus, which then signals effectors to take corrective action. Temperature decreases, restoring homeostasis.

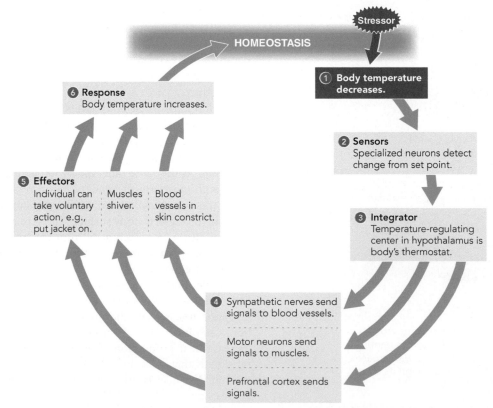

(b) **When body temperature decreases.** Sensors detect any decrease in body temperature below its homeostatic range. They send signals to the hypothalamus, which then signals effectors to take corrective action. Temperature increases, restoring homeostasis.

Many animals adjust to challenging temperature changes

Animals adjust to seasonal changes, a process called **acclimatization.** A familiar example is the thickening of a dog's coat in the winter. As water temperature decreases during fall and winter, a trout's enzyme systems decrease their level of activity, allowing the trout to remain active at the lowest metabolic cost.

When stressed by cold, many small endotherms sink into **torpor,** a short-term state in which metabolic rate decreases, sometimes dramatically. Torpor saves the energy that the animal would use to maintain a high body temperature. Instead, body temperature decreases below normal levels. The decrease in body temperature is brought about by a decrease in the temperature set point in the hypothalamus. Heart and respiratory rates decrease, and animals are less responsive to external stimulation. Daily torpor occurs in some small endotherms, such as hummingbirds and shrews. We can think of torpor as an adaptive hypothermia that helps animals survive during times of cold temperatures.

Hibernation is long-term torpor in response to winter cold and scarcity of food. Animals that hibernate store unsaturated fats to use as energy sources. **Estivation** is a state of torpor caused by lack of food or water during periods of high temperature. During estivation, some mammals retreat to their burrows. The cactus mouse enters a state of hibernation during the winter in response to cold and scarcity of food. In the summer, it estivates in response to lack of either food or water.

CHECKPOINT 39.3

- *What are some costs and benefits of ectothermy? How do ectotherms adjust body temperature?*
- *What are some costs and benefits of endothermy?*
- **VISUALIZE** *How is body temperature regulated in humans? Draw a diagram to illustrate your answer.*

SUMMARY: FOCUS ON LEARNING OBJECTIVES

39.1 Tissues, Organs, and Organ Systems *(page 816)*

1 Compare the structure and function of the four main kinds of animal tissues: epithelial, connective, muscle, and nervous tissues.

- A **tissue** consists of a group of similarly specialized cells that associate to perform specific functions. **Epithelial tissue** (*epithelium*) forms a continuous layer, or sheet, of cells covering a body surface or lining a body cavity. Epithelial tissue functions in protection, absorption, secretion, and sensation.
- **Connective tissue** consists of relatively few cells separated by an **intercellular substance,** composed of **fibers** scattered throughout a **matrix.** The intercellular substance contains three types of fibers.
- Connective tissue contains specialized cells such as **fibroblasts** and **macrophages.** Connective tissue joins other tissues of the body, supports the body and its organs, and protects underlying organs.
- **Muscle** tissue consists of cells specialized to contract. Each cell is an elongated muscle fiber containing many contractile units called **myofibrils. Nervous tissue** consists of elongated cells called neurons, specialized for transmitting impulses, and **glial cells,** which support and nourish the neurons.

2 Compare the main types of epithelial tissue and describe their functions.

- Epithelial cells may be *squamous, cuboidal,* or *columnar* in shape. Epithelial tissue may be *simple, stratified,* or *pseudostratified* (summarized in Table 39-1).
- *Simple squamous epithelium* lines blood vessels and the air sacs in the lungs; it permits exchange of materials by diffusion. *Simple cuboidal epithelium* and *columnar epithelium* line passageways and are specialized for secretion and absorption. *Stratified squamous epithelium* forms the outer layer of the skin and lines passageways into the body; it provides protection. *Pseudostratified epithelium* also lines passageways and protects underlying tissues.
- Some epithelial tissue is specialized to form **glands. Goblet cells** are unicellular glands that secrete mucus. Goblet cells are **exocrine glands** that secrete their product through a duct onto an exposed epithelial surface. In contrast, **endocrine glands** release hormones into the **interstitial fluid** or blood.
- An *epithelial membrane* consists of a sheet of epithelial tissue and a layer of underlying connective tissue. A **mucous membrane** lines a cavity that opens to the outside of the body. A **serous membrane** lines a body cavity that does not open to the outside.

3 Compare the main types of connective tissue and describe their functions.

- The cells of connective tissue are embedded in an intercellular substance that consists of microscopic *collagen fibers, elastic fibers,* and *reticular fibers* (thin branched fibers) scattered through a **matrix,** a thin gel of polysaccharides. **Loose connective tissue** consists of fibers running in various directions through a semifluid matrix; it forms a covering for nerves, blood vessels, and muscles.
- **Dense connective tissue** is strong but less flexible than loose connective tissue. It forms **tendons,** cords that connect muscles to bones, and **ligaments,** cables that connect bones to one another.
- Elastic connective tissue consists of bundles of parallel elastic fibers; it is found in lung tissue and in walls of large arteries. *Reticular connective tissue,* which consists of interlacing reticular fibers, forms a supporting framework for many organs.
- **Adipose tissue** is made up of fat cells; it is found along with loose connective tissue in subcutaneous tissue.
- **Cartilage** consists of **chondrocytes** that lie in lacunae, small cavities in a hard matrix. **Osteocytes** secrete and maintain the matrix of **bone.** Unlike cartilage, bone is quite vascular. Cartilage and bone form the skeleton of vertebrates.
- **Blood** and **lymph** are circulating tissues that help various parts of an animal communicate with one another. The intercellular substances of blood and lymph are more fluid than those of other tissues.

4 Contrast the three types of muscle tissue and describe their functions.

- **Skeletal muscle** is striated and under voluntary control. Each elongated, cylindrical **muscle fiber** has several nuclei. When skeletal muscles contract, they move parts of the body.
- **Cardiac muscle** is also striated, but its contractions are involuntary. Its elongated, cylindrical fibers branch and fuse; each fiber has one or two central nuclei. When this muscle contracts, the heart pumps the blood.
- **Smooth muscle** contracts involuntarily; its elongated, spindle-shaped fibers lack striations. Each fiber has a single central nucleus. Smooth muscle is responsible for movement of body organs; for example, it pushes food through the digestive tract.

5 Relate the structure of the neuron to its function.

- The elongated **neuron** is adapted for receiving and transmitting information. **Dendrites** receive signals and transmit them to the **cell body.** The **axon** transmits signals away from the cell body to other neurons or to a muscle or gland. A **synapse** is a junction between neurons.

6 Briefly describe the organ systems of a mammal and summarize the functions of each organ system.

- Tissues and **organs** work together, forming **organ systems.** In mammals 11 organ systems work together to carry out the functions required by the **organism:** the **integumentary system, skeletal system, muscular system, nervous system, endocrine system, cardiovascular system, lymphatic system,** which functions as part of the **immune system, respiratory, digestive, urinary,** and **reproductive systems** (summarized in Figure 39-4). Each organ system functions to maintain homeostasis.

39.2 Regulating the Internal Environment *(page 828)*

7 Define *homeostasis* and contrast negative and positive feedback systems.

- **Homeostasis** is the balanced internal environment, or steady state. The control processes that maintain these conditions are **homeostatic mechanisms,** mainly **negative feedback systems.** When a stressor causes a change in some steady state, a response is triggered that counteracts the change.

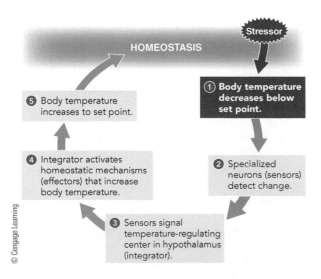

A **sensor** detects the change, a deviation from the normal condition or **set point.** The sensor signals an **integrator,** or control center. Based on the output of the sensor, the integrator activates one or more **effectors,** organs or processes that restore the steady state.

- In a **positive feedback system,** a deviation from the steady state sets off a series of changes that intensify (rather than reverse) the changes.

39.3 Regulating Body Temperature *(page 830)*

8 Compare the costs and benefits of being an ectotherm; and describe strategies ectotherms use to adjust their body temperature.

- Animals have structural, behavioral, and physiological strategies for **thermoregulation,** the process of maintaining body temperature within certain limits despite changes in the surrounding temperature.
- In **ectotherms** body temperature depends to a large extent on the temperature of the environment. A benefit of ectothermy is that very little energy is used to maintain metabolic rate. A disadvantage is that activity may be limited by daily and seasonal temperature conditions. Many ectotherms use behavioral strategies to adjust body temperatures.

9 Compare the costs and benefits of being an endotherm; and describe strategies endotherms use to adjust their body temperature.

- **Endotherms** have homeostatic mechanisms for regulating body temperature within a narrow range. The most important benefit of endothermy is a high metabolic rate. Another advantage is that constant body temperature allows a higher rate of enzyme activity. Many endotherms are active even in low winter temperatures. A disadvantage of endothermy is its high energy cost.

10 Describe strategies animals use to adjust to challenging temperature changes.

- **Acclimatization** is the process of adjustment to seasonal changes.
- When challenged by a drop in surrounding temperature, many small endotherms enter a state of torpor. **Torpor** is an adaptive hypothermia; body temperature is maintained below normal levels. **Hibernation** is long-term torpor in response to winter cold. **Estivation** is torpor caused by lack of food or water during summer heat.

Know and Comprehend

1. Tissue that contains fibroblasts and a great deal of intercellular substance is (a) connective tissue (b) muscle tissue (c) nervous tissue (d) pseudostratified epithelium (e) simple squamous epithelium

2. Tissue that contracts and is striated and involuntary would most likely be found in (a) the leg (b) the wall of the stomach (c) the exocrine glands (d) body structures requiring very rapid contraction (e) the heart

3. Which organ system has the homeostatic function of helping regulate volume and composition of blood and body fluids? (a) integumentary (b) muscular (c) reproductive (d) urinary (e) exocrine

4. Most homeostatic functions in the body are maintained by (a) exocrine glands (b) negative feedback systems (c) set points (d) stressors (e) positive feedback systems

5. Which of the following is *not* true of torpor? (a) it is an adaptive state of low body temperature (b) the temperature set point in the hypothalamus decreases (c) metabolic rate increases (d) it is a strategy used by some endotherms (e) respiratory rate decreases

6. An ectotherm (a) has a higher rate of enzyme activity than a typical endotherm (b) has a variety of homeostatic mechanisms for regulating body temperature (c) depends on sensors in the hypothalamus to regulate temperature (d) may use behavioral strategies to help adjust body temperature (e) must expend more energy on thermoregulation than an endotherm

Apply and Analyze

7. **VISUALIZE** Draw (a) simple cuboidal epithelium lining a kidney tubule and (b) loose connective tissue.

8. **VISUALIZE** Draw a flowchart showing the relationship among organ systems, tissues, cells, and organs.

9. **PREDICT** Jim has lost a great deal of epithelium due to a chemical burn. What effects might this change have on his body and its ability to function?

10. **PREDICT** The intercellular substance of the connective tissue in a dog's skin is decreasing due to a rare disease. What effect might this change have on the dog's body?

11. **PREDICT** A high concentration of carbon dioxide in the blood and interstitial fluid results in more rapid breathing. What effect would rapid breathing have on homeostasis?

Evaluate and Synthesize

12. **EVOLUTION LINK** From an evolutionary perspective, why do you think most animals are ectotherms? (*Hint:* What are some benefits of ectothermy?)

13. **SCIENCE, TECHNOLOGY, AND SOCIETY** Imagine that you are a health care professional. If a patient told you that she had a family history of breast cancer, would you advise her to be genetically tested? Why or why not? What if you had a family history of cancer? Would you want to be tested?

To access course materials, such as Aplia and other companion resources, please visit **www.cengagebrain.com.**

Introduction to Ecology: Population Ecology

© Joe Belanger/Shutterstock.com

A population of Mexican poppies. Mexican poppies (*Eschsolzia mexicana*), which thrive on gravelly desert slopes, bloom in the desert after the winter rains.

KEY CONCEPTS

53.1 A population can be described in terms of its density, dispersion, birth and death rates, growth rate, survivorship, and age structure.

53.2 Changes in population size are caused by natality, mortality, immigration, and emigration.

53.3 Population size may be influenced by density-dependent factors and density-independent factors.

53.4 Life history traits of a population are adaptations that affect the ability of individuals to survive and reproduce.

53.5 A metapopulation consists of two or more local populations with dispersal occurring among them.

53.6 Human population structure differs among countries in ways that are primarily related to differences in level of development.

The science of **ecology** is the study of how living organisms and the physical environment interact in an immense and complicated web of relationships. Biologists call the interactions among organisms **biotic factors** and those between organisms and their nonliving, physical environment **abiotic factors.** Abiotic factors include precipitation, temperature, pH, wind, and chemical nutrients. Ecologists formulate hypotheses to explain such phenomena as the distribution and abundance of life, the ecological roles of specific species, the interactions among species in communities, and the importance of ecosystems in maintaining the health of the biosphere. They then test these hypotheses.

The focus of ecology can be local or global, specific or generalized, depending on what questions the scientist is asking and trying to answer. Ecology is the broadest field in biology, with explicit links to evolution and every other biological discipline. It includes studies on transfer of information among organisms and analyses of the transfer of energy for life. Its universality encompasses subjects that are not traditionally part of biology. Earth science, geology, chemistry, oceanography, climatology, and meteorology are extremely important to ecology, especially when ecologists examine the abiotic environment of planet Earth. Because humans are part of Earth's web of life, all our activities, including economics and politics, have profound ecological implications. *Environmental science,* a scientific discipline with ties to ecology, focuses on how humans interact with the environment.

As you learned in Chapter 1, most ecologists are interested in the levels of biological organization including and above the level of the individual organism: population, community, ecosystem, landscape, and biosphere. Each level has its own characteristic composition, structure, and functioning.

An individual belongs to a **population,** a group consisting of members of the same species that live together in a prescribed area at the same time. The boundaries of the area are defined by the ecologist performing a particular study. A population ecologist might study a population of microorganisms, animals, or plants, like the Mexican poppies in the photograph, to see how individuals within it live and interact with one another, with other species in their community, and with their physical environment.

In this chapter we begin our study of ecological principles by focusing on the study of populations as functioning systems and end with a discussion of the human population. Subsequent chapters examine the interactions among different populations within communities (Chapter 54), the dynamic exchanges between communities and their physical environments (Chapter 55), the characteristics of Earth's major biological ecosystems (Chapter 56), and biological diversity and conservation biology (Chapter 57).

53.1 FEATURES OF POPULATIONS

LEARNING OBJECTIVE

1 Define *population density* and *dispersion,* and describe the main types of population dispersion.

Populations exhibit characteristics distinctive from those of the individuals of which they are composed. Some features discussed in this chapter that characterize populations are population density, population dispersion, birth and death rates, growth rates, survivorship, and age structure.

Although communities consist of all the populations of all the different species that live together within an area, populations have properties that communities lack. Populations, for example, share a common gene pool (see Chapter 19). Consequently, natural selection can cause changes in allele frequencies in populations. As a result, allele frequency changes resulting from natural selection occur in populations. Natural selection therefore acts directly to produce adaptive changes in populations and only indirectly affects the community level.

Population ecology considers both the number of individuals of a particular species that are found in an area and the dynamics of the population. **Population dynamics** is the study of changes in populations: how and why those numbers increase or decrease over time. Population ecologists try to determine the processes common to all populations. They study how a population interacts with its environment, such as how individuals in a population compete for food or other resources and how predation, disease, and other environmental pressures affect the population. Population growth, whether of bacteria, maples, or giraffes, cannot increase indefinitely because of such environmental pressures.

Additional aspects of populations that interest biologists are their reproductive success or failure (extinction), their evolution, their genetics, and the way they affect the normal functioning of communities and ecosystems. Biologists in applied disciplines, such as forestry, agronomy (crop science), and wildlife management, must understand population ecology to manage populations of economic importance, such as forests, field crops, game animals, or fishes. Understanding the population dynamics of endangered and threatened species plays a key role in efforts to prevent their slide to extinction. Knowledge of population ecology helps in efforts to prevent the increase of pest populations to levels that cause significant economic or health effects.

Density and dispersion are important features of populations

The concept of population size is meaningful only when the boundaries of that population are defined. Consider, for example, the difference between 1000 mice in 100 hectares (250 acres) and 1000 mice in 1 hectare (2.5 acres). Often a population is too large to study in its entirety. Researchers examine such a population by sampling a part of it and then expressing the population in terms of density. Examples include the number of dandelions per square meter of lawn, the number of water fleas per liter of pond water, and the number of cabbage aphids per square centimeter of cabbage leaf. **Population density,** then, is the number of individuals of a species per unit of area or volume at a given time.

Different environments vary in the population density of any species they can support. This density may also vary in a single habitat from season to season or year to year. For example, red grouse are ground-dwelling game birds whose populations are managed for hunting. Consider two red grouse populations in the treeless moors of northwestern Scotland, at locations only 2.5 km (1.5 mi) apart. At one location the population density remained stationary during a three-year period, but at the other site it almost doubled in the first two years and then declined to its initial density in the third year. The reason was likely a difference in habitat. Researchers had experimentally burned the area where the population density increased initially and then decreased. Young heather shoots (*Calluna vulgaris*) produced after the burn provided nutritious food for the red grouse. So, population density may be determined in large part by biotic or abiotic factors in the environment that are external to the individuals in the population.

The individuals in a population often exhibit characteristic patterns of **dispersion,** or spacing, relative to one another. Individuals may be spaced in a random, clumped, or uniform dispersion. **Random dispersion** occurs when individuals in a population are spaced throughout an area in a manner that is unrelated to the presence of others (FIG. 53-1a). Of the three major types of dispersion, random dispersion is least common and hardest to observe in nature, leading some ecologists to question its existence. Trees of the same species, for example, sometimes appear to be distributed randomly in a tropical rain forest. However, an international team of 13 ecologists studied six tropical forest plots that were 25 to 52 hectares (62 to 130 acres) in area and reported that most of the 1000 tree species observed were clumped and not randomly dispersed. (Ecologists determine both clumped and uniform dispersion by statistically testing for differences from an assumed random distribution.) Random dispersion may occur infrequently because important environmental factors affecting dispersion usually do not occur at random. Flour beetle larvae in a container of flour are randomly dispersed, but their environment (flour) is unusually homogeneous.

Perhaps the most common spacing is **clumped dispersion,** also called **aggregated distribution** or **patchiness,** which occurs when individuals are concentrated in specific parts of the habitat. Clumped dispersion often results from the patchy

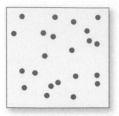

(a) Random dispersion, illustrated for comparison, rarely, if ever, occurs in nature.

Andrew G. Wood/Science Source

(b) Clumped dispersion is evident in the schooling behavior of certain fish species. Shown are bluestripe snappers (*Lutjanus kasmira*), photographed in Hawaii. This introduced fish, which grows to 30 cm (12 in.), may be displacing native fish species in Hawaiian waters.

Robert Hernandez/Science Source

(c) Uniform dispersion is characteristic of these nesting Cape gannets (*Morus capensis*) on the coast of South Africa. The birds space their nests more or less evenly.

Figure 53-1 Dispersion of individuals within a population
© Cengage Learning

distribution of resources in the environment. It also occurs among animals because of the presence of family groups and pairs, and among plants because of limited seed dispersal or asexual reproduction. An entire grove of aspen trees, for example, may originate asexually from a single plant. Clumped dispersion may sometimes be advantageous because

social animals derive many benefits from their association. Many fish species, for example, associate in dense schools for at least part of their life cycle, possibly because schooling may reduce the risk of predation for any particular individual (**FIG. 53-1b**). The many pairs of eyes of schooling fish tend to detect predators more effectively than a single pair of eyes of a single fish. When threatened, schooling fish clump together more closely, making it difficult for a predator to single out an individual.

Uniform dispersion occurs when individuals are more evenly spaced than would be expected from a random occupation of a given habitat. A nesting colony of seabirds, in which the birds are nesting in a relatively homogeneous environment and place their nests at a more or less equal distance from one another, is an example of uniform dispersion (**FIG. 53-1c**). What might this spacing pattern tell us? In this case, uniform dispersion may occur as a result of nesting territoriality. Aggressive interactions among the nesting birds as they peck at one another from their nests cause each pair to place its nest just beyond the reach of nearby nesting birds. Uniform dispersion also occurs when competition among individuals is severe, when plant roots or leaves that have been shed produce toxic substances that inhibit the growth of nearby plants, or when animals establish feeding or mating territories.

Some populations have different spacing patterns at different ages. Competition for sunlight among same-aged sand pine in a Florida scrub community resulted in a change over time from either random or clumped dispersion when the plants were young to uniform dispersion when the plants were old. Sand pine is a fire-adapted plant with cones that do not release their seeds until they have been exposed to high temperatures (45°C to 50°C or higher). As a result of seed dispersal and soil conditions following a fire, the seedlings grow back in dense stands that exhibit random or slightly clumped dispersion. Over time, however, many of the more crowded trees tend to die from shading or competition, resulting in uniform dispersion of the surviving trees (**TABLE 53-1**).

CHECKPOINT 53.1

- *What is the difference between population density and dispersion?*
- **CONNECT** *What are some biological advantages of a clumped dispersion? What are some disadvantages?*

TABLE 53-1	**Dispersion in a Sand Pine Population in Florida**	
TREE TRUNKS EXAMINED	**DENSITY (per m²)**	**DISPERSION**
All (alive and dead)	0.16	Random
Alive only	0.08	Uniform

Source: Adapted from Laessle, A.M. "Spacing and Competition in Natural Stands of Sand Pine." *Ecology,* Vol. 46, pp. 65–72, 1965. Data were collected 51 years after a fire.

53.2 CHANGES IN POPULATION SIZE

One goal of science is to discover common patterns among separate observations. As mentioned previously, population ecologists wish to understand general processes that are shared by many different populations, so they develop mathematical models based on equations that describe the dynamics of a single population. Population models are not perfect representations of a population, but models help illuminate complex processes. Moreover, mathematical modeling enhances the scientific process by providing a framework with which experimental population studies can be compared. We can test a model and see how it fits or does not fit with existing data. Data that are inconsistent with the model are particularly useful because they demand that we ask how the natural system differs from the mathematical model that we developed to explain it. As more knowledge accumulates from observations and experiments, the model is refined and made more precise.

Population size, whether of sunflowers, elephants, or humans, changes over time. On a global scale, this change is ultimately caused by two factors, expressed on a per capita (i.e., per individual) basis: **natality,** the average per capita birth rate; and **mortality,** the average per capita death rate. In humans the birth rate is usually expressed as the number of births per 1000 people per year and the death rate as the number of deaths per 1000 people per year.

To determine the rate of change in population size, we must also take into account the time interval involved, that is, the change in time. To express change in equations, we employ the Greek letter delta (Δ). In equation (1), ΔN is the change in the number of individuals in the population, Δt the change in time, N the number of individuals in the existing population, b the natality, and d the mortality.

$$(1)\ \Delta N/\Delta t = N(b - d)$$

The **growth rate (r),** or rate of change (increase or decrease) of a population on a per capita basis, is the birth rate minus the death rate:

$$(2)\ r = b - d$$

As an example, consider a hypothetical human population of 10,000 in which there are 200 births per year (i.e., by convention, 20 births per 1000 people) and 100 deaths per year (10 deaths per 1000 people):

$$r = 20/1000 - 10/1000 = 0.02 - 0.01 = 0.01, \text{ or } 1\% \text{ per year}$$

A modification of equation (1) tells us the rate at which the population is growing at a particular instant in time, that is, its instantaneous growth rate (dN/dt). (The symbols dN and dt are the mathematical differentials of N and t, respectively; they are not products, nor should the d in dN or dt be confused with the death rate, d.) Using differential calculus, this growth rate can be expressed as follows:

$$(3)\ dN/dt = rN$$

where N is the number of individuals in the existing population, t the time, and r the per capita growth rate.

Because $r = b - d$, if individuals in the population are born faster than they die, r is a positive value and population size increases. If individuals in the population die faster than they are born, r is a negative value and population size decreases. If r is equal to zero, births and deaths match, and population size is stationary despite continued reproduction and death.

Dispersal affects the growth rate in some populations

In addition to birth and death rates, **dispersal,** which is movement of individuals among populations, must be considered when examining changes in populations on a *local* scale. There are two types of dispersal: immigration and emigration. **Immigration** occurs when individuals enter a population and thus increase its size. **Emigration** occurs when individuals leave a population and thus decrease its size. The growth rate of a local population must take into account birth rate (b), death rate (d), immigration rate (i), and emigration rate (e) on a per capita basis. The per capita growth rate equals the birth rate minus the death rate, plus the immigration rate minus the emigration rate:

$$(4)\ r = (b - d) + (i - e)$$

For example, the growth rate of a human population of 10,000 that has 200 births (by convention, 20 per 1000), 100 deaths (10 per 1000), 10 immigrants (1 per 1000), and 100 emigrants (10 per 1000) in a given year would be calculated as follows:

$$r = (20/1000 - 10/1000) + (1/1000 - 10/1000)$$
$$= 0.001, \text{ or } 0.1\% \text{ per year}$$

Each population has a characteristic intrinsic rate of increase

The maximum rate at which a population of a given species could increase under ideal conditions, when resources are abundant and its population density is low, is known as its **intrinsic rate of increase (r_{max}).** Different species have different intrinsic rates of increase. A particular species' intrinsic rate of increase is influenced by several factors. They include the age at which reproduction begins, the fraction of the **lifespan** (duration of the individual's life) during which the individual is capable of reproducing, the number of reproductive periods per lifetime, and the number of offspring the individual is capable of producing during each period of reproduction. These factors, which we discuss in greater detail later in the chapter, determine whether a particular species has a large or small intrinsic rate of increase.

Generally, large species such as blue whales and elephants have the smallest intrinsic rates of increase, whereas microorganisms have the greatest intrinsic rates of increase. Under ideal conditions (an environment with unlimited resources), certain bacteria can reproduce by binary fission every 20 minutes. At this rate of growth, a single bacterium would increase to a population of more than one billion in just ten hours!

If we plot the population size versus time under optimal conditions, the graph has a J shape that is characteristic of **exponential population growth,** which is the accelerating population growth rate that occurs when optimal conditions allow a constant per capita growth rate (FIG. 53-2). When a population grows exponentially, it grows faster as it gets larger.

Regardless of which species we are considering, whenever a population is growing at its intrinsic rate of increase, population size plotted versus time gives a curve of the same shape. The only variable is time. It may take longer for an elephant population than for a bacterial population to reach a certain size (because elephants do not reproduce as rapidly as bacteria), but both populations will always increase exponentially as long as their per capita growth rates remain constant.

No population can increase exponentially indefinitely

Certain populations may grow exponentially for brief periods. Exponential growth has been experimentally demonstrated in certain insects and in cultures of bacteria or protists (by continually supplying nutrients and removing waste products). However, organisms cannot reproduce indefinitely at their intrinsic

rate of increase because the environment sets limits. These limits include such unfavorable environmental conditions as the limited availability of food, water, shelter, and other essential resources (resulting in increased competition) as well as limits imposed by disease and predation.

In the earlier example, bacteria in nature would never be able to reproduce unchecked for an indefinite period because they would run out of food and living space, and poisonous wastes would accumulate in their vicinity. With crowding, bacteria would also become more susceptible to parasites (high population densities facilitate the spread of infectious organisms such as viruses among individuals) and predators (high population densities increase the likelihood of a predator catching an individual). As the environment deteriorated, their birth rate (b) would decline and their death rate (d) would increase. Conditions might worsen to a point where d would exceed b, and the population would decrease. The number of individuals in a population, then, is controlled by the ability of the environment to support it. As the number of individuals in a population (N) increases, environmental limits act to control population growth.

Over longer periods, the rate of population growth may decrease to nearly zero. This leveling out occurs at or near the limits of the environment to support the population. The **carrying capacity (K)** represents the largest population that can be maintained for an indefinite period by a particular environment, assuming that there are no changes in that environment. In nature the carrying capacity is dynamic and changes in response to environmental changes. An extended drought, for example, could decrease the amount of vegetation growing in an area; this change, in turn, would lower the carrying capacity for deer and other herbivores in that environment.

When a population regulated by environmental limits is plotted over longer periods, the curve has a characteristic S shape (FIG. 53-3). The curve shows the population's initial exponential increase (note the curve's J shape at the start, when environmental limits are few), followed by a leveling out as the carrying capacity of the environment is approached. The S-shaped growth curve, also called **logistic population growth,** can be modeled by a modified growth equation called a *logistic equation.* The logistic model of population growth was developed to explain population growth in continually breeding populations. Similar models exist for populations that have specific breeding seasons.

The logistic model describes a population increasing from a small number of individuals to a larger number of individuals that are ultimately limited by the environment. The logistic equation takes into account the carrying capacity of the environment:

$$(5)\ dN/dt = rN[(K - N)/K]$$

Note that part of the equation is the same as equation (3). The added element, $[(K - N)/K]$, reflects a decline in growth as a population size approaches its carrying capacity. When the number of organisms (N) is small, the rate of population growth is unchecked by the environment because the expression

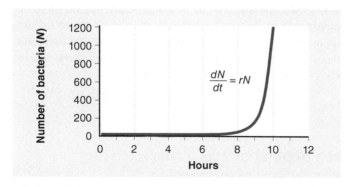

$$\frac{dN}{dt} = rN$$

Figure 53-2 *Animation* **Exponential population growth**

When bacteria divide every 20 minutes, their numbers (expressed in millions) increase exponentially. The curve of exponential population growth has a characteristic J shape. The ideal conditions under which bacteria or other organisms reproduce exponentially rarely occur in nature, and when they do, they are of short duration.

© Cengage Learning

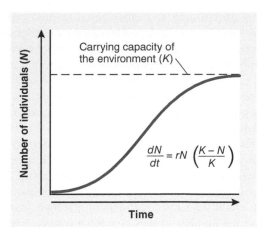

Figure 53-3 *Animation* **Carrying capacity and logistic population growth**

In many laboratory studies, exponential population growth slows as the carrying capacity (K) of the environment is approached. The logistic model of population growth, when plotted, has a characteristic S-shaped curve.
© Cengage Learning

[(K − N)/K] has a value of almost 1. As the population (N) begins to approach the carrying capacity (K), however, the growth rate declines because the value of [(K − N)/K] approaches zero.

Although the S curve is an oversimplification of how most populations change over time, it does appear to fit some populations that have been studied in the laboratory as well as a few that have been studied in nature. For example, Georgyi F. Gause, a Russian ecologist who conducted experiments during the 1930s, grew a population of a single species, *Paramecium caudatum*, in a test tube. He supplied a limited amount of food (bacteria) daily and replenished the growth medium occasionally to eliminate the accumulation of metabolic wastes. Under these conditions, the population of *P. caudatum* increased exponentially at first; then its growth rate declined to zero, and the population size leveled off (see Fig. 54-5, middle graph).

A population rarely stabilizes at K (carrying capacity), but it may temporarily rise higher than K. It will then drop back to, or below, the carrying capacity. Sometimes a population that overshoots K will experience a *population crash,* an abrupt decline from high to low population density. Such an abrupt change is commonly observed in bacterial cultures, zooplankton, and other populations whose resources have been exhausted.

The carrying capacity for reindeer, which live in cold northern habitats, is determined largely by the availability of winter forage. In 1910, humans introduced a small herd of 26 reindeer onto one of the Pribilof Islands of Alaska. The herd's population increased exponentially for about 25 years until there were approximately 2000 reindeer, many more than the island could support, particularly in winter. The reindeer overgrazed the vegetation until the plant life was almost wiped out. Then, in slightly longer than a decade, as reindeer died from starvation, the number of reindeer plunged to 8, one-third the size of the original introduced population. Recovery of subarctic and arctic vegetation after overgrazing by reindeer can take 15 to 20 years, during which time the carrying capacity for reindeer is greatly reduced.

● **CHECKPOINT 53.2**

- *What effect does each of the following have on population size: natality, mortality, immigration, and emigration?*
- **CONNECT** *How does a J-shaped population growth curve differ from an S-shaped curve in terms of intrinsic rate of increase and carrying capacity?*
- **VISUALIZE** *Sketch simple graphs representing the long-term growth of two populations of bacteria cultured in test tubes, one in which the nutrient medium is replenished and the other in which it is not replenished.*

53.3 FACTORS INFLUENCING POPULATION SIZE

● **LEARNING OBJECTIVE**

4 Contrast the influences of density-dependent and density-independent factors on population size and give examples of each.

Certain natural mechanisms influence population size. Factors that affect population size fall into two categories: density-dependent factors and density-independent factors. These two sets of factors vary in importance from one species to another and, in most cases, probably interact simultaneously to determine the size of a population.

Density-dependent factors regulate population size

Sometimes the influence of an environmental factor on the individuals in a population varies with the density or crowding of that population. If a change in population density alters how an environmental factor affects that population, the environmental factor is said to be a **density-dependent factor.**

As population density increases, density-dependent factors tend to slow population growth by causing an increase in death rate and/or a decrease in birth rate. The effect of these density-dependent factors on population growth increases as the population density increases; that is, density-dependent factors affect a larger proportion, not just a larger number, of the population. Density-dependent factors can also affect population growth when population density declines by decreasing the death rate and/or increasing the birth rate. Thus, density-dependent factors tend to regulate a population at a relatively constant size that is near the carrying capacity of the environment. (Keep in mind, however, that the carrying capacity of the environment frequently changes.) Density-dependent factors are an excellent example of a **negative feedback system** (FIG. 53-4).

Predation, disease, and competition are examples of density-dependent factors. As the density of a population increases, predators are more likely to find an individual of a given prey species than before. When population density is high, the members of a population encounter one another

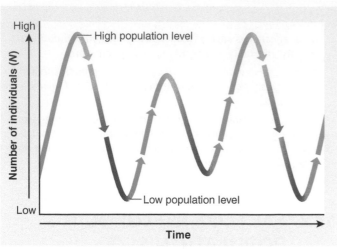

High

KEY

→ Density-dependent factors are increasingly severe: Population peaks and begins to decline.

→ Density-dependent factors are increasingly relaxed: Population bottoms out and begins to increase.

Figure 53-4 Density-dependent factors and negative feedback

When the number of individuals in a population increases, density-dependent factors cause a decline in the population. When the number of individuals in a population decreases, a relaxation of density-dependent factors allows the population to increase.

© Cengage Learning

more frequently than previously, and the chance of their transmitting parasites and infectious disease organisms increases. As population density increases, so does competition for resources such as living space, food, cover, water, minerals, and sunlight; eventually, the point may be reached at which many members of a population fail to obtain the minimum amount of whatever resource is in shortest supply. At higher population densities, density-dependent factors raise the death rate and/or lower the birth rate, inhibiting further population growth. The opposite effect occurs when the density of a population decreases. Predators are less likely to encounter individual prey, parasites and infectious diseases are less likely to be transmitted from one host to another, and competition among members of the population for resources such as living space and food declines.

Density-dependent factors may explain what makes certain populations fluctuate cyclically over time Lemmings are small, stumpy-tailed rodents that are found in colder regions of the Northern Hemisphere (**FIG. 53-5**). They are herbivores that feed on sedges and grasses in the arctic tundra. It has long been known that lemming populations have a three- to four-year cyclical oscillation that is often described as "boom or bust." That is, the population increases dramatically and then crashes; the population peaks may be 100 times as high as the low points in the population cycle. Many other populations, such as snowshoe hares and red grouse, also exhibit cyclic fluctuations.

What is the driving force behind these fluctuations? Several hypotheses have been proposed to explain the cyclical

periodicity of lemming and other boom-or-bust populations, and many involve density-dependent factors. One possibility is that as a prey population becomes more dense, it overwhelms its food supply; as a result, the population declines. In the lemming example, researchers have studied the shape of several lemming population curves during their oscillations; the data suggest that lemming populations crash because they overgraze the plants, not because predators eat them.

Another explanation is that the population density of predators, such as long-tailed jaegers (birds related to gulls that eat lemmings), increases in response to the increasing density of prey. Few jaegers breed when the lemming population is low. However, when the lemming population is high, most jaegers breed, and the number of eggs per clutch is greater than usual. As more predators consume the abundant prey, the prey population declines. Later, with fewer prey in an area, the population of predators declines (some disperse out of the area, and fewer offspring are produced).

In a long-term study of collared lemmings in Greenland, researchers at the University of Helsinki, Finland, observed four-year cycles of lemming population density that were not affected by availability of food or living space. They developed a model in which the fluctuations in the lemming population are most accurately predicted by those of another species, the stoat. The population of the stoat, a member of the weasel family that preys almost exclusively on lemmings, peaks a year after a peak in the lemming population. On the other hand, populations of three other lemming predators—snowy owls, arctic foxes, and long-tailed skuas (birds related to gulls)—respond more immediately to changes in the lemming population and thus tend to stabilize the population cycle established by the stoats.

Climate change may also be affecting lemming population dynamics. Researchers from the University of Oslo, Norway,

Tom McHugh/Science Source

Figure 53-5 Lemming

The brown lemming (*Lemmus trimucronatus*) lives in the arctic tundra. Although lemming populations have been studied for decades, much about the cyclic nature of lemming population oscillations and their effects on the rest of the tundra ecosystem is still not well understood. This species ranges from Alaska eastward to the Hudson Bay.

and a group of international collaborators have observed a correlation between climate and lemming cycles. They found that lemming populations increase in the years in which they can survive by eating moss in the space between the ground and the snow pack. Populations are reduced in warmer years, when slight melting and refreezing of the snow eliminates this space.

Parasites may also interact with their hosts to cause regular cyclic fluctuations. Detailed studies of red grouse have shown that even managed populations in wildlife preserves may have significant cyclic oscillations. Reproduction in red grouse is related to the density of parasitic nematodes (roundworms) living in adult intestines. Fewer birds breed successfully when adults are infected with worms; thus, a high density of worms leads to a population crash. Hypothesizing that red grouse populations fluctuate in response to the parasites, ecologists at the University of Stirling in Scotland successfully reduced or eliminated population fluctuations in several red grouse populations. They did so by catching and orally treating the birds with a chemical that causes worms to be ejected from their bodies.

Competition is an important density-dependent factor

Competition is an interaction among two or more individuals that attempt to use the same essential resource, such as food, water, sunlight, or living space, that is in limited supply. The use of the resource by one of the individuals reduces the availability of that resource for other individuals. Competition occurs both within a given population (**intraspecific competition**) and among populations of different species (**interspecific competition**). We consider the effects of intraspecific competition here; interspecific competition is discussed in Chapter 54.

Individuals of the same species compete for a resource in limited supply by interference competition or by exploitation competition. In **interference competition,** also called **contest competition,** certain dominant individuals obtain an adequate supply of the limited resource at the expense of other individuals in the population; that is, the dominant individuals actively interfere with other individuals' access to resources. In **exploitation competition,** also called **scramble competition,** all the individuals in a population "share" the limited resource more or less equally so that at high population densities none of them obtains an adequate amount. The populations of species in which exploitation competition operates often oscillate over time, and there is always a risk that the population size will drop to zero. In contrast, those species in which interference competition operates experience a relatively small drop in population size, caused by the death of individuals that are unable to compete successfully.

Intraspecific competition among red grouse involves interference competition. When red grouse populations are small, the birds are less aggressive, and most young birds establish a feeding territory (an area defended against other members of the same species). However, when the population is large, establishing a territory is difficult because there are more birds than there are territories and the birds are therefore much more

aggressive. Those birds without territories often die from predation or starvation. Thus, birds with territories use a larger share of the limited resource (the territory with its associated food and cover), whereas birds without territories cannot compete successfully.

The moose population on Isle Royale, Michigan, the largest island in Lake Superior, provides a vivid example of exploitation competition that is similar to that of the reindeer population on the Pribilof Islands (discussed earlier). Isle Royale differs from most islands in that large mammals can walk to it when the lake freezes over in winter. The minimum distance to be walked is 24 km (15 mi), however, so this movement has happened infrequently. Around 1900, a small herd of moose wandered across the ice of frozen Lake Superior and reached the island for the first time. By 1934, the moose population on the island had increased to about 3000 and had consumed almost all the edible vegetation. In the absence of this food resource, there was massive starvation in 1934. More than 60 years later, in 1996, a similar die-off claimed 80% of the moose after they had again increased to a high density. Thus, exploitation competition for scarce resources can result in dramatic population oscillations.

The effects of density-dependent factors are difficult to assess in nature Most studies of density dependence have been conducted in laboratory settings where all density-dependent (and density-independent) factors except one are controlled experimentally. Populations in natural settings, however, are exposed to a complex set of variables that continually change. As a result, in natural communities it is difficult to evaluate the relative effects of different density-dependent factors.

Ecologists from the University of California, Davis noted that few spiders occur on tropical islands inhabited by lizards, whereas more spiders and more species of spiders are found on lizard-free islands. Deciding to study these observations experimentally, David Spiller and Thomas Schoener staked out plots of vegetation (mainly seagrape shrubs) and enclosed some of them with lizard-proof screens (FIG. 53-6). Some of the plots were emptied of all lizards; each control enclosure had approximately nine lizards. Nine web-building spider species were observed in the enclosures. Spiders were counted approximately 30 times from 1989 to 1994. During the 4.5 years of observations reported here, spider population densities were higher in the lizard-free enclosures than in enclosures with lizards. Moreover, the enclosures without lizards had more species of spiders. Therefore, we might conclude that lizards control spider populations.

Even this relatively simple experiment, though, may be explained by a combination of two density-dependent factors: predation (lizards eat spiders) and interspecific competition (lizards compete with spiders for insect prey; i.e., both spiders and lizards eat insects). In this experiment the effects of the two density-dependent factors in determining spider population size cannot be evaluated separately. Additional lines of evidence support the actions of both competition and predation at these sites.

What is the influence of density-dependent factors on population size in a natural habitat?

HYPOTHESIS: Lizards reduce the size of spider populations.

EXPERIMENT: Researchers conducted a field experiment in which they constructed enclosed plots (see photograph); spiders and insects could pass freely into and out of the enclosures, but the lizards could not. Some plots included lizards; the other plots were lizard-free. The spiders were periodically counted over a period of 4.5 years. An earlier experiment indicated that the enclosures themselves have no effect on the number of web-building spiders.

R. Gustafson/Visuals Unlimited

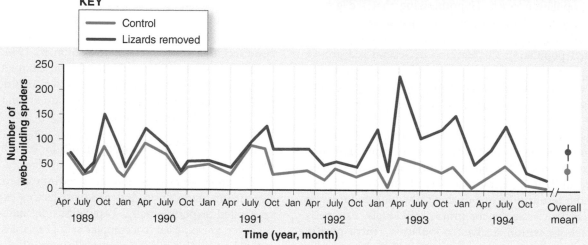

RESULTS AND CONCLUSION: The graph of the mean number of web-building spiders at each count per enclosure with lizards (*control, blue*) and per enclosure with lizards removed (*red*) demonstrates that the number of web-building spiders was consistently higher in the absence of lizards. Lizards may control spider populations by preying on them, by competing with them for insect prey, or by a combination of these factors.

SOURCE: Graph from Spiller, D.A., and T.W. Schoener. "Lizards Reduce Spider Species Richness by Excluding Rare Species." *Ecology*, Vol. 79, No. 2, 1998. Copyright © 1998 Ecological Society of America. Reprinted with permission.

Figure 53-6 Interaction of density-dependent factors

PREDICT Note that the spider populations fluctuated during the experiment, although the lizard-free populations were consistently larger. Formulate a hypothesis relating to whether such fluctuations are due to biotic factors, abiotic factors, or a combination, and devise a way to test it.

Density-independent factors are generally abiotic

Any environmental factor that affects the size of a population but is not influenced by changes in population density is called a **density-independent factor.** Such factors are typically abiotic. Random weather events that reduce population size serve as density-independent factors. They often affect population density in unpredictable ways. A killing frost, severe blizzard, or hurricane, for example, may cause extreme and irregular reductions in a vulnerable population, regardless of its size, and thus may be considered largely density-independent.

Consider a density-independent factor that influences mosquito populations in arctic environments. These insects

produce several generations per summer and achieve high population densities by the end of the season. A shortage of food does not seem to be a limiting factor for mosquitoes, nor is there any shortage of ponds in which to breed. What puts a stop to the skyrocketing mosquito population is winter. Not a single adult mosquito survives winter, and the entire population must grow afresh the next summer from the few eggs and hibernating larvae that survive. Thus, severe winter weather is a density-independent factor that affects arctic mosquito populations.

Density-independent and density-dependent factors are often inter-related. Social animals, for example, often resist dangerous weather conditions by collective behavior, as in the case of sheep huddling together in a snowstorm. In this case it appears that the greater the population density of the sheep, the better their ability to resist the environmental stress of a density-independent event (such as a snowstorm).

CHECKPOINT 53.3

- *What are three examples of density-dependent factors that affect population growth?*
- *What are three density-independent factors?*

53.4 LIFE HISTORY TRAITS

LEARNING OBJECTIVES

5 Contrast semelparous and iteroparous reproduction.
6 Distinguish among species exhibiting an *r* strategy, those with a *K* strategy, and those that do not easily fit either category.
7 Describe Type I, Type II, and Type III survivorship curves and explain how life tables and survivorship curves indicate mortality and survival.

Each species is uniquely suited to its lifestyle. Many years pass before a young magnolia tree flowers and produces seeds, whereas an annual plant grows from seed, flowers, and dies within a single season. A mating pair of black-browed albatrosses produces a single chick every year, but a mating pair of gray-headed albatrosses produces a single chick biennially (every other year).

Species that expend their energy in a single, immense reproductive effort are said to be **semelparous.** Most insects and invertebrates, many plants, and some species of fish exhibit semelparity. Pacific salmon, for example, hatch in fresh water and swim to the ocean, where they live until they mature. Adult salmon swim from the ocean back into the same rivers or streams in which they hatched to spawn (reproduce). After they spawn, the salmon die.

Agaves are semelparous plants that are common in arid tropical and semitropical areas. The thick, fleshy leaves of the agave plant are crowded into a rosette at the base of the stem. Commonly called the century plant because it was mistakenly thought to flower only once in a century, agaves can flower after they are ten years old or so, after which the entire plant dies (FIG. 53-7).

Many species are **iteroparous** and exhibit repeated reproductive cycles—that is, reproduction during several breeding seasons—throughout their lifetimes. Iteroparity is common in most vertebrates as well as in perennial herbaceous plants, shrubs, and trees. The timing of reproduction, earlier or later in life, is a crucial aspect of iteroparity and involves trade-offs. On the one hand, reproducing earlier in life may mean a reduced likelihood of survival (because an individual is expending energy toward reproduction instead of its own growth), which reduces the potential for later reproduction. On the other hand, reproducing later in life means that the individual has less time for additional reproductive events.

R. Gustafson/Visuals Unlimited

Figure 53-7 Semelparity
Agaves flower once and then die. The agave is a succulent with sword-shaped leaves arranged as a rosette around a short stem. Shown is *Agave shawii*, whose leaves grow to 61 cm (2 ft). Note the floral stalk, which can grow more than 3 m (10 ft) tall.

Ecologists try to understand the adaptive consequences of various **life history traits,** such as semelparity and iteroparity. Adaptations such as reproductive rate, age at maturity, and **fecundity** (potential capacity to produce offspring), all of which are a part of a species' life history traits, influence an organism's survival and reproduction. The ability of an individual to reproduce successfully, thereby making a genetic contribution to future generations of a population, is called its **fitness** (recall the discussion of fitness in Chapter 19).

Although many different life histories exist, some ecologists recognize two extremes: *r*-selected species and *K*-selected species. As you read the following descriptions of *r* selection and *K* selection, keep in mind that these concepts, although useful, oversimplify most life histories. Species tend to possess a combination of *r*-selected and *K*-selected traits as well as traits that cannot be classified as either *r*-selected or *K*-selected. In addition, some populations within a species may exhibit the characteristics of *r* selection, whereas other populations in different environments may assume *K*-selected traits.

Populations described by the concept of *r* **selection** have traits that contribute to a high population growth rate. Recall that *r* designates the per capita growth rate. Because such organisms have a high *r*, biologists call them *r* **strategists** or *r***-selected species.** Small body size, early maturity, short lifespan, large broods, and little or no parental care are typical of many *r* strategists, which are usually opportunists found in variable, temporary, or unpredictable environments where the probability of long-term survival is low. Some of the best examples of *r* strategists are insects, such as mosquitoes, and plants such as the poppies shown in the chapter-opening photograph. Following a rainy period, these desert annuals rapidly grow from seed, flower and set seed, and then die.

In populations described by the concept of *K* **selection,** traits maximize the chance of surviving in an environment where the number of individuals is near the carrying capacity (*K*) of the environment. These organisms, called *K* **strategists** or *K***-selected species,** do not produce large numbers of offspring. They characteristically have long lifespans with slow development, late reproduction, large body size, and a low reproductive rate. *K* strategists tend to be found in relatively constant or stable environments, where they have a high competitive ability. Redwood trees as well as most tropical rainforest trees are classified as *K* strategists. Animals that are *K* strategists typically invest in parental care of their young. Tawny owls (*Strix aluco*), for example, are *K* strategists that pair-bond for life, with both members of a pair living and hunting in adjacent, well-defined territories. Their reproduction is regulated in accordance with the resources, especially the food supply, present in their territories. In an average year, 30% of the birds do not breed at all. If food supplies are more limited than initially indicated, many of those that do breed fail to incubate their eggs. Rarely do the owls lay the maximum number of eggs that they are physiologically capable of laying, and breeding is often delayed until late in the season, when the rodent populations on which they depend have become large. Thus, the behavior of tawny owls ensures better reproductive success of the individual and leads to a stable population at or near the carrying capacity of the environment. Starvation, an indication that the tawny owl population has exceeded the carrying capacity, rarely occurs.

Life tables and survivorship curves indicate mortality and survival

A **life table** can be constructed to show the mortality and survival data of a population or **cohort,** a group of individuals of the same age, at different times during their lifespan. Insurance companies were the first to use life tables, using them to calculate the relationship between a client's age and the likelihood of the client surviving to pay enough insurance premiums to cover the cost of the policy. Ecologists construct such tables for animals and plants based on data that rely on a variety of population sampling methods and age determination techniques.

TABLE 53-2 shows a life table for a cohort of 530 gray squirrels. The first two columns show the units of age (years) and the number of individuals in the cohort that were alive at the beginning of each age interval (the actual data collected in the field by the ecologist). The values for the third column (the proportion alive at the beginning of each age interval) are calculated by dividing each number in column 2 by 530, the number of squirrels in the original cohort. The values in the fourth column (the proportion dying during each age interval) are calculated using the values in the third column and subtracting the number of survivors at the beginning of the next interval from those alive at the beginning of the current interval. For example, the proportion dying during interval 0–1 years is $1.000 - 0.253 = 0.747$. The far right column, the death rate for each age interval, is calculated by dividing the proportion dying during the age interval (column 4) by the proportion alive at the beginning of the age interval (column 3). For example, the death rate for the age interval 1–2 years is $0.147 \div 0.253 = 0.581$.

Survivorship is the probability that a given individual in a population or cohort will survive to a particular age. Plotting the logarithm (base 10) of the number of surviving individuals against age, from birth to the maximum age reached by any individual, produces a **survivorship curve. FIGURE 53-8** shows the three main survivorship curves that ecologists recognize.

In *Type I survivorship,* as exemplified by bison and humans, the young and those at reproductive age have a high probability of surviving. The probability of survival decreases more rapidly with increasing age; mortality is concentrated later in life. **FIGURE 53-9** shows a survivorship curve for a natural population of Drummond phlox, an annual native to

TABLE 53-2	Life Table for a Cohort of 530 Gray Squirrels (*Sciurus carolinensis*)			
AGE INTERVAL (YEARS)	NUMBER ALIVE AT BEGINNING OF AGE INTERVAL	PROPORTION ALIVE AT BEGINNING OF AGE INTERVAL	PROPORTION DYING DURING AGE INTERVAL	DEATH RATE FOR AGE INTERVAL
0–1	530	1.000	0.747	0.747
1–2	134	0.253	0.147	0.581
2–3	56	0.106	0.032	0.302
3–4	39	0.074	0.031	0.418
4–5	23	0.043	0.021	0.488
5–6	12	0.022	0.013	0.591
6–7	5	0.009	0.006	0.666
7–8	2	0.003	0.003	1.000
8–9	0	0.000	0.000	—

Source: Adapted from Smith, R.L., and T.M. Smith. *Elements of Ecology*, 4th ed., Table 13.1, p. 150. Benjamin/Cummings Science Publishing, San Francisco, 1998.

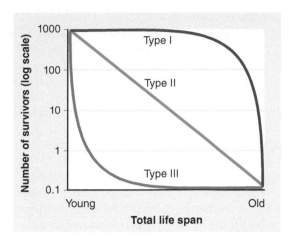

Figure 53-8 *Animation* **Survivorship curves**

These curves represent the ideal survivorships of species in which mortality is greatest in old age (Type I), spread evenly across all age groups (Type II), and greatest among the young (Type III). The survivorship of most organisms can be compared to these curves.

© Cengage Learning

East Texas that became widely distributed in the southeastern United States after it escaped from cultivation. Because most Drummond phlox seedlings survive to reproduce, after germination the plant exhibits a Type I survivorship that is typical of annuals.

In *Type III survivorship* the probability of mortality is greatest early in life, and those individuals that avoid early death subsequently have a high probability of survival, that is, the probability of survival increases with increasing age. Type III survivorship is characteristic of oysters; young oysters have three free-swimming larval stages before settling down and secreting a shell. These larvae are vulnerable to predation, and few survive to adulthood.

In *Type II survivorship,* which is intermediate between Types I and III, the probability of survival does not change with age. The probability of death is equally likely across all age groups, resulting in a linear decline in survivorship. This constancy probably results from essentially random events that cause death with little age bias. Although this relationship between age and survivorship is rare, some lizards have Type II survivorship.

The three survivorship curves are generalizations, and few populations exactly fit one of the three. Some species have one type of survivorship curve early in life and another type as adults. Herring gulls, for example, start out with a Type III survivorship curve but develop a Type II curve as adults (**FIG. 53-10**). The survivorship curve shown in this figure is characteristic of birds in general. Note that most death occurs almost immediately after hatching, despite the protection and care given to the chicks by the parent bird. Herring gull chicks die from predation or attack by other herring gulls, inclement weather, infectious diseases, or starvation following death of the parent. Once the chicks become independent, their survivorship increases dramatically, and death occurs at about the same rate throughout their remaining lives. Few or no herring gulls die from the degenerative diseases of "old age" that cause death in most humans.

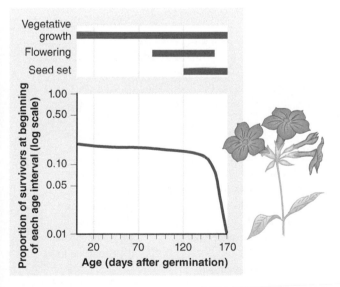

Figure 53-9 Survivorship curve for a Drummond phlox population

Drummond phlox has a Type I survivorship after germination of the seeds. *Bars above the graph* indicate the various stages in the Drummond phlox life history. Data were collected from Nixon, Texas, in 1974 and 1975. Survivorship on the y-axis begins at 0.296 instead of 1.00 because the study took into account death during the seed dormancy period prior to germination (*not shown*). (From Leverich, W.J., and D.A. Levin. "Age-Specific Survivorship and Reproduction in *Phlox drummondii*." *American Naturalist*, Vol. 113, No. 6, p. 1148, 1979. Copyright © 1979 University of Chicago Press. Reprinted with permission.)

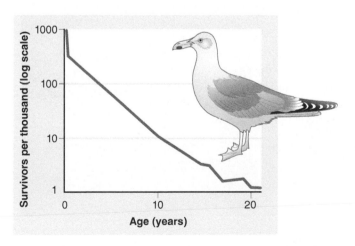

Figure 53-10 Survivorship curve for a herring gull population

Herring gulls (*Larus argentatus*) have Type III survivorship as chicks and Type II survivorship as adults. Data were collected from Kent Island, Maine, during a five-year period in the 1930s; baby gulls were banded to establish identity. The very slight increase just prior to 20 years of age is due to sampling error. (Paynter, R.A., Jr. "A New Attempt to Construct Lifetables for Kent Island Herring Gulls." *Bulletin of the Museum of Comparative Zoology*, Vol. 133, No. 11, pp. 489–528, 1966.)

- *What are the advantages of semelparity? of iteroparity? Are there disadvantages?*
- **CONNECT** *Why is parental care of young a common characteristic of K strategists?*
- *Do all survivorship curves neatly fit the Type I, II, or III models? Explain.*

53.5 METAPOPULATIONS

LEARNING OBJECTIVE

8 Define *metapopulation* and distinguish between source habitats and sink habitats.

The natural environment is a heterogeneous **landscape** consisting of interacting ecosystems that provide a variety of habitat patches. Landscapes, which are typically several to many square kilometers in area, cover larger land areas than individual ecosystems. Consider a forest, for example. The forest landscape is a mosaic of different elevations, temperatures, levels of precipitation, soil moisture, soil types, and other properties. Because each species has its own habitat requirements, this heterogeneity in physical properties is reflected in the different organisms that occupy the various patches in the landscape (**FIG. 53-11**). Some species occur in very narrow habitat ranges, whereas others have wider habitat distributions.

Population ecologists have discovered that many species are not distributed as one large population across the landscape. Instead, many species exist as a series of local populations distributed in distinct habitat patches. Each local population has its own characteristic demographic features, such as birth, death, emigration, and immigration rates. A population that is divided into several local populations among which individuals occasionally disperse (emigrate and immigrate) is known as a **metapopulation.** For example, note the various local populations of red oak on the mountain slope in Figure 53-11b.

The spatial distribution of a species occurs because different habitats vary in suitability, from unacceptable to preferred. The preferred sites are more productive habitats that increase the likelihood of survival and reproductive success for the individuals living there. Good habitats, called **source habitats,** are areas where local reproductive success is greater than local mortality. *Source populations* generally have greater population densities than populations at less suitable sites, and surplus individuals in the source habitat disperse and find another habitat in which to settle and reproduce.

Individuals living in lower quality habitats may suffer death or, if they survive, poor reproductive success. Lower quality habitats, called **sink habitats,** are areas where local reproductive success is less than local mortality. Without immigration from other areas, a *sink population* declines until extinction occurs. If a local population becomes extinct, individuals from a source habitat may recolonize the vacant habitat at a later time. Source and sink habitats, then, are linked to one another by dispersal (**FIG. 53-12**).

(a) This early spring view from Newfound Gap Rd., Great Smoky Mountains National Park, gives some idea of the heterogeneity of the landscape. During the summer, when all the vegetation is a deep green, the landscape appears homogeneous.

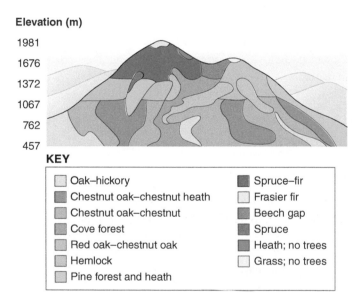

Elevation (m)

1981
1676
1372
1067
762
457

KEY

☐ Oak–hickory	■ Spruce–fir
■ Chestnut oak–chestnut heath	☐ Frasier fir
■ Chestnut oak–chestnut	■ Beech gap
■ Cove forest	■ Spruce
☐ Red oak–chestnut oak	■ Heath; no trees
☐ Hemlock	☐ Grass; no trees
■ Pine forest and heath	

(b) An evaluation of the distribution of vegetation on a typical west-facing slope in the Great Smoky Mountains National Park reveals that the landscape consists of patches. Chestnut oak is a species of oak (*Quercus prinus*); chestnut heath is an area within chestnut oak forest where the trees are widely scattered and the slopes underneath are covered by a thick growth of laurel (*Kalmia*) shrubs; cove forest is a mixed stand of deciduous trees.

Figure 53-11 The mosaic nature of landscapes

(Adapted from Whittaker, R.H. "Vegetation of the Great Smoky Mountains." *Ecological Monographs*, Vol. 26, 1956.)

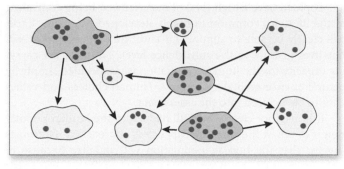

KEY

○ (shaded) Source population in a suitable habitat

○ (open) Sink population in a low-quality habitat

• Individual within a local population

→ Dispersal event

Figure 53-12 Source and sink populations in a hypothetical metapopulation

The local populations in the habitat patches shown here collectively make up the metapopulation. Source habitats provide individuals that emigrate and colonize sink habitats. Studied over time, the metapopulation is shown to exist as a shifting pattern of occupied and vacant habitat patches.
© Cengage Learning

Metapopulations are becoming more common as humans alter the landscape by fragmenting existing habitats to accommodate homes and factories, agricultural fields, and logging. As a result, the concept of metapopulations, particularly as it relates to endangered and threatened species, has become an important area of study in conservation biology.

CHECKPOINT 53.5

• **CONNECT** *What roles do source habitats and sink habitats play in the dynamic nature of a metapopulation?*

53.6 HUMAN POPULATIONS

LEARNING OBJECTIVES

9 Summarize the history of human population growth.

10 Explain how highly developed and developing countries differ in population characteristics such as infant mortality rate, total fertility rate, replacement-level fertility, and age structure.

11 Distinguish between people overpopulation and consumption overpopulation.

Now that we have examined some of the basic concepts of population ecology, we can apply those concepts to the human population. Examine FIGURE 53-13, which shows the world increase in the human population since the development of agriculture approximately 10,000 years ago. Now look back at Figure 53-2 and compare the two curves. The characteristic J curve of exponential population growth shown in Figure 53-13 reflects the decreasing

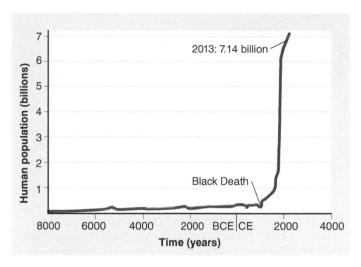

Figure 53-13 Human population growth

During the last 1000 years, the human population has been increasing nearly exponentially. Population experts predict that the population will level out during the 21st century, forming the **S** curve observed in other species. (Black Death refers to a devastating disease, probably bubonic plague, that decimated Europe and Asia in the 14th century.)
© Cengage Learning

amount of time it has taken to add each additional billion people to our numbers. It took thousands of years for the human population to reach 1 billion, a milestone that took place around 1800. It took 130 years to reach 2 billion (in 1930), 30 years to reach 3 billion (in 1960), 15 years to reach 4 billion (in 1975), 12 years to reach 5 billion (in 1987), and 12 years to reach 6 billion (in 1999). The world population reached 7.14 billion in 2013, and the United Nations projects that it will rise to more than 8 billion by 2025.

Thomas Malthus (1766–1834), a British clergyman and economist, was one of the first to recognize that the human population cannot continue to increase indefinitely (see Chapter 18). He pointed out that human population growth is not always desirable (a view contrary to the beliefs of his day and to those of many people even today) and that the human population is capable of increasing faster than the food supply. He maintained that the inevitable consequences of population growth are famine, disease, and war.

The world population is currently increasing by about 84 million people per year. This rise is not caused by an increase in the birth rate (*b*). In fact, the world birth rate has actually declined during the past 200 years. The increase in population is due instead to a dramatic decrease in the death rate (*d*). This decrease in mortality has occurred primarily because greater food production, better medical care, and improved sanitation practices have increased the life expectancies of a great majority of the global population. For example, from 1920 to 2000, the death rate in Mexico fell from approximately 40 per 1000 individuals to 4 per 1000, whereas the birth rate dropped from approximately 40 per 1000 individuals to 24 per 1000 (FIG. 53-14). As of 2013 Mexico's birth rate had continued to fall, to about 19 per 1000, and its death rate remained at 4 per 1000.

The human population has reached a turning point. Although our numbers continue to increase, the world per capita growth rate (*r*) has declined over the past several years, from a peak of

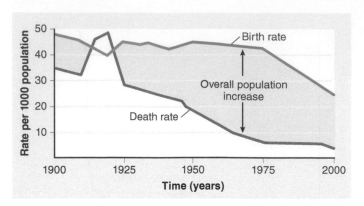

Figure 53-14 Birth and death rates in Mexico, 1900 to 2000
Both birth and death rates declined during the 20th century, but because the death rate declined much more than the birth rate, Mexico has experienced a high growth rate. (The high death rate prior to 1920 was caused by the Mexican Revolution; Population Reference Bureau.)
© Cengage Learning

2.2% per year in the mid-1960s to 1.2% per year in 2013. Population experts at the United Nations and the World Bank have projected that the growth rate may continue to slowly decrease until zero population growth is attained. Thus, exponential growth of the human population may end, and if it does, the S curve will replace the J curve. Demographers project that **zero population growth,** the point at which the birth rate equals the death rate ($r = 0$), will occur toward the end of the 21st century.

The latest (2013) projections available through the Population Reference Bureau, based on data from the United Nations, forecast that the human population will exceed 9.7 billion in the year 2050. This forecast is a "medium" projection; such population projections are "what-if" exercises. Given certain assumptions about future tendencies in natality, mortality, and dispersal, population experts can calculate an area's population for a given number of years into the future. Population projections indicate the changes that may occur, but they must be interpreted with care because they vary depending on what assumptions have been made. Small differences in fertility as well as death rates produce large differences in population forecasts.

The main unknown factor in any population growth scenario is Earth's carrying capacity. According to Joel Cohen of the Earth Institute at Columbia University, most published estimates of how many people Earth can support range from 4 billion to 16 billion. These estimates vary so widely because of the assumptions that are made about standard of living, resource consumption, technological innovations, and waste generation. If we want all people to have a high level of material well-being equivalent to the lifestyles common in highly developed countries, Earth will clearly be able to support far fewer humans than if everyone lives just above the subsistence level. Thus, Earth's carrying capacity for the human population is not decided simply by natural environmental constraints. Human choices and values have to be factored into the assessment.

It is also not clear what will happen to the human population if or when the carrying capacity is approached. Optimists suggest that the human population will stabilize because of a decrease in the birth rate. Some experts take a more pessimistic view and predict that the widespread degradation of our environment caused by our ever-expanding numbers will make Earth uninhabitable for humans and other species. These experts contend that a massive wave of human suffering and death will occur. Some experts think that the human population has already exceeded the carrying capacity of the environment, a potentially dangerous situation that threatens our long-term survival as a species.

Not all countries have the same growth rate

Although world population figures illustrate overall trends, they do not describe other important aspects of the human population story, such as population differences from country to country. Human **demographics,** the science that deals with human population statistics such as size, density, and distribution, provides information on the populations of various countries. As you probably know, not all parts of the world have the same rates of population increase. Countries can be classified into two groups, highly developed and developing, based on their rates of population growth, degrees of industrialization, and relative prosperity (TABLE 53-3).

Highly developed countries, such as the United States, Canada, France, Germany, Sweden, Australia, and Japan, have low rates of population growth and are highly industrialized relative to the rest of the world. Highly developed countries have the lowest birth rates in the world. Indeed, some highly developed countries such as Germany have birth rates just below that needed to sustain the population and are thus

TABLE 53-3	Comparison of 2013 Population Data in Selected Developed and Developing Countries		
	DEVELOPED	DEVELOPING	
	(HIGHLY DEVELOPED) UNITED STATES	(MODERATELY DEVELOPED) BRAZIL	(LESS DEVELOPED) ETHIOPIA
Fertility rate	1.9	1.8	4.8
Doubling time	140 years	78 years	27 years
Infant mortality rate	5.9 per 1000	21 per 1000	52 per 1000
Life expectancy at birth	79 years	74 years	62 years
GNI PPP per capita (U.S. $)	$50,610	$11,720	$1040
Married women 15–49 using modern contraception	73%	77%	27%

Source: Population Reference Bureau.

declining slightly in numbers. Highly developed countries also have low **infant mortality rates** (the number of infant deaths per 1000 live births). The infant mortality rate of the United States in 2013, for example, was 5.9, compared with a world infant mortality rate of 40.

Highly developed countries also have longer life expectancies (79 years at birth in the United States versus 70 years worldwide) and higher average GNI PPP per capita ($50,610 in the United States versus $11,690 worldwide) than other countries. GNI PPP per capita is gross national income (GNI) in purchasing power parity (PPP) divided by midyear population. It indicates the amount of goods and services an average citizen of that particular region or country could buy in the United States.

Developing countries fall into two subcategories: moderately developed and less developed. Mexico, Turkey, Thailand, and most countries of South America are examples of *moderately developed countries*. Their birth rates and infant mortality rates are generally higher than those of highly developed countries, but the rates are declining. Moderately developed countries have a medium level of industrialization, and their average GNI PPP per capita is lower than those of highly developed countries.

Bangladesh, Niger, Ethiopia, Laos, and Cambodia are examples of *less developed countries*. These countries have the highest birth rates, the highest infant mortality rates, the lowest life expectancies, and the lowest average GNI PPP per capita in the world.

One way to represent the population growth of a country is to determine the **doubling time**, the amount of time it would take for its population to double in size assuming that its current growth rate did not change. A simplified formula for doubling time (t_d) is $t_d = 70 \div r$. (The actual formula involves calculus and is beyond the scope of this text. This simplified formula actually has many practical applications; e.g., you can use it to estimate how long it will take to double your money in a savings account at a specific rate of compound interest.)

A look at a country's doubling time identifies it as a highly, moderately, or less developed country: the shorter the doubling time, the less developed the country. At rates of growth in 2013, the approximate doubling time is 30 years for Ethiopia, 35 years for Laos, 58 years for Turkey, 175 years for Thailand, 140 years for the United States, and 175 years for France.

It is also instructive to examine **replacement-level fertility**, the number of children a couple must produce to "replace" themselves. Replacement-level fertility is usually given as 2.1 children in highly developed countries and 2.7 children in developing countries. The number is always greater than 2.0 because some children die before they reach reproductive age. Higher infant mortality rates are the main reason that replacement levels in developing countries are greater than in highly developed countries. The **total fertility rate**—the average number of children born to a woman during her lifetime—is 2.5 worldwide, which is well above replacement levels. However, it has fallen below replacement levels, to 1.6, in the highly developed countries. The total fertility

rate in the United States is 1.9, which is higher than in other industrialized countries.

The population in many developing countries is beginning to approach stabilization. The fertility rate must decline for the population to stabilize (**TABLE 53-4**; note the general decline in total fertility rate from the 1960s to 2013 in selected developing countries). The total fertility rate in developing countries has decreased from an average of 6.1 children per woman in 1970 to 3.0 in 2013 (excluding China), or 2.6 if China is included. Fertility is highly variable among developing countries, and although the fertility rates in most of these countries have declined, it should be remembered that most still exceed replacement-level fertility. Consequently, the populations in these countries are still increasing. Also, even when fertility rates equal replacement-level fertility, population growth will still continue for some time. To understand why, we now examine the age structure of various countries.

The age structure of a country helps predict future population growth

To predict the future growth of a population, it is important to know its **age structure**, which is the number and proportion of people at each age in a population. The number of males and number of females at each age, from birth to death, are represented in an **age structure diagram.**

The overall shape of an age structure diagram indicates whether the population is increasing, stationary, or shrinking (**FIG. 53-15**). The age structure diagram for less developed countries is shaped like a pyramid. Because the largest percentage of the population is in the pre-reproductive age group (i.e., 0 to 14 years of age), the probability of future population growth is great. A strong **population growth momentum** exists because when all these children mature they will become the parents of the next generation, and this group of parents will be larger than the previous group. Thus, even if the fertility rates in

TABLE 53-4	Fertility Changes in Selected Developing Countries	
	TOTAL FERTILITY RATE	
COUNTRY	1960–1965	2013
Bangladesh	6.7	2.3
Brazil	6.2	1.8
China	5.9	1.5
Egypt	7.1	3.0
Guatemala	6.9	3.9
India	5.8	2.4
Kenya	8.1	4.5
Mexico	6.8	2.2
Nepal	5.9	2.6
Nigeria	6.9	6.0
Thailand	6.4	1.6

Source: Population Reference Bureau.

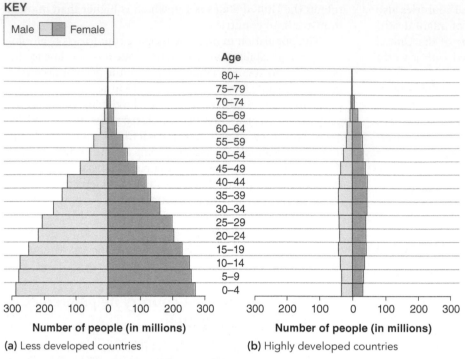

KEY

Male ▢ ▣ Female

Age

| 80+ |
| 75–79 |
| 70–74 |
| 65–69 |
| 60–64 |
| 55–59 |
| 50–54 |
| 45–49 |
| 40–44 |
| 35–39 |
| 30–34 |
| 25–29 |
| 20–24 |
| 15–19 |
| 10–14 |
| 5–9 |
| 0–4 |

300 200 100 0 100 200 300
Number of people (in millions)
(a) Less developed countries

300 200 100 0 100 200 300
Number of people (in millions)
(b) Highly developed countries

Figure 53-15 *Animation* **Age structure diagrams**

These age structure diagrams for **(a)** less developed countries and **(b)** highly developed countries indicate that less developed regions have a greater percentage of young people than do highly developed countries. As a result, less developed countries are projected to have greater population growth than are highly developed countries. (Adapted from Population Reference Bureau using data from United Nations, World Population Prospects: The 2002 Revision, 2003.)

Most of the world population increase since 1950 has taken place in developing countries as a result of the younger age structure and the higher-than-replacement-level fertility rates of their populations. In 1950, 66.8% of the world's population was in the developing countries in Africa, Asia (minus Japan), and Latin America. Between 1950 and 2013, the world's population more than doubled in size, but most of that growth occurred in developing countries. As a reflection of this growth, in 2013 the people in developing countries had increased to more than 82% of the world's population. Most of the population increase that will occur during the 21st century will also take place in developing countries, largely the result of their young age structures. These countries, most of which are poor, are least able to support such growth.

these countries decline to replacement level (i.e., couples have smaller families than their parents did), the population will continue to grow for some time. Population growth momentum can have either a positive value (i.e., the population will grow) or a negative value (i.e., the population will decline). However, it is usually discussed in a positive context, to explain how the future growth of a population is affected by its present age distribution.

In contrast, the more tapered bases of the age structure diagrams of highly developed countries with slowly growing, stable, or declining populations indicate that a smaller proportion of the population will become the parents of the next generation. The age structure diagram of a stable population, one that is neither growing nor shrinking, demonstrates that the number of people at pre-reproductive and reproductive ages are approximately the same. Also, a larger percentage of the population is older—that is, post-reproductive—than in a rapidly increasing population. Many countries in Europe have stable populations. In a population that is shrinking in size, the pre-reproductive age group is smaller than either the reproductive or post-reproductive group. Germany, Russia, and Bulgaria are examples of countries with slowly shrinking populations.

Worldwide, 26% of the human population is younger than age 15. When these people enter their reproductive years, they have the potential to cause a large increase in the growth rate. Even if the birth rate does not increase, the growth rate will increase simply because more people are reproducing.

Environmental degradation is related to population growth and resource consumption

The relationships among population growth, use of natural resources, and environmental degradation are complex, but we can make two useful generalizations.

First, although the amount of resources essential to an individual's survival may be small, a rapidly increasing population tends to overwhelm and deplete a country's soils, forests, and other natural resources. Thus, **people overpopulation** occurs when the environment is worsening from too many people, even if those people consume few resources per person. People overpopulation is the current problem in many developing nations.

Second, in affluent highly developed nations, individual resource demands are large, far above requirements for survival. **Consumption overpopulation** occurs when people in more affluent nations exhaust resources and degrade the global environment through excessive consumption and "throwaway" lifestyles.

The effects of human populations on the environment are explored in more detail in Chapter 57.

CHECKPOINT 53.6

- *What is the reason for the dramatic increase in the world population over the last 200 years?*
- *CONNECT Why is replacement-level fertility greater in developing countries than in highly developed countries? Explain your answer.*
- *How can a single child born in the United States have a greater effect on the environment and natural resources than a dozen children born in Kenya?*

53.1 Features of Populations *(page 1145)*

1 Define *population density* and *dispersion*, and describe the main types of population dispersion.

- **Population density** is the number of individuals of a species per unit of area or volume at a given time.

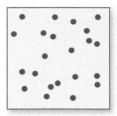 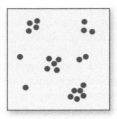 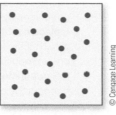

Random dispersion   **Clumped dispersion**   **Uniform dispersion**

- Population **dispersion** (spacing) may be **random dispersion** (unpredictably spaced), **clumped dispersion** (clustered in specific parts of the habitat), or **uniform dispersion** (evenly spaced).

53.2 Changes in Population Size *(page 1147)*

2 Explain the four factors (natality, mortality, immigration, and emigration) that produce changes in population size and solve simple problems involving these changes.

- Population size is affected by the average per capita birth rate (*b*), average per capita death rate (*d*), and two measures of **dispersal:** average per capita **immigration** rate (*i*) and average per capita **emigration** rate (*e*).
- The **growth rate (*r*)** is the rate of change (increase or decrease) of a population on a per capita basis. On a global scale (when dispersal is not a factor), $r = b - d$. Populations increase in size as long as the average per capita birth rate (**natality**) is greater than the average per capita death rate (**mortality**).
- For a local population (where dispersal is a factor), $r = (b - d) + (i - e)$.

3 Define *intrinsic rate of increase* and *carrying capacity*, and explain the differences between J-shaped and S-shaped growth curves.

 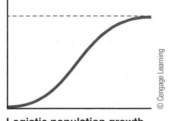

Exponential population growth   **Logistic population growth**

- **Intrinsic rate of increase (*r*$_{max}$)** is the maximum rate at which a species or population could increase in number under ideal conditions.
- Although certain populations exhibit an accelerated pattern of growth known as **exponential population growth** for limited periods of time (the J-shaped curve), eventually the growth rate decreases to around zero or becomes negative.
- Population size is modified by limits set by the environment. The **carrying capacity (*K*)** of the environment is the largest population that can be maintained for an indefinite time by a particular environment. **Logistic population growth,** when plotted, shows a characteristic S-shaped curve. Seldom do natural populations follow the logistic growth curve very closely.

53.3 Factors Influencing Population Size *(page 1149)*

4 Contrast the influences of density-dependent and density-independent factors on population size and give examples of each.

- **Density-dependent factors** regulate population growth by affecting a larger proportion of the population as population density rises. Predation, disease, and competition are examples.
- **Density-independent factors** limit population growth but are not influenced by changes in population density. Hurricanes and blizzards are examples.

53.4 Life History Traits *(page 1153)*

5 Contrast semelparous and iteroparous reproduction.

- **Semelparous** species expend their energy in a single, immense reproductive effort. **Iteroparous** species exhibit repeated reproductive cycles throughout their lifetimes.

6 Distinguish among species exhibiting an *r* strategy, those with a *K* strategy, and those that do not easily fit either category.

- Although many different combinations of life history traits exist, some ecologists recognize two extremes: *r* strategy and *K* strategy.
- An *r* strategy emphasizes a high growth rate. Organisms characterized as ***r* strategists** often have small body sizes, high reproductive rates, and short **lifespans,** and they typically inhabit variable environments.
- A *K* strategy maintains a population near the carrying capacity of the environment. Organisms characterized as ***K* strategists** often have large body sizes, low reproductive rates, and long lifespans, and they typically inhabit stable environments.
- The two strategies oversimplify most life histories. Many species combine *r*-selected and *K*-selected traits as well as traits that cannot be classified as either *r*-selected or *K*-selected.

7 Describe Type I, Type II, and Type III survivorship curves and explain how life tables and survivorship curves indicate mortality and survival.

- A **life table** shows the mortality and survival data of a population or **cohort**—a group of individuals of the same age—at different times during the population's lifespan.
- **Survivorship** is the probability that a given individual in a population or cohort will survive to a particular age. There are three general **survivorship curves:** *Type I survivorship,* in which mortality is greatest in old age; *Type II survivorship,* in which mortality is spread evenly across all age groups; and *Type III survivorship,* in which mortality is greatest among the young.

53.5 Metapopulations *(page 1156)*

8 Define *metapopulation* and distinguish between source habitats and sink habitats.

- Many species exist as a **metapopulation,** a set of local populations among which individuals are distributed in distinct habitat patches across a **landscape,** which is a large area of terrain (several to many square kilometers) composed of interacting ecosystems.

- Within a metapopulation, individuals occasionally disperse from one local habitat to another by emigration and immigration. **Source habitats** are preferred sites where local reproductive success is greater than local mortality. Surplus individuals disperse from source habitats. **Sink habitats** are lower quality habitats where individuals may suffer death or, if they survive, poor reproductive success. If extinction of a local *sink population* occurs, individuals from a *source population* may recolonize the vacant habitat at a later time.

53.6 Human Populations *(page 1157)*

9 Summarize the history of human population growth.

- The world population increases by more than 84 million people per year and reached 7.14 billion in 2013.
- Although our numbers continue to increase, the per capita growth rate (r) has declined over the past several years, from a peak in 1965 of about 2% per year to a 2013 growth rate of 1.2% per year.
- Scientists who study human **demographics** (human population statistics) project that the world population will become stationary ($r = 0$, or **zero population growth**) by the end of the 21st century.

10 Explain how highly developed and developing countries differ in population characteristics such as infant mortality rate, total fertility rate, replacement-level fertility, and age structure.

- *Highly developed countries* have the lowest birth rates, lowest infant mortality rates, lowest total fertility rates, longest life expectancies, and highest GNI PPP per capita (a measure of the amount of goods and services the average citizen could purchase in the United States) of all countries. *Developing countries* have the highest birth rates, highest infant mortality rates, highest total fertility rates, shortest life expectancies, and lowest GNI PPP per capita.
- The **age structure** of a population greatly influences population dynamics. It is possible for a country to have **replacement-level fertility** and still experience population growth if the largest percentage of the population is in the pre-reproductive years. A young age structure causes a positive **population growth momentum** as the very large pre-reproductive age group matures and becomes parents.

11 Distinguish between people overpopulation and consumption overpopulation.

- Developing countries tend to have **people overpopulation,** in which population increase degrades the environment even though each individual uses few resources.
- Highly developed countries tend to have **consumption overpopulation,** in which each individual in a slow-growing or stationary population consumes a large share of resources, which results in environmental degradation.

TEST YOUR UNDERSTANDING

Know and Comprehend

1. Population _____ is the number of individuals of a species per unit of habitat area or volume at a given time. (a) dispersion (b) density (c) survivorship (d) age structure (e) demographics
2. The per capita growth rate of a population where dispersal is not a factor is expressed as (a) $i + e$ (b) $b - d$ (c) dN/dt (d) $rN(K - N)$ (e) $(K - N) \div K$
3. The maximum rate at which a population could increase under ideal conditions is known as its (a) total fertility rate (b) survivorship (c) intrinsic rate of increase (d) doubling time (e) age structure
4. When r is a positive number, the population size is (a) stable (b) increasing (c) decreasing (d) either increasing or decreasing, depending on interference competition (e) either increasing or stable, depending on whether the species is semelparous
5. In a graph of population size versus time, a J-shaped curve is characteristic of (a) exponential population growth (b) logistic population growth (c) zero population growth (d) replacement-level fertility (e) population growth momentum
6. The largest population that can be maintained by a particular environment for an indefinite period is known as a (a) semelparous population (b) population undergoing exponential growth (c) metapopulation (d) population's carrying capacity (e) source population
7. Giant bamboos live many years without reproducing, then send up a huge flowering stalk and die shortly thereafter. Giant bamboo is therefore an example of (a) iteroparity (b) a source population (c) a metapopulation (d) an r strategist (e) semelparity
8. Predation, disease, and competition are examples of _____ factors. (a) density-dependent (b) density-independent (c) survivorship (d) dispersal (e) semelparous
9. _____ competition occurs within a population, and _____ competition occurs among populations of different species. (a) Interspecific; intraspecific (b) Intraspecific; interspecific (c) Type I survivorship; Type II survivorship (d) Interference; exploitation (e) Exploitation; interference
10. A highly developed country has a (a) long doubling time (b) low infant mortality rate (c) high GNI PPP per capita (d) a and b (e) a, b, and c
11. The continued growth of a population with a young age structure, even after its fertility rate has declined, is known as (a) population doubling (b) iteroparity (c) population growth momentum (d) r selection (e) density dependence

Apply and Analyze

12. Which of the following patterns of cars parked along a street is an example of uniform dispersion? (a) five cars parked next to one another in the middle, leaving two empty spaces at one end and three empty spaces at the other end (b) five cars parked in this pattern: car, empty space, car, empty space, and so on (c) five cars parked in no discernible pattern, sometimes having empty spaces on each side and sometimes parked next to another car
13. A female elephant bears a single offspring every two to four years. Based on this information, which survivorship curve do you think is representative of elephants? Explain your answer.

Evaluate and Synthesize

14. Explain why the population size of a species that competes by interference competition is often near the carrying capacity, whereas the population size of a species that competes by exploitation competition is often greater than or below the carrying capacity.

15. **EVOLUTION LINK** In developing his scientific theory of evolution by natural selection, Charles Darwin considered four main observations: heritable variation among individuals in a population, overproduction of offspring, limits on population growth, and differential reproductive success. Compare how these observations may apply to populations that tend to fit the concepts of *r* selection and *K* selection.

16. **INTERPRET DATA** In Bolivia, 35% of the population is younger than age 15, and 5% is older than 65. In Austria, 14% of the population is younger than 15, and 18% is older than 65. Which country will have the highest growth rate over the next two decades? Explain your answer.

17. **INTERPRET DATA** The 2013 population of the Netherlands was 16.8 million, and its land area is 15,768 square miles. The 2013 population of the United States was 316.2 million, and its land area is 3,717,796 square miles. Which country has the greater population density?

18. **INTERPRET DATA** The population of India in 2013 was 1,276.5 million, and its growth rate was 1.5% per year. Calculate the 2014 population of India.

19. **INTERPRET DATA** The world population in 2013 was 7.14 billion, and its annual growth rate was 1.2%. If the birth rate was 20 per 1000 people in the year 2013, what was the death rate, expressed as number per 1000 people?

20. **INTERPRET DATA** Consider the age structure diagrams for counties (a) and (b). Which diagram is consistent with negative growth momentum? Why?

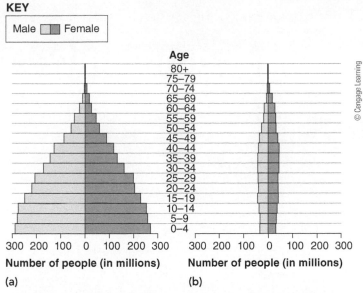

KEY

Male ☐ Female

(a) Number of people (in millions)

(b) Number of people (in millions)

21. **SCIENCE, TECHNOLOGY, AND SOCIETY** In what ways has technology contributed to consumption overpopulation? Can you propose some applications of technology that might help alleviate its effects?

To access course materials, such as Aplia and other companion resources, please visit **www.cengagebrain.com**.

54 | Community Ecology

Luis Javier Sandoval/Getty Images

Mangrove root community. Spreading mangrove roots at the water and land interface provide shelter for many species of animals including fish, invertebrates, and amphibians.

KEY CONCEPTS

54.1 A community consists of populations that live in the same place at the same time. Community ecologists focus on questions concerning the number of species, the relative abundance of each species, interactions among species, and resistance of the community to environmental disturbances (natural and human-made).

54.2 Both dominant species and keystone species have community-wide effects on energy flow and community structure: dominant species because of their large biomass or abundance, and keystone species despite their relatively small biomass or abundance.

54.3 Factors that influence community diversity include the number, variety, and abundance of species. Field experiments with plants beginning in the 1990s suggest that more diverse communities have a greater stability, or resistance to change.

54.4 Most ecologists think that communities are loose associations of organisms that have similar environmental requirements and therefore live together in the same environment. Following a disturbance, communities undergo succession from pioneer communities to mature communities.

I n Chapter 53 we examined the dynamics of populations. In the natural world, most populations are part of a **community,** which consists of an association of populations of different species that live and interact in the same place at the same time. The definition for *community* is deliberately broad because it refers to ecological categories that vary greatly in size, lack precise boundaries, and are rarely completely isolated.

Smaller communities nest within larger communities. A mangrove forest is a community, but so are the interlacing roots that support each tree (see photograph). Mangrove roots, anchored in sediment made up of sand and peat, are breeding grounds and nurseries for crabs, shrimp, and many commercially important fish. Blue crabs, lizards, and turtles feed on insects, algae, and dead animal material. Small mammals scurry among the roots, and manatees and alligators find shelter from the tropical sun. Mangrove root surfaces are home to invertebrates, algae, bacteria, archaea, and fungi, which provide nutrients for other organisms. Mangroves also filter excess nutrients and some toxic pollutants from the water.

Organisms exist in an abiotic (nonliving) environment that is as essential to their lives as their interactions with one another. Minerals, air, water, and sunlight are just as much a part of a bat's environment, for example, as the flowers it pollinates and from which it takes nectar and insects. A biological community and its abiotic environment together compose an **ecosystem.** Like communities, ecosystems are broad entities that refer to ecological units of various sizes.

We now present some of the challenges in trying to find common patterns and processes that govern communities. The living community is emphasized in this chapter. The abiotic components of ecosystems, including energy flow and trophic structure (feeding relationships), nutrient cycling, and climate, are considered in Chapter 55.

54.1 COMMUNITY STRUCTURE AND FUNCTIONING

LEARNING OBJECTIVES

1 Define *ecological niche* and distinguish between an organism's fundamental niche and its realized niche.

2 Define *competition* and distinguish between interspecific and intraspecific competition.

3 Summarize the concepts of the competitive exclusion principle, resource partitioning, and character displacement.

4 Define *predation* and describe the effects of natural selection on predator–prey relationships.

5 Distinguish among mutualism, commensalism, and parasitism, and give examples of each.

Communities exhibit characteristic properties that populations lack. These properties, known collectively as *community structure* and *community functioning,* include the number and types of species present, the relative abundance of each species, the interactions among different species, community resilience to disturbances, energy and nutrient flow throughout the community, and productivity. **Community ecology** is the description and analysis of patterns and processes within the community. Finding common patterns and processes in a wide variety of communities—for example, a pond community, a pine forest community, and a sagebrush desert community—helps ecologists understand community structure and functioning.

Communities are exceedingly difficult to study because a large number of individuals of many different species interact with one another and are interdependent in a variety of ways. Species compete with one another for food, water, living space, and other resources. (Used in this context, a *resource* is anything from the environment that meets needs of a particular species.) Some organisms kill and eat other organisms or cause disease.

Some species form intimate associations with one another, whereas other species seem only distantly connected. Certain species interact in positive ways in a process known as **facilitation,** which modifies and enhances the local environment for other species. For example, alpine plants in harsh mountain environments grow faster and larger and reproduce more successfully when certain other plants are growing nearby (**FIG. 54-1**).

(a) *Laretia acaulis* plants increase the survival rate of certain nearby plants at 2800 m (9100 ft) in the Andes Mountains of Chile. The effect is less pronounced at higher elevations.

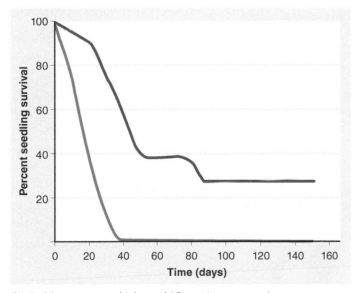

(b) Field mouse-ear chickweed (*Cerastium arvense*) plants were planted and grown within (*red*) and outside (*blue*) clumps of *Laretia acaulis.*

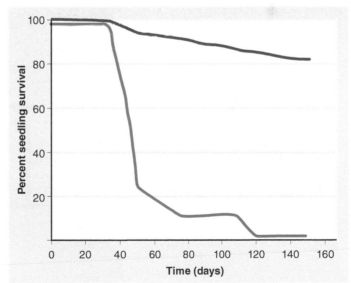

(c) Alpine barley (*Hordeum comosum*) plants were planted and grown within (*red*) and outside (*blue*) clumps of *Laretia acaulis.*

Figure 54-1 Facilitation in alpine communities

(**b** and **c,** Adapted from Cavieres, L.A., et al. "Positive Interactions between Alpine Plant Species and the Nurse Cushion Plants *Laretia acaulis* Do Not Increase with Elevation in the Andes of Central Chile." 2006, *New Phytologist,* 169:59–69.)

Also, each organism plays one of three main roles in community life: producer, consumer, or decomposer. Unraveling the many positive and negative, direct and indirect interactions of organisms living together as a community is one of the goals of community ecologists.

Community interactions are complex and often not readily apparent

During the late 1990s, an intricate relationship emerged among acorn production, white-footed mice, deer, gypsy moth population growth, and the potential occurrence of Lyme disease in humans (FIG. 54-2). Large-scale experiments conducted in oak forests of the northeastern United States linked bumper acorn crops, which occur every three to four years, to booming mouse populations (the mice eat the acorns). Because the mice also eat gypsy moth pupae, high acorn conditions also lead to low populations of gypsy moths. This outcome helps the oaks because gypsy moths cause serious defoliation. However, abundant acorns also attract tick-bearing deer to oak forests. The ticks' hungry offspring feed on the mice, which often carry the Lyme disease–causing bacterium. The bacterium infects the maturing ticks and, in turn, spreads to humans who are bitten by affected ticks. In 2006, scientists concluded that it is possible to predict which years pose the greatest potential threat of Lyme disease to humans based on when oaks are most productive. They determined that the risk of Lyme disease is greater two years following a bumper acorn crop than in other years.

Within a community, no species exists independently of other species. As the preceding example shows, the populations of a community interact with and affect one another in complex ways that are not always obvious. Three main types of interactions occur among species in a community: competition, predation, and symbiosis. Before we address these interactions, however, we need to examine the way of life of a given species in its community.

The niche is a species' ecological role in the community

Every species is thought to have its own ecological role within the structure and function of a community; we call this role its **ecological niche.** Although the concept of ecological niche has been in use in ecology since early in the 20th century, Yale ecologist G. E. Hutchinson first described in 1957 the multidimensional nature of the niche that is accepted today. An ecological niche takes into account all biotic and abiotic aspects of the species' existence, that is, all the physical, chemical, and biological factors that the species needs to survive, remain healthy, and reproduce. A niche includes the local environment in which a species lives, its **habitat.** A niche also encompasses what a species eats, what eats it, what organisms it competes with, and how it interacts with and is influenced by the abiotic components of its environment, such as light, temperature, and moisture. The niche thus represents the totality of adaptations by a species to its environment, its use of resources, and the lifestyle to which it is suited. Although

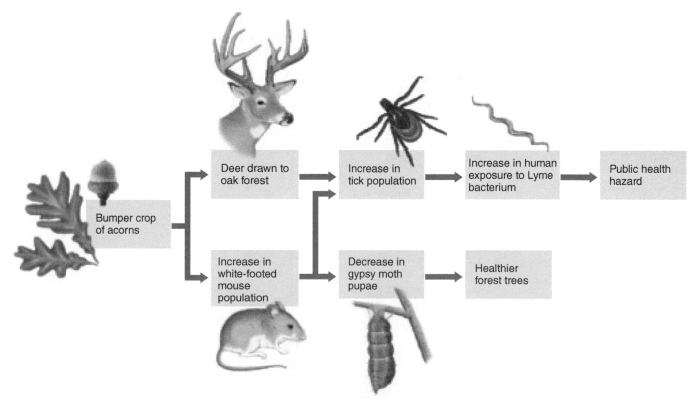

Figure 54-2 Connections to the size of an acorn crop

When there is a bumper crop of acorns, more mice survive and breed in winter, and more deer are attracted to oak forests. Both mice and deer are hosts of ticks that may carry the Lyme disease bacterium to humans. Abundant mice also reduce gypsy moth populations, thereby improving the health of forest trees.

© Cengage Learning

a complete description of an organism's ecological niche involves many dimensions and is difficult to define precisely, ecologists usually confine their studies to one or a few niche variables, such as feeding behaviors or ability to tolerate temperature extremes.

The ecological niche of a species is far broader hypothetically than in actuality. A species is usually capable of using much more of its environment's resources or of living in a wider assortment of habitats than it actually does. The potential ecological niche of a species is its **fundamental niche,** but various factors, such as competition with other species, may exclude it from part of this fundamental niche. Thus, the lifestyle that a species actually pursues and the resources it actually uses make up its **realized niche.**

An example may help make this distinction clear. The green anole, a lizard native to Florida and other southeastern states, perches on trees, shrubs, walls, or fences during the day, waiting for insect and spider prey (FIG. 54-3a). In the past, these little lizards were widespread in Florida. Several decades ago, however, a related species, the brown anole introduced from Cuba into southern Florida, spread northward up the Florida peninsula and quickly became common (FIG. 54-3b). Suddenly, the green anoles became rare, apparently driven out of their habitat by competition from the slightly larger brown anoles. Careful investigation, however, disclosed that green anoles were still around. They were now confined largely to the vegetation in wetlands and to the foliated crowns of trees, where they were less easily seen.

The habitat portion of the green anole's fundamental niche includes the trunks and crowns of trees, exterior house walls, and many other locations. Once the brown anoles became established in the green anole habitat, they drove the green anoles from all but wetlands and tree crowns; competition between the two species shrank the green anoles' realized niche (FIGS. 54-3c and d). Because communities consist of numerous species, many of which compete to some extent, the interactions among them produce each species' realized niche.

Limiting resources restrict the ecological niche of a species

A species' structural, physiological, and behavioral adaptations determine its tolerance for environmental extremes. If any feature of an environment lies outside the bounds of its tolerance, the species cannot live there. Just as you would not expect to find a cactus living in a pond, you would not expect water lilies in a desert.

The environmental factors that actually determine a species' ecological niche are difficult to identify. For this reason, the concept of ecological niche is largely abstract, although some of its dimensions can be experimentally determined. Any environmental resource that, because it is scarce or unfavorable, tends to restrict the ecological niche of a species is called a **limiting resource.**

Most of the limiting resources that have been studied are simple variables, such as the soil's mineral content, temperature extremes, and precipitation amounts. Such investigations have disclosed that any factor either exceeding the tolerance of a species or present in quantities smaller than the required minimum limits the presence of that species in a community. By their interaction, such factors help define the ecological niche for a species.

Limiting resources may affect only part of an organism's life cycle. For example, although adult blue crabs live in fresh or slightly brackish water, they do not become permanently established in such areas because their larvae (immature forms) require salt water. Similarly, the ring-necked pheasant, a popular game bird native to Eurasia, has been widely introduced in North America but has not become

Danita Delimont/Getty Images

Robert Clay/Visuals Unlimited, Inc.

(a) Green anole lizard with dragonfly prey. The green anole (*Anolis carolinensis*) is the only anole species native to North America. Males are about 12.5 cm (5 in.) long; females are slightly smaller. (Photographed on Jefferson Island, Louisiana.)

(b) The brown anole (*A. sagrei*), which is 15.2 cm (6 in.) long, was introduced to Florida. It is native to Cuba and the Bahamas.

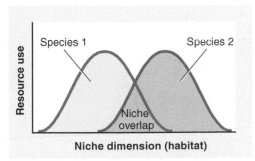

(c) Positions of the two species along a single niche dimension (in this case, habitat). Species 1 represents the green anole, and Species 2 represents the brown anole. The fundamental niches of the two lizards overlap.

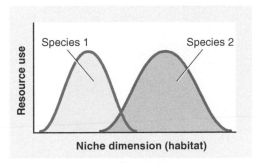

(d) The brown anole outcompetes the green anole in the area where their niches overlap, restricting the niche of the green anole.

Figure 54-3 *Animation* **Effect of competition on an organism's realized niche**
© Cengage Learning

established in the southern United States. The adult birds do well there, but the eggs do not develop properly in the warmer southern temperatures.

Biotic and abiotic factors influence a species' ecological niche In the 1960s, U.S. ecologist Joseph H. Connell investigated biotic and abiotic factors that affect the distribution of two barnacle species in the rocky *intertidal zone* along the coast of Scotland. The intertidal zone is a challenging environment, and organisms in the intertidal zone must tolerate exposure to the drying air during low tides. Barnacles are sessile crustaceans whose bodies are covered by a shell of calcium carbonate (see Fig. 31-21a). When the shell is open, feathery appendages extend to filter food from the water.

Along the coast of Scotland, more adults of one barnacle species, *Semibalanus balanoides* (formerly called *Balanus balanoides*), are attached on lower rocks in the intertidal zone than are adults of the other species, *Chthamalus stellatus* (**FIG. 54-4**). The distributions of the two species do not overlap, although immature larvae of both species live together in the intertidal zone. Connell manipulated the two populations to determine what factors were affecting their distribution. When he removed *Chthamalus* from the upper rocks, *Semibalanus* barnacles did not expand into the vacant area. Connell's experiments showed that *Chthamalus* is more resistant than *Semibalanus* to desiccation

when the tide retreats. However, when Connell removed *Semibalanus* from the lower rocks, *Chthamalus* expanded into the lower parts of the intertidal zone. The two species compete for space, and *Semibalanus*, which is larger and grows faster, outcompetes the smaller *Chthamalus* barnacles.

Competition among barnacle species for the limiting resource of living space was one of the processes that Connell's research demonstrated. We now examine other aspects of competition that various ecologists have revealed in both laboratory and field studies.

Competition is intraspecific or interspecific

Competition occurs when two or more individuals attempt to use the same essential resource, such as food, water, shelter, living space, or sunlight. Because resources are often in limited supply in the environment, their use by one individual decreases the amount available to others (**TABLE 54-1**). If a tree in a dense forest grows taller than surrounding trees, for example, it absorbs more of the incoming sunlight. Less sunlight is therefore available for nearby trees that are shaded by the taller tree. Competition occurs among individuals within a population (**intraspecific competition**) or between different species (**interspecific competition**). (Intraspecific competition was discussed in Chapter 53.)

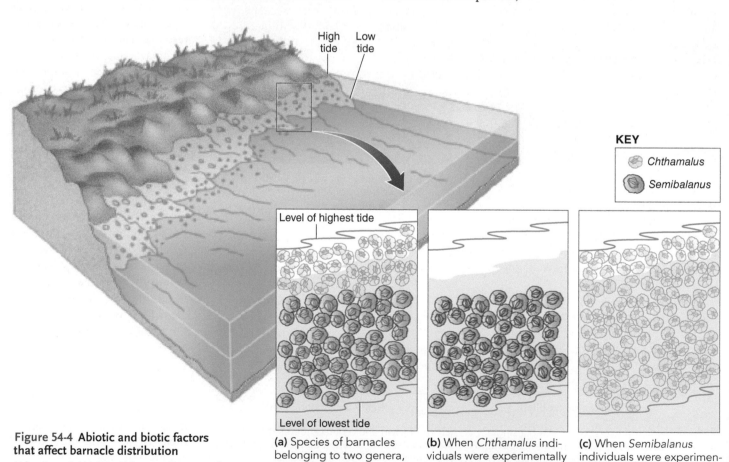

Figure 54-4 Abiotic and biotic factors that affect barnacle distribution

(After Connell, J.H. "The Influence of Interspecific Competition and Other Factors on the Distribution of the Barnacle *Chthamalus stellatus*." *Ecology*, Vol. 42, 1961.)

(a) Species of barnacles belonging to two genera, *Chthamalus* and *Semibalanus*, grow in the intertidal zone of a rocky shore in Scotland.

(b) When *Chthamalus* individuals were experimentally removed, *Semibalanus* individuals did not expand into their section of the rock.

(c) When *Semibalanus* individuals were experimentally removed, *Chthamalus* individuals spread into the empty area.

KEY

Chthamalus

Semibalanus

TABLE 54-1	Ecological Interactions among Species		
INTERACTION		EFFECT ON SPECIES 1	EFFECT ON SPECIES 2
Competition between species 1 and species 2		Harmful	Harmful
Predation of species 2 (prey) by species 1 (predator)		Beneficial	Harmful
Symbiosis			
Mutualism of species 1 and species 2		Beneficial	Beneficial
Commensalism of species 1 with species 2		Beneficial	No effect
Parasitism by species 1 (parasite) on species 2 (host)		Beneficial	Harmful

© Cengage Learning

Ecologists traditionally assumed that competition is the most important determinant of both the number of species found in a community and the size of each population. Today ecologists recognize that competition is only one of many interacting biotic and abiotic factors that affect community structure. Furthermore, competition is not always a straightforward, direct interaction. Several kinds of flowering plants, for example, live in a young pine forest and presumably compete with the conifers for such resources as soil moisture and soil minerals. Their relationship, however, is more complex than simple competition. The flowers produce nectar that is consumed by some insect species that also prey on needle-eating insects, thereby reducing the number of insects feeding on pines. It is therefore difficult to assess the overall effect of flowering plants on pines. If the flowering plants were removed from the community, would the pines grow faster because they were no longer competing for necessary resources? Or would the increased presence of needle-eating insects (caused by fewer predatory insects) inhibit pine growth?

Short-term experiments in which one competing plant species is removed from a forest community have often demonstrated an improved growth for the remaining species. However, very few studies have tested the long-term effects on forest species of removing a single competing species. These long-term effects may be subtle, indirect, and difficult to ascertain; they may lessen or negate the short-term effects of competition for resources.

Competition between species with overlapping niches may lead to competitive exclusion

When two species are similar, as are the green and brown anoles or the two species of barnacles, their fundamental niches may overlap. However, based on experimental and modeling work, many ecologists think that no two species indefinitely occupy the same niche in the same community. According to the **competitive exclusion principle,** it is hypothesized that one species excludes another from its niche as a result of interspecific competition. Although it is possible for species to compete for some necessary resource without being total competitors, two species with absolutely identical ecological niches cannot coexist. Coexistence occurs, however, if the overlap between the two niches is reduced. In the lizard example, direct competition between the two species was reduced as the brown anole excluded the green anole from most of its former habitat.

The initial evidence that interspecific competition contributes to a species' realized niche came from a series of laboratory experiments by Russian biologist Georgyi F. Gause in the 1930s. In one study Gause grew populations of two species of protozoa, *Paramecium aurelia* and the larger *P. caudatum,* in controlled conditions (FIG. 54-5). When grown in separate test tubes—that is, in the absence of the second species—the population of each species quickly increased to a level imposed by the resources and remained there for some time thereafter. When grown together, however, only *P. aurelia* thrived, whereas *P. caudatum* dwindled and eventually died out. Under different sets of culture conditions, *P. caudatum* prevailed over *P. aurelia.* Gause interpreted these results to mean that although one set of conditions favored one species, a different set favored the other. Nonetheless, because both species were so similar, in time one or the other would eventually triumph. Similar experiments with competing species of fruit flies, mice, beetles, and annual plants have supported Gause's results: one species thrives, and the other eventually dies out.

Thus, competition has adverse effects on species that use a limited resource and may result in competitive exclusion of one or more species. It therefore follows that over time natural selection should favor individuals of each species that avoid or reduce competition for environmental resources. Reduced competition among coexisting species as a result of each species' niche differing from the others in one or more ways is called **resource partitioning.** Resource partitioning is well-documented in animals; studies in tropical forests of Central America and South America demonstrate little overlap in the diets of fruit-eating birds, primates, and bats that coexist in the same habitat. Although fruits are the primary food for several hundred bird, primate, and bat species, the wide variety of fruits available has allowed fruit eaters to specialize, which reduces competition.

Resource partitioning may also include timing of feeding, location of feeding, nest sites, and other aspects of a species' ecological niche. Princeton ecologist Robert MacArthur's study of five North American warbler species is a classic example of resource partitioning (FIG. 54-6). Although initially the warblers' niches seemed nearly identical, MacArthur found that individuals of each species spend most of their feeding time in different portions of the spruces and other conifer trees they frequent. They also move in different directions through the canopy, consume different combinations of insects, and nest at slightly different times.

Difference in root depth is an example of resource partitioning in plants. For example, three common annuals found in certain abandoned fields are smartweed, Indian mallow, and bristly foxtail. Smartweed roots extend deep into the soil, Indian mallow roots grow to a medium depth, and bristly foxtail roots are shallow. This difference reduces competition for the same soil resources—water and minerals—by allowing the plants to exploit different portions of the resource.

Character displacement is an adaptive consequence of interspecific competition

Sometimes populations of two similar species occur together in some locations and separately

Can competitive exclusion be demonstrated in the laboratory under controlled conditions?

HYPOTHESIS: When two species of paramecia (ciliated protozoa) are grown together in a mixed culture, one species outcompetes the other.

EXPERIMENT: Gause grew two species of paramecia, both separately and together.

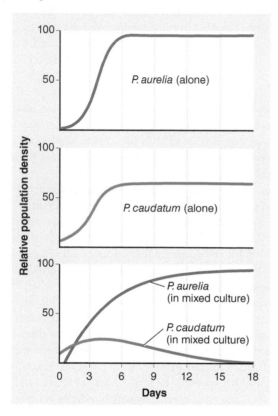

RESULTS AND CONCLUSION: The *top* and *middle graphs* show how each species of *Paramecium* flourishes when grown alone. The *bottom graph* shows how they grow together, in competition with each other. In a mixed culture, *P. aurelia* outcompetes *P. caudatum*, resulting in competitive exclusion.

SOURCE: Adapted from Gause, G.F. *The Struggle for Existence.* Williams and Wilkins, Baltimore, 1934.

Figure 54-5 *Animation* **G.F. Gause's classic experiment on interspecific competition**

PREDICT What would happen to the two competing cultures shown in the bottom graph if a medium containing a nutrient that could be metabolized only by *P. caudatum* replaced the existing growth medium at day 6?

in others. Where their geographic distributions overlap, the two species tend to differ more in their structural, ecological, and behavioral characteristics than they do where each occurs in separate geographic areas. Such divergence in traits in two similar species living in the same geographic area is known as **character displacement.** Biologists think that character

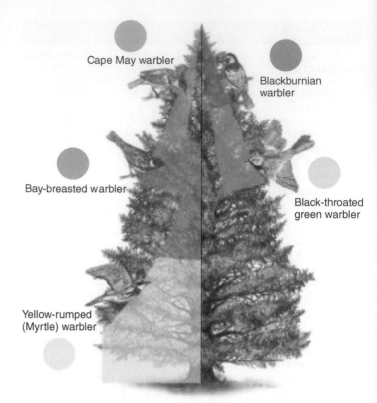

Figure 54-6 Resource partitioning
Each warbler species spends at least half its foraging time in its designated area of a spruce tree, thereby reducing the competition among warbler species. (After MacArthur, R.H. "Population Ecology of Some Warblers of Northeastern Coniferous Forests." *Ecology,* Vol. 39, 1958.)

displacement reduces competition between two species because their differences give them somewhat different ecological niches in the same environment.

There are several well-documented examples of character displacement between two closely related species. The flowers of two *Solanum* species in Mexico are quite similar in areas where either one or the other occurs. However, where their distributions overlap, the two species differ significantly in flower size and are pollinated by different kinds of bees. In other words, character displacement reduces interspecific competition, in this case for the same animal pollinator.

The bill sizes of Darwin's finches provide another example of character displacement (**FIG. 54-7**). On large islands in the Galápagos where the medium ground finch (*Geospiza fortis*) and the small ground finch (*G. fuliginosa*) occur together, their bill depths are distinctive. *Geospiza fuliginosa* has a smaller bill depth that enables it to crack small seeds, whereas *G. fortis* has a larger bill depth that enables it to crack medium-sized seeds. However, *G. fortis* and *G. fuliginosa* also live on separate islands. Where the two species live separately, bill depths are about the same intermediate size, perhaps because there is no competition from the other species.

Although these examples of the coexistence of similar species are explained in terms of character displacement, the character displacement hypothesis has been demonstrated in nature in only a few instances. In 2006, Peter and Rosemary

Can character displacement be demonstrated in the wild?

HYPOTHESIS: Two species of finches are more different where they occur together than where they occur separately.

EXPERIMENT: Two species of Darwin's finches in the Galápagos were observed on islands where they occur separately and on an island where they exist together. Bill depth **(a),** which varies considerably in the two species, was measured in the different environments.

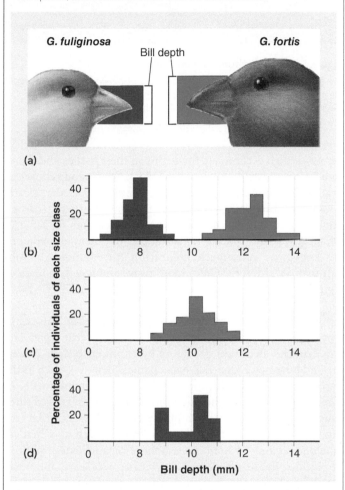

RESULTS AND CONCLUSION: (b) Where the two species are found on the same island (Santa Cruz), *G. fuliginosa* (*red*) has a smaller average bill depth than *G. fortis* (*blue*). Where they occur on separate islands (**c,** on Daphne Major, and **d,** on Los Hermanos), the average bill depths of each are similar. Thus, they illustrate character displacement.

SOURCE: After Lack, D. *Darwin's Finches.* Cambridge University Press, Cambridge, 1947.

Figure 54-7 **Character displacement**

PREDICT If *G. fuliginosa* were removed from the shared island, would you expect the beaks of the *G. fortis* population to change over time? In what way?

Grant, who have studied Darwin's finches in the Galápagos Islands since the 1970s, reported in the journal *Science* another example of character displacement in Darwin's finches. The medium ground finch (*G. fortis*) originally lived on one of the small Galápagos islands by itself. Different *G. fortis* individuals had varying beak sizes that allowed them to eat small, medium, or large seeds. However, in recent years the large ground finch (*G. magnirostris*) colonized the island and began to compete with the medium ground finch for the larger seeds. A severe drought reduced the seed supply, putting additional pressure on the medium finch population. In response, the medium ground finch's beak quickly diverged, becoming significantly smaller in length, depth, and width on average than it had been. The altered population of medium ground finches now consumes small seeds almost exclusively; their small beaks cannot crack the larger seeds preferred by the large ground finch.

Natural selection shapes the bodies and behaviors of both predator and prey

Predation is the consumption of one species, the *prey,* by another, the *predator* (see Table 54-1). Predation includes animals eating other animals as well as animals eating plants (*herbivory*). Predation has resulted in an evolutionary "arms race," with the evolution of predator strategies (more efficient ways to catch prey) and prey strategies (better ways to escape the predator). A predator that is more efficient at catching prey exerts a strong selective force on its prey. Over time, adaptations that reduce the probability of being captured may evolve in the prey species. In turn, these adaptations exert a strong selective force on the predator. This type of interdependent evolution of two interacting species is known as **coevolution** (see discussion of coevolution in Chapter 37).

We now consider several adaptations related to predator–prey interactions, including predator strategies (pursuit and ambush) and prey strategies (plant defenses and animal defenses). Keep in mind as you read these descriptions that such strategies are not "chosen" by the respective predators or prey. New traits arise randomly in a population as a result of genetic changes. Some new traits are beneficial, some are harmful, and others have no effect. Beneficial strategies, or traits, persist in a population because such characteristics make the individuals that have them well suited to thrive and reproduce. In contrast, characteristics that make the individuals that have them poorly suited to their environment tend to disappear in a population.

Pursuit and ambush are two predator strategies A brown pelican sights its prey—a fish—while in flight. Less than 2 seconds after diving into the water at a speed as great as 72 km/h (45 mph), it has its catch. Orcas, formerly known as killer whales, hunt in packs and often herd salmon or tuna into a cove so that they are easier to catch. Any trait that increases hunting efficiency, such as the speed of brown pelicans or the intelligence of orcas, favors predators that pursue their prey. Because these carnivores must process information quickly

Figure 54-8 Ambush

A yellow crab spider (*Misumena vatia*) blends into its surroundings, waiting for an unwary insect to visit the flower. An effective predator strategy, ambush relies on surprising the prey.

Figure 54-9 Plant chemical defenses

Toxic chemicals protect the common milkweed (*Asclepias syriaca*). Its leaves are poisonous to most herbivores except monarch caterpillars (*Danaus plexippus*) and a few other insects. Monarch caterpillars have bright aposematic coloration.

during the pursuit of prey, their brains are generally larger, relative to body size, than those of the prey they pursue.

Ambush is another effective way to catch prey. The yellow crab spider, for example, is the same color as the white or yellow flowers on which it hides (**FIG. 54-8**). This camouflage keeps unwary insects that visit the flower for nectar from noticing the spider until it is too late. It also fools birds that prey on the crab spider.

Predators that *attract* prey are particularly effective at ambushing. For example, a diverse group of deep-sea fishes called anglerfish possess rodlike bioluminescent lures close to their mouths to attract prey (see Fig. 32-14c).

Chemical protection is an effective plant defense against herbivores

Plants cannot escape predators by fleeing, but they have several physical and chemical adaptations that protect them from being eaten. The presence of spines, thorns, tough leathery leaves, or even thick wax on leaves discourages foraging herbivores from grazing. Other plants produce an array of protective chemicals that are unpalatable or even toxic to herbivores. The active ingredients in such plants as marijuana and tobacco affect hormone activity and nerve, muscle, liver, and kidney functions and may discourage foraging by herbivores. Interestingly, many of the chemical defenses in plants are useful to humans. India's neem tree, for example, contains chemicals effective against more than 100 species of herbivorous insects, mites, and nematodes. Nicotine from tobacco, pyrethrum from chrysanthemum, and rotenone from the derris plant are other examples of chemicals extracted and used as insecticides.

Milkweeds are an excellent example of the biochemical coevolution between plants and herbivores (**FIG. 54-9**). Milkweeds produce alkaloids and cardiac glycosides, chemicals that are poisonous to all animals except a small group of insects. The ability to either tolerate or metabolize the milkweed toxins has evolved in these insects. They eat milkweeds and avoid competition from other herbivorous insects because few others tolerate milkweed toxins. Predators also learn to avoid these

insects, which accumulate the toxins in their tissues and therefore become toxic themselves. The black, white, and yellow coloration of the monarch caterpillar, a milkweed feeder, clearly announces its toxicity to predators that have learned to associate bright colors with illness. Conspicuous colors or patterns, which advertise a species' unpalatability to potential predators, are known as **aposematic coloration** (pronounced "ap'-uh-suh-mat'-ik"; from the Greek *apo,* "away," and *semat,* "a mark or sign"), or **warning coloration.**

Animal prey possess various defensive adaptations to avoid predators Many animals, such as prairie voles and woodchucks, flee from predators by running to their underground burrows. Others have mechanical defenses, such as the barbed quills of a porcupine and the shell of a pond turtle. To discourage predators, the porcupine fish inflates itself to three times its normal size by pumping water into its stomach (see Fig. 32-14a). Some animals live in groups, such as a herd of antelope, colony of honeybees, school of anchovies, or flock of pigeons. Because a group has so many eyes, ears, and noses watching, listening, and smelling for predators, this social behavior decreases the likelihood of a predator catching any one of them unaware.

Chemical defenses are also common among animal prey. The South American poison arrow frog (*Dendrobates*) stores poison in its skin. (These frogs obtain the toxins from ants and other insects in their diet.) The frog's bright aposematic coloration prompts avoidance by experienced predators (see Fig. 32-18a). Snakes and other animals that have tried once to eat a poisonous frog do not repeat their mistake! Other examples of aposematic coloration occur in the striped skunk, which sprays acrid chemicals from its anal glands, and the bombardier beetle, which spews harsh chemicals at potential predators (see Fig. 7-8).

Some animals have **cryptic coloration,** colors or markings that help them hide from predators by blending into their physical surroundings. Certain caterpillars resemble twigs so closely that

Figure 54-10 Cryptic coloration

The mossy leaf-tailed gecko (*Uroplatus sikorae*) hunts for insects by night and sleeps pressed against a tree branch by day. It is virtually invisible when it sleeps (look closely to see its head and front foot). Photographed in a rain forest in southern Madagascar.

you would never guess that they were animals unless they moved. Pipefish are slender green fish that are almost perfectly camouflaged in green eelgrass. Leaf-tailed geckos in southern Madagascar resemble dead leaves or mossy bark, depending on the species (FIG. 54-10). Such cryptic coloration has been preserved and accentuated by means of natural selection. Predators are less likely to capture animals with cryptic coloration than other animals, Such

animals are therefore more likely to live to maturity and produce offspring that also carry the genes for cryptic coloration.

Sometimes a defenseless species (a *mimic*) is protected from predation by its resemblance to a species that is dangerous in some way (a *model*). Such a strategy is known as **Batesian mimicry.** Many examples of this phenomenon exist. For example, a harmless scarlet king snake looks so much like a venomous coral snake that predators may avoid it (FIG. 54-11). Interestingly, the range of the scarlet king snake extends far beyond that of the coral snake. In an area where coral snakes do not occur, having the coloration of the model confers no special advantage to the king snake and may be harmful, triggering natural selection. This seems to be the case: scientists have reported that scarlet king snake populations located far from coral snakes have undergone natural selection and look less like their model.

In **Müllerian mimicry** different species (*co-models*), all of which are poisonous, harmful, or distasteful, resemble one another. Although their harmfulness protects them as individual species, their similarity in appearance works as an added advantage because potential predators more easily learn a single common aposematic coloration. Scientists hypothesize that viceroy and monarch butterflies are an example of Müllerian mimicry (see *Inquiring About: Mimicry in Butterflies*).

Symbiosis involves a close association between species

Symbiosis is any intimate relationship or association between members of two or more species. Usually, symbiosis involves one species living on or in another species. The partners of a symbiotic relationship, called **symbionts,** may benefit from, be unaffected by, or be harmed by the relationship (see Table 54-1). Examples of symbiosis occur across all the domains and kingdoms of life. Most of the thousands, or perhaps even millions, of symbiotic associations are products of coevolution. Symbiosis takes three forms: mutualism, commensalism, and parasitism.

(a) Scarlet king snake.

(b) Eastern coral snake.

Figure 54-11 Batesian mimicry

In this example **(a)** the scarlet king snake (*Lampropeltis triangulum elapsoides*) is the mimic, and **(b)** the eastern coral snake (*Micrurus fulvius fulvius*) is the model. Note that the red and yellow warning colors touch on the coral snake but do not touch on the harmless mimic.

Why do some butterfly species resemble one another? The monarch butterfly (*Danaus plexippus*), for example, is an attractive insect found throughout much of North America (see figure, *left side*). As a caterpillar, it feeds exclusively on milkweed leaves. The milky white liquid produced by the milkweed plant contains poisons that the insect tolerates but that remain in its tissues for life. When a young bird encounters and tries to eat its first monarch butterfly, the bird becomes sick and vomits. Thereafter, the bird avoids eating the distinctively marked insect.

Many people confuse the viceroy butterfly (*Limenitis archippus;* see figure, *right side*) with the monarch. The viceroy, which is found throughout most of North America, is approximately the same size, and the color and markings of its wings are almost identical to those of the monarch. As caterpillars, viceroys eat cottonwood, aspen, and willow leaves, which apparently do not contain poisonous substances.

During the past century, it was thought that the viceroy butterfly was a tasty food for birds but that its close resemblance to monarchs gave it some protection against being eaten. In other words, birds that had learned to associate the distinctive markings and coloration of the monarch butterfly with its bad taste tended to avoid viceroys because they were similarly marked. The viceroy butterfly

was therefore considered a classic example of Batesian mimicry.

In 1991, ecologists David Ritland and Lincoln Brower of the University of Florida reported the results of an experiment that tested the long-held notion that birds like the taste of viceroys but avoid eating them because of their resemblance to monarchs. They removed the wings of different kinds of butterflies—monarchs, viceroys, and several tasty species—and fed the seemingly identical wingless bodies to red-winged blackbirds. The results were surprising: monarchs and viceroys were equally distasteful to the birds.

As a result of this work, ecologists are re-evaluating the evolutionary significance of different types of mimicry. Rather than an example of Batesian mimicry, monarchs and viceroys may be an example of Müllerian mimicry, in which two or more different species that are distasteful or poisonous have come to resemble each other during the course of evolution. This likeness provides an adaptive advantage because predators learn quickly to avoid all butterflies with the coloration and markings of monarchs and viceroys. As a result, fewer butterflies of either species die, and more individuals survive to reproduce.

Thomas C. Emmel

Müllerian mimicry. Evidence suggests that monarch (*left*) and viceroy (*right*) butterflies are an example of Müllerian mimicry, in which two or more poisonous, harmful, or distasteful organisms resemble each other.

Benefits are shared in mutualism **Mutualism** is a symbiotic relationship in which both partners benefit. Mutualism is either obligate (essential for the survival of both species) or facultative (either partner can live alone under certain conditions).

The association between *nitrogen-fixing bacteria* of the genus *Rhizobium* and legumes (plants such as peas, beans, and clover) is an example of mutualism (see Fig. 55-9). Nitrogen-fixing bacteria, which live inside nodules on the roots of legumes, supply the plants with most of the nitrogen they require to manufacture such nitrogen-containing compounds as chlorophylls, proteins, and nucleic acids. The legumes supply sugars and other energy-rich organic molecules to their bacterial symbionts.

Another example of mutualism is the association between reef-building animals and dinoflagellates called **zooxanthellae.** These symbiotic protists live inside cells of the coral polyp (the coral forms a vacuole around the algal cell), where they photosynthesize and provide the animal with carbon and nitrogen compounds as well as oxygen (**FIG. 54-12**). Calcium carbonate skeletons form around the coral bodies much faster when zooxanthellae are present; their faster growth helps the corals dominate their location on a reef. The corals, in turn, supply the zooxanthellae with waste products

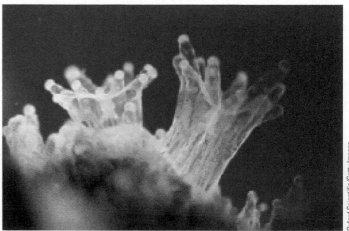

Oxford Scientific/Getty Images

Figure 54-12 Mutualism

The greenish brown specks in these polyps of stony coral (*Pocillopora*) are zooxanthellae, algae that live symbiotically within the coral's translucent cells and supply the coral with carbon and nitrogen compounds. In return, the coral provides the zooxanthellae with nitrogen in the form of ammonia.

such as ammonia, which the algae use to make nitrogen compounds for both partners.

Mycorrhizae are mutualistic associations between fungi and the roots of plants. The association is common; biologists think that nearly 90% of all plant species have mycorrhizae. The fungus, which grows around and into the root as well as into the surrounding soil, absorbs essential minerals, especially phosphorus, from the soil and provides them to the plant. In return, the plant provides the fungus with organic molecules produced by photosynthesis. Plants grow more vigorously in the presence of mycorrhizal fungi (see Figs. 29-19 and 36-11), and they better tolerate environmental stressors such as drought and high soil temperatures. Indeed, some plants cannot maintain themselves under natural conditions if the fungi with which they normally form mycorrhizae are not present.

Humans and bacteria also share mutualistic relationships. Recall in Chapter 25 that we discussed the intestinal component of the human microbiome, which receives shelter and nutrients in exchange for breaking down complex carbohydrates and vitamin production. In addition, human intestinal microbiota ferment unused materials, prevent colonization of pathogenic bacteria, and strengthen the immune system. Recent research also suggests that intestinal microbiota are involved in endocrine and neurological functions and may play a major role in diseases such as diabetes and obesity.

Commensalism is taking without harming

Commensalism is a type of symbiosis in which one species benefits and the other one is neither harmed nor helped. One example of commensalism is the relationship between social insects and scavengers, such as mites, beetles, or millipedes, which live in the social insects' nests. Certain types of silverfish, for example, move along in permanent association with marching columns of army ants and share the abundant food caught in the ant raids. The army ants derive no apparent benefit or harm from the silverfish.

Another example of commensalism is the relationship between a host tree and its epiphytes, which are smaller plants, such as orchids, ferns, or Spanish moss, attached to the host's branches (FIG. 54-13). The epiphyte anchors itself to the tree but does not obtain nutrients or water directly from it. Living on the tree enables it to obtain adequate light, water (as rainfall dripping down the branches), and required minerals (washed out of the tree's leaves by rainfall). Thus, the epiphyte benefits from the association, whereas the tree is apparently unaffected. (Epiphytes harm their host, however, if they are present in a large enough number to block sunlight from the host's leaves; in this instance, the relationship is no longer commensalism.)

Parasitism is taking at another's expense

Parasitism is a symbiotic relationship in which one member, the **parasite**, benefits, whereas the other, the **host**, is adversely affected. The parasite obtains nourishment from its host. A parasite rarely kills its host directly but may weaken it, rendering it more vulnerable to predators, competitors, or abiotic stressors. When a parasite causes disease and sometimes the death of a host, it is called a **pathogen**.

Ticks and other parasites that live outside the host's body are called **ectoparasites**. Figure 32-9 shows a lamprey, an ectoparasite on fish. Parasites such as tapeworms that live within the host are called **endoparasites**. Parasitism is a successful lifestyle; by one estimate, more than two-thirds of all species are parasites, and nearly 1000 species of parasites (including fungi, bacteria, and

Pete Oxford/Getty Images

Figure 54-13 Commensalism

Spanish moss (*Tillandsia usneoides*) is a gray-colored epiphyte that hangs suspended from larger plants in the southeastern United States. Spanish moss is not a moss but a flowering plant in the bromeliad, or pineapple, family. It often grows 6 m (20 ft) or longer, but it is not a parasite and rarely harms the host tree. Spanish moss provides shelter to small animals such as bats, spiders, and snakes.

viruses) live in or on the human species alone! Examples of human parasites include *Entamoeba histolytica*, an amoeba that causes amoebic dysentery; *Plasmodium*, an apicomplexan that causes malaria; a variety of parasitic worms, such as blood flukes, tapeworms, pinworms, and hookworms (see Figs. 31-9 and 31-11); and *Pseudomonas aeruginosa*, an opportunistic bacterium responsible for many urinary tract and respiratory system infections.

Since the 1980s, wild and domestic honeybees in the United States have been dying off. According to the U.S. Department of Agriculture, many beekeepers have lost one-third to one-half of their bees each winter from a condition called colony collapse disorder. Habitat loss, severe weather, pesticide use, and higher pathogen load, as well as the mite *Varroa destructor* and smaller tracheal mites, have contributed to the problem. Although research continues, many scientists believe that a combination of stressors may be the major reason for the continued honeybee decline (FIG. 54-14).

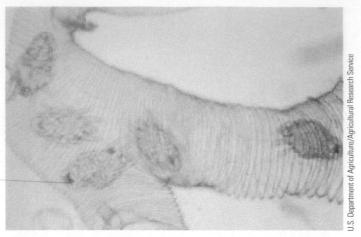

U.S. Department of Agriculture/Agricultural Research Service

100 μm

Figure 54-14 Parasitism

Microscopic tracheal mites (*Acarapis woodi*) are endoparasites that live in the tracheal tubes of honeybees, clogging their airways so that they cannot breathe efficiently. Tracheal mites also suck the bees' circulatory fluid, weakening and eventually killing them. Entomologists think that the larger varroa mites (*not shown*), which are ectoparasites that also feed on the circulatory fluid, are more devastating to honeybee populations than are tracheal mites. Mites may also transmit viruses to their honeybee hosts.

CHECKPOINT 54.1

- **CONNECT** *How are acorns, gypsy moths, and Lyme disease related?*

- *Why is an organism's realized niche usually narrower, or more restricted, than its fundamental niche?*

- **CONNECT** *Which principle of community ecology is illustrated by the following example: Two closely related species of small fish occupy the upper two feet of water when they occur in separate ponds, but if they are in the same pond, species a is more often found in the uppermost foot, and species b in the foot below.*

- *Name the three kinds of symbiosis and give an example of each.*

54.2 STRENGTH AND DIRECTION OF COMMUNITY INTERACTIONS

LEARNING OBJECTIVES

6 Distinguish between keystone species and dominant species.
7 Distinguish between bottom-up and top-down processes in ecosystem regulation.

There is a great deal of variation in the strength and direction of interactions among species within ecological communities. Some species, known as *keystone species*, are present in a community in low abundance and/or biomass but have strong effects on their communities. Other species, known as *dominant species*, exert strong effects on their communities because they are present in great abundance and/or biomass.

Two types of control affect ecological communities, bottom-up processes and top-down processes. In *bottom-up processes* nutrient availability or food organisms whose population is directly affected by nutrient availability affect the abundance of other community organisms. In *top-down processes* predators impact the abundance of other populations in the community. We now examine these aspects of interactions among species within ecological communities.

Other species of a community depend on or are greatly affected by keystone species

Certain species, called **keystone species,** are crucial in determining the nature of the entire community, that is, its species composition and ecosystem functioning. Keystone species are usually not the most abundant species in the community. Although present in relatively small numbers, the individuals of a keystone species profoundly influence the entire community because they often impact the amount of available food, water, or some other resource. Thus, the effect of keystone species is greatly disproportionate to their abundance. Identifying and protecting keystone species are crucial goals of conservation biology (see Chapter 57). If a keystone species disappears from a community, many other species in that community may become more common or rarer, or may even disappear.

The term *keystone* species was coined by ecologist Robert T. Paine in 1969, based on his experimental studies along the Pacific coast in the state of Washington (FIG. 54-15). Paine removed a predatory sea star, *Pisaster ochraceus*, from a rocky intertidal community that included barnacles, mussels, limpets, and chitons, all of which the sea star preyed on. He observed the changes in community structure that resulted and compared these changes to a nearby control area in which the sea stars were left intact. After the sea stars were removed, about half of the 15 species disappeared from the test area, crowded out by certain mussel and barnacle populations, which increased rapidly when freed from predation by the sea stars. Paine noted that when a keystone predator such as the sea star is removed from a community, the species diversity of that community changes dramatically.

One problem with the concept of keystone species is that it is often difficult to measure all the direct and indirect effects of a keystone species on an ecosystem. Consequently, most evidence for the existence of keystone species is based on indirect observations rather than on experimental manipulations. For example, consider the fig tree. Because fig trees produce a continuous crop of fruits, they may be keystone species in tropical rain forests of Central America and South America. Fruit-eating monkeys, birds, bats, and other fruit-eating vertebrates of the forest do not normally consume large quantities of figs in their diets.

During that time of the year when other fruits are less plentiful, however, fig trees become important in sustaining fruit-eating vertebrates. It is therefore assumed that should the fig trees disappear, most of the fruit-eating vertebrates would also disappear. In turn, should the fruit eaters disappear, the

1176 CHAPTER 54

Figure 54-15 Rocky intertidal community at low tide

Pisaster sea stars and chitons cling to the rock during low tide. *Pisaster* sea stars range in color from purple to brown to orange. Photographed in the summer in the Pacific Northwest.

spatial distribution of other fruit-bearing plants would become more limited because the fruit eaters help disperse their seeds. Thus, protecting fig trees in such tropical rainforest ecosystems probably increases the likelihood that monkeys, birds, bats, and many other tree species will survive. The question is whether this anecdotal evidence of fig trees as keystone species is strong enough for policy makers to grant special protection to fig trees.

Like the *Pisaster* sea stars, many keystone species are top predators; for example, consider the gray wolf. Where wolves were hunted to extinction, populations of elk, deer, and other larger herbivores increased exponentially. As these herbivores overgrazed the vegetation, many plant species that could not tolerate such grazing pressure disappeared. Smaller animals such as rodents, rabbits, and insects declined in number because the plants they depended on for food were now less abundant. The number of foxes, hawks, owls, and badgers that prey on these small animals decreased, as did the number of ravens, eagles, and other scavengers that eat wolf-kill. Thus, the disappearance of the wolf resulted in communities with considerably less biological diversity.

The reintroduction of wolves to Yellowstone National Park in 1995 has given ecologists a unique opportunity to study the impact of a keystone species. The wolf's return has already caused substantial changes for other residents in the park. The top predator's effects have ranged from altering relationships among predator and prey species to transforming vegetation profiles. Coyotes are potential prey for wolves, and wolf packs have decimated some coyote populations. A reduction in coyotes has allowed populations of the coyotes' prey, such as ground squirrels and chipmunks, to increase. Scavengers such as ravens, bald eagles, and grizzly bears have benefited from dining on scraps from wolf-kills.

Biologists believe prey populations of elk in Yellowstone may now be in balance with the wolf population. Researchers have also recorded increases in the numbers of bear and cougar, which also feed on elk, resulting in a more balanced, healthier ecosystem.

Dominant species influence a community as a result of their greater size or abundance

In contrast to keystone species, which have a large impact out of proportion to their abundance, **dominant species** greatly affect the community because they are very common. Trees, the dominant species of forests, change the local environment. Trees provide shade, which changes both the light and moisture availability on the forest floor. Trees provide numerous habitats and *microhabitats* (such as a hole in a tree trunk or a rotting log) for other species. Forest trees also provide food for many organisms and therefore play a large role in energy flow through the forest ecosystem. Similarly, cordgrass (*Spartina*) is the dominant species in salt marshes, prairie grass in grasslands, and kelp in kelp beds. Animals are also dominant species. Corals, for example, are dominant species in coral reefs, and cattle are dominant species in overgrazed rangelands. Typically, a community has one or a few dominant species, and most other species are relatively rare.

Ecosystem regulation occurs from the bottom up and top down

One question that ecologists have recently considered is which regulatory process—bottom-up or top-down—is more significant in the regulation of various ecosystems. Both energy flow (see Fig. 1-8) and cycles of matter are involved in bottom-up and top-down processes. **Bottom-up processes** are based on **food webs,** the interconnected series of organisms through which energy flows in an ecosystem. Food webs always have plants or other producers at the first (lowest) trophic level (FIG. 54-16a). (A *trophic level* is an organism's position in a food web; e.g., producers are the first trophic level, and plant-eating herbivores are the second level.) In a sense, the biogeochemical cycles that regenerate necessary nutrients such as nitrates and phosphates for producers to assimilate are located "under" the first trophic level. Thus, bottom-up

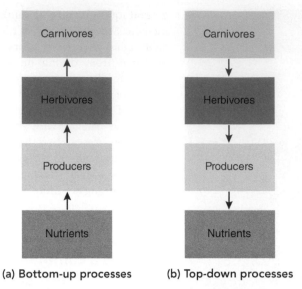

(a) Bottom-up processes   (b) Top-down processes

Figure 54-16 Bottom-up and top-down processes
© Cengage Learning

processes regulate ecosystem function by nutrient cycling and by availability of other resources. If bottom-up processes dominate an ecosystem, the availability of resources such as water or soil minerals controls the number of producers, which controls the number of herbivores, which controls the number of carnivores. (Recall from Chapter 53 that *limiting resources* tend to restrict the ecological niches of organisms, thereby affecting population size.)

Bottom-up processes apparently predominate in certain aquatic ecosystems in which nitrogen or phosphorus is limiting. An experiment in which phosphorus was added to a phosphorus-deficient river (the Kaparuk River in Alaska) resulted in an increase in algae, followed over time by increased populations of aquatic insects, other invertebrates, and fishes.

In contrast, **top-down processes** regulate ecosystem function by trophic interactions, particularly from the highest trophic level (**FIG. 54-16b**). Ecosystem regulation by top-down processes occurs because carnivores eat herbivores, which eat producers, which impacts levels of nutrients. If top-down processes dominate an ecosystem, the effects of an increase in the population of top predators cascade down the food web through the herbivores and producers. In fact, top-down processes are also known as a *trophic cascade.*

A change in the feeding preferences of orcas, off the coast of Alaska, provides an excellent example of a trophic cascade. A few decades ago, when orcas began preying on sea otters, the sea otter population sharply declined. As sea otters have declined, the number of sea urchins, which sea otters eat, has increased. Sea urchins eat kelp, the producers at the base of the food web, and the increase in the number of sea urchins has caused a decline in kelp populations. Kelp forests help reduce levels of carbon dioxide, a greenhouse gas that contributes to climate warming (discussed in Chapter 57).

Top-down regulation appears to predominate in ecosystems with few trophic levels and low species richness. Such ecosystems may have only one or a few species of dominant herbivores, but those species have a strong impact on the producer populations. An excellent example of top-down regulation—reindeer introduced to the Pribilof Islands of Alaska overgrazed the vegetation until the plants were almost wiped out—was discussed in Chapter 53.

It may be that top-down and bottom-up regulatory processes are not mutually exclusive. In a 13-year study of a thorn-scrub community in north-central Chile, ecologists demonstrated that top-down regulation predominates in certain small desert mammals and plant species. However, during periodic El Niño events (discussed later in the chapter), the increase in precipitation resulted in bottom-up increases in producers and consumers. In this ecosystem it appears that both top-down and bottom-up regulatory processes are important in trophic dynamics over an extended period.

CHECKPOINT 54.2

- *Both dominant and keystone species exert strong effects on the character of a community, but in different ways. How do dominant species and keystone species differ?*
- **PREDICT** *Biologists think that the reintroduction of wolves to Yellowstone National Park will ultimately result in a more varied and lush plant composition. How could that occur? Is it an example of a bottom-up or top-down process? Why?*

54.3 COMMUNITY BIODIVERSITY

LEARNING OBJECTIVES

8 Summarize the main determinants of species richness in a community and relate species richness to community stability.
9 State the results of the analysis of the distance effect in South Pacific bird species.

Species diversity, species richness, and species evenness vary greatly from one community to another and are influenced by many biotic and abiotic factors. **Species diversity** is a measure of both the number of species within a community (*species richness*) and the relative importance of each species, based on its abundance, productivity, or size.

Species richness, the number of species in a community, is determined by counting the species of interest. Tropical rain forests and coral reefs are examples of communities with extremely high species richness. In contrast, geographically isolated islands and mountaintops exhibit low species richness. **Species evenness** tells us about the relative abundance of one species compared to other species (**FIG. 54-17**).

Ecologists have developed various mathematical expressions, such as the *Shannon index,* to represent species diversity quantitatively. These *diversity indices* enable ecologists to compare species diversity in different communities. Conservation biologists use diversity indices as part of a comprehensive approach to saving biodiversity.

(a) Low species evenness. In this community the abundance of broomsedge is high relative to the abundance of other wildflowers (burdock, yarrow, and oxeye daisy). Therefore, the community has low species evenness.

(b) High species evenness. In this community each species has the same abundance, and the community has high species evenness.

Figure 54-17 Species evenness

Shown are two hypothetical communities with different species evenness but the same species richness (i.e., each has four species of wildflowers).

© Cengage Learning

A community in which the vegetation is structurally complex generally provides animals with more kinds of food and hiding places than a community with a lower structural complexity.

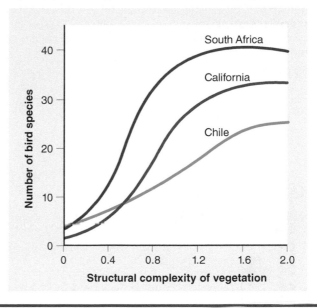

Figure 54-18 Effect of community complexity on species richness

Data were compiled in comparable chaparral habitats (shrubby and woody areas) in Chile, South Africa, and California. The structural complexity of vegetation (*x*-axis) is a numerically assigned gradient of habitats, based on height and density of vegetation, from low complexity (very dry scrub) to high complexity (woodland). (After Cody, M.L., and J.M. Diamond, eds. *Ecology and Evolution of Communities.* Harvard University Press, Cambridge, MA, 1975.)

PREDICT What would a species richness graph look like if the data were compiled from a tundra habitat?

Ecologists seek to explain why some communities have more species than others

What determines the number of species in a community? No single conclusive answer exists, but several explanations appear plausible. They include the structural complexity of habitats, geographic isolation, habitat stress, closeness to the margins of adjacent communities, dominance of one species over others, and geologic history. Although these and other environmental factors have positive or negative effects on species richness, there are exceptions and variations in every explanation. Some explanations vary at different spatial scales: an explanation that seems to work at a large geographic scale (such as a continent) may not work at a smaller local scale (such as a meadow).

In many habitats species richness is related to the structural complexity of habitats. In terrestrial environments the types of plants growing in an area typically determine structural complexity. A structurally complex community, such as a forest, offers a greater variety of potential ecological niches than does a simple community, such as an arid desert or semiarid grassland

(FIG. 54-18). An already complex habitat, such as a coral reef, may become even more complex if species potentially capable of filling vacant ecological niches evolve or migrate into the community because these species create "opportunities" for additional species. Thus, it appears that species richness is self-perpetuating to some degree.

Species richness is inversely related to the geographic isolation of a community. Isolated island communities are generally much less diverse than are communities in similar environments found on continents. This difference is due partly to the *distance effect,* the difficulty encountered by many species in reaching and successfully colonizing the island (FIG. 54-19). Also, sometimes species become locally extinct as a result of random events. In isolated habitats such as islands or mountaintops, locally extinct species are not readily replaced. Isolated areas are usually small and have fewer potential ecological niches.

Generally, species richness is inversely related to the environmental stress of a habitat. Only those species capable of tolerating extreme conditions live in an environmentally stressed community. Thus, the species richness of a highly polluted

Does the geographic isolation of a community affect its species richness?

HYPOTHESIS: Islands close to the mainland (or to a large island) have a higher species richness than the islands that are farther from the mainland.

EXPERIMENT: The number of bird species was cataloged on South Pacific islands that are various distances from New Guinea, a source of colonizing species for these smaller islands. Each point on the graph represents a different island.

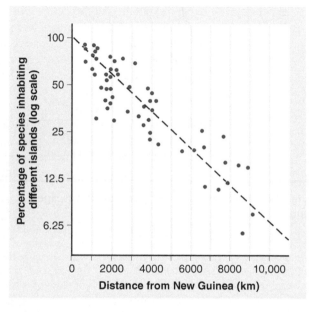

RESULTS AND CONCLUSION: The percentage of South Pacific bird species found on each island in the South Pacific is related to its distance from New Guinea. (New Guinea has 100% of the bird species living in that region.) Thus, species richness declines as the distance from New Guinea increases.

SOURCE: After Diamond, J.M. "Biogeographic Kinetics: Estimation of Relaxation Times for Avifaunas of Southwest Pacific Islands." *Proceedings of the National Academy of Sciences*, Vol. 69, 1972.

Figure 54-19 The distance effect

PREDICT Approximately what percentage of species have colonized islands 5000 km from New Guinea? 8000 km from New Guinea? Based on your answers, explain the relationship between species richness and geographic isolation.

---

stream is low compared with that of a nearby pristine stream. Similarly, the species richness of high-latitude (farther from the equator) communities exposed to harsh climates is lower than that of lower latitude (closer to the equator) communities with milder climates (FIG. 54-20). This observation, known as the *species richness–energy hypothesis,* suggests that different latitudes affect species richness because of variations in solar energy. Greater energy may permit more species to coexist in a given region. Although the equatorial countries of Colombia,

Ecuador, and Peru occupy only 2% of Earth's land, they contain a remarkable 46,000 native plant species. The continental United States and Canada, with a significantly larger land area, host a total of 19,000 native plant species. Ecuador alone contains more than 1600 native species of birds, twice as many as the United States and Canada combined.

Species richness is usually greater at the margins of distinct communities than in their centers. The reason is that an **ecotone,** a transitional zone where two or more communities meet, contains all or most of the ecological niches of the adjacent communities as well as some that are unique to the ecotone (see Fig. 56-24). This change in species composition produced at ecotones is known as the **edge effect.**

Species richness is reduced when any one species enjoys a position of dominance within a community; a dominant species may appropriate a disproportionate share of available resources, thus crowding out, or outcompeting, other species. Ecologist James H. Brown of the University of New Mexico has addressed species composition and richness in experiments conducted since 1977 in the Chihuahuan Desert of southeastern Arizona. In one experiment the removal of three dominant species, all kangaroo rats, from several plots resulted in an increased diversity of other rodent species. This increase was ascribed both to lowered competition for food and to an altered habitat because the abundance of grass species increased dramatically after the removal of the kangaroo rats.

Species richness is greatly affected by geologic history. Many scientists think that tropical rain forests are old, stable communities that have undergone relatively few widespread disturbances through Earth's history. (In ecology a **disturbance** is any event in time that disrupts community or population structure.) During this time, myriad species evolved in tropical rain forests. In contrast, glaciers have repeatedly altered temperate and arctic regions during Earth's history. An area recently vacated by glaciers will have low species richness because few species have had a chance to enter it and become established. The idea that older, more stable habitats have greater species richness than habitats subjected to frequent, widespread disturbances is known as the *time hypothesis.*

Species richness may promote community stability

Traditionally, most ecologists assumed that community stability—the ability of a community to withstand disturbances—is a consequence of community complexity. That is, ecologists hypothesized that a community with considerable species richness is more stable than a community with less species richness. According to this view, the greater the species richness, the less critically important any single species should be. With many possible interactions within the community, it appears unlikely that any single disturbance could affect enough components of the system to make a significant difference in its functioning.

Supporting evidence for this hypothesis is found in destructive outbreaks of pests being more common in cultivated fields, which have a low species richness, than in natural

Species richness increases along a polar ⟶ equatorial gradient. This correlation has been observed for many organisms, from plants to primates, in both terrestrial and marine environments.

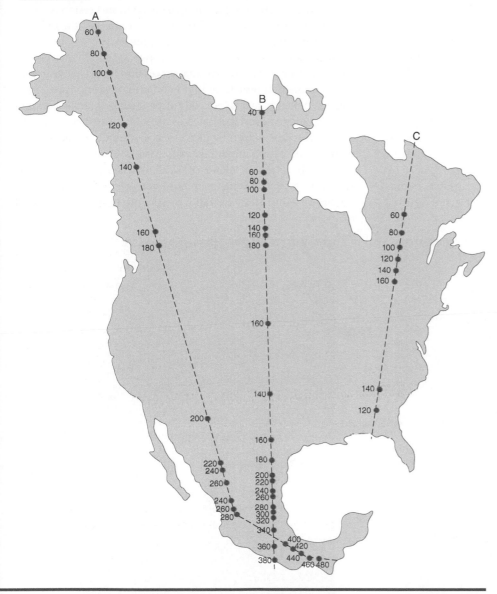

Figure 54-20 Effect of latitude on species richness of breeding birds in North America

The species richness for three north–south transects (A, B, and C) are shown. Note that the overall number of breeding bird species is greater at lower latitudes toward the equator than at higher latitudes. However, this pattern is strongly modified by other factors, such as precipitation and surface features (e.g., mountains). (After Cook, R.E. "Variation in Species Density of North American Birds." *Systematic Zoology,* Vol. 18, 1969.)

PREDICT How might an increase in temperature over time (climate change) affect species richness in Alaska?

strengthened the link between species richness and community stability. In their initial study, they established and monitored 207 plots of various grassland species in Minnesota for seven years. During the study period, Minnesota's worst drought in 50 years occurred (1987–1988). The ecologists found that those plots with the greatest number of plant species lost less ground cover, as measured by dry weight, and recovered faster than species-poor plots. Later studies by Tilman and his colleagues supported these conclusions and showed a similar effect of species richness on community stability during non-drought years. Similar work by almost three dozen ecologists at eight grassland sites in Europe also supports the link between species richness and community stability.

Some scientists do not agree with the conclusions of Tilman and other research groups that the presence of more species confers greater community stability. These critics argue that it is difficult to separate species number from other factors that could affect productivity. They suggest that it would be better to start with established ecosystems and study what happens to their productivity when plants are removed.

Another observation that adds a layer of complexity to the species richness–community stability debate is that populations of individual species within a species-rich community often vary significantly from year to year. It may seem paradoxical that variation within populations of individual species relates to the stability of the entire community. When you consider all the interactions among the organisms in a community, however, it is obvious that some species benefit at the expense of others. If one species declines in a given year, other species that compete with it may flourish. Thus, if an ecosystem contains more species, it is likely that at least some will be resistant to any given disturbance.

communities with a greater species richness. As another example, the almost complete loss of the American chestnut tree to the chestnut blight fungus had little ecological effect on the moderately diverse Appalachian woodlands of which it was formerly a part.

Ongoing studies by David Tilman of the University of Minnesota and John Downing of the University of Iowa have

⊙HECKPOINT 54.3

- **CONNECT** *How is the species richness of a community related to geographic isolation?*
- **CONNECT** *How is the structural complexity of habitats relevant to species richness?*
- **CONNECT** *How is the species richness of a community related to the environmental stress of a habitat?*

54.4 COMMUNITY DEVELOPMENT

LEARNING OBJECTIVES

10 Define *succession* and distinguish between primary and secondary succession.

11 Describe the intermediate disturbance hypothesis.

12 Discuss the two traditional views of the nature of communities: Clements's organismic model and Gleason's individualistic model.

A community does not spring into existence full-blown; rather, it develops gradually through a series of stages, each dominated by different organisms. The process of community development over time, which involves species in one stage being replaced by different species, is called **succession.** An area is initially colonized by certain early successional species that give way over

time to others, and then, in turn, give way much later to late-successional species.

Succession is usually described in terms of the changes in the species composition of an area's vegetation, although each successional stage also has its own characteristic kinds of animals and other species. The time involved in succession is on the order of tens, hundreds, or thousands of years, not the millions of years involved in the evolutionary time scale.

Ecologists distinguish between two types of succession: primary and secondary. **Primary succession** is the change in species composition over time in a habitat that was not previously inhabited by organisms. No soil exists when primary succession begins. Bare rock surfaces, such as recently formed volcanic lava and rock scraped clean by glaciers, are examples of sites where primary succession might take place (FIG. 54-21).

The Indonesian island of Krakatoa has provided scientists with a perfect long-term study of primary succession in a tropical rain forest. In 1883, a volcanic eruption destroyed

(a) After the glacier's retreat, lichens initially colonize the gravel moraine. Mosses and shallow rooted herbs such as mountain avens (*Dryas*) follow.

(b) Dense mats of low-growing *Dryas* plants dominate the landscape, stabilizing the thin layer of developing soil.

(d) As the condition of the soil improves, Sitka spruce (*Picea sichensis*) replaces the alder community. After several hundred years, the forest consists of Sitka spruce and western hemlock (*Tsuga heterophylla*).

(c) Alders replace the *Dryas* community. Both alders (*Alnus*) and *Dryas* have nitrogen-fixing bacteria in root nodules that improve the nitrogen content of the soil.

Figure 54-21 *Animation* **Primary succession following retreating glaciers**
Ecologists have documented primary succession as glaciers have retreated at Glacier Bay, Alaska.

virtually all life on the island. Ecologists have surveyed the ecosystem during the years since the devastation to document the return of life-forms. In the 1990s, ecologists found that the progress of primary succession was extremely slow, in part because of Krakatoa's isolation (recall the distance effect discussed earlier in the chapter). Many species are limited in their ability to disperse over water. Krakatoa's forest, for example, may have only one-tenth the tree species richness of undisturbed tropical rain forest of nearby islands. The lack of plant diversity has, in turn, limited the number of colonizing animal species. In a forested area of Krakatoa where zoologists would expect more than 100 butterfly species, for example, there are only 2.

Secondary succession is the change in species composition that takes place after some disturbance removes the existing vegetation; soil is already present at these sites. Abandoned agricultural fields or open areas produced by forest fires are common examples of sites where secondary succession occurs. During the summer of 1988, wildfires burned approximately one-third of Yellowstone National Park. This natural disaster provided a valuable chance for ecologists to study secondary succession in areas that had been forests. After the conflagration, gray ash covered the forest floor, and most of the trees, although standing, were charred and dead. Secondary succession in Yellowstone has occurred rapidly since 1988. Less than a year later, in the spring of 1989, trout lily and other herbs sprouted and covered much of the ground. By 1998, a young forest of knee-high to shoulder-high lodgepole pines dominated the area. Douglas fir seedlings also began appearing in 1998. Ecologists continue to monitor the changes in Yellowstone as secondary succession unfolds.

Disturbance influences succession and species richness

Early studies suggested that succession inevitably progressed to a stable and persistent community, known as a *climax community*, which was determined solely by climate. Periodic disturbances, such as fires or floods, were not thought to exert much influence on climax communities. If the climax community were disturbed in any way, it would return to a self-sustaining, stable equilibrium in time.

This traditional view of stability has fallen out of favor. The apparent end-point stability of species composition in a "climax" forest is probably the result of how long trees live relative to the human lifespan. It is now recognized that forest communities never reach a state of permanent equilibrium but instead exist in a state of continual disturbance. The species composition and relative abundance of each species vary in a mature community over a range of environmental gradients, although the community retains a relatively uniform appearance overall.

Because all communities are exposed to periodic disturbances, both natural and human-induced, ecologists have long tried to understand the effects of disturbance on species richness. A significant advance was the development of the **intermediate disturbance hypothesis** by Joseph H. Connell.

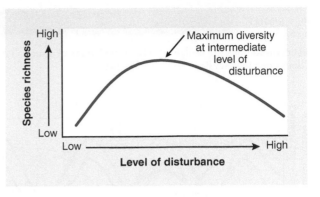

Figure 54-22 Intermediate disturbance hypothesis
Species richness is greatest at an intermediate level of disturbance. (After Connell, J.H. "Diversity in Tropical Rain Forests and Coral Reefs." *Science*, Vol. 199, 1978.)

When he examined species richness in tropical rain forests and coral reefs, he proposed that species richness is greatest at moderate levels of disturbance (FIG. 54-22). At a moderate level of disturbance, the community is a mosaic of habitat patches at different stages of succession; a range of sites exists, from those that were recently disturbed to those that have not been disturbed for many years. When disturbances are frequent or intense, only those species best adapted to earlier stages of succession persist, whereas low levels of disturbance allow late-successional species to dominate to such a degree that other species disappear. For example, when periodic wildfires are suppressed in forests, reducing disturbance to a low level, some of the "typical" forest herbs decline in number or even disappear.

One of the difficulties with the intermediate disturbance hypothesis is defining precisely what constitutes an "intermediate" level of disturbance. Despite this problem, the intermediate disturbance hypothesis has important ramifications for conservation biology because it tells us that we cannot maintain a particular community simply by creating a reserve around it. Both natural and human-induced disturbances will cause changes in species composition, and humans may have to intentionally intervene to maintain the species richness of the original community. What kind of and how much human intervention is necessary to maintain species richness is controversial (we discuss this issue in Chapter 57).

Ecologists continue to study community structure

One of the major issues in community ecology, from the early 1900s to the present, is the nature of communities. Are communities highly organized systems of predictable species, or are they abstractions produced by the minds of ecologists?

U.S. botanist Frederick E. Clements (1874–1945) was struck by the worldwide uniformity of large tracts of vegetation, such as tropical rain forests in South America, Africa, and Southeast Asia. He also noted that even though the species

Most communities are individualistic associations of species rather than distinct units that act like "superorganisms."

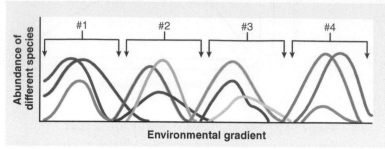

(a) Organismic model. According to this hypothesis, communities are organized as distinct units. Each of the four communities shown (*numbered brackets*) consists of an assemblage of distinct species (*each colored curve represents a single species*). The arrows indicate ecotones, regions of transition along community boundaries.

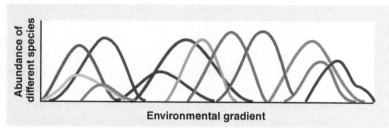

(b) Individualistic model. This model predicts a more random assemblage of species along a gradient of environmental conditions.

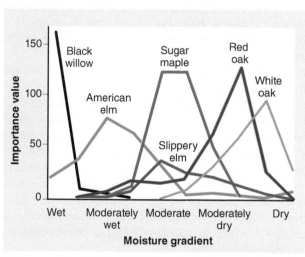

(c) Tree species in Wisconsin forests, which are distributed along a moisture gradient, more closely resemble the individualistic model. The "importance value" (*y-axis*) of each species in a given location combines three aspects (population density, frequency, and size).

Figure 54-23 Nature of communities

(a and b: © Cengage Learning; c: Adapted from Curtis, J.T. *The Vegetation of Wisconsin.* University of Wisconsin Press, Madison, 1959.)

VISUALIZE Create a graph with the same *x*-axis and *y*-axis titles as Figure 54-23c and show what the curves for a palm tree and a cactus might look like.

composition of a community in a particular habitat may be different from that of a community in a habitat with a similar climate elsewhere in the world, overall the components of the two communities are usually similar. He viewed communities as something like "superorganisms" whose member species cooperated with one another in a manner that resembled the cooperation of the parts of an individual organism's body. Clements's view was that a community went through certain stages of development, like the embryonic stages of an organism, and eventually reached an adult state; the developmental process was succession, and the adult state was the climax community. This cooperative view of the community, called the **organismic model,** stresses the interaction of the members, which tend to cluster in tightly knit groups within discrete community boundaries (**FIG. 54-23a**).

Opponents of the organismic model, particularly U.S. ecologist Henry A. Gleason (1882–1975), held that biological interactions are less important in the production of communities than are environmental gradients (such as climate and soil) or even chance. Indeed, the concept of a community is questionable. It may be a classification category with no reality, reflecting little more than the tendency of organisms with similar environmental requirements to live in similar places. This school of thought, called the **individualistic model,** emphasizes species individuality, with each species having its own particular abiotic living requirements. It holds that communities are therefore not interdependent associations of organisms. Rather, each species is independently distributed across a continuum of areas that meets its own individual requirements (**FIG. 54-23b**).

Debates such as this one over the nature of communities are an integral part of the scientific process because they fuel discussion and research that lead to a better understanding of broad scientific principles. Studies testing the organismic and individualistic hypotheses of communities do not support Clements's interactive concept of communities as discrete units. Instead, most studies favor the individualistic model. As shown in **FIGURE 54-23c,** tree species in Wisconsin forests are distributed in a gradient from wet to dry environments. Also, studies of plant and animal movements during the past 14,000 years support the individualistic model because it appears that individual species, not entire communities, became redistributed in response to changes in climate.

CHECKPOINT 54.4

- *How does primary succession differ from secondary succession?*
- *What is Connell's intermediate disturbance hypothesis?*
- *How do the organismic and individualistic models of the nature of communities differ?*

54.1 Community Structure and Functioning *(page 1165)*

1 Define *ecological niche* and distinguish between an organism's fundamental niche and its realized niche.

- The distinctive lifestyle and role of an organism in a community is its **ecological niche.** An organism's ecological niche takes into account all abiotic and biotic aspects of the organism's existence. An organism's **habitat** (where it lives) is one of the parameters used to describe the niche.

- Organisms potentially exploit more resources and play a broader role in the life of their community than they actually do. The potential ecological niche for an organism is its **fundamental niche,** whereas the niche it actually occupies is its **realized niche.**

2 Define *competition* and distinguish between interspecific and intraspecific competition.

- **Competition** occurs when two or more individuals attempt to use the same essential resource, such as food, water, shelter, living space, or sunlight.

- Competition occurs among individuals within a population (**intraspecific competition**) or between different species (**interspecific competition**).

3 Summarize the concepts of the competitive exclusion principle, resource partitioning, and character displacement.

- According to the **competitive exclusion principle,** two species cannot occupy the same niche in the same community for an indefinite period; one species is excluded by another as a result of competition for a limiting resource.

- The evolution of differences in resource use, known as **resource partitioning,** reduces competition between similar species.

- Competition among some species is reduced by **character displacement,** in which their structural, ecological, and behavioral characteristics diverge where their ranges overlap.

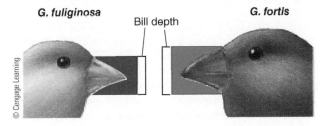

G. fuliginosa   Bill depth   *G. fortis*

© Cengage Learning

4 Define *predation* and describe the effects of natural selection on predator–prey relationships.

- **Predation** is the consumption of one species (the *prey*) by another (the *predator*). During **coevolution** between predator and prey, more efficient ways to catch prey evolve in the predator species, and better ways to escape the predator evolve in the prey species.

5 Distinguish among mutualism, commensalism, and parasitism, and give examples of each.

- **Symbiosis** is any intimate or long-term association between two or more species. The three types of symbiosis are mutualism, commensalism, and parasitism.

- In **mutualism** both partners benefit. Three examples of mutualism are *nitrogen-fixing bacteria* and legumes, **zooxanthellae** and corals, and **mycorrhizae** (fungi and plant roots).

- In **commensalism** one organism benefits and the other is unaffected. Two examples of commensalism are silverfish and army ants, and epiphytes and larger plants.

- In **parasitism** one organism (the **parasite**) benefits and the other (the **host**) is harmed. One example of parasitism is mites that grow in or on honeybees. Some parasites are **pathogens** that cause disease.

54.2 Strength and Direction of Community Interactions *(page 1176)*

6 Distinguish between keystone species and dominant species.

- **Keystone species** are present in relatively small numbers but are crucial in determining the species composition and ecosystem functioning of the entire community.

- In contrast to keystone species, which have an effect that is out of proportion to their abundance, **dominant species** greatly affect the community of which they are a part because they are very common.

7 Distinguish between bottom-up and top-down processes in ecosystem regulation.

- If **bottom-up processes** dominate an ecosystem, the availability of resources such as minerals controls the number of producers (i.e., the lowest trophic level), which controls the number of herbivores, which controls the number of carnivores.

- **Top-down processes** regulate ecosystems from the highest trophic level, by consumers eating producers. If top-down processes dominate an ecosystem, an increase in the number of top predators cascades down the food web through the herbivores and producers.

54.3 Community Biodiversity *(page 1178)*

8 Summarize the main determinants of species richness in a community and relate species richness to community stability.

- Community complexity is expressed in terms of **species richness,** the number of species within a community, and **species diversity,** a measure of the relative importance of each species within a community based on abundance, productivity, or size.

- Species richness is often great in a habitat that has structural complexity; in a community that is not isolated (the distance effect) or severely stressed; in a community where more energy is available (the species richness–energy hypothesis); in **ecotones** (transition zones between communities); and in communities with long histories without major **disturbances,** events that disrupt community or population structure.

- Several studies suggest that species richness may promote community stability.

9 State the results of the analysis of the distance effect in South Pacific bird species.

- The number of bird species found on each island in the South Pacific is inversely related to its geographic isolation, that is, to its distance from New Guinea. Species richness declines as the distance from New Guinea increases.

54.4 Community Development (page 1182)

10 Define *succession* and distinguish between primary and secondary succession.

- **Succession** is the orderly replacement of one community by another. **Primary succession** occurs in an area that has not previously been inhabited (such as bare rock). **Secondary succession** begins in an area where there was a pre-existing community and well-formed soil (such as abandoned farmland).

11 Describe the intermediate disturbance hypothesis.

- Disturbance affects succession and species richness. According to the **intermediate disturbance hypothesis,** species richness is greatest at moderate levels of disturbance, which create a mosaic of habitat patches at different stages of succession.

12 Discuss the two traditional views of the nature of communities: Clements's organismic model and Gleason's individualistic model.

- The **organismic model** views a community as a "super-organism" that goes through certain stages of development (succession) toward adulthood (climax). According to this view, biological interactions are primarily responsible for species composition, and organisms are highly interdependent.

- Most ecologists support the **individualistic model,** which challenges the concept of a highly interdependent community. According to this model, abiotic environmental factors are the primary determinants of species composition in a community, and organisms are somewhat independent of one another.

TEST YOUR UNDERSTANDING

Know and Comprehend

1. A symbiotic association in which organisms are beneficial to one another is known as (a) predation (b) interspecific competition (c) intraspecific competition (d) commensalism (e) mutualism

2. A species' _____ is the totality of its adaptations, its use of resources, and its lifestyle. (a) habitat (b) ecotone (c) ecological niche (d) competitive exclusion (e) coevolution

3. Primary succession occurs on (a) bare rock (b) newly cooled lava (c) abandoned farmland (d) a and b (e) a, b, and c

4. The tendency for two similar species to differ from each other more markedly in areas where they occur together is known as (a) Müllerian mimicry (b) Batesian mimicry (c) resource partitioning (d) competitive exclusion (e) character displacement

5. Competition with other species helps determine an organism's (a) ecotone (b) fundamental niche (c) realized niche (d) limiting resource (e) ecosystem

6. "Complete competitors cannot coexist" is a statement of the principle of (a) primary succession (b) limiting resources (c) Müllerian mimicry (d) competitive exclusion (e) character displacement

7. Based on current evidence, monarch and viceroy butterflies are probably an example of (a) Batesian mimicry (b) character displacement (c) resource partitioning (d) Müllerian mimicry (e) cryptic coloration

8. The _____ signifies that species richness is greater where two communities meet than at the center of either community. (a) edge effect (b) fundamental niche (c) character displacement (d) realized niche (e) limiting resource

9. An unpalatable species demonstrates its threat to potential predators by displaying (a) character displacement (b) limiting resources (c) cryptic coloration (d) aposematic coloration (e) competitive exclusion

10. A limiting resource does all the following *except* that it (a) tends to restrict the ecological niche of a species (b) is in short supply relative to a species' need for it (c) limits the presence of a species in a given community (d) results in an intermediate disturbance (e) may be limiting for only part of an organism's life cycle

Apply and Analyze

11. An ecologist studying several forest-dwelling, insect-eating bird species does not find any evidence of interspecific competition. The most likely explanation is (a) lack of a keystone species

(b) low species richness (c) pronounced intraspecific competition (d) coevolution of predator–prey strategies (e) resource partitioning

12. Support for the individualistic model of community structure includes (a) the decline of honeybees because of two species of parasitic mites (b) the identification of fig trees as a keystone species in tropical forests (c) the competitive exclusion of one *Paramecium* species by another (d) the distribution of trees along a moisture gradient in Wisconsin forests (e) the effects of the removal of a dominant rodent species from an Arizona desert

Evaluate and Synthesize

13. In your opinion, are humans a dominant species or a keystone species? Explain your answer.

14. Many plants that produce nodules for nitrogen-fixing bacteria are common on disturbed sites. Explain how these plants might simultaneously compete with and facilitate other plant species.

15. **EVOLUTION LINK** The rough-skinned newt, which lives in western North America, stores a poison in its skin and is avoided by predators. However, several populations of garter snakes have undergone one or a few mutations that enable them to tolerate the toxin, and these snakes eat the newts with no ill effects. How has natural selection affected this predator–prey relationship? Based on what you have learned about evolutionary arms races, predict what may happen to the newts and the poison-resistant garter snakes over time.

16. **EVOLUTION LINK** Competition is an important part of Darwin's scientific theory of evolution by natural selection, and the evolution of features that reduce competition increases a population's overall fitness. Relate this idea to character displacement and resource partitioning in Darwin's finches.

17. **INTERPRET DATA** Examine the top and middle graphs in Figure 54-5. Are these examples of exponential or logistic population growth? Where is *K* in each graph? (You may need to refer to Chapter 53 to answer these questions.)

18. **SCIENCE, TECHNOLOGY, AND SOCIETY** Describe the ecological niche of humans. How have science and technology changed our realized niche during the past 1000 years?

 To access course materials, such as Aplia and other companion resources, please visit **www.cengagebrain.com.**

Ecosystems and the Biosphere | 55

Planet Earth has often been compared to a vast spaceship, inhabited by diverse communities of organisms. As Earth orbits around the sun, these organisms use the sun's energy to produce oxygen, transfer energy, and recycle water and minerals (inorganic nutrients) with great efficiency. Yet none of these ecological processes would be possible without the abiotic (nonliving) environment of spaceship Earth. As the sun warms the planet, it powers the hydrologic cycle (causes precipitation), drives ocean currents and atmospheric circulation patterns, and produces much of the climate to which organisms have adapted. The sun also supplies the energy that almost all organisms use to carry on life processes.

Individual communities and their abiotic environments are **ecosystems,** which are the basic units of ecology. An ecosystem encompasses all the interactions among organisms living together in a particular place and among those organisms and their abiotic environment. **Ecosystem ecology** is a subfield of ecology that studies energy flow and the cycling of chemicals among the interacting biotic and abiotic parts of an ecosystem.

Ecosystem interactions are complex because each organism responds not only to other organisms but to conditions in the atmosphere, soil, and water. In turn, organisms exert an effect on the abiotic environment, as when a beaver dam creates a pond in a formerly forested area (see photograph). The pond is formed as the beaver builds an island lodge that will be safe from predators. However, the beaver dam also regulates the flow of water in the stream or river: it holds back water during rainy periods and releases a controlled amount of water throughout the year, even during periods of drought.

Like communities, ecosystems vary in size, lack precise boundaries, and are nested within larger ecosystems. Earth's largest ecosystem is the biosphere, which consists of all Earth's communities and their interactions and connections with the planet's abiotic environment: its water, soil, rock, and atmosphere.

Gerry Ellis/Getty Images

Beaver pond. American beavers (*Castor canadensis*) constructed this dam out of branches and mud, converting a creek into a lake. Photographed on Lake Silver Horn, Alaska.

KEY CONCEPTS

55.1 Studying the energy content of the different trophic levels provides insight into how energy flows through the biotic and abiotic components of ecosystems.

55.2 Carbon, nitrogen, water, and other materials cycle through both biotic and abiotic parts of ecosystems.

55.3 The abiotic environment—including solar radiation, the atmosphere, the ocean, climate, and fire—helps shape the biotic portion of ecosystems.

55.4 Ecosystem ecologists focus on chemical, physical, and biological processes of ecosystems to learn how ecosystems function.

55.1 ENERGY FLOW THROUGH ECOSYSTEMS

LEARNING OBJECTIVES

1 Summarize the concept of energy flow through a food web.
2 Explain typical pyramids of numbers, biomass, and energy.
3 Distinguish between gross primary productivity and net primary productivity.

The passage of energy in a one-way direction through an ecosystem is known as **energy flow.** Energy enters an ecosystem as radiant energy (sunlight), a tiny portion (less than 1%) of which *producers* trap and use during photosynthesis. The energy, now in chemical form, is stored in the bonds of organic (carbon-containing) molecules such as glucose. When cellular respiration breaks these molecules apart, energy becomes available (in the form of ATP) to do work, such as repairing tissues, producing body heat, moving about, or reproducing. As the work is accomplished, energy escapes the organisms and dissipates into the environment as heat. Ultimately, this heat energy radiates into space. Thus, once an organism has used energy, the energy is unavailable for reuse (FIG. 55-1). (See also the discussion of the second law of thermodynamics in Chapter 7.)

In an ecosystem energy flow occurs in **food chains,** in which energy from food passes from one organism to the next in a sequence. **Primary producers,** also called *autotrophs,* form the beginning of the food chain by capturing the sun's energy through photosynthesis. Producers, by incorporating the chemicals they manufacture into their own *biomass* (living material), become potential food resources for other organisms. Plants are the most significant producers on land, whereas algae and cyanobacteria are important producers in aquatic environments. (Alternative producers are photoheterotrophs and chemoautotrophs discussed in Chapters 9 and 25.) All other organisms in a community are **consumers,** also called *heterotrophs,* which extract energy from organic molecules produced by other organisms.

Food chains are divided into **trophic levels** (from the Greek *tropho,* which means "nourishment"). Producers occupy the first trophic level. **Herbivores,** which occupy the second trophic level, are *primary consumers* that eat plants. They obtain the chemical energy of the producers' molecules and the building materials used to construct their own tissues. Herbivores are, in turn, consumed by **carnivores,** *secondary consumers* that reap the energy stored in the herbivores' molecules. *Tertiary consumers* are carnivores that eat secondary consumers. **Omnivores** are consumers that eat a variety of organisms, both plant and animal. Omnivores and consumers occupy third or higher trophic levels depending on what they eat.

KEY POINT

Ecologists gain insights into how ecosystems function by examining energy flow and the energy content of each trophic level.

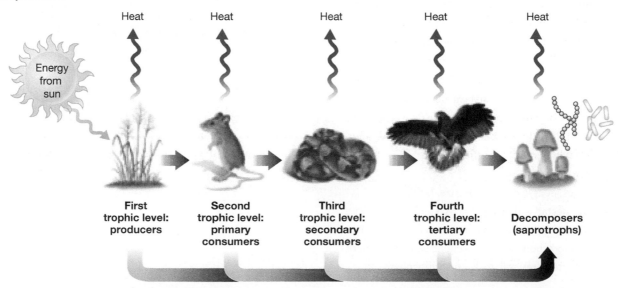

Figure 55-1 *Animation* **Energy flow through ecosystems**
Energy enters ecosystems from an external source (the sun) and exits as heat loss.
PREDICT Which organism(s) would have the longest survival rate if the sun ceased to generate energy?
© Cengage Learning

Some consumers, called **detritus feeders,** or **detritivores,** eat **detritus,** which is dead organic matter that includes animal carcasses, leaf litter, wood, and feces. Detritivores and microbial decomposers break down dead organisms and waste products. **Decomposers,** also called **saprotrophs,** are a subset of detritus feeders. Decomposers include microbial heterotrophs and fungi. These organisms supply themselves with energy by externally breaking down organic molecules in remains (carcasses and body wastes) and ingesting the inorganic products. They typically release simple inorganic molecules, such as carbon dioxide and mineral salts, which may be reused by producers. Most bacteria and fungi are important decomposers of all members of the food chain. (See Chapters 25 and 29.)

Simple food chains such as the one described rarely occur in nature because few organisms eat just one kind, or are eaten by just one other kind, of organism. More typically, the flow of energy and materials through ecosystems takes place in accordance with a range of food choices for each organism. In an ecosystem of average complexity, hundreds of alternative pathways are possible. Thus, a **food web,** which is a complex of interconnected food chains, is a more realistic model of the flow of energy and materials through ecosystems (FIG. 55-2).

Because food chains and food webs are descriptions of "who eats whom," they indicate the negative effects predators have on their prey. For example, consider a simple food chain: grass ⟶ field mouse ⟶ owl. The owl, which kills and eats mice, obviously exerts a negative effect on the mouse population; in like manner, field mice, which eat grass seeds, reduce the grass population.

A trophic level in a food web also influences other trophic levels to which it is not directly linked. Producers and top carnivores do not usually exert direct effects on one another, yet each indirectly affects the other. In our example, the owls help the grasses by keeping the population of seed-eating mice under control. Likewise, the grasses benefit owls by supporting a population of mice on which the owl population feeds. These

Food webs in all but the simplest ecosystems are too complex to depict all their species and links in a simple diagram. Some links are stronger than others. As food webs change over time, new links are added, and some links are deleted.

Figure 55-2 *Animation* **A food web at the edge of an Eastern deciduous forest**
This diagram illustrates only a few of the thousands of species and links that might be part of a food web at the edge of a deciduous forest.
PREDICT What could happen to this food web if drought conditions occurred?
© Cengage Learning

indirect interactions may be as important in food-web dynamics as direct predator–prey interactions.

The most important thing to remember about energy flow in ecosystems is that it is linear, or a one-way system. That is, energy moves along a food web from one trophic level to the next trophic level. Once an organism has used energy, however, it is lost as heat and is unavailable to any other organism in the ecosystem.

Ecological pyramids illustrate how ecosystems work

Ecologists sometimes compare trophic levels by determining the number of organisms, the biomass, or the relative energy found at each level. This information is presented graphically as **ecological pyramids.** The base of each ecological pyramid represents the producers, the next level is the primary consumers (herbivores), the level above that is the secondary consumers (carnivores), and then tertiary consumers (carnivores), and so on. The relative area of each bar of the pyramid is proportional to what is being demonstrated.

A **pyramid of numbers** shows the number of organisms at each trophic level in a given ecosystem, with a larger area illustrating greater numbers for that section of the pyramid. In most pyramids of numbers, fewer organisms occupy each successive trophic level. Thus, in African grasslands the number of herbivores, such as zebras and wildebeests, is greater than the number of carnivores, such as lions. Inverted pyramids of numbers, in which higher trophic levels have more organisms than lower trophic levels, are often observed among decomposers, parasites, and herbivorous insects. One tree provides food for thousands of leaf-eating insects, for example. Pyramids of numbers are of limited usefulness because they do not indicate the biomass of the organisms at each level, nor do they indicate the amount of energy transferred from one level to another.

A **pyramid of biomass** illustrates the total biomass at each successive trophic level. **Biomass** is a quantitative estimate of the total mass, or amount, of living material; it indicates the amount of fixed energy at a particular time. Biomass units of measure vary: biomass may be represented as total volume, dry weight, or live weight. Typically, these pyramids illustrate a progressive reduction of biomass in succeeding trophic levels (**FIG. 55-3a**). Assuming an average biomass reduction of about 90% for each trophic level, 10,000 kg of grass should support 1000 kg of grasshoppers, which in turn support 100 kg of frogs. (The 90% reduction in biomass is an approximation; actual biomass reduction from one trophic level to the next varies widely.) If we use this logic, the biomass of frog eaters (such as snakes) could weigh,

at most, only about 10 kg. From this brief exercise, you see that although carnivores do not eat producers, a large producer biomass is required to support carnivores in a food web.

Occasionally, we find an inverted pyramid of biomass in which the primary consumers outweigh the producers (**FIG. 55-3b**). In these instances, herbivores such as fishes and zooplankton (protozoa, tiny crustaceans, and immature stages of many aquatic animals) consume large numbers of producers, which are usually unicellular algae that are short-lived and reproduce quickly. Thus, although at any point in time relatively few algae are present, the rate of biomass production of the primary consumers is much less than that of the producers.

A **pyramid of energy** indicates the energy content, often expressed as kilocalories (or kilojoules), per square meter per year of the biomass of each trophic level. A common method ecologists use to measure energy content is to burn a sample of tissue in a calorimeter; the heat released during combustion is measured to determine the energy content of the organic material in the sample. Energy pyramids always have large bases and get progressively smaller through succeeding trophic levels to show that most energy dissipates into the environment when there is a transition from one trophic level to the next. Less energy reaches each successive trophic level from the level beneath it because those organisms at the lower level use some of the energy to perform work, and some of it is lost as heat (**FIG. 55-4**). (Remember that no biological process is 100% efficient.) The second law of thermodynamics explains why there are few trophic levels: energy pyramids are short because of the dramatic reduction in energy content that occurs at each successive trophic level.

Ecosystems vary in productivity

The **gross primary productivity (GPP)** of an ecosystem is the rate at which energy is captured during photosynthesis.[1] Thus,

---

[1] Gross and net primary productivities are referred to as primary because plants and other producers occupy the first position in food webs.

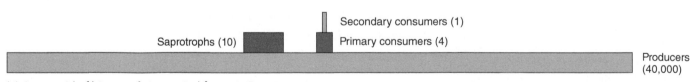

(a) A pyramid of biomass for a tropical forest in Panama.

Saprotrophs (10)
Secondary consumers (1)
Primary consumers (4)
Producers (40,000)

Primary consumers (21)

Producers (4)

(b) An inverted biomass pyramid, such as that for plankton in the English Channel, occurs when a highly productive lower trophic level experiences high rates of turnover. Plankton are free-floating, mainly microscopic algae and animals.

Figure 55-3 Pyramids of biomass

These pyramids are based on the biomass at each trophic level and generally have a pyramid shape with a large base and progressively smaller areas for each succeeding trophic level. Biomass values are in grams of dry weight per square meter. (**a, b,** Adapted from Odum, E. P. *Fundamentals of Ecology,* 3rd ed., W. B. Saunders Company, Philadelphia, 1971, and based on studies by F. B. Golley and G. I. Child **[a]** and H. W. Harvey **[b].**)

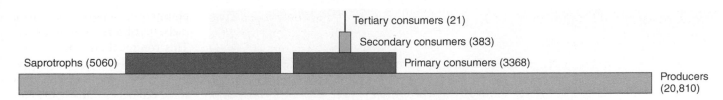

Figure 55-4 *Animation* **Pyramid of energy**

A pyramid of energy for Silver Springs, Florida, represents energy flow, the functional basis of ecosystem structure. Energy values are in kilocalories per square meter per year. Note the substantial loss of usable energy from
one trophic level to the next. The Silver Springs ecosystem is complex, but tape grass (producers), spiral-shelled
snails (primary consumers), young river turtles (secondary consumers), gar (fish; tertiary consumers), and
bacteria and fungi (saprotrophs) are representative organisms. When they are young, river turtles are carnivores
and consume snails, aquatic insects, and worms; as adults, river turtles are herbivores. (Based on Odum, H. T.
"Trophic Structure and Productivity of Silver Springs, Florida." *Ecological Monographs*, Vol. 27, 1957.)

GPP is the total amount of photosynthetic energy captured in a given period. Of course, plants and other producers must respire to provide energy for their life processes, and cellular respiration acts as a drain on photosynthetic output. Energy that remains in plant tissues after cellular respiration has occurred is called **net primary productivity (NPP).** That is, NPP is the amount of bio-mass (the energy stored in plant tissues) found in excess of that broken down by a plant's cellular respiration for normal daily activities. NPP represents the rate at which this organic matter is actually incorporated into plant tissues to produce growth.

net primary productivity	=	gross primary productivity	−	plant respiration
(plant growth per unit area per unit time)		(total photosynthe-sis per unit area per unit time)		(per unit area per unit time)

Only the energy represented by net primary productiv-ity is available for consumers, and of this energy only a por-tion is actually used by them. Both GPP and NPP are expressed as energy per unit area per unit time (e.g., kilojoules of energy fixed by photosynthesis per square meter per year) or as dry weight (e.g., grams of carbon incorporated into tissue per square meter per year).

Ecologists use different methods to measure net primary productivity, such as through calorimetry (previously described) and change in dry biomass per unit time. Scientists also deter-mine NPP by measuring carbon dioxide uptake and oxygen uptake over time. Another method to assess NPP in plants is through recording the change in chlorophyll *a* concentration, which measures daily carbon dioxide fixation.

Herbivores and other consumers eventually consume all of a plant's net primary production. What happens to this energy? Consider the transfer of net primary production from a plant to a deer that eats the plant. Much of the energy stored in the plant material that the deer consumes—about 25%—is not digested and is lost in its feces. (This energy is not lost from the ecosystem because detritivores and decomposers will make use of it; it is lost from the deer's point of view, however.) Per-haps 55% of the energy that the deer takes in as food is released during cellular respiration and used to do work such as muscle

contraction and to maintain and repair the deer's body. The remaining energy—less than 20%—is available to produce new biomass, that is, new tissues. This net energy available for bio-mass production by consumer organisms is called **secondary productivity.** An ecosystem's secondary productivity is based on its primary productivity.

Many factors may interact to determine primary productiv-ity. Some plants are more efficient than others in fixing carbon. Environmental factors are also important. They include the availability of solar energy, minerals, and water; other climate factors; the degree of maturity of the community; and the sever-ity of human modification of the environment.

These factors are difficult to assess, particularly on a large scale. The summer of 2003, which was extremely hot and dry in Europe, provided ecologists with a chance to measure primary productivity changes in response to these unusual conditions. Based on their measurements, they estimate that GPP throughout Europe was reduced by 30% as a result of the heat and drought.

Ecosystems differ strikingly in their primary productivi-ties (**FIG. 55-5** and **TABLE 55-1**). On land, tropical rain forests have the highest productivity, probably as a result of the abundant rainfall, warm temperatures, and intense sunlight. As you might expect, tundra, because of its short, cool growing season, and deserts, because of their lack of precipitation, are the least pro-ductive terrestrial ecosystems. In ecosystems with comparable annual temperatures (e.g., temperate deciduous forest, temper-ate grassland, and temperate desert), water availability affects NPP. Availability of essential minerals such as nitrogen and phosphorus also affects NPP.

Wetlands (swamps and marshes) connect terrestrial and aquatic environments and are extremely productive. The most productive aquatic ecosystems are algal beds, coral reefs, and estuaries. The lack of available minerals in the sunlit region of the open ocean makes this area extremely unproductive, equiva-lent to an aquatic desert. Earth's major aquatic and terrestrial ecosystems are discussed in Chapter 56.

As primary productivity increases, species richness declines Ecologists have observed that an ecosystem's species richness declines with increasing productivity. For example, the resource-poor depths of the Atlantic Ocean's abyssal plain have

NEO NASA Earth Observations. Image made by Reto Stockli, NASA's Earth Observatory Team, using data provided by the MODIS Land Science Team.

Figure 55-5 View of Earth's net primary productivity

The colors on this NASA satellite image indicate how quickly plants took carbon in for every square meter of land during August, 2013. Values range from −1.0 gram of carbon per square meter per day (*tan*) to 6.5 grams per square meter per day (*dark green*). A negative value indicates that decomposition or respiration was greater than carbon production; more carbon was released to the atmosphere than plants captured. The least productive areas are deserts. The most productive regions are tropical rain forests. Images like this allow scientists to assess changes in productivity over time.

phosphorus inputs from fossil fuels, fertilizers, and livestock. This continual enrichment may make Earth's ecosystems increasingly productive, a shift that some ecologists think could cost the world a substantial loss of species richness. (Other factors that affect species richness were discussed in Chapter 54.)

Humans consume an increasingly greater percentage of global primary productivity Humans consume far more of Earth's resources than do any of the other millions of animal species. Peter Vitousek and co-workers at Stanford University calculated in 1986 how much of the global NPP is appropriated for the human economy.

more species richness than productive shallow waters near the coasts. Ecologists are designing experiments to help explain the pattern, which has been documented with rodents in Israel, birds in South America, and large mammals in Africa. Mathematical ecosystem models suggest that a less productive environment has a *patchy distribution of resources* that reduces competition and allows a greater variety of organisms to coexist.

The bad news for global biodiversity is that humans are constantly enriching the environment, such as with nitrogen and

When both direct and indirect human effects are accounted for, Vitousek estimated that humans use 32% to 40% of land-based annual NPP. Since 1986, scientists have done additional research on global ecology, resulting in improved data sets. In 2001, Stuart Rojstaczer and co-workers at Duke University used satellite-based data to determine a conservative estimate of land-based annual NPP appropriation by humans at 32%.

The take-home message from Vitousek's and Rojstaczer's research is simple. Essentially, human use of global productivity is competing with other species' needs for energy. Our use of so much of the world's productivity may contribute to the loss, through extinction or genetic impoverishment, of many species that have unique roles in maintaining functional ecosystems. Clearly, at these levels of consumption and exploitation of Earth's resources, human population growth threatens the planet's ability to support all its occupants.

TABLE 55-1	**Net Primary Productivity (NPP) for Selected Ecosystems**

ECOSYSTEM	AVERAGE NPP (g dry matter/m²/year)
Algal beds and reefs	2500
Tropical rain forest	2200
Swamp and marsh	2000
Estuaries	1500
Temperate evergreen forest	1300
Temperate deciduous forest	1200
Savanna	900
Boreal (northern) forest	800
Woodland and shrubland	700
Agricultural land	650
Temperate grassland	600
Upwelling zones in ocean	500
Lake and stream	250
Arctic and alpine tundra	140
Open ocean	125
Desert and semidesert scrub	90
Extreme desert (rock, sand, ice)	3

Source: Based on Whittaker, R. H. *Communities and Ecosystems*, 2nd ed. Macmillan, New York, 1975.

Some toxins persist in the environment

You have seen how energy flows through food chains in ecosystems. Before leaving the discussion of food chains, let us consider how certain toxins, including some pesticides, radioactive isotopes, heavy metals such as mercury, and industrial chemicals such as polychlorinated biphenyls (PCBs), enter and pass through food chains. The effects of the pesticide DDT on some bird species first drew attention to the problem. Falcons, pelicans, bald eagles, ospreys, and many other birds are sensitive to traces of DDT in their tissues. A substantial body of scientific evidence indicates that one effect of DDT on these birds is that their eggs have extremely thin, fragile shells that usually break during incubation, causing the chicks' deaths. In 1962, U.S. biologist Rachel Carson published *Silent Spring*, which heightened public awareness about the dangers of DDT and other pesticides. After 1972, the year DDT was banned in the United States, the reproductive success of many birds gradually improved.

Does DDT exhibit biological magnification as it moves through a food chain?

HYPOTHESIS: DDT, a persistent insecticide, increases in concentration at each level of a food chain.

EXPERIMENT: Biologists sampled the concentration of DDT in various organisms of a Long Island salt marsh.

TROPHIC LEVEL	AMOUNT OF DDT IN TISSUE
Tertiary consumer	Ring-billed gull (75.5 ppm)
Secondary consumer	Atlantic needlefish (2.07 ppm)
Secondary consumer	American eel (0.28 ppm)
Primary consumer	Shrimp (0.16 ppm)
Producers, primary consumers	Plankton (0.04 ppm)

RESULTS AND CONCLUSION: The level of DDT increased in the tissues of various organisms as DDT moved through the food chain from producers to consumers. Ring-billed gulls at the top of the food chain had approximately 1 million times as much DDT in their tissues as the concentration of DDT in the water (0.00005 ppm). (Plankton consisted of a mixture of phytoplankton and zooplankton.)

SOURCE: Based on data from Woodwell, G. M., C. F. Worster Jr., and P. A. Isaacson. "DDT Residues in an East Coast Estuary: A Case of Biological Concentration of a Persistent Insecticide." *Science*, Vol. 156, May 12, 1967.

Figure 55-6 Biological magnification of DDT (expressed as parts per million) in a Long Island salt marsh

PREDICT How might DDT be passed on by the ring-billed gull, and what might be the consequences?

The effect of DDT on birds is the result of three characteristics of DDT (and other toxins that cause problems in food webs): its persistence, bioaccumulation, and biological magnification. Some toxins are extremely stable and may take many years to break down into less toxic forms. The **persistence** of synthetic pesticides and industrial chemicals is a result of their novel chemical structures. These toxins accumulate in the environment because ways to degrade them have not evolved in natural decomposers such as bacteria.

When an organism does not metabolize (break down) or excrete a persistent toxin, the toxin simply gets stored, usually in fatty tissues. Over time, the organism may accumulate high concentrations of the toxin. The buildup of such a toxin in an organism's body is known as **bioaccumulation.**

Organisms at higher trophic levels in food webs tend to store greater concentrations of bio-accumulated toxins in their bodies than do those at lower levels. The increase in concentration as the toxin passes through successive levels of the food web is known as **biological magnification.**

As an example of the concentrating characteristic of persistent toxins, consider a food chain studied in a Long Island salt marsh that was sprayed with DDT over a period of years for mosquito control (FIG. 55-6). Although this example involved a bird at the top of the food chain, it is important to recognize that

all top carnivores, from fishes to humans, are at risk from biological magnification of persistent toxins. Because of this risk, currently approved pesticides have been tested to ensure that they do not persist and accumulate in the environment.

CHECKPOINT 55.1

- **VISUALIZE** *Draw a diagram tracing energy flow through a food web such as one found in a deciduous forest.*
- **CONNECT** *What are trophic levels, and how are they related to ecological pyramids?*
- *How do gross primary productivity (GPP) and net primary productivity (NPP) differ?*

55.2 CYCLES OF MATTER IN ECOSYSTEMS

LEARNING OBJECTIVE

4 Describe the main steps in each of these biogeochemical cycles: the carbon, nitrogen, phosphorus, and hydrologic cycles.

Matter moves in numerous cycles from one part of an ecosystem to another; that is, it moves from one organism to another (in food chains) and from living organisms to the abiotic environment and back again. We call these cycles of matter **biogeochemical cycles** because they involve biological, geologic, and chemical interactions. For all practical purposes, matter cannot escape from Earth's boundaries. The materials organisms use cannot be "lost," although this matter can end up in locations outside the reach of organisms for a long period. Usually, materials are reused and often recycled both within and among ecosystems.

We discuss four different biogeochemical cycles of matter—carbon, nitrogen, phosphorus, and water—as representative of all biogeochemical cycles. These four cycles are particularly important to organisms because they involve materials used to make the chemical components of cells.

Carbon dioxide is the pivotal molecule in the carbon cycle

Proteins, nucleic acids, lipids, carbohydrates, and other molecules essential to life contain carbon. Carbon is present in the atmosphere as the gas carbon dioxide (CO_2), which makes up approximately 0.04% of the atmosphere. It is also present in the ocean and fresh water as dissolved carbon dioxide, that is, carbonate (CO_3^{2-}) and bicarbonate (HCO_3^-); other forms of dissolved inorganic carbon; and dissolved organic carbon from decay processes. Carbon is also present in rocks such as limestone ($CaCO_3$). The global movement of carbon between the abiotic environment, including the atmosphere and ocean, and organisms is known as the **carbon cycle** (FIG. 55-7).

During photosynthesis, plants, algae, and cyanobacteria remove carbon dioxide from the air and *fix*, or incorporate, it into organic compounds such as glucose. Plants use much of the glucose to make cellulose, starch, amino acids, nucleic acids, and other compounds.

Many of these compounds are used as fuel for cellular respiration by the producer that made them, by a consumer that eats the producer, or by a decomposer that breaks down the remains of the producer or consumer. The process of cellular respiration returns carbon dioxide to the atmosphere. A similar carbon cycle occurs in aquatic ecosystems between aquatic organisms and dissolved carbon dioxide in the water (not shown in Figure 55-7).

Some archaea fix carbon using atmospheric CO_2. Other archaea, the methanogens, are decomposers and are the major source of methane in the atmosphere. The methanogens significantly contribute to global climate change (see discussion of methanogens in Chapter 25).

Sometimes the carbon in biological molecules is not recycled back to the abiotic environment for a long time and remains in reservoirs, or sinks, indefinitely. Carbon stored in the wood

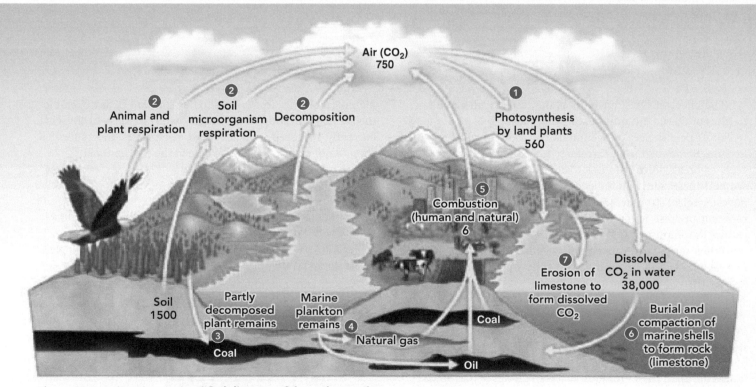

Figure 55-7 *Animation* **A simplified diagram of the carbon cycle**

All but a tiny fraction of Earth's estimated 10^{23} g of carbon is buried in sedimentary rocks and fossil fuel deposits. The values shown for some of the active pools in the global carbon budget are expressed as 10^{15} g of carbon. For example, the soil contains an estimated 1500 × 10^{15} g of carbon. (Values from Schlesinger, W. H. *Biogeochemistry: An Analysis of Global Change*, 2nd ed., Academic Press, San Diego, 1997, and several other sources.)

© Cengage Learning

of trees may stay for several hundred years or even longer. Also, millions of years ago vast coal beds formed from the bodies of ancient trees that were buried and subjected to anaerobic conditions before they had fully decayed. Similarly, the oils of unicellular marine organisms probably gave rise to the underground deposits of oil and natural gas that accumulated in the geologic past. Coal, oil, and natural gas, called **fossil fuels** because they formed from the remains of ancient organisms, are vast deposits of carbon compounds, the end products of photosynthesis that occurred millions of years ago.

The process of burning, or combustion, may return the carbon in coal, oil, natural gas, and wood to the atmosphere. In combustion organic molecules are rapidly oxidized (combined with oxygen) and converted to carbon dioxide and water with an accompanying release of light and heat.

An even greater amount of carbon that is stored for millions of years is incorporated into the shells of marine organisms. When these organisms die, their shells sink to the ocean floor, and sediments cover them, forming seabed deposits thousands of meters thick. The deposits are eventually cemented together to form limestone, a sedimentary rock. Earth's crust is dynamically active, and over millions of years, sedimentary rock on the bottom of the seafloor may lift to form land surfaces. When the process of geologic uplift exposes limestone, chemical and physical weathering processes slowly erode it away. This returns carbon to the water and atmosphere, where it is available to participate in the carbon cycle once again.

Human activities have disturbed the global carbon budget Before the Industrial Revolution, around 1750, the global carbon cycle was in a steady state. Enormous amounts of carbon moved to and from the atmosphere, ocean, and terrestrial ecosystems, but these movements within the global carbon cycle just about canceled out one another.

Since 1750, our industrial society has required a lot of energy, and we have burned increasing amounts of fossil fuels—coal, oil, and natural gas—to obtain this energy. This trend, along with a greater combustion of wood as a fuel and the burning of large sections of tropical forest, has released CO_2 into the atmosphere at a rate greater than the natural carbon cycle can handle.

Earth's ocean absorbs much of this excess CO_2 from the atmosphere. In the ocean some dissolved CO_2 is converted to carbonic acid (H_2CO_3), which is acidifying surface ocean waters. The pH of modern surface waters is about 0.1 pH unit lower than it was in preindustrial times, and models predict up to 1.4 pH units of further acidification during the next 300 years. *Ocean acidification* harms marine organisms, particularly those that produce skeletons and shells of calcium carbonate ($CaCO_3$), which dissolve in the presence of acid.

The level of atmospheric CO_2 increased dramatically beginning in the last half of the 20th century (see Fig. 57-16), and this rise of CO_2 has initiated human-induced changes in global climate. Global climate change will result in a rise in sea level, changes in precipitation patterns, death of forests, extinction of organisms, and problems for agriculture. It will force the displacement of thousands or even millions of people, particularly from coastal areas. (Chapter 57 contains a more thorough discussion of increasing atmospheric CO_2 and the potential effects of global climate change.)

Bacteria and archaea are essential to the nitrogen cycle

Nitrogen is crucial for all organisms because it is an essential part of proteins, nucleic acids, and chlorophyll. Because Earth's atmosphere is about 78% nitrogen gas (N_2), it would appear that there could be no possible shortage of nitrogen for organisms. However, molecular nitrogen is so stable that it does not readily combine with other elements. Therefore, the N_2 molecule must be broken apart before the nitrogen atoms combine with other elements to form proteins, nucleic acids, and chlorophyll. Chemical reactions that break up N_2 and combine nitrogen with other elements require a great deal of energy.

The **nitrogen cycle,** in which nitrogen cycles between the abiotic environment and organisms, has five steps: nitrogen fixation, nitrification, assimilation, ammonification, and denitrification (**FIG. 55-8**). Certain bacteria and archaea are exclusively involved in all these steps except assimilation.

The first step in the nitrogen cycle, biological **nitrogen fixation,** involves conversion of gaseous nitrogen (N_2) to ammonia (NH_3). This process fixes nitrogen into a form that organisms can use. Combustion, volcanic action, lightning discharges, and industrial processes also fix nitrogen as nitrate (NO_3^-). Certain archaea and nitrogen-fixing bacteria, including cyanobacteria and certain other free-living and symbiotic bacteria, carry on biological nitrogen fixation in soil and aquatic environments. These nitrogen-fixing prokaryotes employ an enzyme called **nitrogenase** to break up molecular nitrogen and combine the resulting nitrogen atoms with hydrogen.

Because nitrogenase functions only in the absence of oxygen, the prokaryotes that fix nitrogen insulate the enzyme from oxygen in some way. Some nitrogen-fixing prokaryotes live beneath layers of oxygen-excluding slime on the roots of several plant species. Other important nitrogen-fixing bacteria, in the genus *Rhizobium*, live in oxygen-excluding swellings, or **nodules,** on the roots of legumes such as beans and peas and some woody plants (**FIG. 55-9**; also see Table 25-3).

In aquatic environments bacteria and archaea perform most nitrogen fixation. Filamentous cyanobacteria have special oxygen-excluding cells called **heterocysts** that function to fix nitrogen (see Table 25-3). Some water ferns have cavities in which cyanobacteria live, in a manner comparable to the way *Rhizobium* lives in root nodules of legumes. Other cyanobacteria fix nitrogen in symbiotic association with cycads and other terrestrial plants or as the photosynthetic partner of certain lichens.

The second step of the nitrogen cycle is **nitrification** (see Fig. 55-8), the conversion of ammonia (NH_3) or ammonium (NH_4^+), formed when water reacts with ammonia, to nitrate (NO_3^-). Soil bacteria are responsible for the two-phase process of nitrification, which furnishes these bacteria, called *nitrifying bacteria,* with energy.

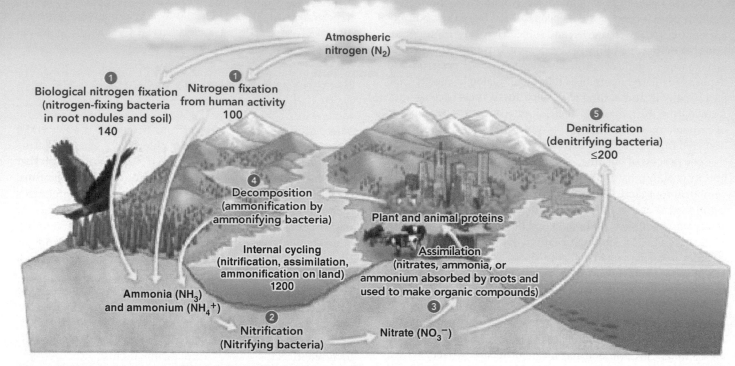

Figure 55-8 *Animation* **A simplified diagram of the nitrogen cycle**

The largest pool of nitrogen, estimated at 3.9×10^{21} g, is in the atmosphere. The values shown for selected nitrogen fluxes in the global nitrogen budget are expressed as 10^{12} g of nitrogen per year and represent terrestrial values. For example, each year humans fix an estimated 100×10^{12} g of nitrogen. (Values from Schlesinger, W. H. *Biogeochemistry: An Analysis of Global Change*, 2nd ed., Academic Press, San Diego, 1997, and several other sources.)
© Cengage Learning

In the third step, **assimilation,** roots absorb ammonia (NH_3), ammonium (NH_4^+), or nitrate (NO_3^-) formed by nitrogen fixation and nitrification, and incorporate the nitrogen into proteins, nucleic acids, and chlorophyll. When animals consume plant tissues, they assimilate nitrogen by taking in plant nitrogen compounds and converting them to animal nitrogen compounds.

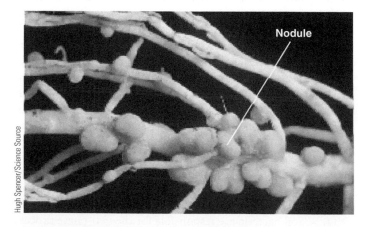

Figure 55-9 Root nodules and nitrogen fixation

Root nodules on the roots of a pea plant provide an oxygen-free environment for nitrogen-fixing *Rhizobium* bacteria that live in them.

The fourth step, **ammonification,** is the conversion of organic nitrogen compounds into ammonia (NH_3) and ammonium ions (NH_4^+). Ammonification begins when organisms produce nitrogen-containing wastes such as urea in urine and uric acid in the wastes of birds (see Fig. 48-1). As these substances, along with the nitrogen compounds in dead organisms, decompose, nitrogen is released into the abiotic environment as ammonia (NH_3). The bacteria that perform ammonification in both the soil and aquatic environments are called *ammonifying bacteria*. Most available nitrogen in the soil derives from the recycling of organic nitrogen by ammonification.

The fifth step of the nitrogen cycle is **denitrification,** the reduction of nitrate (NO_3^-) to gaseous nitrogen (N_2). Denitrifying prokaryotes reverse the action of nitrogen-fixing and nitrifying prokaryotes by returning nitrogen to the atmosphere as nitrogen gas. Denitrifying prokaryotes are anaerobic and therefore live and grow best where there is little or no free oxygen. For example, they are found deep in the soil near the water table, an environment that is nearly oxygen-free.

Human activities have changed the global nitrogen budget Human activities have disturbed the balance of the global nitrogen cycle. During the 20th century, humans more than doubled the amount of fixed nitrogen (nitrogen that has been chemically combined with hydrogen, oxygen, or carbon) entering the global nitrogen cycle. The excess nitrogen is seriously altering many terrestrial and aquatic ecosystems.

Large quantities of nitrogen fertilizer, for commercial farming operations and for residential use, are produced from nitrogen gas for agriculture. The increasing use of fertilizer has resulted in higher crop yields, but there are negative environmental effects from human-produced nitrogen. Nitrogen fertilizer is extremely mobile and is easily transferred from the land to rivers to estuaries to the ocean. Thus, the overuse of commercial fertilizer on the land causes water-quality problems that may help explain long-term declines in many coastal fisheries. The amount of nitrate or ammonium in most aquatic ecosystems is in limited supply and limits the growth of algae. Rain washes fertilizer into rivers and lakes, where it stimulates the growth of algae, some of which are toxic. As these algae die, their decomposition by bacteria robs the water of dissolved oxygen, which in turn causes other aquatic organisms, including many fishes, to suffocate.

Nitrates from fertilizer also leach (dissolve and wash down) through the soil and contaminate groundwater. Many people who live in rural areas drink groundwater. Groundwater contaminated by nitrates is dangerous, particularly for infants and small children.

Another human activity that affects the nitrogen cycle is the combustion of fossil fuels. When fossil fuels are burned, the nitrogen locked in organic compounds in the fuel is chemically altered and transferred to the atmosphere. In addition, the high temperature of combustion converts some atmospheric nitrogen to **nitrogen oxides.** Automobile exhaust is one of the main sources of nitrogen oxides. Nitrogen oxides are a necessary ingredient in the production of **photochemical smog,** a mixture of several air pollutants that injure plant tissues, irritate eyes, and cause respiratory problems in humans.

Nitrogen oxides also react with water in the atmosphere to form nitric acid (HNO_3) and nitrous acid (HNO_2). When these and other acids leave the atmosphere as precipitation (rain, sleet, snow, or hail), they decrease the pH of surface waters (lakes and streams) and soils. **Acid precipitation** includes rain, snow, fog, or dust that is unusually acidic (pH below 5.6). Acid precipitation has been linked to declining animal populations in aquatic ecosystems. On land, acid precipitation alters soil chemistry: certain essential minerals, such as calcium and potassium, wash out of the soil and are therefore unavailable for plants. Nitrous oxide (N_2O), one of the nitrogen oxides, retains heat in the atmosphere (like CO_2) and so promotes global climate change.

Nitrous oxide also contributes to the depletion of ozone in the stratosphere. (See Chapter 2 for a discussion of acids and pH, and Chapter 57 for a discussion of global climate change and stratospheric ozone depletion.)

The phosphorus cycle lacks a gaseous component

Phosphorus does not exist in a gaseous state and therefore does not enter the atmosphere. In the **phosphorus cycle,** phosphorus cycles from the land to sediments in the ocean and back to the land (FIG. 55-10).

As water runs over rocks containing phosphorus, it gradually erodes the surface and carries off inorganic phosphate (PO_4^{3-}). The erosion of phosphorus rocks releases phosphate into the soil, where it is taken up by roots in the form of inorganic phosphates. Once in cells, phosphates are incorporated into a variety of biological molecules, including nucleic acids, ATP, and the phospholipids that make up cell membranes. Animals obtain most of their required phosphorus from the food they eat, although in some places drinking water may contain a substantial amount of inorganic phosphate. Phosphate released by decomposers becomes part of the pool of inorganic phosphate in the soil that plants reuse. Thus, like carbon and nitrogen, phosphorus moves through the food web as one organism consumes another.

Phosphorus cycles through aquatic ecosystems in much the same way as through terrestrial ecosystems. Dissolved phosphate enters aquatic ecosystems through absorption by algae and aquatic plants, which zooplankton and larger organisms consume. In turn, a variety of fishes and mollusks eat the zooplankton. Ultimately, decomposers break down wastes and dead organisms to release inorganic phosphate into the water, making it available for use again by aquatic producers.

Phosphate can be lost for varying time periods from biological cycles. Streams and rivers carry some phosphate to the ocean, where it is deposited on the seafloor and remains for millions of years. The geologic process of uplift may someday expose these reservoirs of seafloor sediments as new land surfaces, from which phosphate will be once again eroded. Phosphate deposits are also mined for agricultural use in phosphate fertilizers.

Humans affect the natural cycling of phosphorus In natural terrestrial communities, very little phosphorus is lost from the cycle, but few communities today are in a natural state, that is, unaltered in some way by humans. Land-denuding practices, such as the clear-cutting of timber, and erosion of agricultural and residential lands accelerate phosphorus loss from the soil into waterways. Excess phosphorus enriches the water, causing algal blooms that rob the water of dissolved oxygen. For practical purposes, phosphorus that washes from the land into the ocean is permanently lost from the terrestrial phosphorus cycle (and from further human use) because it remains in the ocean for millions of years.

Ecologists are also concerned that we are mining phosphorus faster than is sustainable. At its current rate of use, U.S. deposits of phosphorus will probably be depleted during the 21st century. There are currently no substitutes for phosphorus or synthetic methods to produce it.

Water moves among the ocean, land, and atmosphere in the hydrologic cycle

Life would be impossible without water, which makes up a substantial part of the mass of most organisms. All species, prokaryotes and eukaryotes, use water as a medium for chemical

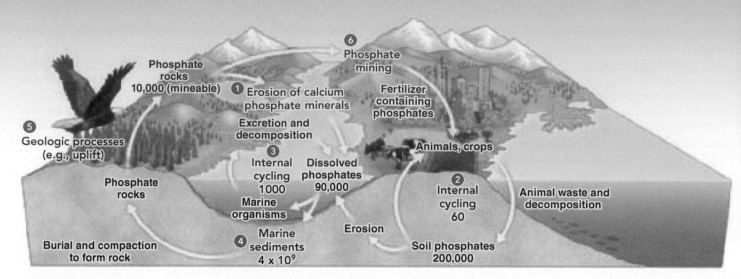

Figure 55-10 *Animation* **A simplified diagram of the phosphorus cycle**
Some values of the global phosphorus budget are given, in units of 10^{12} g phosphorus per year. For example, each year an estimated 60×10^{12} g of phosphorus cycles from the soil to terrestrial organisms and back to the soil. (Values from Schlesinger, W. H. *Biogeochemistry: An Analysis of Global Change*, 2nd ed., Academic Press, San Diego, 1997, and several other sources.)
© Cengage Learning

reactions as well as for the transport of materials within and among cells. (Recall from Chapter 2 that water has many unique properties that help shape the continents, moderate climate, and allow organisms to survive.)

In the **hydrologic cycle,** water continuously circulates from the ocean to the atmosphere to the land and back to the ocean (**FIG. 55-11**). Water moves from the atmosphere to the land and ocean in the form of precipitation. Water that evaporates from the ocean surface and from soil, streams, rivers, and lakes eventually condenses and forms clouds in the atmosphere. In addition, **transpiration,** the loss of water vapor from land plants, adds a considerable amount of water vapor to the atmosphere. Roughly 97% of the water a plant absorbs from the soil is transported to the leaves, where it is lost by transpiration.

Water may evaporate from land and re-enter the atmosphere directly. Alternatively, it may flow in rivers and streams to coastal **estuaries,** where fresh water meets the ocean. The movement of surface water from land to ocean is called *runoff,* and the area of land drained by runoff is called a *watershed.* Water also percolates (seeps) downward in the soil to become *groundwater,* where it is trapped and held for a time. The underground caverns and porous layers of rock in which groundwater is stored are called *aquifers.* Groundwater may reside in the ground for hundreds to many thousands of years, but eventually it supplies water to the soil, streams and rivers, plants, and the ocean. The human removal of more groundwater than precipitation or melting snow recharges, called *aquifer depletion,* eliminates groundwater as a water resource.

Regardless of its physical form (solid, liquid, or vapor) or location, every molecule of water eventually moves through the hydrologic cycle. Tremendous amounts of water cycle annually between Earth and its atmosphere. The volume of water entering the atmosphere from the ocean each year is estimated at

about 425,000 km³. Approximately 90% of this water re-enters the ocean directly as precipitation over water; the remainder falls on land. As is true of the other cycles, water (in the form of glaciers, polar ice caps, and certain groundwater) can be lost from the cycle for thousands of years.

CHECKPOINT 55.2

- **CONNECT** *What are the roles of the following processes in the carbon cycle: photosynthesis, cellular respiration, combustion, and erosion?*

- **VISUALIZE** *Draw a diagram showing the five steps in the nitrogen cycle and explain what happens in each step.*

- *How does the phosphorus cycle proceed without a gaseous component?*

55.3 ABIOTIC FACTORS IN ECOSYSTEMS

LEARNING OBJECTIVES

5 Summarize the effects of solar energy on Earth's temperatures.
6 Discuss the roles of solar energy and the Coriolis effect in the generation of global air and water flow patterns.
7 Give two causes of regional precipitation differences.
8 Discuss the effects of fire on certain ecosystems.

You have seen how ecosystems depend on the abiotic environment to supply energy and essential materials (in biogeochemical cycles). Other abiotic factors such as solar radiation, the

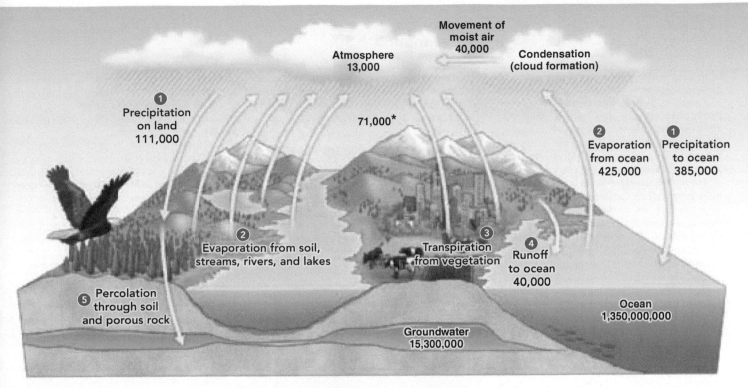

Figure 55-11 *Animation* **A simplified diagram of the hydrologic cycle**

The global water budget values shown for pools are expressed as cubic kilometers; values for fluxes (movements associated with arrows) are in cubic kilometers per year. The *starred value* (71,000 km³/yr) is the sum of both transpiration and evaporation from soil, streams, rivers, and lakes. (Values from Schlesinger, W. H. *Biogeochemistry: An Analysis of Global Change,* 2nd ed., Academic Press, San Diego, 1997, and several other sources.)
© Cengage Learning

atmosphere, the ocean, climate, and fire also affect ecosystems. For a given abiotic factor, each organism living in an ecosystem has an optimal range in which it survives and reproduces. Water and temperature are probably the two abiotic factors that most affect organisms in ecosystems.

The sun warms Earth

The sun makes life on Earth possible. Without the sun's energy, the temperature on planet Earth would approach absolute zero (0 K or −273°C), and all water would be frozen, even in the ocean. The sun powers the hydrologic cycle, carbon cycle, and other biogeochemical cycles and is the primary determinant of climate. Photosynthetic organisms capture the sun's energy and use it to make organic compounds that almost all forms of life require. Most of our fuels, such as wood, oil, coal, and natural gas, represent solar energy captured by photosynthetic organisms. Without the sun, almost all life on Earth would cease (see *Inquiring About: Life without the Sun* for an interesting exception).

The sun's energy, which is the product of a massive nuclear fusion reaction, is emitted into space in the form of electromagnetic radiation, especially ultraviolet, visible, and infrared radiation. About one-billionth of the total energy that the sun releases strikes the atmosphere, and of this tiny trickle of energy, a minute part operates the biosphere. On average, clouds and surfaces—especially snow, ice, and the ocean—immediately reflect away

30% of the solar radiation that falls on Earth (FIG. 55-12). Earth's surface and atmosphere absorb the remaining 70%, which runs the water cycle, drives winds and ocean currents, powers photosynthesis, and warms the planet. Ultimately, the continual radiation of long-wave infrared (heat) energy returns all this energy to space. If heat gains did not exactly balance losses, Earth would heat up or cool down.

Temperature changes with latitude The most significant local variations in Earth's temperature are produced because the sun's energy does not uniformly reach all places. Our planet's roughly spherical shape and the tilted angle of its axis produce significant variation in the exposure of the surface to sunlight. The sun's rays strike almost vertically near the equator, concentrating the energy and producing warmer temperatures. Near the poles the sun's rays strike more obliquely and, as a result, are spread over a larger surface area. Also, rays of light entering the atmosphere obliquely near the poles must pass through a deeper envelope of air than those entering near the equator. This angle causes more of the sun's energy to be scattered and reflected back into space, which further lowers temperatures near the poles. Thus, the solar energy that reaches polar regions is less concentrated and produces lower temperatures than elsewhere.

Temperature changes with season Earth's inclination on its axis (23.5 degrees from a line drawn perpendicular to the orbital plane) primarily determines the seasons.

Is the sun the energy source for all ecosystems? A notable exception was discovered in the late 1970s in a series of hydrothermal vents in the eastern Pacific where seawater apparently had penetrated and been heated by the radioactive rocks below. During its time within Earth, the water had become charged with inorganic mineral compounds, including hydrogen sulfide (H_2S).

No light is available for photosynthesis, but hydrothermal vents support a rich ecosystem that contrasts with the surrounding "desert" of the deep-ocean floor. Giant, blood-red tube worms almost 3 m (10 ft) in length cluster in great numbers around the vents (see figure). Other animals around the hydrothermal vents include unique species of clams, crabs, barnacles, and mussels.

Scientists initially wondered what energy source sustains the organisms in this dark environment. Most deep-sea communities depend on the organic matter that drifts down from the surface waters; in other words, they rely on energy ultimately derived from photosynthesis. Hydrothermal vent communities, however, are too densely clustered and too productive to be dependent on chance encounters with organic material from surface waters.

Instead, chemoautotrophic prokaryotes occupy the base of the food web in these aquatic oases.

These prokaryotes have enzymes that catalyze the oxidation of hydrogen sulfide, yielding water plus sulfur or sulfate. Such chemical reactions are exergonic and provide the energy required to fix CO_2

dissolved in the water into organic compounds. Many of the animals consume the prokaryotes directly by filter-feeding, but others, such as the giant tube worms, get their energy from prokaryotes that live in their tissues.

Scientists continue to generate questions about hydrothermal vent communities. How do the organisms find and colonize vents, which are ephemeral and widely scattered on the ocean floor? How have the inhabitants of these communities adapted to survive the harsh living conditions, including high pressure, high temperatures, and toxic chemicals? As vent community research continues, scientists hope to discover answers to these and other questions.

Hydrothermal vent ecosystem. Chemoautotrophic prokaryotes living in the tissues of these tube worms (*Riftia pachyptila*) extract energy from hydrogen sulfide to manufacture organic compounds. These worms lack digestive systems and depend on the organic compounds the prokaryotes provide, along with materials filtered from the surrounding water. Also visible in the photograph are some filter-feeding clams (*yellow*) and a crab (*white*).

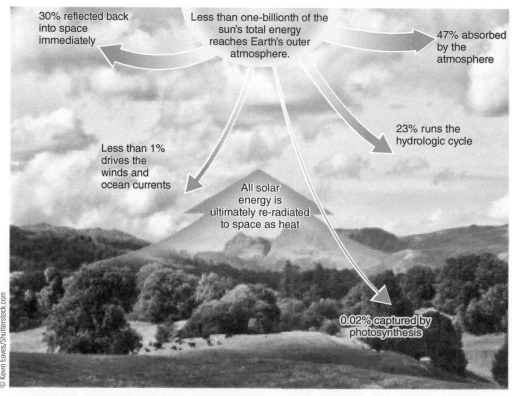

Figure 55-12 *Animation* The fate of solar radiation that reaches Earth

Most of the energy released by the sun never reaches Earth. The solar energy that does reach Earth warms the planet's surface, drives the hydrologic and other biogeochemical cycles, produces the climate, and powers almost all life through the process of photosynthesis.

© Cengage Learning

During half of the year (March 21 to September 22), the Northern Hemisphere tilts toward the sun, concentrating the sunlight and making the days longer (FIG. 55-13). During the other half of the year (September 22 to March 21), the Northern Hemisphere tilts away from the sun, giving it a lower concentration of sunlight and shorter days. The orientation of the Southern Hemisphere is just the opposite at these times. Summer in the Northern Hemisphere corresponds to winter in the Southern Hemisphere.

The atmosphere contains several gases essential to organisms

The atmosphere is an invisible layer of gases that envelops Earth. Oxygen (21%) and nitrogen (78%) are the predominant gases in the atmosphere, accounting for about 99% of dry air; other gases, including argon, carbon dioxide, neon, and

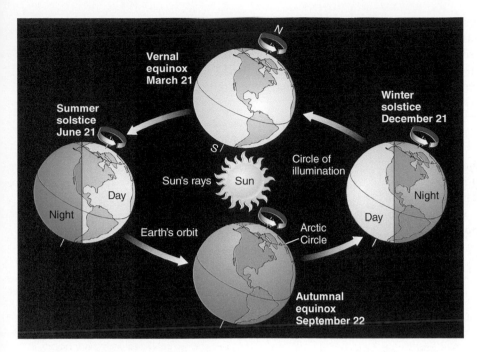

Figure 55-13 Seasonal changes in temperature

Earth's inclination on its axis remains the same as Earth travels around the sun. Thus, the sun's rays hit the Northern Hemisphere obliquely during winter months and more directly during summer months. In the Southern Hemisphere, the sun's rays are oblique during the winter, which corresponds to the Northern Hemisphere's summer. At the equator, the sun's rays are approximately vertical on March 21 and September 22.

© Cengage Learning

causing this air to expand and rise. As the warm air rises, it flows away from the equator, cools, and sinks again (FIG. 55-14). Much of it recirculates to the same areas it left, but the remainder splits and flows in two directions, toward the poles. The air chills enough to sink to the surface at about 30 degrees north and south latitudes. Similar upward movements of warm air and its subsequent flow toward the poles occur at higher latitudes, farther from the equator. At the poles, the cold polar air sinks and flows toward the lower latitudes, generally beneath the warm air that simultaneously flows toward the poles. The constant motion of air transfers heat from the equator toward the poles, and as the air returns, it cools the land over which it passes. This continuous turnover moderates temperatures over Earth's surface.

The atmosphere exhibits complex horizontal movements In addition to global circulation patterns, the atmosphere exhibits complex horizontal movements called **winds.** The nature of wind, with its turbulent gusts, eddies, and lulls, is difficult to understand or predict. It results in part from differences in

helium, make up the remaining 1%. In addition, water vapor and trace amounts of various air pollutants, such as methane, ozone, dust particles, pollen, microorganisms, and chlorofluorocarbons (CFCs), are present. Atmospheric oxygen is essential to plants, animals, and other organisms that respire aerobically; and plants and other photosynthetic organisms also require carbon dioxide.

The atmosphere performs several essential ecological functions. It protects Earth's surface from most of the sun's ultraviolet radiation and X-rays as well as from lethal amounts of cosmic rays from space. Without this atmospheric shielding, life as we know it would cease. Although the atmosphere protects Earth from high-energy radiation, visible light and some infrared radiation can penetrate it, and they warm the surface and the lower atmosphere. This interaction between the atmosphere and solar energy is responsible for weather and climate.

Organisms depend on the atmosphere, but they also help maintain and, in certain instances, modify its composition. For example, atmospheric oxygen increased to its present level as a result of billions of years of photosynthesis. Today, an approximate balance between oxygen-producing photosynthesis and oxygen-using aerobic respiration helps maintain the level of atmospheric oxygen.

The sun drives global atmospheric circulation In large measure, differences in temperature that are due to variations in the amount of solar energy at different locations on Earth drive the circulation of the atmosphere. The warm surface near the equator heats the air with which it comes into contact,

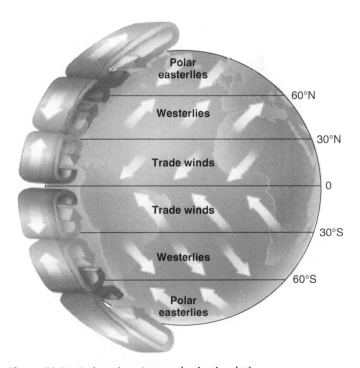

Figure 55-14 *Animation* Atmospheric circulation

The greatest solar energy input occurs at the equator and heats air most strongly in that area. The air rises and travels poleward (*left*) but is cooled in the process, so much of it descends again around 30 degrees latitude in both hemispheres. At higher latitudes, the patterns of air movement are more complex.

© Cengage Learning

atmospheric temperature and pressure changes, Earth's rotation, and uneven heating of the oceans and continents.

The gases that constitute the atmosphere have weight and exert a pressure that is, at sea level, about 1013 millibars (14.7 lb/in.²). Air pressure is variable, however, and changes with altitude, temperature, and humidity. Winds tend to blow from areas of high atmospheric pressure to areas of low pressure; the greater the difference and proximity between the high and low pressure areas, the stronger the wind.

Earth's rotation influences the direction that wind blows. Because Earth rotates from west to east, wind swerves to the right in the Northern Hemisphere and to the left in the Southern Hemisphere. This tendency of moving air to be deflected from its path by Earth's rotation is known as the **Coriolis effect.**

The global ocean covers most of Earth's surface

The global ocean is a huge body of salt water that surrounds the continents and covers almost three-fourths of Earth's surface.

It is a single, continuous body of water, but geographers divide it into four sections separated by the continents: the Pacific, Atlantic, Indian, and Arctic Oceans. The Pacific Ocean, which covers one-third of Earth's surface and contains more than half of Earth's water, is the largest by far.

Winds drive surface ocean currents The persistent prevailing winds blowing over the ocean produce mass movements of surface ocean water known as **ocean currents** (FIG. 55-15). The prevailing winds generate circular ocean currents called *gyres.* For example, in the North Atlantic, the tropical trade winds tend to blow toward the west, whereas the westerlies in the midlatitudes blow toward the east (see Fig. 55-14). This movement helps establish a clockwise gyre in the North Atlantic. Thus, surface ocean currents and winds tend to move in the same direction, although there are many variations on this general rule.

The Coriolis effect is partly responsible for the paths that surface ocean currents travel. Earth's rotation from west to east causes surface ocean currents to swerve to the right in the

KEY POINT

The driving force of wind produces Earth's major surface ocean currents.

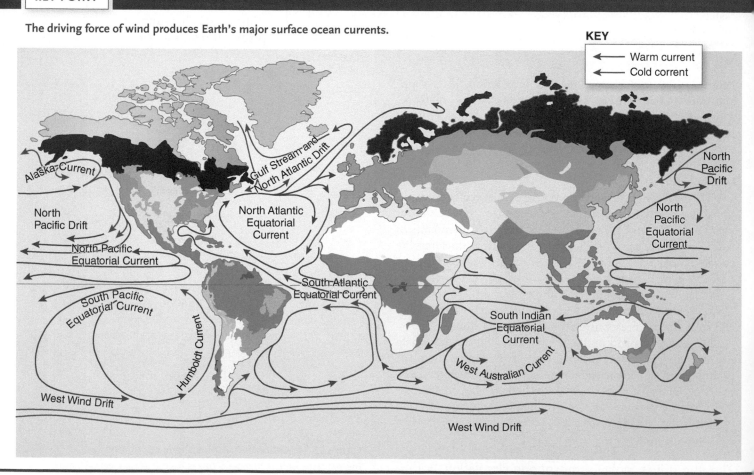

Figure 55-15 Major surface ocean currents
Each current has characteristic temperature and flow patterns.
© Cengage Learning

PREDICT How could currents be affected by global climate change?

Northern Hemisphere, producing a clockwise gyre of water currents. In the Southern Hemisphere, ocean currents swerve to the left, producing a counterclockwise gyre.

The ocean interacts with the atmosphere The ocean and the atmosphere are strongly linked. Wind from the atmosphere affects the ocean currents, and heat from the ocean affects atmospheric circulation. One of the best examples of the interaction between ocean and atmosphere is the **El Niño–Southern Oscillation (ENSO)** event. ENSO is a periodic warming of surface waters of the tropical eastern Pacific that alters both oceanic and atmospheric circulation patterns and results in unusual weather in areas far from the tropical Pacific. Normally, westward-blowing trade winds restrict the warmest waters to the western Pacific (near Australia). Every three to seven years, however, the trade winds weaken, and the warm water mass expands eastward to South America, raising surface temperatures in the eastern Pacific. Ocean currents, which normally flow westward in this area, slow down, stop altogether, or even reverse and go eastward. The phenomenon is called El Niño, which is Spanish for "the (Christ) child," because the warming usually reaches the fishing grounds off Peru just before Christmas. Most ENSOs last from one to two years. La Niña (Spanish for "the girl"), the opposite phase, is the cold phase, of the ENSO cycle and occurs when cold ocean waters return.

An ENSO event changes biological productivity in parts of the ocean. The warmer sea-surface temperatures and accompanying changes in ocean circulation patterns off the west coast of South America prevent colder, nutrient-laden deeper waters from **upwelling** (coming to the surface) (FIG. 55-16). The lack of nutrients in the water results in a severe decrease in the populations of anchovies and many other marine fishes. Other species, such as shrimp and scallops, thrive during an ENSO event. Along the Pacific coast of North America, ENSO shifts the distribution of tropical fishes northward and even affects the salmon run in Alaska.

Climate profoundly affects organisms

Climate is the average weather conditions, plus extremes (records), that occur in a given place over a period of years. The two most important factors that determine an area's climate are temperature (both average temperature and temperature extremes) and precipitation (both average precipitation and seasonal distribution). Other climate factors include wind, humidity, fog, cloud cover, and lightning-caused wildfires. Unlike weather, which changes rapidly, climate generally changes slowly, over hundreds or thousands of years.

Day-to-day variations, day-to-night variations, and seasonal variations are also important dimensions of climate that affect organisms. Latitude, elevation, topography, vegetation, distance from the ocean or other large bodies of water, and location on a continent or other landmass all influence temperature, precipitation, and other aspects of climate.

Earth has many different climates, and because they are relatively constant for many years, organisms have adapted to them. The wide variety of organisms on Earth evolved in part

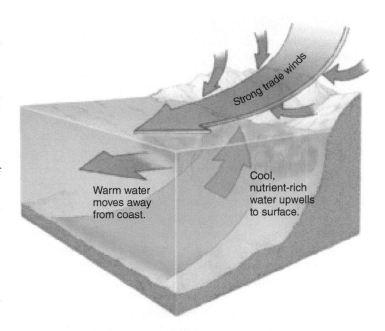

Figure 55-16 *Animation* **Upwelling**
Coastal upwelling, where deeper waters come to the surface, occurs in the Pacific Ocean along the South American coast. Upwelling provides nutrients for microscopic algae, which in turn support a complex food web. Coastal upwelling weakens considerably during years with ENSO events, temporarily reducing fish populations.
© Cengage Learning

because of the many different climates, ranging from cold, snow-covered, polar climates to hot, tropical climates where it rains almost every day.

Air and water movements and surface features affect precipitation patterns Precipitation varies from one location to another and has a profound effect on the distribution and kinds of organisms present. One of the driest places on Earth is in the Atacama Desert in Chile, where the average annual rainfall is 0.05 cm (0.02 in.). In contrast, Mount Waialeale in Hawaii, Earth's wettest spot, receives an average annual precipitation of 1200 cm (472 in.).

Differences in precipitation depend on several factors. The heavy-rainfall areas of the tropics result mainly from the uplifting of moisture-laden air. High surface-water temperatures (recall the enormous amount of solar energy striking the equator) cause the evaporation of vast quantities of water from tropical parts of the ocean. Prevailing winds blow the resulting moist, warm air over landmasses. Land surfaces warmed by the sun heat the air and cause moist air to rise. As it rises, the air cools, and its moisture-holding ability decreases. (Cool air holds less water vapor than warm air.) When air reaches its saturation point, it cannot hold any additional water vapor; clouds form, and water is released as precipitation. The air eventually returns to the surface on both sides of the equator near the Tropics of Cancer and Capricorn (latitudes 23.5 degrees north and south, respectively). By then, most of the moisture has precipitated so that dry air returns to the equator. This dry air makes little biological difference over the ocean, but its lack of moisture produces some of the great subtropical deserts, such as the Sahara.

Air is also dried during long journeys over landmasses. Near the windward (side from which the prevailing wind blows) coasts of continents, rainfall may be heavy. However, in the temperate zones—the areas between the tropical and polar zones—continental interiors are usually dry because they are far from the ocean that replenishes water vapor in the air passing over it.

Mountains force air to rise, removing moisture from humid air. As it gains altitude, the air cools, clouds form, and precipitation typically occurs, primarily on the windward slopes of the mountains. As the air mass moves down on the other side of the mountain, it is warmed, and clouds then evaporate, thereby lessening the chance of precipitation of any remaining moisture. This situation exists on the west coast of North America, where precipitation falls on the western slopes of mountains that are close to the coast. The dry lands on the sides of the mountains away from the prevailing wind (in this case, east of the mountain range) are called **rain shadows** (FIG. 55-17).

Microclimates are local variations in climate Differences in elevation, in the steepness and direction of slopes, and therefore in exposure to sunlight and prevailing winds may produce local variations in climate known as **microclimates,** which are sometimes quite different from their overall surroundings. Patches of sun and shade on a forest floor, for example, produce a variety of microclimates for plants, animals, and microorganisms living there. The microclimate of an organism's habitat is of primary importance because it is the climate that an organism actually experiences and must cope with. (Keep in mind, however, that microclimates are largely affected by the regional climates in which they are located.)

Sometimes organisms modify their own microclimate. For example, trees modify the local climate within a forest so that in summer the temperature is usually lower, and the relative humidity greater, than outside the forest. The temperature and humidity beneath the litter of the forest floor differ still more; in the summer the microclimate of this area is considerably cooler and moister than the surrounding forest. As another example, many desert-dwelling animals burrow to avoid surface climate conditions that would kill them in minutes. The cooler daytime microclimate in their burrows permits them to survive until night, when the surface cools off and they come out to forage or hunt.

Fires are a common disturbance in some ecosystems

Wildfires, which are fires started by lightning, are an important ecological force in many geographic areas. Those areas most prone to wildfires have wet seasons followed by dry seasons. Vegetation that grows and accumulates during the wet season dries out enough during the dry season to burn easily. When lightning hits vegetation or ground litter, it ignites the dry organic material, and a fire spreads through the area.

Fires have several effects on organisms. First, combustion frees the minerals that were locked in dry organic matter. The ashes remaining after a fire are rich in potassium, phosphorus, calcium, and other minerals essential for plant growth. With the arrival of precipitation, vegetation flourishes following a fire. Second, fire removes plant cover and exposes the soil. This change stimulates the germination and establishment of seeds requiring bare soil as well as encourages the growth of shade-intolerant plants. Third, fire causes increased soil erosion because it removes plant cover, leaving the soil more vulnerable to wind and water.

African savanna, California chaparral, North American grasslands, and ponderosa pine forests of the western United States are some fire-adapted ecosystems (see Chapter 56). Fire helps maintain grasses as the dominant vegetation in grasslands by removing fire-sensitive hardwood trees.

Humans try to prevent fires, and sometimes this effort has disastrous consequences. When fire is excluded from a fire-adapted ecosystem, deadwood and other plant litter accumulate. As a result, when a fire does occur, it can be very destructive. The sometimes deadly wildfires in Colorado and other western states and provinces are blamed in part on decades of suppressing fires in the region. Prevention of fire also converts grassland to woody vegetation and facilitates the invasion of fire-sensitive trees into fire-adapted forests.

Controlled burning is a tool of ecological management in which the undergrowth and plant litter are deliberately burned under controlled conditions before they have accumulated to dangerous levels (FIG. 55-18). Controlled burns are also used to suppress fire-sensitive trees, thereby maintaining the natural fire-adapted ecosystem. In a 2010 study of fire reintroduction in Sierra Nevada forests reported in *Ecosphere,* Karen Webster and Charles Halpern explored two decades of changes in plant diversity and abundance following reintroduction and repeated use of fire in previously unmanaged forests. Results from their research suggest that repeated controlled burning can gradually enhance the diversity and abundance of understory species and may enhance the dispersal of those species impacted by fire exclusion. More research needs to be conducted on when controlled burning is appropriate or how often it should be carried out. Moreover, there are major practical, political, and educational issues that must be addressed in implementing controlled burns.

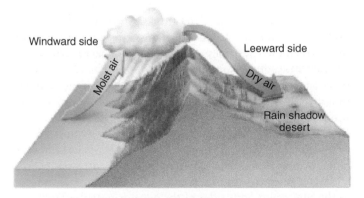

Figure 55-17 *Animation* **Rain shadow**

A rain shadow is the arid or semiarid land that occurs on the leeward side of a mountain. Such a rain shadow occurs east of the Cascade Range in Washington State. The western side of the range receives more than 500 cm of precipitation annually, whereas the eastern side receives 40 to 50 cm.
© Cengage Learning

Figure 55-18 Controlled burn as a tool of ecological management
This aerial view of a controlled burn shows the leading edge of the fire, or fire line.

CHECKPOINT 55.3

- *What basic forces determine the circulation of the atmosphere?*
- *What basic forces produce the main ocean currents?*
- **CONNECT** *What are some of the factors that produce regional differences in precipitation?*

55.4 STUDYING ECOSYSTEM PROCESSES

LEARNING OBJECTIVE

9 Briefly describe some of the long-term ecological research conducted at Hubbard Brook Experimental Forest.

Ecologists conduct detailed ecosystem studies in laboratory simulations and in the field to measure such processes as energy flow, the cycling of nutrients, and the effects of natural and human-induced disturbances (e.g., air pollution, tree harvesting, and land-use changes). Some ecosystem studies, such as those performed at the Hubbard Brook Experimental Forest (HBEF), a 3100-hectare (7750-acre) reserve in the White Mountain National Forest in New Hampshire, are long term. Beginning in the late 1950s and continuing to the present, HBEF has been the site of numerous studies that address the hydrology (e.g., precipitation, surface runoff, and groundwater flow), biology, geology, and chemistry of forests and associated aquatic ecosystems. The National Science Foundation (NSF) has designated HBEF as one of its 24 long-term ecological research sites.

Many of the experiments at HBEF are based on field observations. For example, salamander populations were originally surveyed in forest communities in 1970 and have been resurveyed in recent years. Other studies involve manipulative experiments. In 1978, scientists added dilute sulfuric acid to a small stream in HBEF to study the chemical and biological effects of acidification. This experiment was of practical value because acid precipitation, a form of air pollution, has acidified numerous lakes and streams in industrialized countries.

Several researchers have studied the effects on HBEF stream ecosystems of **deforestation,** the clearance of large expanses of forest for agriculture or other uses. When a forest is removed, the total amount of water and minerals that flow into streams increases drastically. A concrete dam called a *catchment* can be constructed across a stream so that ecologists can measure the flow of water and chemical components out of the ecosystem. Catchments help scientists to measure the quantity, timing, and quality of water flowing from a forested watershed. Typically, outflow is measured in two separate ecosystems: one serves as a control, and one is experimentally manipulated. These studies demonstrate that deforestation causes soil erosion and leaching of essential minerals that result in decreased soil fertility. The summer temperatures in streams running through deforested areas are higher than in shady streams running through uncut forests. Many stream organisms do not fare well in deforested areas, in part because they are adapted to cooler temperatures.

Detailed studies such as those at HBEF provide ecologists with insights into how ecological processes function in individual ecosystems. Ecologists compare these data with similar information from other ecosystem studies to develop generalized insights into how ecosystems are structured and how they function. Long-term ecosystem experiments enable ecologists to evaluate and predict the effects of environmental change, including human-induced change.

Ecosystem experiments also contribute to our practical knowledge about how to maintain water quality, wildlife habitat, and productive forests. **Ecosystem management,** a conservation approach that emphasizes restoring and maintaining the quality of an entire ecosystem rather than the conservation of individual species, makes use of such knowledge.

Ecologists are also studying the causes of food-web flips and ecosystem collapse to recognize tipping points. A food-web flip occurs when there is a major persistent change in the sequences of organisms eating and being eaten by one another. As reported in *Science,* a team from University of Wisconsin–Madison led by Stephen Carpenter examined 30 years of research on Peter Lake, Wisconsin, and developed mathematical models to recognize early signs of tipping points. The researchers identified signs of change in an endangered food web 15 months before it flipped. Continued research in this area may enhance our ability to recognize warning signs to protect ecosystems from natural and human effects before irreversible or costly damage occurs.

CHECKPOINT 55.4

- *What are some of the environmental effects observed in the deforestation study at Hubbard Brook Experimental Forest?*

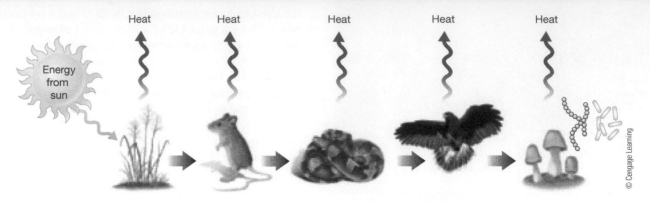

55.1 Energy Flow Through Ecosystems (page 1188)

1 Summarize the concept of energy flow through a food web.

- **Energy flow** through an ecosystem is linear, from the sun to producer to consumer to decomposer. Much of this energy is converted to heat as it moves from one organism to another, so organisms occupying the next **trophic level** cannot use it.

- Trophic relationships may be expressed as **food webs,** which show the many alternative pathways that energy may take among the producers, consumers, and decomposers of an ecosystem.

2 Explain typical pyramids of numbers, biomass, and energy.

- **Ecological pyramids** typically express the progressive reduction in numbers of organisms, biomass, and energy found in successive trophic levels. A **pyramid of numbers** shows the number of organisms at each trophic level in a given ecosystem. A **pyramid of biomass** shows the total biomass at each successive trophic level. A **pyramid of energy** indicates the energy content of the biomass of each trophic level.

3 Distinguish between gross primary productivity and net primary productivity.

- **Gross primary productivity (GPP)** of an ecosystem is the rate at which photosynthesis captures energy. **Net primary productivity (NPP)** is the energy that remains (as biomass) after plants and other producers carry out cellular respiration.

55.2 Cycles of Matter in Ecosystems (page 1193)

4 Describe the main steps in each of these biogeochemical cycles: the carbon, nitrogen, phosphorus, and hydrologic cycles.

- Carbon dioxide is the important gas of the **carbon cycle.** Carbon enters plants, algae, and cyanobacteria as CO_2, which photosynthesis incorporates into organic molecules. Cellular respiration, combustion, and erosion of limestone return CO_2 to the water and atmosphere, where it is again available to producers.

- The **nitrogen cycle** has five steps. **Nitrogen fixation** is the conversion of nitrogen gas to ammonia. **Nitrification** is the conversion of ammonia or ammonium to nitrate. **Assimilation** is the conversion of nitrates, ammonia, or ammonium to proteins and other nitrogen-containing compounds by plants; conversion of plant proteins into animal proteins is also assimilation. **Ammonification** is the conversion of organic nitrogen to ammonia and ammonium ions. **Denitrification** is the conversion of nitrate to nitrogen gas.

- The **phosphorus cycle** has no biologically important gaseous compounds. Phosphorus erodes from rock as inorganic phosphate, which the roots of plants absorb from the soil. Animals obtain the phosphorus they need from their diets. Decomposers release inorganic phosphate into the environment. When phosphorus washes into the ocean and is subsequently deposited in seabeds, it is lost from biological cycles for millions of years.

- The **hydrologic cycle** involves an exchange of water between the land, ocean, atmosphere, and organisms. Water enters the atmosphere by evaporation and **transpiration** and leaves the atmosphere as precipitation. On land, water filters through the ground or runs off to lakes, rivers, and the ocean. Aquifers are underground caverns and porous layers of rock in which groundwater is stored.

55.3 Abiotic Factors in Ecosystems (page 1198)

5 Summarize the effects of solar energy on Earth's temperatures.

- Of the solar energy that reaches Earth, 30% is immediately reflected away; the atmosphere and surface absorb the remaining 70%. Ultimately, all absorbed solar energy is reradiated into space as infrared (heat) radiation.

- A combination of Earth's roughly spherical shape and the tilted angle of its axis concentrates solar energy at the equator and dilutes it at the poles; the tropics are hotter and less variable in climate than are temperate and polar areas.

6 Discuss the roles of solar energy and the Coriolis effect in the generation of global air and water flow patterns.

- Visible light and some infrared radiation warm the surface and the lower part of the atmosphere. Atmospheric heat transferred from the equator to the poles produces movement of warm air toward the poles and of cool air toward the equator.

- **Winds** result in part from differences in atmospheric pressure and from the **Coriolis effect,** the tendency of moving air or water, because of Earth's rotation, to be deflected to the right in the Northern Hemisphere and to the left in the Southern Hemisphere.

- Surface **ocean currents** result in part from prevailing winds and the Coriolis effect.

7 Give two causes of regional precipitation differences.

- Latitude, elevation, topography, vegetation, distance from the ocean or other large bodies of water, and location on a continent or other landmass influence precipitation.

- Precipitation is greatest where warm air passes over the ocean, absorbs moisture, and then cools, such as in areas where mountains force humid air upward. Deserts develop in the **rain shadows** of mountain ranges or in continental interiors.

8 Discuss the effects of fire on certain ecosystems.
- Fire frees the minerals locked in dry organic matter, removes plant cover and exposes the soil, and increases soil erosion. Many ecosystems, such as savanna, chaparral, grasslands, and certain forests, contain fire-adapted organisms.

55.4 Studying Ecosystem Processes *(page 1205)*

9 Briefly describe some of the long-term ecological research conducted at Hubbard Brook Experimental Forest.
- Hubbard Brook Experimental Forest (HBEF) in New Hampshire is the site of numerous studies that address the hydrology (precipitation, surface runoff, and groundwater flow), biology (effects of deforestation and changes in salamander populations), geology, and chemistry (acid precipitation) of forests and associated aquatic ecosystems.

TEST YOUR UNDERSTANDING

Know and Comprehend

1. The movement of matter is _____ in ecosystems, and the movement of energy is _____. (a) linear; linear (b) linear; cyclic (c) cyclic; cyclic (d) cyclic; linear (e) cyclic; linear or cyclic

2. A complex of interconnected food chains in an ecosystem is called (a) an ecosystem (b) a pyramid of numbers (c) a pyramid of biomass (d) a biosphere (e) a food web

3. The quantitative estimate of the total amount of living material is called (a) biomass (b) energy flow (c) gross primary productivity (d) plant respiration (e) net primary productivity

4. Which of the following equations shows the relationship between gross primary productivity (GPP) and net primary productivity (NPP)? (a) GPP = NPP − photosynthesis (b) NPP = GPP − photosynthesis (c) GPP = NPP − plant respiration (d) NPP = GPP − plant respiration (e) NPP = GPP − animal respiration

5. Which of the following processes increase(s) the amount of atmospheric carbon in the carbon cycle? (a) photosynthesis (b) cellular respiration (c) combustion (d) a and c (e) b and c

6. In the nitrogen cycle, gaseous nitrogen is converted to ammonia during (a) nitrogen fixation (b) nitrification (c) assimilation (d) ammonification (e) denitrification

7. The conversion of ammonia to nitrate, known as _____, is a two-step process performed by soil bacteria. (a) nitrogen fixation (b) nitrification (c) assimilation (d) ammonification (e) denitrification

8. Which biogeochemical cycle does not have a gaseous component but cycles from the land to sediments in the ocean and back to the land? (a) carbon cycle (b) nitrogen cycle (c) phosphorus cycle (d) hydrologic cycle (e) neither a nor c has a gaseous component

9. Which of the following processes is *not* directly involved in the hydrologic cycle? (a) transpiration (b) evaporation (c) precipitation (d) nitrification (e) condensation

10. The periodic warming of surface waters of the tropical eastern Pacific that alters both oceanic and atmospheric circulation patterns is known as (a) upwelling (b) prevailing wind (c) ocean current (d) El Niño–Southern Oscillation (e) Coriolis effect

11. A mountain range may produce a downwind arid (a) upwelling (b) rain shadow (c) ocean current (d) microclimate (e) ecological pyramid

Apply and Analyze

12. **VISUALIZE** Draw the simplest stable ecosystem you can imagine.

13. **PREDICT** How might a food web change if all decomposers were eliminated from it?

14. Why is the cycling of matter essential to the long-term continuance of life?

15. What would happen to the nitrogen cycle if all bacteria were absent? Explain your answer.

Evaluate and Synthesize

16. Would the microclimate of an ant be the same as that of an elephant living in the same area? Why or why not?

17. **INTERPRET DATA** Examine Figure 55-3b (shown here). Explain why this pyramid of biomass is inverted. In other words, how can 4 g of producers support 21 g of primary consumers?

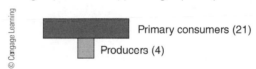
© Cengage Learning
Primary consumers (21)
Producers (4)

18. **INTERPRET DATA** Scientists have compiled databases of large forest wildfires in the western United States and compared them to climate and land-surface data. Examine the graph showing wildfire frequency compared to average spring–summer temperature. Do you see a correlation? If so, describe it. Based on these data, do you think that climate warming is causing more wildfires? Explain your answer.

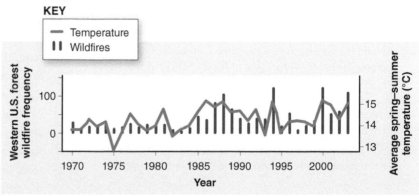

Source: Adapted from Westerling, A. L., H. G. Hidalgo, D. R. Cayan, and T. W. Swetnam. "Warming and Earlier Spring Increase Western U.S. Forest Wildfire Activity." *Science*, Vol. 313, Aug. 18, 2006.

19. **SCIENCE, TECHNOLOGY, AND SOCIETY** How do humans alter the nitrogen cycle, and what can scientists, engineers, and the public do to mitigate the damage?

To access course materials, such as Aplia and other companion resources, please visit **www.cengagebrain.com.**

56 Ecology and the Geography of Life

© Ed Endicott/Alamy

Black-tailed prairie dog. Prairie dogs (*Cynomys ludovicianus*) never wander far from their burrows, which they use to escape from predators.

KEY CONCEPTS

56.1 Climate, particularly temperature and precipitation, affects the distribution of Earth's major biomes, such as tropical rain forests and tundra.

56.2 Abiotic factors—such as water salinity, amount of dissolved oxygen, availability of essential minerals, light, and water depth—influence the distribution of organisms in aquatic ecosystems.

56.3 Ecotones—areas of transition where two communities meet and intergrade—provide diverse conditions that encourage species richness.

56.4 Earth has six biogeographic realms, each consisting of a major landmass separated by deep water, mountains, or a desert.

Earth has many different environments. *Natural selection* affects an organism's ability to survive and reproduce in a given environment. In natural selection both **abiotic** (nonliving) and **biotic** (living) factors eliminate the least-fit individuals in a population. Over time, succeeding generations of organisms that live in each biome or major aquatic ecosystem become better adapted to local environmental conditions.

Black-tailed prairie dogs are superbly adapted to their environment. Their teeth and digestive tracts are modified to eat and easily digest the seeds and leaves of grasses that grow in great profusion on the Great Plains of western North America.

Prairie dogs live in large colonies of about 500 individuals. The eyes of every individual in the colony watch for potential danger, and when they see it, prairie dogs call out to warn the rest of the colony (see photograph). When danger approaches, each prairie dog dives into its underground home. Each burrow has at least two openings and consists of an elaborate network of long tunnels with several chambers: a nursery for the young, a sleeping chamber, a toilet chamber, and a listening chamber (close to an entrance). Piles of excavated soil surround the burrow entrances and help prevent flooding during rainstorms.

To survive winter, black-tailed prairie dogs sleep in their burrows. Their metabolism slows, and they subsist on the stored fat in their bodies. They do not truly hibernate, however, and may leave their burrows to look for food when the weather warms.

Like prairie dogs, each species has structural, behavioral, and physiological adaptations for its own particular environment. As you examine Earth's major terrestrial and aquatic ecosystems, including the species characteristic of each, think about the variety of adaptations that natural selection has produced in organisms in response to their particular environments.

56.1 BIOMES

LEARNING OBJECTIVES

1 Define *biome* and briefly describe the nine major terrestrial biomes, giving attention to the climate, soil, and characteristic plants and animals of each.

2 Describe at least one human effect on each of the biomes discussed.

A **biome** is a large, relatively distinct terrestrial region that has similar climate, soil, plants, and animals regardless of where it occurs. Because it covers such a large geographic area, a biome encompasses many interacting landscapes. Recall from Chapter 53 that a **landscape** is a large land area (several to many square kilometers) composed of interacting ecosystems.

Biomes largely correspond to major climate zones, with temperature and precipitation being most important (FIG. 56-1). Near the poles, temperature is generally the overriding climate factor, whereas in tropical and temperate regions, precipitation becomes more significant than temperature. Other abiotic factors to which biomes are sensitive include temperature extremes,

---

KEY POINT

The distribution of the world's biomes is largely the result of climate patterns, which determine an area's water (measured as precipitation) and energy (measured as temperature).

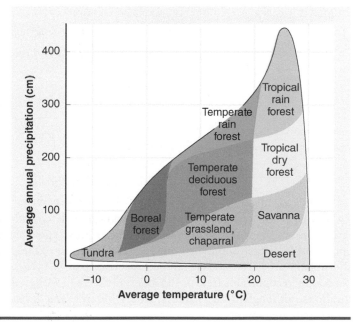

Figure 56-1 Using precipitation and temperature to identify biomes

Factors such as soil type, fire, and seasonality of climate affect whether temperate grassland or chaparral develops. (Adapted from Whittaker, R. H. *Communities and Ecosystems*, 2nd ed. Macmillan, New York, 1975.)

PREDICT As global climate continues to change, how might Earth's biomes be affected?

---

rapid temperature changes, floods, droughts, strong winds, and fires (see section on fires in Chapter 55).

We discuss nine major biomes in this chapter: tundra, boreal forest, temperate rain forest, temperate deciduous forest, temperate grassland, chaparral, desert, savanna, and tropical rain forest. Although we discuss each biome as a distinct entity, biomes intergrade into one another at their boundaries.

Tundra is the cold, boggy plains of the far north

Tundra (also called **arctic tundra**) occurs in extreme northern latitudes wherever snow melts seasonally (FIG. 56-2). In the Southern Hemisphere, the **Antarctic tundra,** located on the Antarctic Peninsula and nearby islands, is home to animals such as penguins and elephant seals. Plant life in this warmer, slightly moister region of Antarctica consists of many mosses and lichens and some liverworts and fungi, but only two species of vascular plants. A third similar ecosystem, located in the higher elevations of mountains, above the tree line, is called **alpine tundra** (see *Inquiring About: The Distribution of Vegetation on Mountains*).

Arctic tundra has long, harsh winters and extremely short summers. Although the growing season, with its warmer temperatures, is as short as 50 days, the days are long. Above the Arctic Circle, the sun does not set at all for many days in midsummer, although the amount of light at midnight is only one-tenth that at noon. There is little precipitation (10 to 25 cm, or 4 to 10 in., per year) over much of the tundra, and most of it falls during summer months.

Tundra soils tend to be geologically young (with the exception of Antarctic tundra) because most were formed only after

Figure 56-2 Arctic tundra

Because of the short growing season and permafrost in arctic tundra, only small, hardy plants grow in this northernmost biome that encircles the Arctic Ocean. Photographed during autumn in Alaska.

Does the type of vegetation change at different elevations on a mountain? Hiking up a mountain is similar to traveling toward the North Pole with respect to the major life zones encountered (see figure). This elevation–latitude similarity occurs because the temperature drops as one climbs a mountain, just as it does when one travels north; the temperature drops about 6°C (11°F) with each 1000-m increase in elevation. The types of species growing on the mountain change as the temperature changes.

Deciduous trees, which shed their leaves every autumn, may cover the base of a mountain in Colorado, for example. At higher elevations, where the climate is colder and more severe, a coniferous *subalpine forest* resembling boreal forest grows. Spruces and firs are the dominant trees here.

Higher still, the forest thins, and the trees become smaller, gnarled, and shrublike. These twisted, shrublike trees, called *krummholz* (a German word meaning "crooked wood"), are found at their elevational limit (the *tree line*). The exact elevation at which the tree line occurs depends on the latitude and distance from the ocean. In the Rocky Mountains, between 35° and 50° north latitude, the tree line drops 100 m with each 1° latitude northward.

Above the tree line, where the climate is quite cold, a kind of tundra occurs, with vegetation composed of grasses, sedges, and small tufted plants, most of which are hardy perennials. Some alpine plants (e.g., buttercups) are lowland species that have adapted to the alpine environment, whereas other plants (e.g., mountain douglasia) live exclusively in the mountains. This tundra is called *alpine tundra* to distinguish it from arctic tundra. At the top of the mountain, a permanent ice cap or snowcap might be found, similar to the nearly lifeless polar land areas.

Important environmental differences exist between high elevations and high latitudes that affect the types of organisms found in each place. Alpine tundra typically lacks permafrost and receives more precipitation than does arctic tundra. High elevations of temperate mountains do not have the great extremes of day length that are associated with the changing seasons in high-latitude biomes. The intensity of solar radiation is greater at high elevations than at high latitudes. At high elevations, the sun's rays pass through less atmosphere, which results in greater exposure to ultraviolet radiation (less is filtered out by the atmosphere) than occurs at high latitudes.

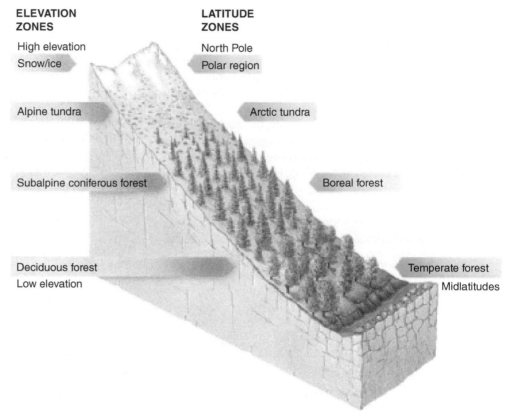

Comparison of elevation and latitude zones. The cooler temperatures at higher elevations of a mountain produce a series of ecosystems similar to those encountered when going toward the North Pole.
© Cengage Learning

the last Ice Age.[1] These soils are usually nutrient poor and have little organic litter (dead leaves and stems, animal droppings, and remains of organisms) in the uppermost layer of soil. Although the soil surface melts during the summer, tundra has a layer of permanently frozen ground called **permafrost** that varies in depth and thickness. Because permafrost interferes with drainage, the thawed upper zone of soil is usually waterlogged during the summer. Limited precipitation, combined with low temperatures, flat topography (surface features), and permafrost, produces a landscape of broad, shallow lakes, sluggish streams, and bogs.

Low species richness and low primary productivity characterize tundra. Mosses, lichens (such as reindeer moss), grasses, and grasslike sedges dominate tundra vegetation; most of these short plants are herbaceous perennials that live 20 to 100 years. No readily recognizable trees or shrubs grow except in sheltered locations, although dwarf willows, dwarf birches, and other dwarf trees are common.

Year-round animal life of the tundra includes voles, weasels, arctic foxes, gray wolves, snowshoe hares, ptarmigan, snowy owls, musk oxen, and lemmings (see Figure 53-5 and the discussion of lemming population cycles in Chapter 53). In the summer caribou migrate north to the tundra to graze on sedges, grasses, and dwarf willow. Dozens of bird species also migrate north in summer to nest and feed on abundant insects.

---

[1] Glacier ice, which occupied about 30% of Earth's land during the last Ice Age, began retreating about 17,000 years ago. Today, glacier ice occupies about 10% of the land surface.

Mosquitoes, blackflies, and deerflies survive the winter as eggs or pupae and occur in great numbers during summer weeks.

Tundra regenerates quite slowly after it has been disturbed. Even casual use by hikers causes damage. Long-lasting injury, likely to persist for hundreds of years, has been done to large portions of the arctic tundra as a result of oil exploration and military use.

Boreal forest is the evergreen forest of the north

Just south of the tundra lies the **boreal forest,** also known as *coniferous forest* or **taiga.** (Conifers are cone-bearing evergreens.) The boreal forest, which stretches across both North America and Eurasia, is the world's largest biome, covering approximately 11% of Earth's land (FIG. 56-3). A biome comparable to the boreal forest is not found in the Southern Hemisphere because it has no land at the corresponding latitudes. Winters are extremely cold and severe, although not as harsh as in the tundra. Boreal forest receives little precipitation, perhaps 50 cm (20 in.) per year, and its soil is typically acidic, low in minerals (inorganic nutrients), and has a deep layer of partly decomposed conifer needles at the surface. Boreal forest contains numerous ponds and lakes in water-filled depressions dug by grinding ice sheets during the last Ice Age.

White and black spruces, balsam fir, eastern larch, and other conifers dominate the boreal forest, but **deciduous** trees such as aspen or birch, which shed their leaves in autumn, form striking stands. Conifers have many drought-resistant adaptations, such as needlelike leaves with a minimal surface area to reduce water loss (see Fig. 34-9). Such an adaptation enables conifers to withstand the "drought" of the northern winter months, when roots do not absorb water because the ground is frozen. Natural selection also favors conifers in the boreal forest because, being evergreen, they resume photosynthesis as soon as warmer temperatures return.

Animal life of the boreal forest includes some larger species, such as caribou (which migrate from the tundra to the boreal forest for winter), wolves, bears, and moose. However, most animal life is medium-sized to small and includes rodents, rabbits, and fur-bearing predators such as lynx, sable, and mink. Most species of birds are seasonally abundant but migrate to warmer climates for winter. Insects are numerous, but there are few amphibians and reptiles except in the southern boreal forest.

Most of the boreal forest is not suitable for agriculture because of its short growing season and mineral-poor soil. The boreal forest, which is harvested primarily by clear-cutting, is currently the primary source of the world's industrial wood and wood fiber.

Temperate rain forest has cool weather, dense fog, and high precipitation

Coniferous **temperate rain forest** grows on the northwestern coast of North America. Similar vegetation exists in southeastern Australia and in southwestern South America. Annual precipitation in this biome is high, from 200 to 380 cm (80 to 150 in.); condensation of water from dense coastal fog augments the annual precipitation. The proximity of temperate rain forest to the coastline moderates the temperature so that seasonal fluctuation is narrow; winters are mild, and summers are cool. Temperate rain forest has a relatively nutrient-poor soil, although its organic content may be high. Cool temperatures slow the activity of bacterial and fungal decomposers. Thus, needles and large fallen branches and trunks accumulate on the ground as litter that takes many years to decay and release inorganic minerals to the soil.

The dominant vegetation type in the North American temperate rain forest is large evergreen trees, such as western hemlock, Douglas fir, Sitka spruce, and western red cedar. Temperate rain forest is rich in epiphytic vegetation, which consists of smaller plants that grow nonparasitically on the trunks and branches of large trees (FIG. 56-4). Epiphytes in this biome are mainly mosses, lichens, and ferns, all of which also carpet the ground. Squirrels, wood rats, mule deer, elk, numerous bird species (such as jays, nuthatches, and chickadees), several species of reptiles (such as painted turtles and western terrestrial garter snakes), and amphibians (such as Pacific giant salamanders and Pacific treefrogs) are common temperate rainforest animals.

Temperate rain forest, one of the richest wood producers in the world, supplies us with lumber and pulpwood. It is also one of the most complex ecosystems in terms of species richness. Care must be taken to avoid overharvesting original old-growth forest because such an ecosystem takes hundreds of years to develop. When the logging industry harvests old-growth forest, it typically replants the area with a monoculture (a single species) of trees that it harvests in 40- to 100-year cycles. Thus, the old-growth forest ecosystem, once harvested, never has a chance to redevelop. A small fraction of the original, old-growth temperate rain forest in Washington, Oregon, and northern California remains untouched. These stable forest ecosystems provide biological habitat for many organisms, including 40 endangered and threatened species.

Beth Davidow/Visuals Unlimited

Figure 56-3 Boreal forest
Boreal forest is coniferous forest that occurs in cold regions of the Northern Hemisphere adjacent to the tundra. Photographed in Yukon, Canada.

Figure 56-4 Temperate rain forest

Large amounts of precipitation characterize temperate rain forest. Note the epiphytes hanging from the branches of coniferous trees. Photographed in Olympic National Park in Washington State.

Temperate deciduous forest has a canopy of broad-leaf trees

Seasonality (hot summers and cold winters) is characteristic of **temperate deciduous forest,** which occurs in temperate areas where precipitation ranges from about 75 to 126 cm (30 to 50 in.) annually. Typically, the soil of a temperate deciduous forest consists of both a topsoil rich in organic material and a deep, clay-rich lower layer. As organic materials decay, mineral ions are released. If roots of living trees do not absorb these ions, they leach into the clay, where they may be retained.

Broad-leaf hardwood trees, such as oak, hickory, maple, and beech, which lose their foliage annually dominate temperate deciduous forests of the northeastern and Mid-Atlantic United States (**FIG. 56-5**). The trees of the temperate deciduous forest form a dense canopy that overlies saplings and shrubs.

Temperate deciduous forests originally contained a variety of large mammals such as mountain lions, wolves, bison, and other species now regionally extinct, plus deer, bears, and many small mammals and birds (such as wild turkeys, blue jays, and scarlet tanagers). Both reptiles (such as box turtles and rat snakes) and amphibians (such as spotted salamanders and wood frogs) abounded, together with a denser and more varied insect life than exists today.

In Europe and North America, logging and land clearing for farms, tree plantations, and cities have removed much of the

Figure 56-5 Temperate deciduous forest

The broad-leaf trees that dominate the temperate deciduous forest shed their leaves before winter. Photographed during autumn at the Durance River in France.

original temperate deciduous forest. Where it has regenerated, temperate deciduous forest is often in a seminatural state, highly modified by humans for recreation, livestock foraging, timber harvest, and other uses. Although these returning forests do not have the biological diversity of virgin stands, many forest organisms have successfully become re-established. For example, in the eastern United States, white-tailed deer populations were decimated by hunting by 1900. As large parts of forests were modified for agricultural use and large predators (wolves and panthers) were eliminated, the white-tailed deer population rebounded. In fact, many regions consider the animals an agricultural or suburban nuisance and have had variable success in controlling the deer population.

Worldwide, temperate deciduous forest was among the first biomes to be converted to agricultural use. In Europe and Asia, many soils that originally supported temperate deciduous forest have been cultivated by traditional agricultural methods for thousands of years without a substantial loss in fertility. During the 20th century, however, intensive agricultural practices were adopted; along with overgrazing and deforestation, these methods have contributed to the degradation of some agricultural lands.

Temperate grasslands occur in areas of moderate precipitation

Summers are hot, winters are cold, fires help shape the landscape, and rainfall is often uncertain in **temperate grasslands.** Annual precipitation averages 25 to 75 cm (10 to 30 in.). In grasslands with less precipitation, minerals tend to accumulate in a marked layer just below the topsoil. These minerals tend to leach out of the soil in areas with more precipitation. Grassland soil contains considerable organic material because surface parts of many grasses die off each winter and contribute to the organic content of the soil (the roots and rhizomes survive underground). Many grasses are sod formers: their roots and rhizomes form a thick, continuous underground mat.

Moist temperate grasslands, also known as *tallgrass prairies,* occur in the United States in Iowa, western Minnesota, eastern Nebraska, and parts of other midwestern states and across Canada's prairie provinces. Although few trees grow except

Figure 56-6 Temperate grassland
The Nature Conservancy owns this tallgrass prairie preserve in Oklahoma. Like other moist temperate grasslands, it is mostly treeless but contains a profusion of grasses and other herbaceous flowering plants. As bison graze on the plants, they affect community structure and diversity.

native grasses, reducing the amount of food available for grazing animals. Fires in such altered ecosystems are more catastrophic, and the deep roots of these invasive plants tap into water, altering the area's hydrology. Scientists are studying why this change is occurring. Many think that climate change, increased droughts, overgrazing, and fire suppression all play a role.

Chaparral is a thicket of evergreen shrubs and small trees

Some hilly temperate environments have mild winters with abundant rainfall combined with extremely dry summers. Such Mediterranean climates, as they are called, occur not only in the area around the Mediterranean Sea, but also in California, Western Australia, portions of Chile, and South Africa. In southern California this environment is called **chaparral.** This vegetation type is also known as maquis in the Mediterranean region, mallee scrub in Australia, matorral in Chile, and Cape scrub in Africa. Chaparral soil is thin and infertile. Frequent fires occur naturally in this environment, particularly in late summer and autumn.

Chaparral vegetation looks strikingly similar in different areas of the world, even though the individual species are quite different. A dense growth of evergreen shrubs, often of drought-resistant pine or scrub oak trees, dominates chaparral (**FIG. 56-7**). During the rainy winter season the landscape may be lush and green, but during the hot, dry summer, the plants lie dormant. Trees and shrubs often have hard, small, leathery leaves that resist water loss. Many plants are also fire-adapted and grow best in the months following a fire. Such growth is possible because fire releases minerals that were tied up in the plants that burned. With the new availability of essential minerals, plants sprout vigorously during winter rains. Mule deer, wood rats, brush rabbits, skinks and other lizards, and many species of birds (such as Anna's hummingbird, scrub jay, and bushtit) are common animals of the chaparral.

Fires, which occur at irregular intervals in California chaparral vegetation, often consume expensive homes built on the hilly chaparral landscape. Unfortunately, efforts to control naturally occurring fires sometimes backfire. Denser, thicker vegetation tends to accumulate when periodic fires are prevented; then, when a fire does occur, it is much more severe. Removing the chaparral vegetation, whose roots hold the soil in place, also causes problems; witness the mud slides that sometimes occur during winter rains in these areas.

near rivers and streams, grasses, some as tall as 2 m (6.5 ft), grow in great profusion in the deep, rich soil (**FIG. 56-6**). Before most of this area was converted to arable land, it was covered with herds of grazing animals, particularly bison. The principal predators were wolves, although in sparser, drier areas, coyotes took their place. Smaller fauna included prairie dogs and their predators (foxes, black-footed ferrets, and birds of prey such as prairie falcons), western meadowlarks, bobolinks, reptiles (such as gopher snakes and short-horned lizards), and great numbers of insects.

Shortgrass prairies, in which the dominant grasses are less than 0.5 m (1.6 ft) tall, are temperate grasslands that receive less precipitation than the moister grasslands just described but more precipitation than deserts. In the United States, shortgrass prairies occur in the eastern half of Montana, the western half of South Dakota, and parts of other midwestern states; they also appear in western Alberta in Canada. The plants grow in less abundance than in the moister grasslands, and occasionally some bare soil is exposed.

The North American grassland, particularly the tallgrass prairie, was so well suited to agriculture that little of it remains. More than 90% has vanished under the plow, and the remainder is so fragmented that almost nowhere can we see even an approximation of what European settlers saw when they settled in the Midwest. Today, the tallgrass prairie is considered North America's rarest biome.

In recent decades, woody shrubs and small trees such as juniper have invaded many of the world's grasslands in North and South America, Africa, and Australia. These plants displace

Harvey Payne

Figure 56-7 Chaparral

Chaparral, which consists primarily of drought-resistant evergreen shrubs and small trees, develops where hot, dry summers alternate with mild, rainy winters. Photographed in northwest Arizona.

Deserts are arid ecosystems

Deserts are dry areas found in temperate (*cold deserts*) and subtropical or tropical regions (*warm deserts*). North America has four distinct deserts. The Great Basin Desert in Nevada, Utah, and neighboring states is a cold desert dominated by sagebrush. The Mojave Desert in Nevada and California is a warm desert known for its Joshua trees (a type of yucca with an erect, woody stem). The Chihuahuan Desert, home of century plants (agaves; see Fig. 53-7), is a warm desert found in Texas, New Mexico, and Mexico. The warm Sonoran Desert, with its many species of cacti, is found in Arizona, California, and Mexico (**FIG. 56-8**).

The low water-vapor content of the desert atmosphere leads to daily temperature extremes of heat and cold, so a major change in temperature occurs in each 24-hour period. Deserts vary greatly depending on the amount of precipitation they receive, which is generally less than 25 cm (10 in.) per year. A few deserts are so dry that virtually no plant life occurs in them. As a result of sparse vegetation, desert soil is low in organic material but often high in mineral content, particularly the salts NaCl, $CaCO_3$, and $CaSO_4$.

Desert vegetation includes both perennials (cacti, yuccas, Joshua trees, and sagebrushes) and, after a rain, flowering annuals. Desert plants tend to have reduced leaves or no leaves, an adaptation that conserves water. In cacti such as the giant saguaro, for example, the stem carries out photosynthesis and also expands accordion-style to store water; the leaves are modified into spines, which discourage herbivores. Other desert plants shed their leaves for most of the year, growing only during the brief moist season.

Desert animals tend to be small. During the heat of the day, they remain under cover or return to shelter periodically, whereas at night they come out to forage or hunt. In addition to desert-adapted insects, there are many specialized desert reptiles (such as desert iguanas, desert tortoises, and rattlesnakes) and a few desert-adapted amphibians

Figure 56-8 Desert

Summer rainfall characterizes the warmer deserts of North America, such as the Sonoran Desert shown here. The Sonoran Desert contains many species of cacti, including the large, treelike saguaro (*Carnegiea gigantea*), which grows 15 to 18 m (50 to 60 ft) tall. Photographed in Arizona.

(such as western spadefoot toads). Mammals include such rodents as the American kangaroo rat, which does not need to drink water but subsists solely on the water content of its food (primarily seeds and insects). American deserts are also home to jackrabbits, and kangaroos live in Australian deserts. Carnivores such as the African fennec fox and some birds of prey, especially owls, live on rodents and rabbits. During the driest months of the year, many desert insects, amphibians, reptiles, and mammals tunnel underground, where they remain inactive; this period of dormancy is known as *estivation.*

Humans have altered North American deserts in several ways. Off-road vehicles damage desert vegetation, which sometimes takes years to recover. When the top layer of desert soil is disturbed, erosion occurs more readily than when the soil is undamaged, and less vegetation grows to support native animals. Another problem is that certain cacti and desert tortoises have become rare as a result of poaching. Houses, factories, and farms built in desert areas require vast quantities of water, which must be imported from distant areas. Irrigation of desert soils often causes them to become salty and unfit for crops or native vegetation. Increased groundwater consumption by many desert cities has caused groundwater levels to drop. Aquifer depletion in U.S. deserts is particularly critical in central and southern Arizona and southwestern New Mexico and is an increasing concern in southern California, Nevada, and Utah.

Savanna is a tropical grassland with scattered trees

The **savanna** biome is a tropical grassland with widely scattered clumps of low trees (FIG. 56-9). Savanna is found in areas of relatively low or seasonal rainfall with prolonged dry periods. Temperatures in savannas vary little throughout the year, and precipitation, not temperature (as in temperate grasslands), regulates seasons. Annual precipitation is 85 to 150 cm (34 to 60 in.). Savanna soil is low in essential minerals, in part because it is strongly leached. Savanna soil is often rich in aluminum, which resists leaching, and in places the aluminum reaches levels that are toxic to many plants. Although the African savanna is best known, savanna also occurs in South America and northern Australia.

Wide expanses of grasses interrupted by occasional trees characterize savanna. Trees such as *Acacia* bristle with thorns that provide protection against herbivores. Both trees and grasses have fire-adapted features, such as extensive underground root systems, that enable them to survive seasonal droughts as well as periodic fires that sweep through the savanna.

The world's greatest assemblage of hoofed mammals occurs in the African savanna. Here live great herds of herbivores, including wildebeests, antelopes, giraffes, zebras, and elephants. Large predators, such as lions and hyenas, kill and scavenge the herds. In areas of seasonally varying rainfall, the herds and their predators may migrate annually.

Savanna is rapidly being fragmented and converted to range-land for cattle and other domesticated animals, which are replacing the big herds of wild animals. The problem is particularly acute in Africa, which has the most rapidly growing human population of any continent. In some places severe overgrazing by domestic animals has contributed to the conversion of marginal savanna into desert, a process known as **desertification.** In desertification the reduced grass cover caused by overgrazing allows wind and water to erode the soil; erosion removes the topsoil and decreases the soil's ability to support crops or livestock. Desertification has also become a serious problem in South America, Mexico, and the Caribbean due to overgrazing, farming, and drought. (Desertification is not restricted to savanna. Temperate grasslands and tropical dry forests can also be degraded to desert.)

There are two basic types of tropical forests

There are many kinds of tropical forests, but ecologists generally classify them as one of two types: tropical dry forests or tropical rain forests. **Tropical dry forests** occur in regions with a wet season and a dry season (usually two to three months each year). Annual precipitation is 150 to 200 cm (60 to 80 in.). During the dry season, many tropical trees shed their leaves and remain dormant, much as temperate trees do during the winter. India, Brazil, Thailand, and Mexico are some of the countries

Figure 56-9 Savanna
In this photograph of African savanna in Tanzania, the smaller animals in the foreground are Thomson's gazelles (*Gazella thomsonii*), and the larger ones near the trees are wildebeests (*Connochaetes taurinus*).

Carlyn Iverson

that have tropical dry forests. Tropical dry forests intergrade with savanna on their dry edges and with tropical rain forests on their wet edges. Logging and overgrazing by domestic animals have fragmented and degraded many tropical dry forests.

The annual precipitation of **tropical rain forests** is 200 to 450 cm (80 to 180 in.). Much of this precipitation, which occurs almost daily, comes from locally recycled water that enters the atmosphere by transpiration from the forest's own trees. Tropical rain forests are often located in areas with ancient, highly weathered, mineral-poor soil. Little organic matter accumulates in such soils. Because temperatures are high and soil moisture is abundant year-round, decay organisms and detritus-feeding ants and termites decompose organic litter quite rapidly. Vast networks of roots and mycorrhizae quickly absorb minerals from decomposing materials. Thus, minerals of tropical rain forests are tied up in the vegetation rather than in the soil.

Tropical rain forests are found in Central and South America, Africa, and Southeast Asia. A tropical rain forest is very productive despite the scarcity of minerals in the soil. Its plants, stimulated by abundant solar energy and precipitation, capture considerable energy by photosynthesis. Of all the biomes, the tropical rain forest is unrivaled in species richness.

Most trees of tropical rain forests are evergreen flowering plants. A fully developed rain forest has several distinct stories of vegetation (**FIG. 56-10**). The topmost story, called the *emergent layer*, consists of the crowns of the oldest, tallest trees, some 40 m (130 ft) or more in height; these trees are exposed to direct sunlight and are subject to the warmest temperatures, lowest humidities, and strongest winds. The next story, the *canopy*, reaches a height of 30 to 35 m (100 to 115 ft) and lets in little sunlight for the support of the sparse *understory*, shrub layer, and ground layer, all of which consist of smaller plants specialized for life in the shade as well as seedlings of taller trees. Vegetation of tropical rain forests is generally not dense at ground level except near stream banks or where a fallen tree has opened the canopy.

Tropical rainforest trees support extensive epiphytic communities of smaller plants such as orchids and bromeliads. Although epiphytes grow in crotches of branches, on bark, or even on the leaves of their hosts, most use their host trees only for physical support, not for nourishment.

Figure 56-10 Tropical rain forest

Tropical rainforest vegetation is stratified. Except at river banks, tropical rain forest has a closed canopy that admits little light to the forest floor. The animals highlighted in this figure occupy a variety of ecological niches in the rain forest. (Adapted from Miller, G. T. and Spoolman, S. E. *Living in the Environment,* 17th ed. Cengage/Brooks Cole, Belmont, CA, 2012, p. 162, Figure 7-15.)

Because little light penetrates to the understory, many plants living there are adapted to climb already-established host trees. Lianas (woody tropical vines), some as thick as a human thigh, twist up through the branches of tropical rainforest trees. Once in the canopy, lianas grow from the upper branches of one tree to another, connecting the tops of the trees and providing a walkway for many of the canopy's residents.

Not counting bacteria and other soil-dwelling organisms, about 90% of tropical rainforest organisms live in the middle and upper canopies. Rainforest animals include the most abundant and varied insect, reptile, and amphibian fauna on Earth. Birds, too, are diverse, with some specialized to consume fruits (such as parrots), some to consume nectar (such as hummingbirds and sunbirds), and others to consume insects. Most rainforest mammals, such as sloths and monkeys, live only in the trees and never climb down to the ground. Some large ground-dwelling mammals, including elephants, are also found in tropical rain forests.

Unless strong conservation measures are initiated soon, human population growth and agricultural and industrial expansion in tropical countries may spell the end of tropical rain forests by the early 22nd century. Many rainforest species may become extinct before they are even identified and scientifically described. (Tropical rainforest destruction is discussed in detail in Chapter 57.)

To review, examine FIGURE 56-11, which shows the geographic distribution of the world's biomes.

CHECKPOINT 56.1

- CONNECT *What climate and soil factors produce the major biomes?*
- CONNECT *What representative organisms are found in each of these forest biomes: boreal forest, temperate deciduous forest, temperate rain forest, and tropical rain forest?*
- CONNECT *In which biome do you live? Does it match the description given in this text? If not, explain the discrepancy.*
- CONNECT *How does tundra compare to desert? How does temperate grassland compare to savanna?*

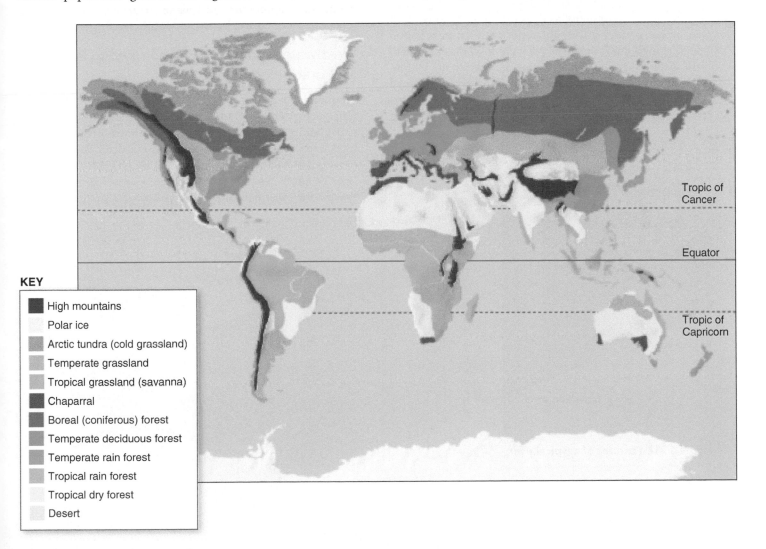

KEY

■ High mountains
■ Polar ice
■ Arctic tundra (cold grassland)
■ Temperate grassland
■ Tropical grassland (savanna)
■ Chaparral
■ Boreal (coniferous) forest
■ Temperate deciduous forest
■ Temperate rain forest
■ Tropical rain forest
■ Tropical dry forest
■ Desert

Tropic of Cancer

Equator

Tropic of Capricorn

Figure 56-11 The world's major biomes
This simplified diagram shows sharp boundaries between biomes. Biomes actually intergrade at their boundaries, sometimes over large areas. Note that mountains are keyed separately because they have variable vegetation. (Adapted from Miller, G. T. and Spoolman, S. E. *Living in the Environment,* 17th ed. Cengage/Brooks Cole, Belmont, CA, 2012, p. 153, Figure 7-7.)

56.2 AQUATIC ECOSYSTEMS

Aquatic "biomes" do not exist in the sense that aquatic ecologists do not distinguish aquatic ecosystems based on the dominant form of vegetation. Aquatic ecosystems are classified primarily on abiotic factors, such as salinity, that help determine an aquatic life zone's boundaries. **Salinity,** the concentration of dissolved salts in a body of water, affects the kinds of organisms present in aquatic ecosystems, as does the amount of dissolved oxygen. Because water greatly interferes with the penetration of light, floating aquatic organisms that photosynthesize remain near the water's surface, and vegetation attached to the bottom grows only in shallow water. In addition, low levels of essential minerals often limit the number and distribution of organisms in certain aquatic environments. Other abiotic determinants of species composition in aquatic ecosystems include water depth, temperature, pH, and presence or absence of waves and currents.

Aquatic ecosystems contain three main ecological categories of organisms: free-floating plankton, strongly swimming nekton, and bottom-dwelling benthos. **Plankton** are usually small or microscopic organisms that are relatively feeble swimmers. For the most part, they are carried about at the mercy of currents and waves. They are unable to swim far horizontally, but some species are capable of large vertical migrations and are found at different depths of water at different times of the day or at different seasons. Plankton are generally subdivided into two major categories: phytoplankton and zooplankton. **Phytoplankton** (photosynthetic cyanobacteria and free-floating algae) are producers that form the base of most aquatic food webs. **Zooplankton** are nonphotosynthetic organisms that include protozoa, tiny crustaceans, and the larval stages of many animals. **Nekton** are larger, actively swimming organisms such as fishes, turtles, and whales. **Benthos** are bottom-dwelling organisms that fix themselves to one spot (sponges, oysters, and barnacles), burrow into the sand (many worms and echinoderms), or walk or swim about on the bottom (crayfish, aquatic insect larvae, and brittle stars).

Freshwater ecosystems are linked to land and marine ecosystems

Freshwater ecosystems include streams and rivers (flowing-water ecosystems), ponds and lakes (standing-water ecosystems), and marshes and swamps (freshwater wetlands). Each type of freshwater ecosystem has its own specific abiotic conditions and characteristic organisms. Although freshwater ecosystems occupy a relatively small portion—about 2%—of Earth's surface, they are important in the hydrologic cycle because they

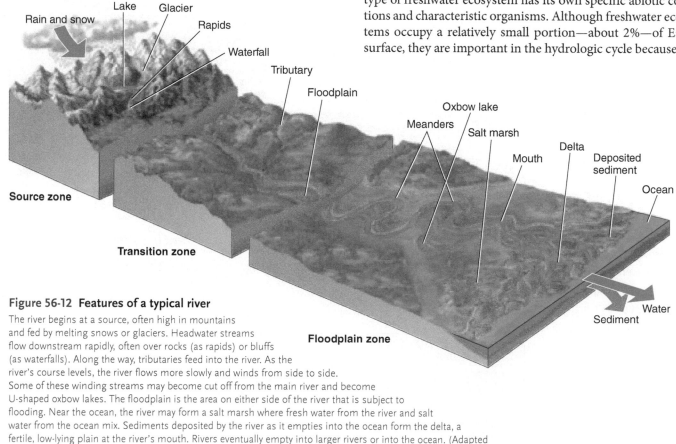

Figure 56-12 Features of a typical river

The river begins at a source, often high in mountains and fed by melting snows or glaciers. Headwater streams flow downstream rapidly, often over rocks (as rapids) or bluffs (as waterfalls). Along the way, tributaries feed into the river. As the river's course levels, the river flows more slowly and winds from side to side. Some of these winding streams may become cut off from the main river and become U-shaped oxbow lakes. The floodplain is the area on either side of the river that is subject to flooding. Near the ocean, the river may form a salt marsh where fresh water from the river and salt water from the ocean mix. Sediments deposited by the river as it empties into the ocean form the delta, a fertile, low-lying plain at the river's mouth. Rivers eventually empty into larger rivers or into the ocean. (Adapted from Miller, G. T. and Spoolman, S. E. *Living in the Environment,* 17th ed. Cengage/Brooks Cole, Belmont, CA, 2012, p. 183, Figure 8-18.)

assist in recycling precipitation that flows as surface runoff to the ocean (see discussion of hydrologic cycle in Chapter 55). Freshwater habitats also provide homes for many species.

Streams and rivers are flowing-water ecosystems Many different conditions exist along the length of a stream or river (**FIG. 56-12**). The nature of a **flowing-water ecosystem** changes greatly from its source (where it begins) to its mouth (where it empties into another body of water). Headwater streams (small streams that are the sources of a river) are usually shallow, clear, cold, swiftly flowing, and highly oxygenated. In contrast, rivers downstream from the headwaters are wider and deeper, cloudy (i.e., they contain suspended particulates), not as cold, slower flowing, and less oxygenated than headwater streams. Surrounding forest may shade certain parts of the stream or river, whereas other parts may be exposed to direct sunlight. Along parts of a stream or river, groundwater wells up through sediments on the bottom. This local input of water moderates the water temperature so that summer temperatures are cooler and winter temperatures are warmer than in adjacent parts of the flowing-water ecosystem.

The kinds of organisms in flowing-water ecosystems vary greatly from one stream to another, depending primarily on the strength of the current. In streams with fast currents, inhabitants have adaptations such as suckers to attach themselves to rocks so that they are not swept away. The larvae of blackflies, for example, attach themselves with suction discs located on the ends of their abdomens. Some stream inhabitants, such as immature water-penny beetles, have flattened bodies that

enable them to slip under or between rocks. The water-penny beetle larva gets its common name from its flattened, nearly circular shape. Alternatively, inhabitants such as the brown trout are streamlined and muscular enough to swim in the current.

Streams and rivers depend on land for much of their energy. In headwater streams up to 99% of the energy input comes from detritus (dead organic material such as leaves) carried from the land into streams and rivers by wind or surface runoff. Downstream, rivers contain more producers and therefore depend slightly less on detritus as a source of energy than do the headwaters.

Human activities have several adverse effects on rivers and streams, including water pollution and the impacts of dams built to contain the water of rivers or streams. Pollution, such as sewage and fertilizer runoff, alters the physical environment of a flowing-water ecosystem and changes the biotic component downstream from the pollution source. Dams change the nature of flowing-water ecosystems, both upstream and downstream from the dam location. A dam causes water to back up, resulting in flooding of large areas of land and formation of a reservoir, which destroys terrestrial habitat. Below the dam, the once-powerful river is reduced to a relative trickle, so the flowing-water ecosystem is altered.

Ponds and lakes are standing-water ecosystems Zonation characterizes **standing-water ecosystems.** A large lake has four basic zones: the littoral, limnetic, profundal, and benthic zones (**FIG. 56-13**). Smaller lakes and ponds typically lack a profundal zone.

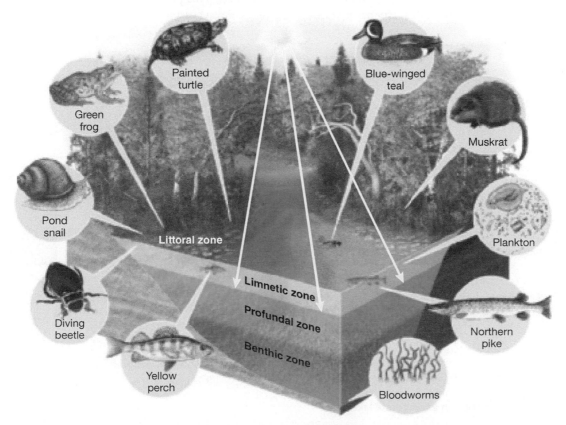

Figure 56-13 *Animation* **Zonation in a large, deep, temperate lake**
A lake is a standing-water ecosystem surrounded by land. A large lake has littoral, limnetic, profundal, and benthic zones. (Adapted from Miller, G. T. and Spoolman, S. E. *Living in the Environment*, 17th ed. Cengage/Brooks Cole, Belmont, CA, 2012, p. 182, Figure 8-16.)

The **littoral zone** is a shallow-water area along the shore of a lake or pond. It includes rooted, emergent vegetation, such as cattails and bur-reeds (flowering wetland plants), plus several deeper-dwelling aquatic plants and algae. The littoral zone is the most productive zone of the lake. Photosynthesis is greatest in the littoral zone, in part because light is abundant and because the littoral zone receives nutrient inputs from surrounding land that stimulate the growth of plants and algae. In addition, ponds and lakes—like streams and rivers—depend on detritus carried from the land for much of their energy. Animals of the littoral zone include frogs and their tadpoles, turtles, worms, crayfish and other crustaceans, insect larvae, and many fishes such as perch, carp, and bass. Surface dwellers, such as water striders and whirligig beetles, are found in the quieter areas.

The **limnetic zone** is the open water beyond the littoral zone, that is, away from the shore; it extends down as far as sunlight penetrates to permit photosynthesis. The main organisms of the limnetic zone are microscopic phytoplankton and zooplankton. Larger fishes also spend some of their time in the limnetic zone, although they may visit the littoral zone to feed and reproduce. Because of the depth of this zone, less vegetation grows in the limnetic zone than in the littoral zone.

Beneath the limnetic zone of a large lake is the **profundal zone.** Because light does not penetrate effectively to this depth, plants and algae do not live in this zone. Food drifts into the profundal zone from the littoral and limnetic zones. Bacteria and archaea decompose dead plants and animals that reach the profundal zone, thus liberating minerals. These minerals are not effectively recycled because no photosynthetic organisms

are present to absorb them and incorporate them into the food web. As a result, the profundal zone tends to be both mineral rich and anaerobic (oxygen deficient), with few organisms other than anaerobic bacteria and archaea occupying it.

The **benthic zone** is the bottom layer of the lake. Decomposers, detritus feeders, and some fish live here. These organisms depend mainly on organic matter that drifts down from the upper zones.

Thermal stratification in temperate lakes The marked layering of large temperate lakes caused by light penetration is accentuated by **thermal stratification,** in which the temperature changes sharply with depth (FIG. 56-14a). Thermal stratification occurs because the summer sunlight penetrates and warms surface water, making it less dense. (Recall from Chapter 2 that the density of water is greatest at 4°C; both above and below this temperature, water is less dense.) In summer, cool (and therefore *more* dense) water remains at the lake bottom and is separated from warm (and therefore *less* dense) water above by an abrupt temperature transition called the **thermocline.** Seasonal distribution of temperature and oxygen (more oxygen dissolves in water at cooler temperatures) affects the distribution of fish in the lake.

In temperate lakes falling temperatures in autumn cause a mixing of the lake waters called the **fall turnover** (FIG. 56-14b). As surface water cools, its density increases, and it sinks and displaces the less dense, warmer, mineral-rich water beneath. Warmer water then rises to the surface where it, in turn, cools and sinks. This process of cooling and sinking continues until the lake reaches a uniform temperature throughout.

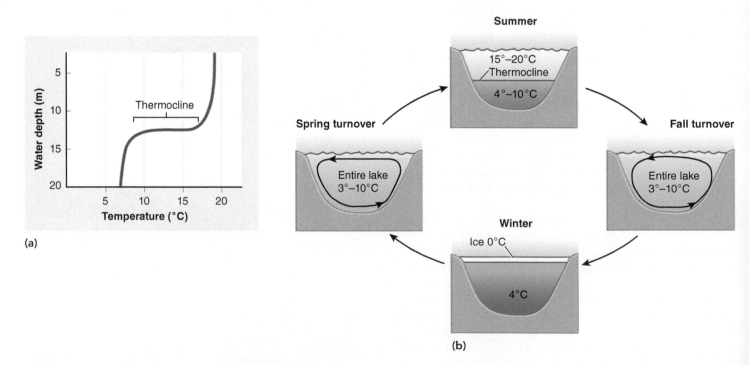

(a)

(b)

Figure 56-14 Thermal stratification in a temperate lake

(a) Temperature varies at different depths during the summer. There is an abrupt temperature transition, the thermocline. **(b)** During fall and spring turnovers, a mixing of upper and lower layers of water brings oxygen to the oxygen-depleted depths of the lake and minerals to the mineral-deficient surface waters.
© Cengage Learning

In winter, surface water cools to below 4°C, its temperature of greatest density. Ice, which forms at 0°C, is less dense than cold water. Thus, ice forms on the surface, and the water on the lake bottom is warmer than the ice on the surface. In spring, a **spring turnover** occurs as ice melts and surface water reaches 4°C. Surface water again sinks to the bottom, and bottom water returns to the surface. As summer arrives, thermal stratification occurs once again.

The mixing of deeper, nutrient-rich water with surface, nutrient-poor water during the fall and spring turnovers brings essential minerals to the surface and oxygenated water to the bottom. The sudden presence of large amounts of essential minerals in surface waters encourages the development of large algal and cyanobacterial populations, which may form temporary **blooms** in the fall and spring.

Increased nutrients and algal growth The presence of high levels of plant and algal nutrients such as nitrogen and phosphorus causes *enrichment,* the fertilization of a body of water. Excess amounts of these nutrients enter waterways from sewage and from fertilizer runoff from lawns and fields. The water in an enriched pond or lake is cloudy because of the vast numbers of algae and cyanobacteria that the nutrients support.

The species composition is different in enriched and unenriched lakes. For example, an unenriched lake in the northeastern United States may contain pike, sturgeon, and whitefish in the deeper, colder part of the lake where there is a higher concentration of dissolved oxygen. In contrast, the deeper, colder levels of water in enriched lakes are depleted of dissolved oxygen because of the greater amount of decomposition on the lake floor. Fishes such as pike, sturgeon, and whitefish die out, and fishes such as catfish and carp, which tolerate lower concentrations of dissolved oxygen, replace them.

Enrichment is reversible and has declined in North America since the 1970s because legislation limits the phosphate content of detergents and because better sewage treatment plants have been constructed. Agriculture is the leading source of water-quality impairment of U.S. surface waters today. Major causes of enrichment problems in waterways include fertilizer runoff, animal wastes, and sewage plant residues. States and communities continue to improve storm water management practices, and many have passed laws to ban phosphate fertilizers.

Freshwater wetlands are transitional between aquatic and terrestrial ecosystems **Freshwater wetlands,** which are usually covered by shallow water for at least part of the year, have characteristic soils and water-tolerant vegetation. They include marshes, dominated by grasslike plants, and swamps, in which woody trees or shrubs dominate (**FIG. 56-15**). Freshwater wetlands also include hardwood bottomland forests (lowlands along streams and rivers that are periodically flooded), prairie potholes (small, shallow ponds that formed when glacial ice melted at the end of the last Ice Age), and peat moss bogs (peat-accumulating wetlands where sphagnum moss dominates).

Wetlands are valued as a wildlife habitat for migratory waterfowl and many other bird species, beavers, otters, muskrats, and game fishes. Wetlands are holding areas for excess water when rivers flood their banks. The floodwater stored in wetlands then drains slowly back into the rivers, providing a steady flow of water throughout the year. Wetlands also serve as groundwater recharging areas. One of their most important roles is to trap and hold pollutants in the flooded soil, thereby cleansing and purifying the water. Such important environmental functions as these are known as **ecosystem services.**

Wetlands were once considered wastelands, areas to be filled in or drained so that farms, housing developments, and industrial plants could be built on them. Wetlands are also breeding places for mosquitoes and therefore were viewed as a menace to public health. The crucial ecosystem services that wetlands provide are widely recognized today, and wetlands have some legal protection. Despite this recognition of their value, agriculture, pollution, engineering (dams), and urban and suburban development continue to threaten wetlands.

Estuaries occur where fresh water and salt water meet

Where the ocean meets the land, there may be one of several kinds of ecosystems: a rocky shore, a sandy beach, an intertidal mudflat, or a tidal estuary. An **estuary** is a coastal body of water, partly surrounded by land, with access to the open ocean and a large supply of fresh water from rivers. Water levels in an estuary rise and fall with the tides, and salinity fluctuates with tidal cycles, the time of year, and precipitation. Salinity also changes gradually within the estuary, from fresh water at the river entrance to salty ocean water at the mouth of the estuary. Because estuaries undergo marked daily, seasonal, and annual variations in temperature, salinity, and other physical properties, estuarine organisms have a wide tolerance to such changes.

Figure 56-15 Freshwater swamp

Trees, such as bald cypress (*shown*), dominate freshwater swamps. In this wetland, photographed in northeastern Texas, a floating carpet of tiny aquatic plants covers the water's surface.

Gregory J. Dimijian/Science Source

Figure 56-16 Salt marsh
Cordgrass (*Spartina alterniflora*) is the dominant vegetation in this salt marsh in Georgia.

and nurseries for commercially important fish and shellfish species, such as blue crabs, shrimp, mullet, and spotted sea trout. Mangrove branches are nesting sites for many species of birds, such as pelicans, herons, egrets, and roseate spoonbills. Mangroves are under assault from coastal development, including aquaculture facilities, and unsustainable logging. Some countries, such as the Philippines, Bangladesh, and Guinea-Bissau, have cut down more than two-thirds of their mangrove forests. In the United States, commercial developers, home builders, and some residents continue to sidestep conservation laws by destroying mangroves to provide waterfront properties with unobstructed views.

Estuaries are among the most fertile ecosystems in the world, often having much greater productivities than the adjacent ocean or freshwater river (see Table 55-1). This high productivity is the result of four factors: (1) the action of tides promotes a rapid circulation of nutrients and helps remove waste products; (2) minerals, transported from land into streams and rivers emptying into the estuary, provide nutrients; (3) the high level of light that penetrates the shallow water supports photosynthesis; and (4) the presence of many plants provides an extensive photosynthetic carpet and also mechanically traps detritus, forming the basis of detritus food webs. Most commercially important fishes and shellfish spend their larval stages in estuaries among the protective tangle of decaying stems.

Temperate estuaries usually contain **salt marshes,** shallow wetlands in which salt-tolerant grasses dominate (FIG. 56-16). Uninformed people have often considered salt marshes as worthless, empty stretches of land. As a result, people have used them as dumps, severely polluting them, or filled them with dredged bottom material to form artificial land for residential and industrial development. A large part of the estuarine environment is lost in this way, along with many of its ecosystem services, such as biological habitats, sediment and pollution trapping, groundwater supply, and storm buffering (salt marshes absorb much of the energy of a storm surge and therefore prevent flood damage elsewhere).

Mangrove forests, the tropical equivalent of salt marshes, cover perhaps 70% of tropical and subtropical coastal mudflats where tides and waves fluctuate (FIG. 56-17; Chapter 54 introduction). Like salt marshes, mangrove forests provide valuable ecosystem services. Mangrove roots stabilize the sediments, preventing coastal erosion and providing a barrier against the ocean during storms. Their interlacing roots are breeding grounds

Marine ecosystems dominate Earth's surface

Although lakes and the ocean are comparable in many ways, they have many differences. Depths of even the deepest lakes

Figure 56-17 Mangroves
Red mangroves (*Rhizophora mangle*) have stiltlike roots that support the tree. Many animals live in the complex root systems of mangrove forests. Photographed at low tide along the coast of Florida in Biscayne National Park.

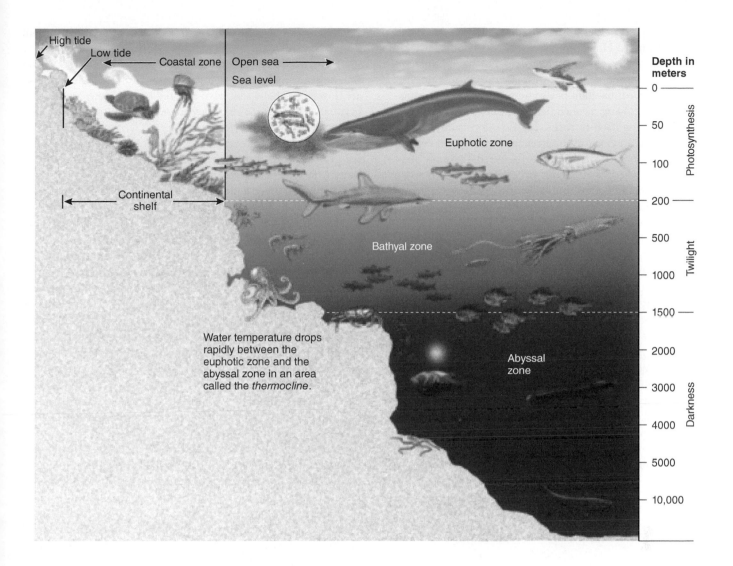

Figure 56-18 *Animation* **Vertical zones in an ocean**

The euphotic zone, the brightly lit upper region of an ocean, is inhabited by plankton and plankton-eating nekton. The bathyal zone, which receives little sunlight, does not support phytoplankton. Zooplankton and some invertebrates and fish live in the bathyal zone. The dark, cold abyssal zone is inhabited by some sponges, clams, oysters, squid, worms, and fish. Many organisms that inhabit the abyssal zone are filter feeders that depend on organic material that drifts down from the upper layers.

Note that the slopes of the ocean floor are not as steep as shown; they are exaggerated to save space. (Adapted from Miller, G. T. and Spoolman, S. E. *Living in the Environment*, 17th ed. Cengage/Brooks Cole, Belmont, CA, 2012, p. 173, Figure 8-6.)

do not approach those of the ocean, which has areas that extend more than 6 km (3.6 mi) below the sunlit surface. Tides and currents profoundly influence the ocean. Gravitational pulls of both the sun and the moon produce two tides a day throughout most areas of the ocean, but the height of those tides varies with season, local topography, and phases of the moon (full moons and new moons cause the highest tides).

The immense, complex marine environment is subdivided into several zones: the intertidal zone, the benthic (ocean floor) environment, and the pelagic (ocean water) environment (FIG. 56-18). The pelagic environment is, in turn, divided into two provinces: the neritic province and the oceanic province.

The intertidal zone is transitional between land and ocean The **intertidal zone** is the shoreline area between low tide and high tide. Although high levels of light and nutrients, together with an abundance of oxygen, make the intertidal zone a biologically productive environment, it is also a stressful one. If an intertidal beach is sandy, inhabitants must contend with a constantly shifting environment that threatens to engulf them and gives them scant protection against wave action. Consequently, most sand-dwelling organisms, such as mole crabs, are continual and active burrowers. Because they follow the tides up and down the beach, most do not have any notable adaptations to survive drying or exposure.

A rocky shore provides a fine anchorage for seaweeds and invertebrate animals. However, it is exposed to constant wave action when immersed during high tides and to drying and temperature changes when exposed to the air during low tides. A typical rocky-shore inhabitant has some way of sealing in moisture, perhaps by closing its shell, if it has one, plus a powerful means of anchoring itself to rocks. Mussels, for example, have horny, threadlike anchors, and barnacles have special cement glands. Rocky-shore intertidal algae (seaweeds) usually have thick, gummy polysaccharide coats, which dry out slowly when exposed, and flexible bodies not easily broken by wave action (**FIG. 56-19**). Some rocky-shore community inhabitants hide in burrows or crevices at low tide.

Seagrass beds, kelp forests, and coral reefs are part of the benthic environment The **benthic environment** is the ocean floor. It is divided into zones based on distance from land, light availability, and depth. The benthic environment consists of sediments (mostly sand and mud) in which many marine animals, such as worms and clams, burrow. Archaea and bacteria are common in marine sediments, and living archaea and bacteria have been found in deeply buried ocean sediments at least 800 m (2600 ft) below the ocean floor at several different sites in the Pacific Ocean.

The **abyssal zone** is that part of the benthic environment that extends from a depth of 4000 to 6000 m (2.5 to 3.7 mi). (In Chapter 55 *Inquiring About: Life without the Sun* describes some of the unusual organisms in hydrothermal vents in the abyssal zone.) The **hadal zone** is that part of the benthic environment deeper than 6000 m.

Here we describe benthic communities in shallow ocean waters: seagrass beds, kelp forests, and coral reefs. **Sea grasses** are flowering plants that have adapted to complete submersion in ocean water (**FIG. 56-20**). They are not true grasses. Sea grasses live in shallow water, to depths of 10 m (33 ft), where they receive enough light to photosynthesize efficiently. Extensive beds of sea grasses occur in quiet temperate, subtropical, and tropical waters; no sea grasses live in polar waters.

Sea grasses have a high primary productivity and are therefore ecologically important in shallow marine areas. Their roots and rhizomes stabilize the sediments, reducing surface erosion.

Sea grasses provide food and habitat for many marine organisms. In temperate waters ducks and geese eat sea grasses; in tropical waters manatees, green turtles, parrot fish, sturgeon fish, and sea urchins eat them. These herbivores consume only about 5% of the sea grasses. The remaining 95% eventually enter the detritus food web when the sea grasses die and bacteria decompose them. In turn, a variety of animals such as mud shrimp, lug worms, and mullet consume the bacteria. Seagrass beds have been severely damaged and depleted by water pollution and by boat propellers. Fortunately, many coastal communities and environmental organizations are replanting seagrass beds and educating boaters about the importance of healthy seagrass ecosystems.

Kelps, which may reach lengths of 60 m (200 ft), are the largest brown algae (see Fig. 26-11b). Kelps are common in cooler temperate marine waters of both the Northern and Southern Hemispheres. They are especially abundant in relatively shallow waters (depths of about 25 m, or 82 ft) along rocky coastlines. Kelps are photosynthetic and are therefore the primary food producers for the kelp forest ecosystem. Kelp forests also provide habitats for many marine animals. Tube worms, sponges, sea cucumbers, clams, crabs, fishes (such as tuna), and mammals

Figure 56-19 Seaweeds in a rocky intertidal zone

Sea palms (*Postelsia*), which are 50 to 75 cm (20 to 30 in.) tall, are common on the rocky Pacific coast from Vancouver Island to California. The bases of these brown algae are firmly attached to the rocky substrate, enabling them to withstand heavy surf action. Photographed at low tide.

Figure 56-20 Seagrass bed

Turtle grasses (*Thalassia*) have numerous invertebrates and algal epiphytes attached to their leaves. These shallow underwater meadows of marine flowering plants are ecologically important for shelter and food for many organisms. Photographed in the Red Sea, Egypt.

(such as sea otters) find refuge in the algal blades. Some animals eat the blades, but kelps are consumed mainly in the detritus food web. Bacteria that decompose dead kelp provide food for sponges, tunicates, worms, clams, and snails. Kelp beds support a diversity of life that almost rivals that found in coral reefs.

Coral reefs, which are built from accumulated layers of calcium carbonate ($CaCO_3$), are found in warm (temperature usually greater than 21°C), shallow sea water. The living portions of coral reefs grow in shallow waters where light penetrates. Many coral reefs are composed principally of red coralline algae that require light for photosynthesis. Coral animals also require light for the large number of symbiotic dinoflagellates, known as **zooxanthellae,** which live and photosynthesize in their tissues (see Fig. 54-12). Although species of coral without zooxanthellae exist, only those with zooxanthellae build reefs. In addition to obtaining nitrogen compounds from the zooxanthellae living inside them, coral animals capture food at night, using their stinging tentacles to paralyze small animals that drift nearby.

Coral reefs grow slowly as coral organisms build on the calcareous remains of countless organisms before them. The warm, shallow waters in which coral reefs are found are often poor in nutrients. Other factors favor high productivity, however, including the presence of symbiotic zooxanthellae, warm temperatures, and plenty of sunlight.

Coral reef ecosystems are the most diverse of all marine environments and contain hundreds or even thousands of species of fishes and invertebrates, such as giant clams, sea urchins, sea stars, sponges, brittle stars, sea fans, and shrimp (FIG. 56-21). The Great Barrier Reef, along the northeastern coast of Australia, occupies only 0.1% of the ocean's surface, but 8% of the world's fish species live there. The multitude of relationships and interactions that occur at coral reefs is comparable only to those in tropical rain forests among terrestrial ecosystems. As in the rain forest, competition is intense, particularly for light and space to grow.

In addition to providing habitat for a wide variety of marine organisms, coral reefs are ecologically important because they protect coastlines from shoreline erosion. They also provide humans with seafood, pharmaceuticals, and income from tourism and recreation. Although coral formations are important ecosystems, they are rapidly being degraded and destroyed. According to the United Nations Environment Program, 27% of the world's coral reefs are at high risk. Coral reefs of Southeast Asia, which contain the most species of all coral reefs, are the most threatened of any region.

In some areas, silt washing downstream from clear-cut inland forests has smothered reefs under a layer of sediment. Some scientists hypothesize that high salinity resulting from the diversion of fresh water to supply the growing human population is killing Florida reefs. Overfishing, pollution from sewage discharge and agricultural runoff, oil spills, boat groundings, fishing with dynamite or cyanide, hurricane damage, disease, coral bleaching, land reclamation, tourism, and the mining of corals for building material are also taking a heavy toll. (Coral reefs are also discussed in Chapter 31.)

The neritic province consists of shallow waters close to shore The **neritic province** is the open ocean that overlies the continental shelves, that is, the ocean floor from the shoreline to a depth of 200 m (650 ft). Organisms that live in the neritic province are floaters or swimmers (FIG. 56-22). The upper reaches of the neritic province make up the **euphotic zone,** which extends from the surface to a depth of approximately 100 m (325 ft). Enough light penetrates the euphotic zone to support photosynthesis.

Large numbers of phytoplankton, particularly diatoms in cooler waters and dinoflagellates in warmer waters, produce food by photosynthesis and are thus the base of food webs. Zooplankton (including tiny crustaceans; jellyfish; comb jellies; protists such as foraminiferans; and larvae of barnacles, sea urchins, worms, and crabs) feed on phytoplankton.

Plankton-eating nekton, such as herring, sardines, squid, manta rays, and baleen whales, consume zooplankton. These, in turn, become prey for carnivorous nekton such as sharks, tuna, dolphins, and toothed whales. Nekton are thought to be mostly confined to the shallower neritic waters (less than 60 m, or 195 ft, deep) because that is where their food is. However,

Figure 56-21 Coral reef organisms

A panoramic view of a coral reef in the Indian Ocean off the coast of the Maldives shows a few of the many animals that live on and around coral reefs. The fish in the foreground are blue-green damselfish (*Chromis viridis*).

Reinhard Dirscherl/Getty Images

Figure 56-22 Fish in the open ocean

Rough triggerfish (*Canthidermis maculatus*) are tropical fish usually found in the open ocean to depths of 92 m (300 ft). Sometimes they spend time on deep rocky slopes. Photographed in the Pacific Ocean near Hawaii.

tentacles. Fishes of the oceanic province are strikingly adapted to darkness and food scarcity. For example, the gulper eel's huge jaws enable it to swallow large prey (**FIG. 56-23**). (An organism that encounters food infrequently needs to eat as much as possible when it has the chance.) The lizardfish has strong pelvic fins that stabilize it in deep underwater currents. The many, long, folding teeth in its jaw and on its tongue maintain a tight hold on its prey. Many animals of the oceanic province have illuminated organs that enable them to see one another to mate or to capture food. Adapted to drifting or slow swimming, these fishes often have reduced bone and muscle mass.

not much is known about the behavior and migration patterns of marine nekton. Many fishes appear to be wide-ranging. For example, an individual fish tagged on one side of an ocean may be recaptured on the other side a few months later. Whether the fish traveled alone or in a school is not known at this time.

The oceanic province makes up most of the ocean The average depth of the world's ocean is 4000 m (2.4 mi). The **oceanic province** is that part of the open ocean that covers the deep-ocean basin, that is, the ocean floor at depths more than 200 m (650 ft). It is the largest marine environment and contains about 75% of the ocean's water. Cold temperatures, high hydrostatic pressure, and absence of sunlight characterize the oceanic province. These environmental conditions are uniform throughout the year.

Most organisms of the oceanic province depend on **marine snow**, organic debris that drifts down into the unlit **aphotic region** from the upper, lighted regions. Organisms of this little-known realm are filter-feeders, scavengers, or predators. Many are invertebrates, some of which attain great sizes. The giant squid, for example, measures up to 18 m (59 ft) in length, including its

Human activities are harming the ocean Because the ocean is so vast, many individuals have difficulty realizing how seriously human activities negatively impact and harm it. Development of resorts, cities, industries, transportation, and agriculture along coasts alters or destroys many coastal ecosystems, including mangrove forests, salt marshes, seagrass beds, and coral reefs. Coastal and marine ecosystems receive pollution from land, from rivers emptying into the ocean, and from

Figure 56-23 Gulper eel from the oceanic province

The gulper eel (*Saccopharynx lavenbergi*) uses its "trap-door" jaws to swallow prey as large as itself. The tail, of which only a small portion is shown, makes up most of the length of a gulper eel's body. Gulper eels grow to 1.8 m (6 ft). Shown is a live specimen, photographed in an aquarium aboard ship after being captured at a depth of 1500 m (4921 ft) off southern California.

atmospheric contaminants that enter the ocean via precipitation. Disease-causing viruses and bacteria from human sewage contaminate shellfish and other seafood and sometimes threaten public health. Millions of tons of trash, including plastic, fishing nets, and packaging materials, end up in coastal and marine ecosystems; some of this trash entangles and kills marine organisms.

Less visible ocean contaminants, including fertilizers, pesticides, heavy metals, pharmaceuticals, and synthetic chemicals from agriculture and industry, continue to be detected in increasing amounts. Coastal dead zones, caused by runoff of fertilizers and burning fossil fuels, have been reported in more than 400 locations. These dead zones have severely depleted dissolved oxygen levels in bottom waters.

Offshore mining and oil drilling pollute the neritic province with oil and other contaminants. Millions of ships dump oily ballast and other wastes overboard in the neritic and oceanic provinces. Fishing is highly mechanized, and new technologies can remove every single fish in a targeted area of the ocean. Scallop dredges and shrimp trawls are dragged across the benthic environment, destroying entire communities with a single swipe. Most countries recognize the importance of the ocean to life on this planet, but few have the resources or programs to protect and manage the ocean effectively.

CHECKPOINT 56.2

- **PREDICT** *Imagine that the ocean plankton suddenly disappeared. What effect would that have on the nekton and benthos?*

- **CONNECT** *What environmental factors are most important in determining the adaptations of organisms that live in aquatic environments?*

- *How do you distinguish between freshwater wetlands and estuaries? between flowing-water and standing-water ecosystems?*

- **CONNECT** *Compare and contrast the four main marine environments.*

- **CONNECT** *Which aquatic ecosystem is often compared to tropical rain forests? Why?*

56.3 ECOTONES

LEARNING OBJECTIVE

7 Define *ecotone* and describe some of its features.

We have discussed the various terrestrial biomes and aquatic ecosystems as if they were distinct and separate entities, but within landscapes, ecosystems intergrade with one another at their boundaries. The transition zone where two communities or biomes meet and intergrade is called an **ecotone** (see Chapter 54). Ecotones range in size from quite small, such as the area where an agricultural field meets a woodland or where a stream flows through a forest, to continental in scope. For example, at the

border between tundra and boreal forest, an extensive ecotone exists that consists of tundra vegetation interspersed with small, scattered conifers. Such ecotones provide habitat diversity. In fact, often a greater variety and density of organisms populate ecotones than live in either adjacent ecosystem (**FIG. 56-24**).

Ecologists who study ecotones look for adaptations that enable organisms to survive there. They also examine the relationship between species richness and ecotones and how

---

KEY EXPERIMENT

Does species richness vary among ecotones and their adjoining communities?

HYPOTHESIS: Ecotones have greater species richness than the communities they connect.

EXPERIMENT: Plant species were sampled for two communities in southwestern Oregon and for the ecotone between them. The communities, one with nonserpentine soil and one with serpentine soil, are defined largely by soil conditions. Nonserpentine soils (samples 1 to 10) are "normal" soils. Serpentine soils (samples 18 to 28) contain high levels of elements such as chromium, nickel, and magnesium that are toxic to many plants.

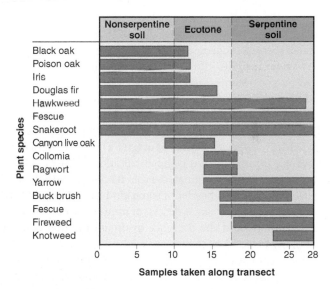

RESULTS AND CONCLUSION: The various plant species found in the two communities (*yellow* and *blue*) and in the ecotone between them (*green*) are shown in the graph. The ecotone had a greater richness than either adjoining community.

SOURCE: Modified from White, C. D. "Vegetation-Soil Chemistry Correlations in Serpentine Ecosystems." Ph.D. dissertation, University of Oregon, Eugene, 1971. Reprinted with permission of Dr. Charles D. White.

Figure 56-24 Ecotones and species richness
Note that the two fescues in the figure are different species.

CONNECT Why were fireweed and knotweed samples not found in the ecotone area?

ecotones change over time. Long-term, or longitudinal, studies of ecotones have revealed they are far from static. The ecotone boundary between desert and semiarid grassland in southern New Mexico, for example, has moved since the 1950s as the desert ecosystem has continued its expansion into the grassland.

CHECKPOINT 56.3

● *What habitat feature is characteristic of an ecotone?*

56.4 BIOGEOGRAPHY

LEARNING OBJECTIVE

8   Define *biogeography* and briefly describe Wallace's biogeographic realms.

The study of the geographic distribution of plants and animals is called **biogeography** (see Chapter 18). Biogeographers search for patterns in geographic distribution and try to explain how such patterns arose, including where populations originated, how they spread, and when. Biogeographers recognize that geologic and climate changes such as mountain building, continental drift (encompassed in the theory of *plate tectonics,* which describes the continents as moving plates floating on Earth's mantle), and periods of extensive glaciation influence the distribution of species. Biogeography is linked to evolutionary history and provides insights into how organisms may have interacted in ancient ecosystems. Studying biogeography helps us understand the continuum between ancient and modern ecosystems.

One tenet of biogeography is that each species originated only once. The particular place where such origination occurred is known as the species' **center of origin.** The center of origin is not a single point; rather, it is the distribution of the population when the new species originated. From its center of origin, each species spreads until a barrier of some kind halts it. Examples of barriers include an ocean, a desert, or a mountain range; unfavorable climate; and the presence of organisms that compete successfully for food or shelter.

Most plant and animal species have characteristic geographic distributions. The **range** of a particular species is that portion of Earth in which it is found. The range of some species may be a relatively small area. For example, wombats, the marsupial equivalent of groundhogs, are found only in drier parts of southeastern Australia and nearby islands. Such localized, native species are said to be **endemic;** that is, they are not found anywhere else in the world. In contrast, some species have a nearly worldwide distribution and occur on more than one continent or throughout much of the ocean. Such species are said to be **cosmopolitan.**

One of the early observations of biogeographers was that the ranges of different species do not include everywhere that they *could* survive. Central Africa has elephants, gorillas, chimpanzees, lions, antelopes, umbrella trees, and guapiruvu trees, whereas areas in South America with a similar climate have none of them. These animals and plants originated in Africa

after continental drift had already separated the supercontinent Pangaea into several landmasses. The organisms could not expand their range into South America because the Atlantic Ocean was an impassable barrier. Likewise, the ocean was a barrier to South American monkeys, sloths, tapirs, balsa trees, and snakewood trees, none of which are found in Africa.

Land areas are divided into six biogeographic realms

As the various continents were explored and their organisms studied, biologists observed that the world could be divided into major blocks of vegetation, such as forests, grasslands, and deserts, and that these vegetation types corresponded to specific climates. The relationship between animal distribution, geography, and climate was not deduced until 1876. At that time, Alfred Russel Wallace, who independently and concurrently discovered the same scientific theory of evolution by natural selection as Charles Darwin, divided Earth's land areas into six major biogeographic realms: the Palearctic, Nearctic, Neotropical, Ethiopian, Oriental, and Australian (FIG. 56-25). A major barrier separates each of the six biogeographic realms from the others and helps maintain each region's biological distinctiveness.

Many biologists quickly embraced Wallace's classification system, which is still considered valid today. However, human activities, such as the intentional and unintentional introduction of foreign species, are contributing to a homogenization of the biogeographic realms (see Chapter 57).

Refer to Figure 56-25 as we briefly consider some of the characteristic animals in each realm. The *Nearctic* and *Palearctic realms* are more closely related than the other regions, especially in their northern parts, where they share many animals such as wolves, hares, and caribou. This similarity may be due to a land bridge that has periodically connected Siberia and Alaska. This bridge was present until late in the Pleistocene epoch, about 10,000 years ago. Animals adapted to cold environments likely dispersed between Asia and North America along this bridge.

The *Neotropical realm* was almost completely isolated from the Nearctic realm and other landmasses for most of the past 70 million years. During this time, many marsupial species evolved. The isthmus of Panama, which formed a dryland connection about 3 million years ago, linked North and South America and provided a route for dispersal. Only three species—the opossum, armadillo, and porcupine—are descendants of animals that survived the northward dispersal from South America, but many species, such as the tapir and llama, are descendants of animals that survived the southward dispersal from North America. Competition from these species caused many of South America's marsupial species to go extinct.

The Sahara Desert separates the *Ethiopian realm* from other landmasses. The Ethiopian realm contains the most varied vertebrates of all six realms. Some overlap exists between the Ethiopian realm and *Oriental realm* because a land bridge with a moist climate linked Africa to Asia during the Miocene and Pliocene epochs. The Oriental realm has the fewest endemic species of all the tropical realms.

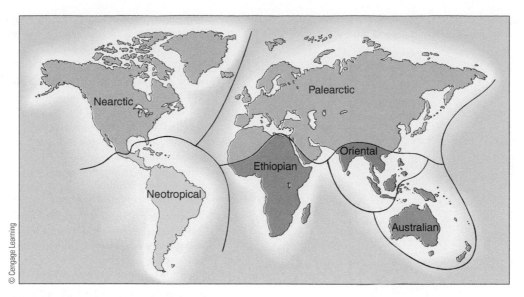

Figure 56-25 Wallace's biogeographic realms

Certain unique species characterize each of the six biogeographic realms. The boundary between the Oriental and Australian realms, for example, is a deep-water gap. Wallace noted that hornbills, Sumatran tigers, orangutans, and tree shrews live west of the boundary, whereas tree kangaroos, cockatoos, birds of paradise, and cuscus live east of the boundary. Many of the Australian species are endemic; that is, they evolved in Australia and are found nowhere else. Wallace's studies of biogeography helped him develop his scientific theory of evolution by natural selection.

The *Australian realm* has not had a land connection with other regions for more than 85 million years. It has no native placental mammals, and marsupials and monotremes, including the duck-billed platypus and the spiny anteater, dominate it. Adaptive radiation of the marsupials during their long period of isolation led to species with ecological niches similar to those of placental mammals of other realms (see Fig. 32-28).

CHECKPOINT 56.4

- *What is biogeography, and what do biogeographers do?*
- *Which biogeographic realm has been separated from the other biogeographic realms for the longest period? What animals characterize this biogeographic realm?*

SUMMARY: FOCUS ON LEARNING OBJECTIVES

56.1 Biomes *(page 1209)*

1 Define *biome* and briefly describe the nine major terrestrial biomes, giving attention to the climate, soil, and characteristic plants and animals of each.

- A **biome** is a large, relatively distinct terrestrial region with characteristic climate, soil, plants, and animals.
- A frozen layer of subsoil (**permafrost**) and low-growing vegetation that is adapted to extreme cold and a short growing season characterize **tundra** (also called **arctic tundra**), the northernmost biome. **Alpine tundra,** at higher elevations above the tree line, and **Antarctic tundra** of the Southern Hemisphere are also included in the tundra biome classification.
- Conifers—which are adapted to cold winters, a short growing season, and acidic, mineral-poor soil—dominate the **boreal forest,** or **taiga.**
- Large conifers dominate **temperate rain forest,** which receives high precipitation.

- **Temperate deciduous forest** occurs where precipitation is relatively high and soils are rich in organic matter. Broad-leaf trees that lose their leaves seasonally dominate temperate deciduous forest.
- **Temperate grassland** typically has a deep, mineral-rich soil and has moderate but uncertain precipitation.
- Thickets of small-leaf evergreen shrubs and trees and a climate of wet, mild winters and dry summers characterize **chaparral.**
- **Desert,** found in both temperate (cold deserts) and subtropical or tropical regions (warm deserts) with low levels of precipitation, is inhabited by organisms with specialized water-conserving adaptations.
- Tropical grassland, called **savanna,** has widely scattered trees interspersed with grassy areas. Savanna occurs in tropical areas with low or seasonal rainfall.
- Mineral-poor soil and high rainfall that is evenly distributed throughout the year characterize **tropical rain forest.** Tropical rain forest has high species richness and high productivity.

A rain forest has several stories of vegetation: emergent layer, canopy, understory, shrub layer, and ground layer.

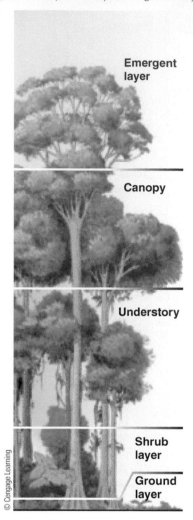

Emergent layer

Canopy

Understory

Shrub layer

Ground layer

© Cengage Learning

2 Describe at least one human effect on each of the biomes discussed.

- Oil exploration and military exercises result in long-lasting damage to tundra. Clear-cut logging destroys boreal and temperate rain forests. Temperate deciduous forests are removed for logging, farms and tree plantations, and land development.

- Human population growth and its accompanying agricultural and industrial expansion threaten most of the world's tropical rain forests.

- Farmland has replaced most temperate grasslands; savannas are increasingly converted to rangeland for cattle. Development of hilly chaparral results in mud slides and costly fires. Land development in deserts reduces wildlife habitat.

56.2 Aquatic Ecosystems (page 1218)

3 Explain the important environmental factors that affect aquatic ecosystems.

- In aquatic ecosystems important environmental factors include **salinity** (concentration of dissolved salts), amount of dissolved oxygen, availability of light, levels of essential minerals, water depth, temperature, pH, and presence or absence of waves and currents.

4 Distinguish among plankton, nekton, and benthos.

- Aquatic life is ecologically divided into **plankton** (free-floating organisms), **nekton** (strongly swimming organisms), and **benthos** (bottom-dwelling organisms).

- **Phytoplankton** includes photosynthetic algae and cyanobacteria; **zooplankton** includes protozoa, tiny crustaceans, and the larval stages of many animals.

5 Briefly describe the various freshwater, estuarine, and marine ecosystems, giving attention to the environmental characteristics and representative organisms of each.

- Freshwater ecosystems include flowing-water ecosystems, standing-water ecosystems, and freshwater wetlands. In **flowing-water ecosystems,** the water flows in a current. Flowing-water ecosystems have few phytoplankton and depend on detritus from the land for much of their energy.

- Large **standing-water ecosystems** (freshwater lakes) are divided into zones on the basis of water depth. The marginal **littoral zone** contains emergent vegetation and algae. The **limnetic zone,** open water away from the shore that extends as far down as sunlight penetrates, contains phytoplankton, zooplankton, and larger fishes. The deep, dark **profundal zone** holds little life other than bacterial decomposers.

- **Freshwater wetlands** are transitional between fresh water and terrestrial ecosystems. They are usually covered at least part of the year by shallow water and have characteristic soils and vegetation. Freshwater wetlands perform many valuable **ecosystem services.**

- An **estuary** is a coastal body of water, partly surrounded by land, with access to both the ocean and a large supply of fresh water from rivers. Salinity fluctuates with tidal cycles, the time of year, and precipitation. Temperate estuaries usually contain **salt marshes,** whereas **mangrove forests** dominate tropical coastlines.

- Four important marine environments are the intertidal zone, the benthic environment, the neritic province, and the oceanic province. The **intertidal zone** is the shoreline area between low tide and high tide. Organisms of the intertidal zone have adaptations to resist wave action and being exposed to air during low tide.

- The **benthic environment** is the ocean floor. **Sea grasses, kelps,** and **coral reefs** are important benthic communities in shallow ocean waters.

- The **neritic province** is open ocean from the shoreline to a depth of 200 m. Organisms that live in the neritic province are all floaters or swimmers. The **euphotic zone** is the upper part of the neritic province, where enough light penetrates to support photosynthesis. Phytoplankton are the base of the food web in the euphotic zone.

- The **oceanic province** is that part of the open ocean that is deeper than 200 m. Its uniform environment is one of darkness, cold temperature, and high pressure. Animal inhabitants of the oceanic province are either predators or scavengers that subsist on **marine snow,** detritus that drifts down from other areas of the ocean.

6 Describe at least one human effect on each of the aquatic ecosystems discussed.

- Water pollution and dams adversely affect flowing-water ecosystems. Increased nutrients, supplied by human activities, stimulate algal growth, resulting in enriched ponds and lakes.
- Agriculture, pollution, and land development threaten wetlands and estuaries. Pollution, coastal development, offshore mining and oil drilling, and overfishing threaten marine ecosystems.

56.3 Ecotones *(page 1227)*

7 Define *ecotone* and describe some of its features.

- An **ecotone** is the transition zone where two communities or biomes meet and intergrade. Ecotones provide habitat diversity and are often populated by a greater variety of organisms than lives in either adjacent ecosystem.

56.4 Biogeography *(page 1228)*

8 Define *biogeography* and briefly describe Wallace's biogeographic realms.

- **Biogeography** is the study of the geographic distribution of plants and animals, including where populations came from, how they got there, and when. Each species originated only once, at its **center of origin.** From its center of origin, each species spreads until a physical, environmental, or biological barrier halts it. The **range** of a particular species is that portion of Earth in which it is found.
- Alfred Russel Wallace divided Earth's land areas into six major biogeographic realms: the Palearctic, Nearctic, Neotropical, Ethiopian, Oriental, and Australian. Each realm is biologically distinct because a mountain range, desert, deep water, or other barrier separates it from the others.

TEST YOUR UNDERSTANDING

Know and Comprehend

1. The northernmost biome, known as _____, typically has little precipitation, a short growing season, and permafrost. (a) chaparral (b) boreal forest (c) tundra (d) northern deciduous forest (e) savanna
2. Forests of the northeastern and middle Atlantic United States, which have broad-leaf hardwood trees that lose their foliage annually, are called (a) temperate deciduous forests (b) tropical dry forests (c) boreal forests (d) temperate rain forests (e) tropical rain forests
3. The deepest, richest soil in the world occurs in (a) temperate rain forest (b) tropical rain forest (c) savanna (d) temperate grassland (e) chaparral
4. This biome, with its thicket of evergreen shrubs and small trees, is found in areas with Mediterranean climates. (a) temperate rain forest (b) tropical rain forest (c) savanna (d) temperate grassland (e) chaparral
5. This biome is a tropical grassland interspersed with widely spaced trees. (a) temperate rain forest (b) tropical rain forest (c) savanna (d) temperate grassland (e) chaparral
6. This biome has the greatest species richness. (a) temperate rain forest (b) tropical rain forest (c) savanna (d) temperate grassland (e) chaparral
7. Organisms in aquatic environments fall into three categories: free-floating _____, strongly swimming _____, and bottom-dwelling _____. (a) nekton; benthos; plankton (b) nekton; plankton; benthos (c) plankton; benthos; nekton (d) plankton; nekton; benthos (e) benthos; nekton; plankton
8. Emergent vegetation grows in the _____ zone of freshwater lakes. (a) littoral (b) limnetic (c) profundal (d) neritic (e) intertidal
9. The _____ is open ocean from the shoreline to a depth of 200 m. (a) benthic environment (b) intertidal zone (c) neritic province (d) oceanic province (e) aphotic region
10. The transition zone where two ecosystems or biomes meet and intergrade is called (a) a biosphere (b) an aphotic region (c) a thermocline (d) a biogeographic realm (e) an ecotone
11. Which biogeographic realm has been separated from the other landmasses for more than 85 million years? (a) Ethiopian (b) Palearctic (c) Nearctic (d) Oriental (e) Australian

Apply and Analyze

12. **INTERPRET DATA** Develop a hypothesis to explain why animals adapted to the desert are usually small. How would you test your hypothesis?
13. **INTERPRET DATA** Examine Figure 56-1. What is the lowest average annual precipitation characteristic of tropical rain forests? the highest? What is the range of average temperature in tropical rain forests?
14. **INTERPRET DATA** Examine Figure 56-24. How many of the sampled species are found in the nonserpentine soil? in the serpentine soil? in the ecotone? What generalization about ecotones do these data support?

Evaluate and Synthesize

15. **PREDICT** What would happen to the organisms in a river with a fast current if a dam were built? Would there be any differences in habitat if the dam were upstream or downstream of the organisms in question? Explain your answers.
16. **EVOLUTION LINK** When a black-tailed prairie dog or other small animal dies, other prairie dogs bury it. Develop a hypothesis to explain how this behavior may be adaptive. How would you test this hypothesis?
17. **SCIENCE, TECHNOLOGY, AND SOCIETY** Imagine that you are a graduate student working with university scientists on the effects on sea turtles of the 2010 oil spill in the Gulf of Mexico. What technologies might you employ to collect data for your research? Knowing that the turtles' life cycle includes laying eggs on beaches, how would you involve local communities in your research?

To access course materials, such as Aplia and other companion resources, please visit **www.cengagebrain.com.**

57 Biological Diversity and Conservation Biology

Cross River gorilla, *Gorilla gorilla diehli*. Will this critically endangered species survive?

KEY CONCEPTS

57.1 Never before in Earth's history has biodiversity been threatened with mass extinction in such a compressed time period by one species: *Homo sapiens*.

57.2 Conservation biology is a multidisciplinary science that studies human effects on biodiversity and devises practical solutions to address these effects.

57.3 Globally, removal of large expanses of forest for timber, agriculture, and other uses is contributing to the loss of biological diversity and valuable ecosystem services.

57.4 Scientists continue to provide evidence of global climate change, which is adversely affecting biodiversity, human health, and agriculture.

The Cross River gorilla, *Gorilla gorilla diehli*, was discovered early in the 20th century (see photograph). It was eventually identified as a fourth subspecies of gorilla and second member of the western lowland gorilla family. This rarest of all the great apes lives in small groups in highland forests of Nigeria and western Cameroon. Cross River gorillas, listed as critically endangered (estimated population 250 to 300), are rapidly facing extinction due to habitat loss caused by human destruction. Local people have cut down, or destroyed, much of the forests for lumber, cattle grazing, and agriculture. The gorillas are hunted and poached for bush meat.

The World Wildlife Federation (WWF) reports that these gorillas also face the risk of inbreeding and loss of genetic diversity due to their small population size and the low rate of genetic exchange between the different subpopulations. The WWF has partnered with the Wildlife Conservation Society and the governments of Nigeria and Cameroon to protect the fragile Cross River gorilla groups by establishing a sanctuary, enforcing laws, and supporting government management of the Campo Ma'an National Park in Cameroon and the surrounding buffer zone. Both Cameroon and Nigeria are working with local people to educate about sustainable use of forest resources and to promote alternative sources of income, such as tourism. Plans for the survival of the Cross River gorillas will focus on developing protected corridors of forest habitat that will allow safe movement of gorillas between different groups to increase genetic diversity.

Humans are very closely related to gorillas, both in our evolutionary development and genetically. In 2012, researchers reported in *Nature* that when the western lowland gorilla genome was sequenced, they found that 15% of the human genome was more closely related to gorillas than to chimpanzees. Scientists also confirmed that the gorilla is about 98% genetically identical to us. Further, we share some rapidly evolving genes with gorillas, which may facilitate medical research of such ailments as heart disease and dementia. The study increases our understanding of human evolution and, according to the researchers, "connects us to a time when our existence was more tenuous, and in doing so, highlights the importance of protecting and conserving these remarkable species."

The Cross River gorilla decline underscores how humans have negatively affected biological diversity. For example, according to the International Union for the Conservation of Nature (IUCN), which monitors the status of Earth's biological diversity, as many as one-fourth of the world's mammals are at risk of extinction. Our recognition of this serious situation and our efforts to address the damage we have caused may well be what ultimately ensures our own human survival.

In this chapter we focus on declining biological diversity and conservation biology. We discuss deforestation and climate change, two major environmental issues that negatively affect biological diversity.

57.1 THE BIODIVERSITY CRISIS

LEARNING OBJECTIVES

1 Identify various levels of biodiversity: genetic diversity, species richness, and ecosystem diversity.
2 Distinguish among threatened species, endangered species, and extinct species.
3 Discuss at least four causes of declining biological diversity and identify the most important causes.

The human species (*Homo sapiens*) has been present on Earth for about 195,000 years (see Chapter 22), which is a brief span of time compared with the age of our planet, some 4.6 billion years. Despite our relatively short tenure on Earth, our biological effect on other species is unparalleled. Our numbers have increased dramatically—the human population reached 7.14 billion in 2013—and we have expanded our biological range, moving into almost every habitat on Earth.

Wherever we have lived, we have altered the environment and shaped it to meet our needs. In only a few generations, we have transformed the face of Earth, placed a great strain on Earth's resources and resilience, and profoundly affected other species. As a result of these changes, we must all be concerned about **environmental sustainability** (or simply, *sustainability*), the ability to meet humanity's current needs without compromising the ability of future generations to meet their needs. The effect of humans on the environment merits special study in biology, not merely because we ourselves are humans but because our impact on the rest of the biosphere is so extensive.

Extinction, the death of a species, occurs when the last individual member of a species dies. (We introduced the important concept of extinction in Chapter 20.) Although extinction is a natural biological process, human activities have greatly accelerated it (**FIG. 57-1**). According to the 2005 Millennium Ecosystem Assessment report, extinction is happening at about 1000 times more rapidly as the normal background rate of extinction. The burgeoning human population has forced us to spread to almost all areas of Earth. Whenever humans invade an area, the habitats of many plants and animals are disrupted or destroyed, which can contribute to their extinction.

Biological diversity, also called **biodiversity,** is the variation among organisms (**FIG. 57-2**). Biological diversity includes much more than simply **species richness,** the number of species of archaea, bacteria, protists, plants, fungi, and animals. Biological diversity occurs at all levels of ecological organization, from populations to ecosystems. It takes into account **genetic diversity,** the genetic variety within a species, both among individuals within a given population and among geographically separate populations. (An individual species may have hundreds of genetically distinct populations.) Biological diversity also includes **ecosystem diversity,** the variety of ecosystems found on Earth: the forests, prairies, deserts, lakes, coastal estuaries, coral reefs, and other ecosystems.

Biologists must consider all three levels of biological diversity—species richness, genetic diversity, and ecosystem diversity—as they address the human impact on biodiversity. For example, the disappearance of populations (i.e., a decline in

Passenger pigeon Great auk Dodo Golden toad Aepyornis

Figure 57-1 Selected animal extinctions

These animals became extinct largely as a result of human activities such as destruction of their habitats and hunting. (Adapted from Miller, G. T., and S. E. Spoolman. *Living in the Environment,* 16th ed. Brooks/Cole, Belmont, CA, 2009.)

Genetic diversity affects a population's ability to thrive, which in turn affects species richness within an ecosystem. Ultimately, species richness helps determine ecosystem diversity across a large area.

(a) Genetic diversity in an American oystercatcher population.

(b) Species richness in an East Coast sandy shore ecosystem.

(c) Ecosystem diversity across an entire region (ocean and shore).

Figure 57-2 **Levels of biodiversity**

The single unduplicated chromosome below each oystercatcher represents the genetic variation among individuals within a population. Conservation at all three ecological levels must occur to protect biological diversity.

PREDICT What might happen to this oystercatcher population if another population of oystercatchers migrates to the area and competes for food and space?

© Cengage Learning

genetic diversity) indicates an increased risk that a species will become extinct (a decline in species richness). Biologists perform detailed analyses to quantify how large a population must be to ensure a given species' long-term survival. The smallest population that has a high chance of enduring into the future is known as the **minimum viable population (MVP)**.

Biological diversity is currently decreasing at an unprecedented rate (see *Inquiring About: Declining Amphibian Populations*). For example, the IUCN Red List of Threatened Plants, which is based on 20 years of data collection and analysis around the world, lists about 34,000 species of plants currently threatened with extinction. Because Red Lists are not yet available for many tropical countries, it is difficult to know the true scale of the biodiversity crisis.

We may have entered the greatest period of mass extinction in Earth's history, but the current situation differs from previous periods of mass extinction in several respects. First, its cause is directly attributable to human activities. Second, it is occurring in a tremendously compressed period (just a few decades as opposed to hundreds of thousands of years), much faster than rates of speciation (or replacement). Perhaps even more sobering, larger numbers of plant species are becoming extinct today than in previous mass extinctions. Because plants are the base of terrestrial food webs, extinction of animals that depend on plants is not far behind. It is crucial that we determine how the loss of biodiversity affects the stability and functioning of ecosystems, which make up our life-support system.

The legal definition of an **endangered species,** as stipulated by the U.S. Endangered Species Act, is a species in imminent danger of extinction throughout all or a significant part of its range. (The area in which a particular species is found is its **range.**) Unless humans intervene, an endangered species will probably become extinct.

When extinction is less imminent but the population of a particular species is quite small, the species is classified as threatened. The legal definition of a **threatened species** is a species likely to become endangered in the foreseeable future, throughout all or a significant part of its range.

Endangered and threatened species represent a decline in biological diversity because as their numbers decrease, their genetic diversity is severely diminished. Endangered and threatened species are at greater risk of extinction than species with greater genetic variability because long-term survival and evolution depend on genetic diversity (see the section on genetic drift in Chapter 19).

Endangered species have certain characteristics in common

Many threatened and endangered species share certain characteristics that may make them more vulnerable to extinction. Some of these characteristics include having an extremely small (localized) range, requiring a large territory, living on islands, having a low reproductive success, needing specialized breeding areas, and possessing specialized feeding habits.

What is happening to our amphibian populations? Since the 1970s, many of the world's frog populations have dwindled or disappeared. According to the IUCN Global Amphibian Assessment, as many as 168 amphibian species may have disappeared since 1980 and are presumed extinct. About one-third of all amphibian species are in decline, and more than 40% are at risk of becoming extinct by 2060 if they are not taken into captivity.

The declines are not limited to areas with obvious habitat destruction (such as drainage of wetlands where frogs live), degradation from pollutants, or overharvesting. Some remote, pristine locations also show dramatic declines in amphibians. Researchers have reported evidence that pollutants, infectious diseases, and climate change are all factors in these declines.

Agricultural chemicals are implicated in amphibian declines in California's Sierra Nevadas. Frog populations on the eastern slopes are relatively healthy, but about eight species are declining on the western slopes, where prevailing winds carry residues of 15 different pesticides from the Central Valley's agricultural region. Agricultural chemicals are also implicated in amphibian declines on the eastern shore of Maryland and in Ontario, Canada. Researchers at the University of South Florida found that atrazine (an herbicide) combined with phosphate fertilizer increased trematode

(a parasitic flatworm) infection and suppressed the immune system, making it difficult for amphibians to fight parasitic infections.

Infectious diseases are strongly implicated in some of the declines. In 1998, a chytrid (fungus) was first connected to amphibian declines. Climate change may be exacerbating chytrid-induced amphibian deaths, and this factor continues to be investigated. At certain altitudes and temperatures, the chytrid has infected and killed 85% of the amphibians.

The discovery of amphibians with deformities adds another layer of complexity to the amphibian crisis (see photograph). Frogs with extra legs, extra toes, eyes located on the shoulder or back, deformed jaws, missing legs, missing toes, or missing eyes usually die before they reproduce. Predators easily catch frogs with extra or missing legs. Deformed amphibians have been reported on four continents and in almost all states in the United States.

Biologists have investigated many possible causes of amphibian deformities during development, and no single factor explains the deformities found in all locations. Several pesticides affect normal development in frog embryos. Also, infecting tadpoles with a trematode causes the adults that develop from the tadpoles to exhibit limb deformities. Multiple environmental stressors, such as habitat loss, disease, and pollution, may interact synergistically with one another to cause deformities.

Frog deformity. Pollution and parasites are implicated in developmental abnormalities in amphibians, such as this Pacific tree frog.

Many endangered species have a small natural range, which makes them particularly prone to extinction if their habitat is altered. The Tiburon mariposa lily, for example, is found nowhere in nature except on a single hilltop near San Francisco. Wildfire or development of that hilltop would almost certainly cause the extinction of this species.

Species that need extremely large territories may be threatened with extinction when all or part of their territory is modified by human activity. The California condor, for example, is a scavenger bird that lives off carrion and requires hundreds of square kilometers of undisturbed territory to find adequate food. The condor is slowly recovering from the brink of extinction. From 1987 to 1992, it existed only in zoos and was not found in nature. A program to reintroduce zoo-bred California condors into the wild began in 1992. Currently, there are more than 350 condors, with more than half of them living in the wild in California, Arizona, Utah, and Baja California. The condor story is not an unqualified success, however; the condors have yet to become a self-sustaining population that replaces its numbers without captive breeding.

Many **endemic** island species are endangered. (*Endemic* means that they are local species not found anywhere else in the world.) These species often have small populations that cannot be replaced by immigration if their numbers decline. Because

they evolved in isolation from competitors, predators, and disease organisms, island species have few defenses when such organisms are introduced, usually by humans. It is not surprising that of the 171 bird species that have become extinct in the past few centuries, 155 of them lived on islands.

For a species to survive, its members must be present within their range in large enough numbers for males and females to mate. The minimum viable population that ensures reproductive success varies from one type of organism to another. For all species, when the population size falls below the MVP, the population goes into a decline and becomes susceptible to extinction.

Endangered species often have low reproductive rates. The female blue whale produces a single calf every other year, whereas no more than 6% of swamp pinks, an endangered species of small flowering plant, produce flowers in a given year (**FIG. 57-3**). Some endangered species breed only in specialized areas; for example, the green sea turtle lays its eggs on just a few beaches.

Highly specialized feeding habits endanger a species. In nature, the giant panda eats only bamboo. Periodically, all the bamboo plants in a given area flower and die together; when that occurs, panda populations face starvation. Like many other endangered species, giant pandas are also endangered

Figure 57-3 The swamp pink, an endangered species
The swamp pink (*Helonias bullata*) lives in boggy areas of the eastern United States. Photographed in Killens Pond State Park, Delaware.

Because direct and indirect causes of decreased biodiversity interact in complex ways, declining biodiversity is addressed from a systems biology perspective rather than from a more-specific perspective.

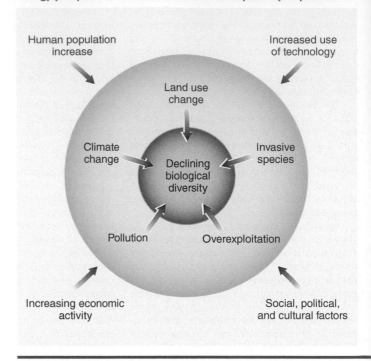

Figure 57-4 *Animation* Causes of declining biological diversity
Indirect causes (*blue*) of decreasing biodiversity interact with and amplify the effects of one another and of direct causes (*green*). Note that each of these causes can be traced to human activities.

CONNECT Give an example of how an indirect effect could positively change a direct effect.

© Cengage Learning

because their habitat has been fragmented, and there are few intact habitats where they can survive. China's 1600 wild giant pandas live in 24 isolated habitats that represent a small fraction of their historic range.

Human activities contribute to declining biological diversity

Species become endangered and extinct for a variety of reasons, including the destruction or modification of habitats (i.e., land use change) and the production of pollution, including the greenhouse gases that cause climate change. Humans also upset the delicate balance of organisms in a given area by introducing invasive species, which compete with native organisms. Overexploitation through overfishing, hunting, and poaching is also a factor. **FIGURE 57-4** shows the interactions between these direct causes of declining biological diversity and indirect human factors such as human population increase.

To save species, we must protect their habitats Most species facing extinction today are endangered by destruction, fragmentation, or degradation of natural habitats. Building roads, parking lots, bridges, and buildings; clearing forests to grow crops or graze domestic animals; and logging forests for timber all take their toll on natural habitats. Draining marshes converts aquatic habitats to terrestrial ones, whereas building dams and canals floods terrestrial habitats (**FIG. 57-5**).

Because most organisms require a particular type of environment, habitat destruction reduces their biological range and ability to survive.

Humans often leave small, isolated patches of natural landscape that roads, fences, fields, and buildings completely surround. In ecological terms *island* refers not only to any landmass surrounded by water but also to any isolated habitat surrounded by an expanse of unsuitable territory. Accordingly, a small patch of forest surrounded by agricultural and suburban lands is considered an island.

Habitat fragmentation, the breakup of large areas of habitat into small, isolated segments (i.e., islands), is a major threat to the long-term survival of many populations and species (**FIG. 57-6**). Species from the surrounding "developed" landscape may intrude into the isolated habitat (the *edge effect,* discussed in Chapter 54), whereas rare and wide-ranging species that require a large patch of undisturbed habitat may disappear altogether. Habitat fragmentation encourages the spread of *invasive species,* disease organisms, and other "weedy" species and makes it difficult for organisms to migrate. Generally, habitat fragments support only

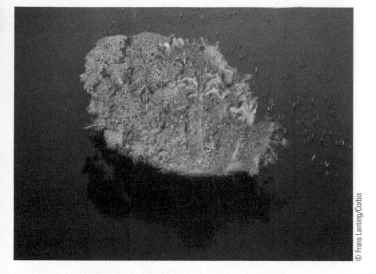

Figure 57-5 Habitat destruction
This tiny island lies in the Panama Canal. It was once a hilltop in a forest that was flooded when the canal was built.

a fraction of the species found in the original, unaltered environment. However, much remains to be learned about precisely how habitat fragmentation affects specific populations, species, and ecosystems.

Human activities that produce acid precipitation and other forms of pollution indirectly modify habitats left undisturbed and in their natural state. Acid precipitation, also called acid rain or industrial precipitation, has contributed to the decline of large stands of forest trees and to the biological death of many freshwater lakes in, for example, the Adirondack Mountains and Nova Scotia. Acid rain is especially problematic in much of Eastern Europe and around industrial regions of China. Other types of pollutants, such as chemicals from industry and agriculture, organic pollutants from sewage, acid wastes seeping from mines, thermal pollution from the heated wastewater of industrial plants, and radioactive contamination, also adversely affect organisms.

To save native species, we must control intrusions of invasive species Biotic pollution, the introduction of a foreign species into an area where it is not native, often upsets the balance among the organisms living in that area and interferes with the ecosystem's normal functioning. Unlike other forms of pollution, which may be cleaned up, biotic pollution is usually permanent. The foreign species may prey on native species or compete with them for food or habitat. If the foreign species causes economic or environmental harm, it is known as an **invasive species.** Generally, a foreign competitor or predator harms local organisms more than do native competitors or predators. Most invasive species lack natural agents (such as parasites, predators, and competitors) that would otherwise control them. Also, without a shared evolutionary history, most native species typically are less equipped to cope with invasive species. Although foreign species sometimes spread into new areas on their own, humans are

How does habitat fragmentation affect predation of juvenile bay scallops in a marine environment?

HYPOTHESIS: Predation of juvenile bay scallops is greater in patchy areas of sea grass than in undisturbed (continuous) seagrass meadows.

EXPERIMENT: Predation rates of juvenile bay scallops were measured over a four-week period in three seagrass environments: continuous, patchy, and very patchy.

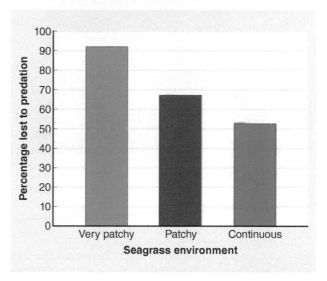

RESULTS AND CONCLUSION: The lowest rate of predation (52%) occurred in the continuous seagrass meadow, and the highest predation rate (92%) occurred in the very patchy environment. The patchy (fragmented) areas provided the predators with easier access to the young scallops than did the continuous area. It was also more difficult for the predators to intrude from surrounding areas into the continuous seagrass meadow.

SOURCE: Irlandi, E. A., W. G. Ambrose, and B. A. Orando. "Landscape Ecology and the Marine Environment: How Spatial Configuration of Seagrass Habitat Influences Growth and Survival of the Bay Scallop." *Oikos,* Vol. 72, 1995.

Figure 57-6 Effects of habitat fragmentation in a shallow marine environment

PREDICT What is likely to happen to bay scallop populations if seagrass environments continue to deteriorate and become more fragmented?

usually responsible for such introductions, either knowingly or accidentally.

One of North America's greatest biological threats is the zebra mussel, a native of the Caspian Sea. It was probably introduced by a foreign ship that flushed ballast water into the Great Lakes in 1985 or 1986. Since then, the tiny freshwater mussel, which clusters in extraordinary densities, has massed on hulls of boats, piers, buoys, water intake systems, and, most damaging of all, on native clam and mussel shells. The zebra mussel's large appetite for algae, phytoplankton, and zooplankton is also cutting into the food supply of native fishes,

Figure 57-7 Zebra mussels clog a pipe
Thumbnail-sized zebra mussels (*Dreissena polymorpha*) have caused billions of dollars in damage in addition to displacing native clams and mussels.

mussels, and clams, threatening their survival. The zebra mussel is currently found throughout most of the Mississippi River and its tributary rivers. According to the U.S. Coast Guard, the United States spends about $5 billion each year to control the spread of the zebra mussel and to repair damage such as clogged pipes (FIG. 57-7).

Islands are particularly susceptible to the introduction of invasive species. In Hawaii the introduction of sheep has imperiled both the mamane tree (because the sheep eat it) and a species of honeycreeper, an endemic bird that relies on the tree for food. Hawaii's plants evolved in the absence of herbivorous mammals and therefore have no defenses against introduced sheep, pigs, goats, and deer.

Other human activities affect biodiversity directly or indirectly Sometimes species become endangered or extinct as a result of deliberate efforts to eradicate or control their numbers, often because they prey on game animals or livestock. In the past, ranchers, hunters, and government agents decimated populations of large predators such as the wolf, mountain lion, and grizzly bear. Some animals are killed because their lifestyles cause problems for humans. The Carolina parakeet, a beautiful green, red, and yellow bird endemic to the southeastern United States, was extinct by 1920, exterminated by farmers because it ate fruit from their trees.

Unregulated hunting, or overhunting, has caused the extinction of certain species in the past but is now strictly controlled in most countries. The passenger pigeon was one of the most common birds in North America in the early 1800s, but a century of overhunting resulted in its extinction in the early 1900s.

Illegal commercial hunting, or *poaching,* endangers larger animals such as the tiger, cheetah, and snow leopard, whose beautiful furs are quite valuable. Rhinoceroses are slaughtered for their horns (used for ceremonial dagger handles in the Middle East and for purported medicinal purposes in Asian medicine). Elephants are poached for their ivory tusks. Bears are killed for their gallbladders (which Asian doctors use to treat ailments ranging from indigestion to hemorrhoids). Bushmeat—meat from wild animals, including rare primates, elephants, anteaters, and great apes—is sold to urban restaurants. Although laws protect these animals, demand for their products on the black market has promoted illegal hunting, particularly in impoverished countries where a sale of contraband products can support a family for months.

Shark finning, removing a shark's fin and throwing the animal back in the ocean to die, has caused a third of the world's shark species to become endangered, according to the International Union for the Conservation of Nature (IUCN). The fins are sold to China and other Asian countries for shark fin soup and medicinal purposes. One million sharks were reportedly harvested in 2012. Sharks play an important role in maintaining ecosystems and many are keystone species. Many countries have passed laws banning any trading in shark fins, or restricting harvest of depleted species, but laws have been difficult to enforce and are easy to circumvent. Recently, phylogenetic DNA testing has been developed to identify illegal catches of banned species using samples of confiscated fins and shark soup.

Commercial harvest is the collection of live organisms from nature. Most commercially harvested organisms end up in zoos, aquaria, biomedical research labs, circuses, and pet stores. For example, several million birds are commercially harvested each year for the pet trade, but many die in transit, and many more die from improper treatment in their owners' homes. At least 40 parrot species are now threatened or endangered, in part because of commercial harvest. Although it is illegal to capture endangered animals from the wild, a thriving black market exists, mainly because collectors in the United States, Europe, and Japan pay large sums for rare tropical birds (FIG. 57-8).

Commercial harvest also threatens plants. Many unique or rare plants have been so extensively collected from the wild that they are now classified as endangered. Included are certain carnivorous plants, wildflower bulbs, cacti, and orchids. In contrast, carefully monitored and regulated commercial use of animal and plant resources creates an economic incentive to ensure that these resources do not disappear.

CHECKPOINT 57.1

- *What are the three levels of biological diversity?*
- PREDICT *Which organism is more likely to become extinct: an endangered species or a threatened species? Explain your answer.*
- CONNECT *How does habitat fragmentation contribute to declining biological diversity?*
- CONNECT *How do invasive species contribute to the biodiversity crisis?*

Figure 57-8 Illegal commercial harvesting

These hyacinth macaws (*Anodorhynchus hyacinthus*) were seized in French Guiana in South America as part of the illegal animal trade there. The hyacinth macaw population has been seriously reduced in South America.

Jany Sauvanet/NHPA/Photoshot

57.2 CONSERVATION BIOLOGY

LEARNING OBJECTIVES

4 Define *conservation biology* and compare in situ and ex situ conservation measures.

5 Describe the benefits and shortcomings of the U.S. Endangered Species Act and the Convention on International Trade in Endangered Species of Wild Flora and Fauna.

Conservation biology is the scientific study of how humans impact organisms and of the development of strategies to protect biological diversity. Conservation biologists develop models, design experiments, and perform fieldwork to address a wide range of questions. For example, what are the processes that influence a decline in biological diversity? How do we protect and restore populations of endangered species? If we are to preserve entire ecosystems and landscapes, which ones are the most important to save?

Conservation biologists have determined that a single large area of habitat capable of supporting several populations is more effective at safeguarding an endangered species than several habitat fragments, each capable of supporting a single population. Also, a large area of habitat typically supports greater species richness than several habitat fragments.

Conservation is more successful when habitat areas for a given species are in close proximity rather than far apart. If an area of habitat is isolated from other areas, individuals may not effectively disperse from one habitat to another. Because the presence of humans adversely affects many species, habitat areas that lack roads or are inaccessible to humans are better than human-accessible areas.

According to conservation biologists, it is more effective and, ultimately, more economical to preserve intact ecosystems in which many species live than to try to preserve individual species. Conservation biologists generally consider it a higher priority to preserve areas with greater biological diversity.

Conservation biology includes two problem-solving approaches that save organisms from extinction: in situ and ex situ conservation. **In situ conservation,** which includes the establishment of parks and reserves, concentrates on preserving biological diversity in nature. A high priority of in situ conservation is identifying and protecting sites that harbor a great deal of diversity.

With increasing demands on land, in situ conservation cannot preserve all types of biological diversity. Sometimes only ex situ conservation can save a species. **Ex situ conservation** conserves individual species in human-controlled settings. Breeding captive species in zoos and storing seeds of genetically diverse plant crops are examples of ex situ conservation.

In situ conservation is the best way to preserve biological diversity

Protecting animal and plant habitats—that is, conserving and managing ecosystems as a whole—is the single best way to protect biological diversity. Many nations have set aside areas for wildlife habitats. Such natural ecosystems offer the best strategy for the long-term protection and preservation of biological diversity. Currently, more than 160,000 national parks, marine sanctuaries, wildlife refuges, forests, and other areas are protected throughout the world. Nearly 15% of the world's land area is protected, but only 1.7% of ocean area is set aside.

Unfortunately, many protected areas have multiple uses that sometimes conflict with the goal of preserving species. National parks provide for recreational needs, for example, whereas national forests are used for logging, grazing, and mineral extraction. The mineral rights to many wildlife refuges are privately owned, and oil, gas, and other mineral development has occurred on some wildlife refuges.

Protected areas are not always an effective strategy to preserve biological diversity, particularly in developing countries where biological diversity is greatest, because there is little money or expertise to manage them. Another shortcoming of the world's protected areas is that many are in lightly populated mountain areas, tundra, and the driest deserts, places that often have spectacular scenery but relatively few kinds of species. In reality, such remote areas are often designated reserves because they are unsuitable for commercial development.

In contrast, ecosystems in which biological diversity is greatest often receive little attention. Protected areas are urgently needed in tropical rain forests, the tropical grasslands and savannas of Brazil and Australia, and dry forests that are widely scattered around the world. Desert organisms are underprotected in northern Africa and Argentina, and the species of many islands and temperate river basins also need protection.

Many of these unprotected areas are part of what some biologists have identified as the world's 25 **biodiversity hotspots** (FIG. 57-9). The hotspots collectively make up 1.4% of Earth's land but contain as many as 44% of all vascular plant species, 29% of the world's endemic bird species, 27% of endemic mammal species, 38% of endemic reptile species, and 53% of endemic amphibian species. More than 20% of the world's human population lives in the hotspots. Fifteen of the 25 hotspots are tropical, and 9 are mostly or solely islands. The 25 hotspots are somewhat arbitrary because additional hotspots are recognized when different criteria are used.

Not all conservation biologists support focusing limited conservation resources on protecting biodiversity hotspots because doing so ignores the many **ecosystem services** provided by entire ecosystems that are rapidly vanishing due to habitat destruction. For example, the vast boreal forests in Canada and Russia are critically important to the proper functioning of the global carbon and nitrogen cycles. Conservation organizations

do not recognize them as hotspots, however, and these forests are being logged at unprecedented rates. Landscape ecology takes a larger view of ecosystem conservation.

Landscape ecology considers ecosystem types on a regional scale The subdiscipline of ecology that studies the connections in a heterogeneous **landscape** consisting of multiple interacting ecosystems is known as **landscape ecology.** Increasingly, biologists are focusing efforts on preserving biodiversity in landscapes. What, though, is the minimum ecosystem/landscape size needed to preserve species numbers and distributions?

One long-term study addressing this question in tropical rain forests is the Biological Dynamics of Forest Fragment Project (formerly the Minimum Critical Size of Ecosystems Project), which is studying a series of Amazonian rainforest fragments varying in size from 1 to 100 hectares (One hectare is equal to 2.471 acres.) (FIG. 57-10). Preliminary data from this study, which began in 1979, indicate that smaller forest fragments do not maintain their ecological integrity. For example, large trees

---

KEY POINT

Biodiversity hotspots are areas of the world that are critically important because they contain a disproportionate number of the world's endemic species.

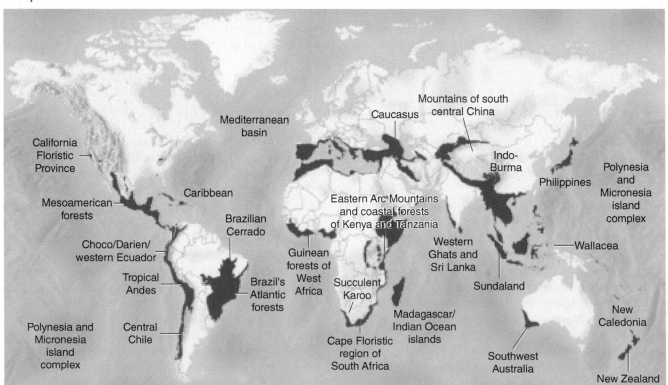

Figure 57-9 *Animation* **Biodiversity hotspots**

Rich in endemic species, these hotspots are under pressure from the number of humans living in them. (Adapted from Miller, G. T. and S. E. Spoolman. *Living in the Environment,* 17th ed., 2012, p. 243, Figure 10-27. Brooks Cole/Cengage Learning. Data from Center for Applied Biodiversity Science at Conservation International.)

PREDICT How could a large human population in a hotspot area be turned into an advantage?

Figure 57-10 Biological Dynamics of Forest Fragment Project
Shown are 1-hectare and 10-hectare plots of a long-term (about three decades) study under way in Brazil on the effects of fragmentation on Amazonian rain forest. Plots with an area of 100 hectares are also under study, along with identically sized sections of intact forest, which are controls.

near forest edges often die or are damaged from exposure to wind, desiccation (from lateral exposure of the forest fragment to sunlight), and invasion by parasitic woody vines. In addition, biologists have documented that various species adapted to forest interiors do not prosper in the smaller fragments and eventually die out, whereas species adapted to forest edges invade the smaller fragments and thrive.

Unfortunately, human colonization and other activities are threatening the Biological Dynamics of Forest Fragment Project itself. Recently, a 1,100-km (683.1 mi) road was paved nearby, expanding agriculture, logging, and hunting opportunities. Should human expansion spread into the research site, the potential benefits that might be derived from understanding the effects of forest fragmentation will be lost.

To remedy widespread habitat fragmentation and its associated loss of biodiversity, conservation biologists have proposed linking isolated fragments with **habitat corridors,** strips of habitat connecting isolated habitat patches. Habitat corridors allow wildlife to move about so they can feed, mate, and recolonize habitats after local extinctions take place. Research has also shown that habitat fragments linked by habitat corridors retain more native plant species than do isolated fragments.

Habitat corridors range from a local scale (such as an overpass that allows wildlife to cross a road safely) to a landscape scale that connects separate reserves. The minimum corridor width for landscape-scale corridors varies depending on the size of home ranges for various species. For example, to link two reserves and protect wolves in Minnesota, the corridor must have a minimum width of 12 km (7.2 mi), whereas the minimum corridor width for bobcats in South Carolina must be 2.5 km (1.5 mi).

The United Nations Educational, Scientific, and Cultural Organization (UNESCO) Program on Man and the Biosphere (MAB) has established **biosphere reserves** to protect biodiversity. Each reserve consists of three zones: core, buffer, and transition. The core zone contains a protected ecosystem and allows for nondestructive research and education. The surrounding buffer zone is used for environmental education, ecotourism, recreation, and research. The transition zone consists of local farms, fisheries, and towns where stakeholders collaborate to oversee and sustainably develop the biosphere's resources. Maintaining biodiversity is a major principle of environmental sustainability.

Restoring damaged or destroyed habitats is the goal of restoration ecology Increasingly, countries are reclaiming disturbed lands and converting them into areas with high biological diversity. **Restoration ecology,** in which the principles of ecology are used to return a degraded environment to one that is more functional and sustainable, is an important part of in situ conservation. Costa Rica is an important success story. By the 1980s, ranchers had cleared so much forest to provide land for grazing and farmers had cleared so much land for growing coffee trees that only about 20% of Costa Rica's tropical forests remained. Then, this small, but ecologically important, country made a commitment to restore and protect its rich biodiversity. Economic and other incentives were offered for restoring and protecting its lands. Once again, forests cover more than 50% of its land area and Costa Rica has become a global leader in environmental sustainability (FIG. 57-11).

One of the oldest and most extensive ecological restoration projects in the United States was undertaken in the early 1930s by the University of Wisconsin–Madison Arboretum. The university ecologists have developed several distinct natural communities on damaged agricultural land (FIG. 57-12). These communities include a tallgrass prairie, a xeric (dry) prairie, savannas, and several types of pine and maple forests native to Wisconsin. More than 300 species have been restored.

Restoration of disturbed lands not only creates biological habitats but also has additional benefits, such as the regeneration of soil that agriculture or mining damaged. Restoration ecology is an important aspect of conservation biology.

Ex situ conservation attempts to save species on the brink of extinction

Zoos, aquaria, and botanical gardens are valuable because they provide the public with informal learning and education opportunities to understand the importance of biodiversity and conservation. These facilities work to save certain endangered species from extinction. Eggs are collected from nature, or the remaining few animals are captured and bred in zoos and other research facilities.

Artificial insemination and host mothering can be used to increase the number of offspring. In **artificial insemination** sperm can be collected from a suitable male of a rare species and used to impregnate a selected female, which may be located in another zoo, or even another country. In **host mothering** a female of a rare species is treated with fertility drugs, which cause her to produce multiple eggs. Eggs are collected, fertilized with sperm, and surgically implanted into females of a related but less rare species, which later give birth to offspring of the rare species (see *Inquiring About: Novel Origins,* in Chapter 50). Plans are under way to clone endangered species, such as the giant panda, that do not reproduce well in captivity. Hormone patches are being developed to stimulate reproduction in endangered birds; the patch is attached under the female bird's wing.

A few spectacular successes have occurred in captive-breeding programs, in which large enough numbers of a species have been produced to re-establish small populations in the wild. Conservation efforts, for example, let the bald eagle make a remarkable comeback in the contiguous states, and in 2007, the U.S. Fish and Wildlife Service (FWS) removed the bald eagle from the endangered list.

Attempting to save a species on the brink of extinction is usually expensive, and only a small proportion of endangered species can be saved. Moreover, zoos, aquaria, and botanical gardens do not have the space to try to save all endangered species. Conservation biologists must therefore set priorities on which species to attempt to save. Zoos have traditionally focused on large, charismatic animals, such as pandas, bald eagles, and whooping cranes, because the public is interested in them. However, such conservation efforts ignore millions of ecologically important species. Clearly, controlling unchecked human development so that species do not become endangered in the first place is a more effective way to protect and maintain natural habitat.

The Endangered Species Act provides some legal protection for species and habitats

In 1973, the *Endangered Species Act (ESA)* was passed in the United States, authorizing the FWS to protect endangered and threatened species in the United States and abroad. Most other countries now have similar legislation. The FWS conducts a detailed study of a species to determine if it should be listed as endangered or threatened (TABLE 57-1). The ESA provides legal protection to listed species, reducing their danger of extinction. For example, the act makes it illegal to sell or buy any product made from an endangered or threatened species.

The ESA requires officials of the FWS to select critical habitats and design a recovery plan for each species listed. The recovery plan includes an estimate of the current population size, an

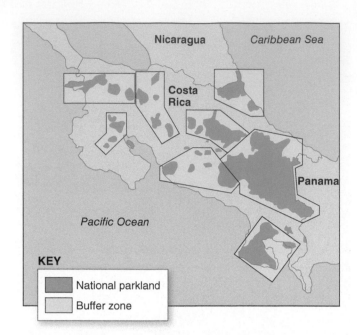

Figure 57-11 Restoration ecology and biodiversity conservation in Costa Rica

Costa Rica has won international awards for restoring its tropical forests and protecting its rich biodiversity. Its protected natural parklands (*green*) are surrounded by buffer zones (*yellow*), which are used for *sustainable* agriculture, cattle grazing, forestry, logging, fishing, and ecotourism. (Adapted from Miller, G. T. and S. E. Spoolman. *Living in the Environment,* 17th ed., 2012, p. 241, Figure 10-26. Brooks Cole/Cengage Learning.)

analysis of what factors contributed to its endangerment, and a list of activities that may help the species recover.

The ESA is considered one of the strongest pieces of environmental legislation in the United States, in part because species are designated as endangered or threatened entirely on biological grounds. Economic considerations cannot influence the designation of endangered or threatened species. Biologists generally agree that as a result of passage of the ESA in 1973, fewer species became extinct than would have had the law not been passed.

The ESA is also a very controversial piece of environmental legislation. For example, the ESA does not provide compensation for private property owners who suffer financial losses because they cannot develop their land if a threatened or endangered species lives there. The ESA has also interfered with some federally funded development projects.

It currently takes about 15 years for a candidate species with declining numbers to be listed as threatened or endangered. This backlog is due to both the high cost of evaluating each species and the limited funds allocated to the FWS for these studies. Meanwhile, more than 80 species on the ESA's "candidate list" have become extinct since 1973, without ever being classified as threatened or endangered.

(a) The restoration of the prairie by the University of Wisconsin–Madison Arboretum was at an early stage in 1935. The men are digging holes to plant prairie grass sod.

(b) The prairie as it looks today. This picture was taken at about the same location as the 1935 photograph.

Figure 57-12 Restoring damaged lands

The ESA is geared more to saving a few popular or unique endangered species than to saving the much larger number of less popular species that perform valuable ecosystem services. About one-third of the annual funding for the ESA is used to help just ten species. Less glamorous plants, fungi, bacteria and archaea, and insects, however, play central roles in ecosystems and contribute. Prokaryotes and fungi, for example, provide the critically important ecosystem service of breaking down dead organic materials into simple substances (CO_2, water, and minerals) that are subsequently recycled to plants and other autotrophs.

Conservation biologists and numerous conservation organizations support a stronger ESA to manage whole ecosystems and maintain complete biological diversity rather than attempt to save endangered species as isolated entities. This approach

TABLE 57-1	Organisms Listed as Endangered or Threatened in the United States, 2012	
TYPE OF ORGANISM	NUMBER OF ENDANGERED SPECIES	NUMBER OF THREATENED SPECIES
Mammals	69	16
Birds	78	15
Reptiles	14	22
Amphibians	16	11
Fishes	80	51
Snails	33	13
Clams	72	12
Crustaceans	20	3
Insects	55	10
Spiders	12	0
Flowering plants	668	150
Conifers and cycads	2	1
Ferns, other plants	28	2
Corals	0	2
Lichens	2	0

Source: U.S. Fish and Wildlife Service.

offers collective protection to many declining species rather than to a few specific species.

International agreements provide some protection for species and habitats

The *Convention on International Trade in Endangered Species of Wild Flora and Fauna (CITES)* is an international agreement that went into effect in 1975. Originally drawn up to protect endangered animals and plants considered valuable in the highly lucrative international wildlife trade, CITES bans hunting, capturing, and selling of endangered or threatened species and regulates trade of organisms listed as potentially threatened. Unfortunately, enforcement of this treaty varies from country to country, and even where enforcement exists, the penalties are minimal. As a result, illegal trade in rare, commercially valuable species continues.

The goals of CITES often stir up controversy over such issues as who actually owns the world's wildlife and whether global conservation concerns take precedence over competing local interests. These conflicts often highlight socioeconomic differences between wealthy consumers of products protected by CITES and poor people who trade the endangered organisms.

Another international treaty, the *Convention on Biological Diversity,* requires that each signatory nation inventory its own biodiversity and develop a **national conservation strategy,** a detailed plan for managing and preserving the biological diversity of that specific country.

57.3 DEFORESTATION

LEARNING OBJECTIVES

6 Discuss the ecosystem services of forests and describe the consequences of deforestation.

7 State at least three reasons forests (tropical rain forests and boreal forests) are disappearing today.

The most serious problem facing the world's forests and their biological diversity is **deforestation,** the temporary or permanent clearance of large expanses of forest for agriculture or other uses (FIG. 57-13). According to the UN Food and Agriculture Organization, between 2000 and 2010 forests declined by about 5.2 million hectares each year (an area equal to the size of Costa Rica).

When forests are destroyed, their valuable ecosystem services are no longer available to the environment or to people who depend on them. Deforestation increases soil erosion and thus decreases soil fertility. Soil erosion causes increased sedimentation of waterways, which harms downstream aquatic ecosystems by reducing light penetration, covering aquatic organisms, and filling in waterways. Uncontrolled soil erosion, particularly on steep deforested slopes, causes mudflows that

Figure 57-13 *Animation* **Deforestation**
Aerial view of clear-cut areas in the Gifford Pinchot National Forest in southwestern Washington State. The lines are roads built at taxpayer expense to haul away logs.

Gary Braasch/Getty Images

endanger human lives and property and reduces production of hydroelectric power as silt builds up behind dams. In drier areas deforestation can lead to the formation of deserts.

Deforestation contributes to the loss of biological diversity. Many species have limited ranges within a forest, particularly in the tropics, making these species especially vulnerable to habitat destruction or modification. Migratory species, such as birds and butterflies, also suffer from tropical deforestation.

By trapping and absorbing precipitation, forests on hillsides and mountains help protect nearby lowlands from floods. When a forest is cut down, the watershed cannot absorb and hold water as well, and the total amount of surface runoff flowing into rivers and streams increases. This increased runoff not only causes soil erosion, but also puts lowland areas at extreme risk of flooding.

Deforestation may affect regional and global climate changes. Transpiring trees release substantial amounts of moisture into the air. This moisture falls back to the surface in the hydrologic cycle. When a large forest is removed, rainfall may decline, and droughts may become common in that region. Studies suggest that the local climate has become drier in parts of Brazil where tracts of the rain forest have been burned. Temperatures rise slightly in a deforested area because there is less evaporative cooling from the trees.

Deforestation increases global temperature by releasing carbon stored in the trees into the atmosphere as carbon dioxide, which enables the air to retain heat. The carbon in forests is released immediately if the trees are burned or more slowly when unburned parts decay. If trees are harvested and logs are removed, roughly one-half of the forest carbon remains as dead materials (branches, twigs, roots, and leaves) that decompose, releasing carbon dioxide. When an old-growth forest is harvested, it may take 200 years for the replacement forest to accumulate the amount of carbon that was stored in the original forest.

Why are tropical rain forests continuing to disappear?

Most of the remaining undisturbed tropical rain forests, in the Amazon and Congo River basins of South America and Africa, continue to be cleared and burned at a rate unprecedented in human history. Tropical rain forests are also being rapidly destroyed in southern Asia, Indonesia, Central America, and the Philippines.

Several studies show a strong statistical correlation between population growth and deforestation. More people need more food and fuel, so they clear forests for agricultural expansion and burn wood for personal use. However, tropical deforestation cannot be attributed simply to population pressures. The main causes of deforestation vary from place to place, and a variety of economic, social, and governmental factors interact to cause deforestation. Government policies sometimes provide incentives that favor the removal of forests. For example, in the late 1950s the Brazilian government constructed the Belem–Brasilia Highway, which cut through the Amazon Basin and opened the Amazonian frontier for settlement (FIG. 57-14). Sometimes economic conditions encourage deforestation. The farmer who converts more forest to pasture can maintain a larger herd of cattle, which is a good hedge against inflation.

If we keep in mind that tropical deforestation is a complex problem, three agents are probably the most immediate causes of deforestation in tropical rain forests: subsistence agriculture, commercial logging, and cattle ranching. Other reasons for the destruction of tropical forests include the development of hydroelectric power, which inundates large areas of forest; mining, particularly when ore smelters burn charcoal produced from rainforest trees; and plantation-style agriculture of crops such as sugarcane, bananas, and palm oil.

Subsistence agriculture, in which a family produces enough food to feed itself, accounts for nearly 50% of tropical deforestation. In many developing countries where tropical rain forests are located, many people do not own the land on which they live and work and must clear the forest to grow food. Land reform in Brazil, Madagascar, Mexico, the Philippines, Thailand, and many other countries is slowly easing some of the pressure of subsistence farmers on tropical forests as deforestation is decoupled from economic growth.

Subsistence farmers often follow loggers' access roads, cut down the trees, burn the area, and plant crops immediately. This method is known as **slash-and-burn agriculture.** Yields from the first crop are often quite high because the nutrients that were in the trees are now available in the soil. In a few years, however, soil productivity declines, and the farmer must move to a new part of the forest and repeat the process. Cattle ranchers often claim the abandoned land because it can still support livestock.

Slash-and-burn agriculture carried out on a small scale, with periods of 20 to 100 years between cycles, is sustainable. The forest regrows rapidly after a few years of farming. However, when millions of people try to obtain a living in this way, the land is not allowed to lie uncultivated long enough to recover. Globally, at least 180 million subsistence farmers obtain a living from slash-and-burn agriculture.

About 14% of tropical deforestation is the result of commercial logging, and vast tracts of tropical rain forests, particularly in Southeast Asia, are harvested for export abroad. Some tropical countries still allow commercial logging to proceed much faster than is sustainable because it supplies them with much-needed revenues. In the final analysis, uncontrolled tropical deforestation does not contribute to economic development; rather, it reduces or destroys the value of an important natural resource.

Approximately 10% of tropical rainforest destruction is carried out to provide open rangeland for cattle. Cattle ranching is particularly important in Central America. Much of the beef raised on these ranches, which foreign companies often own, is exported to restaurant chains in North America and Europe. After the forests are cleared, cattle graze on the land for as long as 20 years, after which time the soil fertility is depleted. When that occurs, shrubby plants, or *scrub savanna*, take over the range.

Why are boreal forests disappearing?

Tropical rain forests are not the only forests at risk from deforestation. Extensive logging of certain boreal forests began in the late 1980s and continues today. Coniferous evergreen

Figure 57-14 Human settlements in Brazil's tropical rain forest

This satellite photograph shows numerous smaller roads extending perpendicularly from the main roads. As people settle along the roads, they clear out more and more forest (*dark green*) for their croplands and pastures (*tans* and *pinks*).

NRSC/Science Source

trees such as spruce, fir, cedar, and hemlock dominate these northern forests of Alaska, Canada, Scandinavia, and northern Russia.

Boreal forests, harvested primarily by clear-cut logging, are currently the primary source of the world's industrial wood and wood fiber. More than 1 million hectares (2.5 million acres) of Canadian forests are logged annually, and most of Canada's forests are under logging tenures. (*Tenures* are agreements between provinces and companies that give companies the right to cut timber.) Canada is the world's biggest timber exporter, and most of its forest products are exported to China and the United States. In 2010, Canada reached an agreement between loggers and environmentalists to protect a huge part of the Canadian boreal forest, 1.4 billion acres of wilderness containing mostly never-harvested woodland. Extensive tracts of boreal forests in Russia are also harvested, although exact estimates are unavailable. Alaska's boreal forests are also at risk because the U.S. government may increase logging on public lands there in the near future.

CHECKPOINT 57.3

- *What are three ecosystem services that forests provide?*
- *What are two reasons for deforestation in tropical rain forests? What is the main reason for deforestation of boreal forests?*

57.4 CLIMATE CHANGE

LEARNING OBJECTIVES

8 Name at least three greenhouse gases and explain how greenhouse gases contribute to climate change.
9 Describe how climate change may affect sea level, precipitation patterns, organisms (including humans), and food production.

Earth's average temperature is based on daily measurements from several thousand land-based meteorological stations around the world as well as data from weather balloons, orbiting satellites, transoceanic ships, and hundreds of sea-surface buoys with temperature sensors. *Data indicate that the ten warmest years since the mid-1800s have occurred between 1998 and 2012.* The 1990s was the warmest decade of the 20th century, and the early 2000s continued the warming trend (FIG. 57-15). Earth's rapidly changing climate imposes stress on many living organisms and is already having a negative effect on biological diversity.

Scientists worldwide have studied **climate change** for several decades. As the evidence has accumulated, a strong consensus was reached that the 21st century will experience significant rapid climate change and that this change has been caused mainly by human activities. Governments around the world organized the United Nations' Intergovernmental Panel on Climate Change (IPCC) in 1988 to review all published literature about global climate change, especially recent research, and provide an update of knowledge on the scientific, technical, and

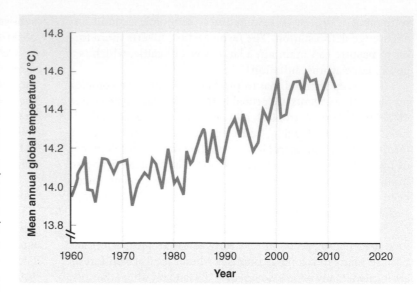

Figure 57-15 Mean annual global temperature, 1960 to 2011

Data are presented as surface temperatures (°C) for 1960, 1965, and every year thereafter. The measurements, which naturally fluctuate, clearly show the warming trend of the last several decades. (Data from Surface Air Temperature Analysis, Goddard Institute for Space Studies, NASA.)

socioeconomic aspects of climate change. Observed and projected effects of climate change in each IPCC report have been progressively worse. The 2013 IPCC Fifth Assessment Report concluded that human-produced air pollutants caused most of the climate change and increased ocean water temperatures observed in the prior 55 years. The IPCC report projects global surface temperature increase is likely to exceed 1.5 to 2.0°C (2.7 to 3.6°F) by the year 2100. Additionally, the global ocean will continue to warm, which will affect ocean circulation, and will undergo further acidification.

Sea levels will rise more rapidly during the 21st century (compared with observations from 1970–2010) as glaciers and ice sheet shrinking will continue to rapidly increase. Thus, Earth will likely become warmer during the 21st century than it has been for several million years.

Greenhouse gases cause climate change

The World Meteorological Organization recently reported a 29% increase in the warming effect of greenhouse gases between 1990 and 2010; carbon dioxide accounted for 80% of this increase. Carbon dioxide (CO_2), methane (CH_4), and nitrous oxide (N_2O) are the three most prevalent and long-lived greenhouse gases, excluding water vapor. Surface ozone (O_3) and hydrochlorofluorocarbons (HCFCs) also continue to accumulate in the atmosphere as a result of human activities (TABLE 57-2). The concentration of atmospheric CO_2 has increased 39% since the start of the industrial era in 1750, recorded at 400 parts per million in 2013 (FIG. 57-16). Burning carbon-containing fossil fuels—coal, oil, and natural gas—accounts for about three-fourths of human-made carbon dioxide emissions to the atmosphere. Land conversion, such as when forests are logged or burned, also releases carbon dioxide. Trees normally remove carbon dioxide from the atmosphere during photosynthesis, but tree removal prevents this process.

TABLE 57-2	Changes in Selected Atmospheric Greenhouse Gases, Preindustrial Times to Present	
GAS	ESTIMATED PREINDUSTRIAL CONCENTRATION	PRESENT CONCENTRATION
Carbon dioxide	288 ppm*	400 ppm
Methane	848 ppb†	1866 ppb
Nitrous oxide	285 ppb	324 ppb
Tropospheric ozone	25 ppb	34 ppb
CFC-12	0 ppt‡	530 ppt
CFC-11	0 ppt	237 ppt

Note: The preindustrial value is for the 17th and 18th centuries.

*ppm = parts per million
†ppb = parts per billion
‡ppt = parts per trillion

Source: Carbon Dioxide Information Analysis Center, Environmental Sciences Division, Oak Ridge National Laboratory.

Climate change occurs because greenhouse gases absorb infrared radiation (heat) in the atmosphere. This absorption slows the natural heat flow into space, warming the lower atmosphere. Some of the heat from the lower atmosphere is transferred to the ocean and raises its temperature as well. This atmospheric retention of heat is a natural phenomenon that has made Earth habitable for its millions of species.

Because carbon dioxide and other gases trap the sun's radiation somewhat like glass does in a greenhouse, the natural trapping of heat in the atmosphere is called the **greenhouse effect,** and the gases that absorb infrared radiation are known as **greenhouse gases.** This natural heating of the atmosphere prevents Earth from becoming a frozen planet. However, the additional warming produced when increased levels of gases produced by human activities absorb additional infrared radiation, called the **enhanced greenhouse effect,** has potentially catastrophic implications as atmospheric and ocean temperatures continue to rise (FIG. 57-17).

Although current rates of fossil fuel combustion and deforestation are high, causing the carbon dioxide level in the atmosphere to increase markedly, scientists think that the warming trend is slower than the increasing level of carbon dioxide might indicate. The reason is that water requires more heat to raise its temperature than gases in the atmosphere do. (Recall the high specific heat of water discussed in Chapter 2.) As a result, the ocean takes longer to warm than the atmosphere. Most climate scientists think that warming will be more pronounced in the second half of the 21st century than in the first half.

Methane gas, the second most prevalent greenhouse gas, has increased 158% since 1750, mostly due to cattle grazing, rice planting, fossil fuel exploitation, and landfills. Human activities currently account for 60% of methane emissions, whereas nearly 40% of emissions are naturally occurring. The natural methane emissions are also growing and are expected to increase still more as northern permafrost thaws and tropical wetlands emissions increase.

Nitrous oxide (N_2O) is now the third most important greenhouse gas and is found at levels 20% higher than in 1750. Its concentration is increasing rapidly due to use of nitrogen containing fertilizers and manure. The effect of nitrous oxide over the past century is nearly 300 times greater than equal emissions of carbon dioxide and is contributing to the destruction of the stratospheric ozone layer, which protects us from harmful solar ultraviolet rays. (See *Inquiring About: Stratospheric Ozone Depletion from Industrial Chemicals.*)

What are the probable effects of climate change?

We now consider some of the probable effects of climate change, including changes in sea level; changes in precipitation patterns; effects on biological diversity, including humans; and effects on agriculture. These changes will persist for centuries because many greenhouse gases remain in the atmosphere for hundreds of years. Furthermore, even after greenhouse gas concentrations have stabilized, scientists think that Earth's mean surface temperature will continue to rise because the ocean adjusts to climate change on a delayed time scale.

With climate change, the global average sea level is rising As Earth's overall temperature increases, major thawing of glaciers and the polar ice caps is taking place. In addition to sea-level rise caused by the retreat of glaciers and thawing of polar ice, the sea level will rise due to thermal expansion of the warming ocean. Water, like other substances, expands as it warms.

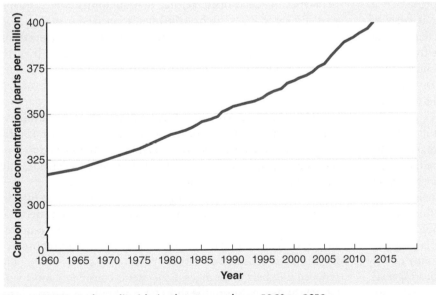

Figure 57-16 Carbon dioxide in the atmosphere, 1960 to 2013

Note the steady increase in the concentration of atmospheric carbon dioxide. Measurements are taken at the Mauna Loa Observatory, Hawaii, far from urban areas where factories, power plants, and motor vehicles emit carbon dioxide. (Data from Scripps Institution of Oceanography, University of California, La Jolla, California.)

Greenhouse gases accumulating in the atmosphere are causing an enhanced greenhouse effect, resulting in climate change. Human activity is largely responsible for these changes.

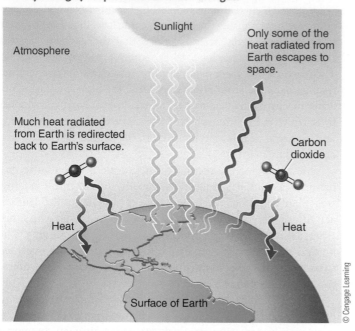

Figure 57-17 *Animation* **Enhanced greenhouse effect**

The buildup of carbon dioxide and other greenhouse gases in the atmosphere absorbs some of the outgoing infrared (heat) radiation and redirects it back to Earth's surface. As a result, the atmosphere, land, and ocean are warming.

CONNECT How can we slow the accumulation of greenhouse gases in the atmosphere?

The IPCC estimates that sea level will rise 18 to 59 cm (0.6 to 1.9 ft) by 2100 and notes that it could be even higher. Such an increase will flood low-lying coastal areas, such as parts of southern Louisiana and south Florida. Coastal areas that are not inundated will likely suffer erosion and other damage from more frequent and more intense weather events such as hurricanes. Countries particularly at risk include Bangladesh, Egypt, Vietnam, Mozambique, and many island nations such as the Maldives.

With climate change, precipitation patterns will change Computer simulations of weather changes from climate warming indicate that precipitation patterns will be altered, causing some areas such as midlatitude continental interiors to have more frequent droughts. At the same time, heavier snowstorms and rainstorms may cause more frequent flooding in other areas. Changes in precipitation patterns could impact the availability and quality of fresh water in many places. Arid or semiarid areas, such as the Sahel region just south of the Sahara Desert, may have the most serious water shortages as the climate warms. Closer to home, water experts predict more water shortages in the western United States because warmer winter temperatures will cause more precipitation to fall as rain rather than snow; melting snow currently provides 70% of stream flows in that region during summer months.

The frequency and intensity of storms over warm surface waters may also increase. A computer model developed by National Oceanic and Atmospheric Administration (NOAA) scientists predicts how climate change may affect hurricanes. When the model was run with a sea-surface temperature 2.2°C warmer than today, more intense hurricanes resulted. (The question of whether hurricanes will occur *more frequently* in a warmer climate continues to be studied.) Increases in storm frequency and intensity are expected because as the atmosphere warms, more water evaporates, which in turn releases more energy into the atmosphere. (Recall the discussion of water's heat of vaporization in Chapter 2.) This energy generates unusually powerful storms.

With climate change, the ranges of organisms are changing Dozens of studies report on the effects of climate change on organisms, from flowering times in plants to breeding times in birds. For example, researchers determined that populations of zooplankton in the California Current have declined 80% since 1951, apparently because the current has warmed slightly. (The California Current flows from Oregon southward along the California coast.) The decline in zooplankton has affected the entire ecosystem's food web, and populations of seabirds and plankton-eating fishes have also declined.

Warmer temperatures in Antarctica—since 1960, the average annual temperature on the Antarctic Peninsula has increased 2.6°C (5°F)—have contributed to reproductive failure in Adélie penguins. The birds normally lay their eggs in snow-free rocky outcrops, but the warmer temperatures have caused increased snowfall (recall that warmer air holds more moisture), which melts when the birds incubate the eggs. The melted snow forms cold pools of slush that kill the developing chick embryos.

Biologists generally agree that climate change will have an especially severe effect on plants, which cannot migrate as quickly as animals when environmental conditions change. (The speed of seed dispersal has definite limitations.) During past climate changes, such as during the glacial retreat that took place some 12,000 years ago, the upper limit of dispersal for tree species was probably 200 km (124 mi) per century. If Earth warms as much during the 21st century as projections indicate, the ranges for some temperate tree species may shift northward as much as 480 km (300 mi).

The U.S. Department of Agriculture reports hardiness zones, based on the average low temperature in an area. Hardiness zones, which indicate which plants will do well at different locations around the country, have already shifted considerably over the past twenty-five years.

Each species reacts to changes in temperature differently. In response to climate change, some species will probably become extinct, particularly those with narrow temperature requirements, those confined to small reserves or parks, and those living in fragile ecosystems. Other species may survive in greatly reduced numbers and ranges. Ecosystems considered most vulnerable to species loss in the short term are polar seas, coral reefs and atolls, prairie wetlands, coastal wetlands, tundra, boreal forests, tropical forests, and mountains, particularly alpine tundra.

In response to climate change, some species may disperse into new environments or adapt to the changing conditions in

Stratospheric Ozone Depletion from Industrial Chemicals

The **stratosphere,** which encircles planet Earth some 10 to 45 km (6 to 28 mi) above the surface, contains a layer of **ozone (O₃).** The ozone layer shields Earth's surface from about 95% of the harmful ultraviolet (UVA and UVB) radiation from the sun (see Figure 1). Ozone is a form of oxygen that is a human-made pollutant in the lower atmosphere, but is a naturally produced, essential part of the stratosphere. Ozone in the lower atmosphere is converted back to oxygen in a few days and so does not replenish the ozone depleted in the stratosphere.

A slight thinning in the ozone layer over Antarctica forms naturally for a few months each year. In 1985, however, scientists observed more thinning than usual. This increased ozone thinning, which begins each September, is commonly referred to as the "ozone hole" (see Figure 2). During the 1990s, the ozone-thinned area continued to grow, and by 2000 it had reached the record size of 28.3 million km² (11.3 million mi²), larger than the North American continent.

Certain chemicals, such as chlorine- and bromine-containing substances, catalyze ozone destruction, destroying stratospheric ozone. The primary chemicals responsible for ozone loss in the stratosphere are a group of chlorine compounds called *chlorofluorocarbons (CFCs),* which were used as propellants in aerosol cans, coolants in air conditioners and refrigerators, and solvents and cleaners for the electronics industry. Additional compounds that also attack ozone include halocarbons (used in many fire extinguishers), methyl bromide (a pesticide), methyl chloroform (an industrial solvent), and carbon tetrachloride (used in many industrial processes, including the manufacture of pesticides and dyes).

After release into the troposphere (lowest part of Earth's atmosphere), CFCs and similar compounds slowly drift up to the stratosphere. There, ultraviolet radiation breaks them down, releasing chlorine. (Similarly, methyl bromide releases bromine.)

The thinning in the ozone layer over Antarctica occurs annually between September and November (spring in the Southern Hemisphere). At this time, two important conditions occur: sunlight returns to the polar region, and the *circumpolar vortex,* a mass of cold air that circulates around the southern polar region and isolates it from the warmer air in the rest of the planet, is well developed.

The cold air causes polar stratospheric clouds to form; these clouds contain ice crystals to which chlorine and bromine adhere, making them available to destroy ozone. The sunlight promotes the chemical reaction in which chlorine or bromine breaks ozone molecules apart, converting them into O₂ molecules. The chemical reaction in which ozone is destroyed does not alter the chlorine or bromine, and thus a single chlorine or bromine atom breaks down many thousands of ozone molecules. The chlorine and bromine remain in the stratosphere for many years. When the circumpolar vortex breaks up each year, the ozone-depleted air spreads northward, diluting ozone levels in the stratosphere over New Zealand, Australia, South America, and South Africa.

As the ozone layer is depleted, more ultraviolet radiation reaches Earth's surface. Increased levels of UV radiation disrupt ecosystems. For example, the productivity of Antarctic phytoplankton, the microscopic drifting algae that are the base of the Antarctic food web, has declined

from increased exposure to UVB. Biologists have also documented direct damage to natural populations of Antarctic fish. High levels of UV radiation may also damage crops and forests. Excessive exposure to UV radiation has been linked to human health problems, such as cataracts, severe sunburns, skin cancer, and a weakened immune system.

If ozone were to disappear from the stratosphere, Earth would become unlivable for most forms of life. The world's nations have addressed this serious environmental problem. In 1987, representatives from many countries signed the **Montreal Protocol,** an agreement that limited production of CFCs. Industrial companies that manufacture CFCs quickly developed substitutes.

International cooperation has continued to be a major force in repairing the ozone layer. Production of CFCs, carbon tetrachloride, and methyl chloroform has been completely phased out in the United States and other countries. Methyl bromide will be phased out by 2015 in most countries. Hydrochlorofluorocarbons will be phased out in 2020 in high-income countries and in 2030 in lower-income countries. Satellite measurements taken in 1997 provided the first evidence that the levels of ozone-depleting chemicals were starting to decline in the stratosphere. International agreements regarding ozone have now been signed by all independent countries in the world (about 196). However, reversing environmental damage is often a very slow process. Stratospheric ozone levels are not expected to return to 1980 levels until 2068, and 1950 levels are not expected until 2108!

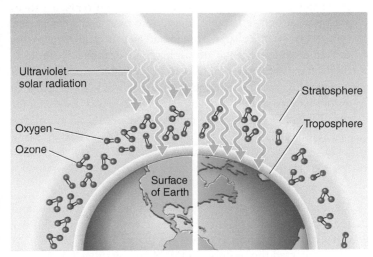

Figure 1 Ultraviolet radiation and the ozone layer. Stratospheric ozone absorbs 99% of incoming UV radiation, effectively shielding Earth's surface (*left*). When stratospheric ozone is reduced (*right*), more high-energy UV radiation penetrates the atmosphere to the surface, where it harms organisms. Stratospheric ozone thinning is accelerated by certain human-produced chemical compounds containing chlorine or bromine.

© Cengage Learning

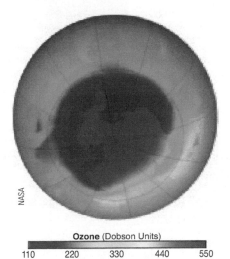

Ozone (Dobson Units)

110   220   330   440   550

Figure 2 Ozone thinning. A computer-generated image of part of the Southern Hemisphere, taken in 2009, showing ozone thinning (*purple* and *blue areas*). The ozone-thinned area is moved about by air currents. (Dobson units measure stratospheric ozone. They are named after British scientist Gordon Dobson, who studied ozone levels over Antarctica during the late 1950s.)

their present habitats. Climate change may not affect certain species, whereas other species may emerge as winners, with greatly expanded numbers and ranges. Those considered most likely to prosper include weeds, pests, and disease-carrying organisms, all of which are generalists that are already common in many different environments.

Climate change will have a more pronounced effect on human health in developing countries Data linking climate change and human health problems continue to accumulate. Since 1950, the United States has experienced an increased frequency of extreme heat-stress events, which are extremely hot, humid days during summer months. Heat-related deaths among elderly and other vulnerable people have been increasing now for many years worldwide.

Climate change has also affected human health indirectly. Mosquitoes and other disease carriers have expanded their range into the newly warm areas and are spreading malaria, dengue fever, yellow fever, Rift Valley fever, and viral encephalitis. As many as 50 million to 80 million additional cases of malaria are predicted to occur annually in tropical, subtropical, and temperate areas.

High-income countries are less vulnerable to such disease outbreaks because of better housing (which keeps mosquitoes outside), medical care, pest control, and public health measures such as water treatment plants. Dengue fever, however, has been increasing in Texas and the Florida Keys. The Centers for Disease Control recently reported a strain of dengue fever unique to the Florida Keys, indicating that the disease has been evolving in the region for many years. In 2012, the United States reported a 70% increase in cases of dengue fever. Mexico has recognized thousands of new cases of dengue fever, especially in the Yucatan and surrounding areas where tourism is prevalent.

Climate change may increase problems for agriculture Numerous studies show that the rising sea level will inundate river deltas, which are some of the world's best agricultural lands. The Nile River (Egypt), Mississippi River (United States), and Yangtze River (China) are examples of river deltas that have been studied. Certain agricultural pests and disease-causing organisms will probably proliferate. As mentioned earlier, climate change will likely increase the frequency and duration of droughts and, in some areas, crop-damaging floods.

On a regional scale, current climate-change models forecast that agricultural productivity will increase in some areas and decline in others. Models have suggested that Canada and Russia will increase their agricultural productivity in a warmer climate, whereas tropical and subtropical regions, where many of the world's poorest people live, will decline in agricultural productivity. Central America and Southeast Asia may experience some of the greatest declines in agricultural productivity.

We know how to prevent emission of greenhouse gases, for example, by reducing use of fossil fuels and replacing them with low-carbon renewable energy resources and solar energy (FIG. 57-18). We are also aware of strategies for removing excess carbon dioxide from the atmosphere, for example, by protecting wetlands and planting trees that store CO_2. The question is whether the global community of nations will work together to solve this very serious problem effectively, as they are doing for the problem of stratospheric ozone depletion.

Prevention

Cut fossil fuel use (especially coal)

Shift from coal to natural gas

Put a price on greenhouse gas emissions

Improve energy efficiency

Shift to renewable energy resources

Transfer energy efficiency and renewable energy technologies to developing countries

Reduce deforestation

Use more sustainable agriculture and forestry

Reduce poverty

Slow population growth

Cleanup

Remove CO_2 from smokestack and vehicle emissions

Store (sequester) CO_2 by planting trees

Sequester CO_2 in soil by using no-till cultivation and taking cropland out of production

Sequester CO_2 deep underground (with no leaks allowed)

Sequester CO_2 in the deep ocean (with no leaks allowed)

Repair leaky natural gas pipelines and facilities

Use animal feeds that reduce CH_4 emissions from cows (belching)

Figure 57-18 Slowing climate change: solutions
This figure shows some strategies we could use to slow atmospheric warming. Reducing the use of fossil fuel, especially coal, is a major prevention strategy. Shifting to renewable energy resources, including solar energy, is another critical action for decreasing greenhouse gas emissions. Because trees and wetlands remove carbon dioxide from the atmosphere, protecting forests and wetlands and planting trees will reduce carbon dioxide in the atmosphere. (Adapted from Miller, G. T. and S. E. Spoolman. *Living in the Environment,* 17th ed., 2012, p. 513, Figure 19-16. Brooks Cole/Cengage Learning.)

THE FUTURE?

We hope that your study of biology has helped you understand that we humans are interdependent with millions of other organisms: our fellow travelers on Planet Earth. We humans have impacted the biosphere more than any other species, and we have seriously disrupted its fragile web of interconnected ecosystems. We are not immune to the environmental damage that we have produced. In fact, we will share the fate of other species on the planet.

We humans differ from other organisms, however, in our capacity to reflect on the consequences of our actions and to alter our behavior accordingly. Humans, both individually and collectively, can bring about change. A global commitment to sustainable living is the key to ensuring the biosphere's survival. The fate of future generations and of the biosphere depends on our decisions and our actions.

CHECKPOINT 57.4

- *What is the enhanced greenhouse effect? What causes the enhanced greenhouse effect?*
- **PREDICT** *What are some of the significant problems that climate change may cause during the 21st century?*

SUMMARY: FOCUS ON LEARNING OBJECTIVES

57.1 The Biodiversity Crisis *(page 1233)*

1 Identify various levels of biodiversity: genetic diversity, species richness, and ecosystem diversity.

- **Genetic diversity** is the genetic variety within a species, both within a given population and among geographically separate populations. **Species richness** is the number of species of archaea, bacteria, protists, plants, fungi, and animals. **Ecosystem diversity** is the variety of Earth's ecosystems, such as forests, prairies, deserts, lakes, coastal estuaries, and coral reefs.

2 Distinguish among threatened species, endangered species, and extinct species.

- A species' **extinction** occurs when its last individual member dies. A species whose severely reduced numbers throughout all or a significant part of its **range** put it in imminent danger of extinction is classified as an **endangered species.** When extinction is less imminent but the population is quite small, a species is classified as a **threatened species.**

Golden toad

© Cengage Learning

3 Discuss at least four causes of declining biological diversity and identify the most important causes.

- Human activities that reduce biological diversity include habitat loss and **habitat fragmentation,** pollution, introduction of **invasive species,** pest and predator control, illegal commercial hunting, and **commercial harvest.** Of these, habitat loss and fragmentation are the most significant.

57.2 Conservation Biology *(page 1239)*

4 Define *conservation biology* and compare in situ and ex situ conservation measures.

- **Conservation biology** is the study of how humans affect organisms and of the development of ways to protect biological diversity.

- Efforts to preserve biological diversity in the wild, known as **in situ conservation,** are urgently needed in the world's **biodiversity hotspots.** Increasingly, biologists are focusing efforts on preserving biodiversity in entire ecosystems and **landscapes,** which consist of multiple interacting ecosystems.

- **Ex situ conservation** involves conserving individual species in human-controlled settings. Breeding captive species in zoos and storing seeds of genetically diverse plant crops are examples.

5 Describe the benefits and shortcomings of the U.S. Endangered Species Act and the Convention on International Trade in Endangered Species of Wild Flora and Fauna.

- The Endangered Species Act (ESA) authorizes the U.S. Fish and Wildlife Service to protect endangered and threatened species, both in the United States and abroad. Conservationists would like to strengthen the ESA to manage whole ecosystems rather than endangered species and individual entities.

- At the international level, the Convention on International Trade in Endangered Species of Wild Flora and Fauna (CITES) protects endangered animals and plants considered valuable in the highly lucrative international wildlife trade. Enforcement varies from country to country; where enforcement exists, penalties are not severe, so illegal trade in rare species continues.

57.3 Deforestation *(page 1244)*

6 Discuss the ecosystem services of forests and describe the consequences of deforestation.

- Forests provide many **ecosystem services,** including wildlife habitat, protection of watersheds, prevention of soil erosion, moderation of climate, and protection from flooding.

- **Deforestation** is the temporary or permanent clearance of forests for agriculture or other uses. Deforestation increases soil erosion and decreases soil fertility; contributes to loss of biological diversity; adversely affects watersheds; and may affect regional and global climate changes.

7 State at least three reasons why forests (tropical rain forests and boreal forests) are disappearing today.

- Forests are destroyed to provide subsistence farmers with agricultural land, to produce timber, to provide open rangeland for cattle, and to supply fuel wood. **Subsistence agriculture,** in which a family produces enough food to feed itself, accounts for much of tropical rainforest deforestation. Extensive logging of boreal forests in Alaska, Canada, and Russia is the world's primary source of industrial wood and wood fiber.

- In **slash-and-burn agriculture,** trees are cut down and burned so that crops can be grown in the soil. Yields from the first crop are high because the nutrients that were in the trees are now available in the soil. When soil productivity declines, the farmer moves to a new part of the forest and repeats the process.

57.4 Climate Change *(page 1246)*

8 Name at least three major greenhouse gases and explain how greenhouse gases contribute to climate change.

- **Greenhouse gases**—carbon dioxide, methane, nitrous oxide, surface ozone, and chlorofluorocarbons—cause the **greenhouse effect,** in which the atmosphere retains heat and warms Earth's surface. Increased levels of human-produced greenhouse gases in the atmosphere are causing concerns about an **enhanced greenhouse effect,** which is additional warming produced by increased levels of gases that absorb infrared radiation.

9 Describe how climate change may affect sea level, precipitation patterns, organisms (including humans), and food production.

- During the 21st century, **climate change** is causing a rise in sea level. Precipitation patterns are changing, resulting in more frequent droughts in some areas and more frequent flooding in other areas.
- Biologists think that climate change will cause some species to go extinct, some to be unaffected, and others to expand their numbers and ranges. Data linking climate change and human health problems (particularly in developing countries) are accumulating.
- Problems for agriculture include increased flooding, increased droughts, and declining agricultural productivity in tropical and subtropical areas.

TEST YOUR UNDERSTANDING

Know and Comprehend

1. Which of the following statements about extinction is *not* correct? (a) extinction is the permanent loss of a species (b) extinction is a natural biological process (c) once a species is extinct, it never reappears (d) human activities have little impact on extinctions (e) thousands of plant and animal species are currently threatened with extinction

2. An endangered species (a) is severely reduced in number (b) is in imminent danger of becoming extinct throughout all or a significant part of its range (c) usually does not have reduced genetic variability (d) is not in danger of extinction in the foreseeable future (e) a and b

3. The most important reason for declining biological diversity is (a) air pollution (b) introduction of foreign (invasive) species (c) habitat destruction and fragmentation (d) illegal commercial hunting (e) commercial harvesting

4. Habitat corridors (a) surround a given habitat (b) cut through a continuous habitat, producing an edge effect (c) vary in width depending on the species they are designed to protect (d) are an important strategy of ex situ conservation (e) have been widely adopted by restoration ecologists

5. In situ conservation (a) includes breeding captive species in zoos (b) includes seed storage of genetically diverse crops (c) concentrates on preserving biological diversity in the wild (d) focuses exclusively on large, charismatic animals (e) a and b

6. Restoration ecology (a) is the study of how humans impact organisms (b) returns a degraded environment as close as possible to its former state (c) is an example of ex situ conservation (d) has been used to successfully reverse the decline in amphibian populations (e) is an important provision of the Endangered Species Act

7. About 60% of tropical rainforest deforestation is the result of (a) commercial logging (b) cattle ranching (c) hydroelectric dams (d) mining (e) subsistence agriculture

8. Climate change occurs because (a) carbon dioxide and other greenhouse gases react chemically to produce excess heat (b) Earth has too many greenhouses and other glassed buildings (c) volcanic eruptions produce large quantities of sulfur and other greenhouse gases (d) carbon dioxide and other greenhouse gases trap infrared radiation in the atmosphere (e) carbon dioxide and other greenhouse gases allow excess heat to pass out of the atmosphere

9. **CONNECT** What gas is a human-made pollutant in the lower (surface) atmosphere but a natural and beneficial gas in the stratosphere? (a) CO_2 (b) CH_4 (c) O_3 (d) CFCs (e) N_2O

10. Where is stratospheric ozone depletion most pronounced? (a) over Antarctica (b) over the equator (c) over South America (d) over North America and Europe (e) over Alaska and Siberia

Apply and Analyze

11. Why might captive-breeding programs that reintroduce species into natural environments fail?

12. **CONNECT** Conservation biologists often say that their discipline is less about biology than it is about economics and human decision making. What do you think that they mean?

13. A more descriptive name for *Homo sapiens* is *Homo dangerous*. Explain this specific epithet, given what you have learned in this chapter.

Evaluate and Synthesize

14. **EVOLUTION LINK** Because new species will eventually evolve to replace those that humans are driving to extinction, why is declining biological diversity such a threat?

15. **EVOLUTION LINK** Biologists have wondered how introduced species that would probably have limited genetic variation (due to the founder effect) survive and adapt so successfully that they become invasive. Part of the answer may be that invasive species are the result of multiple introductions instead of a single one. Explain how multiple introductions from a species' native

area to an introduced area could increase that species' invasion success.

16. **EVOLUTION LINK** Conservation biologists have altered the evolution of salmon populations in captive-breeding programs. Wild female salmon tend to produce fewer but larger eggs because the large eggs contain more nutrients for the offspring than smaller eggs, giving each individual a greater chance to survive. After just a few generations, however, captive-bred females now lay greater numbers of small eggs. Suggest a possible adaptive advantage for many small eggs in the captive-bred environment. What would you predict regarding the reproductive success of captive-bred females released in the wild?

17. **INTERPRET DATA** Study the graph, which shows the combined effects of various factors on biological diversity in 12 different terrestrial and aquatic ecosystems. Which factor is most important overall? Why do you think that climate change and increasing atmospheric CO_2 are represented as separate factors? What is nitrogen pollution? (Adapted from Sala, O. E., et al. *Science*, Vol. 287, 2000.)

18. **SCIENCE, TECHNOLOGY, AND SOCIETY** If you were given the task of developing a policy for the United States to deal with global climate change during the next 50 years, what would you propose? Explain your answer by describing how science, technology, and society would play a role in your policy.

aplia To access course materials, such as Aplia and other companion resources, please visit **www.cengagebrain.com.**

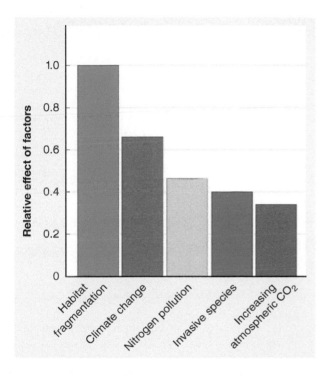

Appendix A
Periodic Table of the Elements

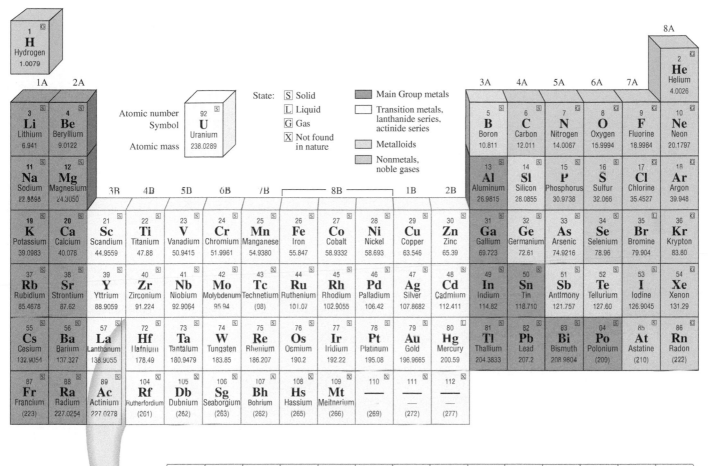

© Cengage Learning

Appendix B
Classification of Organisms

The system of cataloging organisms used in this book is described in Chapter 1 and in Chapters 23 through 32. In this tenth edition of *Biology*, we use the three-domain classification. The three domains are Bacteria, Archaea, and Eukarya (eukaryotes). We also discuss the five "supergroups" of eukaryotes based on molecular data. The kingdoms Plantae, Fungi, and Animalia are assigned to domain Eukarya. The protists are members of domain Eukarya, but are no longer considered a kingdom. We assign them to several supergroups.

In this classification overview, we have included select groups. (We have also omitted many groups, especially extinct ones.) We have omitted viruses from this survey because they are not considered living organisms and are not assigned to any of the three domains.

PROKARYOTES

Domains Bacteria and Archaea are made up of prokaryotic organisms. They are distinguished from eukaryotic organisms by their smaller ribosomes and absence of membranous organelles, including the absence of a discrete nucleus surrounded by a nuclear envelope. Prokaryotes reproduce mainly asexually by binary fission. When present, flagella are simple and solid; they do not have the 9 + 2 microtubule structure typical of eukaryotes.

DOMAIN BACTERIA, KINGDOM BACTERIA

Very large, diverse group of prokaryotic organisms. Typically unicellular, but some form colonies or filaments. Mainly chemoheterotrophic, but some groups are photoautotrophic or photoheterotrophic, and some are chemoautotrophic. Bacteria are nonmotile or move by rotating flagella. Typically have peptidoglycan in their cell walls. Estimated 100,000 to 200,000 species. Bacterial nomenclature and taxonomic practices are controversial and changing. See Table 25-3.

Proteobacteria   Large, diverse group of gram-negative bacteria. Five subgroups are designated alpha, beta, gamma, delta, and epsilon. The alpha proteobacteria group includes *Rhizobium* and rickettsias. Beta proteobacteria include the bacterium that causes gonorrhea. Gamma proteobacteria include the enterobacteria, the group to which the intestinal bacterium *Escherichia coli* belongs, and the purple sulfur bacteria. The delta proteobacteria group includes the myxobacteria, and the epsilon bacteria include *Helicobacter*, which can cause peptic ulcers.

Gram-positive bacteria   Diverse group; includes actinomycetes, lactic acid bacteria, mycobacteria, streptococci, staphylococci, clostridia. Thick cell wall of peptidoglycan; many produce spores.

Mycoplasmas   Lack cell walls. Extremely small bacteria bounded by plasma membrane. May have evolved from gram-positive bacteria.

Cyanobacteria   Gram negative, photosynthetic.

Chlamydias   Gram negative; lack peptidoglycan in their cell walls. Energy parasites dependent on host for ATP.

Spirochetes   Gram negative; spiral-shaped bacteria with flexible cell walls.

DOMAIN ARCHAEA, KINGDOM ARCHAEA

Prokaryotes with unique cell membrane structure and cell walls lacking peptidoglycan. Also distinguished by their ribosomal RNA, lipid structure, and specific enzymes. About 225 named species. Based on molecular data, there are four main clades: **Crenarchaeota, Euryarchaeota, Korarchaeota,** and **Nanoarchaeota.** Archaea are common to most environments, including the human digestive tract, but many are found in extreme environments such as hot springs, sea vents, dry and salty seashores, boiling mud, and near ash-ejecting volcanoes. Three main types of archaea (not clades) based on their metabolism and ecology are *methanogens, extreme halophiles,* and *extreme thermophiles.* See Fig. 25-10.

Methanogens   Anaerobes that produce methane gas from simple carbon compounds.

Extreme halophiles   Inhabit saturated salt solutions.

Extreme thermophiles   Grow at 70°C or higher; some thrive above boiling point. Antarctic archaea live in very cold (1.8°C) environments.

DOMAIN EUKARYA, PROTISTS

Primarily unicellular or simple multicellular eukaryotic organisms that do not form tissues and that exhibit relatively little division of labor. Most modes of nutrition occur in this group. Life cycles may include both sexually and asexually reproducing phases and may be extremely complex, especially in parasitic forms. Locomotion is by cilia, flagella, amoeboid movement, or by other means; flagella and cilia have 9 + 2 structure. Many biologists recognize five supergroups: Excavates, Chromalveolates, Rhizarians, Archaeplastids, and Unikonts.

Excavates Unicellular protists that have deep, or excavated, oral (feeding) groove. Have atypical, greatly modified mitochondria or lack them. Many are endosymbionts. Currently include diplomonads, parabasilids, euglenoids, and trypanosomes.

Diplomonads Excavates with one or two nuclei, no functional mitochondria, no Golgi complex, and up to eight flagella.

Parabasilids Anaerobic, flagellated excavates that often live in animals. Include trichonymphs and trichomonads.

Euglenoids and trypanosomes Unicellular flagellates with crystalline rod in flagella; some free-living and some pathogenic. Many are heterotrophic, but some (about one-third) have plastids and are photosynthetic. At least 900 species.

Chromalveolates Diverse protists that may have originated as a result of secondary endosymbiosis in which an ancestral cell engulfed a red alga. Include alveolates (dinoflagellates, ciliates, and apicomplexans) and stramenopiles (water molds, diatoms, golden algae, and brown algae).

Alveolates Chromalveolates with alveoli, flattened vesicles located inside plasma membrane.

Dinoflagellates Unicellular (some colonial), photosynthetic, biflagellate. Cell walls composed of overlapping cell plates; contain cellulose. Contain chlorophylls *a* and *c* and carotenoids, including fucoxanthin. About 2000 to 4000 species.

Ciliates Unicellular protists that move by means of cilia. Reproduction is asexual by binary fission or sexual by conjugation. About 7200 species.

Apicomplexans Parasitic unicellular protists that lack specific structures for locomotion. At some stage in life cycle, they develop spores (small infective agents). Some pathogenic. About 3900 species.

Stramenopiles Diverse group; most have motile cells with two flagella, one with tiny, hairlike projections off shaft; no flagella in some. Include water molds, diatoms, golden algae, and brown algae.

Water molds Consist of branched, coenocytic mycelia. Cellulose and/or chitin in cell walls. Produce biflagellate asexual spores. Sexual stage involves production of oospores. Some parasitic. About 700 species.

Diatoms Unicellular (some colonial), photosynthetic. Most nonmotile, but some move by gliding. Cell walls composed of silica rather than cellulose. Contain chlorophylls *a* and *c* and carotenoids, including fucoxanthin. At least 100,000 species estimated.

Golden algae Unicellular (some colonial), photosynthetic, biflagellate (some lack flagella). Cells covered by tiny scales of either silica or calcium carbonate. Contain chlorophylls *a* and *c* and carotenoids, including fucoxanthin. About 1000 species.

Brown algae Multicellular, often quite large (kelps). Photosynthetic; contain chlorophylls *a* and *c* and carotenoids, including fucoxanthin. Biflagellate reproductive cells. About 1500 species.

Rhizarians Amoeboid cells that often have tests (shells). Include forams and actinopods.

Foraminiferans (forams) Unicellular protists that produce calcareous tests (shells) with pores through which cytoplasmic projections extend, forming sticky net to entangle prey.

Actinopods Unicellular protists that produce axopods (long, filamentous cytoplasmic projections) that protrude through pores in their siliceous shells.

Archaeplastids Photosynthetic organisms with chloroplasts bounded by outer and inner membranes. This monophyletic group includes Plantae (land plants) and protists (red algae and green algae).

Red algae Most multicellular (some unicellular), mainly marine. Some (coralline algae) have bodies impregnated with calcium carbonate. No motile cells. Photosynthetic; contain chlorophyll a, carotenoids, phycocyanin, and phycoerythrin. About 5000 species.

Green algae Unicellular, colonial, and multicellular forms. Some motile and flagellate. Photosynthetic; contain chlorophylls a and b and carotenoids. About 17,000 species.

Unikonts Cells that have a single flagellum or are amoebas with no flagella. Have a triple-gene fusion that is lacking in other eukaryotes. Includes organisms currently classified in two kingdoms, Animalia and Fungi, and certain protists (amoebozoa and opisthokonts).

Amoebozoa Amoeboid protists that lack tests and move by means of lobose pseudopodia. Include amoebas, plasmodial slime molds, and cellular slime molds.

Amoebas Free-living and parasitic unicellular protists whose movement and capture of food are associated with pseudopodia.

Plasmodial slime molds Spend part of life cycle as thin, streaming, multinucleate plasmodium that creeps along on decaying leaves or wood. Flagellate or amoeboid reproductive cells; form spores in sporangia. About 700 species.

Cellular slime molds Vegetative (nonreproductive) form is unicellular; move by pseudopods. Amoeba-like cells aggregate to form multicellular pseudoplasmodium that eventually develops into fruiting body that bears spores. About 50 species.

Opisthokonts Opisthokonts (Greek opistho, "rear," and kontos, "pole") have a single posterior flagellum in flagellate cells. Includes animals, fungi, and choanoflagellates.

Choanoflagellates Have a single flagellum surrounded at its base by a collar of microvilli. Probably related to the common ancestor of animals.

DOMAIN EUKARYA, KINGDOM PLANTAE

Multicellular eukaryotic organisms with differentiated tissues and organs. Cell walls contain cellulose. Cells frequently contain large vacuoles; photosynthetic pigments in plastids. Photosynthetic pigments are chlorophylls *a* and *b* and carotenoids. Nonmotile. Reproduce both asexually and sexually, with alternation of gametophyte (*n*) and sporophyte (2*n*) generations. Some biologists classify plants as Archaeplastids (along with red algae and green algae).

Phylum Bryophyta *Mosses*   Nonvascular plants that lack xylem and phloem. Marked alternation of generations with dominant gametophyte generation. Motile sperm. Gametophytes generally form dense green mat consisting of individual plants. At least 9900 species.

Phylum Hepatophyta *Liverworts*   Nonvascular plants that lack xylem and phloem. Marked alternation of generations with dominant gametophyte generation. Motile sperm. Gametophytes of certain species have flat, liverlike thallus; other species more mosslike in appearance. About 6000 species.

Phylum Anthocerophyta *Hornworts*   Nonvascular plants that lack xylem and phloem. Marked alternation of generations with dominant gametophyte generation. Motile sperm. Gametophyte is small, flat, green thallus with scalloped edges. Spores produced on erect, hornlike stalk. About 100 species.

Phylum Pteridophyta   Vascular plants with dominant sporophyte generation. Reproduce by spores. Motile sperm.

Ferns   Generally homosporous. Gametophyte is free-living and photosynthetic. About 11,000 species.

Whisk ferns   Homosporous. Sporophyte stem branches dichotomously; lacks true roots and leaves. Gametophyte is subterranean and nonphotosynthetic and forms mycorrhizal relationship with fungus. About 12 species.

Horsetails   Homosporous. Sporophyte has hollow, jointed stems and reduced, scalelike leaves. Gametophyte is tiny photosynthetic plant. About 15 species.

Phylum Lycopodiophyta *Club mosses*   Sporophyte plants are vascular with branching rhizomes and upright stems that bear microphylls. Although modern representatives are small, some extinct species were treelike. Some homosporous; others heterosporous. Motile sperm. About 1200 species.

Phylum Coniferophyta *Conifers*   Heterosporous vascular plants with woody tissues (trees and shrubs) and needle-shaped or scalelike leaves. Most are evergreen. Seeds usually borne naked on surface of cone scales. Nutritive tissue in seed is haploid female gametophyte tissue. Nonmotile sperm. About 630 species.

Phylum Cycadophyta *Cycads*   Heterosporous, vascular, dioecious plants that are small and shrubby or larger and palmlike. Produce naked seeds in conspicuous cones. Flagellate sperm. About 140 species.

Phylum Ginkgophyta *Ginkgo*   Broadleaf deciduous trees that bear naked seeds directly on branches. Dioecious. Contain vascular tissues. Flagellate sperm. Ginkgo tree is only living representative. One species.

Phylum Gnetophyta *Gnetophytes*   Woody shrubs, vines, or small trees that bear naked seeds in cones. Contain vascular tissues. Possess many features similar to flowering plants. About 70 species.

Phylum Anthophyta *Flowering plants or angiosperms*   Largest, most successful group of plants. Heterosporous; dominant sporophytes with extremely reduced gametophytes. Contain vascular tissues. Bear flowers, fruits, and seeds (enclosed in fruit; seeds contain endosperm as nutritive tissue). Double fertilization. More than 300,000 species.

DOMAIN EUKARYA, KINGDOM FUNGI

Eukaryotic, mainly multicellular organisms with cell walls containing chitin. Heterotrophs that secrete digestive enzymes onto food source and then absorb predigested food. Most decomposers, but some parasites. Body form typically a mycelium. Cells usually haploid or dikaryotic, with brief diploid period following fertilization. Reproduce by means of spores, which may be produced sexually or asexually. No flagellate stages except in chytrids. Classified as opisthokonts (along with choanoflagellates and animals) because flagellate cells, where present, have a single posterior flagellum (Greek *opistho,* "rear," and *kontos,* "pole").

Phylum Chytridiomycota *Chytridiomycetes or chytrids*   Parasites and decomposers found mainly in fresh water. Motile cells (gametes and zoospores) contain single, posterior flagellum. Reproduce both sexually and asexually. About 1000 species.

Phylum Zygomycota *Zygomycetes (molds)*   Important decomposers; some are insect parasites. Produce sexual resting spores called *zygospores* and nonmotile, haploid, asexual spores in sporangium. Hyphae are coenocytic. Many are heterothallic (two mating types). About 1100 species.

Phylum Glomeromycota *Glomeromycetes*   Symbionts that form intracellular mycorrhizal associations within roots of most trees and herbaceous plants. Reproduce asexually with large, multinucleate spores called *blastospores.* About 200 species.

Phylum Ascomycota *Ascomycetes or sac fungi (yeasts, powdery mildews, molds, morels, truffles)*   Important symbionts; 98% of lichen-forming fungi are ascomycetes; some form mycorrhizae. Sexual reproduction: form ascospores in sacs called *asci.* Asexual reproduction: produce spores called *conidia,* which pinch off from conidiophores. Hyphae usually have perforated septa. Dikaryotic stage. About 32,000 species.

Phylum Basidiomycota *Basidiomycetes or club fungi (mushrooms, bracket fungi, puffballs)*   Many form mycorrhizae with tree roots. Sexual reproduction: form basidiospores on basidium. Asexual reproduction uncommon. Heterothallic. Hyphae usually have perforated septa. Dikaryotic stage. More than 30,000 species.

DOMAIN EUKARYA, KINGDOM ANIMALIA

Eukaryotic, multicellular heterotrophs with differentiated cells. In most animals, cells are organized to form tissues, tissues form organs, and tissues and organs form specialized organ systems that carry on specific functions. Most have a well-developed nervous system and respond adaptively to changes in their environment. Most are capable of locomotion during some time in their life cycle. Most diploid and reproduce sexually; flagellate haploid sperm unites with large, nonmotile, haploid egg, forming diploid zygote that undergoes cleavage. Classified as opisthokonts (along with choanoflagellates and fungi) because flagellate cells, when present, have a single posterior flagellum (Greek *opistho*, "rear," and *kontos*, "pole").

Phylum Porifera *Sponges*   Mainly marine; solitary or colonial. Body bears many pores through which water circulates. Food is filtered from water by collar cells (choanocytes). Asexual reproduction by budding; external sexual reproduction in which sperm are released and swim to internal egg. Larva is motile. About 10,000 species.

Phylum Cnidaria *Hydras, jellyfish, sea anemones, corals*   Marine, with a few freshwater species; solitary or colonial; polyp and medusa forms. Radial symmetry. Tentacles surrounding mouth. Stinging cells (cnidocytes) contain stinging structures called *nematocysts*. Planula larva. About 10,000 species.

Phylum Ctenophora *Comb jellies*   Marine; free-swimming. Biradial symmetry. Two tentacles and eight longitudinal rows of cilia resembling combs; animal moves by means of these bands of cilia. About 150 species.

Protostomes: Lophotrochozoa

Most are true coelomates (characterized by a body cavity completely lined with mesoderm). Spiral, determinate cleavage; mouth typically develops from blastopore. There are two branches of protostomes: Lophotrochozoa and Ecdysozoa. The Lophotrochozoa include the platyhelminths, nemerteans (ribbon worms), mollusks, annelids, the lophophorate phyla, and the rotifers. The name *Lophotrochozoa* comes from two characteristics of some animals in this clade: the lophophore, a ciliated ring of tentacles surrounding the mouth in three small groups of animals, and the trochophore larva that characterizes its two major groups: the mollusks and annelids.

Phylum Platyhelminthes *Flatworms*   Acoelomate (no body cavity); region between body wall and internal organs filled with tissue. Planarians are free-living; flukes and tapeworms are parasitic. Body dorsoventrally flattened; cephalization; three tissue layers. Simple nervous system with ganglia in head region. Excretory organs are protonephridia with flame cells. About 20,000 species.

Phylum Nemertea *Proboscis worms (also called ribbon worms)*   Long, dorsoventrally flattened body with complex proboscis used for defense and for capturing prey. Functionally acoelomate but have small true coelom in proboscis. Definite organ systems. Complete digestive tract. Circulatory system with blood. About 1200 species.

Phylum Mollusca *Snails, clams, squids, octopods*   Unsegmented, soft-bodied true coelomate animals usually covered by dorsal shell. Have ventral, muscular foot. Most organs located above foot in visceral mass. Shell-secreting mantle covers visceral mass and forms mantle cavity, which contains gills. Trochophore and/or veliger larva. More than 80,000 species.

Phylum Annelida *Segmented worms: polychaetes, earthworms, leeches*   True coelomates; both body wall and internal organs are segmented. Body segments separated by septa. Some have nonjointed appendages. Setae used in locomotion. Closed circulatory system; metanephridia; specialized regions of digestive tract. Trochophore larva. About 15,000 species.

Phylum Brachiopoda *Lamp shells*   One of lophophorate phyla. Marine; body enclosed between two shells. About 325 species.

Phylum Phoronida   One of lophophorate phyla. Tube-dwelling marine worms. About 20 species.

Phylum Bryozoa   One of lophophorate phyla. Mainly marine; sessile colonies produced by asexual budding. About 4500 species.

Phylum Rotifera *Wheel animals*   Aquatic, microscopic. Anterior end has ciliated crown that looks like wheel when cilia beat. Posterior end tapers to foot. Characterized by pseudocoelom (body cavity not completely lined with mesoderm). Constant number of cells in adult. About 2000 species.

Protostomes: Ecdysozoa

Animals in this group of protostomes characterized by ecdysis (molting).

Phylum Nematoda *Roundworms: ascaris, hookworms, pinworms*   Slender, elongated, cylindrical worms; covered with cuticle. Characterized by pseudocoelom (body cavity not completely lined with mesoderm). Free-living and parasitic forms. More than 25,000 species.

Phylum Arthropoda *Arachnids (spiders, mites, ticks), crustaceans (lobsters, crabs, shrimp), insects, centipedes, millipedes*   Segmented animals with paired, jointed appendages and hard exoskeleton made of chitin. Open circulatory system with dorsal heart. Hemocoel occupies most of body cavity, and coelom is reduced. More than 1 million species.

Deuterostomes

True coelomates with radial, indeterminate cleavage. Blastopore develops into anus, and mouth forms from second opening. At some time in their life cycle most deuterostomes (except echinoderms) develop pharyngeal slits, openings that connect the pharynx with the outside environment.

Phylum Echinodermata *Sea stars, sea urchins, sand dollars, sea cucumbers* Marine. Pentaradial symmetry as adults; bilateral symmetry as larvae. Endoskeleton of small, calcareous plates. Water vascular system; tube feet for locomotion. About 7000 species.

Phylum Hemichordata *Acorn worms* Marine with ring of cilia around mouth. Anterior muscular proboscis is connected by collar region to long, wormlike body. Larval form resembles echinoderm larva. About 100 species.

Phylum Chordata *Subphylum Urochordata (tunicates), subphylum Cephalochordata (lancelets), subphylum Vertebrata (fishes, amphibians, reptiles, including birds, mammals)* Notochord; dorsal, tubular nerve cord; postanal tail; and endostyle. About 60,000 species.

Appendix C
Understanding Biological Terms

Your task of mastering new terms will be greatly simplified if you learn to dissect each new word. Many terms can be divided into a prefix, the part of the word that precedes the main root; the word root itself; and often a suffix, a word ending that may add to or modify the meaning of the root. As you progress in your study of biology, you will learn to recognize the more common prefixes, word roots, and suffixes. Such recognition will help you analyze new terms so that you can more readily determine their meaning and will help you remember them.

Prefixes

a-, ab- from, away, apart (*abduct,* move away from the midline of the body)

a-, an-, un- less, lack, not (*asymmetrical,* not symmetrical)

ad- (also **af-, ag-, an-, ap-**) to, toward (*adduct,* move toward the midline of the body)

allo- different (*allometric growth,* different rates of growth for different parts of the body during development)

ambi- both sides (*ambidextrous,* able to use either hand)

andro- a man (*androecium,* the male portion of a flower)

anis- unequal (*anisogamy,* sexual reproduction in which the gametes are of unequal sizes)

ante- forward, before (*anteflexion,* bending forward)

anti- against (*antibody,* proteins that have the capacity to react against foreign substances in the body)

auto- self (*autotroph,* organism that manufactures its own food)

bi- two (*biennial,* a plant that takes two years to complete its life cycle)

bio- life (*biology,* the study of life)

circum-, circ- around (*circumcision,* a cutting around)

co-, con- with, together (*congenital,* existing with or before birth)

contra- against (*contraception,* against conception)

cyt- cell (*cytology,* the study of cells)

di- two (*disaccharide,* a compound made of two sugar molecules chemically combined)

dis- apart (*dissect,* cut apart)

ecto- outside (*ectoderm,* outer layer of cells)

end-, endo- within, inner (*endoplasmic reticulum,* a network of membranes found within the cytoplasm)

epi- on, upon (*epidermis,* upon the dermis)

ex-, e-, ef- out from, out of (*extension,* a straightening out)

extra- outside, beyond (*extraembryonic membrane,* a membrane that encircles and protects the embryo)

gravi- heavy (*gravitropism,* growth of a plant in response to gravity)

hemi- half (*cerebral hemisphere,* lateral half of the cerebrum)

hetero- other, different (*heterozygous,* having unlike members of a gene pair)

homeo- unchanging, steady (*homeostasis,* reaching a steady state)

homo-, hom- same (*homologous,* corresponding in structure; *homozygous,* having identical members of a gene pair)

hyper- excessive, above normal (*hypersecretion,* excessive secretion)

hypo- under, below, deficient (*hypotonic,* a solution whose osmotic pressure is less than that of a solution with which it is compared)

in-, im- not (*incomplete flower,* a flower that does not have one or more of the four main parts)

inter- between, among (*interstitial,* situated between parts)

intra- within (*intracellular,* within the cell)

iso- equal, like (*isotonic,* equal osmotic pressure)

macro- large (*macronucleus,* a large, polyploid nucleus found in ciliates)

mal- bad, abnormal (*malnutrition,* poor nutrition)

mega- large, great (*megakaryocyte,* giant cell of bone marrow)

meso- middle (*mesoderm,* middle tissue layer of the animal embryo)

meta- after, beyond (*metaphase,* the stage of mitosis after prophase)

micro- small (*microscope,* instrument for viewing small objects)

mono- one (*monocot,* a group of flowering plants with one cotyledon, or seed leaf, in the seed)

oligo- small, few, scant (*oligotrophic lake,* a lake deficient in nutrients and organisms)

oo- egg (*oocyte,* cell that gives rise to an egg cell)

paedo- a child (*paedomorphosis,* the preservation of a juvenile characteristic in an adult)

para- near, beside, beyond (*paracentral,* near the center)

peri- around (*pericardial membrane,* membrane that surrounds the heart)

photo- light (*phototropism,* growth of a plant in response to the direction of light)

poly- many, much, multiple, complex (*polysaccharide,* a carbohydrate composed of many simple sugars)

post- after, behind (*postnatal,* after birth)

pre- before (*prenatal,* before birth)

pseudo- false (*pseudopod,* a temporary protrusion of a cell, i.e., "false foot")

retro- backward (*retroperitoneal,* located behind the peritoneum)

semi- half (*semilunar,* half-moon)

sub- under (*subcutaneous tissue,* tissue immediately under the skin)

super-, supra- above (*suprarenal,* above the kidney)

sym- with, together (*sympatric speciation,* evolution of a new species within the same geographic region as the parent species)

syn- with, together (*syndrome,* a group of symptoms that occur together and characterize a disease)

trans- across, beyond (*transport,* carry across)

Suffixes

-able, -ible able (*viable,* able to live)

-ad used in anatomy to form adverbs of direction (*cephalad,* toward the head)

-asis, -asia, -esis condition or state of (*euthanasia,* state of "good death")

-cide kill, destroy (*biocide,* substance that kills living things)

-emia condition of blood (*anemia,* a blood condition in which there is a lack of red blood cells)

-gen something produced or generated or something that produces or generates (*pathogen,* an organism that produces disease)

-gram record, write (*electrocardiogram,* a record of the electrical activity of the heart)

-graph record, write (*electrocardiograph,* an instrument for recording the electrical activity of the heart)

-ic adjective-forming suffix that means *of* or *pertaining to* (*ophthalmic,* of or pertaining to the eye)

-itis inflammation of (*appendicitis,* inflammation of the appendix)

-logy study or science of (*cytology,* study of cells)

-oid like, in the form of (*thyroid,* in the form of a shield, referring to the shape of the thyroid gland)

-oma tumor (*carcinoma,* a malignant tumor)

-osis indicates disease (*psychosis,* a mental disease)

-pathy disease (*dermopathy,* disease of the skin)

-phyll leaf (*mesophyll,* the middle tissue of the leaf)

-scope instrument for viewing or observing (*microscope,* instrument for viewing small objects)

Some Common Word Roots

abscis cut off (*abscission,* the falling off of leaves or other plant parts)

angi, angio vessel (*angiosperm,* a plant that produces seeds enclosed within a fruit or "vessel")

apic tip, apex (*apical meristem,* area of cell division located at the tips of plant stems and roots)

arthr joint (*arthropods,* invertebrate animals with jointed legs and segmented bodies)

aux grow, enlarge (*auxin,* a plant hormone involved in growth and development)

blast a formative cell, germ layer (*osteoblast,* cell that gives rise to bone cells)

brachi arm (*brachial artery,* blood vessel that supplies the arm)

bry grow, swell (*embryo,* an organism in the early stages of development)

cardi heart (*cardiac,* pertaining to the heart)

carot carrot (*carotene,* a yellow, orange, or red pigment in plants)

cephal head (*cephalad,* toward the head)

cerebr brain (*cerebral,* pertaining to the brain)

cervic, cervix neck (*cervical,* pertaining to the neck)

chlor green (*chlorophyll,* a green pigment found in plants)

chondr cartilage (*chondrocyte,* a cartilage cell)

chrom color (*chromosome,* deeply staining body in nucleus)

cili small hair (*cilium,* a short, fine cytoplasmic hair projecting from the surface of a cell)

coleo a sheath (*coleoptile,* a protective sheath that encircles the stem in grass seedlings)

conjug joined (*conjugation,* a sexual phenomenon in certain protists)

cran skull (*cranial,* pertaining to the skull)

decid falling off (*deciduous,* a plant that sheds its leaves at the end of the growing season)

dehis split (*dehiscent fruit,* a fruit that splits open at maturity)

derm skin (*dermatology,* study of the skin)

ecol dwelling, house (*ecology,* the study of organisms in relation to their environment, i.e., "their house")

enter intestine (*enterobacteria,* a group of bacteria that includes species that inhabit the intestines of humans and other animals)

evol to unroll (*evolution,* descent with modification, gradual directional change)

fil a thread (*filament,* the thin stalk of the stamen in flowers)

gamet a wife or husband (*gametangium,* the part of a plant, protist, or fungus that produces reproductive cells)

gastr stomach (*gastrointestinal tract,* the digestive tract)

glyc, glyco sweet, sugar (*glycogen,* storage form of glucose)

gon seed (*gonad,* an organ that produces gametes)

gutt a drop (*guttation,* loss of water as liquid "drops" from plants)

gymn naked (*gymnosperm,* a plant that produces seeds that are not enclosed with a fruit, i.e., "naked")

hem blood (*hemoglobin,* the pigment of red blood cells)

hepat liver (*hepatic,* of or pertaining to the liver)

hist tissue (*histology,* study of tissues)

hydr water (*hydrolysis,* a breakdown reaction involving water)

leuk white (*leukocyte,* white blood cell)

menin membrane (*meninges,* the three membranes that envelop the brain and spinal cord)

morph form (*morphogenesis,* development of body form)

my, myo muscle (*myocardium,* muscle layer of the heart)

myc a fungus (*mycelium,* the vegetative body of a fungus)

nephr kidney (*nephron,* microscopic unit of the kidney)

neur, nerv nerve (*neuromuscular,* involving both the nerves and muscles)

occiput back part of the head (*occipital,* back region of the head)

ost bone (*osteology,* study of bones)

path disease (*pathologist,* one who studies disease processes)

ped, pod foot (*bipedal,* walking on two feet)

pell skin (*pellicle,* a flexible covering over the body of certain protists)

phag eat (*phagocytosis,* process by which certain cells ingest particles and foreign matter)

phil love (*hydrophilic,* a substance that attracts, i.e., "loves," water)

phloe bark of a tree (*phloem,* food-conducting tissue in plants that corresponds to bark in woody plants)

phyt plant (*xerophyte,* a plant adapted to xeric, or dry, conditions)

plankt wandering (*plankton,* microscopic aquatic protists that float or drift passively)

rhiz root (*rhizome,* a horizontal, underground stem that superficially resembles a root)

scler hard (*sclerenchyma,* cells that provide strength and support in the plant body)

sipho a tube (*siphonous,* a type of tubular body form found in certain algae)

som body (*chromosome,* deeply staining body in the nucleus)

sor heap (*sorus,* a cluster or "heap" of sporangia in a fern)

spor seed (*spore,* a reproductive cell that gives rise to individual offspring in plants, protists, and fungi)

stom a mouth (*stoma,* a small pore, i.e., "mouth," in the epidermis of plants)

thigm a touch (*thigmotropism,* plant growth in response to touch)

thromb clot (*thrombus,* a clot within a blood vessel)

troph nourishment (*heterotroph,* an organism that must depend on other organisms for its nourishment)

tropi turn (*thigmotropism,* growth of a plant in response to contact with a solid object, such as a tendril "turning" or wrapping around a wire fence)

visc pertaining to an internal organ or body cavity (*viscera,* internal organs)

xanth yellow (*xanthophyll,* a yellowish pigment found in plants)

xyl wood (*xylem,* water-conducting tissue in plant, the "wood" of woody plants)

zoo an animal (*zoology,* the science of animals)

Appendix D
Abbreviations

The biological sciences use a great many abbreviations and with good reason. Many technical terms in biology and biological chemistry are both long and difficult to pronounce. When confronted with something like NADPH or EPSP, it can be difficult for beginners to understand the reference. Here, for your ready reference, are some of the common abbreviations used in biology.

A adenine
ABA abscisic acid
ABC transporters ATP-binding cassette transporters
ABP androgen-binding protein
ACTH adrenocorticotropic hormone
AD Alzheimer's disease
ADA adenosine deaminase
ADH antidiuretic hormone
ADP adenosine diphosphate
AIDS acquired immunodeficiency syndrome
AMP adenosine monophosphate
amu atomic mass unit (dalton)
ANP atrial natriuretic peptide
APC anaphase-promoting complex *or* antigen-presenting cell
AS Angelman syndrome
ATP adenosine triphosphate
AV node or **valve** atrioventricular node or valve (of heart)
B lymphocyte or **B cell** lymphocyte responsible for antibody-mediated immunity
BAC bacterial artificial chromosome
BH brain hormone (of insects)
BMI body mass index
BMR basal metabolic rate
BR brassinosteroid
bya billion years ago
C cytosine
C$_3$ three-carbon pathway for carbon fixation (Calvin cycle)
C$_4$ four-carbon pathway for carbon fixation
cal calories
CAM crassulacean acid metabolism
cAMP cyclic adenosine monophosphate
CAP catabolite activator protein
CCK cholecystokinin
CD4 T cell T helper cell (T$_H$); T cell with a surface marker designated CD4
CD8 T cell T cell with a surface marker designated CD8; includes T cytotoxic cells (T$_C$)
Cdk cyclin-dependent protein kinase
cDNA complementary deoxyribonucleic acid
CFCs chlorofluorocarbons
CFTR cystic fibrosis transmembrane conductance regulator

cGMP cyclic guanosine monophosphate
CITES Convention on International Trade in Endangered Species of Wild Flora and Fauna
CNS central nervous system
CNVs copy number variations
CO cardiac output
CoA coenzyme A
COPD chronic obstructive pulmonary disease
CP creatine phosphate
CPR cardiopulmonary resuscitation
CREB cyclic AMP response element binding protein
CRF corticotropin releasing factor
CSF cerebrospinal fluid
CVA cardiovascular accident
CVS cardiovascular system
CVS chorionic villus sampling
DAG diacylglycerol
DNA deoxyribonucleic acid
DOC dissolved organic carbon
E_A activation energy (of an enzyme)
ECG electrocardiogram
ECM extracellular matrix
EEG electroencephalogram
EKG electrocardiogram
EM electron microscope or micrograph
ENSO El Niño–Southern Oscillation
EPSP excitatory postsynaptic potential (of a neuron)
ER endoplasmic reticulum
ERK extracellular signal-regulated kinases
ES cells embryonic stem cells
EST expressed sequence tag
F$_1$ first filial generation
F$_2$ second filial generation
Fab portion the part of an antibody that binds to an antigen
Factor VIII blood-clotting factor (absent in certain hemophiliacs)
FAD/FADH$_2$ flavin adenine dinucleotide (oxidized and reduced forms, respectively)
FAP fixed action pattern
F$_c$ portion the part of an antibody that interacts with cells of the immune system
FISH fluorescent in situ hybridization
FSH follicle-stimulating hormone
G free energy
G guanine
G protein cell-signaling molecule that requires GTP
G$_1$ phase first gap phase (of the cell cycle)
G$_2$ phase second gap phase (of the cell cycle)
G3P glyceraldehyde-3-phosphate

GA gibberellin

GAA Global Amphibian Assessment (by World Conservation Union)

GABA gamma-aminobutyric acid

GH growth hormone (somatotropin)

GHIH growth hormone–inhibiting hormone

GHRH growth hormone–releasing hormone

G_i A G protein that inhibits adenylyl cyclase

GINA Genetic Information Nondiscrimination Act

GIP glucose-dependent insulinotropic peptide

GnRH gonadotropin-releasing hormone

GPP gross primary productivity

G_s A G protein that stimulates adenylyl cyclase

GTP guanosine triphosphate

GWA genome-wide association

H enthalpy

Hb hemoglobin

HBEF Hubbard Brook Experimental Forest

HBO_2 oxyhemoglobin

HCFCs hydrochlorofluorocarbons

hCG human chorionic gonadotropin

HD Huntington disease

HDL high-density lipoprotein

HFCs hydrofluorocarbons

HGH human growth hormone

HIV human immunodeficiency virus

HLA human leukocyte antigen

HPV human papillomavirus

HUGO Human Genome Organization

IAA indole acetic acid (natural auxin)

Ig immunoglobulin, as in IgA, IgG, etc.

IGF insulin-like growth factor

IP_3 inositol trisphosphate

IPCC United Nations Intergovernmental Panel on Climate Change

iPSCs induced pluripotent stem cells

IPSP inhibitory postsynaptic potential (of a neuron)

IUCN World Conservation Union

IUD intrauterine device

J joules

JH juvenile hormone (of insects)

kb kilobase

kcal kilocalories

kJ kilojoules

LDH lactate dehydrogenase enzyme

LDL low-density lipoprotein

LH luteinizing hormone

LM light microscope or micrograph

lncRNA long noncoding RNA

LSD lysergic acid diethylamide

LTP long-term potentiation

LUCA last universal common ancestor

MAO monoamine oxidase

MAP mitogen-activated protein

MAPs microtubule-associated proteins

MH molting hormone (ecdysone)

MHC major histocompatibility complex

MI myocardial infarction

miRNA microribonucleic acid

miRNA microRNA

MPF mitosis-promoting factor

MRI magnetic resonance imaging

mRNA messenger RNA

MSAFP maternal serum a-fetoprotein

MSH melanocyte-stimulating hormone

mtDNA mitochondrial DNA

MTOC microtubule organizing center

MVP minimum viable population

mya million years ago

9 + 2 structure cilium or flagellum (of a eukaryote)

9 × 3 structure centriole or basal body (of a eukaryote)

$n, 2n$ the chromosome number of a gamete and of a zygote, respectively

NAD^+/NADH nicotinamide adenine dinucleotide (oxidized and reduced forms, respectively)

$NADP^+$/NADPH nicotinamide adenine dinucleotide phosphate (oxidized and reduced forms, respectively)

NAG N-acetyl glucosamine

NK cell natural killer cell

NLS nuclear localization signal

NMDA N-methyl-D aspartate (an artificial ligand)

NO nitric oxide

NPP net primary productivity

NPY neuropeptide Y

NSF National Science Foundation

P generation parental generation

P53 a tumor suppressor gene

P680 reaction center of photosystem II

P700 reaction center of photosystem I

PABA para-aminobenzoic acid

PAMPs pathogen-associated molecular patterns

PCR polymerase chain reaction

PEP phosphoenolpyruvate

Pfr phytochrome (form that absorbs far-red light)

PGA phosphoglycerate

PGD preimplantation genetic diagnosis

PID pelvic inflammatory disease

PIF3 phytochrome-interacting factor 3

piRNA piwi-associated RNA

PKU phenylketonuria

PNS peripheral nervous system

Pr phytochrome (form that absorbs red light)

pre-mRNA precursor messenger RNA (in eukaryotes)

PRR pattern recognition receptor

PTH parathyroid hormone

PWS Prader-Willi syndrome

r growth rate of a population

RAO recent African origin

RAS reticular activating system

RBC red blood cell (erythrocyte)

REM sleep rapid-eye-movement sleep

RFLP restriction fragment length polymorphism

r_{max} intrinsic rate of increase (of a population)

RNA ribonucleic acid

RNAi RNA interference

rRNA ribosomal RNA

rubisco ribulose bisphosphate carboxylase/oxygenase

RuBP ribulose bisphosphate

S entropy

S phase DNA synthetic phase (of the cell cycle)

SA node sinoatrial node (of heart)

SAR systemic acquired resistance (in plants)

SCID severe combined immunodeficiency

SEM scanning electron microscope or micrograph

siRNA small interfering RNA

snoRNA small nucleolar RNA

SNPs single nucleotide polymorphisms ("snips")

snRNA small nuclear RNA

snRNPs small nuclear ribonucleoprotein complexes ("snurps")

SRP signal-recognition particle

SRP RNA signal recognition particle ribonucleic acid

SSB protein single-strand binding protein

ssp subspecies

STD sexually transmitted disease

STI sexually transmitted infection

STR short tandem repeat

T thymine

T_3 triiodothyronine

T_4 thyroxine

T lymphocyte or **T cell** lymphocyte responsible for cell-mediated immunity

T_C **lymphocyte** T cytotoxic cell (CD8 T cell)

T_H **lymphocyte** T helper cell (CD4 T cell)

TATA box base sequence in eukaryotic promoter

TCA cycle tricarboxylic acid cycle (citric acid cycle, Krebs cycle)

TCR T-cell receptor

TEM transmission electron microscope or micrograph

Tm tubular transport maximum

TNF tumor necrosis factor

TRH thyroid-releasing hormone

tRNA transfer RNA

TSH thyroid-stimulating hormone

U uracil

UV light ultraviolet light

WBC white blood cell (leukocyte)

Appendix E
Answers

CHAPTER 1

CHECKPOINT

1.1 • Information transmission, energy transfer, and evolution are considered basic to life because organisms must be able to send and receive information within their own bodies and with other organisms and their environment; organisms must be able to transfer energy from one form to another to perform life functions; populations of organisms must change over time, or evolve, to survive as their environment changes. • Consumers are dependent on producers for food and energy. Producers and consumers are dependent on decomposers for recycling nutrients. Organisms are interdependent for maintaining the needed balance of gases in the atmosphere. **1.2** • Living organisms differ from a rock because they are characterized by cellular organization, growth and development, self-regulated metabolism, the ability to respond to stimuli, reproduction, and adaptation to environmental change. • If an organism's homeostatic mechanisms failed, the organism could not maintain metabolic processes and it would die. **1.3** • The levels of organization within an organism are the chemical level (atoms and molecules), cells, tissues, organs, and organ systems. • Ecosystems include all of the other categories; because they are the most complex, they interact with the most other biological systems. **1.4** • The function of DNA is to transmit genetic information from one generation to the next through information coded in sequences of nucleotides. • A nervous system transmits information through electrical impulses and chemical compounds, called neurotransmitters. **1.5** • A forest ecosystem would include producers (flowering plants, bushes, trees), primary consumers (grasshoppers, rabbits, worms), secondary consumers (birds, coyote, snakes), and decomposers (bacteria, fungi, archaea). • Consumers depend on producers to provide energy captured from the sun by photosynthesis and stored as carbohydrates. Consumers depend on decomposers to break down complex compounds, releasing nutrients and elements for reuse by producers and consumers. **1.6** • *Python* is the genus name for the African rock python. • The tree showing the major forms of life may be modified as scientists obtain additional data about evolutionary relationships. • The sharp claws and teeth of tigers may have been an evolutionary advantage (improved predation and defensive ability) that began as a random mutation and was selected for in the tiger's environment and then passed on to future generations, becoming an important adaptation in the tiger population. **1.7** • A good hypothesis is reasonably consistent with well-established facts, generates predictions that can be tested, yields test results that are repeatable by independent researchers, and is falsifiable, or can be proved false through testing. • A controlled experiment consists of an experimental group and a control group, which are treated identically except for a variable treatment of the experimental group. • Systems biology depends on information generated by the reductionist approach to yield basic information about components of biological systems.

FIGURE QUESTIONS

FIG. 1-9 Smog and discharge from factories, utilities, and automobiles can reduce sunshine over broad areas, causing decreased photosynthetic activity and death in plants and algae, which results in less food, or available energy, for animals. Gases released into the atmosphere can cause acidified precipitation, which damages leaves of producers and increases carbon dioxide levels, which further increases climate change. **FIG. 1-10** The mushroom would first be classified into a domain (Eukarya), then kingdom (Fungi). Physical and molecular information would help to determine phylum, class, order, family, genus, and species of the mushroom. **FIG. 1-11** The protists do not share enough common characteristics to be classified as a kingdom and have been placed in five "supergroups" based on their commonalities to better reflect how they are evolutionally related. **FIG. 1-16** The cell may be able to carry out life processes under the direction of the donor nucleus. **FIG. 1-17** Results from the repeated experiment might be similar but may not be identical to the result from the previous experiment.

TEST YOUR UNDERSTANDING

1. c 2. e 3. c 4. d 5. b 6. c 7. e 8. d 9. See Fig. 1-11. 10. Failure of the homeostatic mechanism could cause the organism to die. Further explanation relies on a logical description and discussion of the homeostatic mechanism selected for example. 11. A good hypothesis is reasonably consistent with well-established facts, generates predictions that can be tested, yields test results that are repeatable by independent researchers, and is falsifiable, or can be proved false through testing. Examples here will vary. 12. Any answer is acceptable if logically presented and defended. 13. Reductionists study the simplest components of biological processes to understand the whole, while systems biology researchers take the large amounts of reductionist-derived data and do computer analyses to understand the big picture of how biological systems function. Systems biology depends on reductionism because it relies on information generated by the reductionist approach to yield basic information about components and large data sets. The systems approach is more likely to consider emergent properties. 14. The second graph shows the number of chimpanzees who successfully employed learned tool use and retained the knowledge, or remembered, after two months. As time passes, a learned skill may be forgotten. 15. Evolution depends on transfer of information because organisms must be able to recognize changes in their environment to be able to respond and for the population to adapt. Transfer of information depends on evolution because chemical, electrical, and behavioral components must change, or adapt, as the environment changes in order for life to continue. 16. Any response that is defended by logical argument is acceptable. 17. Any subjective response that is defended by logical argument is acceptable.

CHAPTER 2

CHECKPOINT

2.1 • All atoms of an element have the same atomic number, corresponding to the number of protons in the nucleus. Different isotopes of the same element have different atomic masses, depending on their number of neutrons. • A radioisotope is an unstable isotope of an element that can decay, releasing a radioactive particle, such as a β particle. Radioisotopes are used in research to label biological molecules used to trace biochemical pathways, follow the transport of molecules in cells and tissues, and determine the sequence of genetic information in DNA. • Electrons occupying different orbitals of the same electron shell are at the same principal energy level (i.e., have similar energies). **2.2** • A radioisotope can substitute for a nonradioactive atom of the same element because both isotopes have the same chemical characteristics. • Structural formulas contain the most information because they illustrate the structural arrangement of atoms in the compound, as well as their types and numbers. • One gram of hydrogen atoms would contain one mole, or 6.02×10^{23} particles of hydrogen atoms. Two grams of hydrogen molecules (one mole of H_2) would also contain 6.02×10^{23} particles. **2.3** • A chemical compound consists of atoms of two or more different elements combined in a fixed ratio. Not all compounds are made up of molecules. For example, sodium chloride is not a molecule because the sodium and chloride atoms are not joined by covalent bonds. • An atom or molecule can become an anion by gaining one or more electrons; a molecule can also become an anion by losing one or more protons. An atom or molecule can become a cation by losing one or more electrons; a molecule can also become a cation by gaining one or more protons. • Ionic bonds are formed by an attraction between the positive charge of a cation and the negative charge of an anion. Covalent bonds are formed between atoms that share electrons. • Weak forces, such as hydrogen bonds and van der Waals interactions, can produce strong forces when large numbers of these bonds occur over short distances between regions of molecules. **2.4** • In redox reactions energy is transferred in the form of electrons. **2.5** • Water molecules are formed by polar covalent bonds between oxygen and two hydrogen atoms. The region around the oxygen atom is slightly negative and the regions around the hydrogen atoms are slightly positive, allowing hydrogen bonds to form between the oxygen atom of one water molecule and a hydrogen atom of another water molecule. • Hydrogen bonding is responsible for water's high specific heat, which affects the freezing and boiling points of water. Hydrogen bonding also affects the spacing of water molecules in ice, making ice less dense and allowing ice to float on liquid water. The high water content of organisms helps them maintain relatively constant internal temperatures. The high heat of vaporization of water also allows organisms to dissipate heat through evaporative cooling. • Weak forces such as hydrogen bonds have collective strength when many work together. **2.6** • A solution with a [H^+] of 10^{-2} has a pH of 2.0. Its hydroxide ion concentration is 10^{-12}. The solution is strongly acidic. Its [H^+] is one-tenth that of a solution with a pH of 1.0. • Adding a reactant or removing a product would shift the system to the right, resulting in the formation of more product. Adding a product or removing a reactant would shift the system to the left, resulting in the formation of more reactant. • Buffers prevent excessive acidity or alkalinity from occurring in organisms, helping to maintain cellular and extracellular environments within a narrow range of pH. Strong acids or bases cannot work as buffers because there are few undissociated molecules present relative to

the dissociated components of the system. This prevents a dynamic equilibrium from forming, which can allow associated or dissociated components to be produced. • Electrolytes, such as acids, bases, and salts, dissociate to form anions and cations in solution, allowing the solution to conduct electric current.

FIGURE QUESTIONS

FIG. 2-1 Examine the Bohr model for oxygen (atomic number 8) in Figure 2-1. A Bohr model for fluorine would have an additional electron in its valence shell. **FIG. 2-5** An N_2 molecule has 2 electrons in each inner shell and 5 electrons in each valence shell. There are 3 pairs of electrons bonded between the two atoms.

TEST YOUR UNDERSTANDING

1. c 2. e 3. a 4. b 5. c 6. d 7. a 8. a 9. d 10. e 11. e 12. e 13. Refer to Figure 2-1 to construct your diagram. Element A would be expected to donate electrons. Element B would most likely share electrons. Element C would be expected to accept electrons. 14. HCl is the reactant. H^+ and Cl^- are the products. The expression indicates that this is an irreversible reaction. HCl is a strong acid and could not be used as a buffer because there would be very little undissociated HCl remaining after the reaction. 15. You should not immerse your hand. The solution has a pH of 12, which is strongly basic. 16. If hydrogen bonds were stronger, the freezing point of water would be higher, its boiling point would be higher, and it would have a higher specific heat and heat of vaporization. If hydrogen bonds were weaker, these properties would be lower than for existing water. 17. Water is the most fundamental indicator because its unique properties make it unlikely that life could evolve in its absence.

CHAPTER 3

CHECKPOINT

3.1 • Carbon–carbon bonds can produce a wide variety of 3-D molecular shapes because the four possible covalent bonds do not form in a single plane. Carbon–carbon bonds can consist of single, double, or triple bonds that are strong and not easily broken. These bonds can form unbranched or branched chains as well as rings that can be joined, forming complex 3-D structures. • See Figure 3-3 for examples of different types of isomers. Isomers with the same molecular formula have different physical and chemical properties. Cells can distinguish between isomers and usually only one will be biologically active. • See Table 3-1 for the structures and properties of functional groups. • Nonpolar groups lack

distinct charged regions and do not interact readily with water. Polar, acidic, and basic groups are hydrophilic. They have charged regions that associate with polar water molecules. • See Figure 3-5 for an illustration of how water molecules participate in condensation and hydrolysis reactions. **3.2** • Hydrogen bonding between polysaccharides occurs between the hydroxyl groups of the sugar units. Your drawing should show that these bonds occur within a single molecule of the storage polysaccharide, resulting in a helical structure (see Fig. 3-9c). The hydrogen bonds in structural polysaccharides occur between different molecules, forming bundles of fibers (see Fig. 3-10a). **3.3** • Saturated fatty acids contain flexible, unbranched hydrocarbon chains. Adjacent saturated fatty acids can align with each other, and associate by van der Waals interactions along the length of the chains. This makes them more solid at a given temperature by limiting the motions of the chains. Unsaturated fatty acids contain double bonds that produce bends in the chains, preventing them from aligning closely with adjacent chains, reducing the number of van der Waals interactions. *Cis* fatty acids are more liquid than saturated fatty acids at a given temperature. *Trans* fatty acids contain double bonds that do not produce a bend in the chain. These mimic the properties of saturated fatty acids and are more solid at a given temperature than *cis* fatty acids. • Phospholipids are amphipathic molecules. These molecules can form a bilayer in which their hydrophobic fatty acid chains associate in the center of the two layers and the hydrophilic head groups interact with water on the outer surfaces of the bilayer. Triacylglycerols and diacylglycerols are more hydrophobic molecules that tend to form spherical oil droplets in water. This minimizes their interactions with surrounding water molecules and maximizes interactions between their hydrophobic hydrocarbon chains. **3.4** • See Figures 3-16 and 3-17 for representative amino acid structures and the properties of their side chains (R groups). The amino and carboxyl groups participate in peptide bond formation between amino acid subunits. If they are exposed (not part of a peptide bond), the amino group can assume positive charge and the carboxyl group can have a negative charge, depending on the pH of the medium. The R group can consist of any of a number of different functional groups that confer different shapes and properties to the amino acid. Nonpolar R groups are found on hydrophobic amino acids; polar R groups are found on more hydrophilic amino acids. Acidic and basic amino acids have negatively and positively charged side chains, respectively. • The primary structure of a polypeptide influences its secondary and tertiary structures through the differing structural and chemical properties of the amino acids in the polypeptide chain. Interactions between amino acids within the chain, such as hydrogen bonding, ionic bonding, hydrophobic interactions, and disulfide bonding can result in the formation of complex folds and structural domains within the polypeptide. **3.5** • See Figs. 3-24a and 3-25. Pyrimidine subunits in RNA consist of cytosine and uracil. The 5-carbon sugar in RNA is ribose. To convert this sugar to deoxyribose found in DNA, the 3' hydroxyl group of the ribose would be removed, and if the pyrimidine base were uracil, a methyl group would have to be added to convert it to thymine. **3.6** • Refer to the following pairs of figures to compare differences between the indicated molecules: pentose and hexose sugars—Figs. 3-6b and c; disaccharides and sterols—Figs. 3-8 and 3-15; amino acids and monosaccharides—Figs. 3-17 and 3-6; phospholipid and triacylglycerol—Figs. 3-13a and 3-12b; protein and polysaccharide—Figs. 3-18, 3-19, and 3-21, as well as 3-9b and 3-10b; nucleic acid and protein—Figs. 3-18, 3-19, and 3-21 and 3-25.

FIGURE QUESTIONS

FIG. 3-13 Unlike bilayer-forming phospholipids, triacylglycerols lack the hydrophilic head groups needed to associate with water. They would not be able to form organized bilayer structures. **FIG. 3-20** Secondary structure is based on a regular repeating sequence of atoms in the backbone. Insertion of an additional carbon atom between the α-carbon and the peptide bond carbon in some amino acids would disrupt secondary structure by altering the distances between the atoms involved in hydrogen bond formation. **FIG. 3-21** Leucine and valine would associate through hydrophobic interactions. Alanine (a nonpolar amino acid) would not interact with serine (a polar amino acid). Lysine and arginine are positively charged, basic amino acids and would repel each other. Glutamic acid has a negative charge and would form an ionic interaction with positively charged lysine.

TEST YOUR UNDERSTANDING

1. d 2. b 3. e 4. c 5. c 6. a 7. a 8. b 9. c 10. e 11. b 12. b and c or c and d 13. Sulfur would not be able to form hydrogen or ionic bonds with positively charged atoms found in proteins and other biological molecules. 14. Hydrogen bonds and van der Waals interactions can produce strong bonding when many of these bonds and interactions occur within a region of a biological molecule. Examples include α-helical regions and β-sheet regions of proteins and van der Waals interactions between fatty acid chains of membrane lipids. 15. All forms of life share many common components of biological molecules, including the nucleotides of nucleic acids, amino acids of proteins, fatty acids of membrane and storage lipids, and monosaccharides found in complex carbohydrates. These suggest that the use of these building blocks to form many different types of biological structures evolved early in the history of life. 16. Although there are very large combinations of amino acid sequences that can be generated for polypeptides, evolutionary processes select only the small number of sequences that have structures and functions that provide a selective advantage to the organism. 17. The existence of only one of two different kinds of enantiomers for amino acids suggests that the first cells to evolve had L-amino acids and that this feature has been conserved in all their descendants.

CHAPTER 4

CHECKPOINT

4.1 • Because cells, the basic units of life, only come from pre-existing cells, it follows that their lineage extends to very ancient times. • Membrane barriers are required to maintain the appropriate internal chemical environments for cellular functions. • DNA is used for information storage in all cells. • ATP is one convenient form of chemical energy used by all cells. • Small surface areas relative to large internal volumes prevent/restrict the movement of materials into, out of, and throughout the cells. **4.2** • Magnification that exceeds the limits of resolution (the equivalent of sharp focus) cannot improve the observation of fine structural details. • Each method provides different information about the structure or function of a cellular component. For example, microscopy can reveal the location of a protein within the cell and its association with cellular structures. Immunoprecipitation provides information about the quantity of the protein and other proteins that bind to it. Biochemical analyses provide structural and functional information about the protein. **4.3** • DNA, cell membranes, protein synthesis. • Plants have cell walls, chloroplasts, vacuoles, and plasmodesmata. Animal cells have centrioles. • Membrane-enclosed organelles provide cellular compartments with unique chemical environments for specialized functions. **4.4** • DNA is highly organized as chromatin (with RNA and protein); ribosomal RNA is synthesized in the nucleoli; and the nuclear lamina helps organize nuclear contents. • The nuclear envelope and nuclear pores provide selective entry and exit for large macromolecules and macromolecular complexes, such as RNAs, ribosomes, nuclear proteins, etc. • Large molecules, such as large proteins, RNA molecules, and macromolecular complexes are bound to specialized proteins that selectively import their "cargo" into or out of the nucleus through the nuclear pores. Small molecules such as ions and small polypeptides can freely diffuse through the nuclear pores. **4.5** • The rough ER typically consists of flattened membranous sheets that are studded with ribosomes on the cytosolic membrane surfaces. A primary function of the rough ER involves the synthesis of membrane proteins and proteins that are translocated through the ER membrane into the ER lumen. The smooth ER is typically made up of tubular membranous structures. Some regions of the smooth ER carry out membrane and storage lipid biosynthesis; others are involved in numerous functions including detoxification reactions, calcium storage, and various protein modifications. • The *cis* face of the Golgi complex receives proteins from membrane vesicles derived from the ER and initiates modfication of those proteins. The proteins are sequentially modified as they move through the Golgi complex. At the *trans* face of the Golgi complex, proteins are sorted into specialized transport vesicles that are targeted to the plasma membrane or other organelles in the cell such as lysosomes. • See Figure 4-15 for steps in the manufacture and secretion of cellular proteins. • Chloroplasts and mitochondria are organelles that contain multiple membrane compartments involved in the conversion of energy from one form to another. A major function of mitochondria is the breakdown (oxidation) of carbon compounds to form ATP. A primary function of chloroplasts is the capture of energy from light that is then stored in reduced carbon compounds. (See Fig. 4-19.) **4.6** • Cytoskeletal structures maintain cell shape, anchor intracellular structures and membranes, and are involved in the movement of cells and intracellular organelles. The endomembrane system is involved in many different cellular functions, including protein biosynthesis and modification, membrane formation, and membrane trafficking. • Microtubules and microfilaments are fiber-like structures that can be rapidly assembled and disassembled. Both are involved in different types of cellular and intracellular movements. Microtubules are hollow cylinders that can serve as intracellular tracks for organellar movement using molecular motors. Microtubules are also components of cilia and flagella used for cellular locomotion. Microfilaments can generate force and intracellular movement by rapidly assembling and disassembling. Combined with motor proteins such as myosins, microfilaments can also generate force and intracellular movement. • Microtubules are bundled, cylinder-like elements of cilia and flagella; they provide movement when bent by motor proteins such as dynein. **4.7** • The glycocalyx surrounds most cells as a cell coat that extends from the plasma membrane. It is formed by polysaccharides. • Fibronectins are extracellular matrix (ECM) glycoproteins that bind to integrins, which are plasma membrane receptor proteins.

FIGURE QUESTIONS

FIG. 4-11 Ribosomes are assembled in the nucleus and move from the inside of the nucleus to the cytosol through the nuclear pores. **FIG. 4-12** The protein fragment containing the hypothetical NLS sequence would bind to the importin attached to the beads. **FIG. 4-15** The vesicles would be unable to dock with the plasma membrane and release their contents. **FIG. 4-19** Cells would break down the available glucose, but would not be able to produce glucose in the chloroplasts. **FIG. 4-22** The cell would not be able to maintain its appropriate shape or move. **FIG. 4-26** Cilia would not be able to bend if the linking proteins were inflexible or absent.

TEST YOUR UNDERSTANDING

1. d 2. d 3. d 4. e 5. d 6. b 7. a 8. c 9. See Figs. 4-20 and 4-21. 10. None of the measurements agree. Observer 2 is most likely correct if the cells are prokaryotic (0.002 mm = 2 μm); observer 3 is most likely correct if the cells are eukaryotic (2 $\times$ 10^4 nm = 20 μm). 11. Consider the following in formulating your answer: Membranous organelles provide the cell with compartments with unique environments. Fibrous cytoskeletal components provide for structure and movement. 12. Mutant a is probably defective in the formation of ER-derived transport vesicles or in movement of vesicles to the Golgi; mutant b probably has a defect in the formation of secretory vesicles on the *trans* face of the Golgi complex. 13. In formulating your answer, consider features common to all cells, including plasma membranes, ribosomes, DNA, and ATP. 14. Consider the origins and applications of different methods used to study the structures and functions of cells.

CHAPTER 5

CHECKPOINT

5.1 • Phospholipids and sterols are the primary determinants of membrane lipid bilayer fluidity. • See Figs. 5-4 and 5-6. • Sugars are added to proteins in the lumens of the ER and Golgi complexes. **5.2** • Specific molecules move across bilayers through transmembrane proteins that form highly selective channels or pumps. • Some membrane proteins respond to signals. Extracellular parts of transmembrane proteins can bind or link to proteins on the surface of neighboring cells. **5.3** • Water, as well as very small, nonpolar molecules. • Channels function as highly selective pores. Transporters bind specific ions or molecules and change shape to move

bound substrates across membranes. • Aquaporins are specific channel proteins that move water across the bilayer. **5.4** • Isotonic conditions result in no change in plant or animal cells. Under hypertonic conditions plant cells undergo plasmolysis due to water loss; they become turgid under hypotonic conditions. Hypertonic conditions cause animal cells to shrink; under hypotonic conditions they swell and may possibly burst. • The energy source for diffusion and facilitated diffusion is a chemical concentration gradient. • The net movement of particles in a concentration gradient is from a region of high concentration to low concentration. Simple diffusion and facilitated diffusion do not differ in the direction of net particle movement. **5.5** • Active transport requires a source of metabolic energy, such as ATP. • In cotransport, the transport of a substance down its concentration gradient provides the energy to drive the transport of the other substance against its concentration gradient. **5.6** • Both exocytosis and endocytosis move materials across the plasma membrane by vesicular transport mechanisms. • Phagocytosis moves large solid particles across the membrane; pinocytosis moves dissolved molecules. • The steps for the sequence of events for receptor mediated endocytosis are outlined in Figure 5-22. **5.7** • Both desmosomes and tight junctions form strong attachments between neighboring cells. Desmosomes form strong sheets of cells; tight junctions prevent passage of materials through intercellular spaces. • Both plasmodesmata and gap junctions allow the movement of water, ions, and small molecules between the cytosols of neighboring cells. Gap junctions form protein-based channels between neighboring cells; plasmodesmata form continuous membrane-lined channels between the plasma membranes of neighboring cells.

FIGURE QUESTIONS

FIG. 5-5 If the proteins labeled with the green fluorescent antibody were linked to cytoplasmic microtubules, they would not immediately become distributed over the entire hybrid cell. **FIG. 5-16** If equal numbers of Na$^+$ and K$^+$ ions were moved in each pump cycle, chemical gradients of the two different ions would be generated, but there would be no electrical gradient produced. **FIG. 5-18** The energy source for glucose transport is the cotransport of Na$^+$ ions down their concentration gradient. If the Na$^+$/K$^+$ pump were inhibited, the Na$^+$ gradient would disappear, blocking the ability of the symporter to transport glucose. **FIG. 5-22** Humans who produce an LDL-receptor protein with a missing membrane-spanning region exhibit very high levels of cholesterol in the blood because their cells are unable to bind and remove it.

1. c 2. e 3. a 4. b 5. d 6. e 7. b 8. e 9. e 10. The stimulated cells have ten times as many GLUT4 proteins in their plasma membranes as unstimulated cells. 11. Consider that plant cells are held in relatively fixed positions by their cell walls, and also that plant cell walls may act as barriers to many types of molecules. 12. Consider that the properties of cell membranes include their ability to form compartments that maintain unique chemical environments. Can you think of other ways this could have been accomplished in the origin of life? 13. Early evolution of transport proteins would have greatly improved the ability of cells to maintain high internal concentrations of essential molecules and allowed cells to interact with their external molecular environments in a controlled way. These functions would have needed to be provided by some other mechanism if transport proteins had evolved later.

CHAPTER 6

CHECKPOINT

6.1 • The sequence of events involved in cell signaling are: *signal transmission* (synthesis and release of signal molecules), *signal reception* (binding of signals to target cell receptors), *signal transduction* (conversion and amplification of extracellular signals to intracellular signals), and *response* (conversion of the final signal into a cellular response that alters some cellular process). • Signal transduction results in the conversion of an extracellular signal into an intracellular form. Multiple intracellular signals are typically produced in the process, activating and/or deactivating multiple genes and proteins. **6.2** • Neurotransmitters are molecules that transmit signals across synapses between adjacent nerve cells. • Animal hormones are typically secreted by cells into the interstitial fluid. Some may bind to neighboring target cells, whereas others enter the blood to be transported to distant targets. • Endocrine and paracrine regulation are similar in that both involve the production of hormones secreted by ductless glands into the interstitial fluid. Paracrine hormones act locally, diffusing directly to their target cells. Endocrine regulation typically involves the transport of hormones through the blood to other parts of the body. **6.3** • Receptor proteins have binding sites that recognize specific signal molecules. • Receptor up-regulation occurs in response to low concentrations of signaling molecules, increasing the sensitivity of that cell to that particular signal. Receptor down-regulation occurs when concentrations of signaling molecules remain high over extended times, decreasing the sensitivity of the down-regulated cell to that specific signal • Cell-surface receptors contain an external *signal-binding domain,* a *membrane-spanning domain,* and an *internal cytoplasmic domain.* Each type of cell-surface receptor contains a unique signal-binding domain that binds a specific type of signal molecule. • Intracellular receptors bind signal molecules that can diffuse into the cell through the plasma membrane. The activated intracellular receptors are typically transcription factors that regulate the expression of specific genes. **6.4** • The binding of a signal molecule to a cell surface receptor alters the shape of the receptor protein, resulting in conformational changes in its intracellular domain. These changes trigger the activation of intracellular enzymes that produce or activate intracellular signaling molecules. For example, a signaling molecule binds to a receptor that activates a G protein; adenylyl cyclase is activated and catalyzes the conversion of many ATPs to cyclic AMP; cyclic AMP activates many protein kinases, which phosphorylate many proteins, leading to one or more responses. • Second messenger molecules are produced intracellularly in large quantities in response to an extracellular signal. • Scaffold proteins tightly organize the proteins involved in a signal transduction pathway so that they can interact efficiently. Loss of a scaffold protein could result in significant slowing of the signaling pathway, reducing the effectiveness of the response. **6.5** • Cells respond to signals by opening or closing ion channels, altering enzyme activities, or by changing patterns of gene expression • Refer to Figure 6-14 as an example of signal amplification. • The failure to terminate signal transmission can lead to maintenance of the signal, resulting in continuation of a now-inappropriate response such as a failure to close certain ion channels. **6.6** • The observation that choanoflagellates and animals have similar protein kinases suggests that cell signaling became important at very early stages of animal evolution.

FIGURE QUESTIONS

FIG. 6-2 If a cell were exposed to a drug that blocked the activity of signaling molecule A, signal molecule B and other signaling molecules downstream of B would not be activated. There would be no changes in membrane permeability, metabolic processes, and gene expression controlled by that signaling pathway. **FIG. 6-12** If the Ras protein is continuously activated, any of the downstream components of the signaling pathway (Raf, Mek, or ERK) might prove to be good candidates for a drug target aimed to prevent cancerous growth. All of these components act as steps in the pathway to activation of cellular growth.

FIG. 6-13 If the altered LH receptor were activated in the absence of LH, its signaling pathway would be continuously activated, resulting in the constant activation of oocyte maturation and ovulation.

TEST YOUR UNDERSTANDING

1. a 2. e 3. d 4. c 5. a 6. a 7. c 8. d 9. c 10. Binding of a hormone to a G protein–linked receptor results in the formation of many second messengers along with the activation of a number of different protein kinases. Each of these types of signals can result in the activation (or deactivation) of different sets of genes and enzymes, leading to the blocking of DNA synthesis, directional growth toward a mating partner, and other physiological events associated with mating in yeast. 11. The identification of hundreds of protein kinase genes in humans indicates that these enzymes play major roles in the regulation of many different physiological functions in human cells. Since each kinase activates or deactivates a specific set of proteins in response to specific cellular signals, the large number of different kinases indicates that many different types of responses are controlled by these enzymes. 12. d 13. b 14. You might hypothesize that plants and animals have common ancestors. Because they share many of the basic molecular components involved in membrane and organellar structure, growth, metabolism, and cell division, a number of these molecules might have been selected as molecular signals. Similarities in plant and animal signaling include protein kinases and G protein receptors that employ GTP or trigger the synthesis of modified forms of ATP (cAMP) as signals. For the differences in signaling, consider the different structures and functions of plant and animal cells. Plants have cell walls and cells communicate through plasmodesmata, whereas animals can communicate via the extracellular fluid through receptors on membrane surfaces. Plants also respond to different types of stimuli, including light, which could lead to the evolution of receptors and different types of light-sensitive signal molecules. 15. The occurrence of G protein–linked receptors and signal transduction pathways found in plants and animals as well as fungi and algae suggests that these signal pathways may have evolved very early in a common ancestor of all these organisms. This suggests that these molecules and pathways existed in ancient organisms early in the evolutionary process. 16. Tyrosine kinase signaling proteins trigger different types of signal transduction pathways in different cell types, depending on which types of signal transduction proteins are present. Drugs that inhibit tyrosine kinases in cancer cells may also inhibit tyrosine kinases that may be required for certain essential cellular functions in normal cells.

CHAPTER 7

CHECKPOINT

7.1 • See Fig. 7-1. Kinetic energy is used to stretch the spring. Work is performed. The stretched spring has stored potential energy. Potential energy is converted to kinetic energy as the spring is released. **7.2** • First law of thermodynamics: energy cannot be created or destroyed, but can be converted from one form of energy to another. Second law of thermodynamics: when energy is converted from one form to another, some of the usable energy is converted to heat and dissipated into the surroundings. This results in the amount of usable energy in the universe available to do work decreasing with time. • Organisms succeed in the struggle with the second law because they are open systems. They can capture energy from their surroundings to do work. Although this allows living systems to increase in order, the total entropy of the universe (organisms plus their surroundings) always increases over time. **7.3** • In a reaction in which enthalpy decreases and entropy increases, ΔG has a negative value. The reaction is exergonic. • Reaction 2 can do work. **7.4** • (1) X + ATP $\longrightarrow$ X–P + ADP; (2) X–P $\longrightarrow$ Y + P_i. If the ratio of ATP to ADP were to become 1:1, ATP requiring reactions would not work effectively because the ATP/ADP system would be near equilibrium. **7.5** • Reduced compounds have more energy available than oxidized forms. They contain electrons that can be transferred to oxidizing agents, transferring energy in the process. **7.6** • An enzyme reduces the energy of activation of a chemical reaction, speeding up the reaction. • An active site of an enzyme is a region involved in the conversion of a substrate to its product. An allosteric site is a binding site on the enzyme for a molecule that regulates the enzyme's activity. • Temperature and pH affect an enzyme's structure, and thus its activity, by promoting the formation or breaking of hydrogen bonds and number of electrical charges within the protein. • Allosteric inhibition is noncompetitive. The allosteric regulatory molecule binds at a site other than the active site of the enzyme.

FIGURE QUESTION

FIG. 7-10 The reaction would not proceed if ΔG had a positive value. A reaction cannot proceed spontaneously if the products will have more energy than the reactants.

TEST YOUR UNDERSTANDING

1. e 2. d 3. b 4. c 5. b 6. c 7. b 8. b 9. b 10. e 11. a 12. The use of ATP/ADP by all organisms suggests that their role in energy metabolism evolved very early in the history of life among

ancestors that are common for all living organisms. 13. The statement misinterprets the second law of thermodynamics. Entropy always increases only in a closed system such as the entire universe. Organisms are open systems that can extract energy from their surroundings, which can be used to build greater complexity. 14. The reaction is exergonic. The free energy of the products is less than the free energy of the reactants. 15. Reaction 2 is capable of performing work. 16. If the inhibition is competitive, increasing the succinate concentration should reverse the inhibition of the enzyme.

CHAPTER 8

CHECKPOINT

8.1 • Glucose loses electrons, becoming oxidized. • Oxygen serves as an electron acceptor in most cells. **8.2** • ATPs available from one molecule of glucose: (1) glycolysis produces a net yield of 2 ATPs from substrate-level phosphorylation in the cytosol; (2) acetyl CoA formation in the mitochondria does not produce ATP; (3) the citric acid cycle produces a net yield of 2 ATPs from substrate-level phosphorylation in the mitochondria; (4) oxidative phosphorylation produces a net yield of 32–34 ATPs produced from NADH and $FADH_2$ in the mitochondria through electron transport and chemiosmosis. • The electron transport chain functions in the transport of H^+ ions from the mitochondrial matrix across the inner mitochondrial membrane, establishing a proton gradient. Energy stored across the mitochondrial inner membrane in the form of the proton gradient powers ATP synthesis as protons flow back across the inner membrane through the ATP synthase complex. The ATP synthase complex catalyzes the formation of ATP using the energy from proton movement through the complex. • NAD^+ and FAD accept electrons derived from the breakdown of glucose and its products, forming NADH and $FADH_2$. These high-energy electrons are then passed to membrane proteins in the electron transport chain, powering the transport of H^+ ions across the inner membrane to establish the proton gradient used to synthesize ATP. Oxygen is the terminal electron acceptor from the electron transport chain. In the process it is reduced to H_2O. • If most of the ADP in the cell were converted to ATP, oxidative phosphorylation would slow because of a lack of ADP to be converted to ATP. **8.3** • Humans obtain energy from a low carbohydrate diet by converting lipids and other biological molecules in their food into molecular intermediates of glycolysis or the citric acid cycle. • Amino acids from food supplies must be deaminated before the carbon chain can be

metabolized through glycolysis or the citric acid cycle. • Refer to Figure 8-13. Show in your diagram that fatty acids are broken down to form acetyl coenzyme A before being metabolized through aerobic respiration in the citric acid cycle. **8.4** • An equivalent number of hydrogen atoms removed from glucose during glycolysis are transferred to NAD^+ to form NADH. When oxygen is present, the NADH is recycled to NAD^+ through electron transport and oxidative phosphorylation. An equivalent number of these hydrogen atoms is used in the formation of H_2O when the electrons are passed to molecular oxygen during that process. In the absence of oxygen, NAD^+ is recycled from NADH by passing the electrons (and an equivalent number of hydrogen atoms) to organic molecules, forming ethanol and carbon dioxide or lactate. • The ATP yield from fermentation is much lower than that from aerobic respiration because the energy released from the glucose in the form of reduced NADH and $FADH_2$ cannot be used to form large amounts of ATP through electron transport and oxidative phosphorylation. • Chemiosmosis is not involved in fermentation, but anaerobic respiration does involve an electron transport chain (with a terminal electron acceptor other than oxygen) and chemiosmosis.

FIGURE QUESTIONS

FIG. 8-3 In glycolysis, 2 molecules of G3P will yield 4 ATPs, whereas glucose will consume 2 molecules of ATP in the formation of G3P, yielding a net gain of only 2 ATPs. Two molecules of G3P will yield 4 molecules of ATP and 2 molecules of NADH in glycolysis; no energy is captured from pyruvate in glycolysis because it is the end product in the pathway. **FIG. 8-8** If complex III were missing, complex I and complex II would not be able to pass on their electrons down the chain to complex IV and molecular oxygen. Complex I and complex II would remain in a reduced state and would not be able to recycle NADH and $FADH_2$ to the NAD^+ and FAD needed to accept new electrons generated from the citric acid cycle. **FIG. 8-9** If the cells were placed in a basic (low H^+ concentration) environment, a proton gradient would not exist and ATP synthesis would not take place. **FIG. 8-11** If ATP synthases were removed, electron transport would still create a proton gradient across the membrane, but ATP synthesis would not take place. **FIG. 8-14** Anaerobic respiration, because in that process high-energy electrons are transferred from NADH to an electron transport chain that synthesizes ATP by chemiosmosis.

TEST YOUR UNDERSTANDING

1. d 2. a 3. a 4. b 5. c 6. d 7. d 8. e 9. b 10. c 11. d 12. The proton gradient represents a state of low entropy because the proton gradient is highly organized with high H^+ concentrations

in the intermembrane space and low H^+ in the matrix. 13. The first phase of glycolysis involves the coupling of the exergonic reactions of ATP hydrolysis to the endergonic phosphorylation of glucose to form fructose 1,6 bisphosphate. The second phase of glycolysis involves the coupling of the exergonic reactions of the hydrolysis of phosphate and the removal of electrons from G3P to the endergonic phosphorylation of ADP to form ATP and the reduction of NAD^+ to form NADH. 14. If the inner mitochondrial membrane were readily permeable to H^+ ions, the coupling of electron transport to ATP synthesis could not occur because a proton gradient could not be formed across the membrane. 15. Refer to Figure 8-11 in constructing your diagram. 16. When you lose weight, carbon-containing compounds (especially fatty acids) become oxidized, yielding carbon dioxide and water. 17. The universal occurrence of the identical reactions of glycolysis in all organisms indicates that glycolysis evolved at early stages in the origin of life, in cells that became the ancestors of all modern organisms. 18. The need for photosynthetic organisms to continuously replenish oxygen today indicates that aerobic respiration could not have evolved without the previous evolution of oxygen-releasing photosynthetic processes.

CHAPTER 9

CHECKPOINT

9.1 • Red light has the longer wavelength. • Violet light has the higher energy per photon. **9.2** • Refer to Figure 9-4b. The line should be colored green. One side of the line should be labeled the thylakoid lumen. The other side should be labeled the chloroplast stroma. • The matching of the action spectrum of photosynthesis with combined spectra of chlorophylls *a* and *b* indicates that these molecules are the primary mechanism for capturing light energy for photosynthesis. Photosynthesis would be less efficient if their absorption spectra coincided exactly because fewer wavelengths of light in the red and blue regions would be captured, losing those sources of energy. • Fluorescence results from release of a low-energy photon from a molecule that has captured a photon with higher energy. That low-energy photon cannot be used to drive photosynthesis. **9.3** • Molecular oxygen is more oxidized than the oxygen in a water molecule. • Carbon fixation reactions are dependent on ATP and NADPH molecules produced during the light-dependent reactions of photosynthesis. **9.4** • Molecular oxygen is released as a waste product through the splitting of water as electrons are transferred to photosystem II. In aerobic respiration molecular oxygen is the terminal electron acceptor for the mitochondrial electron transport chain, forming water in the process. • Photophosphorylation of ADP to form ATP involves the transport of electrons energized in photosystem II. Their energy is used to form a proton gradient across the thylakoid membrane. ATP is formed when protons diffuse back, through the ATP synthase complexes in the thylakoid membrane. • Cyclic electron transport through photosystem I cannot drive photosynthesis. While ATP can be generated through this process, it does not produce NADPH required for photosynthesis. **9.5** • Phase 1 of the Calvin cycle (CO_2 uptake phase) involves the fixation of carbon when CO_2 reacts with RuBP to form PGA. In phase 2 (carbon reduction phase) PGA is converted to G3P using energy from ATP and NADPH formed during the light-dependant reactions. G3Ps are converted to carbohydrate or remain in the cycle in phase 3 (RuBP regeneration phase, which also requires ATP energy). • A decrease in entropy occurs during CO_2 uptake due to the fixation of the CO_2 into a carbon skeleton by combining it with RuBP. This reaction is exergonic because RuBP is a high-energy molecule. Its formation required energy from ATP and NADPH earlier in the cycle. • Photorespiration requires oxygen and produces CO_2 and H_2O; it differs from aerobic cellular respiration in that ATP is not produced. • C_3, C_4, and CAM plants all have rubisco, which is used to fix CO_2 through the reaction with RuBP at the beginning of the Calvin cycle. Only C_4 and CAM plants employ PEP carboxylase as a way of initially capturing CO_2 prior to the Calvin cycle. **9.6** • Green plants obtain energy from light. They obtain carbon through the fixation of CO_2. Humans obtain energy and carbon from reduced carbon compounds derived from food. **9.7** • Root cells obtain energy and organic molecules from sugars transported through plant vascular tissues from photosynthetic tissues. • Molecular oxygen in the atmosphere is produced by photosynthetic organisms.

FIGURE QUESTIONS

FIG. 9-7 We would expect the bacteria to be distributed in the area corresponding to the yellow/green part of the spectrum if their photosynthetic pigments had a maximal absorption at those wavelengths. **FIG. 9-11** If photosystem I were missing, there would be no terminal electron acceptor to receive the electrons derived from water in photosystem II, so all photosynthesis would stop. **FIG. 9-13** If an inhibitor prevented protons from being pumped across the thylakoid membrane, ATP could not be synthesized using energy captured by photosystem I. As long as $NADP^+$ is available, NADPH could be produced by

electron transport through photosystems II and I. **FIG. 9-14** If the 2:10 ratio of G3P molecules leaving the Calvin cycle were to become a 4:8 ratio, the cycle would run down because the pool of G3P would become depleted with each turn of the cycle, leaving insufficient G3P molecules to continue the formation of RuBP.

TEST YOUR UNDERSTANDING

1. a 2. d 3. a 4. e 5. c 6. a 7. c 8. b 9. Refer to Figure 9-13. The interior compartment should be labeled thylakoid lumen. The exterior should be chloroplast stroma. The proton gradient should show high levels in the lumen and low in the stroma. ATP is synthesized in the stroma. 10. Compare your sketch to Figure 8-11. For chloroplasts, protons are pumped into the innermost compartment (the thylakoid lumen); in mitochondria protons are pumped out of the innermost compartment (the matrix). The direction doesn't matter as long as the ATP synthase complex is oriented correctly with respect to the proton gradient. 11. Not all autotrophs use energy from light. Chemoautotrophs capture energy from reduced inorganic compounds such as hydrogen sulfide, nitrite, or ammonia. 12. All actively metabolizing plant cells require energy (in the form of ATP, NADH, and other reduced compounds) for growth, development, and maintenance that is generated through mitochondrial functions. 13. High-energy electrons in glucose became energized during the light-dependant reactions of photosynthesis. 14. Photoautotrophs could sustain life on Earth without the presence of chemoheterotrophs. Chemoheterotrophs, however, could not survive without sources of energy and carbon skeletons provided by photoautotrophs. 15. The common occurrence of ATP synthase complexes among bacteria, chloroplasts, and mitochondria suggests that these enzyme systems must have evolved early in the history of life. 16. The absorption spectrum indicates that these pigments absorb purple and blue light. Their color would be a mixture of reflected green, yellow, orange, and red light that is not absorbed by the pigments. 17. Some strategies for increasing the food supply might involve engineering food crops to more efficiently carry out photosynthesis and carbon fixation. One strategy might be to produce a more efficient form of the carbon-fixing enzyme rubisco. Another might be to increase the productivity of traditional C_3 food crops for growth in arid and hot climates by incorporating C_4 and CAM enzyme systems into the plant photosynthetic tissues.

CHAPTER 10

CHECKPOINT

10.1 • Informational units on chromosomes are called genes. Genes consist of sequences within DNA molecules that encode information needed to carry out one or more specific cell functions. • DNA found within a nucleus is very long compared to the diameter of the nucleus. In order to address the large differences between chromosome length and nuclear dimensions, DNA molecules are packaged in a highly organized way in chromosomes. **10.2** • The stages of the cell cycle consist of G_1, S, G_2, and M phases. DNA is replicated during the S phase. • The stages in mitosis are: *prophase*—chromosomes shorten and condense; *prometaphase*—chromosomes begin to move to cell's midplane; *metaphase*—duplicated chromosomes align on the metaphase plate; *anaphase*—chromatids (each now a chromosome) separate and move toward opposite poles of the cell; and *telophase*—two nuclei are formed and cytokinesis usually occurs, giving rise to two cells. **10.3** • Cell-cycle checkpoints temporarily block key events in the cell cycle from being activated, ensuring that the previous phase of the cell cycle has been completed before the cell cycle can proceed. • Two types of molecular controls that control the onset of different stages of the cell cycle are (1) the association of Cdk with cyclin to form M-Cdk, which triggers the M phase, and (2) the degradation of M-Cdk, allowing daughter cells formed by mitosis to enter G_1. **10.4** • Homologous chromosome pairs are present in diploid cells. Only one member of a homologous chromosome pair is present in a haploid cell. • Meiosis is a process of cell division resulting in the formation of haploid cells. Mitosis is a process of cell division that produces daughter cells that are genetically identical to the original cell. • Haploid cells can divide by mitosis. They cannot undergo meiotic cell division because they do not contain pairs of homologous chromosomes. **10.5** • In animals, somatic cells are produced by mitosis, and gametes by meiosis. In plants, cells of the $2n$ sporophyte and n gametophyte generations are produced by mitosis. Plant spores (n) are produced by sporophyte cells by meiosis; plant gametes are produced by gametophyte cells by mitosis. • Many protists remain haploid throughout most of their life cycle. Two haploid gametes can fuse through fertilization, however, to form a diploid zygote, which subsequently undergoes meiosis to restore the haploid chromosome number.

FIGURE QUESTIONS

FIG. 10-4 Histone H1 is involved in the packing of 10 nm nucleosomes, forming 30 nm packed nucleosome fibers. **FIG. 10-8** If cohesins failed to separate, two daughter chromosomes might move to the same pole, resulting in one cell that has two copies of a given chromosome and a sister cell that has no copies of that same chromosome. If the chromatids dissociated prematurely in late prophase, the separated chromosomes would not arrange properly on the metaphase plate and might not separate equally into the two daughter cells. **FIG. 10-10** If spindle microtubules disassembled at their polar ends, the distances between the bleached areas and the poles would be decreased. **FIG. 10-13** Refer to Figure 10-9. If the cell were arrested at the metaphase–anaphase checkpoint, chromosomes would stay aligned at the metaphase plate of the cell. **FIG. 10-14** If cyclin were not degraded in step 4, cells formed by mitosis would not enter into the G_1 phase.

TEST YOUR UNDERSTANDING

1. c 2. d 3. e 4. d 5. c 6. c 7. b 8. b 9. Refer to Figures 10-6 and 10-7. 10. The DNA content of a cell doubles as the cells progress through the S phase of interphase. The number of chromosomes does not change. At the end of the S phase, each chromosome consists of two identical DNA molecules as chromatids. 11. For a cell with 5 chromosomes:

	Number of Duplicated Chromosomes	Number of Unduplicated Chromosomes	Number of Kinetochores
Prophase (number per cell)	5	0	10
Metaphase (number per cell)	5	0	10
Telophase (number per nucleus)	0	5	5

The cell is haploid because an odd number of chromosomes indicates that there are no pairs of homologous chromosomes. 12. For a diploid cell with 14 chromosomes:

	Number of Duplicated Chromosomes	Number of Unduplicated Chromosomes	Number of Tetrads
Beginning of prophase I (number per cell)	14	0	0
End of prophase I (number per cell)	14	0	7
End of telophase II (number per nucleus)	0	7	0

13. Honeybee drones are produced by an asexual mechanism with no fusion of gametes. 14. Seeds develop from a flower pollinated by the same plant through sexual reproduction resulting from the fusion of two haploid gametes. 15. The chromosomal mechanisms of mitosis are similar in organisms as diverse as seaweeds and mammals, indicating an evolutionary relationship between these groups of organisms. 16. During unfavorable conditions, sexual reproduction involving meiotic recombination and fusion of gametes would ensure a more genetically diverse generation than the identical progeny produced by asexual reproduction. Greater genetic diversity within a generation increases the chance of survival of at least some offspring as new environmental conditions emerge.

CHAPTER 11

CHECKPOINT

11.1 • A single diploid individual can have a maximum of two different alleles for a genetic locus. • Segregation cannot be demonstrated between crosses of either two homozygous dominant individuals or two homozygous recessive individuals. All progeny in those crosses will either show a homozygous dominant or homozygous recessive phenotype. • A monohybrid cross involves only one locus and cannot be used to demonstrate independent assortment. To observe independent assortment, you need individuals heterozygous for two different loci. **11.2** • The F_1 individuals crossed would be $YyRr \times YyRr$. To produce yellow round seeds a plant must be $Y\_R\_$ (probability in this cross = $\%_{16}$). • The product rule and the sum rule are used to obtain the result. **11.3** • If two loci are unlinked, the ratio of genotypes to phenotypes in a two-point testcross is 1:1:1:1. • Unlinked genes reside on different chromosomes. Crossing-over occurs only between homologous chromosomes. The mechanism of recombination for unlinked genes is independent assortment. • The map distance between the two loci is 5 map units. • The Y chromosome determines male sex in humans and most other mammals. • Dosage compensation is required in mammals because females have roughly twice as many genes on their two X chromosomes as males, who have only one X chromosome. In females, one X chromosome is inactivated in most cells to balance the number of active X chromosome genes between males and females. One of the two X chromosomes is active in some cells, and the other X is active in other cells, leading to variegated expression (on a cell by cell basis) of many X-linked genes. **11.4** • For ABO blood types, the A allele and the B allele are codominant, and are both fully expressed in heterozygotes. For traits with incomplete dominance, both alleles are expressed, but the phenotype is a mixture of the two traits, as in the pink flower color of heterozygous four o'clocks. • A trait with multiple alleles means that more than two different alleles for a locus can occur in a population. Only two alleles, however, can occur within an individual. Polygenic inheritance refers to a phenotypic trait that is produced by the additive action of alleles of more than one locus in an individual. • Pleiotropy is the ability of a gene to have multiple effects on the phenotype. Epistasis refers to the interaction between alleles of two different loci. • The *norm of reaction* refers to the range of phenotypic possibilities that can develop from a single genotype under different environmental conditions. In the case of the hydrangeas, the range may include a variety of pink, purple, and blue hues, but may not extend to other colors such as yellow.

FIGURE QUESTIONS

FIG. 11-3 All F_2 generation short plants are homozygous recessive. You would be able to discover the genotype of an F_2 generation tall plant by crossing it with an F_2 short plant. If the tall plant is heterozygous, you will obtain a 1:1 ratio of tall and short progeny. If it is homozygous dominant, all progeny will be tall (but heterozygous). **FIG. 11-4** The haploid cells would be spores if meiosis were occurring in a plant and gametes if it were occurring in an animal. **FIG. 11-6** You would expect the same results if the genotypes in the P generation were reversed. **FIG. 11-7** If only one black individual were produced from the test cross, the genotype of the black parent could be either homozygous or heterozygous. If a single brown individual were produced, the genotype of the black parent would be heterozygous. **FIG. 11-8** The results would be the same. Segregation and independent assortment do not act differently depending on parental genotype. **FIG. 11-9** The diagram would be drawn the same (refer to the answer for Figure 11-8). **FIG. 11-11** You would expect a similar excess of parental class progeny and a deficiency of recombinant class progeny, but the classes would be reversed. The parental classes would be *Bbvv* and *bbVv*. The recombinant classes would be *BbVv* and *bbvv*. **FIG. 11-12** Your diagram would be similar to that shown in Figure 11-12. The red homologue would have the genotype *bV* on each chromatid and the blue homologue would have the genotype *Bv*. Following the crossover, the recombinant chromatid of the red homologue would have a blue tip with *B* and the recombinant chromatid of the blue homologue would have a red tip with *b*. **FIG. 11-16** The calico cat would be female. If the cat were black or orange, it could be either a male, or a female homozygous for black or orange. **FIG. 11-17** A pink-flowered (heterozygous) plant crossed with a white-flowered (homozygous) plant would yield a 1:1 ratio of pink- and white-flowered plants. Crossing a pink plant with a red (homozygous) plant would yield a ratio of 1:1 red and pink progeny. **FIG. 11-18** Two *PpRr* chickens would produce offspring in the ratio of 9 walnut, 3 pea, 3 rose, and 1 single-combed. **FIG. 11-19** Two black labs could produce a yellow puppy if the parents were heterozygous (*BbEe*), producing a puppy with a *B_ee* or *bbee* genotype. **FIG. 11-20** Possible genotypes from the class in the middle include all combinations that include 3 "dark" alleles and 3 "light" alleles (*AaBbCc*, *AABbcc*, *AAbbCc*, *aaBBCc*, *aaBbCC*, *AaBBcc*, or *AabbCC*).

TEST YOUR UNDERSTANDING

1. d 2. c 3. c 4. e 5. c 6. b 7. The short-winged genotype is recessive. The parents were both heterozygous for wing length. 8. Hair length: *S* = short hair, *s* = long hair. Coat color: *B* = black, *b* = brown/tan. *BBss* × *bbSS* ⟶ *BbSs* F₁ progeny (black, short hair). If two F₁s are mated, probability of long hair is ¼, and the probability of brown/tan is ¼. ¼ × ¼ = ¹⁄₁₆. The probability of producing a long-haired, brown/tan cat is ¹⁄₁₆. 9. Yes, Richard could be the child of the parents if both were heterozygous (*I^Bi* × *I^Bi*). 10. Rooster: *PpRr*; Hen A: *PpRR*; Hen B: *Pprr*; Hen C: *PPRR*. 11. The cross is a two-point test cross; the loci are linked. Parental classes are *Aabb* and *aaBb*; recombinant classes are *AaBb* and *aabb*. The percentage of recombination between the two loci is 4.6%. The two loci are 4.6 map units apart. 12. Gene *A*

is in the middle if *B* and *C* are 10 map units apart. Gene *C* is in the middle if *B* and *C* are 2 map units apart. 13. (a) Refer to Figure 11-4 to construct a diagram of gene segregation. (b) Refer to Figure 11-9 to diagram alleles that undergo independent assortment. (c) Refer to Figure 11-12 to construct a diagram of two linked loci that undergo recombination. 14. You cannot usually discriminate between the phenotypes of heterozygous and homozygous individuals for genes that exhibit simple Mendelian dominant and recessive inheritance. You may be able to predict the phenotype of an individual if you know the genotype, but keep in mind that the phenotype may be influenced by the environment or by other genes (epistasis). 15. Linked genes recombine through crossing-over during meiosis. Unlinked genes are on nonhomologous chromosomes and recombine through independent assortment during meiosis. 16. The inherited variation among individuals that Darwin observed is caused by the different combinations of alleles of one or more loci found in each individual. 17. Sixty-four individuals were involved in the hypothetical cross. Of those, 1.6% (¹⁄₆₄) had the lightest skin possible and 1.6% had the darkest skin possible.

CHAPTER 12

CHECKPOINT

12.1 • Griffith's work showed that a genetic trait (virulence) could be transferred from one bacterial strain to another. This allowed Avery and his colleagues to determine that the trait was transferred from the DNA that was extracted from the donor strain. • Hershey and Chase knew that proteins of bacteriophages could be specifically labeled with radioactive sulfur and that bacteriophage DNA could be specifically labeled with radioactive phosphorus, allowing them to determine which type of molecule entered a bacterial cell upon infection. **12.2** • Adenine, thymine, guanine, and cytosine nucleotides make up a single strand of DNA. They are linked together through their 5′ phosphate groups that are covalently bonded to the 3′ carbon of the deoxyribose subunit of the next base in the polynucleotide chain. • Watson and Crick determined that double-stranded DNA consisted of two single strands of DNA running in opposite directions to form a helix, with the nitrogenous bases stacked on the inside and their phosphodiester chains on the outside; the bases in the interior of the helix are hydrogen bonded to their complementary bases (A:T and G:C) on the opposite strand. • Chargaff's rules showed that in DNA molecules extracted from different organisms, the amount of adenine was equal to the amount of thymine and the amount of guanine was equal to the amount of cytosine. This corresponded to the base pairing rules for

double-stranded DNA in Watson and Crick's model. **12.3** • Meselson and Stahl were able to separate and identify DNA strands from different generations of bacteria by labeling them with either ¹⁴N or ¹⁵N as they were being replicated. By showing that ¹⁵N-labeled DNA progressed from a dense to intermediate and lighter densities in subsequent generations of growth on ¹⁴N-labeled medium, they demonstrated that DNA was replicated by a semi-conservative mechanism. • The two strands of a DNA molecule run in opposite directions. Because DNA polymerase can only add bases to a growing 3′ end, one strand is replicated in a continuous manner, and the opposite strand is replicated discontinuously. • Eukaryotic cells require telomerase because their DNA is linear, resulting in shortened ends with each round of DNA replication. Bacterial DNA is circular and is replicated completely with each round of replication.

FIGURE QUESTIONS

FIG. 12-1 Heat-killed S cells treated by methods 1 or 2 would still transform the rough cells to virulence. Method 3 would prevent the S cells from transforming R cells into S cells. **FIG. 12-3** The Hershey–Chase experiments reinforced Avery, McCleod, and McCarthy's findings that genes are composed of nucleic acids by showing that only bacteriophage DNA is required to form new bacteriophage particles composed of both DNA and protein. **FIG. 12-9** G:C base pairs are linked by three double bonds; A:T base pairs are linked by two double bonds. It would require more energy to separate the strands (to break the bonds) of G:C–rich DNA than A:T–rich DNA. **FIG. 12-11** Refer to Figures 12-10b and c. Conservative replication would produce a light and heavy band after the first round of replication (no intermediate band). Dispersive replication would produce a smear of bands in the centrifuge after one and two replication cycles.

TEST YOUR UNDERSTANDING

1. c 2. d 3. d 4. e 5. b 6. d 7. b 8. e 9. d 10. b 11. a 12. b 13. Cancer cells are locked in a constant state of growth and cell division. They require active telomerase to maintain continuous cell division without losing essential chromosomal material. 14. Refer to Figures 12-15 and 12-16 to construct your diagram. 15. In drafting your response, consider the properties the genetic material must have, including the ability to store information, the ability to be copied accurately from one generation to the next, and the ability to undergo stable mutations that persist in following generations. Then explain how these properties are found in the structure of DNA. 16. If the radioactive-labeled proteins were found inside the cells, Hershey and Chase would have to argue that the genetic information needed to replicate and assemble bacteriophages was encoded by proteins. 17. DNA is

the universal molecule of inheritance in all cells. This supports evolutionary theory providing a common mechanism for inheritance and the ability to undergo stable changes in inherited traits, providing a source of variable traits for natural selection to act upon.

CHAPTER 13

CHECKPOINT

13.1 • The one gene, one enzyme hypothesis argued that each gene encodes the information to produce a single enzyme. • Garrod showed that a single recessive gene was associated with a missing enzyme; Beadle and Tatum showed that there was a one-to-one correspondence of genes with enzymes; Pauling demonstrated that a mutation in a single gene altered the structure of a single polypeptide chain, refining the definition of a gene (at that time) to "one gene, one polypeptide chain." **13.2** • DNA (transcription) $\longrightarrow$ RNA (translation) $\longrightarrow$ polypeptide. • DNA and RNA are both polynucleotides consisting of strands of nucleotides linked together by phosphodiester bonds. They differ in that DNA molecules are typically double-stranded molecules with deoxyribose as the sugar. RNA molecules are typically single-stranded molecules with ribose as the sugar component. **13.3** • DNA and RNA polymerases are enzymes that assemble polynucleotide chains by adding nucleotides to a growing 3′ end. They form phosphodiester linkages from nucleoside triphosphate subunits. DNA polymerases can only polymerize nucleotides from an existing 3′ end of DNA molecule that is hydrogen-bonded to complementary strand; RNA polymerases do not require a 3′ end of a primer to copy a template DNA strand. • The transcribed RNA would read 5′ AUG ACG UAU UAC UAA 3′. The nontemplate DNA strand would read 5′ ATG ACG TAT TAC TAA 3′. • Eukaryotic mRNAs have a 3′ $\longrightarrow$ 5′ 7-methylguanosine cap at the 5′ end of the molecule and a poly-A tail at the 3′ end of the message. **13.4** • Ribosomes are composed of two subunits. The small subunit contains a single RNA molecule and over 20 different proteins; the large subunit contains two RNA molecules and over 30 proteins. The ribosomal RNAs have catalytic functions and do not encode information about the amino acid sequence of proteins. • Initiation of protein synthesis involves binding of the small ribosomal subunit to the start codon region of the mRNA. The initiator tRNA binds to the start codon, followed by the assembly of the complete ribosome. Elongation is a cyclic process in which amino acids are added, one by one, linked by peptide bonds to the growing polypeptide chain. Elongation proceeds from the 5′ end to the 3′ end of the mRNA and from the amino end to the carboxyl terminal end

of the polypeptide chain. Termination occurs when the ribosome encounters a stop codon in the mRNA. A release factor binds to the ribosomal A site, releasing the polypeptide chain and disassociating the ribosomal subunits and translation complex. • The anticodons are 3′ UAC UGC AUA UUG AAA, and the corresponding amino acid sequence is NH$_2$–Met–Thr–Tyr–Asn–Phe–COOH. **13.5** • The main types of mutations are base-pair substitution mutations (either silent, missense, or nonsense mutations), frameshift mutations, or mutations involving mobile genetic elements. • Silent mutations do not alter the amino acid composition of the protein; missense mutations substitute one amino acid for another in the polypeptide; a nonsense mutation inserts a stop codon, resulting in a shortened polypeptide. Frameshift mutations alter the reading frame, usually resulting in the insertion of a stop codon a short distance from the mutation. **13.6** • RNA interference occurs when small RNA molecules interfere with the expression of genes or their transcripts. • A gene is a unit of inheritance. In molecular terms it is a DNA sequence that contains information used to produce an RNA or protein product. • Retroviruses use reverse transcriptase to synthesize a DNA strand that is complementary to the viral RNA. After the double-stranded DNA provirus is completed, it is integrated into the host cell's DNA.

FIGURE QUESTIONS

FIG. 13-2 Citrulline or arginine would support the growth of a strain missing both enzyme 1 and enzyme 2. **FIG. 13-4** mRNA strand: 5′ AUG ACU UGC GAA UGU UUC 3′; template strand: 3′ TAC TGA ACG CTT ACA AAG 5′ **FIG. 13-9** RNA polymerase will require a helicase activity to unwind the DNA, exposing the template strand; a polymerase activity to form the phosphodiester bonds of the mRNA; and topoisomerase activities to reduce strain on the DNA as the double helix is uncoiled. Each of these activities may involve the actions of two or more proteins. **FIG. 13-12** A mutation in the polyadenylation signal of an mRNA would prevent it from being polyadenylated. This would probably prevent the mRNA from being exported from the nucleus. The absence of a poly-A tail would also affect the stability of the mRNA, as well as prevent it from being properly translated.

TEST YOUR UNDERSTANDING

1. e 2. a 3. b 4. d 5. b 6. a 7. e 8. c 9. a 10. d 11. b 12. e 13. Bacterial and eukaryotic mRNAs are both transcribed by RNA polymerase II enzymes. Transcription is started at initiation sequences that are downstream of the promoter site. Both types of mRNAs are transcribed in a 5′ $\longrightarrow$ 3′ direction as the polymerase travels down the template strand in a 3′ $\longrightarrow$ 5′ direction. Unlike bacterial mRNAs, the 5′ ends of eukaryotic mRNAs are quickly capped after the

initiation of transcription. Intron sequences in the eukaryotic pre-mRNA molecule are removed by spliceosomes and the remaining exons are spliced together. After the poly-A site (which is located 3′ to the mRNA coding sequences) is transcribed, the pre-mRNA is cut and poly-A sequences are added to the 3′ end of the transcript. Transcription of eukaryotic mRNA requires more energy because many of the nucleotides incorporated into the pre-mRNA are removed by intron splicing and are not required for protein synthesis. The formation of the poly-A tail also requires the use of more nucleotides to form the functional mRNA than that found on a corresponding bacterial mRNA molecule. The eukaryotic mRNA offers more opportunities to control gene expression because regulation could occur at the levels of transcription, capping, intron splicing, polyadenylation, and mRNA export from the nucleus. 14. The genetic code was deciphered by adding artificial mRNAs with specific nucleotide sequences to an artificial protein synthesis system. By analyzing the amino acid composition of the resulting polypeptides, researchers could connect specific nucleotide sequences to the genetic code. 15. Transposons would eventually lose the ability to replicate and jump between genes as they acquired mutations that would disrupt their transposable element functions. 16. Refer to Figure 13-23. RNA $\longrightarrow$ (reverse transcriptase) $\longrightarrow$ DNA. Your diagram should show that reverse transcriptase polymerizes the DNA strand in a 5′ $\longrightarrow$ 3′ direction as it reads the RNA strand from a 3′ $\longrightarrow$ 5′ direction. 17. If the irradiated fungus grows on all three media, then it does not have a mutation in a gene affecting its nutritional requirements. If it does not grow on any of the three media, its mutation is unknown, but it does not affect vitamin or amino acid biosynthesis. 18. Prokaryotes may have lost their introns early in evolution because the synthesis of intron-free mRNA may have conferred a selective advantage on the ancestral organisms, by supporting more rapid, energy-efficient growth.

CHAPTER 14

CHECKPOINT

14.1 • Regulation of transcription is the most efficient means of gene regulation in bacteria. • Prokaryotic gene regulation acts primarily through the control of transcription. Eukaryotic gene regulation can act at many different levels of gene expression such as control of transcription, and posttranscriptional mechanisms that include regulation of mRNA processing, nuclear export and stability, and controls of translation, protein activity, and protein stability. **14.2** • Promoter—RNA polymerase binding site; CAP binding site—binds catabolite activator protein when cells have insufficient supply of glucose; operator sequence—binding site for *lac* repressor protein; structural genes—encode enzymes and proteins that function in lactose metabolism. • The *trp* operon encodes a promoter, operator (repressor binding site), and structural genes as does the *lac* operon. • The *trp* operon is a repressible operon because it is usually turned "on" and is only repressed when the cells have sufficient levels of tryptophan; the *lac* operon is inducible because it is only activated when cells have an insufficient supply of glucose and are exposed to the sugar lactose. • Glucose is the preferred carbon source; cells sense glucose levels, and when they are low, cAMP is produced, activating the CAP protein, which binds near the lactose promoter to speed up transcription of the *lac* operon. **14.3** • Bacterial genes are primarily regulated through mechanisms that control the rate of transcription. Eukaryotic genes are regulated at many different levels of gene expression, including transcriptional, posttranscriptional, and posttranslational controls. • Certain eukaryotic genes (e.g., ribosomal RNA genes, egg storage protein genes) that must produce high levels of their products in cells are present in multiple copies to provide high levels of RNA needed to produce high levels of their encoded product. • Chromosome structure affects the expression of eukaryotic genes by controlling its packing. Genes are inactivated in tightly packed and coiled chromosomes (e.g., heterochromatin). Active genes are associated with more loosely packed euchromatin. Chromosome packing is controlled through chemical modifications of histones and the methylation of DNA. • Alternate splicing can produce different proteins by removing or leaving intact some of the pre-mRNA molecule during the splicing process. Refer to Figure 14-15 in constructing your diagram. • See Table 13-1 and Fig. 14-14.

FIGURE QUESTIONS

FIG. 14-2 If the *lac* repressor gene were deleted, the *lac* operon would be activated in the presence or absence of lactose. **FIG. 14-4** If the *trp* operator region were mutated or deleted, the operon would remain active in cells grown with high intracellular levels of tryptophan. **FIG. 14-5** If adenylyl cyclase were activated in the absence of glucose, the *lac* operon would be activated to high levels in cells grown on lactose, with no glucose.

TEST YOUR UNDERSTANDING

1. a 2. c 3. c 4. b 5. c 6. e 7. a 8. c 9. a 10. c 11. c 12. (a) constitutive; (b) inducible; (c) repressible. 13. *Mutant a*: mutation lies within the *trp* operator; *mutant b*: mutation lies within the *trp* promoter; *mutant c*: mutation lies within the *trp* repressor coding sequence. 14. The data suggest that the deletion removed an enhancer sequence that interacts with the gene. 15. The repressor gene needs to be constitutively transcribed and not under the control of the *trp* operon. If it were under the control of the *trp* promoter, it would not be transcribed under repressed conditions. 16. Multiple levels of control probably evolved in eukaryotes due to cell differentiation and the long lifetimes of cells. A eukaryotic cell might encounter many different changes to physiological, metabolic, and nutritional states during its lifetime, requiring different regulatory mechanisms to respond to those changes. 17. Gene regulation is essential in all cells to ensure efficient growth and adaptability to environmental changes. Loss of an essential regulatory element would most likely result in the loss of selective advantage or death.

CHAPTER 15

CHECKPOINT

15.1 • 3′ CCTAG↓G. • Both types of libraries contain fragments of DNA inserted into plasmids that are maintained in a large population of cells (in many cases, *E. coli*). Genomic libraries contain DNA fragments corresponding to parts of chromosomal DNA. Gene sequences in eukaryotic genomic libraries may contain introns. cDNA libraries contain DNA fragments that are copies of mRNA molecules—those DNA fragments do not contain introns. • DNA probes are used to identify specific DNA or RNA fragments in Southern blots and Northern blots by hybridization to base sequences that are complementary to the probe molecules. • If the maximum insert size were 1×10^4 base pairs, the minimum number of plasmids (or colonies of bacteria each containing a single type of plasmid) that would contain the entire genome would be 3×10^5. If the insert size were 350 kb, 8571 plasmids (or colonies) would be required. Actually, many more colonies would be required to isolate a complete genome because some genomic DNA would be inserted multiple times into a plasmid by chance, whereas others might be missed if only the minimum number were used. • PCR amplification allows one to specifically amplify the desired fragment of DNA to be inserted into a plasmid, whereas gene cloning would require sorting through many different clones to find the required gene from a library. **15.2** • For Northern blot analysis, equal amounts of RNAs isolated from the two cell lines are separated according to size by gel electrophoresis. The separated RNAs are transferred to a filter and the filter is exposed to a radioactive probe complementary to the gene of interest. The amount of radioactivity that binds to each of the RNA samples is compared to determine the relative levels of expression between the two cell types. For RT–PCR analysis, the cDNAs of the gene of interest from each cell type are amplified by PCR using fluorescent-labeled primers. The relative levels of fluorescence are compared between the two cell types. For a DNA chip, mRNAs from each cell type are copied into fluorescent-labeled cDNAs using different colors for each cell type. The two cDNA populations are incubated on a DNA chip containing dots of DNA fragments from each gene in the genome. The level of gene expression in the cells is determined by comparing the relative fluorescence intensity of the two colors found in each dot on the chip. • Identify your gene by comparing its sequence to data in the GenBank. Using your derived protein sequence data, search for similar proteins (or parts of your protein) in organisms in which their function is known. **15.3** • The gene might be involved in one of a number of different developmental functions relating to touch, including the development of touch receptor cells, or of nerve cells used to signal touch, or of muscle cells that might respond to the touch signals. **15.4** • The significant medical advantages of recombinant human insulin include the lack of allergic reactions produced by insulin produced by animal sources. • STRs are stretches of short DNA sequences repeated multiple times within the human genome. The number of repeated sequences in each region is highly variable between individuals. By measuring the number of repeated sequences in multiple STR regions, investigators can identify an individual with a very high degree of probability. • Mice have many genes in common with humans. By using targeted gene modifications and mutagenesis of genes in mice that are also found in humans, investigators can gain insights into their functions and develop potential treatments for genetic disorders involving those genes. **15.5** • Environmental risks include the potential for genetically modified organisms to pass on engineered foreign genes to wild relatives or different species, causing unknown environmental problems, such as the production of "super weeds" from herbicide-resistant crops, or the harmful killing of useful insects from crops engineered to produce pesticides.

FIGURE QUESTIONS

FIG. 15-9 Lane 1: homozygous mutant; lane 2: homozygous wild type; lane 3: heterozygote. **FIG. 15-13** Suspect 2's DNA matches the crime scene DNA.

TEST YOUR UNDERSTANDING

1. a 2. b 3. e 4. e 5. a 6. b 7. a 8. a 9. c 10. b 11. d 12. Many eukaryotic genes contain introns, which must be removed from pre-mRNAs. Bacterial cells do not have the spliceosomes required to remove introns and splice together exons to form functional mRNAs. Expressing eukaryotic genes in transgenic plants or animals allows functional mRNAs to be formed through processing by the host organism's splicing apparatus. 13. Knowledge of bacterial genetics led to the discovery of the enzymes,

gene regulation mechanisms, and vector plasmids that were used (and are still used) to develop recombinant DNA technology. We would not have been able to develop genetic engineering methods employed today without the information derived from the years of basic research into bacterial genetics. 14. Suspect 2's DNA matches the evidence. 15. The universality of genetic systems is strong support for the view that all organisms evolved from common ancestors. 16. DNA technologies used today have provided many advances in fields of medicine, pharmaceutics, agriculture, and criminal justice.

CHAPTER 16

CHECKPOINT

16.1 • Human karyotypes provide information about the chromosome composition of the individual. It can identify the existence of chromosome abnormalities such as extra or missing chromosomes, translocated parts of chromosomes, deletions, and inversions. • Pedigree analysis can assist in determining the pattern of inheritance of a specific trait; it complements karyotype analysis, which can identify chromosome abnormalities, and molecular genetic methods, which can identify specific types of mutations in affected genes. • Comparison of an individual's gene sequences with other sequences stored in gene databases can assist in identifying the specific mutations that are involved in a genetic disease. Comparative genome database information can also shed light on the specific function of an affected gene if the function of that gene is known in another organism. • Mice and humans share many genes that have common structures and functions. Comparing a human gene to a similar mouse gene with a known function can give insights into the function of its human counterpart. If the mouse gene's function is not known, genetic manipulation of the mouse gene (by mutation and observing the effect on the mouse's phenotype) can provide insights into function of the homologous human gene. **16.2** • Most cases of Down syndrome are produced by nondisjunction in meiosis associated with an extra chromosome 21. Figure 16-4 illustrates how disjunction works with cases involving sex chromosomes. Draw a similar diagram illustrating how meiotic nondisjunction would produce a gamete with two chromosome 21s. • Cri du chat syndrome involves a deletion in chromosome 5. • Fragile X syndrome involves a weak region near the tip of an X chromosome, associated with many repeats of a CGG sequence that disrupts a gene involved in nerve cell function. • Genomic imprinting is a form of epigenetic inheritance (see Chapter 14), usually due to methylation

of specific regions of DNA within a chromosome. **16.3** • Phenylketonuria and Tay-Sachs diseases are autosomal recessive genetic diseases. • Huntington's disease is inherited as an autosomal dominant trait. • Hemophilia A is inherited as an X-linked recessive disease. **16.4** • Gene therapy is a strategy for treating genetic disease by introducing a normal, therapeutic allele into the individual, usually by employing a viral vector to move the allele into target cells. A potential concern is that the viral vectors might be toxic or trigger severe reactions by the patient's immune system. **16.5** • The advantages of amniocentesis, chorionic villus sampling, and preimplantation genetic diagnoses are that genetic diseases in the fetus can be detected during a pregnancy. Disadvantages are that none of these tests are foolproof. With amniocentesis, the results of the test are not obtained until well into the second trimester. Most of the conditions it detects are incurable, making it more difficult to safely terminate the pregnancy. Chorionic villus sampling results are obtained earlier, reducing those potential risks. Preimplantation diagnosis is not as accurate as the first two methods but is used to detect potential diseases in embryos prior to implantation. It is used for patients who have possible risk factors, allowing physicians to screen healthy embryos for implantation. • The goals of genetic screening for newborns are to detect potential genetic diseases that can be addressed by early treatment of the disease. The goals of genetic screening in adults are to determine potential risk factors of having children with inherited diseases. **16.6** • Many different types of genetic disorders occur in all human populations. It would be incorrect to assume that certain individuals or populations carry most of the abnormal alleles. • The incidence of autosomal recessive diseases depends on the frequency of the abnormal allele in the population. Each parent must contribute a recessive allele to produce offspring with the disease. Parents who are closely related have a higher probability of each having the same abnormal allele, resulting in a higher risk of offspring who will develop that disease. • Health and life insurance companies base their insurance rates on the probability that an individual will be healthy or live to a certain age. If the companies knew that a person were harboring genes that might cause poor health or death at an early age, they would be in a position to refuse to insure that individual.

FIGURE QUESTION

FIG. 16-4 An XY sperm would give rise to Klinefelter syndrome, a 0 sperm (no sex chromosome) would give rise to Turner syndrome, and a YY sperm would give rise to an XYY karyotype.

TEST YOUR UNDERSTANDING

1. e 2. c 3. e 4. a 5. d 6. c 7. e 8. a 9. d 10. e 11. a 12. (a) Test the potential parents for the Tay-Sachs allele. If both carry the recessive allele, perform preimplantation diagnosis for in vitro fertilization, or chorionic villi sampling during early pregnancy. (b) There is low risk of genetic disease if the young man is unaffected. (c) There is no significant risk of inheriting X-linked hemophilia A given that the young woman's male parent is unaffected. (d) Offer the young man testing for the Huntington's gene, particularly if he intends to have children. He should receive counseling regarding the implications for his own future, should he test positive. (e) There is a duty to respect the patient's wishes. Some would argue that there is a moral duty to advise the patient that she should inform the sons of her condition if they intend to have children before the mother's diagnosis is revealed to them. 13. Genes contribute to a large part of the physical makeup of the individual. Many types of disorders and behaviors, however, are complex and may have multiple genetic and environmental components. 14. Chromosome deletions usually result in the removal of many genes, whereas a frameshift mutation typically results in the shortening of some part of a single gene's product. If a small deletion were to occur within a specific gene, then the expression of that gene might be affected in a similar way to a frameshift mutation within the same gene. 15. It is likely that the approximately 500 identical DNA segments shared by mice and humans contain genetic information that is essential to both species and has been conserved in evolution. 16. About one-half of the individuals carrying a Huntington's disease allele will have developed symptoms by the age of 48; approximately three-fourths will have symptoms by the age of 58.

CHAPTER 17

CHECKPOINT

17.1 • The principle of nuclear equivalence is demonstrated by the Steward, Gurdon, and Wilmut experiments that show that a differentiated cell nucleus can be reprogrammed to support the development of an organism to adulthood. This demonstrates that the genes in a differentiated cell nucleus are equivalent to the genes found in embryonic cells. • Wilmut's team recognized that the embryonic nucleus was arrested in metaphase II of meiosis, whereas the donor cell for the adult nucleus is usually in the middle of the S phase of the cell cycle. By withholding nutrients, the group was able to force the donor cells into the G_0 state, synchronizing the cell cycles of the donor nucleus and the egg cytoplasm. • Induced pluripotent stem cells are produced from differentiated cells by reactivating genes that are "locked" in an inactive state during development through epigenetic changes involving DNA methylation, histone modifications, and the production of inhibitory micro-RNAs. The ability to activate genes that can convert differentiated cells to pluripotent cells supports the principle of nuclear equivalence because it demonstrates that these genes have not been lost or irreparably altered during the differentiation process. **17.2** • *Drosophila* development involves an anterior–posterior body plan that is found in many invertebrates and vertebrates. *C. elegans* has a rigid developmental plan and transparent cells that allow investigators to follow the lineage of every somatic cell. Both *Drosophila* and *C. elegans* have short life cycles and are genetically well characterized, facilitating the isolation and analysis of developmental mutations. Many genes affecting the development of multicellular organisms were first discovered with *Drosophila*. *Arabidopsis* is a small, fast-growing plant with a small genome used to study development in plants. *M. musculus* is a model organism for studying development in mammals, including humans. It has a short lifespan compared to other mammals, it is easily raised in captivity, and methods have been developed for the production and analysis of strains with developmental mutations. • Transcription factors control the activity of genes. They influence development by activating genes required for the differentiation of specific cells. • Induction involves developmental interactions between cells in which specific cells signal other cells to organize into specialized structures. • Apoptosis refers to programmed cell death. For example, during development, certain cells in budding appendages may be programmed to die, forming fingers. **17.3** • Oncogenes are typically growth-activating genes that produce continuous, abnormal growth when the control of their expression is altered. Tumor suppressor genes normally prevent cells from undergoing inappropriate growth and cell division. In cancer cells tumor suppressor genes are inactivated. • When reprogrammed cells interact with older surrounding cells, they may develop as tumors. The use of highly expressed transcription factors that are coded for by oncogenes may contribute to this effect if their expression remains at high levels in the reprogrammed cells.

FIGURE QUESTIONS

FIG. 17-1 Vertebrate organs can contain cells derived from more than one lineage. For example, the cortex of the adrenal gland is derived from mesoderm and the medulla is derived from ectoderm. **FIG. 17-2** Only some of the undifferentiated cells from the root discs produced plantlets, suggesting that not all differentiated plant cells are totipotent. **FIG. 17-3** The egg nucleus would be haploid and it is not clear that it would play a role in the development of

the tadpole. If the nucleus in the unfertilized egg had not been killed, one could argue that the development of the adult frog may have proceeded from the activation of genes in the egg nucleus, rather than those of the differentiated intestinal cell nucleus. It would not be possible to clearly interpret the results from that experiment. **FIG. 17-4** The egg nucleus was haploid; the nucleus from the cultured mammary cell was diploid. **FIG. 17-13** *Hox* genes that are active in the mouse, but not in *Drosophila*, are genes 3, 10, 11, 12, and 13. **FIG. 17-15** Germ line cells in *C. elegans* do not give rise to other types of cells in the individual. They give rise to gametes. Zygotes produced from the fusion of gametes, however, give rise to all of the different cell types in a new individual.

TEST YOUR UNDERSTANDING

1. c 2. d 3. b 4. c 5. d 6. c 7. b 8. d 9. c 10. a 11. b 12. e 13. Almost all developmental processes are controlled through mechanisms that regulate some aspect of gene expression. Specific sets of genes are activated or inactivated during development. Many developmental genes code for transcription factors. 14. Each model organism provides specific characteristics suitable for the efficient analysis of different types of developmental processes. Most have well-characterized genetic systems and short life cycles, allowing for the isolaton of many different types of mutant strains affecting development. 15. A number of genes responsible for the production and maintenance of stem cells are proto-oncogenes that code for transcription factors. Inappropriate expression of these genes causes them to become cancer-driving oncogenes. 16. Many genes involved in the development of *Drosophila* and *C. elegans* also control development in mammals. The common chromosomal organization and function of *Hox* genes in almost all animals with an anterior–posterior axis is a strong argument that modern organisms evolved from a common ancestor. 17. Evo Devo argues that developmental genes (such as the *Hox* genes) that are common in both structure and function represent "molecular fossils" that are important drivers of evolutionary change. The occurrence of mutations in these genes can lead to dramatic morphological changes. This could explain how a new species with a different body plan could rapidly evolve. 18. The resulting flowers will consist of sepals and carpels.

CHAPTER 18

CHECKPOINT

18.1 • Microevolution is the accumulation of small genetic changes in a population; macroevolution involves greater genetic changes,

such as those leading to an ancestral population giving rise to a new species. • Evolution involves aggregate genetic changes that occur among organisms in a population over generations, not the changes that may occur in a particular individual during its life. **18.2** • Aristotle visualized organisms changing over time. His ideas differed from modern evolutionary theory because he did not propose any type of natural process to explain these changes and he envisioned changes as progression or a "scale of nature" in which organisms became more perfect. • Darwin proposed natural selection as the mechanism for evolution; Lamarck's explanation invoked a type of "vital force" that drove organisms to change to become more adapted to their environment during their lifetimes and to pass these adaptations to their descendants. **18.3** • Darwin invoked the well-recognized power of artificial selection in the breeding of new varieties of plants and animals as the basis for his explanation of evolution by natural selection. • Variations that cannot be transmitted to offspring are a dead end and cannot play a role in evolution. • Although Darwin recognized that evolution required natural selection acting on heritable variation in populations, he did not know the mechanism of inheritance. The modern synthesis couples Mendel's explanation of inheritance with an understanding of the genetics of populations. **18.4** • Scientists usually date fossils through comparisons of the sedimentary rock layers in which they are found. • *Mesosaurus* lived prior to the separation of southern Africa and South America by continental drift. • Homologous features are evidence that two groups share a common ancestor. Homoplastic features, which are superficially similar because they are used in similar ways, are evidence of convergent evolution. • In addition to common embryonic morphology among vertebrates, genetic studies (as discussed in Chapter 17) provide strong evidence that evolution builds on pre-existing developmental patterns. • Researchers moved populations of guppies from a high-predation habitat (in which there is natural selection against larger guppies) to a low-predation habitat (in which such selection was absent). Eighteen generations later, they were able to demonstrate heritable changes in the relocated populations such that the guppies matured at a larger size compared to their ancestral population.

FIGURE QUESTIONS

FIG. 18-11 Northwest coast of Europe. **FIG. 18-12** Australia. **FIG. 18-19** Hippopotamus. **FIG. 18-21** You might predict that larger predators introduced into the low-predation habitat would convert it to a high-predation habitat in which there would be natural selection against larger guppies. The expected result might be heritable changes in the population, causing the guppies of future generations to mature at a smaller size on average. Can you think of alternative predictions?

TEST YOUR UNDERSTANDING

1. d 2. b 3. c 4. c 5. b 6. d 7. e 8. b 9. b 10. b
11. Changes that affect developmental patterns. 12. Comparative anatomy; molecular comparisons (including proteins as well as the virtual universality of the genetic code); common developmental patterns and their genetic basis. 13. Darwin meant that a species that possesses heritable variation enabling it to adapt to new challenges is most likely to survive (and reproduce). 14. (a) Natural selection can only work in the present; it cannot anticipate the future. (b) Evolution results from natural selection acting on heritable variation within a population. Although individuals do not themselves evolve, the genetic makeup of the population over time will be influenced by the contributions of individuals possessing heritable characteristics that cause them to be more likely to survive and produce offspring that exhibit those same characteristics. (c) Every organism is a descendant, but not every individual organism becomes an ancestor. Every individual alive today exists because every single one of its direct ancestors in the entire history of life on planet Earth survived long enough to reproduce. (d) Replacement of a single nucleotide can result in the replacement of one amino acid by another, with the potential of producing an altered protein. The new protein may be nonfunctional, or it may possess novel functions. Single nucleotide changes affecting RNAs, particularly those with regulatory functions, may have even greater evolutionary significance. (e) Genetic changes in a population over time constitute microevolution. 15. The information that "limbless" salamanders occupy similar habitats (shallow water) is a clue that that limblessness may have been selected as an adaptation to this particular environment. Think about the kinds of additional information that would help you answer this question more fully. For example: Are there any limbed salamanders that occupy the same habitats? If so, do they have special adaptations? Do the limbless salamanders have any close relatives (perhaps as identified by molecular analysis) that have limbs? If so, what types of habitats do they occupy? 16. Tarsier. 17. Those individuals in a pest population that are genetically resistant to a particular pesticide are more likely to survive exposure and pass on their genes for resistance to their offspring. If exposure to the pesticide continues, there will also be selection for any additional new genes for resistance that may arise through mutations. Therefore, over time the population will consist of a higher proportion of resistant individuals, rendering the pesticide much less effective.

CHAPTER 19

CHECKPOINT

19.1 • Populations. • No. • Frequency of $T = 0.6$. **19.2** • $T = 0.6$; $t = 0.4$; $TT = 0.36$; $Tt = 0.48$. • $A = 0.8$; $a = 0.2$; $AA = 0.64$; $Aa = 0.32$; $aa = 0.04$. • No. The genotype frequencies clearly do not match Hardy–Weinberg expectations. **19.3** • Natural selection. • Mutation is the source of new genetic variation in a population. • Mutation and gene flow are associated with an increase in variation within a population. Populations diverge genetically due to such forces as nonrandom mating, genetic drift, and differences in natural selection. • Stabilizing selection favoring a heterozygous genotype as well as disruptive selection against a heterozygous genotype can change genotype frequencies without changing allele frequencies. Alleles will be maintained in the favored genotypes. **19.4** • There is strong selection against individuals with sickle cell anemia (homozygous recessive). In regions where malaria is a problem, the sickle cell allele is maintained in the population because it confers resistance to malaria on heterozygous persons (relative to homozygous individuals with normal hemoglobin). • Frequency-dependent selection tends to maintain genetic variation within a population over time. • Researchers can test the genetic basis for clinal variation by conducting studies similar to those of Clausen, Keck, and Hiesey (see Fig. 19-9).

FIGURE QUESTIONS

FIG. 19-2 40 mice. **FIG. 19-4** The relationship between wing color and antenna length is unknown, so selection for antenna length would be impossible to predict. **FIG. 19-8** a = 0.7; A = 0.3.

TEST YOUR UNDERSTANDING

1. b 2. b 3. b 4. b 5. b 6. c 7. a 8. e 9. b 10. c
11. d 12. Compare your graphs to those in Figure 19-4. 13. Mutations are the source of all new genetic variation. 14. Natural selection acts on individuals, each of which has a particular phenotype. That phenotype is determined partly by the genotype, so selection on the genotype is indirect. 15. Compared to the United States, the populations of Finland and Iceland are genetically much more homogeneous and occupy more similar environments. This relative lack of variability makes it much easier for researchers to analyze their data and draw meaningful conclusions. 16. The phrase "survival of the fittest" has become a poor way to think about evolution because it is widely misinterpreted by nonscientists. Evolutionary biologists think about fitness in terms of reproductive success in response to selective forces. 17. Amish population: 4.9 out of 1000; general population: 1.0 out of 1 million. 18. If

due to genetic factors, the differences in average weights observed in the natural populations would be similar in the aquarium-raised populations. 19. New information on genetic polymorphism in humans will be useful in understanding the genetic basis of various diseases, with the expectation that new therapeutic approaches may follow. However, this information will be challenging, particularly to individuals, because risk estimates may not be accompanied by useful recommendations and may even create needless worry.

CHAPTER 20

CHECKPOINT

20.1 • The members of a biological species interbreed in nature to produce fertile offspring, but do not interbreed with other species. • The biological species concept does not work well for extinct species, asexually reproducing species, or species in captivity. • A population that meets all the criteria of the biological species concept shares a common gene pool. To the extent that various morphological characteristics are genetically determined, the population is likely to meet the definition of a morphological species. **20.2** • Wood frogs and leopard frogs breed at different times (temporal isolation). They are also subject to behavioral isolation because males use different vocalizations to attract mates. • Temporal isolation involves breeding at different times; behavioral isolation, also known as sexual isolation, is based on differences in reproductive behaviors. • Mechanical isolation is based on differences in reproductive structures. In gametic isolation, incompatibilities between eggs and sperm prevent fertilization. • Hybrid sterility. **20.3** • Mountains, glaciers, rivers, canyons, land barriers, deserts, etc. • Individuals produced by allopolyploidy (hybridization followed by polyploidy) are reproductively isolated. They can form a new species because they can only reproduce with themselves (if self-fertilizing) or with each other, and not with individuals of the two parent species. • Pupfishes: allopatric speciation among isolated springs; cichlids: sympatric speciation within individual lakes. **20.4** • Phyletic gradualism and punctuated equilibrium are not mutually exclusive. Periods of phyletic gradualism, stasis, and rapid evolutionary change can all occur in the course of the evolution of a particular group. **20.5** • The large-scale phenotypic changes that occur when pre-existing structures become modified as evolutionary novelties are associated with the evolution of new species and higher taxa (macroevolution). • The modification of a pre-existing structure (a preadaptation) can occur through relatively minor changes in genetic regulation, thereby quickening the pace of macroevolution. • Paedomorphosis allows a species to occupy a particular habitat for the entire lifespan, without competition from adults of related species. • Mass extinction leaves many ecological niches available to the surviving species. Adaptive radiation may occur as these species evolve to utilize these now unoccupied habitats.

FIGURE QUESTIONS

FIG. 20-9 The $2n = 10$ hybrids would produce $n = 5$ gametes. It is unlikely that it could produce fertile offspring crossed with either species A ($n = 3$ gametes) or species B ($n = 2$ gametes). **FIG. 20-13** Your hypothesis would be supported if the F_1 hybrid females were found to choose red and blue males with equal frequency in well-lit aquaria. **FIG. 20-15** Long-term environmental stability, such as that observed in tropical rain forests, is usually associated with phyletic gradualism. **FIG. 20-18** Future adaptive radiation in the Hawaiian honeycreepers (if it occurs at all) will likely be restricted to human-created habitats because traditional natural habitats are disappearing.

TEST YOUR UNDERSTANDING

1. a 2. a 3. c 4. d 5. b 6. c 7. b 8. e 9. c 10. d 11. Compare your diagrams with Figure 20-9. The F_1 hybrid ($2n = 9$) is unlikely to be fertile. However, if the chromosome number is doubled ($2n = 18$), it is likely that the hybrid could produce $n = 9$ gametes. It would be able to breed with other such hybrids, but not with either of the two parental species. 12. If the original isolated population is small, it could become extinct. However, if it survives it is more likely to diverge genetically from the parent population due to genetic drift and the founder effect. 13. In one sense hawthorn maggot flies and apple maggot flies can be considered an example of speciation that originated through positive assortative mating because they are reproductively isolated by their mate choice behaviors. 14. The human-caused mass extinction that is occurring today may be on a scale that is unprecedented in geological history and many of the potential effects on the future of the human population are unpredictable. 15. April 1 is the only date (of those given) in which both populations are within their breeding season.

CHAPTER 21

CHECKPOINT

21.1 • The origin of life required a reducing atmosphere (i.e., the virtual absence of free molecular oxygen) because of oxygen's reactive and destructive properties. Chemical sources of important elements (particularly carbon, hydrogen, oxygen, and nitrogen) were needed along with energy to power chemical reactions. Time was the fourth requirement, although not as much time as one might think because there is evidence that life arose early in the history of the planet. • According to the prebiotic soup hypothesis, life arose on or close to Earth's surface; the iron–sulfur world hypothesis envisions life originating from molecules produced in hydrothermal vents on the ocean floor. Both hypotheses seek to explain how life could have arisen as the chemical reactions of simple molecules led to greater complexity. **21.2** • Major steps that probably occurred in the origin of cells were the evolution of simple metabolism with an energy source and occurring within a boundary, as well as the evolution of molecular reproduction. • Molecular oxygen (produced by photosynthetic cyanobacteria) increased slowly in the atmosphere. Eventually oxygen rose to levels that poisoned anaerobic organisms but also provided conditions for the evolution of aerobes. • Compare your sketch to Figure 21-8. **21.3** • Prokaryotic cells → eukaryotic cells → multicellular organisms • Fishes → amphibians → reptiles → mammals • Ferns → gymnosperms → flowering plants.

FIGURE QUESTIONS

FIG. 21-2 There would have been no source of carbon for organic molecules if methane had been omitted in the experiment. **FIG. 21-5** Without mutations the selective process would have had nothing to act upon. **FIG. 21-7** The chemical reactions that destroy ozone cause this protective layer to be less effective in screening out ultraviolet radiation, which is harmful to most organisms.

TEST YOUR UNDERSTANDING

1. a 2. b 3. d 4. c 5. e 6. c 7. a 8. a 9. b 10. b 11. c 12. c 13. There was little or no molecular oxygen for aerobic metabolism in bacteria prior to the evolution of oxygen-producing photosynthetic bacteria. 14. Keep in mind that life requires metabolism as well as self-replication. 15. A successful experiment such as the one described would be a demonstration that the origin of life could have occurred through chemical evolution but would not constitute proof. 16. Molecular oxygen (produced by photosynthesis) is the basis for aerobic metabolism. In contrast to anaerobic metabolism, aerobic metabolism makes large amounts of energy available to organisms (see Chapter 8), enabling them to grow to much larger sizes. 17. One hypothesis could be that the molecular fossils (in the form of lipids) were not actually produced by cyanobacteria and therefore do not provide an accurate date for their early presence. An opposing hypothesis might be that cyanobacteria evolved at the early date (2.7 bya), but conditions for formation of structural fossils did not exist or that such fossils are yet to be found. Similarly, one might hypothesize that over 700 million years were required for their numbers to reach a level at which structural fossils would have been reliably produced.

CHAPTER 22

CHECKPOINT

22.1 • Opposable thumb (and possibly big toe); highly flexible digits with fleshy pads at the ends and nails instead of claws. • Eyes positioned at the front of the head. **22.2** • Suborder Prosimii; suborder Tarsiiformes; suborder Anthropoidea. • Monkeys possess tails, which hominoids (apes and humans) lack. **22.3** • The foramen magnum of an ape is situated in the rear of the skull; that of the human is located in the skull base. Unlike modern humans, apes have pronounced supraorbital ridges. The ape jaw is relatively rectangular compared to the more U-shaped jaw of humans. • The human skeleton exhibits multiple adaptations for bipedal posture, including complex curvature of the spine (in contrast to the simply curved ape spine), a pelvis that is shorter and broader than that of an ape, and alignment of all the toes (unlike the opposable big toe of many apes). • Members of genus *Homo* are distinguished from the australopithecines by larger brains, smaller premolars and molars, and evidence of tool use. • *H. erectus* had a larger brain than *H. habilis*, was taller, and made more sophisticated tools. • Compared to *H. sapiens*, *H. neanderthalensis* had larger brains and sturdier builds. They also possessed heavy supraorbital ridges, which are lacking in *H. sapiens*. **22.4** • Early human societies consisted of nomadic hunters and gatherers. Agriculture began with the cultivation of plants around 10,000 years ago, which was usually followed by the domestication of animals. Agriculture freed much of the population from the need to produce food, fostering the cultural evolution that led to the industrial society in which we live today. Not all human societies have gone through these transitions in this way.

FIGURE QUESTIONS

FIG. 22-1 Gorilla. **FIG. 22-2** Gorillas. **FIG. 22-9** Consider the following in placing *Homo floresiensis* and the Denisovans in the chart: The researchers who have been most involved in studies of *H. floresiensis* fossils think that it was an evolutionary offshoot of *H. erectus* that existed from about 38,000–12,000 years ago. Based on fossil dating and molecular evidence, the Denisovans are currently thought to represent a sister group of *H. neanderthalensis*, existing as recently as 50,000 years ago (and possibly as early as 80,000 years ago).

TEST YOUR UNDERSTANDING

1. c 2. a 3. a 4. b 5. e 6. a 7. b 8. b 9. d 10. c 11. c 12. e 13. Scientists have found Neanderthal bones in Europe showing signs of cannibalism and dating from a time when no modern humans were present in that region. You might look for caves with evidence of occupation by *H. sapiens* and Neanderthals at close to the same time. Evidence of violent injuries to the Neanderthal remains, but not the *H. sapiens* remains, would possibly implicate modern humans in the Neanderthals' demise. The evidence would be stronger if the injuries could be shown to differ from the types of injuries Neanderthals have been implicated in inflicting on their own species. 14. Climate change since the last Ice Age has altered the range of reindeer. Humans are an extremely adaptable species, able to live in a wide variety of habitats. 15. Chimpanzees and humans did not exist at the time their lineages are thought to have diverged about 4 million years ago; therefore, their as yet undiscovered most recent common ancestor was a hominoid that was neither a chimpanzee nor a human. 16. As you form your opinion, consider the concept of fitness (both direct fitness and inclusive fitness) as understood by evolutionary biologists today. Do these ideas correspond to popular notions of "survival of the fittest"? Does natural selection apply to humans? Do you think artificial selection plays any role? Do you think that your ideas regarding future human evolution will be influenced by new information regarding the human genome? 17. Your cladogram should show *Ardipithecus* giving rise to *Australopithecus,* which in turn gave rise to *Homo.* You would not include the genus *Paranthropus* because there is no evidence that it was ancestral to *Homo.* 18. (a) African; (b) first migrants out of Africa; (c) Eurasian; (d) Amerindian (native Americans).

CHAPTER 23

CHECKPOINT

23.1 • *Amanita phalloides.* • The categories range from species to domain; as you move up the hierarchy, each taxon is more inclusive than the one below it. • Domain, kingdom, phylum, class, order, family, genus, species. **23.2** • Archaea (archaeons) belong to Domain Archaea; bacteria belong to Domain Bacteria; protists, plants, fungi, and animals belong to Domain Eukarya; white willow belongs to Domain Eukarya, Kingdom Plantae; *Escherichia coli* belongs to Domain Bacteria, Kingdom Bacteria; tapeworms belong to Domain Eukarya, Kingdom Animalia; black bread mold belongs to Domain Eukarya, Kingdom Fungi. • Nodes in a cladogram represent the splitting of two or more new groups from a common ancestor; each node represents the most recent common ancestor of each clade, represented by branches; and the branches diverging from a node share a set of characteristics. **23.3** • Shared ancestral characters are characteristics that were present in an ancestral group and remain present in all groups descended from that ancestor; shared derived characters were present in a *recent* common ancestor and are present in its descendants; homology refers to traits organisms share as a result of their shared ancestry. • Shared ancestral characters are present in all groups descended from a particular ancestor. For example, all mammals have hair, so hair does not help us distinguish between carnivores and marsupials (e.g., kangaroos). However, shared derived characters of marsupials separate them from carnivores. For example, marsupial young are born at an immature stage and complete their development in the mother's pouch. • Molecular biology is helping systematists establish evolutionary relationships. The more similar the macromolecules of various groups of organisms, the more closely related the species are considered to be. • A monophyletic taxon includes an ancestral species and all of its descendants. **23.4** • Systematists use shared derived characters to determine monophyletic groups. • Outgroup analysis is a research method used for estimating which features are shared derived characters in a group of organisms. • In applying the principle of parsimony, systematists select the simplest explanation to interpret the data. **23.5** • Modern systematics helps researchers understand the relationships and origins of viruses and other pathogens; this information helps health professionals understand the source and spread of infections.

FIGURE QUESTIONS

FIG. 23-2 The Archaea are more closely related to the Eukarya; they share a common ancestor as indicated by node B. **FIG. 23-6** The coyote. **FIG. 23-7** Taxa 4, 5, and 6.

TEST YOUR UNDERSTANDING

1. a 2. e 3. c 4. a 5. c 6. c 7. e 8. a 9. d 10. Shared derived characters; molecular data. 11. Domains have been determined based on molecular data and cladistics analyses; historically, animals were assigned to kingdoms less rigorously; for example, systematists have determined that the protists are not a monophyletic group and now assign them to several "supergroups." 12. Similar because they share a common ancestor. 13. Suggests archaea are more closely related to eukaryotes than to bacteria; such data suggests that archaea and eukaryotes share a common ancestor. 14. Figure 23-7a without branch 4 has similar branching; mosses would be represented by branch 1; horsetails and ferns by branches 2 and 3; and gymnosperms and angiosperms by branches 5 and 6. 15. Paraphyletic; monophyletic; polyphyletic.

CHAPTER 24

CHECKPOINT

24.1 • Viruses are not cellular and cannot reproduce without a host; they lack the enzymes and other proteins needed to carry on cellular respiration and other metabolic activities; most viruses lack the components necessary to synthesize proteins. • A virus consists of a core of nucleic acid surrounded by a capsid made of protein subunits. Many viruses are surrounded by an envelope external to the capsid. **24.2** • Viruses can be classified based on their home range (the type of host species the virus can infect), on the type of nucleic acid (DNA or RNA) the virus contains, and whether its nucleic acid is single stranded or double stranded. They can also be classified based on size, shape, and presence of an envelope. **24.3** • Steps in a lytic cycle include attachment, penetration, replication and synthesis, assembly, and release. See Fig. 24-3. • In a lysogenic cycle, a temperate virus integrates into the host DNA. The host is not immediately destroyed. **24.4** • Viruses can enter plants through damaged cells. Viruses can be transmitted from one plant generation to the next through infected seeds or by asexual reproduction. • Some viruses enter animal cells by fusing with the cell's plasma membrane; the entire virus, including the capsid, is released into the animal cell. Other viruses enter by endocytosis. • See Fig. 24-7. **24.5** • Viruses could have evolved from free-living complex cellular ancestors. Later, they became parasitic and through time, lost some of the genes needed for protein synthesis and other cellular activities. • Polydnaviruses do not have genes for making the proteins needed to replicate and produce new viruses. Genes needed for viral replication are found in the wasp genome; the viruses can replicate only in the wasp ovary cells. The wasp injects polydnaviruses along with her eggs into certain caterpillars. These viruses express toxins that interfere with the caterpillar's immune defenses and development. This action allows the wasp eggs to hatch and develop inside the caterpillar. The young wasps feed on the caterpillar. **24.6** • Both viroids and prions are subviral agents; they are smaller and simpler than viruses. Viroids consist of a very short, circular, single strand of naked RNA; they do not have a protective protein coat or proteins to assist in duplication. Viroids infect plants. In contrast, prions are misfolded proteins. They arise spontaneously, mostly as a result of mutation. Prions apparently can aggregate and accumulate in the brain and in certain other tissues where they cause serious damage.

FIGURE QUESTIONS

FIG. 24-3 No, because the tail has proteins that recognize and bind to the host cell. Also, the capsid would not surround phage DNA, leaving it vulnerable to being destroyed. FIG. 24-4 By integrating into the bacterial genome, the virus is reproduced in all of the cell's daughter cells for, potentially, many generations. In this way, the virus population is expanded and disseminated. FIG. 24-6 The cytoplasm contains the materials and organelles necessary to synthesize proteins needed by the new viruses. Also glycoproteins must be transported to the cell membrane in order to envelope new viruses before release. FIG. 24-7 The infected cells replicate, producing daughter cells with integrated proviral DNA. These daughter cells continue to transcribe the proviral DNA and they bud progeny virions. FIG. 24-8 The caterpillar population would increase; the wasp population would decrease; the virus could become extinct because it would no longer have wasps in which to reproduce.

TEST YOUR UNDERSTANDING

1. e 2. a 3. b 4. a 5. c 6. e 7. b 8. b 9. c 10. c 11. Release of viruses from host cell; see Fig. 24-3a, step 5. 12. Viral genomes are single stranded and can be DNA or RNA. 13. Neither has a protective coat; viroids have no proteins; prions have no nucleic acid 14. Polydnaviruses are mutualistic partners with certain wasps. Their relationship is so complex that it is likely they coevolved. Researchers have concluded that the polydnavirus evolved from a nudivirus that infected wasps millions of years ago. In time, the virus genome became incorporated into the wasp genome. Proteins needed for viral replication are now part of the wasp's DNA, and the virus can replicate only in the wasp's ovaries. 15. The regressive hypothesis is supported by discovery of giant viruses. Viruses may have evolved from complex, cellular, free-living ancestors. Later, they became parasitic and through time, lost some of the genes needed for protein synthesis and other cellular activities. 16. Influenza viruses mutate frequently, necessitating ongoing development of new vaccines. The latest advances in nucleic acid technology must be applied to meeting this challenge.

CHAPTER 25

CHECKPOINT

25.1 • Bacteria and archaea differ genetically, in their chemical composition, and anatomically. Unlike archaea, bacteria contain peptidoglycan in their cell walls and can form endospores. Prokaryotes are exclusively single-celled organisms that, in contrast to eukaryotic cells, do not have membrane-enclosed organelles; most have a cell wall that surrounds the plasma membrane, and most have a single, circular DNA molecule instead of linear DNA. • The cell walls of gram-positive bacteria are very thick and consist primarily of peptidoglycan, while the cell walls of gram-negative bacteria have two layers: a thin peptidoglycan layer and a thick outer membrane containing polysaccharides bonded to lipids. Distinguishing between gram-positive and gram-negative bacteria is important for treating certain diseases. For example, penicillin interferes with peptidoglycan synthesis and weakens cell walls of gram-positive bacteria. • Bacterial and eukaryotic flagella are different in structure, mechanism of propulsion, and protein composition. 25.2 • Prokaryotes reproduce asexually by binary fission, budding, or fragmentation. Gene transfer among prokaryotes takes place by three different mechanisms: transformation, transduction, and conjugation. • Transduction contributes to the rapid evolution of bacterial populations through horizontal gene transfer. The transferred bacterial chromosome becomes a recombination of its own original DNA and the DNA from another bacterium, which provides new DNA allowing diversification and adaptation. • The steps that take place during conjugation can be found in Figure 25-8. 25.3 • Chemoheterotrophs obtain energy from organic molecules. • Facultative anaerobes use oxygen for cellular respiration if it is available, but can metabolize anaerobically when necessary. Obligate anaerobes carry out anaerobic respiration using terminal electron acceptors other than oxygen. Some obligate anaerobes are killed by even low concentrations of oxygen. Facultative anaerobes differ from aerobes because they do not require oxygen to carry out cellular respiration. • Prokaryotes obtain nitrogen needed to produce amino acids and nucleic acids by nitrogen fixation in which atmospheric nitrogen is reduced to ammonia. 25.4 • The four phyla of archaea were once thought to inhabit only extreme environments, such as hydrothermal vents and springs, extreme salt water, and oxygen-free environments. Scientists now think archaea may be found everywhere other organisms live. Methanogens produce methane from simple carbon compounds and inhabit oxygen-free environments in sewage, swamps, and the digestive tracts of humans and other animals. Methanogens are important in recycling components of organic products of organisms that inhabit swamps and contribute more than 80% of greenhouse gases to Earth's atmosphere. • See Table 25-3. 25.5 • Bacteria form symbiotic relationships with other organisms. The three forms of symbiosis are mutualism, commensalism, and parasitism. • Biofilms are common along surfaces in aquatic environments and are also found on teeth, contact lenses, pipelines, catheters, and surgical implants. Biofilms consist of many species of bacteria, archaea, fungi, and protists. • Chemoheterotrophs break down dead organisms and waste to their organic components, which recycles nitrogen, oxygen, carbon, phosphorus, and other minerals. Many prokaryotes are important parts of biogeochemical cycles. Cyanobacteria fix carbon dioxide and generate oxygen. • Bioremediation is the process of using microorganisms (and sometimes other organisms) to detoxify or remove oil, gasoline, and other pollutants or toxic chemicals from the environment. The microorganisms break down certain toxins, leaving behind harmless metabolic byproducts. 25.6 • Each of Koch's postulates is important because all four are part of a system, which demonstrate that a specific pathogen causes specific disease symptoms. • Exotoxins are strong poisons produced by bacteria that are either secreted from the cell or leak out when the bacterial cell is destroyed. Endotoxins are components of the cell walls of most gram-negative bacteria, which affect the host only when they are released when the bacteria dies. Exotoxins cause specific symptoms and are destroyed by heating; endotoxins affect the entire body by binding to macrophages of the immune system and are not destroyed by heat.

FIGURE QUESTIONS

FIG. 25-2 A nucleus might be an unnecessary organelle that could interfere with or slow replication, causing prokaryotes to lose their advantage of rapid replication. FIG. 25-8 The F plasmid contains the genetic information for making a sex pilus. Each time an F plasmid is transferred to another cell, that recipient cell can then produce a sex pilus; genetic recombination increases.

TEST YOUR UNDERSTANDING

1. d 2. b 3. b 4. a 5. a 6. c 7. e 8. d 9. e 10. a 11. a 12. See Fig. 25-2. 13. Characteristics of archaea are no peptidoglycan in their cell walls, plasma membranes with branched-chain hydrocarbons (synthesized from isoprene units) bonded to glycerol by ether linkages, and flagella structurally different from bacteria. 14. Consider the ecological and industrial roles prokaryotes have in order to answer this question. 15. Antibiotics impose selective pressure on bacteria by killing susceptible bacteria and leaving those that are resistant to pass on their genes for antibiotic resistance to future generations of bacteria. 16. The public would need to be educated about how to properly take prescribed antibiotics so that they are not contributing to the problem of antibiotic resistance. Society would need to fund research and support the development of new antibiotics.

CHAPTER 26

CHECKPOINT

26.1 • Protists may be photoautotrophic or heterotrophic (obtaining nutrition by absorption or by ingestion). • Protists that are not free living may be involved in symbiotic relationships with other organism (ranging from mutualism, to commensalism, to parasitism). **26.2** • The structure of chloroplasts in different groups of eukaryotes (some with two external membranes and others with three) is evidence that chloroplasts arose through several endosymbiotic events. These events began with primary endosymbiosis of ancient cyanobacteria and continued with subsequent secondary endosymbiosis in some evolutionary lines. • The various groups informally called protists differ widely in their ultrastructural features and molecular composition. These differences are strong evidence that, as a group, the protists do not include all the descendants of a common eukaryote ancestor; hence, they are a paraphyletic group. **26.3** • The mitochondria of excavates are atypical. • Diplomonads include *Giardia intestinalis,* which causes severe diarrhea. *Trichomonas vaginalis,* which causes a sexually transmitted disease in humans, is a parabasilid. The trypanosomes include *Trypanosoma brucei,* which causes African sleeping sickness. **26.4** • The main groups of chromalveolates are the alveolates (characterized by alveloli, flattened vesicles inside their plasma membranes) and stramenopiles (most of which have motile cells with two flagella, one of which bears tiny hairlike projections). • Like dinoflagellates, apicomplexans have alveoli. There is evidence that the chloroplasts of photosynthetic dinoflagellates were derived from a red alga through secondary endosymbiosis; the apicomplexans carry a nonphotosynthetic chloroplast remnant also thought to have originated from a red alga. • A water mold, *Phytophthora infestans,* causes light blight of potatoes and was responsible for the 19th-century Irish potato famine. • Diatoms are major producers in the ocean. Brown algae are also producers and provide habitat for many marine organisms. **26.5** • The term *rhizarian* ("root") refers to the threadlike cytoplasmic projections extended by forams and actinopods. **26.6** • Red algae and green algae share similarities with land plants at the molecular level, and, like land plants, have chloroplasts surrounded by only two external membranes. **26.7** • The cytoplasmic projections of the amoebozoa are rounded and wide (i.e., lobose) as opposed to those of the rhizarians, which are thin and threadlike. • The choanoflagellates are the unikonts most structurally and genetically similar to animals.

FIGURE QUESTIONS

FIG. 26-2 Two. **FIG. 26-3** The common ancestor of the brown algae and the water molds is most likely a stramenopile that evolved before the water mold clade branched off. The likely common ancestor of animals and fungi would be an opisthokont that evolved before the fungal clade branched off. **FIG. 26-17** Unikont.

TEST YOUR UNDERSTANDING

1. c 2. a 3. c 4. b 5. d 6. d 7. b 8. a 9. d 10. e 11. c 12. Compare your sketches to Figures 26-5b (*Euglena*) and 26-8b (*Paramecium*). 13. The protists include many, but not all, of the descendants of the ancestral eukaryote at the base of the cladogram (i.e., land plants, fungi, and animals are not protists). 14. Actin (*red*) is found in the microvilli in the choanoflagellate collar, tubulin (*green*) in the flagellum and as part of the cytoskeleton, and DNA (*blue*) in the nucleus. 15. The available evidence supports the hypothesis that the chloroplast remnant in the cells of the malaria parasite *Plasmodium* evolved by serial endosymbiosis from a red algal chloroplast. Although nonphotosynthetic, it is essential to the parasite's survival and therefore a potential target for drug therapy. Unfortunately, the use of chemotherapies against malaria, and insecticides against the *Anopheles* mosquito, are selecting for the evolution of resistant strains of both the parasite and the vector.

CHAPTER 27

CHECKPOINT

27.1 • Challenges for terrestrial plants include preventing desiccation, obtaining CO_2 for photosynthesis without excessive water loss, providing a means for sperm and egg to meet, and protection of the embryo. • The presence of a waxy cuticle helps prevent desiccation of the plant body, and gas exchange is facilitated by stomata. Various mechanisms have evolved for sperm and egg to meet and embryos are protected within a multicellular female gametangium. • Many lines of molecular evidence link the land plants more closely to the charophytes than to other groups of Archaeplastids. • Compare your diagram to Figure 27-2. **27.2** • The haploid gametophyte generation in mosses includes the following: spores, protonema (each develops from a spore), archegonia (produce egg cells by mitosis), and antheridia (produce sperm by mitosis) • Mosses, liverworts, and hornworts lack vascular tissue and share similar gametophyte dominant life cycles. They most obviously differ in their body forms: mosses (leafy gametophytes), liverworts (thalloid or leafy gametophytes), and hornworts (thalloid gametophytes that give rise to sporophytes that exhibit indeterminate growth). **27.3** • Unlike algae and bryophytes, ferns have dominant sporophytes that possess vascular tissue, as well as stems, leaves (megaphylls), and roots. • Microphylls are small, with a single vascular strand; megaphylls are typically larger and each possesses more than one vascular strand. • The diploid sporophyte generation of ferns includes the following: zygote, roots, rhizome, frond, sorus, and sporangium. • Whisk ferns and horsetails are classified with ferns based on characteristics such as similarities in DNA and sperm structure. • The heterosporous life cycle is characterized by the formation of two kinds of spores and hence two kind of gametophytes: megaspores (give rise to female gametophytes) and microspores (give rise to male gametophytes).

FIGURE QUESTIONS

FIG. 27-2 Both diploid (sporophyte generation) and haploid (gametophyte generation) cells undergo mitosis in the plant life cycle. **FIG. 27-5** The cladogram indicates that all land plants have multicellular embryos (unlike their green algal most recent common ancestor). **FIG. 27-7** Compare your sketch to Figure 27-7, step 3. The tissue of the archegonium belongs to the haploid gametophyte generation and the developing embryo belongs to the new sporophyte generation. **FIG. 27-11** You would not expect *Physcomitrella* to possess genes required to produce functional xylem and phloem because it lacks these tissues. However, evolution builds on pre-existing genetic variation, so it is possible that gene sequences that were important in the evolution of xylem and phloem may be found in the *Physcomitrella* genome. **FIG. 27-13** Ferns. **FIG. 27-16** The fern life cycle is sporophyte dominant, unlike the gametophyte dominant life cycle of mosses. **FIG. 27-19** The heterosporous life cycle, like the basic plant life cycle, consists of a multicellular haploid gametophyte generation and a multicellular diploid sporophyte generation.

TEST YOUR UNDERSTANDING

1. d 2. b 3. d 4. d 5. a 6. b 7. c 8. a 9. c 10. d 11. c 12. c 13. Compare your diagram to Figure 27-19. 14. (a) Plants that are dependent on water for fertilization are limited to aquatic environments or those in which sperm can be transported in a film of water. (b) Unlike homospory, heterospory can lead to a life cycle in which seeds can be formed. Seeds are advantageous for life on land because they provide both protection and nutrition for new sporophyte plants. 15. Nonvascular bryophytes. 16. Based on current evidence, you would probably place the rhyniophytes in the fern clade because they possessed xylem, although their relationship to other ferns remains unclear. Their line would not extend to the tips of the rest of the cladogram because they are all extinct, and it is not clear if any extant group descended directly from them.

CHAPTER 28

CHECKPOINT

28.1 • An ovule is a megasporangium surrounded by integuments. • Unlike the naked seeds of gymnosperms, those of angiosperms are surrounded by an ovary wall. **28.2** • The sporophyte is the dominant generation in the pine. Gymnosperms are commonly wind pollinated, although some, such as cycads, may be pollinated by insects. • Gymnosperms possess seeds, lack free-living gametophytes, and, unlike most seedless plants, are heterosporous. • The four groups of gymnosperms are the conifers, cycads, ginkgoes, and gnetophytes. • Unlike ginkgoes and gnetophytes, cycads produce seeds in cones. Both cycads and ginkgoes have flagellated motile sperm cells (unlike gnetophytes). Ginkgoes have unique fan-shaped leaves and produce exposed seeds; gnetophytes also produce exposed seeds, and unlike all other gymnosperms, have vessel elements in their xylem. **28.3** • The vascular tissue of angiosperms has more efficient components than that of gymnosperms; it includes vessel elements in the xylem and sieve tube elements in the phloem. • The flowering plant life cycle is characterized by a unique double fertilization process, which provides endosperm for the nutrition of the new sporophyte. Angiosperm seeds are enclosed in a fruit, which protects the seeds and promotes their dispersal. • Monocots have embryos with one cotyledon; eudicot embryos have two cotyledons. Refer to Table 28-2 to compare additional distinguishing characteristics. • Fertilization in gymnosperms yields a diploid zygote; double fertilization in angiosperms yields a diploid zygote, plus a triploid cell that develops into the endosperm. **28.4** • Unlike the seed ferns, progymnosperms reproduced by spores (not seeds). • *Archaefructus,* the oldest known fossil angiosperm, had carpels that enclosed ovules. • Based on molecular data, monocots are considered core angiosperms (a sister clade to the eudicots).

FIGURE QUESTIONS

FIG. 28-2 Gnetophytes. **FIG. 28-4** A pine pollen grain is a haploid immature microgametophyte (not a gamete), which will mature to produce sperm (male gametes) by mitosis. **FIG. 28-13** Microspores and megaspores are haploid cells that divide by mitosis to give rise to multicellular microgametophytes and megagametophytes, respectively. Megagametophytes produce eggs (female gametes) and microgametophytes produce sperm (male gametes) by mitosis. **FIG. 28-18** The basal angiosperm *Amborella* lacks vessel elements, which are present in water lilies and star anise. **FIG. 28-19** In gymnosperms the haploid

female gametophyte forms the nutritive tissue in the seed.

TEST YOUR UNDERSTANDING

1. e 2. b 3. d 4. a 5. e 6. d 7. b 8. d 9. a 10. c 11. a 12. c 13. Eudicot angiosperm: five petals, netted leaf veination. 14. Compare your sketch to Figures 28-4 and 28-13. Embryos (new sporophytes) and seed coats (parent sporophyte tissue) are diploid. The gymnosperm nutritive tissue is the haploid female gametophyte; that of the monocot is triploid endosperm. 15. Both seedless and seed plants have the same basic life cycle, with an alteration of multicellular haploid gametophyte and multicellular diploid sporophyte generations. Most seedless plants are homosporous; all seed plants are heterosporous. 16. Bisexual flowers increase the odds that an individual will be able to reproduce sexually because the individual has the potential to become a male parent, a female parent, or both. 17. Algae, mosses, and ferns all require at least a thin film of water for sperm transport in sexual reproduction. Both gymnosperms and angiosperms enclose their gametes and embryos in structures that provide some measure of protection from desiccation, an important adaptation to life on land. 18. Given the information currently available in the fossil record, the progymnosperm clade would branch off from the cladogram after the ferns because they had gymnosperm-like vascular tissue; it would branch off before the evolution of seeds, which they lacked.

CHAPTER 29

CHECKPOINT

29.1 • Fungi are distinguished from other simple eukaryotes by nutrition by absorption from the environment and by cell walls of chitin. • Yeasts are unicellular; molds form filamentous mycelia composed of hyphae. **29.2** • A diploid cell contains two sets of chromosomes in a single nucleus. A dikaryotic cell contains two kinds of nuclei, each with a single set of chromosomes. • Compare your sketch to Figure 29-4. **29.3** • Chytrids, like other opisthokonts but unlike all other fungi, produce flagellate cells at some stage of their life cycle. • Zygomycetes: produce sexual zygospores. Glomeromycetes: sexual spores are large, multinucleate blastospores. Ascomycetes: asci produce sexual ascospores. Basidiomycetes: basidia produce sexual basidiospores. • Compare your diagrams to Figures 29-13 and 29-17. • An ascocarp is a fruiting body that produces ascospores (sexual spores) in asci. A basidiocarp is a fruiting body that produces basidiospores (sexual spores) on basidia. **29.4** • Fungal decomposers recycle important nutrients back into the environment and are particularly important

in breaking down certain materials such as cellulose and lignin. • Plants provide organic nutrients to mycorrhizal fungi, which in turn make soil nutrients available by decomposing organic matter; through their larger surface area, they increase the ability of plant roots to absorb water and minerals. • The photoautotroph is the likely host because it can typically grow well when separated from the fungal partner. The fungal partner does not grow well on its own, so it is the likely parasite. **29.5** • Studies of fungi such as *Saccharomyces, Aspergillus,* and *Neurospora* as model organisms have yielded important insights in biology and medicine. Some fungi produce valuable medications, while others are responsible for causing serious diseases. • Some fungi benefit plants by participating in mycorrhizal associations; by recycling nutrients in the environment, making them available to plants; by degrading toxins in the environment; and by controlling insects and other pests. Other fungi cause serious plant diseases.

FIGURE QUESTIONS

FIG. 29-4 Beadle and Tatum irradiated asexual spores of *Neurospora* to induce mutations, and then selected the mutant strains with differing nutritional requirements. **FIG. 29-7** Animals produce gametes by meiosis. **FIG. 29-9** Haploid gametangia function as gametes in the zygomycete life cycle. **FIG. 29-13** Conidia and ascospores are haploid; the ascocarp is dikaryotic; and the zygote is diploid. **FIG. 29-17** The basidiospore and primary mycelium are haploid; secondary mycelium and basidiocarp are dikaryotic; and the zygote is diploid. **FIG. 29-19** The potential loss of mycorrhizal fungi (negatively affected by acid precipitation) will reduce the ability of their plant partners to obtain water and essential mineral nutrients. The problem can be alleviated by controls on industries responsible for releasing acid-causing pollutants into the atmosphere.

TEST YOUR UNDERSTANDING

1. a 2. b 3. e 4. d 5. d 6. a 7. e 8. c 9. c 10. c 11. b 12. e 13. (a) Dikaryotic. (b) Dikaryotic, preparing for sexual reproduction. (c) Compare your sketches to steps 4 and 5 of Figure 29-17. 14. Fungal mycelia form an extensive, but not easily seen, network of microscopic hyphae in the soil. 15. (a) Fungi are classified as opisthokonts based on molecular data and the presence of platelike cristae in their mitochondria. The flagella of chytrids (the only fungi that have a life cycle that includes flagellate cells) are single and posterior, as in flagellate opisthokonts. (b) Microsporidia are classified as fungi based on gene sequences. (c) Ascomycetes and basidiomycetes are sister clades, thought to have diverged after the evolution of the dikaryotic stage in the life cycle. 16. Fungi, like humans, are eukaryotes. Consequently, there are fewer differences between humans and fungi that can be exploited in the development of safe and

effective treatment options for fungal diseases. 17. *Pro:* The genomes of the fungi that are model organisms provide important insights into the genetic basis of a vast array of processes in other organisms, including humans. Knowledge of the genomes of economically important fungi (both beneficial and harmful) can be exploited in making these fungi more useful or to provide ways to combat them. *Con:* The scientific resources required can be costly and expenditures must be balanced with other important societal and scientific goals (but keep in mind that the latest advances in genome sequencing technology and bioinformatics are reducing, not increasing, costs).

CHAPTER 30

CHECKPOINT

30.1 • Like other animals, sponges are multicellular, eukaryotic heterotrophs; they have an extracellular matrix containing collagen; sponges exchange gases, circulate materials, and dispose of waste; they are capable of locomotion and can reproduce sexually. **30.2** • Advantages of the marine environment for animals are the buoyancy of sea water, which provides support; the large volume of the ocean, which keeps the water temperature relatively stable; and the similar osmotic concentration of animal body fluids and sea water, which helps maintain fluid and salt homeostasis. • Animal adaptations to the terrestrial environment are a body covering that minimizes desiccation, internal respiratory organs that reduce fluid loss; internal fertilization; protective egg, shell, or internal embryo development; skeletal and muscular support; and behavioral and physiological adaptations for maintaining body temperature. **30.3** • The Cambrian radiation was the rapid appearance of a great variety of body plans evidenced by fossils dating to the Early and Middle Cambrian time periods. • According to the current hypothesis, most major groups of animals evolved several hundred million years before they appeared in the fossil record, suggesting that the Cambrian radiation was a rapid evolution of new animal body plans among clades that already existed. • The discovery of *Hox* genes helped biologists understand that similarities in molecular development among different animal groups suggest that they had a common ancestor because all the *Hox* gene groups had evolved by the beginning of the Cambrian period. Further study has shown that regulation by *Hox* gene groups has been linked with the development of wings or legs. **30.4** • Animals are classified based on radial symmetry, in which the animal can be divided into two mirror images by multiple planes through the central axis, or bilateral symmetry, in which an animal can be divided into two mirror images by only one plane through the central axis. • Some differences between protostomes and deuterostomes are in the patterns of cleavage. For example, in early development, early cell division consists of spiral cleavage in protostomes and radial cleavage in deuterostomes. Also, the early four-cell embryo of protostomes exhibits a pattern of determinate cleavage, while the first embryonic cells of deuterostomes undergo indeterminate cleavage. Further, in protostomes the blastula develops into a mouth, while in the deuterostomes the blastula develops into an anus, and the mouth, a second opening, forms later. • Refer to Figure 30-7 for a cladogram illustrating the evolutionary relationships among and major differences between the three main clades of bilateral animals.

FIGURE QUESTION

FIG. 30-6 Nematodes, tardigrades, onychophorans, and arthropods are the animal groups assigned to the Ecdysozoa. The shared derived character present in the Ecdysozoa clade is molting.

TEST YOUR UNDERSTANDING

1. d 2. e 3. b 4. b 5. d 6. c 7. a 8. b 9. c 10. See Fig. 30-6b. 11. You could decide that the organism is an animal if the following criteria are observed: multicellular, eukaryotic, heterotrophic, extracellular matrix containing collagen, locomotion, and sexual reproduction. 12. Large molecular data sets, physical and molecular examination of fossils and existent animals, morphology, and patterns of development were some of the types of data that biologists used to determine these phylogenetic relationships. 13. Any hypothesis that is logically defended is acceptable. 14. The branch would occur just below the node where Lophotrochozoa and Ecdysozoa branch, at the spot labeled protostome pattern.

CHAPTER 31

CHECKPOINT

31.1 • Choanocytes resemble choanoflagellates (protists) in form and function. Many systematists think that sponges and other animals share a common ancestor with choanoflagellates. Choanocytes create water current in the sponge, bringing food and oxygen in and carrying out carbon dioxide and wastes. Choanocytes also phagocytize food particles. • Cnidarians are more highly organized than sponges; they have two-tissue cell layers, a nerve net with simple sense organs, a hydrostatic skeleton for body support and movement, and cnidocytes, with stinging organelles for defense and predation. • See Fig. 31-5. • Ctenophores are like cnidarians in that both have a similar body plan, two cell layers, and a nerve net. Ctenophores are different from cnidarians because they lack nematocysts; their digestive system has a mouth for intake and anal pores for waste removal, while cnidarians have only one opening. **31.2** • Cephalization is an advantage because forward-moving organisms with concentration of sense organs in a head area are better able to search for food, shelter, mates, and be alerted to predators and dangerous conditions. Advantages of having a coelom include room for more complex organ systems with organs attached to the body wall and space for gonads to develop. • Nemerteans are classified as lophotrochozoans because they have a rhynchocoel, which is a remnant of a coelomate ancestor; recent molecular evidence and cladistic analysis place them in the lophotrochozoan clade. • Gastropods have a large, flat foot for locomotion, a mantle that functions as a lung (for land snails), and torsion, which protects the head. They have a slow-moving lifestyle and retreat to their shell when threatened. Cephalopods have very complex eyes; a body containing a siphon, enabling rapid swimming for predation and evasion; and defense mechanisms such as chromatophores and an ink sac. They live a fast-moving predator lifestyle, and many exhibit highly adaptable vertebrate-like behavior. • Flatworms have a simple nervous system and are acoelomate. Mollusks have a muscular foot and a mantle. Annelids have segmented bodies in which each segment has its own muscles, segmented organs, and most members have setae (with the exception of leeches). **31.3** • Nematodes differ from flatworms because they molt, have a thick cuticle, and a pseudocoelom. • Arthropod characteristics for success are segmentation for specialized body functions; an exoskeleton to provide protection from predators and desiccation; paired, jointed appendages, which are modified for diverse functions; and a more developed nervous system, which may include hearing organs, antennae, and compound eyes. • Crustaceans have three body divisions, while chelicerates have two; crustaceans have biramous appendages, while chelicerates are uniramous; crustaceans have antennae, while chelicerates do not; crustaceans develop through larval stages, while most chelicerates exhibit direct development. • Adaptations that have made insects very successful include the specialized insect body plan, ability of many insects to fly, great reproductive capacity, and offensive and defensive adaptations (cryptic coloration, toxins, pheromones).

FIGURE QUESTION

FIG. 31-32 All four stages are diploid; the adult produces haploid gametes.

TEST YOUR UNDERSTANDING

1. a 2. c 3. b 4. d 5. a 6. e 7. b 8. d 9. b 10. e 11. d 12. See Fig. 31-4. 13. Having a coelom resulted in advantages such as highly developed, complex organ systems. Many internal organs are suspended from folds of tissue lining the coelom; these organs, for example, the digestive tube, can move independently of the outer body wall. In some animals, fluid in the coelom helps transport food, oxygen, and wastes; cells bathed by the coelomic fluid can exchange materials such as food, oxygen, and wastes with it. The coelom also provides space for production and storage of gametes. 14. Cephalization was an advantage because centralized sense organs efficiently promoted greater nervous and sensory adaptations (offensive and defensive), but it was a disadvantage to have the majority of sensory organs in the head, which could be easily harmed and destroyed. The arthropod exoskeleton was an evolutionary advantage that provided strong armor and muscle support but was a disadvantage when the animal molted, leaving it vulnerable while waiting for its new exoskeleton to harden. Specialized segmentation was advantageous in the development of legs and wings for locomotion but was a disadvantage if that area became damaged where other segments could no longer substitute for the function. 15. The animal would be classified in the lophotrochozoan clade due to segmented body, bristles, and no observable head. Based on Figure 30-6a, the animal would likely be classified as an annelid, between the unsegmented mollusks and lophophorates, which do have an obvious mouth end. 16. Biologists have recently recognized that animals with very similar body cavities may have great evolutionary and genetic differences based on molecular phylogenetic analyses. 17. Some animals, such as parasites, became adapted to environments in which they no longer used some of their organs, or even organ systems. For example, the tapeworm lives inside the digestive system of its host and absorbs food through its body wall. Through the course of evolution these structures were not selected for, eventually resulting in their loss. Tapeworms no longer have a mouth or digestive system. 18. Insects that undergo complete metamorphosis may be more successful than other insects because the larval form and the adult form are very different and occupy different habitats. They do not compete with each other for food and other resources. 19. Coral reef health is an indicator of the quality and temperature of our oceans. We humans are as dependent on healthy, pollution-free, oceans as are all living organisms on this planet we share. Damage to coral reefs from human-caused water temperature increase, higher acidity from carbon dioxide release, reduced water clarity from contaminants, introduction of toxic pollutants, and physical destruction of reefs are all problems society must address in partnership with scientists to develop successful technologies for remediation.

CHAPTER 32

CHECKPOINT

32.1 • Three shared derived characteristics of deuterostomes are radial cleavage, indeterminate cleavage in which blastopore develops into anus and mouth develops from second opening of embryo, and pharyngeal slits. **32.2** • Three derived characters of echinoderms are adult pentaradial symmetry, allowing them to respond to all directions of their environment; a water vascular system for feeding, gas exchange, and hydrostatic support for locomotion; and a calcium carbonate endoskeleton covered by a ciliated epidermis with spines, which protects them from predation. • Sea stars are different from crinoids because their mouths are on the underside of the disc, not the upper side, and most sea stars are active predators and scavengers, while crinoids move little or are sessile and obtain food by removing microorganisms in suspension. Sea stars are different from sea urchins because they have movable arms, while sea urchins have flattened, fused plates and no arms but do have movable, long, sharp spines that aid locomotion and provide protection. **32.3** • Four shared derived characters of chordates are a notochord; the dorsal, tubular nerve cord; the postanal tail; and an endostyle or thyroid gland. • The chordate nerve chord differs from most other animals because it is dorsal, hollow, and single rather than ventral, solid, and double. • Human jaws are related to early chordate pharyngeal slits because the anterior pharyngeal arches of the slits evolved into jaws during early vertebrate evolution. **32.4** • A tunicate larva has the four chordate characters (notochord; dorsal, tubular nerve chord; postanal tail; and endostyle), while a tunicate adult loses the notochord, postanal tail, and most of the nervous system. • If the organism lacks paired fins, eyes, and jaws, it would be identified as a lancelet instead of a fish. **32.5** • The four shared derived characters of vertebrates are vertebral column, cranium, neural crest cells, and pronounced cephalization with 10 to 12 pairs of cranial nerves and developed sensory organs. • The main classes of fishes are Myxini, Petromyzontida, Chondrichthyes, Actinopterygii, Actinistia, and Dipnoi. The main groups of tetrapods are amphibians, mammals, and reptiles. **32.6** • Like ostracoderms, lampreys and hagfishes do not have paired fins or jaws. • Unlike most other fishes, hagfishes do not have jaws, paired fins, or vertebrae. **32.7** • Placoderms were the first fish to have jaws and paired fins, characteristics that were passed on to modern fishes. Ray-finned fishes underwent adaptive radiation, aided by additional clusters of *Hox* genes, which increased amount of genetic material for evolution and promoted the diversification of modern bony fishes. Lungfishes retained lungs from their sarcopterygian ancestors and evolved fleshy fins from which limbs of tetrapods developed. *Tiktaalik* was a fish that had limblike fins and tetrapod characteristics (movable neck and ribs that supported lungs); it was a transitional form between fishes and tetrapods. • Amphibians undergo metamorphosis in which they lose gills, gill slits, and tail, and grow limbs. Simple lungs and moist skin allow for respiration/gas exchange on land. Mucus-producing glands develop to help maintain skin moisture and make the animal slippery to evade land predators. Many adult amphibians also have glands that secrete poison for protection. **32.8** • Adaptations that allow amniotes to be terrestrial are the amniotic egg, internal fertilization, a body covering that retards water loss, and physiological mechanisms to retain water. • Birds and mammals are endotherms. Advantages of endothermy are high metabolic rate allowing for a high level of activity and decreased vulnerability to temperature fluctuations. • Birds and reptiles are now correctly classified as a single clade based on fossil records and molecular analyses; they evolved from feathered, saurischian dinosaurs, bipedal theropods, which share characteristics such as feet with three digits, thin-walled, hollow bones, and a wishbone. Modern birds also retain reptilian scales on their feet and legs. • Protherian mammals, or monotremes, lay eggs and secrete milk for young (do not have nipples). Metatherian mammals, or marsupials, give birth to undeveloped young that move to a pouch on the mother to continue development. They obtain milk from a nipple in the pouch. Eutherian mammals are attached to a placenta before birth and are born much more developed. Babies obtain milk from nipples on the mother's chest or abdomen.

FIGURE QUESTIONS

FIG. 32-4 The vertebrate nerve cord differentiates into the brain and spinal cord. **FIG. 32-7** The pronounced cephalization that was part of the evolution of vertebrates from jawless fish to tetrapods allowed for a larger, more complex brain. As the brain and sensory organs further evolved, various regulatory and cognitive systems could become more complex; increased brain complexity resulted in greater success in competing with other animals for food and mates. **FIG. 32-20** Birds are more closely related to the extinct branches of reptiles because they share the same archosaur ancestor. Mammals share a distant relationship with all members of the diapsids through the amniotic ancestor at the root of the cladogram.

1. b 2. a 3. d 4. e 5. e 6. c 7. c 8. See Fig. 32-25. 9. Sea urchins are not cnidarians because they have the characteristics of deuterostomes and echinoderms. Radial symmetry may have evolved as an adaptation to the sessile lifestyle of early echinoderms. 10. Birds share the same archosaur ancestor based on fossil records and molecular analyses; they are most closely related to saurischian dinosaurs (now extinct) and share characteristics of the dinosaurs such as bipedal locomotion, feet with three digits, thin-walled, hollow bones, a wishbone, and scales on their legs. 11. Echinoderms and chordates are both members of the deuterostomes and share derived characters at some stage of life such as radial cleavage, indeterminate cleavage in which blastopore develops into anus and mouth develops from second opening of embryo, and pharyngeal slits. 12. Dorsal tubular nerve cord would identify the animal as a chordate. Cranium would place the animal in vertebrates. Skin with scales and two atria/two ventricles would indicate the animal is closely related to a crocodilian, bird, or saurischian dinosaur. The animal discovery would be placed somewhere between crocodilians and birds on the cladogram. 13. Sea turtles can be protected by scientists sharing research about the animals and their needs with the public; educators can inform society about sea turtle conservation and lead activities to improve habitat, reduce poaching, and pass conservation laws; technology can be developed to support more complex research, rehabilitate habitat, control poaching, and improve health care for turtles.

CHAPTER 33

CHECKPOINT

33.1 • Roots absorb water and minerals; shoots bear the leaves, which absorb CO_2 and serve as the main organs of photosynthesis. • The *ground tissue system* carries out photosynthesis, and provides for storage and support. The *vascular tissue system* conducts water, minerals, and carbohydrates. The *dermal tissue system* provides a covering for the plant body. • Parenchyma tissue contains thin-walled parenchyma cells that carry out such functions as photosynthesis, storage, and secretion. Collenchyma tissue consists of collenchyma cells, which provide flexible support by means of their thickened primary cell walls. The sclerenchyma cells (sclerids and fibers) in sclerenchyma tissue have thickened secondary cell walls that provide strong support. • Xylem is the tissue responsible for conduction of water and minerals by means of tracheids (with pits) and vessel elements (with perforations in end walls as well as pits). Sieve tube elements in phloem are responsible for conducting dissolved sugar, which has been moved into them by companion cells. • The epidermis,

the outer covering of the plant body, functions in protection and also includes guard cells in leaves that regulate stomata as well as trichomes, which carry out varied functions. The underlying periderm, like the epidermis, has protective functions. It also contains meristematic and storage cells. **33.2** • Plant meristems provide new cells for growth. Animal growth does not involve meristems. • Secondary growth is an increase in girth; primary growth is an increase in length. • Apical meristems are responsible for primary growth; lateral meristems provide for secondary growth. **33.3** • Cell expansion typically precedes cell differentiation. • Changes in gene activity (differential gene expression) are responsible for pattern formation. • Cells alter the expression of their genes response to positional information received from their environment. These changes bring about pattern formation, which eventually leads to morphogenesis. • Many developmental mutants of *Arabidopsis,* a small plant with a fast life cycle, are available for study. Information gained from these investigations can then be applied to research on other plants.

FIGURE QUESTIONS

FIG. 33-1 Air: CO_2; soil: water. **FIG. 33-2** For transport to take place, the vascular tissue must be continuous throughout the plant. The plant would die because there would be no transport between the leaves and the roots.

TEST YOUR UNDERSTANDING

1. a 2. c 3. d 4. b 5. c 6. c 7. a 8. b 9. b 10. e 11. a 12. Compare your labels to Figure 33-2a. 13. Compare your sketch to Figure 33-11. 14. Compare your sketch to Figure 33-12. Note that your arrow should be perpendicular to the cellulose microfibrils. 15. The initials will still be 4 ft above the ground. The increase in the height of the tree occurred at multiple apical meristems. 16. Unlike dead cells (schlerenchyma), living cells (bone) require maintenance in the form of nutrition, gas exchange, and waste removal. On the other hand, dead cells cannot be repaired or replaced. 17. Vessel elements are more efficient water conductors than are tracheids. It is thought that possession of both tracheids and vessel elements has contributed to the adaptive radiation of angiosperms into a wide variety of environments. 18. The relationship of the genome to various plant functions can be studied more easily in *Arabidopsis* than in most other plants. The pace of research is enhanced when these insights are applied to investigations on commercially important plants.

CHAPTER 34

CHECKPOINT

34.1 • Leaves are covered with a waxy cuticle and may also have trichomes that are specialized to reduce water loss. Gas exchange is limited to stomata, tiny pores whose opening and closing can be controlled. • Mesophyll, the leaf's photosynthetic ground tissue, typically consists of palisade mesophyll under the upper epidermis, and spongy mesophyll below. • A vascular bundle contains xylem (upper) and phloem (below). • Leaf mesophyll cells receive water and dissolved minerals from the xylem; the carbohydrate products of photosynthesis are transported away by the phloem. CO_2 enters the leaf through stomata, which also provide for the exit of excess O_2 (i.e., that not used for respiration by leaf cells). **34.2** • Blue light begins the process of stomatal opening by causing the activation of proton pumps in the plasma membranes of guard cells. It also triggers synthesis of malic acid and hydrolysis of starch. • In stomatal opening, proton pumps (activated by blue light) actively transport H^+ out of the guard cells. This resulting electrochemical gradient is responsible for the opening of voltage-activated ion channels through which K^+ and Cl^- enter the guard cells by facilitated diffusion; water then enters by osmosis. The resulting turgor pressure in the guard cells causes them to change shape, resulting in stomatal opening. The stomata are maintained in an open position during the day due to maintenance of osmotic pressure by sucrose produced by photosynthesis. When sucrose concentration declines at the end of the day, the guard cells lose turgor as they lose water by osmosis and the stomata close. **34.3** • The leaf cuticle and stomata limit water loss by transpiration. • Sunlight, higher temperatures, lower relative humidity, and higher wind speeds all increase the rate of transpiration. • Transpiration benefits plants by making water and minerals available throughout the plant. It is harmful when it results in excess water loss. • In guttation, liquid water is forced out of vein endings in the leaves of small plants as a result of water entering the roots when soil moisture is high and transpiration is negligible. Transpiration is the evaporation of water from aerial parts of the plant. **34.4** • Loss of leaves in autumn is a mechanism to reduce water loss during winter when cold temperatures (and perhaps freezing) make water less available from the soil. • Leaf abscission occurs after enzymes have dissolved the middle lamella between the cells in the abscission zone. • The abscission zone is an area where a leaf petiole attaches to a stem. It is composed mainly of thin-walled parenchyma cells. It also includes cork cells, which will remain with the stem as a protective layer after the leaf has abscissed. **34.5** • Spines, protection from herbivores; tendrils; aid in climbing; bud scales; protection of meristematic tissue. • Bulbs; storage of food; succulent leaves; storage of water. • Certain leaves of carnivorous plants are specialized to capture and digest small animals such as insects.

FIGURE QUESTIONS

FIG. 34-3 Control of developmental processes is not limited to genes that code for transcription factors. Other examples include genes that code for components of signaling pathways, regulatory RNAs, and a great many more. **FIG. 34-10** During photosynthesis during the day, guard cells produce sucrose, which is osmotically active and helps maintain their turgor pressure, keeping the stomata open.

TEST YOUR UNDERSTANDING

1. c 2. d 3. d 4. e 5. d 6. a 7. e 8. c 9. a 10. c 11. a 12. You would expect a higher concentration of guard cells in the lower epidermis. 13. In the stem, an arrangement with the xylem toward the center and the phloem toward the periphery would account for the leaf arrangement (xylem toward the upper epidermis and the phloem toward the lower epidermis). 14. Compare your simple drawing to Figure 34-4. Mesophyll cells and guard cells should contain chloroplasts. 15. A few large leaves present a large area for photosynthesis, but may effectively shade leaves below them and also present a large area for potential water loss. This might not be a great disadvantage in a humid climate. Many small leaves may have less area for photosynthesis, but they will shade each other less. Collectively they can be oriented in many directions to capture light and may lose much less water. 16. Leaf abscission helps prevent water loss during the winter when photosynthesis is negligible and less water is available from the soil. The smaller surface area, thick cuticle, and sunken stomata of conifer leaves (needles) are adaptations that allow conifers to survive winter without leaf abscission. 17. Agricultural plant yields depend on photosynthesis, which in turn depends on availability of CO_2 (through open stomata). Water loss (also through open stomata) reduces plant yields.

CHAPTER 35

CHECKPOINT

35.1 • In a stem cross section, the vascular tissue of a primary eudicot stem is arranged in a circle; vascular bundles of a monocot stem are scattered. • Vascular cambium gives rise to secondary xylem (to the inside) and secondary phloem (to the outside). Cork cambium produces periderm (outer bark). • When secondary growth occurs, the primary tissues become nonfunctional (e.g., primary xylem) or become destroyed (e.g., primary phloem). • Growth rings are a consequence of the differences between springwood (with large-diameter tracheids and vessel elements formed when water is plentiful) and summerwood (with smaller water-conducting cells, formed when water is less available). • Terminal buds form at the tips of stems; axillary buds form in the axils of

plant leaves. **35.2** • Water moves from a region of higher water potential (generally less negative) to a region of lower water potential (generally more negative). • It has been demonstrated that tension–cohesion is strong enough to pull water as high as 130 m. The tallest known tree is 115.7 m high. **35.3** • Xylem transport occurs upward from roots to leaves. Phloem transport is from a source to a sink (upward or downward). • In the pressure–flow model, companion cells load sugar into sieve tube elements at the source and water follows by osmosis. This increases the hydrostatic pressure inside the sieve tube, pushing the contents toward the sink. The hydrostatic pressure is lower at the sink because companion cells unload sugar from the sieve tube elements, causing water to leave by osmosis.

FIGURE QUESTIONS

FIG. 35-3 The irregularly arranged (scattered) vascular bundles of a monocot stem would not provide for regular positioning of a vascular cambium within the stem. **FIG. 35-7** The branch is two years old (two sets of bud scale scars). There are two twigs with terminal buds at the end. **FIG. 35-11** Water would not be able to move from the soil to the root (and might even move out of the root) if the water potential of the soil were more negative than that of the root. **FIG. 35-12** The direction of translocation is from a source (in this case a root where starch is broken down) to a sink (in this case a developing leaf cell). Therefore the direction of transport would be upward in the stem. **FIG. 35-13** Outward movement of fluid would not occur because, unlike phloem, the xylem of a large plant is not under positive pressure.

TEST YOUR UNDERSTANDING

1. d 2. e 3. b 4. b 5. a 6. b 7. e 8. c 9. b 10. a 11. b 12. Compare your drawing to Figure 35-4. The daughter cell formed to the outside of the meristematic cell should be labeled secondary phloem. 13. Periderm or outer bark (which is usually most easily peeled away) consists of remnants of primary phloem, cortex, and epidermis. 14. A tree 150 m tall would exceed the calculated maximum height for xylem transport by tension–cohesion (130 m). 15. One hypothesis would be that tropical vines must be strong and long lived to obtain adequate sunlight by growing to the tops of tall rainforest trees. 16. Water will flow from the cell with higher (less negative) water potential (i.e., -1.5 MPa) to the cell with lower (more negative) water potential (i.e., -1.8 MPa).

CHAPTER 36

CHECKPOINT

36.1 • A fibrous root system is adapted to obtain water from a larger area of the soil surface; a taproot system has access to water

deep underground. • A primary eudicot root has a central stele containing xylem and phloem. The center of the stele of a typical monocot root is occupied by pith surrounded by xylem and phloem arranged in alternating bundles. • Water and dissolved minerals move through the apoplast by way of interconnected cell walls. Water and minerals must cross at least one plasma membrane to enter the symplast, and then move from cell to cell through plasmodesmata. • The Casparian strip prevents materials from entering the center of the root without passing through the plasma membrane of an endodermal cell. • As in the stem, the root vascular cambium produces secondary xylem toward the inside and secondary phloem toward the outside. Cork cambium also contributes to the increase in girth as it produces cork cells and cork parenchyma cells. • Prop roots provide support; buttress roots provide support and help distribute shallow roots around a tree; pneumatophores may assist in gas exchange by submerged roots. **36.2** • Mycorrhizae and root nodules are symbiotic associations that benefit plants. Mycorrhizal fungi aid plant roots in water and mineral uptake and rhizobial bacteria fix nitrogen in root nodules. **36.3** • Minerals supply essential inorganic nutrients; organic matter provides many nutrients and holds water; air supplies oxygen for aerobic respiration and nitrogen that can be used by nitrogen-fixing bacteria; soil water makes water available to plants and dissolves nutrients and gases. • In cation exchange, H^+ pumped into the soil by plant roots releases various mineral cations from negatively charged clay particles, making them available for absorption. • In weathering processes, rock is broken down by acids produced by organisms (particularly carbonic acid formed from carbon dioxide) and by alternating cycles of freezing and thawing. • Macronutrients are required in relatively large quantities (greater than 0.05% dry weight), whereas trace amounts of micronutrients are required. • Human mismanagement can damage soil through mineral depletion, soil erosion, and salt accumulation.

FIGURE QUESTIONS

FIG. 36-4 Many kinds of minerals are carried along dissolved in the water traveling through the nonselective apoplast. To enter the symplast, all minerals must pass through at least one plasma membrane. The plasma membranes therefore act as "gatekeepers" that promote entry of minerals the plant requires, and typically exclude others. **FIG. 36-5** Water enters the endodermal cells by osmosis, which does not require a direct expenditure of energy. Energy is supplied indirectly by the energy-requiring transport of minerals, which creates relatively hypertonic conditions (i.e., lowers the effective water concentration) inside the endodermal cells. **FIG. 36-9** Stem vascular cambium, like root vascular cambium, produces secondary xylem inward and secondary phloem outward.

1. c 2. b 3. b 4. a 5. c 6. c 7. d 8. a 9. d 10. e 11. Compare your sketch to Figure 36-9. 12. The roots of woody plants, like their stems, produce annual rings. You should take a core sample of the root (as you would for a tree trunk) close to the entrance of the mineshaft and count the rings. 13. Without a microscope, look for the presence of root hairs. With a microscope, examine the internal structure in cross section and determine if a stele (characteristic of roots) is present. 14. In roots with secondary growth, all absorption occurs close to the tips, where only primary growth occurs and where the root hairs are found. 15. A shallow root system enables a cactus to capture more water from the infrequent rains that occur in the desert before the water runs off. 16. Understanding development of root hairs could lead to ways of modifying agricultural crops to improve water and mineral absorption. Mycorrhizal associations benefit many plants, and it is possible these benefits could be extended to additional types of agricultural crops. 17. The roots of the common reeds (*Phragmites australis*) absorbed almost all of the selenium. The plants should be uprooted and disposed of in a way that does not release selenium into the environment.

CHAPTER 37

CHECKPOINT

37.1 • Sepals, the outermost flower whorl, are typically more leaflike than the petals, which form the second whorl and are typically colored to attract pollinators. • Stamens and carpels are modified for reproduction. Stamens produce pollen and carpels produce ovules. • The female gametophyte of a flowering plant, produced within an ovule, is an embryo sac containing a haploid egg (which is fertilized to become the zygote) and two haploid polar nuclei (which are fertilized to become the triploid endosperm). • The immature male gametophytes of flowering plants are pollen grains, produced in anthers. **37.2** • Bee. • Wind. • Nectar or pollen are important rewards for many pollinators. Flowers have evolved to have colors that are visible to particular pollinators. Specific plant odors attract specific pollinators. **37.3** • Pollination is delivery of pollen to a flower stigma. Fertilization occurs when a pollen tube delivers sperm to fuse with the egg (producing an embryo) and with the two polar nuclei (producing the endosperm). • A eudicot embryo proceeds through the following stages: proembryo, globular stage embryo, heart stage embryo, torpedo stage embryo, and maturing embryo with two cotyledons. • A fruit is a mature ripened ovary. • Simple fruit develops from a single ovary with a single carpel or several fused carpels; aggregate fruit develops

from a flower that contains several unfused carpels; multiple fruit develops from ovaries of many flowers; accessory fruit develops from other tissues in addition to the ovary. • Animal-dispersed fruits and seeds tend to be edible, or they have barbs or other structures that attach them to the bodies of animals. **37.4** • All plant seeds require water for germination; the young plant would not be able to grow in the absence of water. Many seeds require a period of low temperature before they germinate; this prevents them from germinating in the fall and being unable to survive the winter. Some very small seeds require light for germination, ensuring that they will germinate near the soil surface. • The stem of a eudicot seedling protects its delicate tip by forming a hook as it emerges from the soil. The stem tip of a monocot seedling is enclosed by a protective coleoptile. **37.5** • Rhizomes are horizontal underground stems that produce new aerial shoots. Tubers are storage organs that develop from rhizomes and have axillary buds that can develop into new plants. • A bulb is composed mainly of fleshy leaves attached to short underground stem. The underground stem of a corm is enlarged relative to the papery leaves. • Apomixis is the production of seeds enclosed in fruits without sexual reproduction. It has the advantages of the protections and dispersal methods usually provided by seeds and fruits. **37.6** • As in all organisms, asexual reproduction in plants results in offspring that are like their parents. Conversely, asexual reproduction results in genetically varied offspring. • Genetic variety in the offspring is considered adaptive because it typically results in at least some offspring that are better suited for survival and subsequent reproduction than their parents. However, it is costly because it also results in some less well-adapted offspring.

FIGURE QUESTIONS

FIG. 37-3 Haploid: megaspore, microspore, egg, polar nucleus, generative cell, sperm cell. Diploid: megasporocyte, microsporocyte. **FIG. 37-5** Some additional traits that might affect pollination in monkeyflowers would be scent (important to bumblebees but less so to hummingbirds) and rewards (nectar important to both, pollen more important to bumblebees).

TEST YOUR UNDERSTANDING

1. c 2. d 3. c 4. a 5. c 6. b 7. b 8. d 9. c 10. d 11. a 12. Compare your sketch with Figure 37.1. 13. Compare your sketches with Figures 37-1, 37-11, and 37-12. 14. The offspring of asexual reproduction might be expected to develop close to the parent plant because they are well suited to the same environmental conditions. You could test this hypothesis by growing the offspring in various locations, including close to the parent. Do you think there could be competition between the parent and offspring? 15. (a) Likely asexual. (b) Likely sexual.

(c) Asexual (because all the offspring would be adapted to the parent's climate range) or could be sexual (because some of the offspring might be able to live in a somewhat different climate). 16. Plants produce seeds with elaiosomes to attract ants, which have coevolved to bury the seeds as they make use of the food reward. 17. Because almost all agricultural plants are flowering plants, an improved understanding of the control of their flowering can yield important benefits in agriculture. Similarly, almost every new crop begins with the sowing of seeds, so an understanding of their germination processes can be equally valuable.

CHAPTER 38

CHECKPOINT

38.1 • Phototropins absorb wavelengths other than yellow (which they reflect); they respond to blue light, which is one of the wavelengths they absorb. • Phototropism: directional growth in response to the direction of light; gravitropism: directional growth in response to gravity (either positive or negative); thigmotropism: growth response to a mechanical stimulus. **38.2** • The signal provided by auxin activates a pathway that results in cell walls of target cells becoming acidified. These acidified cell walls are more plastic, enabling them to expand due to the force of the cell's turgor pressure. This cell expansion is a form of growth without cell division. • Auxin is transported from cell to cell in a plant in a unidirectional manner (polar transport). In phototropism, auxin is transported from the lighted side of the stem to the shaded side. Expansion of the cells on the shaded side causes the stem to bend toward the light. • (1) Seed germination: gibberellins, cytokinins, ethylene, brassinosteroids; (2) stem elongation: auxins, gibberellins; (3) fruit ripening: ethylene; (4) leaf abscission: ethylene; (5) seed dormancy: abscisic acid. **38.3** • Phytochrome is the main photoreceptor for photoperiodism and for shade avoidance. • One or more signal transduction pathways are activated when phytochrome undergoes changes in shape in response to light. Some of these pathways activate specific transcription factors that control gene expression. • Cryptochrome plays a role in resetting the biological clock responsible for maintaining circadian rhythms. **38.4** • The production of necrotic lesions is associated with the hypersensitive response. These areas of dead tissue limit or slow the spread of an infection.

FIGURE QUESTIONS

FIG. 38-5 One possible experiment would be to expose the uncovered coleoptiles to directional light for varying times, then cover their tips, and record bending responses. **FIG. 38-6** Coleoptile

tips previously exposed to light could be placed on agar blocks, which would then be exposed to heat at varying temperatures and for varying durations of time. The agar blocks could then be placed on decapitated coleoptiles and the bending responses recorded.

TEST YOUR UNDERSTANDING

1. c 2. a 3. b 4. c 5. e 6. e 7. d 8. b 9. e 10. b 11. 1 → 4 → 3 → 5 → 2 12. (a) Plant will not flower; night length does not exceed 14 hours. (b) Plant will flower; night length exceeds 14 hours. (c) Plant will not flower; night length does not exceed *uninterrupted* 14 hours. 13. The plant will not flower at the equator (night length does not exceed 14 hours). 14. Negatively geotropic shoots grow up, into to the air where CO_2 and light are available to support photosynthesis; positive gravitropic roots grow into the soil where they can absorb water and minerals. 15. A plant with a phytochrome gene mutation that affects flowering time would be at an evolutionary disadvantage for many reasons. For example, it might flower at time when pollen or pollinators are not available. Its seeds might not have time to mature during the growing season or might mature too early and germinate during an unfavorable season. 16. Flowering is 100% when the day length is 10 hours and the night length is 14 hours; flowering is 0% when the day length is 16 hours and the night length is 8 hours. According to the graph, the critical night length for this plant is about 11 hours. 17. There is a growing body of evidence that plant-signaling molecules are involved in a wide range of processes affecting plant growth and development, all of which are of significant agricultural importance.

CHAPTER 39

CHECKPOINT

39.1 • Epithelial tissue forms a continuous sheet of cells covering a body surface or lining a body cavity. Its functions are to protect, absorb, secrete, and sense. Connective tissue consists of few scattered cells separated by intercellular substance, composed of fibers scattered throughout a matrix. Connective tissue joins other tissues of the body, supports the body and its organs, and protects underlying organs. • The air sacs of the lungs are lined with simple squamous epithelium. The cells are flat and arranged in a single layer to permit diffusion and passage of materials where little protection is required. • Skeletal muscle is striated with each elongated muscle fiber containing several nuclei. Skeletal muscles contract voluntarily; they move body parts. For example, they lift and lower arms and legs on demand. Cardiac muscle is striated, but the elongated fibers are branched and fused with only one or two nuclei. Cardiac muscle

contracts involuntarily for the heart to beat; it is a complex network that pumps blood continuously. Smooth muscle is not striated; it is made up of elongated spindle-like fibers, each with one central nucleus. Smooth muscle contracts involuntarily to move body organs; it contracts in the walls of the digestive tract to apply pressure to move food onward; it constricts arteries causing blood pressure to increase. • The respiratory system supplies oxygen to the blood and excretes carbon dioxide. The urinary system removes metabolic waste and excess materials from the blood, produces urine, and helps regulate blood chemistry. The endocrine system works with the nervous system to regulate metabolic activities and other body functions. **39.2** • In a negative feedback system, a change in a steady state triggers a response that counteracts, or reverses, the change. A sensor detects a change, a deviation from the normal condition, or set point. The sensor signals an integrator, or control center. Based on the input of the sensor, the integrator activates homeostatic mechanisms that restore the steady state. The response counteracts the inappropriate change, which restores the steady state. Unlike a negative feedback system, a positive feedback system does not reverse the change; a change in a steady state sets off a response that intensifies the changing condition. **39.3** • A cost of ectothermy is that temperature conditions, daily and seasonal, can limit an animal's activity. A benefit for ectotherms is that they survive on less food and convert more energy from food to growth and reproduction because they do not need to maintain a high metabolic rate. To adjust body temperature, ectotherms may move in or out of the sun to raise or lower temperature; they may migrate as seasons change or hibernate. • A cost of endothermy is that animals must expend considerable energy to maintain body temperature, even when inactive. Benefits of endothermy are a rapid response to internal and external stimuli, and a greater level of activity in cold weather. To help maintain body temperature, endotherms have structural adaptations (feathers, hair, insulating fat), behavioral adaptations, and several physiological mechanisms (shivering, sweating, panting, bringing heat to skin surface) mediated by nervous and endocrine systems. • See Fig. 39-9.

FIGURE QUESTIONS

FIG. 39-5 Glucose concentration in your blood would increase. Your body would respond by negative feedback, releasing insulin into your blood to counteract the glucose until the steady state, or normal condition, is restored. **FIG. 39-7** If we could convert to a negative feedback system, the loss of blood and decrease in blood pressure would initiate factors that would slow the loss of blood by clotting at the wound site and constricting blood vessels.

TEST YOUR UNDERSTANDING

1. a 2. e 3. d 4. b 5. c 6. d 7. See Tables 39-1 and 39-2. 8. Cells → Tissues → Organs → Organ Systems. 9. Loss of epithelium would allow pathogens to enter the body, causing infection; loss of body fluids would lead to dehydration; skin damage could impact sensation and cause extreme pain. If the skin damage is not repaired and systems are not returned to normal state, the patient could go into shock and may die. 10. Joint connections, body, and organ support would deteriorate, and the body would collapse. 11. Rapid breathing is typically shallow. Less oxygen would be inhaled and less carbon dioxide would be exhaled. As a result carbon dioxide concentration would further increase, disrupting homeostasis even more. 12. Most animals are ectotherms; they do not use metabolic energy to maintain a constant body temperature. Compared to endotherms, ectotherms can survive on less food and they expend more energy on growth and reproduction. 13. A health care worker has an obligation to recommend any and all tests that may benefit the patient. A genetic test can provide information necessary for making medical decisions, especially if your family has a history of cancer. Knowing that you may be predisposed toward certain types of cancer can help you and your caregivers make educated decisions to improve your chances for survival.

CHAPTER 40

CHECKPOINT

40.1 • Invertebrates and vertebrates both have epithelial coverings that protect the body. The epithelial coverings may be specialized for gas exchange, secretion, or temperature regulation; skin may contain sensory receptors that obtain information from the surrounding environment. • Birds have feathers and mammals have hair, which provide insulation and help maintain body temperature; amphibians have skin that allows gas exchange and poison secretion; mammals have claws and nails as well as sweat glands, oil glands, and sensory receptors. • Keratin gives skin mechanical strength and reduces water loss. • Melanin is a pigment that contributes to skin color and has a role in reducing ultraviolet radiation damage. **40.2** • The septa separating segments in the annelid worm allow the worm to move with more flexibility, as each segment is independent. • Advantages of the exoskeleton are to protect, transmit force, and reduce water loss; arthropods have modified parts of their exoskeleton that function as tools or weapons. The exoskeleton is a disadvantage for arthropods because their body continues to grow and they must molt, or shed their exoskeleton, which makes them weak and vulnerable to predation, while a new covering grows and hardens. • Axial skeleton main bones are skull, sternum, rib cage, and vertebrae. Appendicular skeleton main bones are clavicle, scapula, humerus, radius, ulna, carpals, metacarpals, phalanges, pelvic girdle, femur, patella, fibula, tibia, tarsals, and metatarsals. • Osteoblasts build up bone by secreting the protein collagen that forms strong bone fibers; hydroxyapatite forms around the fibers and hardens into bone matrix. Osteoclasts break down (resorb) bone by secreting hydrogen ions that dissolve crystals and enzymes that digest collagen. Osteoblasts and osteoclasts work synergistically to shape bones. **40.3** • See Figs. 40-9 and 40-10. Actin is the thin filament; myosin is the thick filament. • For a muscle fiber to contract: (1) Acetycholine, released by a motor neuron, binds with receptors on the muscle fiber, causing depolarization and generation of an action potential. (2) The action potential spreads through the T tubules, releasing calcium ions from the sarcoplasmic reticulum. (3) Calcium ions bind to troponin in the actin filaments, causing the troponin to change shape. The troponin pushes tropomyosin away from the binding sites on the actin filaments. (4) ATP (bound to myosin) is split, putting the myosin head in a high-energy state. Energized myosin heads attach to the exposed binding sites on the actin filaments, forming cross bridges that link the myosin and actin filaments. (5) After myosin attaches to the actin filament, P_i is released, triggering the power stroke. (6) During the power stroke, myosin heads pull the actin filaments toward the center of the sarcomere. ADP is released during the power stroke. (7) The myosin head binds a new ATP, which lets the myosin head detach from the actin. As long as the calcium ion concentration remains elevated, the new ATP is split and the sequence repeats. • ATP is the immediate source of energy for muscle contraction. The hydrolysis of ATP provides the energy to "cock" the myosin. Creatine phosphate is an intermediate energy storage compound for muscle tissue. Glycogen is the fuel stored in muscle fibers. • Skeletal muscle is striated, with each elongated muscle fiber contracting voluntarily to move body parts; arms and legs, for example, lift and lower on demand. Cardiac muscle is striated with elongated fibers that are branched and fused. Cardiac muscle contracts involuntarily for the heart to beat; it is a complex tissue that pumps blood continuously. Smooth muscle is not striated; it is made up of elongated spindle-like fibers. Smooth muscle contracts involuntarily to move body organs; it contracts in the walls of the digestive tract to move food onward; it constricts arteries causing blood pressure to increase.

FIGURE QUESTIONS

FIG. 40-10 The greater the volume of myofibrils in a muscle fiber, the greater the force that the muscle can generate. **FIG. 40-11** If the body stopped producing acetylcholine, action potentials could not be generated. The person would quickly die because the muscles necessary for breathing could not contract.

TEST YOUR UNDERSTANDING

1. c 2. c 3. e 4. b 5. e 6. c 7. The high rate of metabolism in insect flight muscles is adaptive because a great amount of energy must be generated to support flight. This energy is generated by the numerous mitochondria in these muscles. Flight increases the opportunities to exploit additional habitats. 8. See Fig. 40-9. 9. The resulting curve would be similar to the curve in Figure 40-13b, except there would be a third hump added to the graph slightly higher than the second twitch hump. 10. A skeletal muscle shifts function—agonist or antagonist—depending on what action is needed. If each muscle could only perform one function, twice as many muscles would be needed. 11. Muscles are attached to the bones by tendons; the muscles pull on the bones, which causes the bones to act as levers. As muscles weaken, or are not exercised, the bones also lose strength and weaken. 12. Benefits of the arthropod exoskeleton are protection, reduction of water loss, and modified parts that function as tools or weapons; a disadvantage of the exoskeleton is that as their bodies continue to grow, they must molt, making them weak and vulnerable to predation while a new covering grows and hardens. Advantages of the vertebrate skeleton are structural support for organs and locomotion, continued growth and change as the body ages, protection, transmission of muscle forces, and calcium storage for maintaining homeostatic levels of calcium in the blood. Disadvantages of the vertebrate skeleton are degenerative bone and joint diseases, and lack of external protection for many soft tissues. The insect skeleton is adapted to its terrestrial lifestyle: a light, but strong, chitin covering that resists water protects tissues; wings for flight, modified from thoracic exoskeleton; high degree of leverage for powerful muscle use. 13. Human muscle contraction and cellular movement in single-celled organisms both involve actin and myosin. 14. As science has elucidated how joints function, technology has used this knowledge to develop devices and materials to replace destroyed and deteriorated joints. Because humans live longer, joint replacement surgery has become common in developed countries to maintain peoples' active lifestyles. The return of wounded war veterans has driven new demands for high-tech, sophisticated replacement joints. Governments and corporations are investing in needed medical research and development in bioengineering and robot science.

CHAPTER 41

CHECKPOINT

41.1 • The sequence of processes that would allow you to escape the shark are: (1) reception by a sensory receptor; (2) transmission by afferent neuron; (3) integration by interneurons in CNS; (4) transmission by efferent neuron; (5) action by effectors: you yell for help and swim away from the shark. • After neural signals are integrated in the CNS, a neural message is transmitted from the CNS by efferent neurons to effectors. The actions of the effectors are the response to the stimulus. **41.2** • See Fig. 41-2. • A neuron produces and transmits an action potential; it is a cell of the nervous system, made of a cell body containing nucleus and organelles, many branched dendrites extending out from the cell body, and a single long axon. A nerve is a bundle of several hundred axons wrapped in connective tissue. • Astrocytes provide physical support and nutrients for neurons, help regulate the composition of the extracellular fluid in the CNS, communicate with other neurons, and induce synapse formation. Microglia are specialized macrophages that mediate responses to injury and disease by moving to the affected area and removing bacteria and cellular debris. They also release signaling molecules that mediate inflammation and help regulate the number of neurons developing in the brain. **41.3** • Resting potential is mainly due to K^+ easily flowing out of ion channels. Sodium–potassium pumps move Na^+ out and K^+ into the neuron. For some neurons, resting potential is maintained at about -70 mV. • When the threshold level is reached, Na^+ channels open and Na^+ enters the neuron, causing depolarization. The action potential transmits a signal. After signal transmission, the neuron repolarizes; K^+ channels are opened, and K^+ diffuses out of neuron; the neuron then returns to its resting state. • An action potential is an all-or-none response; it is either initiated and continues (self-propagating) or there is no response. A graded potential is a local response that varies in magnitude depending on the strength of the stimulus and fades out within a few millimeters of its origin. • The benefits of saltatory conduction are that it is more rapid and requires less energy than continuous conduction. **41.4** • Biogenic amines have important roles in regulating mood. Dopamine also has a role in motor function. GABA functions as a widespread inhibitory neurotransmitter. • See Fig. 41-11. • EPSPs are produced by a change in membrane potential that brings a neuron closer to the firing level. IPSPs are produced by a change in membrane potential that moves a neuron further from the firing level. **41.5** • Neural integration is the process of summing, or integrating, incoming signals. • Temporal summation occurs when repeated stimuli cause new EPSPs to develop before previous

EPSPs have decayed. Spatial summation occurs when several closely spaced synaptic terminals release neurotransmitters simultaneously, stimulating the postsynaptic neuron at several different places. • In vertebrates most neural integration takes place in the CNS (the brain or spinal cord). **41.6** • See Fig. 41-13.

FIGURE QUESTIONS

FIG. 41-8 Because charybdotoxin blocks K⁺ channels, it would not let the neuron repolarize. **FIG. 41-10** In multiple sclerosis, an autoimmune response destroys and scars myelin along nerves, causing gaps in the myelin covering; this lack of myelin slows or stops the transmission of neural impulses; it can also lead to abnormal nerve signaling ("cross-talk" between neurons). **FIG. 41-11** The neurotransmitter would not be able to bind; the ion channels would not open or close, so no action potential would be generated.

TEST YOUR UNDERSTANDING

1. c 2. d 3. a 4. c 5. d 6. b 7. See Fig. 41-11c. 8. See Fig. 41-11c. The antidepressant/spheres could block reuptake of the neurotransmitter into the presynaptic neuron. 9. (a) Na⁺ ions entering the postsynaptic neuron cause a graded depolarization, or EPSPs. (b) K⁺ diffusing out of a postsynaptic neuron cause IPSPs. (c) Cl⁻ entering a postsynaptic neuron would produce IPSPs. 10. The acetylcholine affects the skeletal and cardiac muscle differently because of the different chemical composition of the two muscles. 11. A person could make future plans, change lifestyle, and obtain help earlier if he/she had a higher risk for AD and knew about the potential risk. Psychological care would need to partner with medical care for the future AD patient. 12. Diseases related to these neurotransmitters could be studied in actual cells as they are produced, and cells could be engineered to provide neurotransmitters for therapeutic reasons. 13. Convergent circuits (signals from many neurons sent to a few) and divergent circuits (signals from one neuron sent to many others) allow for greater neural flexibility and control of stimuli/responses to the environment.

CHAPTER 42

CHECKPOINT

42.1 • The cerebral ganglia of some arthropods differ from the ganglia of flatworms in that the arthropod ganglia have specific functional regions. These areas are specialized for integrating information transmitted to the ganglia from sense organs. • Trends in the evolution of nervous systems include: the number of nerve cells increased; nerve cell bodies became concentrated to form a brain and ganglia; neurons formed nerves and nerve cords; neurons became specialized to perform specific functions; the number of interneurons and complex synaptic contacts increased. • With cephalization, sense organs became concentrated at the front end of the body; this allows the animal to find food and detect enemies and mates more effectively. With the brain located close by, responses can be rapid. **42.2** • See Fig. 42-4. • The CNS consists of the brain where most decisions are made and the spinal cord, which integrates some information itself, and also transmits information from afferent neurons to the brain and from the brain to efferent neurons. The PNS consists of the sensory receptors, the afferent nerves that transmit signals from the sensory receptors to the CNS, and the efferent neurons that transmit signals from the CNS to the muscles and glands. **42.3** • The vertebrate embryonic forebrain subdivides to form the telencephalon, which gives rise to the cerebrum and olfactory bulbs, and to the diencephalon, which gives rise to the thalamus and hypothalamus. The midbrain gives rise to the superior colliculi and the inferior colliculi. The hindbrain gives rise to the cerebellum, pons, and medulla. The cerebrum is the center of intellect, memory, and language, and controls sensory and motor functions. The thalamus is a relay center for motor and sensory messages. The hypothalamus is a major coordinating center for regulating autonomic and somatic responses. It controls body temperature and regulates appetite and water balance. The hypothalamus is important in emotional and sexual responses, and is the link between the nervous and endocrine systems; it also produces certain hormones. The superior colliculi in the midbrain are centers for visual reflexes, and the inferior colliculi are centers for auditory reflexes. The cerebellum regulates motor coordination, muscle tone, posture, and equilibrium. It is important in planning and executing voluntary movements. The pons connects various parts of the brain with one another, and contains respiratory and sleep centers. The medulla contains centers that regulate respiration, heartbeat, and blood pressure. Other reflex centers in the medulla regulate activities such as swallowing, coughing, and vomiting. • The midbrain is the most prominent part of the amphibian brain, and it serves as the main association area. In mammals, the cerebrum is the largest, most complex part of the brain; it serves as the main association area. The cerebellum is also much larger in the mammalian brain than in the amphibian brain. **42.4** • The CNS is encased in bone and covered by three layers of connective tissue, the meninges (dura mater, arachnoid, pia mater). The CNS is also protected by the shock-absorbing cerebrospinal fluid. • The spinal cord transmits information to and from the brain and controls many reflex actions. • See Figs. 42-10a and 42-11a. • The amygdala, part of the limbic system, filters incoming information and evaluates threat. When it perceives danger, the amygdala signals other parts of the brain. Following a traumatic experience, the amygdala may become hypersensitive to possible danger and may over-respond to harmless "triggers." • Learning depends on synaptic plasticity, the ability of synaptic connections to change in response to experience. LTP changes the strength of a synaptic connection. NMDA receptors respond to the neurotransmitter glutamate by opening Ca²⁺ channels. Calcium ions act as second messengers that initiate long-term changes ultimately responsible for LTP. Gene expression and protein synthesis take place during the process of establishing long-term memory. (See Fig. 42-16.) **42.5** • The somatic division of the PNS innervates skeletal muscles and helps maintain posture and balance. The autonomic division of the PNS helps maintain homeostasis in the internal environment; its effectors are smooth muscle, cardiac muscle, and glands. • In general, the sympathetic system stimulates organs to mobilize energy, e.g., it speeds the heart; the parasympathetic system has the opposite effect. Typically, it stimulates organs to conserve and restore energy, e.g., it slows the heart. Sympathetic preganglionic neurons secrete acetylcholine and postganglionic neurons release norepinephrine. Both preganglionic and postganglionic parasympathetic neurons secrete acetylcholine. **42.6** • Alcohol is a CNS depressant; antipsychotic drugs block dopamine receptors and have a calming effect; many SSRI antidepressants elevate mood by blocking serotonin reuptake; amphetamines stimulate release and block reuptake of dopamine and norepinephrine; opiates inhibit dopamine reuptake; and MDMA is a CNS stimulant. (See Table 42-4.)

FIGURE QUESTIONS

FIG. 42-6 During future evolution, the cerebellum and other motor areas of the brain may become smaller because physical activity may continue to decline. Scientists may interfere with evolution by using genetic engineering and technology to produce brains that function more effectively into old age (that is, without cognitive decline); and they may also develop brains with larger, more complex frontal lobes. **FIG. 42-16** Calcium ions activate pathways that lead to LTP. For example, Ca²⁺ activate a pathway leading to insertion of more AMPA receptors in the postsynaptic membrane; more AMPA receptors increase sensitivity to glutamate, resulting in more EPSPs. The EPSPs strengthen the synapse, maintaining the LTP.

TEST YOUR UNDERSTANDING

1. b 2. c 3. d 4. e 5. b 6. a 7. a 8. See Fig. 42-11a. 9. During the evolution of the vertebrate brain, there has been a trend toward greater complexity, particularly of the cerebrum and cerebellum. 10. Parents can stimulate their child's intellectual development by exposing the child to a wide variety of experiences from a very

early age and by giving the child the opportunity to manipulate objects, including electronic devices such as computers. Providing a calm, safe environment enhances learning. 11. The limbic system would quickly assess the danger and send signals to other parts of the brain that would initiate protective action (e.g., running away). 12. The presence of CREB in diverse animals suggests a common ancestor (and that common pathways developed for learning and memory). 13. Because genes are activated during information processing (a critical measure of intelligence), and because genes are inherited, intelligence depends, at least in part, on inheritance of genes that code for information processing.

CHAPTER 43

CHECKPOINT

43.1 • A receptor potential is a change in membrane potential; it is a graded response in which the magnitude of change depends on the strength of the stimulus. In contrast, an action potential is generated only when a neuron becomes sufficiently depolarized to reach its threshold level. In a sensory neuron, receptor potentials depolarize the neuron to threshold level, generating an action potential that transmits the signal to the CNS. • As you continue to hike, your perception of the odor will quickly decrease as sensory adaptation occurs. (The frequency of action potentials decreases, and decreases in neurotransmitter release may occur at the synapses.) • Sensory information is initially integrated in the receptor where receptor potentials produced by various stimuli are integrated by summation. However, integration occurs mainly in the spinal cord and at various locations in the brain, which selects, interprets, and organizes sensations and then converts them to perceptions of stimuli. • Refer to Table 43-1: Classification of Receptors by Type of Energy They Transduce. **43.2** • Mosquitos have thermoreceptors, which can locate an endothermic host. Snakes use thermoreceptors to locate prey or to detect predators. Mammals have thermoreceptors, which detect outside environmental temperature changes. Mammals also have thermoreceptors in the hypothalamus to detect internal changes in temperature and receive and integrate information from receptors on the body surface. **43.3** • Electroreceptors sense differences in electrical potential to detect electric fields for locating prey and for navigation. Electroreceptors also aid in communication, as males and females have different frequencies of electric discharge. • Some animals use electromagnetic reception to facilitate orientation and navigation. **43.4** • Mechanical nociceptors respond to strong tactile stimuli such as cutting, crushing, or pinching; thermal nociceptors respond to temperature extremes (above 45°C or below 5°C); polymodal nociceptors respond to a variety of damaging stimuli, including certain chemicals. • Substance P activates interneurons that transmit the pain message to the opposite side of the spinal cord. Endorphins bind with opiate receptors on the terminals of sensory neurons in the spinal cord to inhibit release of substance P, stopping transmission of the pain signal. **43.5** • Mechanoreceptors help to maintain balance and body position as you walk. Tactile receptors aid orientation and the contact you have with the floor. Proprioceptors help you perceive movement of your legs, arms, and head as you move, and they help maintain balance. • The vestibular apparatus helps maintain equilibrium. The three semicircular canals provide information about turning movements, called angular acceleration. • The sequence of events involved in hearing are as follows: sound waves enter external auditory canal; tympanic membrane vibrates; malleus, incus, and stapes amplify vibrations; oval window vibrates; vibrations are conducted through fluid; basilar membrane vibrates; hair cells in organ of Corti are stimulated; cochlear nerve transmits impulses to the brain. **43.6** • Olfaction and gustation are closely related functions; they occur through chemoreceptors, which allow animals to detect substances in food, air, and water. Information from both systems is sent to the limbic system in the brain. **43.7** • The insect compound eye is structurally and functionally different from the vertebrate eye. The insect eye has many faceted units called ommatidia, each of which consists of a cornea and lens unit made up of photoreceptors called retinular cells. The insect eye can form only coarse mosaic images, and it compensates by superbly detecting movement. Because an insect's eye is sensitive to wavelengths of light in the range from red to ultraviolet (UV), it can see UV light well. The vertebrate eye has an adjustable lens, which can be focused for different distances, an iris, which regulates the amount of light entering the eye, and a retina made up of rod and cone photoreceptor cells. The vertebrate eye can adjust focus to see sharp images. The vertebrate's eye is sensitive to wavelengths ranging from red to violet. • When light strikes rhodopsin, light energy is transduced. Refer to Figure 43-22 for description of the signal transduction pathway. • Light passes through the cornea and then through aqueous fluid, through the lens and through the vitreous body. An image forms on photoreceptor cells in the retina, signaling bipolar cells and then ganglion cells. The optic nerve transmits signals to the thalamus and visual areas of cerebral cortex. • All visual images constructed by the retina are integrated and interpreted in the brain.

FIGURE QUESTIONS

FIG. 43-9 The utricle and saccule would not be able to sense changes in head position and would have no function in a weightless environment. **FIG. 43-10** When you reverse your spinning direction, the endolymph flows in the opposite direction. If you then stop spinning, the position of the stereocilia would return to normal, and action potentials signaling circular rotation would stop. **FIG. 43-11** If the basilar membrane were damaged at its higher, stiff end, the individual would no longer be able to hear high frequency sounds. If the basilar membrane were damaged at its wide, flexible end, the individual would no longer be able to hear lower frequency sounds. (High frequency hearing is greatly impacted by excessive exposure to high frequency and high impact [loud] sounds common to our environment [loud music, cell phones], which damage and destroy cilia.) **FIG. 43-20** Cones, which are responsible for color vision, respond best in daylight. We depend on rods to detect shape and movement in dim light.

TEST YOUR UNDERSTANDING

1. c 2. d 3. a 4. d 5. b 6. c 7. See Fig. 43-18. 8. Although there are only a few types of taste receptors, each different substance sensed by taste receptors is a unique combination of molecules with its own signature. 9. We distinguish quality and intensity of sensory information based on the destination of the sensory neuron (that is, to which structure is the information delivered?); total number of neurons transmitting the signal; total number of action potentials transmitted by the neuron; and frequency of the action potentials. 10. The same proteins in the photoreceptors of many diverse organisms indicate that opsins evolved early and the genes coding for them are highly conserved. 11. The rapid evolution of image-forming eyes and their presence in most animals was an advantage, or edge, for survival. Animals that could see better could detect prey or avoid capture and passed this genetic advantage to their offspring. Most animals without image-forming eyes were unable to compete and many became extinct. 12. Any answer is acceptable if a logical argument is presented.

CHAPTER 44

CHECKPOINT

44.1 • Gases are exchanged by diffusion in hydras and flatworms; earthworms have a closed circulatory system, and gas exchange takes place through the thin walls of capillaries; in insects, gas is exchanged through a system of tubes that are separate from the circulatory system; frogs have a respiratory system with lungs for gas exchange. • In an open circulatory system, a heart pumps hemolymph into vessels that have open ends. The hemolymph bathes the cells directly, and then re-enters the circulatory system through openings in the heart (in arthropods) or through open-ended blood vessels (in mollusks). In closed circulatory systems, blood flows through a continuous circuit of blood vessels. The walls of capillaries are thin enough to permit diffusion of gases, nutrients, and wastes between blood in the vessels and the interstitial fluid that bathes the cells. • The vertebrate circulatory system does the following: transports nutrients from the digestive system and from storage depots to each cell; transports oxygen from respiratory structures to the cells; transports metabolic wastes from each cell to organs that excrete them; transports hormones from endocrine glands to target tissues; helps maintain fluid balance; helps distribute metabolic heat within the body; helps maintain appropriate pH. **44.2** • Alpha globulins include certain hormones and proteins that transport hormones and other compounds, prothrombin, and HDL. Beta globulins include other lipoproteins that transport fats and cholesterol and proteins that transport certain vitamins and minerals. The gamma globulin fraction of plasma contains antibodies. Globulins and albumins help regulate distribution of fluid between plasma and interstitial fluid. Plasma proteins help maintain the pH of the blood within a narrow range. • Red blood cells transport oxygen; neutrophils, the main phagocytic cells in the blood, ingest bacteria. • A shortage of fibrinogen in the blood would prevent clotting. **44.3** • Arteries transport blood away from the heart; veins transport blood toward the heart; and capillaries are the exchange vessels. • If arterioles could not constrict, the body could not regulate blood pressure; also, the body would not be able to regulate the amount of blood going to each tissue or organ. **44.4** • During the evolution of the vertebrate cardiovascular system, structural changes evolved that allow separation of oxygen-rich from oxygen-poor blood; most nonavian reptiles, all avian reptiles (birds), and all mammals have a double circuit of blood flow. In avian reptiles and mammals, the heart has four chambers: two atria and two ventricles. **44.5** • During cardiac conduction, the SA node initiates contraction ⟶ action potential spread through atrial muscle fibers (atria contract) ⟶ action potential delayed briefly in AV node ⟶ action potential spreads into AV bundle ⟶ right and left bundle branches ⟶ Purkinje fibers ⟶ conduct impulses to muscle fibers of both ventricles ⟶ ventricles contract. • When the mitral valve does not close completely, some blood leaks backward into the atrium when the ventricle contracts; less blood flows to the tissues of the body. As a result, the heart pumps harder. This condition can lead to congestive heart failure. • Cardiac output = stroke volume (100 ml per stroke) × heart rate (100 contractions/minute) = 10,000 ml/min (10 L/min). **44.6** • Arteriole constriction increases blood pressure. • Blood pressure in arteries is higher than blood pressure in veins. **44.7** • Blood flowing from the carotid artery to the superior vena cava passes through: carotid artery ⟶ capillaries in brain ⟶ jugular vein ⟶ superior vena cava. Blood

flowing from the renal vein to the renal artery passes through: renal vein ⟶ inferior vena cava ⟶ right atrium ⟶ right ventricle ⟶ pulmonary arteries ⟶ pulmonary capillaries (in lungs) ⟶ pulmonary vein ⟶ left atrium ⟶ left ventricle ⟶ aorta ⟶ renal artery. • Recall that most veins conduct blood to larger veins or to the superior or inferior vena cava. The hepatic portal system is an exception. This vein transports nutrients from the intestine to the liver. In the liver, the hepatic portal vein branches into a network of hepatic sinuses from which nutrients leave the circulation and enter liver cells. The liver stores nutrients that are not immediately needed by other cells. The hepatic sinuses then merge to form hepatic veins. The sequence of blood flow: hepatic portal vein ⟶ hepatic sinuses (in liver) ⟶ hepatic veins. **44.8** • See Figs. 44-19 and 44-20. • The lymphatic system collects excess interstitial fluid and returns it to the blood. **44.9** • Joe is at high risk for cardiovascular disease. • During development of atherosclerotic plaque, endothelial cells respond to oxidized LDLs by releasing compounds that attract monocytes. These white blood cells enter the tissues and trigger an inflammatory response. Cells of the immune system migrate to the area and produce substances that maintain chronic inflammation in the inner layer of the arterial wall. Some macrophages become foam cells, which stimulate the development of fatty streaks. These streaks may be the initial lesion in atherosclerosis.

FIGURE QUESTIONS

FIG. 44-6 Lymph vessels have very small dead ends that infiltrate most tissues in the body. They are one-way vessels that pick up fluid and deliver it into the blood circulation through two small ducts in the shoulder region. **FIG. 44-8** The separation of oxygen-rich blood from oxygen-poor blood in avian reptiles and mammals enables their cardiovascular systems to deliver more oxygen to their tissues. As a result, these animals can maintain a higher metabolic rate than other animals and a constant high body temperature even in cold surroundings. **FIG. 44-11** When the SA node increases its rate of firing, the cardiac cycle speeds up accordingly. **FIG. 44-16** The left ventricle needs a thicker wall than the right ventricle because the left ventricle must contract strongly enough to pump blood at a higher pressure through the higher resistance and longer arterial system. If the right ventricle contracted that powerfully, the lung tissue would be damaged.

TEST YOUR UNDERSTANDING

1. a 2. d. 3. e 4. d 5. e 6. e 7. d 8. d 9. See Fig. 44-6. The thick walls of arteries are adapted to the high pressure they must withstand. Compared to arterial walls, the walls of veins are thin. Capillary walls are only one cell thick, allowing nutrients, oxygen, and other substances to pass through them. 10. The heart rate is carefully

regulated by sympathetic and parasympathetic nerves, which are controlled by a cardiac center in the brain stem. 11. The four-chambered heart allows efficient oxygenation of body tissues, which in turn allows these animals to be endothermic. 12. Fish have a single circuit of blood vessels. Blood leaving the heart passes through the gills, where it is oxygenated. 13. Blood vessels with atherosclerotic plaque deliver less oxygen to the tissues, including the heart itself. In ischemic heart disease the heart muscle is not receiving enough oxygen, particularly during exercise or emotional stress. The remaining two parts of this question ask your opinion. As you reflect on the questions, consider the human misery caused by cardiovascular disease, as well as the monetary cost to society.

CHAPTER 45

CHECKPOINT

45.1 • Adaptive immunity consists of specific defenses that target specific macromolecules. In adaptive immunity the body typically produces antibodies that recognize and bind to specific antigens. Also unlike innate immunity, adaptive immunity is characterized by immunological memory. • Like invertebrates, vertebrates depend on innate immunity for their initial defense against invading pathogens. Unlike invertebrates, vertebrates have highly developed adaptive immunity. **45.2** • The function of pattern recognition receptors is to recognize nonself molecules; these receptors recognize pathogen-associated molecular patterns (PAMPs). • If you had no NK cells, you would be much more vulnerable to virus infections and developing tumors. Macrophages are the main phagocytes in the body. If you had no macrophages, both your innate and adaptive immune systems would be severely impaired. • Cytokines are important signaling molecules with a wide variety of functions. For example, they enhance the inflammatory response, stimulate NK cell activity, and activate lymphocytes. Complement proteins destroy viruses and bacteria; they attract white blood cells to the site of infection; they enhance the inflammatory response • See Fig. 45-3. Main steps in the inflammatory response would include activation of macrophages and mast cells, vasodilation, increased capillary permeability, and increased phagocytosis. **45.3** • Cell-mediated immunity and antibody-mediated immunity are two types of adaptive immunity. Lymphocytes are the key cells in both. T cells (and APCs) are the main cells in cell-mediated immunity. T cells attack foreign cells, cancer cells, and body cells infected by invading pathogens. B cells are responsible for antibody-mediated immunity. B cells mature into plasma cells, which produce specific antibodies. • Antigen-presenting cells (APCs) activate T helper cells. Macrophages, dendritic cells, and B cells function as APCs. • A kidney transplant from a first cousin has a higher probability of success than a transplant from an unknown donor because first cousins are more likely to have more HLA alleles in common. (First cousins have 12.5% of their genes in common.) **45.4** • APCs activate T_H cells (and also activate T_C cells). Activated T cells divide by mitosis to form a clone of activated cells. T_H cells release cytokines that activate T_C cells (and macrophages). T_C cells release proteins that destroy infected cells. **45.5** • See highlighted sequence of events on page 967. • See Fig. 45-8 or 45-9. Antigen–antibody complexes: inactivate pathogens or their toxins; stimulate phagocytes to ingest pathogens; IgG and IgM activate the complement system. • Immunological memory depends on memory B cells and memory T cells; after an infection, these cells remain strategically stationed in the body and can respond rapidly to antigens they have encountered before. • Passive immunity is borrowed immunity; memory cells are not produced and its effects are temporary. **45.6** • Some types of cancer cells can block T_C cells. Other cancer cells decrease their expression of class I MHC molecules, preventing T_C cells from recognizing them. Still others do not produce co-stimulatory molecules needed to activate T_C cells. • HIV enters the body through the mucosa that lines passageways into the body. A protein on the outer envelope of the virus attaches to CD4 on the surface of T_H cells. HIV enters the T_H cell and is reverse-transcribed to produce DNA. Its DNA is then incorporated into the host genome. The virus reproduces itself, causing death of the host cell. Innate immune responses include production of antimicrobial peptides and action by NK cells, dendritic cells, and the complement system. Adaptive immune responses include activation and mobilization of T_C cells. • An autoimmune disease is a failure in self-tolerance. Antibodies and T cells attack the body's own tissues. Viral or bacterial infection often precedes the onset of an autoimmune disease. Molecular mimicry has evolved in some pathogens; these pathogens trick the body by producing molecules that look like self-molecules. Immune cells may not discriminate and may attack the body's similar molecules. Overactivation of cells of the immune system can result in inflammation and autoimmune disease. • See Fig. 45-17. • When tissue from a donor is transplanted to the body of another person, several of the HLA antigens are likely to be different. The recipient's T_H cells and T_C cells recognize the graft as nonself (i.e., foreign) and launch an immune response known as graft rejection. T_C cells, the complement system, and cytokines secreted by T_H cells attack the transplanted tissue and can destroy it within a week.

FIGURE QUESTIONS

FIG. 45-3 Several signs of infection would be evident due to the inflammatory response. The foot would be swollen, red, and warm to the touch at and near the site of the puncture. You would experience pain from your foot and might have a low-grade fever. Pus might be seeping from the wound. **FIG. 45-5** The malignant cells would crowd out other cells in the bone marrow, severely slowing the production of antigen-presenting cells and lymphocytes. **FIG. 45-6** Macrophages, dendritic cells, and B cells function as antigen-presenting cells (APCs). **FIG. 45-8** No. Immunity would be depressed if T_C cells collected in the lymph tissues as plasma cells do. T_C cells are the cellular infantry; they must spread out strategically to discover and destroy incoming pathogens. In contrast, plasma cells remain in the bone marrow and release antibodies into the circulation.

TEST YOUR UNDERSTANDING

1. b 2. c 3. e 4. c 5. a 6. e 7. c 8. b 9. a 10. d 11. See Fig. 45-7, step 3. This diagram shows a T_H cell activating a B cell, which then divides, producing two B cells. 12. Specificity helps make the immune system very efficient. T cells and antibodies are produced that are highly specific for destroying the particular pathogens that invade the body. Diversity gives the immune system the capability of protecting the body from almost any new pathogen that invades (see Fig. 45-11). Immunological memory allows the immune system to "remember" each type of pathogen against which it has already launched an immune response. When it encounters the same pathogen again, the immune system launches a rapid attack. 13. Macrophages are important in both innate and adaptive immune responses. Reduction in macrophages would critically decrease the body's ability to launch an immune response. A significant decrease in macrophages would probably have a more serious negative impact than a decrease in memory B cells because macrophages are first responders. The body could compensate for a decrease in memory B cells by launching a primary immune response. 14. In kindergarten, John has been immunized so is unlikely to develop measles again. Jack will likely develop measles, and his body will develop immunity to the measles virus. Five years later when Judy (who has the measles virus) sneezes on both of them, it is improbable that either John or Jack will develop measles because both of them have immunological memory of the virus. 15. These facts suggest that the genes that encode the enzymes necessary for antibody diversity, an important aspect of adaptive immunity, are very old and that echinoderms and jawed vertebrates share a common ancestor. 16. In forming your opinion, you might consider how we could use technology to better inform the millions of people living in poverty in low-income countries. Also, how could we more rapidly apply new technology to development of new vaccines and treatments?

CHAPTER 46

CHECKPOINT

46.1 • Air has a higher concentration of oxygen; oxygen diffuses faster in air; animals that breathe air expend significantly less energy to obtain oxygen than animals in an underwater habitat. **46.2** • Flatworms can depend on diffusion for gas exchange, but the larger tadpole body requires a respiratory system for gas exchange. • An earthworm exchanges gasses through the body surface. A grasshopper exchanges gases through a system of tracheal tubes, or tracheae. Fish exchange gases through internal or external gills. Birds exchange gases with lungs. • The countercurrent exchange system increases the efficiency of gas exchange because much more oxygen is able to diffuse into the blood when the blood flows through the capillaries in the opposite direction compared with the water. **46.3** • In mammals air enters through the nostrils, then nasal cavities, pharynx, larynx, trachea, bronchi, then bronchioles, and lastly the alveoli. • Gas exchange takes place in the alveoli. Oxygen concentration is lower in the alveoli than in atmospheric air because cells of the body use oxygen during cellular respiration; carbon dioxide concentration is higher in the alveoli than in atmospheric air because carbon dioxide is produced during cellular respiration. • Increased carbon dioxide in the blood lowers the pH (blood becomes more acidic). When blood is more acidic, hemoglobin can unload oxygen more readily. • Breathing would increase as more oxygen is required for cellular respiration. You would also breathe harder to increase ventilation to dispose of excess carbon dioxide. Chemoreceptors in the walls of the aorta and carotid arteries sense lower blood pH, which stimulates chemoreceptors to up-regulate breathing. As the lungs remove carbon dioxide, the blood pH returns to normal and homeostasis is restored. **46.4** • The ciliated mucous lining of the airway traps inhaled particles to remove pollutants from the respiratory system. • When the respiratory defense system is overwhelmed by pollutants, diseases such as chronic bronchitis, pulmonary emphysema, and lung cancer can occur.

FIGURE QUESTIONS

FIG. 46-2 The highly efficient tracheal system of insects delivers oxygen to all parts of the body. **FIG. 46-3** The countercurrent flow functions in the same way for carbon dioxide removal; carbon dioxide is transferred from blood in the capillaries to the surrounding water at the same time oxygen is transferred from the water to the blood in capillaries. **FIG. 46-7** The capillary walls are only one cell thick; millions of pulmonary capillaries act as an interface to readily exchange gases in the alveoli. **FIG. 46-11** If the carbonic anhydrase enzyme were inhibited, carbon dioxide would build up in the red blood cells; net diffusion of carbon dioxide from the body cells into the red blood cells would slow and then cease.

TEST YOUR UNDERSTANDING

1. a 2. a 3. b 4. c 5. d 6. e 7. c 8. e 9. c 10. d 11. See Fig. 46-6. 12. Having millions of alveoli immensely increases the surface area for gas exchange. 13. Strenuous muscle activity would increase acidity of the blood and hemoglobin would unload oxygen more readily. The oxygen–hemoglobin curve would shift to the right. 14. If a terrestrial animal had gills, the gills would not function properly on land; water is required to support the gill structure. The animal with gills would not be able to breathe on land and would die. 15. It would be advantageous for fish that live at the land–water interface to have gills and lungs. The lungs of modern fish serve as swim bladders to control buoyancy. 16. Whales and dolphins were originally land mammals with lungs; when they returned to the sea, they continued to require air to breathe. 17. Further increasing tobacco taxes could encourage users to seek help for their expensive addiction; the collected taxes could pay for addiction treatment research. Also, reducing and gradually eliminating places to smoke may continue to be an effective method to curtail smoking.

CHAPTER 47

CHECKPOINT

47.1 • Carnivorous mammals have canine teeth for stabbing prey; their pointed incisors and canines are adaptations for ripping flesh. • Flatworms have a gastrovascular cavity with only one opening; digestion is completed intracellularly within food vacuoles. Earthworms have a complete digestive tract with a mouth and anus; some regions of the digestive tract are specialized to perform specific food-processing functions. • Various regions are specialized to perform specific functions, and different functions can be carried on simultaneously—for example, at the same time food is being digested in the stomach, nutrients can be absorbed in the small intestine and wastes can be eliminated from the large intestine. **47.2** • Mouth—mechanical and enzymatic digestion begins; pharynx—food swallowed; esophagus—moves food to the stomach; stomach—mechanical and enzymatic digestion; small intestine—digestion and absorption of digested nutrients; large intestine—absorbs water and sodium from the chyme, and bacteria there produce vitamin K and certain B vitamins; anus—opening for

elimination of wastes. • Rugae increase the surface area in the stomach; villi increase the surface area in the small intestine. • Trypsin digests proteins and polypeptides; bile salts mechanically digest fats; gastrin stimulates gastric motility and stimulates gastric glands to secrete pepsinogen and HCl; and lacteals, the central lymph vessel in each villus, absorb chylomicrons (fat droplets). • See Fig. 47-4. **47.3** • Carbohydrates, fats, proteins, vitamins, minerals. • Glucose provides energy; essential amino acids are required to synthesize proteins. • LDLs deliver cholesterol to the cells; they are the main source of the cholesterol that builds up in the walls of arteries, causing cardiovascular disease. **47.4** • When energy input = energy output, body weight remains constant; when energy input is less than energy output, body weight decreases; when energy input is greater than energy output, body weight increases. • BMI is an index of weight in relation to height. • Melanocortins suppress appetite, resulting in decreased food intake and weight loss; NPY stimulates appetite; ghrelin stimulates appetite by activating neurons in the hypothalamus to produce NPY. Leptin signals the hypothalamus about the status of energy stores in adipose tissue. It slows the release of NPY and stimulates release of melanocortins.

FIGURE QUESTIONS

FIG. 47-4 The esophagus would need to be connected to the duodenum. **FIG. 47-9** Lymph tissue in the wall of the gastrointestinal tract contains macrophages, T cells, and other cells of the immune system. These cells are closely positioned to destroy pathogens that enter the body in contaminated food or water. **FIG. 47-10** If gluten remains part of the diet, the mucosa of the small intestine becomes damaged and the villi cannot absorb enough nutrients. This can lead to malnutrition.

TEST YOUR UNDERSTANDING

1. c 2. d 3. d 4. e 5. b 6. d 7. a 8. b 9. c 10. c 11. See Fig. 47-4. 12. You could include an experimental and a control group with about 20 mice in each group. Both groups would be fed the same diet *except* the diet of the experimental group would lack pyridoxine. You could weigh each mouse each day and also note specific health factors, including condition of skin, GI tract function, and presence of convulsions. 13. In their inactive form, proteolytic enzymes do not digest the lining of the GI tract. 14. You could examine the animal's tooth structure, and look for other clues, e.g., sharp claws, size of jaws. 15. Identifying and understanding the actions of the many hormones and other signaling molecules that regulate energy metabolism might lead to the development of new compounds that could inhibit appetite-stimulating compounds or stimulate appetite-suppressing compounds in the body. A cure for obesity would lead to a healthier society and also save billions of dollars each year in health care costs.

CHAPTER 48

CHECKPOINT

48.1 • Osmoregulation maintains salt and water concentrations within homeostatic limits. • Excretory systems help maintain homeostasis through osmoregulation and excretion of metabolic wastes. **48.2** • Some aquatic animals excrete ammonia; insects, certain reptiles, and birds excrete uric acid; and urea is the principal nitrogenous waste excreted by amphibians and mammals. • Excretion of nitrogenous wastes as uric acid conserves water in terrestrial animals. Uric acid and urea are less toxic than ammonia. The body can store concentrated urea without causing damage to tissues. **48.3** • Nephridia consist of simple or branching tubes that open to the outside of the body through pores. The protonephridia of flatworms and nemerteans have blind ends that consist of flame cells with cilia. The cilia propel fluid through the tubules. The metanephridia of annelids and mollusks are open at both ends. As fluid moves through the tubule of a nephridium, water and certain other substances (e.g., glucose) are reabsorbed by capillaries, leaving the waste to be excreted. The Malpighian tubules of insects excrete wastes more selectively than nephridia. Malpighian tubules are slender extensions of the gut wall; they have blind ends that extend into the hemocoel. Cells of the tubule wall actively transport uric acid, potassium ions, and some other substances from the hemolymph into the tubule. Malpighian tubules empty into the gut. Water, some salts, and other solutes are reabsorbed into the hemolymph by a specialized epithelium in the rectum. **48.4** • Marine fishes lose water osmotically and take in salt. To compensate they drink and retain sea water. Specialized cells in their gills excrete salt. Marine cartilaginous fishes retain a high urea concentration, which makes their body fluids hypertonic to sea water, so there is a net inflow of sea water. Freshwater fishes are hypertonic to the fresh water around them, and water continuously moves into the body. Their kidneys excrete large amounts of dilute urine. These fishes also lose salts by diffusion through their gills into the surrounding water. Special gill cells actively transport salt back into the body. • Marine birds ingest sea water and take in a lot of salt in their food. Glands in their heads excrete salt in response to osmotic stress. Marine mammals ingest sea water along with their food. Their kidneys produce concentrated urine, saltier than sea water. Terrestrial birds and mammals have efficient kidneys that conserve water. Birds conserve water by reabsorbing water from the intestine and by excreting uric acid. Mammalian kidneys produce hypertonic urine. **48.5** • The liver produces urea; kidneys produce urine; urinary bladder stores urine; urethra conducts urine out of body. • Filtration is the job of the glomerulus; reabsorption is the job of the renal tubules; secretion takes place in the renal tubules and collecting ducts. • Bowman's capsule ⟶ proximal convoluted tubule ⟶ loop of Henle ⟶ distal convoluted tubule ⟶ collecting duct ⟶ ureter ⟶ urinary bladder. See also Figs. 48-8 and 48-10. • The main actions of the renin–angiotensin–aldosterone pathway are to increase sodium reabsorption, which raises blood pressure. Angiotensin II also raises blood pressure directly by constricting blood vessels, and it stimulates the posterior pituitary to release ADH. In contrast, ANP decreases blood pressure by increasing sodium excretion, dilating afferent arterioles, and inhibiting aldosterone secretion.

FIGURE QUESTIONS

FIG. 48-5 If a shark were swimming in fresh water, its kidneys would need to work harder in order to produce a large volume of dilute urine to compensate for the increase in water entering the shark through osmosis. **FIG. 48-10** Mild dehydration would affect kidney function by reducing the volume of the blood plasma. More water would need to be reabsorbed, and a low volume of more concentrated urine would be produced. **FIG. 48-14** ADH increases water reabsorption, which increases blood volume. By this mechanism, ADH raises arterial blood pressure.

TEST YOUR UNDERSTANDING

1. c 2. d 3. e 4. d 5. a 6. a 7. c 8. d 9. e 10. b 11. e 12. See Fig. 48-10. 13. In someone with diabetes mellitus, the concentration of glucose in the blood exceeds its tubular transport maximum. The excess glucose that cannot be reabsorbed is excreted in the urine. Because the urine is more hypertonic, more water enters it by osmosis. The urine volume increases. 14. Dehydration is a familiar example of a human osmoregulatory challenge. Dehydration results in a lower blood volume and resulting lower blood pressure. These events stimulate increased secretion of ADH and aldosterone. Decreased blood pressure also stimulates renin release, which leads to increased angiotensin II. These hormones increase blood pressure. 15. In planaria, when the salinity of the surrounding water decreases, the number of protonephridia increase. When its environment is less salty, more water enters the planarian's body by osmosis. The protonephridia expel the excess water. 16. The kangaroo rat must conserve water by producing a very low volume of urine. 17. Mammalian kidneys are more efficient than bird kidneys; they can produce more concentrated urine. There is a correlation between the length of the loop of Henle and the ability to concentrate urine. 18. Answers will vary based on your opinion.

CHAPTER 49

CHECKPOINT

49.1 • Target cells are those that are influenced by a particular hormone and have specific binding receptors. • The nervous and endocrine systems work together to maintain homeostasis. Neurons signal gland cells, including endocrine cells, and the nervous system helps regulate many endocrine responses. Some signal molecules can function as either a neurotransmitter or a hormone, depending on their source. • When calcium concentration in the blood decreases below the homeostatic level, a negative feedback system is engaged; the parathyroid glands release more parathyroid hormone, returning the calcium concentration to the homeostatic level. • The four major chemical groups of hormones are fatty acid derivatives, which include prostaglandins; steroid hormones such as cortisol; amino acid derivatives such as epinephrine; and peptide hormones such as glucagon. **49.2** • See Figs. 49-3a and b. • In autocrine signaling a hormone acts on the cells that produce it, while in paracrine signaling a hormone diffuses through interstitial fluid and acts on nearby target cells. • Prostaglandins modify cyclic AMP levels and interact with other hormones to regulate various metabolic activities. **49.3** • Receptors convert an extracellular hormone signal into an intracellular signal that affects some cell process. The hormone does not enter the cell but serves as the first messenger and relays information to a second messenger. The second messenger signals effector molecules that carry out the action. • Steroid hormones are relatively small, lipid-soluble molecules that easily pass through the plasma membrane of the target cell. Peptide hormones, not lipid soluble, bind to specific cell-surface receptors in the plasma membrane. • Many protein hormones bind to G protein–linked receptors. The receptor activates a second messenger such as cyclic AMP, which then catalyzes the conversion of ATP to cAMP. This second messenger relays the signal, activating a protein, such as protein kinase, which leads to a response or change in the cell. **49.4** • Four actions of hormones in invertebrates are helping to regulate metabolism, growth and development, regeneration, and molting. • Juvenile hormone suppresses metamorphosis at each larval molt. With each successive molt, the level of juvenile hormone decreases. **49.5** • The hypothalamus is the link between the nervous and endocrine systems because it regulates endocrine activity and connects both systems anatomically. The anterior pituitary regulates growth and other endocrine glands. The posterior pituitary secretes oxytocin and antidiuretic hormone produced by the hypothalamus.

• See Fig. 49-10. • The beta cells in the pancreas would secrete insulin, lowering blood glucose concentration. Insulin decreases blood glucose concentration, while glucagon increases it; both are regulated by negative feedback systems. • The adrenal glands would be triggered to release large amounts of epinephrine and norepinephrine so you could think quicker, fight harder, and run faster to escape the reptilian jaws. • The adrenal medulla is regulated by the hypothalamus and sympathetic nervous system, while the adrenal cortex is regulated by negative feedback involving the hypothalamus and adrenocorticotropic hormone.

FIGURE QUESTIONS

FIG. 49-4 Because there would be fewer receptors that could become activated, specific protein synthesis would be slowed. **FIG. 49-5** Less cAMP (the second messenger) would be produced, so fewer proteins would be activated, and the effect of the hormone would be decreased. **FIG. 49-13** Less glucagon would be secreted and the glucose concentration in the blood would decrease below normal. The person would experience hypoglycemia.

TEST YOUR UNDERSTANDING

1. c 2. d 3. c 4. e 5. a 6. b 7. e 8. a 9. d 10. See Fig. 49-13. 11. Cells require glucose for cellular respiration. There are many challenges to glucose homeostasis, and multiple hormones work together to regulate carbohydrate metabolism. For example, when the body is under stress, cortisol promotes conversion of other nutrients to glucose. 12. The brain does not store glucose; however, neurons require a steady supply of this fuel molecule. When neurons in the brain are deprived of glucose, the brain is not able to function. The individual may pass out, or if the situation is prolonged, could become comatose or die. 13. Receptors only bind with a specific hormone. An advantage of having complexity in hormone action is the precision that is achieved among and between different body systems and regulatory functions. 14. The receptor for aldosterone may have been a receptor for some ancient, no longer present, similar hormone before aldosterone evolved. 15. Humans have evolved over tens of thousands of years (or longer) to store fat and consume a great deal of food when it is available. This physiological characteristic cannot be rapidly changed, but the dilemma can be addressed psychologically and socially. Scientists and doctors can partner with educators to facilitate public understanding about healthy food consumption, physical exercise, and our human proclivity to stuff ourselves with fatty, sugary foods. More technologies can be developed to stimulate pleasurable physical exercise and to retool the food-processing industry without sacrificing taste.

CHAPTER 50

CHECKPOINT

50.1 • In budding (e.g., in cnidarians) a small part of the parent's body separates from the rest and develops into a new individual. In fragmentation, the body of the parent breaks into several pieces; each piece regenerates the missing parts and develops into a new animal. In parthenogenesis, an unfertilized egg develops into an adult animal. • Compared with sexual reproduction, asexual reproduction is the fastest and most efficient way to reproduce. For example, each cell can produce two new cells. The disadvantage of asexual reproduction is that the offspring has all of the same genes as the single parent (except for mutations); as a result, there is a lack of variability in the population. **50.2** • The testes produce sperm and the male hormone testosterone. • Seminiferous tubules ⟶ epididymis ⟶ vas deferens ⟶ ejaculatory duct ⟶ urethra ⟶ release from body (see Fig. 50-3). • Testosterone stimulates development of the male's primary and secondary sex characteristics, maintains the secondary sex characteristics, and stimulates spermatogenesis. • See Fig. 50-8. **50.3** • In oogenesis, a primary oocyte gives rise to only one ovum; compare to a primary spermatocyte giving rise to four sperm cells during spermatogenesis. • If the secondary oocyte were fertilized, it could not develop without the hormones produced by a corpus luteum. • See Fig. 50-15a. FSH stimulates follicle development. Estrogens stimulate the endometrium to thicken; estrogens are necessary for the development of the sex organs at puberty, and for the development and maintenance of female secondary sex characteristics. **50.4** • If a woman becomes pregnant, hCG signals the corpus luteum to continue to function. • Without sufficient estrogen and progesterone, the embryo would be spontaneously aborted. Estrogen is necessary for the development and maintenance of the uterine wall, and progesterone inhibits uterine contractions that might expel the embryo. • High levels of estrogen secreted by the placenta greatly increase the number of receptors for oxytocin in the uterine wall. As a result, the uterus becomes more responsive to oxytocin, the hormone that stimulates uterine contractions. **50.5** • Muscle tension increases and certain tissues (including tissues in the penis, vagina, and clitoris) become engorged with blood (vasocongestion); heart rate and respiration increase. **50.6** • Hormone methods of contraception inhibit ovulation. • Sterilization would have the greatest impact on the number of unwanted pregnancies; other methods with low failure rates are injectable or implanted hormone contraceptives and IUDs. • A spontaneous abortion, or miscarriage, occurs naturally; a therapeutic abortion is performed when the mother's life is in danger or when there is evidence that the embryo will be grossly abnormal.

50.7 • The two most common STIs in the United States are human papillomavirus (HPV) and *Chlamydia*. • Pelvic inflammatory disease (PID), a serious infection that can lead to infertility, can be caused by chlamydia.

FIGURE QUESTIONS

FIG. 50-8 The testes could not produce testosterone, which would stop sperm production, lower his sex drive, and affect his secondary sex characteristics. **FIG. 50-14** Ovulation does not take place and symptoms of menopause may occur. **FIG. 50-15** FSH would continue to be released and new follicles would develop.

TEST YOUR UNDERSTANDING

1. c 2. e 3. a 4. b 5. e 6. a 7. a 8. e 9. d 10. c 11. See Fig. 50-9b. 12. LH and estrogen; mid to late postovulatory phase; estrogen and progesterone. 13. Cross-fertilization increases variability in the offspring, increasing their chance of surviving in a changing environment. 14. Some animals may have mutations that help them resist parasites. Sexual reproduction allows such beneficial mutations to spread through the population. 15. Sociological factors—historically women have been held responsible for contraception; biological factors—there are more opportunities for intervention in the female. Development of a method of male contraception might focus on reduction of sperm production in the seminiferous tubules, or on methods that would decrease sperm motility or viability. 16. Countries where abortions are legal and safe are most likely higher income countries in which people have easier access to contraception (and can also afford contraception).

CHAPTER 51

CHECKPOINT

51.1 • Cell determination generally precedes cell differentiation. • Pattern formation is the process that leads to morphogenesis through the organization of differentiated cells. The steps in pattern formation include cell-to-cell signaling, cell migrations, changes in cell shape, and apoptosis. **51.2** • Species-specific recognition molecules ensure that sperm and egg are of the same species. Events occurring at the time of fertilization ensure that more than one sperm cannot enter the egg (i.e., prevent polyspermy). • Although the details differ, the cortical reaction serves as a block to polyspermy in both echinoderms and mammals. **51.3** • Compare your sketches to Figure 30-5. • Meroblastic cleavage (cleavage restricted to the blastodisc). • Large amounts of yolk in the egg cytoplasm tend to slow down cleavage in the embryo. As a consequence, the vegetal pole

cells of embryos developing from moderately telolecithal eggs tend to be fewer and larger than the animal pole cells. The yolk of embryos developing from extremely telolecithal eggs does not cleave at all (meroblastic cleavage in reptiles and birds). **51.4** • The archenteron is the embryonic forerunner of the digestive tract. It is formed in sea stars and amphibians, but not in birds. • Large amounts of yolk prevent the simple type of gastrulation that occurs in echinoderms and amphioxus. Instead, the establishment of the three embryonic cell layers is accomplished as cells migrate from the cell surface and move into the interior of the embryo. **51.5** • Ectoderm: outer skin layer, nervous system, and sense organs; mesoderm: notochord, skeleton, muscles, circulatory system, reproductive system; endoderm: lining of digestive tube. Refer to Table 51-1 for a more complete list. • Neural plate cells differentiate in response to inductive signals from the underlying notochord tissue. These cells undergo a process of morphogenesis in which their shapes change, converting the neural plate into the neural tube, which eventually sinks below the surface. The cells of the neural tube subsequently differentiate into specialized cells of the central nervous system. • Neural crest cells are extremely versatile cells that give rise to parts of spinal nerves; they also migrate to various locations in the embryo, giving rise to many structures, including parts of the peripheral nervous system, various sense organs, parts of the head, and pigment-forming cells. **51.6** • Chorion: gas exchange and contributes to placenta in mammals; amnion: protection from desiccation and shocks. • In birds the allantois stores wastes and the yolk sac stores nutrients. In mammals the allantois contributes to the blood vessels in the umbilical cord and blood cells form in the walls of the yolk sac. **51.7** • The human embryo undergoes cleavage while being propelled down the oviduct, developing into a blastocyst (a blastula) after it enters the uterus. Trophoblast cells (the outer cell layer of the blastocyst) secrete enzymes that implant the blastocyst in the uterine wall. • The placenta develops from embryonic tissue (the chorion, which develops from trophoblast cells) and maternal uterine tissue, and serves as the organ of exchange between mother and embryo. • The cerebrum develops lobes at four months; limb buds appear at four weeks. • Rapid changes in the circulatory system are required as the embryo begins to breathe air. Most notably the blood that bypassed the lungs during fetal life becomes redirected to the lungs. In addition, the neonate's digestive system must begin to function because it is no longer supplied by nutrients from the mother.

FIGURE QUESTIONS

FIG. 51-3 Compare your sketch to Figure 51-3g. The innermost cavity is the archenteron, surrounded by the blastocoel. Your sketch should not include the blastopore.

FIG. 51-4 Compare your sketch to Figure 51-4j. It should not include the blastopore. **FIG. 51-5** Compare your sketch to Figures 51-4d and 30-5b. **FIG. 51-6** Compare your sketch to Figure 51-3c. **FIG. 51-8** It is unlikely that development would proceed beyond a few divisions because a blastomere lacking a gray crescent would lack cytoplasmic determinants required to support normal development. **FIG. 51-9** Archenteron: gut; blastopore: anus; blastocoel: nothing.

TEST YOUR UNDERSTANDING

1. b 2. d 3. a 4. d 5. b 6. e 7. b 8. b 9. c 10. b 11. c 12. a 13. The modern view is that eggs and sperm contain genetic instructions that interact with developmental determinants in the egg cytoplasm to direct development. 14. Some teratogenic medications such as thalidomide are of significant medical value, but their use must be carefully regulated to prevent birth defects. 15. A human embryo possesses a notochord, which does not support the adult body as in amphioxus, but is responsible for the induction of the overlying cells to form the neural plate, the forerunner of the dorsal hollow nerve cord, which then develops into the brain and spinal cord. A postanal tail develops, but does not persist (although it is evident in many of our primate relatives). Pharyngeal pouches, pharyngeal grooves, and branchial arches develop in the region of the pharynx. Slits do not form between the pouches and grooves, and they are not used for filter feeding (as in amphioxus) or for respiration (as in fishes). However, they and the branchial arches of supporting tissue give rise to many structures in the head, jaws, and neck (see Section 51.5). These structures have persisted because evolution is conservative and commonly builds pre-existing structures. 16. The placenta allows the embryo to develop within the body of the mother, which affords much more protection than an egg. 17. Consult Table 51-3 and the March of Dimes website for information on environmental influences to be avoided during (and even before) pregnancy. Your challenge as a public health official will be to devise programs that will effectively improve and extend maternal education and care.

CHAPTER 52

CHECKPOINT

52.1 • *Philanthus* performs a complex series of behaviors as she provides for her larva. Her behaviors increase the probability that her offspring will survive. The number of viable offspring an animal produces is a measure of its direct fitness. Therefore, the behaviors of *Philanthus* are adaptive. • Sample answer: A child inherits the capacity to run. However, individuals who want to be Olympic athletes must train for many years to improve their basic capacity to run. These athletes must learn how to modify and improve their muscle structure, form, and speed. • Innate behavior occurs when the animal is physiologically ready. Physiological readiness also affects the capacity for learned behavior. For example, a baby cannot learn to walk or play the piano until her body is physiologically ready. **52.2** • Imprinting is adaptive because the young learn to stay close to their mother, increasing their chance of survival. • Operant conditioning is adaptive because animals learn how to obtain food and other necessities; they also learn how to avoid dangerous or unpleasant stimuli. **52.3** • It is adaptive for some species to be diurnal while others are nocturnal or crepuscular because it decreases competition for food and other resources. • Directional orientation refers to travel in a specific direction. In navigation, an animal must integrate information about distance and time, as well as direction. **52.4** • Optimal foraging is the most efficient way for an animal to obtain food. • Optimal foraging is adaptive because the animals maximize their energy intake per unit of foraging time. This approach may maximize their reproductive success. **52.5** • The costs of living in groups include increased competition for food and habitats, increased risk of attracting predators, increased risk of transmitting disease, and time and energy used to gain and maintain social status. The benefits include defense against predators, help in foraging, and opportunities to receive help from others in the group. • Advantages of pheromones include that they are simple, widespread means of communication, and very little energy is required for their synthesis. They are effective in the dark and can be used to communicate danger, ownership of a territory, and availability for mating. Disadvantages include that they are transmitted slowly and the information that can be conveyed is limited. • The benefits of being dominant in a dominance hierarchy often include greater opportunity to mate and the right to eat first. Limitations include the need to maintain the position, which may require fighting. Subordinate individuals may be protected by the dominant animal, but may not have as much opportunity to mate or eat. • Benefits of territoriality often include a higher probability of mating and exclusive rights to food within the territory. Costs of territoriality include the time and energy expended in staking out and defending a territory and the risks involved in fighting for it. • Although it is the most sophisticated communication known among nonmammals, the dance of bees is highly stereotyped compared with human language. **52.6** • Sexual selection is a type of natural selection for successful mating. Factors that may influence mate choice include rank in a dominance hierarchy, ornamental displays, physical attributes that indicate good health or strength, and gifts presented to the female. • Polygyny is favored when the male is not needed to feed and protect the young; polyandry is favored when more than one male may help in caring for the young and when the males give gifts to the female. Monogamy is uncommon because it reduces direct fitness. • Benefits of courtship rituals include ensuring that the male is really a male and that he is a member of the same species. Rituals also provide opportunity for a female to evaluate a male. • Females who invest in parenting have more to gain than males because females of many vertebrate species produce relatively few, large eggs. The time and energy invested in producing eggs and carrying the developing embryo make it important for the female to continue to protect her investment. In addition, female mammals provide milk to nourish their young. The benefit is viable offspring and increased direct fitness. For males of most species, the costs of investing in parental care are outweighed by the benefits of mating with multiple females, thus increasing their direct fitness. **52.7** • Kin selection increases inclusive fitness through the breeding success of close relatives. Natural selection favors animals that help a relative (altruistic behavior) because the relative's offspring carries some of the helper's alleles. • An animal may benefit from helping a nonrelative because according to the hypothesis of reciprocal altruism, at some later time the animal will be paid back by the animal it helped. When paid back, the animal that is helped may benefit in terms of safety, obtaining food, or in direct fitness. **52.8** • Vertebrate societies are simpler than insect societies, but they are more flexible. • Examples of culture include female orcas teaching their offspring to hunt seals according to the custom of their particular group and chimps teaching others in their group how to use rocks to crack nuts. • According to sociobiologists, social behavior is determined by natural selection.

FIGURE QUESTIONS

FIG. 52-1 *Philanthus* would be unable to find her nest because she would be prevented from learning the necessary visual clues/landmarks. **FIG. 52-3** The impaired male stickleback would be less likely to father offspring so his direct fitness would decrease. **FIG. 52-6** The boy would likely be scared and would cry because he has become conditioned to associate dogs with pain. **FIG. 52-21** The males would not have reduced their level of guarding the eggs.

TEST YOUR UNDERSTANDING

1. a 2. b 3. c 4. d 5. b 6. a 7. d 8. e 9. b 10. e 11. a 12. c 13. The young salamanders described preferred eating more distant relatives, which increased the probability that their own relatives would survive to reproduce; this is an example of inclusive fitness. 14. In experiment 1, the parentals guarded the young

more closely than the eggs. After the young hatched, the parentals perceived that (despite the sneaker males lurking nearby during the egg stage) they were indeed the parents. The increase in care was based on olfactory cues. In experiment 2, the parentals guarded the eggs more closely than the young. After the young hatched, olfactory cues from the offspring indicated lack of paternity. 15. During times of prey scarcity, the groups with three and four females were most likely to be hungry at the end of the day. Perhaps when there are more animals in the group, they can venture farther in search of prey or take down larger prey. 16. The society of a social insect is more rigid and less flexible than human society. Information about behavior is largely transmitted genetically; like culture, genetic information is passed from parent to offspring. The young share the behavior of the parents. An important difference is that the insect society remains rigid and unlikely to change, whereas the human society is more flexible and more likely to change. 17. Sea turtle migration may be adaptive because it reduces competition between sea turtles of various ages. Young turtles are more likely to find food when they do not need to compete with older turtles. Migration may also be adaptive in that turtles return to the beach where their ancestors hatched. Those ancestors survived the conditions on that beach, suggesting that the new generation of offspring will also be able to survive. 18. It is unlikely that sea turtles could adapt to environmental pressures created by humans over a short period of time. Base your opinion on what you have learned in your biology course.

CHAPTER 53

CHECKPOINT

53.1 • Population density is the number of individuals per unit of area or volume. Population dispersion is spacing of individuals relative to one another. • A clumped dispersion can be advantageous to social animals, but it can be disadvantageous if there is competition within the population. **53.2** • Natality (the birth rate) and immigration contribute to population growth; mortality (the death rate) and emigration contribute to population decline. • A J-shaped population growth curve (exponential growth) describes a population at its intrinsic rate of increase (r_{max}). An S-shaped growth curve (logistic growth) describes the decline in a population's growth rate as it approaches its carrying capacity (K), the largest population that can be maintained indefinitely. • Compare your graphs to Figure 53-2 (bacteria could grow exponentially for a time if the medium is to provide nutrients and waste removal) and Figure 53-3 (bacteria

would exhibit logistic growth as they approach their carrying capacity). **53.3** • Three density-dependent factors that influence population growth are predation, disease, and competition. • Density-independent factors include abiotic events such as extreme weather, fires, and floods. **53.4** • In semelparity an organism puts all of its resources into a single reproductive event. These resources tend to improve the chances of success, but all is lost if the effort fails. Iteroparity provides many chances for reproduction; however, the organism's reproductive resources may become depleted by repeated reproductive cycles. • Parental care improves survival of the young when the population is at or near its carrying capacity. • Survivorship curves do not neatly fit the three models: Type I, Type II, and Type III. For example, a species' survivorship curve can be described either early in life compared to later in life. **53.5** • In a metapopulation, excess individuals tend to move from good or source habitats, where population growth is greatest, to less favorable sink habitats where population success is poorer. **53.6** • The dramatic increase in the world population over the last 200 years is attributable to a dramatic decrease in the death rate. • Replacement-level fertility is higher in developing countries because they have higher infant mortality rates than do developed countries. • Unlike a child born in a developing country, a single child born in the United States is a major contributor to consumption overpopulation.

FIGURE QUESTION

FIG. 53-6 As is often the case in science, you will need more information to develop your hypothesis. You will want gather information on such abiotic factors as changes in climate and specific weather events. You will also need information on biotic factors such as organisms other than spiders and lizards (including microorganisms) that may be living within the enclosures and affecting the spider populations.

TEST YOUR UNDERSTANDING

1. b 2. b 3. c 4. b 5. a 6. d 7. e 8. a 9. b 10. e 11. c 12. b 13. The pattern of repeated reproduction exhibited by female elephants is characteristic of Type I survivorship, in which individuals of reproductive age have a high probability of surviving. 14. Interference competition, in which a few individuals obtain adequate resources and others do not, is more sustainable than exploitation competition, which can lead to population booms (exceeding the carrying capacity) and crashes. 15. A population that can be described as *r*-selected is mainly characterized by overproduction of offspring and is kept in check by limits on population growth. A *K*-selected population is more stable; reproductive success is achieved with production of fewer offspring who are more likely to survive and reproduce. 16. Bolivia, with a much higher

percentage of its population entering reproductive age, has greater population growth momentum than Austria, and can be expected to have a higher growth rate over the next two decades. 17. With about 1065 people per square mile, the population density of the Netherlands is much greater than that of the United States (about 85 per square mile). 18. 1295.6 million. 19. 8 per 1000. 20. The diagram depicting population (b), with a very small proportion of its population at reproductive age or prereproductive age is consistent with negative population growth momentum. 21. A few examples of technologies that contribute to consumption overpopulation are those that typically involve the exploitation of fossil fuels (electricity, planes, trains, motor vehicles), rare elements (electronics), and those that produce pollution as a byproduct. New technologies to address some of these problems are being developed all the time. Which ones do you think might be most promising?

CHAPTER 54

CHECKPOINT

54.1 • Abundant acorn crops attract mice to oak forests. Mice eat the acorns, so more mice survive and breed in winter. Gypsy moths cause serious damage to oak trees, but mice also eat gypsy moth pupae, reducing their numbers. Both deer and mice are hosts to ticks. The mice often carry the bacteria that cause Lyme disease. The bacteria infect the ticks and are spread to humans when they are bitten by infected ticks. • The realized niche is usually narrower because factors, such as competition with other species, may exclude an organism from a part of its fundamental niche. • The principle of community ecology illustrated by the example is resource partitioning. • The three kinds of symbiosis are mutualism, commensalism, and parasitism. Refer to Section "Symbiosis involves a close association between species" for examples of each. **54.2** • Dominant species are present in great abundance in a community, while keystone species are present in low abundance. • Reintroduced wolves would reduce the herbivore population (such as deer and elk) which, in turn, would allow more and varied plant species to grow. It is an example of a top-down process because the predators (wolves) impact the abundance of herbivores and producers in the community. **54.3** • Species richness is reduced by geographic isolation due to the distance effect, where species are unable to colonize islands due to distance; species richness can also be reduced by random events in mountain or island habitats, which cause species extinction. Locally extinct species are not readily replaced in these isolated habitats. • The structural complexity of habitats such as forests and coral reefs can enhance species richness because they provide numerous diverse ecological niches. New species may migrate to these areas; and over time, new species may evolve there. • Species richness is inversely related to the environmental stress of a habitat because only species that can tolerate the particular type of environmental stress survive, while species that are unable to adapt to the environmental stress become extinct. **54.4** • Primary succession is the change in species composition over time in a habitat without soil that was not previously inhabited by organisms; secondary succession is the change in species composition that takes place after some disturbance removes the existing vegetation from a habitat containing soil. • Connell's intermediate disturbance hypothesis proposes that species richness is greatest at moderate levels of disturbance where the community is a mosaic of habitats at different stages of succession. • Organismic models of the nature of communities propose that member species cooperate with one another in a manner similar to the cooperation of the parts of an individual organism's body. The community passes through stages of development, like the embryonic stages of an organism, eventually reaching an adult state, or climax community. Individualistic models of the nature of communities propose species individuality, with each species having its own particular abiotic living requirements; communities are not interdependent associations of organisms, and each species is independently distributed across a continuum of areas that meets its own individual requirements.

FIGURE QUESTIONS

FIG. 54-5 *P. caudatum* would show increase in population density similar to the second graph, while *P. aurelia* would decrease in population density. **FIG. 54-7** If the *G. fuliginosa* population were removed from the shared island, the smaller seeds it ate would become more available to *G. fortis*. Over time, a smaller bill depth might evolve in the *G. fortis* population, adapting these finches to the wider seed selection. **FIG. 54-18** A species richness graph compiled from a tundra habitat would likely have fewer bird species because the community would have a lower structural complexity of vegetation. **FIG. 54-19** About 60 percent of species have colonized islands at 2000 km and about 20 percent at 6000 km have colonized. The greater the geographic isolation, the lower the species richness. **FIG. 54-20** A gradual increase in temperature could result in an increase in species richness as more bird species move into a warmer, more favorable habitat. **FIG. 54-23** Palm tree: The curve on the graph would begin at a high number on the *y*-axis at the wet end of the *x*-axis; the slope would decrease down to the dry end of the *x*-axis. Cactus: The curve for the cactus would begin at a low number on the *y*-axis at the wet end of the *x*-axis; the slope would increase as the line approaches the dry side of the *x*-axis.

TEST YOUR UNDERSTANDING

1. e 2. c 3. d 4. e 5. c 6. d 7. d 8. a 9. d 10. d 11. e 12. d 13. Humans are a keystone species as we determine the species composition and functioning of our ecosystem, for better or to our detriment. 14. Plants containing nitrogen-fixing nodules can provide nitrogen in the surrounding soil for other plants to grow but may grow better and faster, excluding other plant species. 15. Natural selection has favored the garter snake and made it a predator of the newt, a role reversal for their predator–prey relationship. Over time, the newt may develop (through natural selection) a new defense to escape the garter snake, again changing the predator–prey balance. 16. Competition among finch populations drives natural selection. Character displacement and resource partitioning both reduce interspecific competition, increasing the overall fitness of the different species. 17. The top and middle graph show logistic population growth. The *K,* or carrying capacity, for the two *Paramecium* growth curves occurs at a point where there is no further increase in population and is indicated by a flat line. 18. The human ecological niche constantly changes and expands as we learn about our surroundings and adapt to the challenges of survival. Science and technology provide us with the means to understand and thrive in our ecological niche. Failure of society to promote an understanding of science and misuse of technology could cause our ecological niche to shrink and endanger our survival. (Answers will vary as to how science and technology have changed our ecological niche over the past 1000 years.)

CHAPTER 55

CHECKPOINT

55.1 • See Fig. 55-2. • A trophic level is each sequential level of matter and energy in a food web, from producers to primary, to secondary, to tertiary consumers; each organism is assigned to a trophic level based on its primary source of nourishment. Ecological pyramids illustrate how food webs work and where members of each trophic level fit. • Gross primary productivity is a measurement of the rate at which energy accumulates in an ecosystem during photosynthesis, while net primary productivity is the energy that remains after plant cellular respiration has occurred. Gross primary productivity minus plant cellular respiration is net primary productivity. **55.2** • During photosynthesis, CO_2 in the air is fixed by plants and some prokaryotes; cellular respiration, combustion, and erosion return CO_2 to the atmosphere. • See Fig. 55-8. • Phosphorus cycles from land and terrestrial organisms to ocean and marine organisms and back to land and terrestrial organisms. **55.3** • The circulation of the atmosphere is primarily driven by the energy from the sun; different temperatures at different locations cause warm air to rise and cooler air to sink, creating movement. Earth's rotation and ocean currents also play a role in atmospheric circulation. • Ocean currents are produced by persistent prevailing winds blowing over the ocean surface; the Coriolis effect causes currents to swerve right in the Northern Hemisphere and left in the Southern Hemisphere. • Factors that produce regional differences in precipitation are wind movement over air and water; landmass features such as mountains, valleys, and deserts; ocean water temperatures; currents; and upwelling. **55.4** • The deforestation study observed that when a forest is removed, the total amount of water and minerals that flow into streams increases drastically. Also deforestation causes soil erosion and leaching of essential minerals, resulting in decreased soil fertility.

FIGURE QUESTIONS

FIG. 55-1 Once the sun ceased to provide light for plant growth, all the organisms would starve. The decomposers would be left to consume the remains before eventually dying themselves. **FIG. 55-2** Plants would produce less and gradually die, leaving many insects and small animals without enough food or shelter. Larger animals would leave as smaller animals disappeared or flew away. Decomposers would consume remains. What was left of the dry, weakened forest would be more susceptible to fire. **FIG. 55-6** The gulls might be consumed by larger birds, which could eventually die from the high bioaccumulation of DDT. When the gulls die, decomposers could be poisoned by consuming the remains. The DDT would not disappear from the salt marsh ecosystem. **FIG. 55-15** Increases in land temperature could cause wind speeds to increase, which would produce stronger currents, causing greater upwelling and dead zones. Water temperature increase would alter density of water near the shore, causing fresh water to flow into oceans and change surface current patterns.

TEST YOUR UNDERSTANDING

1. d 2. e 3. a 4. d 5. e 6. a 7. b 8. c 9. d 10. d 11. b 12. See Fig. 55-1. 13. If all decomposers were eliminated from a food web, organic material from waste and remains would not be broken down to simple inorganic compounds. All other life would eventually cease to exist as inorganic compounds became depleted. 14. The cycling of matter is essential because life requires

accessible building materials for long-term continuance; materials must be reused and recycled within and among ecosystems. 15. The nitrogen cycle would collapse if bacteria were absent because the five steps bacteria perform (nitrogen fixation, nitrification, assimilation, ammonification, and denitrification) are all essential to the cycle. 16. The microclimate for the ant and for the elephant would be different. The ant inhabits a microclimate close to the ground, in moist air and under shade from trees. The elephant's microclimate is a drier atmosphere, surrounded by sunlight and wind. 17. The pyramid is inverted because the plankton (microscopic algae and animals) are highly productive and experience high rates of turnover (are short lived and reproduce rapidly). 18. The graph indicates that wildfires increase as temperatures increase. Climate warming may be causing more wildfires because the second half of the graph (1985–2005) indicates higher temperatures and more fires; more data for a longer period of time may support this observation. 19. Humans alter the nitrogen cycle through overuse of nitrogen fertilizer, raw sewage dumping, and automobile/power plant/factory emissions. Scientists can partner with educators to explain the problem to the public while working with engineers to develop methods to mitigate the current damage and prevent future problems. The public can, in turn, encourage legislators to enact laws and set money aside for reducing nitrogen pollution and for education.

CHAPTER 56

CHECKPOINT

56.1 • Tundra: long, cold winters and short summers, little precipitation; geologically young soil with permanent layer of permafrost. Boreal forest: cold winters and short growing season; acidic, mineral-poor soil. Temperate rainforest: cool weather, dense fog, high precipitation; nutrient-poor soil, which may have high organic content. Temperate deciduous forest: hot summers and cold winters, high precipitation; soils rich in organic matter at surface and deeper clay layer. Temperate grasslands: hot summers and cold winters, moderate to unpredictable precipitation; soils rich in organic matter; roots/rhizomes. Chaparral: mild, wet winters and hot, dry summers; thin and infertile soil. Deserts: cold or warm temperatures, very low precipitation, and soil low in organic material, but high in mineral content. Savanna: tropical temperatures, low rainfall with dry periods; soil low in essential minerals, may be high in aluminum. Tropical dry forests: wet season and dry season, high precipitation; soil with some organic matter but low in essential minerals. Tropical rain

forest: tropical temperatures, high year-round precipitation; old, highly weathered, mineral-poor soil with low organic content. • Boreal forest: caribou, wolves, bears, moose, rodents, lynx, seasonal birds, and few reptiles and amphibians. Temperate deciduous forest: mountain lions, wolves, bison, deer, many small animals, insects, birds, reptiles, and amphibians. Temperate rain forest: mule deer, elk, small rodents, insects, many birds, some reptiles and amphibians. Tropical rain forest: greatest number and diversity of insects, bird, reptiles, and amphibians; sloths, monkeys, elephants. • Answers will vary. • Tundra is generally cold and dry, while deserts may be cold or hot as well as dry. Animals and plants in both tundra and desert are adapted to extreme temperatures and limited water. Temperate grassland has cold winters and more rainfall, while savanna is warm year round and has low rainfall and dry periods. Animals and plants are abundant; drought, fire, and overgrazing are significant in both biomes. **56.2** • If ocean plankton disappeared, plankton-eating nekton would lose their food source and die off. Carnivorous nekton (sharks, whales) would lose much of their food source and die. Benthos would, in turn, lose most of their food sources that float down from the surface, and their population would be decimated as well. The ocean would rapidly lose most living organisms. • Salinity, dissolved oxygen, light availability, water depth, essential minerals, temperature, pH, and presence/absence of waves and currents are environmental factors that determine the adaptations of organisms that live in aquatic environments. • Freshwater wetlands are covered part of the year by shallow water, while estuaries are coastal areas near rivers where fresh water mixes with tidal salt water. In flowing-water ecosystems there is a flowing current; in standing-water ecosystems the top layer, due to light penetration, contains phytoplankton, zooplankton, and fishes, while the lower, dark zone contains mostly prokaryotic decomposers. • The intertidal zone, shoreline area between low tide and high tide, has organisms with adaptations that resist wave action and exposure to air during low tide. The benthic environment, the ocean floor, has sea grasses, kelps, and coral reefs in shallow ocean waters. The neritic province is open ocean from shoreline to 200 m. Organisms are all floaters or swimmers. The euphotic zone, the upper part of the neritic province, has phytoplankton that are the base of the food web. The oceanic province is the part of the open ocean deeper than 200 m. It is dark, cold, and has a high pressure. Animals are either predators or scavengers that subsist on marine snow. • Coral reefs are often compared to tropical rain forests because of their immense diversity of life and high productivity. **56.3** • An ecotone is the transition area where two communities, or biomes, meet and

intergrade. Ecotones occur where agricultural land meets forest, tundra borders a boreal forest, or a river touches land. **56.4** • Biogeography is the study of the geographic distribution of plants and animals. Biogeographers look for patterns in geographic distribution and try to explain how such patterns arose, including where populations originated, how they spread, and when. • The Australian realm has been separated from the other biogeographic realms for the longest period; animals living in the Australian realm include marsupials and monotremes, such as the kangaroo, platypus, and spiny anteater.

FIGURE QUESTIONS

FIG. 56-1 As climate changes, plants, animals, and other organisms will disappear if they are unable to adapt. They may be replaced or outcompeted by species that can adapt more rapidly to these climate changes. **FIG. 56-24** Fireweed and knotweed have adapted to the serpentine soil and would have too much competition to colonize the ecotone area.

TEST YOUR UNDERSTANDING

1. c 2. a 3. d 4. e 5. c 6. b 7. d 8. a 9. c 10. e 11. e 12. Desert animals may be small because they have limited food and water resources. To test this hypothesis, a desert animal experimental group could be provided with abundant amounts of food and water for numerous generations. 13. The lowest average annual precipitation characteristic of tropical rain forests is 225 cm. The highest average annual precipitation is 450 cm. The range of average temperature in tropical rain forests is 20°C–28°C. 14. Eight sampled species are found in the nonserpentine soil. Ten sampled species are found in the serpentine soil. Thirteen are found in the ecotone. The ecotone supports more plant species than serpentine or nonserpentine areas alone. 15. Organisms adapted to a fast current would be displaced by organisms that thrive in still water. Upstream organisms' habitats would probably have still water and flooding close to the dam, while downstream organisms' habitats would now have still water and less water. 16. Prairie dogs may bury the dead animal to keep predators from smelling it as a food source and approaching the hole. Researchers could prevent prairie dogs in an experimental group from burying dead animals; the dead animals could be protected in a cage that would allow odors to escape. Prairie dogs in a control group would be permitted to bury dead animals. 17. Technologies employed for data collection could be coastal and ocean buoys, satellite pictures (visual and IR), and research vessels. Local communities could receive instruction from science educators to count turtle eggs and record breeding data to assist with the research.

CHAPTER 57

CHECKPOINT

57.1 • The three levels of biological diversity are genetic diversity, species richness, and ecosystem diversity. • An endangered species would be at greater immediate risk of extinction because there are fewer surviving members of the species throughout its range compared with a threatened species. • Habitat fragmentation contributes to declining biological diversity because it encourages disease organisms, as well as invasive species that compete with native species. • Invasive species contribute to the biodiversity crisis because they cause more damage to native species than do native competitors or predators. Native species are not usually evolutionarily equipped to deal with invasive species. **57.2** • If conservation biology did not exist, many species would not be protected and could become extinct; biodiversity would plummet. • Landscape biology and restoration ecology are examples of in situ conservation. • In situ conservation helps the greatest number of species because it keeps the ecosystems intact and maintains biodiversity on a large scale. • The U.S. Endangered Species Act is controversial because it pits landowners against conservationists, in most cases without developing effective means of fostering education and cooperation between the groups. It is also a very slow, political, litigious process to list species. **57.3** • Three ecosystem services that forests provide are wildlife habitat, protection of watersheds, and prevention of soil erosion and flooding. • Deforestation in tropical rain forests is caused by subsistence agriculture and slash-and-burn agriculture. The main reason for deforestation of boreal forests is clear-cut logging. **57.4** • The enhanced greenhouse effect involves increased levels of greenhouse gases that absorb infrared (heat) radiation, combined with additional warming of the atmosphere. The enhanced greenhouse effect is caused by human actions, such as industrialization without mitigation of pollutants. • Climate change may cause oceans to rise, ice caps and glaciers to melt and disappear, increased water and atmospheric temperatures, reduction of species and diversity, higher frequency and more intense storm systems and wildfires, and increased disease.

FIGURE QUESTIONS

FIG. 57-2 The oystercatcher population would experience changes in genetic diversity if it interbreeds with the newcomer population or could be reduced or eliminated if competition became extreme. **FIG. 57-4** Effectively addressing social, political, and cultural factors, for example by education, could result in greater societal commitment to addressing and changing the direct effects of declining biodiversity, such as pollution and climate change. **FIG. 57-6** Bay scallop populations will decrease, and the species may no longer be able to survive in that habitat. **FIG. 57-9** A large human population could insulate and protect the endemic species through education, research, and well-planned land use solutions. **FIG. 57-17** Accumulation of greenhouse gases can be slowed by humans changing their lifestyles, such as reducing carbon footprint, purchasing low emission energy and automobiles, and maximizing recycling opportunities.

TEST YOUR UNDERSTANDING

1. d 2. e 3. c 4. c 5. c 6. b 7. e 8. d 9. c 10. a 11. Captive breeding may fail because reintroduced species may no longer be able to compete in their original habitats. 12. Human decisions, good and bad, ultimately affect the outcome of survival of organisms and protection of our planet. 13. Modern humans are the most dangerous species, to ourselves and other inhabitants of Earth. 14. Any loss of species is permanent, and every genetic code and genome could potentially be of future benefit for medicine, research, or other economic interests. 15. Multiple introductions, each under slightly different circumstances (weather, predators, nutrient level), could give some of the invasives the edge to thrive. 16. The production of many smaller eggs could be due to more protected surroundings and nourishment not afforded to eggs in the wild, which would need to be bigger and heartier. Captive-bred females might have lower survival rates than wild females. 17. Habitat fragmentation is most important. Climate change and increasing atmospheric CO_2 are represented as separate factors because they have multiple causes. Nitrogen pollution relates to overuse of fertilizer and nitrogen-containing emissions that cause air pollution. 18. Education and dialogue between the public, scientists, and developers of technology in all countries would be essential to developing and implementing a plan for all residents of Earth that would be sustainable for developed (high income) and developing (lower income) countries.

Glossary

ABC transporters ATP-binding cassette transporters; use ATP energy to transport certain ions, sugars, and polypeptides across cell membranes.

abiotic factors Elements of the nonliving, physical environment that affect a particular organism. Compare with *biotic factors*.

abortion Termination of pregnancy, resulting in the death of the embryo or fetus; abortions can occur spontaneously or can be induced.

abscisic acid (ABA) (ab-sis'-ik) A plant hormone involved in dormancy and responses to stress.

abscission (ab-sizh'-en) The normal (usually seasonal) fall of leaves or other plant parts, such as fruits or flowers.

abscission zone The area at the base of the petiole where the leaf will break away from the stem. Also known as *abscission layer*.

absorption (ab-sorp'-shun) (1) The movement of nutrients and other substances through the wall of the digestive tract and into the blood or lymph. (2) The process by which chlorophyll takes up light for photosynthesis.

absorption spectrum A graph of the amount of light at specific wavelengths that is absorbed as light passes through a substance. Each type of molecule has a characteristic absorption spectrum. Compare with *action spectrum*.

abyssal zone Part of benthic environment that extends from a depth of 4000 to 6000 m.

acanthodians (ak-an-tho'-de-uns) An extinct group of armored jawed fishes; possessed paired spines and pectoral and pelvic fins.

accessory fruit A fruit consisting primarily of tissue other than ovary tissue, e.g., apple, pear. Compare with *aggregate, simple,* and *multiple fruits*.

acclimatization Adjustment to seasonal changes.

acetyl coenzyme A (acetyl CoA) (as'-uh-teel) A key intermediate compound in metabolism; consists of a two-carbon acetyl group covalently bonded to coenzyme A.

acetylcholine (ah"-see-til-koh'-leen) A common neurotransmitter released by cholinergic neurons, including motor neurons.

acetyl group A two-carbon group derived from acetic acid (acetate).

achene (a-keen') A simple, dry fruit with one seed in which the fruit wall is separate from the seed coat, e.g., sunflower fruit.

acid A substance that is a hydrogen ion (proton) donor; acids unite with bases to form salts. Compare with *base*.

acidic solution A solution in which the concentration of hydrogen ions [H⁺] exceeds the concentration of hydroxide ions [OH⁻]. An acidic solution

has a pH less than 7. Compare with *basic solution* and *neutral solution*.

acid precipitation Precipitation that is acidic as a result of both sulfur and nitrogen oxides forming acids when they react with water in the atmosphere.

acoelomate (a-seel'-oh-mate) An animal lacking a body cavity (coelom). Compare with *coelomate* and *pseudocoelomate*.

acquired immune responses See *adaptive immune responses*.

acquired immunodeficiency syndrome (AIDS) A serious, potentially fatal disease caused by the human immunodeficiency virus (HIV).

acromegaly (ak"-roh-meg'-ah-lee) A condition characterized by overgrowth of the extremities of the skeleton, fingers, toes, jaws, and nose. It may be produced by excessive secretion of growth hormone by the anterior pituitary gland.

acrosome reaction (ak' roh-sohm) A series of events in which the acrosome, a caplike structure covering the head of a sperm cell, releases proteolytic (protein-digesting) enzymes and undergoes other changes that permit the sperm to penetrate the outer covering of the egg.

actin (ak'-tin) The protein of which microfilaments consist. Actin, together with the protein myosin, is responsible for muscle contraction.

actin filaments Thin filaments consisting mainly of the protein actin; actin and myosin filaments make up the myofibrils of muscle fibers.

actinopods (ak-tin'-o-podz) Protists characterized by axopods that protrude through pores in their shells. See *rhizarians*.

action potential An electrical signal resulting from depolarization of the plasma membrane in a neuron or muscle cell. Compare with *resting potential*.

action spectrum A graph of the effectiveness of light at specific wavelengths in promoting a light-requiring reaction. Compare with *absorption spectrum*.

activation energy (E_A) The kinetic energy required to initiate a chemical reaction.

activator protein A positive regulatory protein that stimulates transcription when bound to DNA. Compare with *repressor protein*.

active immunity Immunity that develops as a result of exposure to antigens; it can occur naturally after recovery from a disease or can be artificially induced by immunization with a vaccine. Compare with *passive immunity*.

active site A specific region of an enzyme (generally near the surface) that accepts one or more substrates and catalyzes a chemical reaction. Compare with *allosteric site*.

active transport Transport of a substance across a membrane that does not rely on the potential energy of a concentration gradient for the substance being transported and therefore requires an additional energy source (often ATP); includes carrier-mediated active transport, endocytosis, and exocytosis. Compare with *diffusion* and *facilitated diffusion*.

adaptation (1) An evolutionary modification that improves an organism's chances of survival and reproductive success. (2) A decline in the response of a receptor subjected to repeated or prolonged stimulation.

adaptive immune responses Defense mechanisms that target specific macromolecules associated with a pathogen. Includes cell-mediated immunity and antibody-mediated immunity. Also known as *acquired immune responses* or *specific immune responses*. Compare with *innate immune responses*.

adaptive immunity See *adaptive immune responses*.

adaptive radiation The evolution of a large number of related species from an unspecialized ancestral organism.

adaptive zone A new ecological opportunity that was not exploited by an ancestral organism; used by evolutionary biologists to explain the ecological paths along which different taxa evolve.

addiction Physical dependence on a drug, generally based on physiological changes that take place in response to the drug; when the drug is withheld, the addict may suffer characteristic withdrawal symptoms.

Addison's disease Caused by insufficient secretion of aldosterone and cortisol by the adrenal cortex and characterized by progressive anemia, low blood pressure, and inability to respond to stress.

adenine (ad'-eh-neen) A nitrogenous purine base that is a component of nucleic acids and ATP.

adenosine diphosphate (ADP) See *adenosine triphosphate (ATP)*.

adenosine triphosphate (ATP) (a-den'-oh-seen) An organic compound containing adenine, ribose, and three phosphate groups; hydrolysis of the terminal phosphate yields adenosine diphosphate (ADP); of prime importance for energy transfers in cells.

adenylyl cyclase Enzyme responsible for catalyzing the conversion of ATP to cyclic AMP (cAMP).

adhering junction A type of anchoring junction between cells; connects epithelial cells.

adhesion The property of sticking to some other substance. Compare with *cohesion*.

adipose tissue (ad'-i-pohs) Tissue in which fat is stored.

adrenal cortex (ah-dree′-nul kor′-teks) The outer region of each adrenal gland; secretes steroid hormones, including mineralocorticoids and glucocorticoids.

adrenal glands (ah-dree′-nul) Paired endocrine glands, one located just superior to each kidney; secrete hormones that help regulate metabolism and help the body cope with stress.

adrenal medulla (ah-dree′-nul meh-dull′-uh) The inner region of each adrenal gland; secretes epinephrine and norepinephrine.

adrenergic neuron (ad-ren-er′-jik) A neuron that releases norepinephrine or epinephrine as a neurotransmitter. Compare with *cholinergic neuron.*

adrenocorticotropic hormone (ACTH) Hormone secreted by anterior pituitary that regulates glucocorticoid and aldosterone secretion.

adult stem cells Cells derived from body tissues that can differentiate into some specific cell types, e.g., blood cells, neuronal cells, or muscle cells, but not all types of cells found in an organism. See *pluripotent stem cells* and *totipotent stem cells.*

adventitious (ad″-ven-tish′-us) Of plant organs, such as roots or buds, that arise in an unusual position on a plant.

aerobe Organism that grows or metabolizes only in the presence of molecular oxygen. Compare with *anaerobe.*

aerobic (air-oh′-bik) Growing or metabolizing only in the presence of molecular oxygen. Compare with *anaerobic.*

aerobic cellular respiration See *respiration.*

aerobic respiration See *respiration.*

afferent (af′fer-ent) Leading toward some point of reference. Compare with *efferent.*

afferent arteriole In the mammalian kidney, an arteriole that conducts blood into the capillaries that make up a glomerulus; afferent arterioles branch from the renal artery. Compare with *efferent arteriole.*

afferent neurons Neurons that transmit action potentials from sensory receptors to the brain or spinal cord. Compare with *efferent neurons.*

age structure The number and proportion of people at each age in a population. Age structure diagrams represent the number of males and females at each age, from birth to death, in the population.

age structure diagram See *age structure.*

aggregated distribution See *clumped dispersion.*

aggregate fruit A fruit that develops from a single flower with many separate carpels, e.g., raspberry. Compare with *simple, accessory,* and *multiple fruits.*

aging Progressive changes in development in an adult organism.

agnathans (ag-na′-thanz) Jawless fishes; term is mainly used to refer to the earliest vertebrates, which are now extinct.

AIDS See *acquired immunodeficiency syndrome.*

albinism (al′-bih-niz-em) A hereditary inability to form melanin pigment, resulting in light coloration.

albumin (al-bew′-min) A class of protein found in most animal tissues; a fraction of plasma proteins.

aldehyde An organic molecule containing a carbonyl group bonded to at least one hydrogen atom. Compare with *ketone.*

aldosterone (al-dos′-tur-ohn) A steroid hormone produced by the vertebrate adrenal cortex; stimulates sodium reabsorption. See *mineralocorticoids.*

algae (al′-gee) (sing., *alga*) An informal group of unicellular, or simple multicellular, photosynthetic protists that are important producers in aquatic ecosystems.

allantois (a-lan′-toe-iss) An extraembryonic membrane of reptiles, birds, and mammals that stores the embryo's nitrogenous wastes; most of the allantois is detached at hatching or birth.

allele frequency The proportion of a specific allele in the population. Compare with *genotype frequency* and *phenotype frequency.*

alleles (al-leelz′) Genes governing variation of the same character that occupy corresponding positions (loci) on homologous chromosomes; alternative forms of a gene.

allelopathy (uh-leel′-uh-path″-ee) An adaptation in which toxic substances secreted by roots or shed leaves inhibit the establishment of competing plants nearby.

allergen A substance that stimulates an allergic reaction.

allergy A hypersensitivity to some substance in the environment, manifested as hay fever, skin rash, asthma, food allergies, etc.

allometric growth Variation in the relative rates of growth for different parts of the body during development.

allopatric speciation (al-oh-pa′-trik) Speciation that occurs when one population becomes geographically separated from the rest of the species and subsequently evolves. Compare with *sympatric speciation.*

allopolyploid (al″-oh-pol′-ee-ployd) A polyploid whose chromosomes are derived from two species. Compare with *autopolyploid.*

all-or-none response The principle that no variation exists in the strength of a single action potential; only a stimulus strong enough to depolarize the membrane to its critical threshold level results in transmission of an action potential.

allosteric regulators Substances that affect protein function by binding to allosteric sites.

allosteric site (al-oh-steer′-ik) A site on an enzyme other than the active site, to which a specific substance binds, thereby changing the shape and activity of the enzyme. Compare with *active site.*

alpha (α) carbon Asymmetrical carbon in an amino acid to which an amino group, a carboxyl group, a side chain (R group), and a hydrogen are covalently bonded.

alpha cells Pancreatic cells that secrete glucagon.

alpha (α) helix A regular, coiled type of secondary structure of a polypeptide chain, maintained by hydrogen bonds. Compare with *beta (β)-pleated sheet.*

alpine tundra An ecosystem located in the higher elevations of mountains, above the tree line and below the snow line. Compare with *tundra.*

alternation of generations A type of life cycle characteristic of plants and a few algae and fungi in which they spend part of their life in a multicellular *n* gametophyte stage and part in a multicellular 2*n* sporophyte stage.

alternative splicing A genetic mechanism in which exons are spliced in different ways to produce different mRNAs from a single gene.

altruism A type of cooperative behavior in which an individual appears to behave in a way that benefits another rather than itself.

altruistic behavior Behavior in which one individual helps another, seemingly at its own risk or expense.

alveolates Protists that have alveoli, flattened vesicles located just inside the plasma membrane; include the dinoflagellates, apicomplexans, and ciliates. See *chromalveolates;* compare with *stramenopiles.*

alveolus (al-vee′-o-lus) (pl., *alveoli*) (1) An air sac of the lung through which gas exchange with the blood takes place. (2) Saclike unit of some glands, e.g., mammary glands. (3) One of several flattened vesicles located just inside the plasma membrane in alveolate protists.

Alzheimer's disease (AD) A progressive, degenerative brain disorder characterized by amyloid plaques and neurofibrillary tangles.

amacrine cell A lateral interneuron in the retina of the eye; receives signals from bipolar cells and sends signals back to them or to ganglion cells.

amino acid (uh-mee′-no) An organic compound containing an amino group (—NH$_2$) and a carboxyl group (—COOH); may be joined by peptide bonds to form a polypeptide chain.

amino acid derivatives Simplest hormones, such as epinephrine and melatonin, that are derived from amino acids.

aminoacyl–tRNA (uh-mee″-no-ace′-seel) Molecule consisting of an amino acid covalently linked to a transfer RNA.

aminoacyl–tRNA synthetase One of a family of enzymes, each responsible for covalently linking an amino acid to its specific transfer RNA.

amino group A weakly basic functional group; abbreviated —NH$_2$.

ammonification (uh-moe″-nuh-fah-kay′-shun) The conversion of nitrogen-containing organic compounds to ammonia (NH$_3$) by certain soil bacteria (ammonifying bacteria); part of the nitrogen cycle.

amniocentesis (am″-nee-oh-sen-tee′-sis) Sampling of the amniotic fluid surrounding a fetus to obtain information about its development and genetic makeup. Compare with *chorionic villus sampling*.

amnion (am'-nee-on) In terrestrial vertebrates, an extraembryonic membrane that forms a fluid-filled sac for the protection of the developing embryo.

amniotes Terrestrial vertebrates: reptiles, birds, and mammals; animals whose embryos are enclosed by an amnion.

amniotic egg Egg that contains an amnion and other membranes that surround and protect the developing embryo and keep it moist; the evolution of the amniotic egg was one of the adaptations that allowed animals to become completely terrestrial.

amoeba (a-mee'-ba) (pl., *amoebas*) A unicellular protist that moves by means of pseudopodia.

amoebozoa Members of the unikont clade characterized by lobose pseudopodia at some time in the life cycle; include amoebas, plasmodial slime molds, and cellular slime molds. Compare with *opisthokonts*.

amphibians Members of vertebrate class that includes salamanders, frogs, and caecilians.

amphipathic lipid See *amphipathic molecule*.

amphipathic molecule (am"-fih-pa'-thik) A molecule containing both hydrophobic and hydrophilic regions.

ampulla Any small, saclike extension, e.g., the expanded structure at the end of each semicircular canal of the ear.

amygdala Part of the limbic system; filters incoming information and interprets it in the context of emotional needs and survival.

amylase (am'-uh-laze) Starch-digesting enzyme, e.g., human salivary amylase or pancreatic amylase.

amyloid plaques Extracellular deposits in the brain of the peptide amyloid-beta surrounded by degenerating dendrites and axons.

amyloplasts See *leukoplasts*.

anabolic hormone Hormone that promotes tissue growth.

anabolic steroids Synthetic androgens that increase muscle mass, physical strength, endurance, and aggressiveness but cause serious side effects; these drugs are often abused.

anabolism (an-ab'-oh-lizm) The aspect of metabolism in which simpler substances are combined to form more complex substances, resulting in the storage of energy, the production of new cell materials, and growth. Compare with *catabolism*.

anaerobe Organism that can grow or metabolize in the absence of molecular oxygen. See *facultative anaerobe* and *obligate anaerobe*. Compare with *aerobe*.

anaerobic (an"-air-oh'-bik) Growing or metabolizing in the absence of molecular oxygen. Compare with *aerobic*.

anaerobic respiration See *respiration*.

anaphase (an'uh-faze) Stage of mitosis in which the chromosomes move to opposite poles of the cell; anaphase occurs after metaphase and before telophase.

anaphase I See *meiosis* and *meiosis I*.

anaphase II See *meiosis* and *meiosis II*.

anaphase-promoting complex (APC) Enzyme complex responsible for initiating the transition from metaphase to anaphase.

anaphylaxis (an"-uh-fih-lak'-sis) An acute allergic reaction following sensitization to a foreign substance or other substance.

ancestral characters See *shared ancestral characters*.

androgen (an'-dro-jen) Any substance that has masculinizing properties, such as a sex hormone. See *testosterone*.

androgen-binding protein (ABP) A protein produced by Sertoli cells in the testes; binds and concentrates testosterone.

anemia (uh-nee'-mee-uh) A deficiency of hemoglobin or red blood cells.

aneuploidy (an'-you-ploy-dee) Any chromosomal aberration in which there are either extra or missing copies of certain chromosomes.

angiosperms (an'-jee-oh-spermz") The traditional name for flowering plants, a very large (more than 300,000 species), diverse phylum of plants that form flowers for sexual reproduction and produce seeds enclosed in fruits; include monocots and eudicots.

angiotensin I (an-jee-o-ten'-sin) A polypeptide produced by the action of renin on the plasma protein angiotensinogen.

angiotensin II A peptide hormone formed by the action of angiotensin-converting enzyme on angiotensin I; stimulates aldosterone secretion by the adrenal cortex.

animal pole The non-yolky, metabolically active pole of a vertebrate or echinoderm egg. Compare with *vegetal pole*.

anion (an'-eye-on) A particle with one or more units of negative charge, such as a chloride ion (Cl^-) or hydroxide ion (OH^-). Compare with *cation*.

anisogamy (an"-eye-sog'-uh-me) Sexual reproduction involving motile gametes of similar form but dissimilar size. Compare with *isogamy* and *oogamy*.

annelids (an'-eh-lids) Segmented worms with bilateral symmetry and a tubular body that may be partitioned into ringlike segments.

annual plant A plant that completes its entire life cycle in one year or less. Compare with *perennial plant* and *biennial plant*.

Antarctic tundra Treeless biome of Antarctica Peninsula and nearby islands characterized by extremely cold temperatures and containing lichens, mosses, and few vascular plants.

antenna complex The arrangement of chlorophyll, accessory pigments, and pigment-binding proteins into light-gathering units in the thylakoid membranes of photoautotrophic eukaryotes. See *reaction center* and *photosystem*.

antennae (sing., *antenna*) Sensory structures characteristic of some arthropod groups.

anterior Toward the head end of a bilaterally symmetrical animal. Compare with *posterior*.

anterior pituitary The anterior, glandular lobe of the pituitary gland; functions as a classical endocrine gland; secretes growth hormone, prolactin, melanocyte-stimulating hormone, and several tropic hormones. Compare with *posterior pituitary*.

anther (an'-thur) The part of the stamen in flowers that produces microspores and, ultimately, pollen grains.

antheridium (an"-thur-id'-ee-im) (pl., *antheridia*) In plants, the multicellular male gametangium (sex organ) that produces sperm cells. Compare with *archegonium*.

anthocyanins Class of red water-soluble plant pigments.

anthropoid (an'-thra-poid) A member of a suborder of primates that includes monkeys, apes, and humans.

antibody (an'-tee-bod"-ee) A specific protein (immunoglobulin) that recognizes and binds to specific antigens; produced by plasma cells.

antibody-mediated immunity A type of specific immune response in which B cells differentiate into plasma cells and produce antibodies that bind with foreign antigens, leading to the destruction of pathogens. Compare with *cell-mediated immunity*.

anticodon (an"-tee-koh' don) A sequence of three nucleotides in transfer RNA that is complementary to, and combines with, the three-nucleotide codon.

antidiuretic hormone (ADH) (an"-ty-dy-uh-ret'-ik) A hormone secreted by the posterior lobe of the pituitary that controls the rate of water reabsorption by the kidney.

antigen (an'-tih-jen) Any molecule, usually a protein or large carbohydrate, that is specifically recognized as foreign by cells of the immune system.

antigen–antibody complex The combination of antigen and antibody molecules.

antigen-presenting cell (APC) A cell that displays foreign antigens as well as its own surface proteins. Dendritic cells, macrophages, and B cells are APCs.

antimicrobial peptides Soluble molecules that destroy pathogens.

anti-oncogene See *tumor suppressor gene*.

antioxidants Certain enzymes (e.g., catalase and peroxidase), vitamins, and other substances that destroy free radicals and other reactive molecules. Compare with *oxidants*.

antiparallel Said of a double-stranded nucleic acid in which the 5' to 3' direction of the sugar–phosphate backbone of one strand is reversed in the other strand.

antiporter Membrane carrier protein that transports two types of substances in opposite directions. Compare with *uniporter* and *symporter*.

anus (ay'-nus) The distal end and outlet of the digestive tract.

aorta (ay-or'-tah) The largest and main systemic artery of the vertebrate body; arises from the left ventricle and branches to distribute blood to all parts of the body except the lungs.

aphotic region (ay-fote′-ik) The lower layer of the ocean (deeper than 100 m or so) where light does not penetrate.

apical dominance (ape′-ih-kl) The inhibition of axillary (lateral) buds by a shoot tip.

apical meristem (mehr′-ih-stem) An area of dividing tissue, located at the tip of a shoot or root, that gives rise to primary tissues; apical meristems cause an increase in the length of the plant body. Compare with *lateral meristems*.

apicomplexans A group of parasitic protists that lack structures for locomotion and that produce sporozoites as infective agents; malaria is caused by an apicomplexan.

apoenzyme (ap″-oh-en′-zime) Protein portion of an enzyme; requires the presence of a specific coenzyme to become a complete functional enzyme.

apomixis (ap″-uh-mix′-us) A type of reproduction in which fruits and seeds are formed asexually.

apoplast A continuum consisting of the interconnected, porous plant cell walls, along which water moves freely. Compare with *symplast*.

apoptosis (ap-uh-toe′-sis) Programmed cell death; apoptosis is a normal part of an organism's development and maintenance. Compare with *necrosis*.

aposematic coloration The conspicuous coloring of a poisonous or distasteful organism that enables potential predators to easily see and recognize it. Also called *warning coloration*. Compare with *cryptic coloration*.

aquaporin One of a family of transport proteins located in the plasma membrane that facilitate the rapid movement of water molecules into or out of cells.

aquifer Underground caverns and porous layers of rock in which groundwater is stored.

aquifer depletion Human removal of more groundwater than precipitation or melting snow can replace.

arachnids (ah-rack′-nidz) Eight-legged arthropods, such as spiders, scorpions, ticks, and mites.

arachnoid The middle of the three meningeal layers that cover and protect the brain and spinal cord; see *pia mater* and *dura mater*.

arboreal Living in trees.

arbuscules Tree-like branched structures inside root cells produced by hyphae of endomycorrhizal fungi known as glomeromycetes.

Archaea (ar′-key-ah) One of the two prokaryotic domains. The absence of peptidoglycan in their cell walls sets them apart from the bacteria. Compare with *bacteria*.

Archaean eon The period of Earth's history from the formation of the crust approximately 4 billion years ago, until 2.5 billion years ago; life originated during the Archaean.

archaeplastids A monophyletic supergroup of eukaryotes with chloroplasts bounded by outer and inner membranes; include red algae, green algae, and land plants.

archegonium (ar′-ke-go′-nee-um) (pl., *archegonia*) In plants, the multicellular female gametangium (sex organ) that contains an egg. Compare with *antheridium*.

archenteron (ark-en′-ter-on) The central cavity of the gastrula stage of embryonic development that is lined with endoderm; primitive digestive system.

archosaurs (ar′-kuh-sors) Lineage of diapsid vertebrates that includes the extinct dinosaurs and flying reptiles, as well as the extant crocodiles (order Crocodilia) and the birds.

arctic tundra See *tundra*.

Ardipithecus ramidus. See *australopithecines*.

arterial pulse See *pulse, arterial*.

arteriole (ar-teer′-ee-ole) A very small artery. Vasoconstriction and vasodilation of arterioles help regulate blood pressure.

artery A thick-walled blood vessel that carries blood away from a heart chamber and toward the body organs. Compare with *vein*.

arthropod (ar′-throh-pod) An invertebrate that belongs to phylum Arthropoda; characterized by a hard exoskeleton; a segmented body; and paired, jointed appendages.

artificial insemination The impregnation of a female by artificially introducing sperm from a male.

artificial selection The selection by humans of traits that are desirable in plants or animals and breeding only those individuals that have the desired traits. Compare with *natural selection*.

ascocarp (ass′-koh-karp) The fruiting body of an ascomycete.

ascomycete (ass″-koh-my′-seat) Member of a phylum of fungi characterized by the production of nonmotile asexual conidia and sexual ascospores.

ascospore (ass′-koh-spor) One of a set of sexual spores, usually eight, contained in a special spore case (an ascus) of an ascomycete.

ascus (ass′-kus) A saclike spore case in ascomycetes that contains sexual spores called *ascospores*.

asexual reproduction Reproduction in which there is no fusion of gametes and in which the genetic makeup of parent and of offspring is usually identical. Compare with *sexual reproduction*.

assimilation (of nitrogen) The conversion of inorganic nitrogen (nitrate, NO_3^-, or ammonia, NH_3) to the organic molecules of living things; part of the nitrogen cycle.

association areas Areas of the brain that link sensory and motor areas; responsible for thought, learning, memory, language abilities, judgment, and personality.

association neuron See *interneuron*.

assortative mating Sexual reproduction in which individuals pair nonrandomly, i.e., select mates on the basis of phenotype; selection may be positive (mates with the same phenotype) or less commonly negative (mates with opposite phenotypes).

asters Clusters of microtubules radiating out from the poles in dividing cells that have centrioles.

astrocyte A type of glial cell; some are phagocytic; others regulate the composition of the extracellular fluid in the central nervous system.

atherosclerosis (ath″-ur-oh-skle-row′-sis) A progressive disease in which lipid deposits accumulate in the inner lining of arteries, leading eventually to impaired circulation and heart disease.

atom The smallest quantity of an element that retains the chemical properties of that element.

atomic mass The total number of protons and neutrons in an atom; expressed in atomic mass units or daltons.

atomic mass unit (amu) The approximate mass of a proton or neutron; also called a *dalton*.

atomic number The number of protons in the atomic nucleus of an atom, which uniquely identifies the element to which the atom corresponds.

ATP See *adenosine triphosphate*.

ATP synthase Large enzyme complex that catalyzes the formation of ATP from ADP and inorganic phosphate by chemiosmosis; located in the inner mitochondrial membrane, the thylakoid membrane of chloroplasts, and the plasma membrane of prokaryotes.

atrial natriuretic peptide (ANP) A hormone released by the atrium of the heart; helps regulate sodium excretion and lowers blood pressure.

atrioventricular (AV) node (ay″-tree-oh-ventrik′-you-lur) Mass of specialized cardiac tissue that receives an impulse from the sinoatrial node (pacemaker) and conducts it to the ventricles.

atrioventricular (AV) valve (of the heart) A valve between each atrium and its ventricle that prevents backflow of blood. The right AV valve is the tricuspid valve; the left AV valve is the mitral valve.

atrium (of the heart) (ay′-tree-um) A heart chamber that receives blood from the veins.

australopithecines Early hominids that lived between about 6 mya and 1 mya, based on fossil evidence. Include several species in three genera: *Ardipithecus, Australopithecus,* and *Paranthropus*.

Australopithecus afarensis See *australopithecines*.

Australopithecus africanus See *australopithecines*.

Australopithecus anamensis See *australopithecines*.

Australopithecus sediba See *australopithecines*.

autocrine regulation A type of regulation in which a signaling molecule (e.g., a hormone) is secreted into interstitial fluid and then acts on the cells that produce it. Compare with *paracrine regulation*.

autoimmune disease (aw″-toh-ih-mune′) A disease in which the body produces antibodies against its own cells or tissues. Also called *autoimmunity*.

autonomic division (of the PNS) (aw-tuh-nom′-ik) The portion of the peripheral nervous system that controls the visceral functions of the body, e.g., regulates smooth muscle, cardiac muscle, and glands. Its divisions are the sympathetic and parasympathetic systems. Compare with *somatic division* of the PNS.

autopolyploid A polyploid whose chromosomes are derived from a single species. Compare with *allopolyploid*.

autoradiography Method for detecting radioactive decay; radiation causes the appearance of dark silver grains in special X-ray film.

autosome (aw'-toh-sohm) A chromosome other than the sex (X and Y) chromosomes.

autotroph (aw'-toh-trof) An organism that synthesizes complex organic compounds from simple inorganic raw materials; also called *producer* or *primary producer*. Compare with *heterotroph*. See *chemoautotroph* and *photoautotroph*.

auxin (awk'-sin) A plant hormone involved in various aspects of growth and development, such as stem elongation, apical dominance, and root formation on cuttings, e.g., indole acetic acid (IAA).

avirulence Properties that render an infectious agent nonlethal, i.e., unable to cause disease in its host. Compare with *virulence*.

Avogadro's number The number of units (6.02 × 10^{23}) present in one mole of any substance.

axillary bud A bud in the axil of a leaf; also called *lateral bud*. Compare with *terminal bud*.

axon (aks'-on) The long extension of the neuron that transmits nerve impulses away from the cell body. Compare with *dendrite*.

axopods (aks'-o-podz) Long, filamentous, cytoplasmic projections characteristic of actinopods.

B cell (B lymphocyte) The type of white blood cell responsible for antibody-mediated immunity. When stimulated, B cells differentiate to become plasma cells that produce antibodies. Compare with *T cell*.

bacillus (bah-sill'-us) (pl., *bacilli*) A rod-shaped bacterium. Compare with *coccus, spirillum, vibrio,* and *spirochete*.

background extinction The continuous, low-level extinction of species that has occurred throughout much of the history of life. Compare with *mass extinction*.

bacteria (bak-teer'-ee-ah) Prokaryotic organisms that have peptidoglycan in their cell walls; most are decomposers, but some are parasites and others are autotrophs. Bacteria is the name of one of the two prokaryotic domains. Compare with *archaea*.

bacterial artificial chromosome (BAC) Genetically engineered segments of chromosomal DNA with the ability to carry large segments of foreign DNA.

bacteriophage (bak-teer'-ee-oh-fayj) A virus that infects a bacterium (literally, "bacteria eater"). Also called *phage*.

balanced polymorphism (pol"-ee-mor'-fizm) The presence in a population of two or more genetic variants that are maintained in a stable frequency over several generations.

bark The outermost covering over woody stems and roots; consists of all plant tissues located outside the vascular cambium.

baroreceptors (bare"-oh-ree-sep'-torz) Receptors within certain blood vessels that are stimulated by changes in blood pressure.

Barr body A condensed and inactivated X chromosome appearing as a distinctive dense spot in the interphase nucleus of certain cells of female mammals.

basal angiosperms (bay'-sl) Three clades of angiosperms that are thought to be ancestral to all other flowering plants. Compare with *core angiosperms*.

basal body Structure involved in the organization and anchorage of a cilium or flagellum. Structurally similar to a centriole; each is in the form of a cylinder composed of nine triplets of microtubules (9 × 3 structure).

basal metabolic rate (BMR) The amount of energy expended by the body at resting conditions, when no food is being digested and no voluntary muscular work is being performed.

base (1) A substance that is a hydrogen ion (proton) acceptor; bases unite with acids to form salts. Compare with *acid*. (2) A nitrogenous base in a nucleotide or nucleic acid. See *purines* and *pyrimidines*.

basement membrane The thin, noncell layer of an epithelial membrane that attaches to the underlying tissues; consists of tiny fibers and polysaccharides produced by the epithelial cells.

base-pair substitution mutation A change in one base pair in DNA. See *missense mutation* and *nonsense mutation*.

basic solution A solution in which the concentration of hydroxide ions [OH$^-$] exceeds the concentration of hydrogen ions [H$^+$]. A basic solution has pH greater than 7. Compare with *acidic solution* and *neutral solution*.

basidiocarp (ba-sid'-ee-o-karp) The fruiting body of a basidiomycete, e.g., a mushroom.

basidiomycete (ba-sid"-ee-o-my'-seat) Member of a phylum of fungi characterized by the production of sexual basidiospores.

basidiospore (ba-sid'-ee-o-spor) One of a set of sexual spores, usually four, borne on a basidium of a basidiomycete.

basidium (ba-sid'-ee-um) The clublike spore-producing organ of basidiomycetes that bears sexual spores called *basidiospores*.

basilar membrane The multicellular tissue in the inner ear that separates the cochlear duct from the tympanic canal; the sensory cells of the organ of Corti rest on this membrane.

Batesian mimicry (bate'-see-un mim'-ih-kree) The resemblance of a harmless or palatable species to one that is dangerous, unpalatable, or poisonous so that predators are more likely to avoid them. Compare with *Müllerian mimicry*.

B-cell receptors The receptors on B cells that recognize specific antigens.

behavior What an animal does and how the animal does it, usually in response to stimuli in the environment.

behavioral ecology The scientific study of behavior in natural environments from the evolutionary perspective.

behavioral isolation A prezygotic reproductive isolating mechanism in which reproduction between similar species is prevented because each group exhibits its own characteristic courtship behavior; also called *sexual isolation*.

behavior pattern A fixed behavior that, once activated, continues to completion regardless of sensory feedback.

benthic environment Ocean floor divided into zones based on distance from land, light availability, and depth.

benthos (ben'-thos) Bottom-dwelling sea organisms that fix themselves to one spot, burrow into the sediment, or simply walk about on the ocean floor.

berry A simple, fleshy fruit in which the fruit wall is soft throughout, e.g., tomato, banana, grape.

beta cells Pancreatic cells that secrete insulin.

beta (β) oxidation Process by which fatty acids are converted to acetyl CoA before entry into the citric acid cycle.

beta (β)-pleated sheet A regular, folded, sheetlike type of protein secondary structure, resulting from hydrogen bonding between two different polypeptide chains or two regions of the same polypeptide chain. Compare with *alpha (α) helix*.

biennial plant (by-en'-ee-ul) A plant that takes two years to complete its life cycle. Compare with *annual plant* and *perennial plant*.

bikonts One of two main clades of all eukaryotes; had a common ancestor with two flagella. Compare with *unikonts*.

bilateral symmetry A body shape with right and left halves that are approximately mirror images of each other. Compare with *radial symmetry*.

bile The fluid secreted by the liver; emulsifies fats.

binary fission (by'-nare-ee fish'-un) Equal division of a prokaryotic cell into two; a type of asexual reproduction.

binomial system of nomenclature (by-nome'-ee-ul) System of naming a species by the combination of the genus name and a specific epithet.

bioaccumulation The buildup of a persistent toxic substance, such as certain pesticides, in an organism's body.

biodiversity See *biological diversity*.

biodiversity hotspot Biogeographic region that is a significant reservoir of endemic biodiversity and is threatened with continued habitat destruction.

biofilm An irregular layer of microorganisms embedded in the slime they secrete and concentrated at a solid or liquid surface.

biogenic amines A class of neurotransmitters that includes norepinephrine, serotonin, and dopamine.

biogeochemical cycle (bye"-o-jee"-o-kem'-ee-kl) Process by which matter cycles from the living world to the nonliving, physical environment and back again, e.g., the carbon cycle, the nitrogen cycle, and the phosphorus cycle.

biogeography The study of the past and present geographic distributions of organisms.

bioinformatics The storage, retrieval, and comparison of biological information, particularly DNA or protein sequences within a given species and among different species.

biological clocks Mechanisms by which activities of organisms are adapted to regularly recurring changes in the environment. See *circadian rhythm*.

biological diversity The variety of living organisms considered at three levels: genetic diversity, species diversity, and ecosystem diversity. Also called *biodiversity*.

biological magnification The increased concentration of toxic chemicals, such as PCBs, heavy metals, and certain pesticides, in the tissues of organisms at higher trophic levels in food webs.

biological species concept See *species*.

biomass (bye'-o-mas) A quantitative estimate of the total mass, or amount, of living material in a particular ecosystem.

biome (by'-ohm) A large, relatively distinct terrestrial region characterized by a similar climate, soil, plants, and animals, regardless of where it occurs on Earth.

bioremediation A method to clean up a hazardous waste site that uses microorganisms to break down toxic pollutants, or plants to selectively accumulate toxins.

biosphere All Earth's communities of living organisms and their physical environments.

biosphere reserves Zones designed and set aside to protect biodiversity, promote sustainable development, and foster research and conservation education.

bioterrorism The intentional use of biological agents, such as microorganisms or toxins derived from living organisms, to cause death or disease.

biotic factors Elements of the living world that affect a particular organism, i.e., its relationships with other organisms. Compare with *abiotic factors*.

biotic pollution Introduction of a foreign species into an area where it is not native.

biotic potential See *intrinsic rate of increase*.

bipedal Walking on two feet. Compare with *quadripedal*.

bipolar cell A type of neuron in the retina of the eye; receives input from the photoreceptors (rods and cones) and synapses on ganglion cells.

biramous appendages Appendages with two jointed branches extending from their base. Compare with *uniramous appendages*.

blade (1) The thin, expanded part of a leaf. (2) The flat, leaflike structure of certain multicellular algae.

blastocoel (blas'-toh-seel) The fluid-filled cavity of a blastula.

blastocyst The mammalian blastula. See *blastula*.

blastodisc A small disc of cytoplasm at the animal pole of a reptile or bird egg; cleavage is restricted to the blastodisc (meroblastic cleavage).

blastomere A cell of an early embryo.

blastopore (blas'-toh-pore) The primitive opening into the body cavity of an early embryo that may become the mouth (in protostomes) or anus (in deuterostomes) of the adult organism.

blastula (blas'-tew-lah) In animal development, a hollow ball of cells produced by cleavage of a fertilized ovum. In mammalian development, known as a *blastocyst*.

blood A fluid, circulating connective tissue that transports nutrients and other materials through the bodies of many types of animals.

blood pressure The force exerted by blood against the inner walls of the blood vessels.

bloom The sporadic occurrence of huge numbers of algae in freshwater and marine ecosystems.

body mass index (BMI) An index of weight in relation to height; calculated by dividing the square of the weight (square kilograms) by height (meters).

Bohr effect Increased oxyhemoglobin dissociation due to lowered pH; occurs as carbon dioxide concentration increases.

bolting The production of a tall flower stalk by a plant that grows vegetatively as a rosette (growth habit with a short stem and a circular cluster of leaves).

bond energy The energy required to break a particular chemical bond.

bone Principal vertebrate skeletal tissue; a type of connective tissue that consists of cells (osteocytes) embedded in a hard matrix of collagen fibers and minerals, including calcium and phosphate.

bone marrow The soft, cellular tissue that fills the internal spaces of bones; red bone marrow in certain bones produces blood cells.

boreal forest (bor'-ee-uhl) The northern coniferous forest biome found primarily in Canada, northern Europe, and Siberia; also called *taiga*.

bottleneck A sudden decrease in a population size caused by adverse environmental factors; may result in genetic drift; also called *genetic bottleneck* or *population bottleneck*.

bottom-up processes Control of ecosystem function by nutrient cycles and other parts of the abiotic environment. Compare with *top-down processes*.

Bowman's capsule A double-walled sac of cells that surrounds the glomerulus of each nephron.

brachiopods (bray'-kee-oh-podz) The phylum of solitary marine invertebrates having a pair of shells and, internally, a pair of coiled arms with ciliated tentacles; one of the lophophorate phyla.

bracts Modified leaves associated with flower clusters; may be showy and petal-like.

brain A concentration of nervous tissue that controls neural function; in vertebrates, the anterior, enlarged portion of the central nervous system.

brain stem The part of the vertebrate brain that includes the medulla, pons, and midbrain.

branchial Pertaining to the gills or gill region.

brassinosteroid (BR) One of a group of steroids that function as plant hormones and are involved in several aspects of growth and development.

Broca's area Located near motor areas in left frontal lobe; controls our ability to speak; important in language processing and speech comprehension.

bronchiole (bronk'-ee-ole) Air duct in the lung that branches from a bronchus; divides to form air sacs (alveoli).

bronchus (bronk'-us) (pl., *bronchi*) One branch of the trachea and its immediate branches within the lung.

brown alga One of a group of predominantly marine algae that are multicellular and contain the pigments chlorophyll *a* and *c*, and carotenoids, including fucoxanthin.

bryophytes (bry'-oh-fites) Nonvascular plants including mosses, liverworts, and hornworts.

bryozoans Animals belonging to phylum Bryozoa, one of the three lophophorate phyla; form sessile colonies by asexual budding.

bud An undeveloped shoot that develops into flowers, stems, or leaves. Buds are enclosed in bud scales; see *axillary bud* and *terminal bud*.

budding Asexual reproduction in which a small part of the parent's body separates from the rest and develops into a new individual; characteristic of yeasts and certain other organisms.

bud scale A modified leaf that covers and protects a dormant bud.

bud scale scar Scar on a twig left when a bud scale abscises from the terminal bud.

buffer A substance in a solution that tends to lessen the change in hydrogen ion concentration (pH) that otherwise would be produced by adding an acid or base.

bulb A globose, fleshy, underground bud that consists of a short stem with fleshy leaves, e.g., onion.

bundle scar Marks on a leaf scar left when vascular bundles of the petiole break during leaf abscission.

bundle sheath Group of tightly packed cells that form a sheath around the veins of a leaf.

bundle sheath extension Group of support cells that extend from the bundle sheath of a leaf vein toward the upper and/or lower epidermis.

buttress root A bracelike root at the base of certain trees that provides upright support.

C_3 pathway See *C_3 plant*.

C_3 plant Plant that carries out carbon fixation solely by the Calvin cycle. Compare with *C_4 plant* and *CAM plant*.

C_4 pathway See *C_4 plant*.

C_4 plant Plant that fixes carbon initially by a pathway in which the reaction of CO_2 with phosphoenolpyruvate is catalyzed by PEP carboxylase in leaf mesophyll cells; the products are transferred to the bundle sheath cells, where the Calvin cycle takes place. Compare with *C₃ plant* and *CAM plant*.

cadherins Transmembrane proteins that are components of adhering junctions between animal cells.

calcitonin (kal-sih-toh′-nin) A hormone secreted by the thyroid gland that rapidly lowers the calcium content in the blood.

calls Short, simple sounds animals use to communicate.

callus (kal′-us) Undifferentiated tissue formed on an explant (excised tissue or organ) in plant tissue culture.

calmodulin A calcium-binding protein; when bound, it alters the activity of certain enzymes or transport proteins.

calorie The amount of heat energy required to raise the temperature of 1 g of water 1°C; equivalent to 4.184 joules. Compare with *kilocalorie*.

Calvin cycle Cyclic series of reactions in the chloroplast stroma in photosynthesis; fixes carbon dioxide and produces carbohydrate. See *C₃ plant*.

calyx (kay′-liks) The collective term for the sepals of a flower.

cambium See *lateral meristems*.

Cambrian explosion See *Paleozoic era*.

Cambrian period See *Paleozoic era*.

Cambrian radiation See *Paleozoic era*.

cAMP See *cyclic AMP*.

CAM plant Plant that carries out crassulacean acid metabolism; carbon is initially fixed into organic acids at night in the reaction of CO_2 and phosphoenolpyruvate, catalyzed by PEP carboxylase; during the day the acids break down to yield CO_2, which enters the Calvin cycle. Compare with *C₃ plant* and *C₄ plant*.

cGMP See *cyclic GMP*.

cancer cells See *malignant cells*.

cancer driver gene A gene that, when its expression is altered, either by a particular mutation or by certain epigenetic changes, gives a cell a selective growth advantage. See *oncogene*, *proto-oncogene*, and *tumor suppressor gene*.

canines The long pointed teeth of a mammal adapted for piercing prey and tearing food. Compare with *incisors*, *premolars*, and *molars*.

CAP See *catabolite activator protein*.

capacitation Maturation process that enables mammalian sperm to participate in fertilization; takes place in the female reproductive tract.

capillaries (kap′-i-lare-eez) Microscopic blood vessels in the tissues that permit exchange of materials between cells and blood.

capillary action The ability of water to move in small-diameter tubes as a consequence of its cohesive and adhesive properties.

capping See *mRNA cap*.

capsid Protein coat surrounding the nucleic acid of a virus.

capsule (1) The portion of the moss sporophyte that contains spores. (2) A simple, dry, dehiscent fruit that develops from two or more fused carpels and opens along many sutures or pores to release seeds. (3) A gelatinous coat that surrounds some bacteria.

carbohydrate Compound containing carbon, hydrogen, and oxygen, in the approximate ratio of C:2H:O, e.g., sugars, starch, and cellulose.

carbon cycle The worldwide circulation of carbon from the abiotic environment into living things and back into the abiotic environment.

carbon fixation reactions Reduction reactions of photosynthesis in which carbon from carbon dioxide becomes incorporated into organic molecules, leading to the production of carbohydrate. See *Calvin cycle*.

Carboniferous period See *Paleozoic era*.

carbonyl group A polar functional group consisting of a carbon attached to an oxygen by a double bond; found in aldehydes and ketones.

carboxyl group A weakly acidic functional group; abbreviated —COOH.

carcinogen (kar-sin′-oh-jen) An agent that causes cancer or accelerates its development.

cardiac cycle One complete heartbeat.

cardiac muscle Involuntary, striated type of muscle found in the vertebrate heart. Compare with *smooth muscle* and *skeletal muscle*.

cardiac output The volume of blood pumped by the left ventricle into the aorta in 1 minute.

cardiovascular disease Disease of the heart or blood vessels; the leading cause of death in most industrial societies.

cardiovascular system The closed circulatory system of vertebrates that transports oxygen, nutrients, hormones, and other substances, and protects the body against disease; consists of heart and blood vessels.

carnivore (kar′-ni-vor) An animal that mainly feeds on other animals; a mammal belonging to order Carnivora, e.g., wolves or seals.

carotenoids (ka-rot′-n-oidz) A group of yellow to orange plant pigments synthesized from isoprene subunits; include carotenes and xanthophylls.

carpel (kar′-pul) The female reproductive unit of a flower; carpels bear ovules. Compare with *pistil*.

carrier-mediated active transport Transport across a membrane of a substance from a region of low concentration to a region of high concentration; requires both a transport protein with a binding site for the specific substance and an energy source (often ATP).

carrier-mediated transport Any form of transport across a membrane that uses a membrane-bound transport protein with a binding site for a specific substance; includes both facilitated diffusion and carrier-mediated active transport.

carrying capacity (*K*) The largest population that a particular habitat can support and sustain for an indefinite period, assuming there are no changes in the environment.

cartilage A flexible skeletal tissue of vertebrates; a type of connective tissue.

caryopsis (pl., *caryopses*) See *grain*.

Casparian strip (kas-pare′-ee-un) A band of waterproof material around the radial and transverse walls of endodermal root cells.

caspase Any of a group of proteolytic enzymes that are active in the early stages of apoptosis.

catabolism The aspect of metabolism in which complex substances are broken down to form simpler substances; catabolic reactions are particularly important in releasing chemical energy stored by the cell. Compare with *anabolism*.

catabolite activator protein (CAP) A positively acting regulator that becomes active when bound to cAMP; active CAP stimulates transcription of the *lac* operon and other operons that code for enzymes used in catabolic pathways.

catalyst (kat′-ah-list) A substance that increases the speed at which a chemical reaction occurs without being used up in the reaction. Enzymes are biological catalysts.

catecholamine (cat″-eh-kole′-ah-meen) A class of compounds including dopamine, epinephrine, and norepinephrine; these compounds serve as neurotransmitters and hormones.

cation A particle with one or more units of positive charge, such as a hydrogen ion (H^+) or calcium ion (Ca^{2+}). Compare with *anion*.

cation exchange Process in which root cells secrete protons (H^+), which replace cations adhering to soil particles, thereby releasing them for absorption by the roots.

cecum (see′-kum) The blind pouch formed at the junction of the small and large intestine.

CD4 T cell See *T helper cell*.

CD8 T cell See *T cytotoxic cell*.

cDNA library A collection of recombinant plasmids that contain complementary DNA (cDNA) copies of mRNA templates. The cDNA, which lacks introns, is synthesized by reverse transcriptase. Compare with *genomic DNA library*.

cell The basic structural and functional unit of life, which consists of living material enclosed by a membrane.

cell body The large portion of a neuron that contains most of the cytoplasm, the nucleus, and most of the other organelles.

cell cycle Cyclic series of events in the life of a dividing eukaryotic cell; consists of mitosis, cytokinesis, and the stages of interphase.

cell-cycle checkpoints See *cell-cycle control system*.

cell-cycle control system Regulatory molecules that control key events (cell-cycle checkpoints) in the cell cycle; common to all eukaryotes.

cell determination See *determination*.

cell differentiation See *differentiation*.

cell fractionation The technique used to separate the components of cells by subjecting them to centrifugal force. See *differential centrifugation* and *density gradient centrifugation*.

cell-mediated immunity A type of specific immune response carried out by T cells. Compare with *antibody-mediated immunity*.

cell plate The structure that forms during cytokinesis in plants, separating the two daughter cells produced by mitosis.

cell signaling Mechanisms of communication between cells. Cells signal one another with secreted signaling molecules, or a signaling molecule on one cell combines with a receptor on another cell. See *signal transduction*.

cell theory The scientific theory that the cell is the basic unit of life, of which all living things are composed, and that all cells are derived from pre-existing cells.

cellular respiration See *respiration*.

cellular slime mold A group of funguslike amoebozoan protists whose feeding stage consists of unicellular, amoeboid organisms that aggregate to form a pseudoplasmodium during reproduction; compare with *plasmodial slime mold*.

cellulose (sel′-yoo-lohs) A structural polysaccharide consisting of beta glucose subunits; the main constituent of plant primary cell walls.

cell wall The structure outside the plasma membrane of certain cells; may contain cellulose (plant cells), chitin (most fungal cells), peptidoglycan and/or lipopolysaccharide (most bacterial cells), or other material.

Cenozoic era Span of geologic time extending from 66 mya to the present; marked by diversification of mammals, birds, insects, and flowering plants. Divided into Paleogene (66–23 mya), Neogene (23–2.6 mya), and Quaternary (2.6 mya to present) periods.

center of origin The geographic area where a given species originated.

central nervous system (CNS) In vertebrates, the brain and spinal cord. Compare with *peripheral nervous system*.

centrifuge A device used to separate cells or their components by subjecting them to centrifugal force.

centriole (sen′-tree-ohl) One of a pair of small, cylindrical organelles lying at right angles to each other near the nucleus in the cytoplasm of animal cells and certain protist and plant cells; each centriole is in the form of a cylinder composed of nine triplets of microtubules (9 × 3 structure).

centromere (sen′-tro-meer) A specialized constricted region of a chromatid; contains the kinetochore. In cells at prophase and metaphase, sister chromatids are joined in the vicinity of their centromeres.

centrosome (sen′-tro-sowm) An organelle in animal cells that is the main microtubule-organizing center; typically contains a pair of centrioles and is important in cell division.

cephalization The evolution of a head; the concentration of nervous tissue and sense organs at the front end of the animal.

cephalochordates Members of the chordate subphylum that includes the lancelets.

cerebellum (ser-eh-bel′-um) A convoluted subdivision of the vertebrate brain concerned with coordination of muscular movements, muscle tone, and balance.

cerebral cortex (ser-ee′-brul kor′-teks) The outer layer of the cerebrum composed of gray matter and consisting mainly of nerve cell bodies.

cerebrospinal fluid (CSF) The fluid that bathes the central nervous system of vertebrates.

cerebrum (ser-ee′-brum) A large, convoluted subdivision of the vertebrate brain; in humans, it functions as the center for learning, voluntary movement, and interpretation of sensation.

cervix The lower region of the uterus; extends slightly into the vagina.

chaparral (shap″-uh-ral′) A biome with a Mediterranean climate (mild, moist winters and hot, dry summers). Chaparral vegetation is characterized by drought-resistant, small-leaved evergreen shrubs and small trees.

chaperones See *molecular chaperones*.

character An attribute or characteristic of an organism.

character displacement The tendency for two similar species to diverge (become more different) in areas where their ranges overlap; reduces interspecific competition.

Chargaff's rules A relationship in DNA molecules based on nucleotide composition data; the number of adenines equals the number of thymines, and the number of guanines equals the number of cytosines.

charophytes Group of green algae closely related to land plants.

chelicerae (keh-lis′-er-ee) The first pair of appendages in certain arthropods; clawlike appendages located immediately anterior to the mouth and used to manipulate food into the mouth.

chemical bond A force of attraction between atoms in a compound. See *covalent bond, hydrogen bond,* and *ionic bond*.

chemical compound Two or more elements combined in a fixed ratio.

chemical evolution The origin of life from nonliving matter.

chemical formula A representation of the composition of a compound; the elements are indicated by chemical symbols with subscripts to indicate their ratios. See *molecular formula, structural formula,* and *simplest formula*.

chemical symbol The abbreviation for an element; usually the first letter (or first and second letters) of the English or Latin name.

chemical synapse A junction between two neurons in which an action potential in the presynaptic neuron triggers release of a neurotransmitter that crosses the gap and binds to a receptor on the postsynaptic neuron; specific gated ion channels open or close which changes the permeability of the postsynaptic neuron. When threshold level is reached, the postsynaptic neuron transmits an action potential. Compare with *electrical synapse*.

chemiosmosis Process by which phosphorylation of ADP to form ATP is coupled to the transfer of electrons down an electron transport chain; the electron transport chain powers proton pumps that produce a proton gradient across the membrane; ATP is formed as protons diffuse through transmembrane channels in ATP synthase.

chemoautotroph (kee″-moh-aw′-toh-trof) Organism that obtains energy from inorganic compounds and synthesizes organic compounds from inorganic raw materials; includes some bacteria and many archaea. Compare with *photoautotroph, photoheterotroph,* and *chemoheterotroph*.

chemoheterotroph (kee″-moh-het′-ur-oh-trof) Organism that uses organic compounds as a source of energy and carbon; includes animals, fungi, many bacteria, and a few archaea. Compare with *photoautotroph, photoheterotroph,* and *chemoautotroph*.

chemoreceptor (kee″-moh-ree-sep′-tor) A sensory receptor that responds to chemical stimuli.

chemotaxis Movement of a cell or organism in response to certain chemicals.

chemotroph (kee′-moh-trof) Organism that uses organic compounds or inorganic substances, such as iron, nitrate, ammonia, or sulfur, as sources of energy. Compare with *phototroph*. See *chemoautotroph* and *chemoheterotroph*.

chiasma (ky-az′-muh) (pl., *chiasmata*) An X-shaped site in a tetrad usually marking the location where homologous (nonsister) chromatids previously crossed over.

chimera (ky-meer′-uh) An organism consisting of two or more kinds of genetically dissimilar cells.

chitin (ky′-tin) A nitrogen-containing structural polysaccharide that forms the exoskeleton of insects and the cell walls of many fungi.

chlorophyll (klor′-oh-fil) A group of light-trapping green pigments found in most photosynthetic organisms.

chlorophyll *a* See *chlorophyll*.

chlorophyll *b* See *chlorophyll*.

chlorophyll-binding proteins About 15 different proteins associated with chlorophyll molecules in the thylakoid membrane.

chloroplasts (klor′-oh-plastz) Membranous organelles that are the sites of photosynthesis in eukaryotes; occur in some plant and algal cells.

choanocyte (ko-an′-uh-site) A collared, flagellate cell that traps and phagocytizes food particles; found in sponges; also called a *collar cell*.

choanoflagellates Collared flagellate protists; opisthokonts closely related to animals.

cholinergic neuron (kohl″-in-air′-jik) A neuron that releases acetylcholine as a neurotransmitter. Compare with *adrenergic neuron*.

chondrichthyes (kon-drik′-thees) The class of cartilaginous fishes that includes the sharks, rays, and skates.

chondrocytes Cartilage cells.

chordates (kor′-dates) Deuterostome animals that, at some time in their lives, have a cartilaginous, dorsal skeletal structure called a *notochord;* a dorsal, tubular nerve cord; *pharyngeal slits;* a postanal tail; and an *endostyle* (or its derivative, a thyroid gland).

chorion (kor-′ee-on) An extraembryonic membrane in reptiles, birds, and mammals that forms an outer cover around the embryo and in mammals contributes to the formation of the placenta.

chorionic villus sampling (CVS) (kor″ee-on′ik) Study of extraembryonic cells that are genetically identical to the cells of an embryo, making it possible to assess its genetic makeup. Compare with *amniocentesis*.

choroid layer A layer of cells filled with black pigment that absorbs light and prevents reflected light from blurring the image that falls on the retina; the layer of the eyeball outside the retina.

chromalveolates A supergroup composed of diverse protists with few shared characters; most are photosynthetic, and heterotrophic chromalveolates, such as the water molds and ciliates, probably descended from autotrophic ancestors. Divided into two main groups; see *alveolates* and *stramenopiles*.

chromatid (kroh′-mah-tid) One of the two identical halves of a duplicated chromosome; the two chromatids that make up a chromosome are referred to as *sister chromatids*.

chromatin (kro′-mah-tin) The complex of DNA and protein that makes up eukaryotic chromosomes.

chromoplasts Pigment-containing plastids; found mainly in flowers and fruits.

chromosome theory of inheritance A basic principle in biology that states that inheritance can be explained by assuming that genes are linearly arranged in specific locations along the chromosomes.

chromosomes Structures in the cell nucleus that consist of chromatin and contain the genes. The chromosomes become visible under the microscope as distinct structures during cell division.

chylomicrons (kie-low-my′-kronz) Protein-covered fat droplets produced in the intestinal cells; they enter the lymphatic system and are transported to the blood.

chytrid See *chytridiomycete*.

chytridiomycete (ki-trid″-ee-o-my′-seat) A member of a phylum of fungi characterized by the production of flagellate cells at some stage in their life history. Also called *chytrid*.

ciliate (sil′-e-ate) A unicellular protist covered by many short cilia.

cilium (sil′-ee-um) (pl., *cilia*) One of many short, hairlike structures that project from the surface of some eukaryotic cells and are used for locomotion or movement of materials across the cell surface.

circadian rhythm (sir-kay′-dee-un) An internal rhythm that approximates the 24-hour day. See *biological clocks*.

circulatory system The body system that functions in internal transport and protects the body from disease.

cisternae (sing., *cisterna*) Stacks of flattened membranous sacs that make up the Golgi complex.

citrate (**citric acid**) A six-carbon organic acid.

citric acid cycle Series of chemical reactions in aerobic cellular respiration in which acetyl coenzyme A is completely degraded to carbon dioxide and water with the release of metabolic energy that is used to produce ATP; also known as the *Krebs cycle* and the *tricarboxylic acid (TCA) cycle*.

clade A group of organisms containing a common ancestor and all its descendants; a monophyletic group.

cladistics An approach to classification based on recency of common ancestry rather than degree of structural similarity. Also called *phylogenetic systematics*. Compare with *phenetics* and *evolutionary systematics*.

cladogram A branching diagram that illustrates taxonomic relationships based on the principles of cladistics.

class A taxonomic category made up of related orders.

classical conditioning A type of learning in which an association is formed between some normal response to a stimulus and a new stimulus, after which the new stimulus elicits the response.

cleavage Series of mitotic cell divisions, without growth, that converts the zygote to a multicellular blastula.

cleavage furrow A constricted region of the cytoplasm that forms and progressively deepens during cytokinesis of animal cells, thereby separating the two daughter cells.

climate Average weather conditions, plus extremes (records), that occur in a given place over a period of years.

climate change Change in Earth's climate patterns; today mostly caused by increased levels of atmospheric carbon dioxide produced by use of fossil fuels.

cline Gradual change in phenotype and genotype frequencies among contiguous populations that is the result of an environmental gradient.

clitoris (klit′-o-ris) A small, erectile structure at the anterior part of the vulva in female mammals; homologous to the male penis.

cloaca (klow-a′-ka) An exit chamber in some animals that receives digestive wastes and urine; may also serve as an exit for gametes.

clonal expansion The increase in number of T cells or B cells specific for an antigen; occurs

when specific T cells or B cells are activated by the antigen.

clonal selection Lymphocyte activation in which a specific antigen causes activation, cell division, and differentiation only in cells that express receptors with which the antigen binds.

clone (1) A population of cells descended by mitotic division from a single ancestral cell. (2) A population of genetically identical organisms asexually propagated from a single individual. Also see *DNA cloning*.

cloning The process of forming a clone.

closed circulatory system A type of circulatory system in which the blood flows through a continuous circuit of blood vessels; characteristic of annelids, cephalopods, and vertebrates. Compare with *open circulatory system*.

closed system An entity that does not exchange energy with its surroundings. Compare with *open system*.

club mosses A phylum of seedless vascular plants with a life cycle similar to that of ferns.

clumped dispersion The spatial distribution pattern of a population in which individuals are more concentrated in specific parts of the habitat. Also called *aggregated distribution* and *patchiness*. Compare with *random dispersion* and *uniform dispersion*.

cnidarians (ni-dah′-ree-anz) Phylum of animals that have stinging cells called *cnidocytes*, two tissue layers, and radial symmetry; include hydras and jellyfish.

cnidocytes Stinging cells characteristic of cnidarians.

coated pit A depression in the plasma membrane, the cytosolic side of which is coated with the protein clathrin; important in receptor-mediated endocytosis.

coccus (kok′-us) (pl., *cocci*) A bacterium with a spherical shape. Compare with *bacillus, spirillum, vibrio,* and *spirochete*.

cochlea (koke′-lee-ah) The structure of the inner ear of mammals that contains the auditory receptors (organ of Corti).

codominance (koh″-dom′-in-ants) Condition in which two alleles of a locus are expressed in a heterozygote.

codon (koh′-don) A triplet of mRNA nucleotides. The 64 possible codons collectively constitute a universal genetic code in which each codon specifies an amino acid in a polypeptide, or a signal to either start or terminate polypeptide synthesis.

coelacanths A genus of lobe-finned fishes that has survived to the present day.

coelom (see′-lum) The main body cavity of most animals; a true coelom is lined with mesoderm. Compare with *pseudocoelom*.

coelomate (seel′-oh-mate) Animal that has a true coelom. Compare with *acoelomate* and *pseudocoelomate*.

coenocyte (see′-no-site) An organism consisting of a multinucleate cell, i.e., the nuclei are not separated from one another by septa.

coenzyme (koh-en′-zime) An organic cofactor for an enzyme; generally participates in the reaction by transferring some component, such as electrons or part of a substrate molecule.

coenzyme A (CoA) Organic cofactor responsible for transferring groups derived from organic acids.

coevolution The reciprocal adaptation of two or more species that occurs as a result of their close interactions over a long period.

cofactor A nonprotein substance needed by an enzyme for normal activity; some cofactors are inorganic (usually metal ions); others are organic (coenzymes).

cognition The mental processes involved in gaining and using knowledge; cognition is learning and knowing, including awareness, thinking, processing information, reasoning, and awareness of thoughts, perceptions, and self.

cohesin Ring-shaped protein complex responsible for linking sister chromatids during prophase.

cohesion The property of sticking together. Compare with *adhesion*.

cohort A group of individuals of the same age.

colchicine A drug that blocks the division of eukaryotic cells by binding to tubulin subunits, which make up the microtubules, the major component of the mitotic spindle.

coleoptile (kol-ee-op′-tile) A protective sheath that encloses the young stem in certain monocots.

collagens (kol′-ah-gen) Proteins found in the collagen fibers of connective tissues.

collar cell See *choanocyte*.

collecting duct A tube in the kidney that receives filtrate from several nephrons and conducts it to the renal pelvis.

collenchyma (kol-en′-kih-mah) Living cells with moderately but unevenly thickened primary cell walls; collenchyma cells help support the herbaceous plant body.

colon The region of the large intestine that extends from the cecum to the rectum.

colony An association of loosely connected cells or individuals of the same species.

commensalism (kuh-men′-sul-izm) A type of symbiosis in which one organism benefits and the other one is neither harmed nor helped. Compare with *mutualism* and *parasitism*.

commercial harvest The collection of commercially important organisms from the wild. Examples include the commercial harvest of parrots (for the pet trade) and cacti (for houseplants).

community An association of populations of different species living together in a defined habitat with some degree of interdependence. Compare with *ecosystem*.

community ecology The description and analysis of patterns and processes within the community.

compact bone Dense, hard bone tissue found mainly near the surfaces of a bone.

companion cell A cell in the phloem of flowering plants that governs loading and unloading sugar into the sieve tube element for translocation.

compass sense The sense of direction an animal requires to travel in a straight line toward a destination.

competition The interaction among two or more individuals that attempt to use the same essential resource, such as food, water, sunlight, or living space. See *interspecific* and *intraspecific competition*. See *interference* and *exploitation competition*.

competitive exclusion principle The concept that no two species with identical living requirements can occupy the same ecological niche indefinitely.

competitive inhibition Binding of a substance (the competitive inhibitor) to the active site of an enzyme, thus lowering the rate of the reaction catalyzed by the enzyme. Compare with *noncompetitive inhibition*.

competitive inhibitor See *competitive inhibition*.

complement A group of proteins in blood and other body fluids that are activated by an antigen–antibody complex and then destroy pathogens.

complementary base pairing The pairing of bases by hydrogen bond formation in double-stranded nucleic acids according to the base pairing rules: adenine pairs with thymine (in DNA) or uracil (in RNA), and guanine pairs with cytosine.

complementary DNA (cDNA) DNA synthesized by reverse transcriptase, using RNA as a template.

complete flower A flower that has all four parts: sepals, petals, stamens, and carpels. Compare with *incomplete flower*.

complete metamorphosis In insects, the transition during the life cycle from egg to larva, to pupa, and finally, to adult. Larvae have different forms and lifestyles than adults. Compare with *incomplete metamorphosis*.

compound eye An eye, such as that of an insect, consisting of many light-sensitive units called *ommatidia*.

concentration gradient A difference in the concentration of a substance from one point to another, as for example, across a cell membrane.

condensation reaction A reaction in which two monomers are combined covalently through the removal of the equivalent of a water molecule; also called *condensation synthesis*. Compare with *hydrolysis reaction*.

condensin Collective name for protein complex that binds DNA and forms it into coiled loops as part of the chromosome compaction process required for cell division.

cone (1) In botany, a reproductive structure in many gymnosperms that produces either microspores or megaspores. (2) In zoology, one of the conical photoreceptive cells of the retina that is particularly sensitive to bright light and, by distinguishing light of various wavelengths, mediates color vision. Compare with *rod*.

conidiophore (kah-nid′-e-o-for″) A specialized hypha that bears conidia.

conidium (kah-nid′-e-um) (pl., *conidia*) An asexual spore that is usually formed at the tip of a specialized hypha called a *conidiophore*.

conifer (kon′-ih-fur) Any of a large phylum of gymnosperms that are woody trees and shrubs with needlelike, mostly evergreen leaves and with seeds in cones.

conjugation (kon″-jew-gay′-shun) (1) A sexual process in ciliate protists that involves exchange of haploid nuclei with another cell. (2) A mechanism for DNA exchange in bacteria that involves cell-to-cell contact.

connective tissue Animal tissue consisting mostly of an intercellular substance (fibers scattered through a matrix) in which the cells are embedded, e.g., bone.

conodonts Extinct, simple fishlike chordates with large eyes and tooth-like hooks; may have been early vertebrates.

conservation biology A multidisciplinary science that focuses on the study of how humans impact organisms and on the development of ways to protect biological diversity.

constitutive gene A gene that is constantly transcribed.

consumer See *heterotroph*.

consumption overpopulation A situation in which each individual in a human population consumes too large a share of resources; results in pollution, environmental degradation, and resource depletion. Compare with *people overpopulation*.

contest competition See *interference competition*.

continental drift The scientific theory that continents were once joined and later split and drifted apart.

contraception Any method used to intentionally prevent pregnancy.

contractile root (kun-trak′-til) A specialized type of root that contracts and pulls a bulb or corm deeper into the soil.

contractile vacuole A membrane-enclosed organelle found in certain freshwater protists, such as *Paramecium;* appears to have an osmoregulatory function.

control group In a scientific experiment, a group in which the experimental variable is kept constant. The control group, which is as closely matched to the experimental group as possible, provides a standard of comparison used to verify the results of the experiment. Compare with *experimental group*.

controlled burning Tool of ecological management in which the undergrowth and plant litter are deliberately burned under controlled conditions before they have accumulated to dangerous levels.

controlled mating A mating in which the genotypes of the parents are known.

convergence The functional arrangement of neurons in which a neuron receives signals from two or more presynaptic neurons. Compare with *divergence*.

convergent circuit (kun-vur'-jent) A neural pathway in which a postsynaptic neuron is controlled by signals coming from two or more presynaptic neurons. Compare with *divergent circuit*.

convergent evolution (kun-vur'-jent) The independent evolution of structural or functional similarity in two or more distantly related species, usually as a result of adaptations to similar environments.

convolutions The numerous folds of the cerebral cortex.

copy number variations (CNVs) Genetic variation among individuals in a population as measured by segments of DNA that have been gained or lost, compared to a reference genome.

coral bleaching The stress-induced loss of the symbiotic algae that inhabit coral cells.

coral reef Reef found in warm, shallow seas; built by coral which has solidified into layers of calcium carbonate ($CaCO_3$).

core angiosperms The clade to which most angiosperm species belong. Core angiosperms are divided into three subclades: magnoliids, monocots, and eudicots. Compare with *basal angiosperms*.

corepressor Substance that binds to a repressor protein, converting it to its active form, which is capable of preventing transcription.

Coriolis effect (kor"-e-o'-lis) The tendency of moving air or water to be deflected from its path to the right in the Northern Hemisphere and to the left in the Southern Hemisphere. Caused by the direction of Earth's rotation.

cork cambium (kam'-bee um) A lateral meristem that produces cork cells and cork parenchyma; cork cambium and the tissues it produces make up the *periderm* (outer bark) of a woody plant. Compare with *vascular cambium*.

cork cell A cell in the bark that is produced outwardly by the cork cambium; cork cells are dead at maturity and function for protection and reduction of water loss.

cork parenchyma (par-en'-kih-mah) One or more layers of parenchyma cells produced inwardly by the cork cambium.

corm A short, thickened underground stem specialized for food storage and asexual reproduction, e.g., crocus, gladiolus.

cornea (kor'-nee-ah) The transparent covering of an eye.

corolla (kor-ohl'-ah) Collectively, the petals of a flower.

coronary circulation The system of blood vessels that delivers blood to the heart muscle and returns blood from the heart muscle to the right atrium.

corpus callosum (kah-loh'-sum) In mammals, a large bundle of nerve fibers interconnecting the two cerebral hemispheres.

corpus luteum (loo'-tee"-um) The temporary endocrine tissue in the ovary that develops from the ruptured follicle after ovulation; secretes progesterone and estrogen.

cortex (kor'-teks) (1) The outer part of an organ, such as the cortex of the kidney. Compare with *medulla*. (2) The tissue between the epidermis and vascular tissue in the stems and roots of many herbaceous plants.

cortical reaction Process occurring after fertilization that prevents additional sperm from entering the egg; also known as the "slow block to polyspermy."

corticotropin-releasing factor (CRF) Secreted by the hypothalamus in response to stress; stimulates the anterior pituitary to secrete adrenocorticotropic hormone (ACTH).

cortisol A steroid hormone, secreted by the adrenal cortex, that helps the body adjust to long-term stress; stimulates conversion of other nutrients to glucose in the liver, resulting in increased blood glucose concentration.

cosmopolitan species Species that have a nearly worldwide distribution and occur on more than one continent or throughout much of the ocean. Compare with *endemic species*.

cost–benefit analysis An analysis of the costs versus the benefits of a particular behavior; the costs and benefits are typically assessed in terms of direct fitness, an individual's reproductive success.

cotransport The active transport of a substance from a region of low concentration to a region of high concentration by coupling its transport to the transport of a substance down its concentration gradient.

cotyledon (kot"-uh-lee'-dun) The seed leaf of a plant embryo, which may contain food stored for germination.

cotylosaurs The first reptiles; also known as *stem reptiles*.

countercurrent exchange system A biological mechanism that enables maximum exchange between two fluids. The two fluids must be flowing in opposite directions and have a concentration gradient between them.

coupled reactions A set of reactions in which an exergonic reaction provides the free energy required to drive an endergonic reaction; energy coupling generally occurs through a common intermediate.

courtship rituals Behaviors intended to attract or maintain the attention of a potential mate. A courtship ritual may be a signal that triggers nest building, ovulation, or mating.

covalent bond The chemical bond involving shared pairs of electrons; may be single, double, or triple (with one, two, or three shared pairs of electrons, respectively). Compare with *ionic bond* and *hydrogen bond*.

covalent compound A compound in which atoms are held together by covalent bonds; covalent

compounds consist of molecules. Compare with *ionic compound*.

cranial nerves The 10 to 12 pairs of nerves in vertebrates that emerge directly from the brain; they transmit sensory information to the CNS; some cranial nerves transmit motor information from the CNS to effectors.

cranium The bony framework that protects the brain in vertebrates.

crassulacean acid metabolism (CAM) pathway See *CAM plant*.

creatine phosphate An energy-storing compound in muscle cells.

crepuscular animals Animals most active during dusk, dawn, or both, e.g., fiddler crabs and mosquitoes. Compare with *diurnal animals* and *nocturnal animals*.

Cretaceous period See *Mesozoic era*.

cretinism (kree'-tin-izm) A chronic condition caused by lack of thyroid secretion during fetal development and early childhood; results in physical and intellectual disability if untreated.

cri du chat syndrome A human genetic disease caused by losing part of the short arm of chromosome 5 and characterized by intellectual disability, a cry that sounds like a kitten mewing, and death in infancy or childhood.

cristae (kris'-tee) (sing., *crista*) Shelflike or fingerlike inward projections of the inner membrane of a mitochondrion.

cross bridges The connections between myosin and actin filaments in muscle fibers; formed by the binding of myosin heads to active sites on actin filaments.

crossing-over A process in which genetic material (DNA) is exchanged between paired, homologous chromosomes.

crustaceans Members of a subphylum that includes lobsters, crabs, shrimp, barnacles, and their relatives.

cryptic coloration Colors or markings that help some organisms hide from predators by blending into their physical surroundings. Compare with *aposematic coloration*.

cryptochrome A proteinaceous pigment that strongly absorbs blue light; implicated in resetting the biological clock in plants, fruit flies, and mice.

ctenophores (ten'-oh-forz) Phylum of marine animals (comb jellies) whose bodies consist of two layers of cells enclosing a gelatinous mass. The outer surface is covered with comblike rows of cilia, by which the animal moves.

culture Behavior common to a population, that is learned from members of the population, and transmitted from one generation to the next.

cupula In certain mechanoreceptors, the mass of gelatinous material that encloses the tips of stereocilia; secreted by the hair cells.

Cushing's syndrome Hormone disorder caused by overexposure to glucocorticoids; characterized by fat deposited around trunk, facial edema, and high blood glucose level, which causes *adrenal diabetes*. Long-term exposure may lead to permanent diabetes mellitus.

cuticle (kew'-tih-kl) (1) A noncell covering over the epidermis of the aerial parts of plants that reduces water loss; composed mainly of *cutin,* a waxy substance. (2) The outer covering of some animals, such as roundworms.

cyanobacteria (sy-an"-oh-bak-teer'-ee-uh) Prokaryotic photosynthetic microorganisms that possess chlorophyll and produce oxygen during photosynthesis.

cycad (sih'-kad) Any of a phylum of gymnosperms that live mainly in tropical and semitropical regions and have stout stems (to 20 m in height) and fernlike leaves.

cyclic adenosine monophosphate See *cyclic AMP.*

cyclic AMP (cAMP) A form of adenosine monophosphate in which the phosphate is part of a ring-shaped structure; acts as a regulatory molecule and second messenger in organisms ranging from bacteria to humans.

cyclic electron transport In photosynthesis, the cyclic flow of electrons through photosystem I; ATP is formed by chemiosmosis, but no photolysis of water occurs, and O_2 and NADPH are not produced. Compare with *noncyclic electron transport.*

cyclic GMP (cGMP) A form of guanosine monophosphate in which the phosphate is part of a ring-shaped structure; involved in certain cell signaling processes.

cyclic guanosine monophosphate See *cyclic GMP.*

cyclin–Cdk complex See *cyclins.*

cyclin-dependent kinases (Cdks) Protein kinases involved in controlling the cell cycle.

cyclins Regulatory proteins whose levels oscillate during the cell cycle; cyclins associate with cyclin-dependent kinases to form cyclin–Cdk complexes.

cystic fibrosis A genetic disease with an autosomal recessive inheritance pattern; characterized by secretion of abnormally thick mucus, particularly in the respiratory and digestive systems.

cytochromes (sy'-toh-krohmz) Iron-containing heme proteins of an electron transport system.

cytokines Signaling proteins that regulate interactions between cells in the immune system. Important groups include interferons, interleukins, tumor necrosis factors, and chemokines.

cytokinesis (sy"-toh-kih-nee'-sis) Stage of cell division in which the cytoplasm divides to form two daughter cells.

cytokinin (sy"-toh-ky'-nin) A plant hormone involved in various aspects of plant growth and development, such as cell division and delay of senescence.

cytoplasm The plasma membrane and cell contents with the exception of the nucleus.

cytosine A nitrogenous pyrimidine base that is a component of nucleic acids.

cytoskeleton The dynamic internal network of protein fibers that includes microfilaments, intermediate filaments, and microtubules.

cytosol The fluid component of the cytoplasm in which the organelles are suspended.

cytotoxic T cell See *T cytotoxic cell.*

dalton See *atomic mass unit (amu).*

day-neutral plant A plant whose flowering is not controlled by variations in day length that occur with changing seasons. Compare with *long-day, short-day,* and *intermediate-day plants.*

deamination (dee-am-ih-nay'-shun) The removal of an amino group ($-NH_2$) from an amino acid or other organic compound.

decapods Lobsters, crabs, shrimp, crayfish, and other species assigned to order Decapoda, the largest order of crustaceans.

decarboxylation A reaction in which a molecule of CO_2 is removed from a carboxyl group of an organic acid.

deciduous A term describing a plant that sheds leaves or other structures at regular intervals, e.g., during autumn. Compare with *evergreen.*

declarative memory Factual knowledge of people, places, or objects; requires conscious recall of the information.

decomposers Microbial heterotrophs that break down dead organic material and use the decomposition products as a source of energy. Also called *saprotrophs* or *saprobes.*

deductive reasoning The reasoning that operates from generalities to specifics and can make relationships among data more apparent. Compare with *inductive reasoning.* See *hypothetico-deductive approach.*

deforestation The temporary or permanent removal of forest for agriculture or other uses.

dehydrogenation (dee-hy"-dro-jen-ay'-shun) A form of oxidation in which hydrogen atoms are removed from a molecule.

deletion (1) A chromosome abnormality in which part of a chromosome is missing, e.g., cri du chat syndrome. (2) The loss of one or more base pairs from DNA, which can result in a frameshift mutation.

demographics The science that deals with human population statistics, such as size, density, and distribution.

denature (dee-nay'-ture) To alter the physical properties and three-dimensional structure of a protein, nucleic acid, or other macromolecule by treating it with excess heat, strong acids, or strong bases.

dendrites (den'-dritez) Branches of a neuron that receive and conduct nerve impulses toward the cell body. Compare with *axon.*

dendritic cells A set of immune cells present in many tissues that capture antigens and present them to T cells.

dendrochronology (den"-dro-kruh-naal'-uh-gee) A method of dating that uses the annual rings of trees.

denitrification (dee-nie"-tra-fuh-kay'-shun) The conversion of nitrate (NO_3^-) to nitrogen gas (N_2) by certain bacteria (denitrifying bacteria) in the soil; part of the nitrogen cycle.

dense connective tissue A type of tissue that may be irregular, as in the dermis of the skin, or regular, as in tendons.

density-dependent factor An environmental factor whose effects on a population change as population density changes; tends to retard population growth as population density increases and enhance population growth as population density decreases. Compare with *density-independent factor.*

density gradient centrifugation Procedure in which cell components are placed in a layer on top of a density gradient, usually a sucrose solution and water. Cell structures migrate during centrifugation, forming a band at the position in the gradient where their own density equals that of the sucrose solution.

density-independent factor An environmental factor that affects the size of a population but is not influenced by changes in population density. Compare with *density-dependent factor.*

deoxyribonucleic acid (DNA) Double-stranded nucleic acid; contains genetic information coded in specific sequences of its constituent nucleotides.

deoxyribose Pentose sugar lacking a hydroxyl ($-OH$) group on carbon-2'; a constituent of DNA.

depolarization (dee-pol"-ar-ih-zay'-shun) A decrease in the charge difference across a plasma membrane; may result in an action potential in a neuron or muscle cell.

deposit feeder Animal that consumes nutrients by ingesting soil or sediments.

derived characters See *shared derived characters.*

dermal tissue system The tissue that forms the outer covering over a plant; the epidermis or periderm.

dermis (dur'-mis) The layer of dense connective tissue beneath the epidermis in the skin of vertebrates.

desert A temperate or tropical biome in which lack of precipitation limits plant growth.

desertification The degradation of once-fertile land into nonproductive desert; caused partly by soil erosion, deforestation, and overgrazing by domestic animals.

desmosomes (dez'-moh-sohmz) Buttonlike plaques, present on two opposing cell surfaces, that hold the cells together by means of protein filaments that span the intercellular space.

determinate cleavage Type of cleavage, characteristic of protostomes, in which the fate of each cell is determined when the cell is produced. Compare with *indeterminate cleavage.*

determinate growth Growth of limited duration, as for example, in flowers and leaves. Compare with *indeterminate growth*.

determination The developmental process by which one or more cells become progressively committed to a particular fate. Determination is a series of molecular events usually leading to differentiation. Also called *cell determination*.

detritivore (duh-try'-tuh-vore) An organism, such as an earthworm or crab, that consumes fragments of freshly dead or decomposing organisms; also called *detritus feeder*.

detritus (duh-try'-tus) Organic debris from decomposing organisms.

detritus feeder See *detritivore*.

deuteromycetes (doo"-ter-o-my'-seats) An artificial grouping of fungi characterized by the absence of sexual reproduction but usually having other traits similar to ascomycetes; also called *imperfect fungi*.

deuterostomes (doo'-ter-oh-stomes) Animals that belong to the Deuterostomia, one of the major animal clades; include the echinoderms and chordates. Compare with *protostomes*.

development All the progressive changes that take place throughout the life of an organism.

developmental genetics Study of how genes and gene expression affect the differentiation of cells and the development of an organism.

Devonian period See *Paleozoic era*.

diabetes mellitus (mel'-i-tus) The most common endocrine disorder. In type 1 diabetes, there is a marked decrease in the number of beta cells in the pancreas, resulting in insulin deficiency. In the more common type 2 diabetes, insulin receptors on target cells do not bind with insulin (insulin resistance).

diacylglycerol (DAG) (di"-as-il-glis'-er-ol) A lipid consisting of glycerol combined chemically with two fatty acids; also called *diglyceride*. Compare with *monoacylglycerol* and *triacylglycerol*.

dialysis The diffusion of certain solutes across a selectively permeable membrane.

diaphragm In mammals, the muscular floor of the chest cavity; contracts during inhalation, expanding the chest cavity.

diapsids (di-ap'-sids) Members of a clade of amniotes in which the skull has two pairs of temporal openings; includes all extant reptilian groups (including birds) as well as most extinct reptiles. Compare with *synapsids*.

diastole (di-ass'-toh-lee) Phase of the cardiac cycle in which the heart is relaxed. Compare with *systole*.

diatom (die'-eh-tom") A usually unicellular stramenopile alga that is covered by an ornate, siliceous shell consisting of two overlapping halves; an important component of plankton in both marine and fresh waters.

dichotomous branching (di-kaut'-uh-mus) In botany, a type of branching in which one part always divides into two more or less equal parts.

diencephalon See *forebrain*.

differential centrifugation Separation of cell particles according to their mass, size, or density. In differential centrifugation, the supernatant is spun at successively higher revolutions per minute.

differential gene expression The expression of different subsets of genes at different times and in different cells during development.

differentiated cell A specialized cell; carries out unique activities, expresses a specific set of proteins, and usually has a recognizable appearance.

differentiation (dif"-ah-ren-she-ay'-shun) Development toward a more mature state; a process changing a young, relatively unspecialized cell to a more specialized cell. Also called *cell differentiation*.

diffusion The net movement of particles (atoms, molecules, or ions) from a region of higher concentration of that type of particle to a region of lower concentration (i.e., down a concentration gradient), resulting from random motion; also called *simple diffusion*. Compare with *facilitated diffusion* and *active transport*.

digestion The breakdown of food to small molecules.

diglyceride See *diacylglycerol*.

dihybrid cross (dy-hy'-brid) A genetic cross that takes into account the behavior of alleles of two loci. Compare with *monohybrid cross*.

dikaryotic (dy-kare-ee-ot'-ik) Condition of having two nuclei per cell (i.e., $n + n$), characteristic of certain fungal hyphae. Compare with *monokaryotic*.

dimer An association of two monomers (e.g., a disaccharide or a dipeptide).

dinoflagellate (dy"-noh-flaj'-eh-late) A unicellular, biflagellate, typically marine protist that is an important component of plankton; usually photosynthetic.

dioecious (dy-ee'-shus) Having male and female reproductive structures on separate plants; compare with *monoecious*.

dipeptide See *peptide*.

diploblastic (dip-lo-blas'-tik) Animal body plan in which there are only two embryonic tissue layers, the ectoderm and endoderm. Compare with *triploblastic*.

diploid (dip'-loyd) The condition of having two sets of chromosomes per nucleus. Compare with *haploid* and *polyploid*.

diplomonads Small, mostly parasitic excavates with one or two nuclei, no functional mitochondria, and one to four flagella.

directed evolution See *in vitro evolution*.

direct fitness An individual's reproductive success, measured by the number of viable offspring it produces. Compare with *inclusive fitness*.

directional selection The gradual replacement of one phenotype with another because of environmental change that favors phenotypes at one of the extremes of the normal distribution. Compare with *stabilizing selection* and *disruptive selection*.

disaccharide (dy-sak'-ah-ride) A sugar produced by covalently linking two monosaccharides (e.g., maltose or sucrose).

disomy The normal condition in which both members of a chromosome pair are present in a diploid cell or organism. Compare with *monosomy* and *trisomy*.

dispersal The movement of individuals among populations. See *immigration* and *emigration*.

dispersion The pattern of distribution in space of the individuals of a population relative to their neighbors; see *clumped dispersion, random dispersion,* and *uniform dispersion*.

disruptive selection A special type of directional selection in which changes in the environment favor two or more variant phenotypes at the expense of the mean. Compare with *stabilizing selection* and *directional selection*.

distal Remote; farther from the point of reference. Compare with *proximal*.

distal convoluted tubule The part of the renal tubule that extends from the loop of Henle to the collecting duct. Compare with *proximal convoluted tubule*.

disturbance In ecology, any event that disrupts community or population structure.

diurnal animals Animals most active during the day, e.g., pigeons. Compare with *crepuscular animals* and *nocturnal animals*.

divergence The functional arrangement of neurons in which a neuron sends signals to two or more postsynaptic neurons. Compare with *convergence*.

divergent circuit A neural pathway in which a presynaptic neuron stimulates many postsynaptic neurons. Compare with *convergent circuit*.

diving reflex A group of physiological mechanisms, such as decrease in metabolic rate, that are activated when a mammal dives to its limit.

dizygotic twins Twins that arise from the separate fertilization of two eggs; commonly known as *fraternal twins*. Compare with *monozygotic twins*.

DNA See *deoxyribonucleic acid*.

DNA chip See *DNA microarray*.

DNA cloning The process of selectively amplifying DNA sequences so their structure and function can be studied.

DNA fingerprinting The analysis of DNA fragments extracted from an individual; the resulting pattern is unique to that individual.

DNA ligase Enzyme that catalyzes the joining of the 5′ and 3′ ends of two DNA fragments; essential in DNA replication and used in recombinant DNA technology.

DNA methylation A process in which gene inactivation is perpetuated by enzymes that add methyl groups to DNA.

DNA microarray A diagnostic test involving thousands of DNA molecules placed on a glass slide or chip.

DNA polymerases Family of enzymes that catalyze the synthesis of DNA from a DNA template by adding nucleotides to a growing 3' end.

DNA primase Enzyme that begins the process of DNA replication by synthesizing a short RNA segment complementary to the DNA template strand; this RNA strand is subsequently degraded and replaced with DNA

DNA probe A labeled single-stranded DNA fragment used to detect a gene of interest in a hybridization experiment.

DNA provirus Double-stranded DNA molecule that is an intermediate in the life cycle of an RNA tumor virus (retrovirus).

DNA replication The process by which DNA is duplicated; ordinarily a semiconservative process in which a double helix gives rise to two double helices, each with an "old" strand and a newly synthesized strand.

DNA sequencing Procedure by which the sequence of nucleotides in DNA is determined.

domain (1) A structural and functional region of a protein. (2) The broadest taxonomic category; each domain includes one or more kingdoms.

dominance hierarchy A linear "pecking order" into which animals in a population may organize according to status; regulates aggressive behavior within the population.

dominant allele (al-leel′) An allele that is always expressed when it is present, regardless of whether it is homozygous or heterozygous. Compare with *recessive allele.*

dominant species In a community, a species that as a result of its large biomass or abundance exerts a major influence on the distribution of populations of other species.

dopamine A neurotransmitter of the biogenic amine group; important in motor function.

dormancy A temporary period of arrested growth in plants or plant parts such as spores, seeds, bulbs, and buds.

dorsal (dor′-sl) Toward the uppermost surface or back of an animal. Compare with *ventral.*

dosage compensation Genetic mechanism by which the expression of X-linked genes is made equivalent in XX females and XY males; in mammals this is accomplished by rendering all but one X chromosome inactive.

double fertilization A process in the flowering plant life cycle in which there are two fertilizations; one fertilization results in formation of a zygote, whereas the second results in formation of endosperm.

double helix The structure of DNA, which consists of two antiparallel polynucleotide chains twisted around each other.

doubling time The amount of time it takes for a population to double in size, assuming that its current rate of increase does not change. Doubling time can be estimated by dividing 70 by the rate of increase (percent increase per unit of time).

Down syndrome An inherited condition in which individuals have abnormalities of the face, eyelids, tongue, and other parts of the body and exhibit physical and intellectual disability; usually results from trisomy of chromosome 21.

drupe (droop) A simple, fleshy fruit in which the inner wall of the fruit is a hard stone, e.g., peach, cherry.

duodenum (doo″-o-dee′-num) The portion of the small intestine into which the contents of the stomach first enter.

duplication An abnormality in which a set of chromosomes contains more than one copy of a particular chromosomal segment; the translocation form of Down syndrome is an example.

dura mater The tough, outer meningeal layer that covers and protects the brain and spinal cord. Also see *arachnoid* and *pia mater.*

dynamic equilibrium The condition of a chemical reaction when the rate of change in one direction is exactly the same as the rate of change in the opposite direction, i.e., the concentrations of the reactants and products are not changing, and the difference in free energy between reactants and products is zero.

dynein See *microtubule-associated proteins (MAPs).*

ecdysis Molting; shedding outer skin; common process in insects, crustaceans, and snakes.

ecdysone (ek′-dih-sone) See *molting hormone.*

Ecdysozoa A branch of the protostomes that includes animals that molt, such as the rotifers, nematodes, and arthropods.

echinoderms (eh-kine′-oh-derms) Phylum of spiny-skinned marine deuterostome invertebrates characterized by a water vascular system and tube feet; include sea stars, sea urchins, and sea cucumbers.

echolocation Determination of the position of objects by detecting echoes of high-pitched sounds emitted by an animal; a type of sensory system used by bats and dolphins.

ecological niche See *niche.*

ecological pyramid A graphical representation of the relative energy value at each trophic level. See *pyramid of biomass* and *pyramid of energy.*

ecological succession See *succession.*

ecology (ee-kol′-uh-jee) A discipline of biology that studies the interrelations among living things and their environments.

ecosystem (ee′-koh-sis-tem) The interacting system that encompasses a community and its nonliving, physical environment. Compare with *community.*

ecosystem diversity Variety of ecosystems found on Earth such as forests, prairies, deserts, lakes, coastal estuaries, and coral reefs.

ecosystem ecology A subfield of ecology that studies energy flow and the cycling of chemicals among the interacting biotic and abiotic parts of an ecosystem.

ecosystem management A conservation focus that emphasizes restoring and maintaining ecosystem quality rather than the conservation of individual species.

ecosystem services Important environmental services, such as clean air to breathe, clean water to drink, and fertile soil in which to grow crops, that ecosystems provide.

ecotone The transition zone where two communities meet and intergrade.

ectoderm (ek′-toh-derm) The outer germ layer of the early embryo; gives rise to the skin and nervous system. Compare with *mesoderm* and *endoderm.*

ectomycorrhizal fungi See *mycorrhizae.*

ectoparasite A tick or other parasite that lives outside its host's body. Compare with *endoparasite.*

ectotherm An animal whose temperature fluctuates with that of the environment; may use behavioral adaptations to regulate temperature; sometimes referred to as *cold-blooded.* Compare with *endotherm.*

edge effect The ecological phenomenon in which ecotones between adjacent communities often contain a greater number of species or greater population densities of certain species than either adjacent community.

Ediacaran period (ee-dee-ack′-uh-ran″) The last (most recent) period of the Proterozoic eon, from 635 million to 541 million years ago; named for early animal fossils found in the Ediacara Hills in South Australia.

effector (1) A muscle or gland that contracts or secretes in direct response to nerve impulses. (2) In homeostasis, an organ or process that helps restore a steady state.

efferent (ef′-fur-ent) Leading away from some point of reference. Compare with *afferent.*

efferent arteriole In the mammalian kidney, an arteriole that conducts blood away from a glomerulus. Compare with *afferent arteriole.*

efferent neurons Neurons that transmit action potentials from the brain or spinal cord to muscles or glands. Compare with *afferent neurons.*

ejaculation (ee-jak″-yoo-lay′-shun) A sudden expulsion, as in the ejection of semen from the penis.

ejaculatory duct A short duct that passes through the prostate gland and opens into the urethra; receives semen from the vas deferens.

electrical synapse A junction between two neurons in which an action potential in the presynaptic neuron spreads directly to the postsynaptic neuron by way of gap junctions. Compare with *chemical synapse.*

electrochemical gradient A difference in charge and chemical concentration existing between two regions.

electrolyte A substance that dissociates into ions when dissolved in water; the resulting solution can conduct an electric current.

electron A particle with one unit of negative charge and negligible mass, located outside the atomic nucleus. Compare with *neutron* and *proton*.

electron configuration The arrangement of electrons around the atom. In a Bohr model, the electron configuration is depicted as a series of concentric circles.

electronegativity A measure of an atom's attraction for electrons.

electron microscope A microscope capable of producing high-resolution, highly magnified images through the use of an electron beam (rather than light). Transmission electron microscopes (TEMs) produce images of thin sections; scanning electron microscopes (SEMs) produce images of surfaces.

electron shell Group of orbitals of electrons with similar energies.

electron transport system A series of redox reactions during which hydrogens or their electrons are passed along an electron transport chain from one acceptor molecule to another, with the release of energy.

electron transport chain See *electron transport system*.

electrophoresis, gel See *gel electrophoresis*.

electroreceptor A receptor that responds to electrical stimuli.

element A substance that cannot be changed to a simpler substance by a normal chemical reaction.

elimination Ejection of undigested food from the body. Compare with *excretion*.

elongation (in protein synthesis) Cyclic process by which amino acids are added one by one to a growing polypeptide chain. See *initiation* and *termination*.

El Niño–Southern Oscillation (ENSO) (el nee'-nyo) A recurring climatic phenomenon that involves a surge of warm water in the Pacific Ocean and unusual weather patterns elsewhere in the world.

embryo (em'-bree-oh) (1) A young organism before it emerges from the egg, seed, or body of its mother. (2) Developing human until the end of the second month, after which it is referred to as a fetus. (3) In plants, the young sporophyte produced following fertilization and subsequent development of the zygote.

embryonic stem cell (ES cell) A pluripotent stem cell derived from an early stage embryo.

embryo sac The female gametophyte generation in flowering plants.

embryo transfer See *host mothering*.

emergent properties Characteristics of an object, process, or behavior that could not be predicted from its component parts; emergent properties can be identified at each level as we move up the hierarchy of biological organization.

emerging diseases Diseases new to the human population; often appear suddenly. Compare with *re-emerging diseases*.

emigration The movement of individuals out of a population. Compare with *immigration*.

enantiomers (en-an'-tee-oh-merz) Two isomeric chemical compounds that are mirror images.

Encode Project (ENCyclopedia of DNA Elements) An international collaborative project to determine all the functional elements within the human genome. Initial results published in 2012 showed that at least 80% of non-protein-coding human DNA has biochemical functions.

3′ end End of a nucleic acid strand that has a 3′ carbon of deoxyribose (DNA) or ribose (RNA) attached to a hydroxyl group. Compare with *5′ end*.

5′ end End of a nucleic acid strand that has a 5′ carbon of deoxyribose (DNA) or ribose (RNA) attached to a phosphate group. Compare with *3′ end*.

endangered species A species whose numbers are so severely reduced that it is in imminent danger of extinction throughout all or part of its range. Compare with *threatened species*.

endemic species Localized, native species that are not found anywhere else in the world. Compare with *cosmopolitan species*.

endergonic reaction (end'-er-gon"-ik) A nonspontaneous reaction; a reaction requiring a net input of free energy. Compare with *exergonic reaction*.

endocrine gland (en'-doh-crin) A gland that secretes hormones directly into the blood or tissue fluid instead of into ducts. Compare with *exocrine gland*.

endocrine system The body system that helps regulate metabolic activities; consists of ductless glands and tissues that secrete hormones.

endocrinology Study of the endocrine system and endocrine activity, including the production and actions of chemical messengers produced by organs, tissues, and cells.

endocytosis (en"-doh-sy-toh'-sis) The active transport of substances into the cell by the formation of invaginated regions of the plasma membrane that pinch off and become cytoplasmic vesicles. Includes *phagocytosis, pinocytosis,* and *receptor-mediated endocytosis*. Compare with *exocytosis*.

endoderm (en'-doh-derm) The inner germ layer of the early embryo; becomes the lining of the digestive tract and the structures that develop from the digestive tract—liver, lungs, and pancreas. Compare with *ectoderm* and *mesoderm*.

endodermis (en"-doh-der'-mis) The innermost layer of the plant root cortex. Endodermal cells have a waterproof Casparian strip around their radial and transverse walls that ensures that water and minerals enter the xylem only by passing through the endoderm cells.

endolymph (en'-doh-limf) The fluid of the membranous labyrinth and cochlear duct of the ear.

endomembrane system The group of membranous structures in eukaryotic cells that interact through direct connections by vesicles; includes the endoplasmic reticulum, outer membrane of the nuclear envelope, Golgi complex, lysosomes, and the plasma membrane; also called *internal membrane system*.

endometrium (en"-doh-mee'-tree-um) The uterine lining.

endomycorrhizal fungi See *mycorrhizae*.

endoparasite A parasite such as a tapeworm that lives within the host. Compare with *ectoparasite*.

endoplasmic reticulum (ER) (en'-doh-plaz"-mik reh-tik'-yoo-lum) An interconnected network of internal membranes in eukaryotic cells enclosing a compartment, the ER lumen. Rough ER has ribosomes attached to the cytosolic surface; smooth ER, a site of lipid biosynthesis, lacks ribosomes.

endorphins (en-dor'-finz) Neuropeptides that block pain signals; released by certain neurons in the CNS.

endoskeleton (en"-doh-skel'-eh-ton) Bony and/or cartilaginous structures within the body that provide support. Compare with *exoskeleton*.

endosperm (en'-doh-sperm) The 3n nutritive tissue that is formed at some point in the development of all angiosperm seeds.

endospore A resting cell formed by certain bacteria; highly resistant to heat, radiation, and disinfectants.

endostyle A shared derived character of chordates; a groove in the floor of the pharynx that secretes mucus and traps food particles in sea water passing through the pharynx. In vertebrates, the thyroid gland is derived from the endostyle.

endosymbiont (en"-doe-sim'-bee-ont) An organism that lives inside the body or a cell of another kind of organism. Endosymbionts may benefit their host (mutualism) or harm their host (parasitism).

endosymbiosis Type of symbiosis in which one organism lives inside another. See *endosymbiont*.

endothelium (en-doh-theel'-ee-um) The tissue that lines the cavities of the heart, blood vessels, and lymph vessels.

endotherm (en'-doh-therm) An animal that uses metabolic energy to maintain a constant body temperature despite variations in environmental temperature; e.g., birds and mammals. Compare with *ectotherm*.

endotoxin A poisonous substance in the cell walls of gram-negative bacteria. Compare with *exotoxin*.

end product inhibition See *feedback inhibition*.

energy The capacity to do work; expressed in kilojoules or kilocalories.

energy flow Passage of energy in a one-way direction through an ecosystem.

energy of activation See *activation energy*.

enhanced greenhouse effect See *greenhouse effect*.

enhancers Regulatory DNA sequences that enhance gene transcription; can be located long distances away from the actual coding regions of a gene.

enkephalins (en-kef'-ah-linz) Neuropeptides that block pain signals; released by certain neurons in the CNS.

enterocoely (en'-ter-oh-seely) The process by which the coelom forms as a cavity within mesoderm produced by outpocketings of the primitive gut (archenteron); characteristic of many deuterostomes. Compare with *schizocoely*.

enthalpy The total potential energy of a system; sometimes referred to as the "heat content of the system."

entropy (en'-trop-ee) Disorderliness; a quantitative measure of the amount of the random, disordered energy that is unavailable to do work.

environmental resistance Unfavorable environmental conditions, such as crowding, that prevent organisms from reproducing indefinitely at their intrinsic rate of increase.

environmental sustainability The ability to meet humanity's current needs without compromising the ability of future generations to meet their needs.

enzyme (en'-zime) An organic catalyst (usually a protein) that accelerates a specific chemical reaction by lowering the activation energy required for that reaction.

enzyme-linked receptors Transmembrane proteins with a hormone-binding site outside the cell and an enzyme site inside the cell.

enzyme–substrate complex The temporary association between enzyme and substrate that forms during the course of a catalyzed reaction; also called *ES complex*.

eon The largest division of the geologic time scale; eons are divided into eras.

eosinophil (ee-oh-sin'-oh-fil) A type of white blood cell whose cytoplasmic granules absorb acidic stains; functions in parasitic infestations and allergic reactions.

ependymal cells Ciliated cells that line internal cavities of CNS; help produce and circulate cerebrospinal fluid.

epidermis (ep-ih-dur'-mis) (1) An outer layer of cells that covers the body of plants and functions primarily for protection. (2) The outer layer of vertebrate skin.

epididymis (ep-ih-did'-ih-mis) (pl., *epididymides*) A coiled tube that receives sperm from the testis and conveys it to the vas deferens.

epigenetic inheritance Inheritance that involves changes in how a gene is expressed without any change in that gene's nucleotide sequence.

epiglottis A thin, flexible structure that guards the entrance to the larynx, preventing food from entering the airway during swallowing.

epinephrine (ep-ih-nef'-rin) Hormone produced by the adrenal medulla; stimulates the sympathetic nervous system.

epiphyte Plant that grows attached to another plant.

epistasis (ep-ih-sta'-sis) Condition in which certain alleles of one locus alter the expression of alleles of a different locus.

epithelial tissue (ep-ih-theel'-ee-al) The type of animal tissue that covers body surfaces, lines body cavities, and forms glands; also called *epithelium*.

epoch The smallest unit of geologic time; a subdivision of a period.

equilibrium See *dynamic equilibrium, genetic equilibrium*, and *punctuated equilibrium*.

equilibrium potential The membrane potential at which the flow of a particular type of ion inward (due to the electrical gradient) equals the flow of that ion outward (because of the concentration gradient).

era An interval of geologic time that is a subdivision of an eon; eras are divided into periods.

erythroblastosis fetalis (eh-rith"-row-blas-toe'-sis fi-tal'-is) Serious condition in which Rh+ red blood cells (which bear antigen D) of a fetus are destroyed by maternal anti-D antibodies.

erythrocyte (eh-rith'-row-site) A vertebrate red blood cell; contains hemoglobin, which transports oxygen. Compare with *leukocyte*.

erythropoietin (eh-rith"-row-poy'-ih-tin) A peptide hormone secreted mainly by kidney cells; stimulates red blood cell production.

ES complex See *enzyme–substrate complex*.

esophagus (e-sof'-ah-gus) The part of the digestive tract that conducts food from the pharynx to the stomach.

essential amino acid An amino acid that must be provided in the diet because the body cannot make it or cannot make it in sufficient quantities to meet nutritional needs.

essential nutrient A nutrient that must be provided in the diet because the body cannot make it or cannot make it in sufficient quantities to meet nutritional needs, e.g., essential amino acids and essential fatty acids.

ester linkage Covalent linkage formed by the reaction of a carboxyl group and a hydroxyl group, with the removal of the equivalent of a water molecule; the linkage includes an oxygen atom bonded to a carbonyl group.

estivation A state of torpor caused by lack of food or water during periods of high temperature. Compare with *hibernation*.

estrogens (es'-troh-jenz) Female sex hormones produced by the ovary; promote the development and maintenance of female reproductive structures and of secondary sex characteristics.

estuary (es'-choo-wear-ee) A coastal body of water that connects to an ocean, in which fresh water from the land mixes with salt water.

ethology (ee-thol'-oh-jee) The study of animal behavior under natural conditions from the point of view of adaptation.

ethyl alcohol A two-carbon alcohol.

ethylene (eth'-ih-leen) A gaseous plant hormone involved in various aspects of plant growth and development, such as leaf abscission and fruit ripening.

euchromatin (yoo-croh'-mah-tin) A loosely coiled chromatin that is generally capable of transcription. Compare with *heterochromatin*.

eudicot (yoo-dy'-kot) One of the two clades of flowering plants; eudicot seeds contain two cotyledons, or seed leaves. Compare with *monocot*.

euglenoids (yoo-glee'-noidz) A group of mostly freshwater unicellular excavates that move by means of an anterior flagellum and are usually photosynthetic.

Eukarya (yoo"-kar'-ee-ah) The domain that includes all eukaryotes: protists, fungi, plants, and animals.

eukaryote (yoo"-kar'-ee-ote) An organism whose cells have nuclei and other membrane-enclosed organelles. Compare with *prokaryote*.

eukaryotic cell See *eukaryote*.

Eumetazoa (yu"-met-uh-zo'-ah) A clade of animals with true tissues; almost all animals except sponges are eumetazoans.

euphotic zone The upper reaches of the ocean, in which enough light penetrates to support photosynthesis.

eustachian tube (yoo-stay'-shee-un) The auditory tube passing between the middle-ear cavity and the pharynx in vertebrates; permits the equalization of pressure on the tympanic membrane.

eutherians A clade of mammals characterized by a well-developed placenta; the young are more developed at birth than are marsupials.

eutrophic lake A lake enriched with nutrients such as nitrate and phosphate and consequently overgrown with plants or algae.

evergreen A plant that sheds leaves over a long period, so some leaves are always present. Compare with *deciduous*.

Evo Devo The study of the evolution of the genetic control of development.

evolution Any cumulative genetic changes in a population from generation to generation. Evolution leads to differences in populations and explains the origin of all the organisms that exist today or have ever existed.

evolutionary species concept See *phylogenetic species concept*.

evolutionary systematics An approach to classification that considers both evolutionary relationships and the extent of divergence that has occurred since a group branched from an ancestral group. Compare with *cladistics* and *phenetics*.

excavates Flagellated unicellular protists, many of which have a deep (excavated) oral groove; include diplomonds, parabasilids, and euglenoids.

excitatory postsynaptic potential (EPSP) A change in membrane potential that brings a neuron closer to the firing level. Compare with *inhibitory postsynaptic potential (IPSP)*.

excretion (ek-skree′-shun) The discharge from the body of a waste product of metabolism (not to be confused with the elimination of undigested food materials). Compare with *elimination*.

excretory system The body system in animals that functions in osmoregulation and in the discharge of metabolic wastes.

exergonic reaction (ex′-er-gon″-ik) A reaction characterized by a release of free energy. Also called *spontaneous reaction*. Compare with *endergonic reaction*.

exocrine gland (ex′-oh-crin) A gland that excretes its products through a duct that opens onto a free surface, such as the skin (e.g., sweat glands). Compare with *endocrine gland*.

exocytosis (ex″-oh-sy-toh″-sis) The active transport of materials out of the cell by fusion of cytoplasmic vesicles with the plasma membrane. Compare with *endocytosis*.

exon (1) A protein-coding region of a eukaryotic gene. (2) The mRNA transcribed from such a region. Compare with *intron*.

exoskeleton (ex″-oh-skel′-eh-ton) An external skeleton, such as the shell of mollusks or outer covering of arthropods; provides protection and sites of attachment for muscles. Compare with *endoskeleton*.

exotoxin A poisonous substance released by certain bacteria. Compare with *endotoxin*.

experimental group In a scientific experiment, a group in which the experimental variable is manipulated. Compare with *control group*.

exploitation competition Intraspecific competition in which all the individuals in a population "share" the limited resource equally so that at high population densities none of them obtains an adequate amount. Also called *scramble competition*. Compare with *interference competition*.

exponential population growth The accelerating population growth that occurs when optimal conditions allow a constant per capita growth rate. Compare with *logistic population growth*.

ex situ conservation Conservation efforts that involve conserving individual species in human-controlled settings, such as zoos. Compare with *in situ conservation*.

external fertilization The process in which gametes meet outside the body, typically when females release eggs and males release sperm into the surrounding water; occurs in most aquatic invertebrates, bony fishes, and amphibians. Compare with *internal fertilization*.

exteroceptor (ex′-tur-oh-sep″-tor) One of the sense organs that receives sensory stimuli from the outside world, such as the eyes or touch receptors. Compare with *interoceptor*.

extinction The elimination of a species; occurs when the last individual member of a species dies; see *background extinction* and *mass extinction*.

extracellular matrix (ECM) A network of proteins and carbohydrates that surrounds many animal cells.

extraembryonic membranes Multicellular membranous structures that develop from the germ layers of a terrestrial vertebrate embryo but are not part of the embryo itself. See *chorion, amnion, allantois,* and *yolk sac*.

extreme halophiles Certain types of archaea, and few types of bacteria and protists, that inhabit environments with very high salt concentrations.

extreme thermophiles Certain types of archaea that require a very high temperature or very low temperature for growth.

F_1 generation (first filial generation) The first generation of hybrid offspring resulting from a cross between parents from two different true-breeding lines.

F_2 generation (second filial generation) The offspring of the F_1 generation.

facilitated diffusion The passive transport of ions or molecules by a specific carrier protein in a membrane. As in simple diffusion, net transport is down a concentration gradient, and no additional energy has to be supplied. Compare with *diffusion* and *active transport*.

facilitation In ecology, a situation in which one species has a positive effect on other species in the community, for example, by enhancing the local environment.

facultative anaerobe An organism capable of carrying out aerobic cellular respiration but able to switch to fermentation when oxygen is unavailable, e.g., yeast. Compare with *obligate anaerobe*.

FAD/FADH$_2$ Oxidized and reduced forms, respectively, of flavin adenine dinucleotide, a coenzyme that transfers electrons (as hydrogen) in metabolism, including cellular respiration.

fallopian tube See *oviduct*.

fall turnover Mixing of temperate lake waters in autumn, caused by falling temperatures, in which surface water sinks to the bottom and bottom water rises to the surface. Compare with *spring turnover*.

family A taxonomic category made up of related genera.

fast-glycolytic fibers White muscle fibers that generate a lot of power for a brief period; they contract rapidly, fatigue quickly, and obtain most of their ATP from glycolysis. Compare with *fast-oxidative fibers* and *slow-oxidative fibers*.

fast-oxidative fibers Muscle fibers specialized for rapid response; they contract quickly, have an intermediate rate of fatigue, and obtain most of their ATP from aerobic respiration. Compare with *slow-oxidative fibers* and *fast-glycolytic fibers*.

fatty acid A lipid that is an organic acid containing a long hydrocarbon chain, with no double bonds (saturated fatty acid), one double bond (monounsaturated fatty acid), or two or more double bonds (polyunsaturated fatty acid); components of triacylglycerols and phospholipids, as well as monoacylglycerols and diacylglycerols.

fatty acid derivatives Prostaglandins, juvenile hormones of insects, and other compounds derived from fatty acids.

fecundity The potential capacity of an individual to produce offspring.

feedback inhibition A type of enzyme regulation in which the accumulation of the product of a reaction inhibits an earlier reaction in the sequence; also known as *end product inhibition*.

fermentation An anaerobic process by which ATP is produced by a series of redox reactions in which organic compounds serve both as electron donors and terminal electron acceptors.

fern One of a phylum of seedless vascular plants that reproduce by spores produced in sporangia; ferns undergo an alternation of generations between the dominant sporophyte and the gametophyte (prothallus).

fertilization The fusion of two *n* gametes; results in the formation of a 2*n* zygote. Compare with *double fertilization*.

fetus The unborn human offspring from the third month of pregnancy to birth.

fiber (1) In plants, a type of sclerenchyma cell; fibers are long, tapered cells with thick walls. Compare with *sclereid*. (2) In animals, an elongated cell such as a muscle or nerve cell. (3) In animals, the microscopic, threadlike protein and carbohydrate complexes scattered through the matrix of connective tissues.

fibrin An insoluble protein formed from the plasma protein fibrinogen during blood clotting.

fibroblasts Connective tissue cells that produce the fibers and the protein and carbohydrate complexes of the matrix of connective tissues.

fibronectins Glycoproteins of the extracellular matrix that bind to integrins (receptor proteins in the plasma membrane).

fibrous root system A root system consisting of several adventitious roots of approximately equal size that arise from the base of the stem. Compare with *taproot system*.

Fick's law of diffusion A physical law governing rates of gas exchange in animal respiratory systems; states that the rate of diffusion of a substance across a membrane is directly proportional to the surface area and to the difference in pressure between the two sides.

fibrinogen A soluble plasma protein that is converted to the insoluble protein fibrin during blood clotting.

filament (1) In flowering plants, the thin stalk of a stamen; the filament bears an anther at its tip. (2) In muscles, a myofilament; when myofilaments slide past one another, muscle contraction occurs.

fimbriae Hairlike structures that project from the cell surface of some prokaryotes; help bacteria to adhere to one another and to attach to the surfaces of cells they infect.

first law of thermodynamics The law of conservation of energy, which states that the total energy of any closed system (any object plus its surroundings, i.e., the universe) remains constant. Compare with *second law of thermodynamics*.

first messenger A signaling molecule that binds to a receptor on the cell surface, initiating a signal transduction process that leads to the formation of an intracellular *second messenger*.

fissure A groove or furrow, for example the grooves between the convolutions of the cerebral cortex.

fitness See *direct fitness*.

fixed action pattern (FAP) An innate behavior triggered by a sign stimulus.

flagellate A unicellular nonphotosynthetic protist that has one or more long, whiplike flagella.

flagellum (flah-jel′-um) (pl., *flagella*) A long, whiplike structure extending from certain cells and used in locomotion. (1) Eukaryote flagella consist of two central, single microtubules surrounded by nine double microtubules (9 + 2 structure), all covered by a plasma membrane. (2) Prokaryote flagella are filaments rotated by special structures located in the plasma membrane and cell wall.

flame cells Collecting cells that have cilia; part of the osmoregulatory system of flatworms.

flavin adenine dinucleotide See *FAD/FADH₂*.

flowering plants See *angiosperms*.

flowing-water ecosystem A river or stream ecosystem.

fluid mosaic model The currently accepted model of the plasma membrane and other cell membranes, in which protein molecules "float" in a fluid phospholipid bilayer.

fluorescence The emission of light of a longer wavelength (lower energy) than the light originally absorbed.

fluorescent in situ hybridization (FISH) A technique to detect specific DNA segments by hybridization directly to chromosomes; visualized microscopically by using a fluorescent dye.

follicle (fol′-i-kl) (1) A simple, dry, dehiscent fruit that develops from a single carpel and splits open at maturity along one suture to liberate the seeds. (2) A small sac of cells in the mammalian ovary that contains a maturing egg. (3) The pocket in the skin from which a hair grows.

follicle-stimulating hormone (FSH) A gonadotropic hormone secreted by the anterior lobe of the pituitary gland; stimulates follicle development in the ovaries of females and sperm production in the testes of males.

food chain The series of organisms through which energy flows in an ecosystem. Each organism in the series eats or decomposes the preceding organism in the chain. See *food web*.

food web A complex interconnection of all the food chains in an ecosystem.

foraging Feeding behavior; involves locating and selecting food, as well as capturing and gathering it.

foram See *formaminiferan*.

foramen magnum The opening in the vertebrate skull through which the spinal cord passes.

foraminiferan (for″-am-in-if′-er-an) A marine protist that produces a shell, or test, that encloses an amoeboid body. Also called *foram*. See *rhizarians*.

forebrain In the early embryo, one of the three divisions of the developing vertebrate brain; subdivides to form the telencephalon, which gives rise to the cerebrum, and the diencephalon, which gives rise to the thalamus and hypothalamus. Compare with *midbrain* and *hindbrain*.

forest decline A gradual deterioration (and often death) of many trees in a forest; can be caused by a combination of factors, such as acid precipitation, toxic heavy metals, and surface-level ozone.

fossil Parts or traces of an ancient organism usually preserved in rock.

fossil fuel Combustible deposits in Earth's crust that are composed of the remnants of prehistoric organisms that existed millions of years ago, e.g., oil, natural gas, and coal.

founder cell A cell from which a particular cell lineage is derived.

founder effect Genetic drift that results from a small population colonizing a new area.

fovea (foe′-vee-ah) The area of sharpest vision in the retina; cone cells are concentrated here.

fragile site A weak point at a specific location on a chromosome where part of a chromatid appears attached to the rest of the chromosome by a thin thread of DNA.

fragile X syndrome A human genetic disorder caused by a fragile site that occurs near the tip on the X chromosome; effects range from mild learning disabilities to severe intellectual disability and hyperactivity.

fragmentation A method of asexual reproduction in some bacteria, archaea, animals, or plants; a cell or an organism separates into several pieces and each piece develops into a new organism.

frameshift mutation A mutation that results when one or two nucleotide pairs are inserted into or deleted from the DNA. The change causes the mRNA transcribed from the mutated DNA to have an altered reading frame such that all codons downstream from the mutation are changed.

fraternal twins See *dizygotic twins*.

free energy The maximum amount of energy available to do work under the conditions of a biochemical reaction.

free radicals Toxic, highly reactive compounds with unpaired electrons that bond with other compounds in the cell and interfere with normal function.

frequency-dependent selection Selection in which the relative fitness of different genotypes is related to how frequently they occur in the population.

freshwater wetlands Land that is transitional between freshwater and terrestrial ecosystems and is covered with water for at least part of the year, e.g., marshes and swamps.

frontal lobes Include the region of the cerebral cortex anterior to the central sulcus; contain important association and motor areas.

fruit In flowering plants, a mature, ripened ovary. Fruits contain seeds and usually provide seed protection and dispersal.

fruiting body A multicellular structure that contains the sexual spores of certain fungi; refers to the ascocarp of an ascomycete and the basidiocarp of a basidiomycete.

fucoxanthin (few″-koh-zan′-thin) The brown carotenoid pigment found in brown algae, golden algae, diatoms, and dinoflagellates.

functional genomics The study of the roles of genes in cells.

functional group A group of atoms that confers distinctive properties on an organic molecule (or region of a molecule) to which it is attached, e.g., hydroxyl, carbonyl, carboxyl, amino, phosphate, and sulfhydryl groups.

fundamental niche The potential ecological niche that an organism could occupy if there were no competition from other species. Compare with *realized niche*.

fungus (pl., *fungi*) A heterotrophic eukaryote belonging to the opisthokont clade, with chitinous cell walls and a body usually in the form of a mycelium of branched, threadlike hyphae. Most fungi are decomposers; some are parasitic.

G protein One of a group of proteins that bind GTP and are involved in the transfer of signals across the plasma membrane.

G protein–linked receptors Cell surface receptors that activate a G protein in response to binding by a signaling molecule.

G₁ phase The first gap phase within the interphase stage of the cell cycle; G_1 occurs before DNA synthesis (S phase) begins. Compare with *S phase* and *G_2 phase*.

G₂ phase Second gap phase within the interphase stage of the cell cycle; G_2 occurs after DNA synthesis (S phase) and before mitosis. Compare with *S phase* and *G_1 phase*.

gallbladder A small sac that stores bile.

gametangium (gam″-uh-tan′-gee-um) Special multicellular or unicellular structure of plants, protists, and fungi in which gametes are formed.

gamete (gam′-eet) A sex cell; in plants and animals, an egg or sperm. In sexual reproduction, the union of gametes results in the formation of a zygote. The chromosome number of a gamete is designated *n*.

gametic isolation (gam-ee′-tik) A prezygotic reproductive isolating mechanism in which sexual reproduction between two closely related species cannot occur because of chemical differences in the gametes.

gametogenesis The process of gamete formation. See *spermatogenesis* and *oogenesis*.

gametophyte generation (gam-ee′-toh-fite) The *n*, gamete-producing stage in the life cycle of a plant. Compare with *sporophyte generation*.

gamma-aminobutyric acid (GABA) A neurotransmitter that has an inhibitory effect.

ganglion (gang'-glee-on) (pl., *ganglia*) A mass of neuron cell bodies; in vertebrates, refers to aggregations of cell bodies in the peripheral nervous system. Compare with *nucleus* (definition 3).

ganglion cell A type of neuron in the retina of the eye; receives input from bipolar cells.

gap junction Structure consisting of specialized regions of the plasma membrane of two adjacent cells; contains numerous pores that allow the passage of certain small molecules and ions between them.

gastric glands Glands in the wall of the stomach; contain cells that secrete hydrochloric acid, intrinsic factor, and pepsinogen, the precursor of the enzyme pepsin.

gastrin (gas'-trin) A hormone released by the stomach mucosa; stimulates the gastric glands to secrete pepsinogen.

gastrovascular cavity A central digestive cavity with a single opening that functions as both mouth and anus; characteristic of cnidarians and flatworms.

gastrula (gas'-troo-lah) A three-layered embryo formed by the process of gastrulation.

gastrulation (gas-troo-lay'-shun) Process in embryonic development during which the three germ layers (ectoderm, mesoderm, and endoderm) form.

gel electrophoresis Procedure by which proteins or nucleic acids are separated on the basis of size and charge as they migrate through a gel in an electric field.

gemmae (sing., *gemma*) Tiny balls of tissue (borne in *gemmae cups*) used for asexual reproduction by liverworts.

gene A segment of DNA that serves as a unit of hereditary information; includes a transcribable DNA sequence (plus associated sequences regulating its transcription) that yields a protein or RNA product with a specific function.

gene amplification The developmental process in which certain cells produce multiple copies of a gene by selective replication, thus allowing for increased synthesis of the gene product. Compare with *nuclear equivalence* and *genomic rearrangement*.

gene flow The movement of alleles between local populations due to the migration of individuals; can have significant evolutionary consequences.

gene locus See *locus*.

gene pool All the alleles of all the genes present in a freely interbreeding population.

gene therapy Any of a variety of methods designed to correct a disease or alleviate its symptoms through the introduction of normal, therapeutic genes into the affected person's cells.

genetic bottleneck See *bottleneck*.

genetic code See *codon*.

genetic counseling Medical and genetic information provided to couples who are concerned about the risk of abnormality in their children.

genetic diversity Genetic variety within a species both among individuals within a given population and among geographically separate populations.

genetic drift A random change in allele frequency in a small breeding population.

genetic engineering Manipulation of genes, often through recombinant DNA technology. Also called *molecular modification*.

genetic equilibrium The condition of a population that is not undergoing evolutionary change, i.e., in which allele and genotype frequencies do not change from one generation to the next. See *Hardy–Weinberg principle*.

genetic polymorphism (pol"-ee-mor'-fizm) The presence in a population of two or more alleles for a given gene locus.

genetic recombination See *recombination, genetic*.

genetics The science of heredity; includes genetic similarities and genetic variation between parents and offspring or among individuals of a population.

genetic screening A systematic search through a population for individuals with a genotype or karyotype that might cause a serious genetic disease in them or their offspring.

genetic variation Inherited differences among individuals.

genome (jee'-nome) Originally, all the genetic material in a cell or individual organism. The term is used in more than one way depending on context, e.g., an organism's haploid genome is all the DNA contained in one haploid set of its chromosomes, and its mitochondrial genome is all the DNA in a mitochondrion. See *human genome*.

genome-wide association study (GWAS) A comparison of differences in the entire genomes of a population of individuals, e.g., single nucleotide polymorphisms (SNPs), DNA insertions, deletions, or copy number variations.

genomic DNA library A collection of recombinant plasmids in which all the DNA in the genome is represented. Compare with *cDNA library*.

genomic imprinting See *imprinting* (definition 1).

genomic rearrangement A physical change in the structure of one or more genes that occurs during the development of an organism and leads to an alteration in gene expression; compare with *nuclear equivalence* and *gene amplification*.

genomics The emerging field of biology that studies the entire DNA sequence of an organism's genome to identify all the genes, determine their RNA or protein products, and ascertain how the genes are regulated.

genotype (jeen'-oh-type) The genetic makeup of, or combination of alleles in, an individual. Compare with *phenotype*.

genotype frequency The proportion of a particular genotype in the population. Compare with *allele frequency* and *phenotype frequency*.

genus (jee'-nus) A taxonomic category made up of related species.

geographic variation Genetic differences that may exist among different populations within the same species. See *cline* for an example of one type of geographic variation.

geometric isomer One of two or more chemical compounds having the same arrangement of covalent bonds but differing in the spatial arrangement of their atoms or groups of atoms.

germination Resumption of growth of an embryo or spore; occurs when a seed or spore sprouts.

germ layers In animals, three embryonic tissue layers: endoderm, mesoderm, and ectoderm.

germ line cell In animals, a cell that is part of the line of cells that will ultimately undergo meiosis to form gametes. Compare with *somatic cell*.

germplasm Any plant or animal material that may be used in breeding; includes seeds, plants, and plant tissues of traditional crop varieties and the sperm and eggs of traditional livestock breeds.

gibberellin (jib"-ur-el'-lin) A plant hormone involved in many aspects of plant growth and development, such as stem elongation, flowering, and seed germination.

gigantism Abnormally tall growth caused when anterior pituitary secretes excessive amounts of human growth hormone during childhood.

gills (1) Moist, thin structures that extend outward from the body surface onto a respiratory medium (water or air); surfaces for gas exchange, mainly in aquatic animals. (2) The spore-bearing, platelike structures under the caps of mushrooms.

ginkgo (ging'-ko) A member of an ancient gymnosperm group that consists of a single living representative (*Ginkgo biloba*), a hardy, deciduous tree with broad, fan-shaped leaves and naked, fleshy seeds (on female trees).

gland See *endocrine gland* and *exocrine gland*.

glial cells (glee'-ul) In nervous tissue, cells that support and nourish neurons; they also communicate with neurons and have several other functions; also see *astrocyte*, *oligodendrocyte*, *ependymal cells*, and *microglia*.

globulin (glob'-yoo-lin) One of a class of proteins in blood plasma, some of which (gamma globulins) function as antibodies.

glomeromycetes A group of endomycorrhizal fungi that form arbuscular mycorrhizae with the roots of many plants; belong to phylum Glomeromycota.

glomerular filtration The process by which plasma is forced out of the capillaries and into Bowman's capsule as blood flows through the glomerular capillaries at high pressure; it is the first step in the production of urine.

glomerulus (glom-air'-yoo-lus) The cluster of capillaries at the proximal end of a nephron; the glomerulus is surrounded by Bowman's capsule.

glucagon (gloo'-kah-gahn) A hormone secreted by the pancreas that stimulates glycogen breakdown, thereby increasing the concentration of glucose in the blood. Compare with *insulin*.

glucocorticoids Steroid hormones, particularly *cortisol*, produced by the adrenal cortex that are involved in carbohydrate, protein, and fat metabolism. Glucocorticoids have anti-inflammatory properties.

glucose A hexose aldehyde sugar that is central to many metabolic processes.

glutamate An amino acid that functions as the major excitatory neurotransmitter in the vertebrate brain.

glyceraldehyde-3-phosphate (G3P) Phosphorylated three-carbon compound that is an important intermediate in glycolysis and in the Calvin cycle.

glycerol A three-carbon alcohol with a hydroxyl group on each carbon; a component of triacylglycerols and phospholipids, as well as monoacylglycerols and diacylglycerols.

glycine An amino acid that is the main inhibitory neurotransmitter in the spinal cord.

glycocalyx (gly″-koh-kay′-lix) A coating on the outside of an animal cell, formed by the polysaccharide portions of glycoproteins and glycolipids associated with the plasma membrane.

glycogen (gly′-koh-jen) The principal storage polysaccharide in animal cells; formed from glucose and stored primarily in the liver and, to a lesser extent, in muscle cells.

glycolipid A lipid with covalently attached carbohydrates.

glycolysis (gly-kol′-ih-sis) The first stage of cellular respiration as well as fermentation; literally the "splitting of sugar." The metabolic conversion of glucose into pyruvate, accompanied by the production of ATP.

glycoprotein (gly′-koh-pro-teen) A protein with covalently attached carbohydrates.

glycosidic linkage Covalent linkage joining two sugars; includes an oxygen atom bonded to a carbon of each sugar.

glyoxysomes (gly-ox′-ih-sohmz) Membrane-enclosed structures in cells of certain plant seeds; contain a large array of enzymes that convert stored fat to sugar.

gnathostomes (nath′-o-stomes) Vertebrates with jaws.

gnetophyte (nee′-toe-fite) One of a small phylum of unusual gymnosperms that have some features similar to those of flowering plants.

goblet cells Unicellular glands that secrete mucus.

goiter (goy′-ter) An enlargement of the thyroid gland.

golden alga A member of a group of algae, most of which are biflagellate, are unicellular, and contain pigments, including chlorophylls *a* and *c*, and carotenoids, including fucoxanthin.

Golgi complex (goal′-jee) Organelle composed of stacks of flattened, membranous sacs. Mainly responsible for modifying, packaging, and sorting proteins that will be secreted or targeted to other organelles of the internal membrane system or to the plasma membrane; also called *Golgi body* or *Golgi apparatus*.

Golgi tendon organ (goal′-jee) A proprioceptor that responds to tension in contracting muscles and in the tendons that attach muscle to bone.

gonad (goh′-nad) A gamete-producing gland; an ovary or a testis.

gonadotropic hormones (go-nad-oh-troh′-pic) Hormones produced by the anterior pituitary gland that stimulate the testes and ovaries; include follicle-stimulating hormone (FSH) and luteinizing hormone (LH).

gonadotropin-releasing hormone (GnRH) A hormone secreted by the hypothalamus that stimulates the anterior pituitary to secrete the gonadotropic hormones: follicle-stimulating hormone (FSH) and luteinizing hormone (LH).

graded potential A local change in electrical potential that varies in magnitude depending on the strength of the applied stimulus.

gradualism See *phyletic gradualism*.

graft rejection An immune response directed against a transplanted tissue or organ.

grain A simple, dry, one-seeded fruit in which the fruit wall is fused to the seed coat, e.g., corn and wheat kernels. Also called *caryopsis*.

gram-negative bacteria Bacteria with cell walls consisting of a thin peptidoglycan layer and a thick outer membrane. Compare with *gram-positive bacteria*.

gram-positive bacteria Bacteria with cell walls that are very thick and consist mainly of peptidoglycan. Compare with *gram-negative bacteria*.

granulosa cells In mammals, cells that surround the developing oocyte and are part of the follicle; produce estrogens and inhibin.

granum (pl., *grana*) A stack of thylakoids within a chloroplast.

Graves' disease Common form of hyperthyroidism, an autoimmune disease, characterized by extreme weight loss and emotional irritability.

gravitropism (grav″-ih-troh′-pizm) Growth of a plant in response to gravity.

gray crescent The grayish area of cytoplasm that marks the region where gastrulation begins in an amphibian embryo.

gray matter Nervous tissue in the brain and spinal cord that contains cell bodies, dendrites, and unmyelinated axons. Compare with *white matter*.

green alga A member of a diverse group of archaeplastid algae that contain the same pigments as plants (chlorophylls *a* and *b* and carotenoids).

greenhouse effect The natural global warming of Earth's atmosphere caused by the presence of carbon dioxide and other gases that trap the sun's radiation. The additional warming produced when increased levels of greenhouse gases absorb infrared radiation is known as the *enhanced greenhouse effect*.

greenhouse gases Trace gases in the atmosphere that allow the sun's energy to penetrate to Earth's surface but do not allow as much of it to escape as heat.

gross primary productivity (GPP) The rate at which energy accumulates (is assimilated) in an ecosystem during photosynthesis. Compare with *net primary productivity (NPP)*.

ground state The lowest energy state of an atom.

ground tissue system All tissues in the plant body other than the dermal tissue system and vascular tissue system; consists of parenchyma, collenchyma, and sclerenchyma.

groundwater Water stored underground in soil and crevasses, or an aquifer.

growth factors A group of more than 50 extracellular peptides that signal certain cells to grow and divide.

growth hormone (GH) A hormone secreted by the anterior lobe of the pituitary gland; stimulates growth of body tissues; also called *somatotropin*.

growth hormone–inhibiting hormone (GHIH) Hormone secreted by hypothalamus that inhibits growth hormone (GH) secretion.

growth hormone–releasing hormone (GHRH) Hormone secreted by hypothalamus that permits growth hormone (GH) secretion.

growth rate (*r*) The rate of change of a population's size on a per capita basis.

guanine (gwan′-een) A nitrogenous purine base that is a component of nucleic acids and GTP.

guanosine diphosphate (GDP) See *guanosine triphosphate*.

guanosine triphosphate (GTP) An energy transfer molecule similar to ATP that releases free energy with the hydrolysis of its terminal phosphate group, yielding guanosine diphosphate (GDP).

guard cell One of a pair of epidermal cells that adjust their shape to form a stomatal pore for gas exchange.

guttation (gut-tay′-shun) The appearance of water droplets on leaves, forced out through leaf pores by root pressure.

gymnosperm (jim′-noh-sperm) Any of a group of seed plants in which the seeds are not enclosed in an ovary; gymnosperms frequently bear their seeds in cones. Includes four phyla: conifers, cycads, ginkgoes, and gnetophytes.

habitat The natural environment or place where an organism, population, or species lives.

habitat corridors Strips of land connecting isolated habitat patches that allow wildlife to pass through freely.

habitat fragmentation The division of habitats that formerly occupied large, unbroken areas into smaller pieces by roads, fields, cities, and other human land-transforming activities.

habitat isolation A prezygotic reproductive isolating mechanism in which reproduction between similar species is prevented because they live and breed in different habitats.

habituation (hab-it″-yoo-ay′-shun) A type of learning in which an animal becomes accustomed to a repeated, irrelevant stimulus and no longer responds to it.

hadal zone Part of benthic environment of ocean deeper than 6000 m.

hagfishes Jawless marine fishes with a notochord for axial support; lack vertebrae and paired appendages.

hair cells Vertebrate mechanoreceptors that detect movement.

half-life The period of time required for a radio-isotope to change into a different material.

haploid (hap′-loyd) The condition of having one set of chromosomes per nucleus. Compare with *diploid* and *polyploid*.

"hard-wiring" Refers to how neurons signal one another, how they connect, and how they carry out basic functions such as regulating heart rate, blood pressure, and sleep–wake cycles.

Hardy–Weinberg principle The mathematical prediction that allele frequencies do not change from generation to generation in a large population in the absence of microevolutionary processes (mutation, genetic drift, gene flow, natural selection).

haustorium (hah-stor′-ee-um) (pl., *haustoria*) In parasitic fungi, a specialized hypha that penetrates a host cell and obtains nourishment from the cytoplasm.

Haversian canals (ha-vur′-zee-un) Channels extending through the matrix of bone; contain blood vessels and nerves.

heat The total amount of kinetic energy in a sample of a substance.

heat energy The thermal energy that flows from an object with a higher temperature to an object with a lower temperature.

heat of vaporization The amount of heat energy that must be supplied to change one gram of a substance from the liquid phase to the vapor phase.

helicases Enzymes that unwind the two strands of a DNA double helix.

helper T cell See *T helper cell*.

hemichordates A phylum of sedentary, wormlike deuterostomes.

hemizygous (hem″-ih-zy′-gus) Possessing only one allele for a particular locus; a human male is hemizygous for all X-linked genes. Compare with *homozygous* and *heterozygous*.

hemocoel Blood cavity characteristic of animals with an open circulatory system.

hemocyanin A hemolymph pigment that transports oxygen in some mollusks and arthropods.

hemoglobin (hee′-moh-gloh″-bin) The red, iron-containing protein pigment in blood that transports oxygen and carbon dioxide and aids in regulation of pH.

hemolymph (hee′-moh-limf) The fluid that bathes the tissues in animals with an open circulatory system, e.g., arthropods and most mollusks.

hemophilia (hee″-moh-feel′-ee-ah) A hereditary disease in which blood does not clot properly; the forms known as *hemophilia A* (deficient for clotting factor VIII) and *hemophilia B* (deficient for clotting factor IX) exhibit an X-linked, recessive inheritance pattern.

Hensen's node See *primitive streak*.

hepatic (heh-pat′-ik) Pertaining to the liver.

hepatic portal system The portion of the circulatory system that carries blood from the intestine through the liver.

herbivore (erb′-uh-vore) An animal that feeds on plants or algae. Also called *primary consumer*.

heredity The transmission of genetic information from parent to offspring.

hermaphrodite (her-maf′-roh-dite) An organism that has both male and female sex organs; hermaphroditism is the form of sexual reproduction in which a single individual produces both eggs and sperm.

hermaphroditism See *hermaphrodite*.

heterochromatin (het′-ur-oh-kroh′-mah-tin) Highly coiled and compacted chromatin in an inactive state. Compare with *euchromatin*.

heterocyst (het′-ur-oh-sist″) An oxygen-excluding cell of cyanobacteria that is the site of nitrogen fixation.

heterogametic A term describing an individual that produces two classes of gametes with respect to their sex chromosome constitutions. Human males (XY) are heterogametic, producing X and Y sperm. Compare with *homogametic*.

heterospory (het″-ur-os′-pur-ee) Production of two types of *n* spores, microspores (male) and megaspores (female). Compare with *homospory*.

heterothallic (het″-ur-oh-thal′-ik) Pertaining to certain algae and fungi that have two mating types; only by combining a plus strain and a minus strain can sexual reproduction occur. Compare with *homothallic*.

heterotroph (het′-ur-oh-trof) An organism that cannot synthesize its own food from inorganic raw materials and therefore must obtain body-building materials from other organisms. Also called *consumer*. Compare with *autotroph*. See *chemoheterotroph* and *photoheterotroph*.

heterozygote advantage A phenomenon in which the heterozygous condition confers some special advantage on an individual that either homozygous condition does not (i.e., *Aa* has a higher degree of fitness than does *AA* or *aa*).

heterozygous (het-ur″-oh-zye′-gus) Having a pair of unlike alleles for a particular locus. Compare with *homozygous*.

hexose A monosaccharide containing six carbon atoms.

hibernation Long-term torpor in response to winter cold and scarcity of food. Compare with *estivation*.

high-density lipoprotein (HDL) See *lipoprotein*.

hindbrain In the early embryo, one of the three divisions of the developing vertebrate brain; subdivides to form the metencephalon, which gives rise to the cerebellum and pons, and the myelencephalon, which gives rise to the medulla. Compare with *forebrain* and *midbrain*.

hippocampus Part of the limbic system; important in forming and retrieving declarative memories.

histamine (his′-tah-meen) Substance released from mast cells that causes inflammation.

histones (his′-tohnz) Small, positively charged (basic) proteins in the cell nucleus that bind to the negatively charged DNA. See *nucleosomes*.

holdfast The basal structure for attachment to solid surfaces found in multicellular algae.

holoblastic cleavage A cleavage pattern in which the entire embryo cleaves; characteristic of eggs with little or moderate yolk (isolecithal or moderately telolecithal), e.g., the eggs of echinoderms, amphioxus, and mammals. Compare with *meroblastic cleavage*.

homeobox A short (180-nucleotide) DNA sequence that characterizes many homeotic genes as well as some other genes that play a role in development.

homeodomain A functional region of certain transcription factors; consists of approximately 60 amino acids specified by a homeobox DNA sequence and includes a recognition alpha helix, which binds to specific DNA sequences and affects their transcription.

homeostasis (home″-ee-oh-stay′-sis) The balanced internal environment of the body; the automatic tendency of an organism to maintain such a steady state.

homeostatic mechanisms (home″-ee-oh-stat′-ik) The regulatory mechanisms that maintain homeostasis.

homeotic gene (home″-ee-ah′-tik) A gene that controls the formation of specific structures during development. Such genes were originally identified through insect mutants in which one body part is substituted for another.

home range A geographic area that an individual animal seldom or never leaves. Compare with *range*.

hominid See *hominin*.

hominin (hah′-min-in) Any of a group of extinct and living humans. Also called *hominid*.

hominoid (hah′-min-oid) The apes and hominins (hominids).

Homo antecessor Early humans living in about 1.2 mya to 800,000 years ago; some scientists believe that they should be classified with *Homo heidelbergensis*.

Homo erectus Species that originated in Africa about 1.7 mya and then spread to Europe and Asia; may have persisted until 200,000 years ago or later; may be an evolutionary dead end.

Homo ergaster African species that lived from about 2.0 to 1.4 mya; may be a direct ancestor of later humans.

Homo habilis Oldest known species in genus *Homo*; lived in Africa from approximately 2.5 to 1.6 mya.

Homo heidelbergensis Early humans living from about 600,000 to 300,000 years ago; some scientists believe that fossils classified as *Homo antecessor* should be included in *Homo heidelbergensis*.

Homo neanderthalensis Human species living in Europe and western Asia from about 250,000 to 28,000 years ago; may have interbred with modern humans (*Homo sapiens*).

Homo sapiens Modern human species.

homogametic Term describing an individual that produces gametes with identical sex chromosome constitutions. Human females (XX) are homogametic, producing all X eggs. Compare with *heterogametic*.

homologous chromosomes (hom-ol′-ah-gus) Chromosomes that are similar in morphology and genetic constitution. In humans there are 23 pairs of homologous chromosomes; one member of each pair is inherited from the mother, and the other from the father.

homologous features See *homology*.

homologous traits See *homology*.

homology Similarity in different species that results from their derivation from a common ancestor. The features that exhibit such similarity are called *homologous features* or *homologous traits*. Compare with *homoplasy*.

homoplastic features See *homoplasy*.

homoplastic traits See *homoplasy*.

homoplasy Similarity in the characters in different species that is due to convergent evolution, not common descent. Characters that exhibit such similarity are called *homoplastic features* or *homoplastic traits*. Compare with *homology*.

homospory (hoh″-mos′-pur-ee) Production of one type of *n* spore that gives rise to a bisexual gametophyte. Compare with *heterospory*.

homothallic (hoh″-moh-thal′-ik) Pertaining to certain algae and fungi that are self-fertile. Compare with *heterothallic*.

homozygous (hoh″-moh-zy′-gous) Having a pair of identical alleles for a particular locus. Compare with *heterozygous*.

horizontal cell A lateral interneuron in the retina of the eye; receives signals from the photoreceptor cells and sends signals to bipolar cells and amacrine cells.

horizontal gene transfer The transfer of genetic material from one genome to another across species and even domains. Also called *lateral gene transfer*. Compare with *vertical gene transfer*.

hormone A chemical messenger, often produced in one region of the body of a multicellular organism and transported to another region where it signals cells to alter some aspect of growth, development, or metabolism.

hornwort A phylum of spore-producing, nonvascular, thallose plants with a life cycle similar to that of mosses.

horsetails Fern relatives with hollow, jointed stems, to which tiny leaves (reduced megaphylls) are attached in whorls.

host Organism that is adversely affected by a parasite member in a symbiotic relationship.

host mothering The introduction of an embryo from one species into the uterus of another species, where it implants and develops; the host mother subsequently gives birth and may raise the offspring as her own.

host range The specific types of host species a specific infectious agent can infect.

***Hox* genes** Clusters of homeobox-containing genes that specify the anterior–posterior axis of various animals during development.

human chorionic gonadotropin (hCG) A hormone secreted by cells surrounding the early embryo; signals the mother's corpus luteum to continue to function.

human genetics The science of inherited variation in humans.

human genome The totality of genetic information in human cells; includes the DNA content of both the nucleus and mitochondria. See *genome*.

Human Genome Project Initiative completed in 2003 to determine the sequence of bases for a human haploid reference genome of more than 3 billion nucleotide base pairs.

human immunodeficiency virus (HIV) The retrovirus that causes AIDS (acquired immunodeficiency syndrome).

human leukocyte antigen complex (HLA) The MHC in humans. See *major histocompatibility complex*.

humus (hew′-mus) Organic matter in various stages of decomposition in the soil; gives soil a dark brown or black color.

Huntington's disease A genetic disease that has an autosomal dominant inheritance pattern and causes mental and physical deterioration.

hybrid The offspring of two genetically dissimilar parents.

hybrid breakdown A postzygotic reproductive isolating mechanism in which, although an interspecific hybrid is fertile and produces a second (F_2) generation, the F_2 has defects that prevent it from successfully reproducing.

hybrid inviability A postzygotic reproductive isolating mechanism in which the embryonic development of an interspecific hybrid is aborted.

hybridization (1) Interbreeding between members of two different taxa. (2) Interbreeding between genetically dissimilar parents. (3) In molecular biology, complementary base pairing between nucleic acid (DNA or RNA) strands from different sources.

hybrid sterility A postzygotic reproductive isolating mechanism in which an interspecific hybrid cannot reproduce successfully.

hybrid vigor The genetic superiority of an F_1 hybrid over either parent, caused by the presence of heterozygosity for a number of different loci.

hybrid zone An area of overlap between two closely related populations, subspecies, or species in which interbreeding occurs.

hydration Process of association of a substance with the partial positive and/or negative charges of water molecules.

hydrocarbon An organic compound composed solely of hydrogen and carbon atoms.

hydrogen bond A weak attractive force existing between a hydrogen atom with a partial positive charge and an electronegative atom (usually oxygen or nitrogen) with a partial negative charge. Compare with *covalent bond* and *ionic bond*.

hydrologic cycle The water cycle, which includes evaporation, precipitation, and flow to the ocean; supplies terrestrial organisms with a continual supply of fresh water.

hydrolysis reaction Reaction in which a covalent bond between two subunits is broken through the addition of the equivalent of a water molecule; a hydrogen atom is added to one subunit and a hydroxyl group to the other. Compare with *condensation reaction*.

hydrophilic Interacting readily with water; having a greater affinity for water molecules than they have for each other. Compare with *hydrophobic*.

hydrophobic Not readily interacting with water; having less affinity for water molecules than they have for each other. Compare with *hydrophilic*.

hydrophobic interactions The tendency of hydrophobic substances to cluster together due to strong cohesive interactions among surrounding water molecules.

hydroponics (hy″-dra-paun′-iks) Growing plants in an aerated solution of dissolved inorganic minerals, i.e., without soil.

hydrostatic skeleton A type of skeleton found in some invertebrates in which contracting muscles push against a tube of fluid.

hydrothermal vents Fissures in the deep ocean floor that release hot water and inorganic compounds.

hydroxide ion An anion (negatively charged particle) consisting of oxygen and hydrogen; usually written OH^-.

hydroxyl group (hy-drok′-sil) Polar functional group; abbreviated —OH.

hyperpolarize To change the membrane potential so that the inside of the cell becomes more negative than its resting potential.

hyperpolarized The condition of the neuron membrane when the inside of the cell becomes more negative than its resting potential.

hypersecretion Abnormally increased output of a secreted material. Compare with *hyposecretion*.

hypertension Sustained, above normal, mean arterial blood pressure.

hypertonic A term referring to a solution having an osmotic pressure (or solute concentration) greater than that of the solution with which it is compared. Compare with *hypotonic* and *isotonic*.

hypha (hy'-fah) (pl., *hyphae*) One of the threadlike filaments composing the mycelium of a water mold or fungus.

hypocotyl (hy'-poh-kah"-tl) The part of the axis of a plant embryo or seedling below the point of attachment of the cotyledons.

hyposecretion Abnormally reduced output of a secreted material. Compare with *hypersecretion*.

hypothalamus (hy-poh-thal'-uh-mus) Part of the vertebrate brain; in mammals it regulates the pituitary gland, the autonomic system, emotional responses, body temperature, water balance, and appetite; located below the thalamus.

hypothesis A testable statement about the nature of an observation or relationship. Compare with *scientific theory*.

hypothetico-deductive approach Emphasizes the use of deductive reasoning to test hypotheses. Compare with *hypothetico-inductive approach*. See *deductive reasoning*.

hypothetico-inductive approach Emphasizes the use of inductive reasoning to discover new general principles. Compare with *hypothetico-deductive approach*. See *inductive reasoning*.

hypotonic A term referring to a solution having an osmotic pressure (or solute concentration) less than that of the solution with which it is compared. Compare with *hypertonic* and *isotonic*.

hypotrichs A group of dorsoventrally flattened ciliates that exhibit an unusual creeping–darting locomotion.

identical twins See *monozygotic twins*.

illuviation The deposition of material leached from the upper layers of soil into the lower layers.

imaginal discs Paired structures in an insect larva that develop into specific adult structures during complete metamorphosis.

imago (ih-may'-go) The adult form of an insect.

imbibition (im"-bi-bish'-en) The absorption of water by a seed prior to germination.

immigration The movement of individuals into a population. Compare with *emigration*.

immune response Process of recognizing foreign macromolecules and mounting a response aimed at eliminating them. See *innate immune responses* and *adaptive immune responses*; *primary immune responses* and *secondary immune responses*.

immune system The system of molecules and cells that protect the body against pathogens and other foreign agents. In vertebrates, includes lymphatic vessels and other lymph structures.

immunity The ability to recognize and destroy foreign or dangerous macromolecules.

immunodeficiency disease A condition that increases susceptibility to infection; the condition can be inherited or acquired. HIV is the major cause of acquired immunodeficiency in adults.

immunofluorescence Method used to localize molecules in cells or quantify specific molecules in biochemical assays by observing or measuring light emitted from a fluorescent dye joined to an antibody that binds to the specific molecule under study.

immunoglobulin (im-yoon"-oh-glob'-yoo-lin) See *antibody*.

immunological memory The ability of the immune system to remember antigen after contact with them so that it can respond more rapidly if it encounters the same antigens again. Memory B cells and memory T cells are responsible for immunological memory.

imperfect flower A flower that lacks either stamens or carpels. Compare with *perfect flower*.

imperfect fungi See *deuteromycetes*.

implantation The embedding of a developing embryo in the inner lining (endometrium) of the uterus.

implicit memory The unconscious memory for perceptual and motor skills, e.g., riding a bicycle.

imprinting (1) The expression of a gene based on its parental origin; also called *genomic imprinting* or *parental imprinting*. (2) A type of learning by which a young bird or mammal forms a strong social attachment to an individual (usually a parent) or object within a few hours after hatching or birth.

inborn error of metabolism A metabolic disorder caused by the mutation of a gene that codes for an enzyme needed for a biochemical pathway.

inbreeding depression The phenomenon in which inbred offspring of genetically similar individuals have lower fitness (e.g., decline in fertility and high juvenile mortality) than do noninbred individuals.

inbreeding The mating of genetically similar individuals. Homozygosity increases with each successive generation of inbreeding. Compare with *outbreeding*.

incisors Chisel-shaped teeth of a mammal; adapted for biting and cutting food. Compare with *canines*, *premolars*, and *molars*.

inclusive fitness The total of an individual's direct and indirect fitness; includes the genes contributed directly to offspring and those contributed indirectly by kin selection. Compare with *direct fitness*. See *kin selection*.

incomplete dominance A condition in which neither member of a pair of contrasting alleles is completely expressed when the other is present.

incomplete flower A flower that lacks one or more of the four parts: sepals, petals, stamens, and/or carpels. Compare with *complete flower*.

incomplete metamorphosis In insects, a life cycle during which the larva resembles the adult in many ways, but lacks functional wings and reproductive structures. Compare with *complete metamorphosis*.

independent assortment, principle of The genetic principle, first noted by Gregor Mendel, that states that the alleles of unlinked loci are randomly distributed to gametes.

indeterminate cleavage Type of cleavage characteristic of deuterostomes; during early cleavage each cell has the potential of developing into a complete embryo. Compare with *determinate cleavage*.

indeterminate growth Unrestricted growth, as for example, in stems and roots. Compare with *determinate growth*.

index fossils Fossils restricted to a narrow period of geologic time and found in the same sedimentary layers in different geographic areas.

individualistic model Independent view of community, described by Gleason, in which biological interactions are less important in the production of communities than are environmental gradients (such as climate and soil) or even chance. Compare with *organismic model*.

indoleacetic acid (IAA) See *auxin*.

induced fit Conformational change in the active site of an enzyme that occurs when it binds to its substrate.

induced pluripotent stem cell (iPSC) A pluripotent stem cell derived by "reprogramming" or modifying the gene expression patterns of an adult somatic cell.

inducer A molecule that binds to a repressor protein, converting it to its inactive form, which is unable to prevent transcription.

inducible operon An operon that is normally inactive because a repressor molecule is attached to its operator; transcription is activated when an inducer binds to the repressor, making it incapable of binding to the operator. Compare with *repressible operon*.

induction The process by which the differentiation of a cell or group of cells is influenced by interactions with neighboring cells.

inductive reasoning The reasoning that uses specific examples to draw a general conclusion or discover a general principle. Compare with *deductive reasoning*. See *hypothetico-inductive approach*.

infant mortality rate The number of infant deaths per 1000 live births. (A child is an infant during his or her first two years of life.)

inferior vena cava In humans, a very large vein that delivers blood from the lower part of the body to the right atrium. Compare with *superior vena cava*.

inflammation The response of body tissues to injury or infection; the body recruits white blood cells and plasma proteins from the blood to the location of an infection resulting in increased dilation of blood vessels and increased phagocytosis.

inflammatory response See *inflammation*.

inflorescence A cluster of flowers on a common floral stalk.

ingestion The process of taking food (or other material) into the body.

ingroup See *outgroup*.

inhibin A hormone that inhibits FSH secretion; produced by Sertoli cells in the testes and by granulosa cells in the ovaries.

inhibiting hormone A hormone secreted by the hypothalamus that inhibits secretion of a specific hormone by the anterior lobe of the pituitary gland.

inhibitory postsynaptic potential (IPSP) A change in membrane potential that takes a neuron farther from the firing level. Compare with *excitatory postsynaptic potential (EPSP)*.

initiation (of protein synthesis) The first steps of protein synthesis, in which the large and small ribosomal subunits and other components of the translation machinery bind to the 5′ end of mRNA. See *elongation* and *termination*.

initiation codon See *start codon*.

innate behavior Behavior that is inherited and typical of the species; also called *instinct*.

innate immune responses Mechanisms such as physical barriers (e.g., the skin) and phagocytosis that provide immediate and general protection against pathogens. Also called *nonspecific immune responses* or *nonspecific immunity*. Compare with *adaptive immune responses*.

innate immunity See *innate immune responses*.

inner cell mass The cluster of cells in the early mammalian embryo that gives rise to the embryo proper.

inorganic compound A simple substance that does not contain a carbon backbone. Compare with *organic compound*.

inositol trisphosphate (IP₃) A second messenger that increases intracellular calcium concentration and activates enzymes.

insight learning A complex learning process in which an animal adapts past experience to solve a new problem that may involve different stimuli.

in situ conservation Conservation efforts that concentrate on preserving biological diversity in the wild. Compare with *ex situ conservation*.

instinct See *innate behavior*.

insulin (in′-suh-lin) A hormone secreted by the pancreas that lowers blood glucose concentration. Compare with *glucagon*.

insulin resistance See *diabetes mellitus*.

insulin shock A condition in which the blood glucose concentration is so low that the individual may appear intoxicated or may become unconscious and even die; caused by the injection of too much insulin or by certain metabolic malfunctions.

insulin-like growth factors (IGFs) Proteins that mediate responses to growth hormone.

insulin-like growth factor 2 (IGF2) See *insulin-like growth factors*.

integral membrane protein A protein that is tightly associated with the lipid bilayer of a biological membrane; a transmembrane integral protein spans the bilayer. Compare with *peripheral membrane protein*.

integration The process of summing (adding and subtracting) incoming neural signals.

integrins Receptor proteins that bind to specific proteins in the extracellular matrix and to membrane proteins on adjacent cells; transmit signals into the cell from the extracellular matrix.

integumentary system (in-teg″-yoo-men′-tar-ee) The body's covering, including the skin and its nails, glands, hair, and other associated structures.

integuments The outer cell layers that surround the megasporangium of an ovule; develop into the seed coat.

intercellular substance In connective tissues, the combination of matrix and fibers in which the cells are embedded.

interference competition Intraspecific competition in which certain dominant individuals obtain an adequate supply of the limited resource at the expense of other individuals in the population. Also called *contest competition*. Compare with *exploitation competition*.

interferons (in″-tur-feer′-onz) Cytokines produced by animal cells when challenged by a virus; prevent viral reproduction and enable cells to resist a variety of viruses.

integrator In homeostasis, a control center.

intercalated discs (in-ter′-kuh-lay″-ted) The junctions between cells in cardiac muscle; contain gap junctions.

interkinesis The stage between meiosis I and meiosis II. Interkinesis is usually brief; the chromosomes may decondense, reverting at least partially to an interphase-like state, but DNA synthesis and chromosome duplication do not occur.

interleukins A diverse group of cytokines produced mainly by macrophages and lymphocytes.

intermediate disturbance hypothesis In community ecology, the idea that species richness is greatest at moderate levels of disturbance, which create a mosaic of habitat patches at different stages of succession.

intermediate filaments Cytoplasmic fibers that are part of the cytoskeletal network and are intermediate in size between microtubules and microfilaments.

intermediate-day plant A plant that flowers when it is exposed to days and nights of intermediate length but does not flower when the day length is too long or too short. Compare with *long-day, short-day,* and *day-neutral plants*.

internal fertilization The process in which the male delivers sperm into the body of the female (or close to the entrance of the reproductive tract). Compare with *external fertilization*.

internal membrane system See *endomembrane system*.

interneuron (in″-tur-noor′-on) A nerve cell that carries impulses from one nerve cell to another and is not directly associated with either an effector or a sensory receptor. Most interneurons are *association neurons*.

internode The region on a stem between two successive nodes. Compare with *node*.

intersexual selection The process by which females select their mates on the basis of some physical trait that indicates genetic quality or good health; sometimes selection depends on some resource offered by the males. Compare with *intrasexual selection*.

interoceptor (in′-tur-oh-sep″-tor) A sense organ within a body organ that transmits information regarding chemical composition, pH, osmotic pressure, or temperature. Compare with *exteroceptor*.

interphase The stage of the cell cycle between successive mitotic divisions; its subdivisions are the G₁ (first gap), S (DNA synthesis), and G₂ (second gap) phases.

interspecific competition The interaction between members of different species that vie for the same resource in an ecosystem (e.g., food or living space). Compare with *intraspecific competition*.

interstitial cells (of testis) The cells between the seminiferous tubules that secrete testosterone.

interstitial fluid The fluid that bathes the tissues of the body; also called *tissue fluid*.

intertidal zone The marine shoreline area between the high-tide mark and the low-tide mark.

intrasexual selection The process by which individuals of the same sex actively compete for mates. Typically numerous males compete for a limited number of receptive females. Compare with *intersexual selection*.

intraspecific competition The interaction between members of the same species that vie for the same resource in an ecosystem (e.g., food or living space). Compare with *interspecific competition*.

intrinsic rate of increase (r_{max}) The theoretical maximum rate of increase in population size occurring under optimal environmental conditions. Also called *biotic potential*.

intron A non-protein-coding region of a eukaryotic gene and also of the pre-mRNA transcribed from such a region. Introns do not appear in mRNA. Compare with *exon*.

invasive species A foreign species that, when introduced into an area where it is not native, upsets the balance among the organisms living there and causes economic or environmental harm.

inversion A chromosome abnormality in which the breakage and rejoining of chromosome parts results in a chromosome segment that is oriented in the opposite (reverse) direction.

invertebrate An animal without a backbone (vertebral column); invertebrates account for about 95% of animal species.

in vitro Occurring outside a living organism (literally "in glass"). Compare with *in vivo*.

in vitro evolution Test tube experiments that demonstrate that RNA molecules in the RNA world could have catalyzed the many different chemical reactions needed for life. Also called *directed evolution*.

in vitro fertilization The fertilization of eggs in the laboratory prior to implantation in the uterus for development.

in vivo Occurring in a living organism. Compare with *in vitro*.

ion An atom or group of atoms bearing one or more units of electric charge, either positive (cation) or negative (anion).

ion channel–linked receptors Cell surface receptors that open or close specific ion channels in response to binding by a signaling molecule (ligand). Also called *ligand-gated channels.*

ion channels Channels for the passage of ions through a membrane; formed by specific membrane proteins.

ionic bond The chemical attraction between a cation and an anion. Compare with *covalent bond* and *hydrogen bond.*

ionic compound A substance consisting of cations and anions, which are attracted by their opposite charges; ionic compounds do not consist of molecules. Compare with *covalent compound.*

ionization The dissociation of a substance to yield ions, e.g., the ionization of water yields H$^+$ and OH$^-$.

iris The pigmented portion of the vertebrate eye.

iron–sulfur world hypothesis The hypothesis that simple organic molecules that are the precursors of life originated at hydrothermal vents in the deep-ocean floor. Compare with *prebiotic soup hypothesis.*

irreversible inhibitor A substance that permanently inactivates an enzyme. Compare with *reversible inhibitor.*

islets of Langerhans (eye′-lets of lahng′-er-hanz) The endocrine portion of the pancreas that secretes glucagon and insulin, hormones that regulate the concentration of glucose in the blood.

isogamy (eye-sog′-uh-me) Sexual reproduction involving motile gametes of similar form and size. Compare with *anisogamy* and *oogamy.*

isolecithal egg An egg containing a relatively small amount of uniformly distributed yolk. Compare with *telolecithal egg.*

isomer (eye′-soh-mer) One of two or more chemical compounds having the same chemical formula but different structural formulas, e.g., structural and geometrical isomers and enantiomers.

isoprene units Five-carbon hydrocarbon monomers that make up certain lipids such as carotenoids and steroids.

isotonic (eye″-soh-ton′-ik) A term applied to solutions that have identical concentrations of solute molecules and hence the same osmotic pressure. Compare with *hypertonic* and *hypotonic.*

isotope (eye′-suh-tope) An alternative form of an element with a different number of neutrons but the same number of protons and electrons. See *radioisotopes.*

iteroparous Having repeated reproductive cycles throughout a lifetime. Compare with *semelparous.*

jasmonic acid One of a group of lipid-derived plant hormones that affect several processes, such as pollen development, root growth, fruit ripening, and senescence; also involved in defense against insect pests and disease-causing organisms.

jelly coat One of the acellular coverings of the eggs of certain animals, such as echinoderms.

joint The junction between two or more bones of the skeleton.

joint receptors Proprioceptors that detect movement in ligaments.

joule A unit of energy, equivalent to 0.239 calorie.

Jurassic period See *Mesozoic era.*

juvenile hormone (JH) An arthropod hormone that preserves juvenile structure during a molt. Without it, metamorphosis toward the adult form takes place.

juxtaglomerular apparatus (juks″-tah-glo-mer′-yoo-lar) A structure in the kidney that secretes renin in response to a decrease in blood pressure.

K selection A reproductive strategy recognized by some ecologists in which a species typically has a large body size, slow development, and long lifespan and does not devote a large proportion of its metabolic energy to the production of offspring. Compare with *r selection.*

K strategist See *K selection.*

karyogamy (kar-e-og′-uh-me) The fusion of two haploid nuclei; follows fusion (plasmogamy) of cells from two sexually compatible mating types.

karyotype (kare′-ee-oh-type) The chromosomal composition of an individual.

kelp Large brown alga that grows in shallow ocean areas and forms underwater forests.

keratin (kare′-ah-tin) A horny, water insoluble protein found in the epidermis of vertebrates and in nails, feathers, hair, and horns.

ketone An organic molecule containing a carbonyl group bonded to two carbon atoms. Compare with *aldehyde.*

keystone species A species whose presence in an ecosystem largely determines the species composition and functioning of that ecosystem.

kidney The paired vertebrate organ important in excretion of metabolic wastes and in osmoregulation.

killer T cell See *T cytotoxic cell.*

kilobase (kb) 1000 bases or base pairs of a nucleic acid.

kilocalorie The amount of heat required to raise the temperature of 1 kg of water 1°C; also called *Calorie,* which is equivalent to 1000 calories.

kilojoule 1000 joules. See *joule.*

kinases Enzymes that catalyze the transfer of phosphate groups from ATP to acceptor molecules. See *protein kinases.* Compare with *phosphatases.*

kinesin See *microtubule-associated proteins (MAPs).*

kinetic energy Energy of motion. Compare with *potential energy.*

kinetochore (kin-eh′-toh-kore) The portion of the chromosome centromere to which the mitotic spindle fibers attach.

kinetoplastid A single mitochondrion with an organized deposit of DNA; characteristic of trypanosomes.

kinocilium The single, long cilium that projects from the surface of a vertebrate hair cell.

kingdom A broad taxonomic category made up of related phyla; many biologists currently assign living organisms to five kingdoms and several "supergroups."

kin selection A type of natural selection that favors altruistic behavior toward relatives (kin), thereby ensuring that although the chances of an individual's survival are lessened, some of its genes will survive through successful reproduction of close relatives; increases inclusive fitness.

Klinefelter syndrome Inherited condition in which the affected individual is a sterile male with an XXY karyotype.

knockout mice Mouse strain in which both alleles of a gene are functionally disabled in one or more tissues by genetic engineering methods.

Koch's postulates A set of guidelines used to demonstrate that a specific pathogen causes specific disease symptoms.

Krebs cycle See *citric acid cycle.*

krummholz The gnarled, shrublike growth habit found in trees at high elevations, near their upper limit of distribution.

K-selected species See *K selection.*

labyrinth The system of interconnecting canals of the inner ear of vertebrates.

labyrinthodonts The first successful group of tetrapods.

lactate (lactic acid) A three-carbon organic acid.

lactation (lak-tay′-shun) The production or release of milk from the breast.

lacteal (lak′-tee-al) One of the many lymphatic vessels in the intestinal villi that absorb fat.

lagging strand A strand of DNA that is synthesized as a series of short segments, called *Okazaki fragments,* which are then covalently joined by DNA ligase. Compare with *leading strand.*

lamins Polypeptides attached to the inner surface of the nuclear envelope that provide a type of skeletal framework.

lampreys Jawless freshwater and marine fishes with skeletons of cartilage, complete cranium, and rudimentary vertebrae.

landscape A large land area (several to many square kilometers) composed of interacting ecosystems.

landscape ecology The subdiscipline in ecology that studies the connections in a heterogeneous landscape.

large intestine The portion of the digestive tract of humans (and other vertebrates) consisting of the cecum, colon, rectum, and anus.

larva (pl., *larvae*) An immature form in the life history of some animals; may be unlike the parent.

larynx (lare'-inks) The organ at the upper end of the trachea that contains the vocal cords.

lateral line organ In fishes, a sensory organ that detects vibrations caused by waves and other movement in the water.

lateral meristems Areas of localized cell division on the side of a plant that give rise to secondary tissues. Lateral meristems, including the vascular cambium and the cork cambium, cause an increase in the girth of the plant body. Compare with *apical meristem.*

leaching The process by which dissolved materials are washed away or carried with water down through the various layers of the soil.

leader sequence Noncoding sequence of nucleotides in mRNA that is transcribed from the region that precedes (is upstream to) the coding region.

leading strand Strand of DNA that is synthesized continuously. Compare with *lagging strand.*

leaf scar Marks on a stem left when the petiole of a leaf breaks during abscission.

learning The process by which knowledge or skills are acquired as a result of experience; a change in the behavior of an animal that results from experience.

legume (leg'-yoom) (1) A simple, dry fruit that develops from a single carpel and splits open at maturity along two sutures to release seeds. (2) Any member of the pea family, e.g., pea, bean, peanut, alfalfa.

lek A small territory in which males compete for females.

lens The oval, transparent structure located behind the iris of the vertebrate eye; bends incoming light rays and brings them to a focus on the retina.

lenticels (len'-tih-sels) Porous swellings of cork cells in the stems of woody plants; facilitate the exchange of gases.

lepidosaurs (lep'-ih-do-sorz) A lineage of diapsid vertebrates that includes snakes, lizards, and tuataras.

leptin A hormone produced by adipose tissue that signals brain centers about the status of energy stores.

leukocytes (loo'-koh-sites) White blood cells; colorless amoeboid cells that defend the body against disease-causing organisms.

leukoplasts Colorless plastids; include amyloplasts, which are used for starch storage in cells of roots and tubers.

lichen (ly'-ken) A compound organism consisting of a symbiotic fungus and an alga or cyanobacterium.

life history traits Significant features of a species' life cycle, particularly traits that influence survival and reproduction.

lifespan The maximum duration of life for an individual of a species.

life table A table showing mortality and survival data by age of a population or cohort.

ligament (lig'-uh-ment) A connective tissue cable or strap that connects bones to each other or holds other organs in place.

ligand A molecule that binds to a specific site in a receptor or other protein.

ligand-gated channels See *ion channel–linked receptors.*

light-dependent reactions Reactions of photosynthesis in which light energy absorbed by chlorophyll is used to synthesize ATP and usually NADPH. Include *cyclic electron transport* and *noncyclic electron transport.*

light microscope (LM) Microscope in which light is refracted (bent) by glass lenses to produce a magnified image.

lignin (lig'-nin) A substance found in many plant cell walls that confers rigidity and strength, particularly in woody tissues.

limbic system In vertebrates, an action system of the brain. In humans, plays a role in emotional responses, motivation, sexual behavior, autonomic responses, and biological rhythms.

limiting resource An environmental resource that because it is scarce or unfavorable tends to restrict the ecological niche of an organism.

limnetic zone (lim-net'-ik) The open water away from the shore of a lake or pond extending down as far as sunlight penetrates. Compare with *littoral zone* and *profundal zone.*

linkage The tendency for a group of genes located on the same chromosome to be inherited together in successive generations.

linked genes See *linkage.*

lipase (lip'-ase) A fat-digesting enzyme.

lipid Any of a group of organic compounds that are insoluble in water but soluble in nonpolar solvents; lipids serve as energy storage and are important components of cell membranes.

lipoprotein (lip-oh-proh'-teen) A large molecular complex consisting of lipids and protein; transports lipids in the blood. High-density lipoproteins (HDLs) transport cholesterol to the liver; low-density lipoproteins (LDLs) deliver cholesterol to many cells of the body.

littoral zone (lit'-or-ul) The region of shallow water along the shore of a lake or pond. Compare with *limnetic zone* and *profundal zone.*

liver A large, complex organ that secretes bile, helps maintain homeostasis by removing or adding nutrients to the blood, and performs many other metabolic functions.

liverworts A phylum of spore-producing, nonvascular, thallose or leafy plants with a life cycle similar to that of mosses.

local hormones See *local regulators.*

local regulators Prostaglandins (a group of local hormones), growth factors, cytokines, and other soluble molecules that act on nearby cells by paracrine regulation or act on the cells that produce them (autocrine regulation).

locus (pl., *loci*) The place on the chromosome at which the gene for a given trait occurs, i.e., a segment of the chromosomal DNA containing information that controls some feature of the organism; also called *gene locus.*

logistic population growth Population growth that initially occurs at a constant rate of increase over time (i.e., exponential) but then levels out as the carrying capacity of the environment is approached. Compare with *exponential population growth.*

long-day plant A plant that flowers in response to shortening nights; also called *short-night plant.* Compare with *short-day, intermediate-day,* and *day-neutral plants.*

long-night plant See *short-day plant.*

long noncoding RNAs (lncRNAs) Molecules longer than 200 bases responsible for controlling genes by regulating chromatin structure.

long-term memory Memory that stores information for long periods of time; the hippocampus temporarily holds new information and helps place our experiences into categories so they can be consolidated and transferred to the cerebral cortex where they are stored along with similar memories. Compare with *short-term memory.*

long-term potentiation (LTP) Long-lasting increase in the strength of synaptic connections that occurs in response to a series of high-frequency electrical stimuli. Compare with *long-term synaptic depression (LTD).*

long-term synaptic depression (LTD) Long-lasting decrease in the strength of synaptic connections that occurs in response to low-frequency stimulation of neurons. Compare with *long-term potentiation (LTP).*

loop of Henle (hen'-lee) The U-shaped loop of a mammalian kidney tubule that extends down into the renal medulla.

loose connective tissue A type of connective tissue that is widely distributed in the body; consists of fibers strewn through a semifluid matrix.

lophophorates (lof-ah-for'ates) Members of three related invertebrate protostome phyla, characterized by a lophophore, a ciliated ring of tentacles that surrounds the mouth.

Lophotrochozoa A branch of the protostomes that includes the flatworms, nemerteans (proboscis worms), mollusks, annelids, and the lophophorate phyla.

low-density lipoprotein (LDL) See *lipoprotein.*

LUCA Acronym referring to the hypothesized **l**ast **u**niversal **c**ommon **a**ncestor of all living things on Earth today.

lumen (loo'-men) (1) The space enclosed by a membrane, such as the lumen of the endoplasmic reticulum or the thylakoid lumen. (2) The cavity or channel within a tube or tubular organ, such as a blood vessel or the digestive tract. (3) The space left within a plant cell after the cell's living material dies, as in tracheids.

lung An internal respiratory organ that functions in gas exchange; enables an animal to breathe air.

luteinizing hormone (LH) (loot'-eh-ny-zing) Gonadotropic hormone secreted by the anterior pituitary; stimulates ovulation and maintains the corpus luteum in the ovaries of females; stimulates testosterone production in the testes of males.

lymph (limf) The colorless fluid within the lymphatic vessels that is derived from blood plasma; contains white blood cells; ultimately lymph is returned to the blood.

lymphatic system A subsystem of the cardiovascular system; returns excess interstitial fluid (lymph) to the circulation; defends the body against disease organisms.

lymph node A mass of lymph tissue surrounded by a connective tissue capsule; manufactures lymphocytes and filters lymph.

lymphocyte (lim'-foh-site) White blood cell with nongranular cytoplasm that governs immune responses. See *B cell* and *T cell*.

lysis (ly'-sis) The process of disintegration of a cell or some other structure.

lysogenic conversion The change in properties of bacteria that results from the presence of a prophage.

lysogenic cycle (ly-so jen'-ik) A type of phage reproductive cycle in which the viral genome usually becomes integrated into the host DNA as a prophage; it is replicated along with the host DNA and does not kill the host cell. Compare with *lytic cycle*.

lysosomes (ly'-soh-sohmz) Intracellular organelles present in many animal cells; contain a variety of hydrolytic enzymes.

lysozyme An enzyme found in many tissues and in tears and other body fluids; attacks the cell wall of many gram-positive bacteria.

lytic cycle (lit'-ik) A type of phage reproductive cycle in which the release of phages from the bacterial cell results in rapid cell lysis (destruction). Compare with *lysogenic cycle*.

M phase That part of the cell cycle in which mitosis and cytokinesis occur.

macroevolution Large-scale evolutionary events over long time spans. Macroevolution results in phenotypic changes in populations that are significant enough to warrant their placement in taxonomic groups at the species level and higher. Compare with *microevolution*.

macromolecule A very large organic molecule, such as a protein or nucleic acid.

macronucleus A large nucleus found, along with one or several micronuclei, in ciliates. The macronucleus regulates metabolism and growth. Compare with *micronucleus*.

macronutrient An essential element required in fairly large amounts for normal growth. Compare with *micronutrient*.

macrophage (mak'-roh-faje) A large phagocytic cell capable of ingesting and digesting bacteria

and cell debris. Macrophages are also antigen-presenting cells.

magnification The ratio of the size of an image as seen with a microscope to its actual size.

magnoliid One of the clades of flowering plants; magnoliids are core angiosperms that were traditionally classified as "dicots," but molecular evidence indicates they are neither eudicots or monocots.

major histocompatibility complex (MHC) A large cluster of loci that encode the self-antigens present on the surface of most cells; these self-antigens are slightly different in each individual. The term refers to both the loci and to the self-antigens. Also see *human leukocyte antigen complex*.

malignant cells Cancer cells; tumor cells that are able to invade tissue and metastasize.

malignant transformation See *transformation*.

malnutrition Poor nutritional status; results from dietary intake that is either below or above required needs.

Malpighian tubules (mal-pig'-ee-an) The excretory organs of many arthropods.

mammals The class of vertebrates characterized by hair, mammary glands, a diaphragm, and differentiation of teeth.

mammary glands Exocrine glands that secrete milk for the young; a derived character of mammals.

mandible (man'-dih-bl) (1) The lower jaw of vertebrates. (2) Jawlike, external mouthparts of insects.

mangrove forest A tidal wetland dominated by mangrove trees in which the salinity fluctuates between that of sea water and fresh water.

mantle In the mollusk, a fold of tissue that covers the visceral mass and that usually produces a shell.

map unit A unit of a genetic map of a chromosome; 1% recombination between two loci equals one map unit.

marine snow The organic debris (plankton, dead organisms, fecal material, etc.) that "rains" into the dark area of the oceanic province from the lighted region above; the primary food of most organisms that live in the ocean's depths.

marsupials (mar-soo'-pee-ulz) A subclass of mammals, characterized by the presence of an abdominal pouch in which the young, which are born in a very undeveloped condition, are carried for some time after birth.

mass extinction The extinction of numerous species during a relatively short period of geologic time. Compare with *background extinction*.

mast cell A type of cell found in connective tissue; contains histamine and is important in an inflammatory response and in allergic reactions.

mate guarding The male guards his partner after copulation to ensure that she does not copulate with another male.

maternal effect genes Genes of the mother that are transcribed during oogenesis and subsequently

affect the development of the embryo. Compare with *zygotic genes*.

matrix (may'-triks) (1) In cell biology, the interior of the compartment enclosed by the inner mitochondrial membrane. (2) In zoology, nonliving material secreted by and surrounding connective tissue cells; contains a network of microscopic fibers.

matter Anything that has mass and takes up space.

maxillae Appendages used for manipulating food; characteristic of crustaceans.

mechanical isolation A prezygotic reproductive isolating mechanism in which fusion of the gametes of two species is prevented by morphological or anatomical differences.

mechanoreceptor (meh-kan'-oh-ree-sep"-tor) A sensory cell or organ that perceives mechanical stimuli, e.g., touch, pressure, gravity, stretching, or movement.

medulla (meh-dul'-uh) (1) The inner part of an organ, such as the medulla of the kidney. Compare with *cortex*. (2) The most posterior part of the vertebrate brain, lying next to the spinal cord.

medusa A jellyfish-like animal; a free-swimming, umbrella-shaped stage in the life cycle of certain cnidarians. Compare with *polyp*.

megaphyll (meg'-uh-fil) Type of leaf found in horsetails, ferns, gymnosperms, and angiosperms; contains multiple vascular strands (i.e., complex venation). Compare with *microphyll*.

megasporangium (pl., *megasporangia*) In a heterosporous plant, structure in which megaspores are produced. Megasporangia of seed plants are *ovules* that develop into seeds following fertilization. Compare with *microsporangium*.

megaspore (meg'-uh-spor) The *n* spore in heterosporous plants that gives rise to a female gametophyte. Compare with *microspore*.

megasporocyte Cell within a megasporangium that undergoes meiosis to produce four *n* megaspores; also called *megaspore mother cell*. Compare with *microsporocyte*.

meiosis (my-oh'-sis) Process in which a 2*n* cell undergoes two successive nuclear divisions (meiosis I and meiosis II), potentially producing four *n* nuclei; leads to the formation of gametes in animals and spores in plants.

meiosis I The first meiotic division; consists of prophase I, metaphase I, anaphase I, and telophase I; see *meiosis*.

meiosis II The second meiotic division; follows interkinesis and consists of prophase II, metaphase II, anaphase II, and telophase II; see *meiosis*.

melanin A dark pigment present in many animals; contributes to the color of the skin.

melanocortins A group of peptides that appear to decrease appetite in response to increased fat stores.

melanocyte-stimulating hormones (MSH) See *melanocortins*.

melatonin (mel-ah-toh'-nin) A hormone secreted by the pineal gland that plays a role in setting circadian rhythms.

membrane potential A difference in electric charge between the two sides of a membrane.

memory The process of encoding, storing, and retrieving information or learned skills.

memory B cells B cells that continue to produce antibodies after the immune system overcomes an infection.

memory cells B or T cells (lymphocytes) that permit rapid mobilization of immune response on second or subsequent exposure to a particular antigen. See *memory B cells* and *memory T cells*.

memory T cells Cytotoxic or helper T cells that, after participating in an immune response, enter an inactive state until activated by exposure to the same type of antigen.

meninges (meh-nin'-jeez) (sing., *meninx*) The three membranes that protect the brain and spinal cord: the dura mater, arachnoid, and pia mater.

menopause The period (usually occurring between 45 and 55 years of age) in women when the recurring menstrual cycle ceases.

menstrual cycle (men'-stroo-ul) In the human female, the monthly sequence of events that prepares the body for pregnancy.

menstruation (men-stroo-ay'-shun) The monthly discharge of blood and degenerated uterine lining in the human female; marks the beginning of each menstrual cycle.

meristem (mer'-ih-stem) A localized area of mitotic cell division in the plant body. See *apical meristem* and *lateral meristems*.

meroblastic cleavage Cleavage pattern observed in the telolecithal eggs of reptiles and birds, in which cleavage is restricted to a small disc of cytoplasm at the animal pole. Compare with *holoblastic cleavage*.

mesencephalon See *midbrain*.

mesenchyme (mes'-en-kime) A loose, often jelly-like connective tissue containing undifferentiated cells; found in the embryos of vertebrates and the adults of some invertebrates.

mesoderm (mez'-oh-derm) The middle germ layer of the early embryo; gives rise to connective tissue, muscle, bone, blood vessels, kidneys, and many other structures. Compare with *ectoderm* and *endoderm*.

mesoglea (mez-o-glee'-ah) Jellylike layer between the epidermis and gastrodermis in cnidarians and ctenophores.

mesophyll (mez'-oh-fil) Photosynthetic tissue in the interior of a leaf; sometimes differentiated into palisade mesophyll and spongy mesophyll.

Mesozoic era Span of geologic time commonly known as the Age of Reptiles; divided into Triassic (252–201 mya), Jurassic (201–145 mya), and Cretaceous (145–66 mya) periods; ended with the mass extinction of the dinosaurs and many other species.

messenger RNA (mRNA) RNA that specifies the amino acid sequence of a protein; transcribed from DNA.

metabolic pathway A series of chemical reactions in which the product of one reaction becomes the substrate of the next reaction.

metabolic rate Energy use by an organism per unit time. See *basal metabolic rate (BMR)*.

metabolic syndrome Condition that often precedes type 2 diabetes. Symptoms include obesity, large waist circumference, elevated blood glucose concentration, high triglyceride and low HDL ("good" cholesterol) concentrations, and high blood pressure.

metabolism The sum of all the chemical processes that occur within a cell or organism; the transformations by which energy and matter are made available for use by the organism. See *anabolism* and *catabolism*.

metabolism first hypothesis An explanation of the origin of life, in which life began as a self-sustaining, organized system consisting of chemical reactions between simple molecules enclosed within a boundary.

metamorphosis (met"-ah-mor'-fuh-sis) Transition from one developmental stage to another, such as from a larva to an adult. See also *complete metamorphosis* and *incomplete metamorphosis*.

metanephridia (sing., *metanephridium*) The excretory organs of annelids and mollusks; each consists of a tubule open at both ends; at one end a ciliated funnel opens into the coelom, and the other end opens to the outside of the body.

metaphase (met'-ah-faze) The stage of mitosis in which the chromosomes line up on the midplane of the cell (metaphase plate). Occurs after prometaphase and before anaphase.

metaphase I See *meiosis* and *meiosis I*.

metaphase II See *meiosis* and *meiosis II*.

metaphase plate See *metaphase*.

metapopulation A population that is divided into several local populations among which individuals occasionally disperse.

metarterioles Small blood vessels that directly link arterioles with veinules.

metastasis (met-tas'-tuh-sis) The spreading of cancer cells from one organ or part of the body to another.

metencephalon Part of the vertebrate embryonic brain; gives rise to the cerebellum and pons.

methanogens (meth-an'-o-jens) Archaeons that inhabit oxygen-free environments, are obligate anaerobes, and produce methane, an important greenhouse gas.

methyl group A nonpolar functional group; abbreviated —CH_3.

microbiome A community of microorganisms, including their genomes and all their interactions.

microbiota A community of microorganisms that inhabits a particular habitat or site.

microclimate Local variations in climate produced by differences in elevation, in the steepness and direction of slopes, and in exposure to prevailing winds.

microevolution Small-scale evolutionary change caused by changes in allele or genotype frequencies that occur within a population over a few generations. Compare with *macroevolution*.

microfilaments Thin fibers consisting of actin protein subunits; form part of the cytoskeleton.

microfossils Ancient traces (fossils) of microscopic life.

microglia Phagocytic glial cells found in the CNS.

micronucleus One or more smaller nuclei found, along with the macronucleus, in ciliates. The micronucleus is involved in sexual reproduction. Compare with *macronucleus*.

micronutrient An essential element that is required in trace amounts for normal growth. Compare with *macronutrient*.

microphyll (mi'-kro-fil) Type of leaf found in club mosses; contains one vascular strand (i.e., simple venation). Compare with *megaphyll*.

microRNA (miRNA) Single-stranded RNA molecules about 22 nucleotides in length that control the expression of genes at the posttranscriptional level by binding mRNA molecules with base sequences complementary to the miRNA, blocking translation of the mRNA or causing it to be degraded. Also involved in control of transcription of some genes. See also *RNA interference (RNAi)*.

microsphere A protobiont produced by adding water to abiotically formed polypeptides.

microsporangium (pl., *microsporangia*) In a heterosporous plant, structure in which microspores are produced; compare with *megasporangium*.

microspore (mi'-kro-spor) The *n* spore in heterosporous plants that gives rise to a male gametophyte. Compare with *megaspore*.

microsporocyte Cell within a microsporangium that undergoes meiosis to produce four *n* microspores; also called *microspore mother cell*. Compare with *megasporocyte*.

microsporidia Small, unicellular, fungal parasites that infect eukaryotic cells; classified with the zygomycetes.

microtubule-associated proteins (MAPs) Structural proteins that help regulate microtubule assembly and cross-link microtubules to other cytoskeletal polymers; and motors, such as kinesin and dynein, that use ATP to produce movement.

microtubule-organizing center (MTOC) The region of the cell from which microtubules are anchored and possibly assembled. The MTOCs of many organisms (including animals, but not flowering plants or most gymnosperms) contain a pair of centrioles.

microtubules (my-kroh-too'-bewls) Hollow, cylindrical fibers consisting of tubulin protein subunits; major components of the cytoskeleton and found in mitotic spindles, cilia, flagella, centrioles, and basal bodies.

microvilli (sing., *microvillus*) Minute projections of the plasma membrane that increase the surface area of the cell; found mainly in cells concerned with absorption or secretion, such as those lining the intestine or the kidney tubules.

midbrain In vertebrate embryos, one of the three divisions of the developing brain. Also called *mesencephalon*. Compare with *forebrain* and *hindbrain*.

middle lamella The layer composed of pectin polysaccharides that serves to cement together the primary cell walls of adjacent plant cells.

midvein The main, or central, vein of a leaf.

migration (1) The periodic or seasonal movement of an organism (individual or population) from one place to another, usually over a long distance. See *dispersal*. (2) In evolutionary biology, a movement of individuals that results in a transfer of alleles from one population to another. See *gene flow.*

mineralocorticoids (min″-ur-al-oh-kor′-tih-koidz) Hormones produced by the adrenal cortex that regulate mineral metabolism and, indirectly, fluid balance. The principal mineralocorticoid is aldosterone.

minerals Inorganic nutrients ingested as salts dissolved in food and water.

minimum viable population (MVP) The smallest population size at which a species has a high chance of sustaining its numbers and surviving into the future.

mismatch repair A DNA repair mechanism in which special enzymes recognize the incorrectly paired nucleotides and remove them. DNA polymerases then fill in the missing nucleotides.

missense mutation A type of base-pair substitution mutation that causes one amino acid to be substituted for another in the resulting protein product. Compare with *nonsense mutation*.

mitochondria (my″-toh-kon′-dree-ah) (sing., *mitochondrion*) Intracellular organelles that are the sites of oxidative phosphorylation in eukaryotes; include an outer membrane and an inner membrane.

mitochondrial DNA (mtDNA) DNA present in mitochondria that is transmitted maternally, from mothers to their offspring. Mitochondrial DNA mutates more rapidly than nuclear DNA.

mitosis (my-toh′-sis) The division of the cell nucleus resulting in two daughter nuclei, each with the same number of chromosomes as the parent nucleus; mitosis consists of prophase, prometaphase, metaphase, anaphase, and telophase. Cytokinesis usually overlaps the telophase stage.

mitotic spindle Structure consisting mainly of microtubules that provides the framework for chromosome movement during cell division.

mitral valve See *atrioventricular valve*.

mobile genetic element See *transposon*.

model organism A species chosen for biological studies because it has characteristics that allow for the efficient analysis of biological processes. Most model organisms are small, have short generation times, and are easy to grow and study under controlled conditions.

modern synthesis A comprehensive, unified explanation of evolution based on combining previous scientific theories, especially of Mendelian genetics with Darwin's scientific theory of evolution by natural selection.

molars Posterior teeth of a mammal; flattened for crushing and grinding; compare with *incisors, canines,* and *premolars.*

mole The atomic mass of an element or the molecular mass of a compound, expressed in grams; one mole of any substance has 6.02×10^{23} units (Avogadro's number).

molecular anthropology The branch of science that compares genetic material from individuals of regional human populations to help unravel the origin and migrations of modern humans.

molecular chaperones Proteins that help other proteins fold properly. Although chaperones do not dictate the folding pattern, they make the process more efficient.

molecular clock analysis A comparison of the DNA nucleotide sequences of related organisms to estimate when they diverged from one another during the course of evolution.

molecular formula The type of chemical formula that gives the actual numbers of each type of atom in a molecule. Compare with *simplest formula* and *structural formula*.

molecular mass The sum of the atomic masses of the atoms that make up a single molecule of a compound; expressed in atomic mass units (amu) or daltons.

molecular systematics The science that focuses on molecular structure to clarify evolutionary relationships.

molecule The smallest particle of a covalently bonded element or compound; two or more atoms joined by covalent bonds.

mollusks A phylum of coelomate protostome animals characterized by a soft body, visceral mass, mantle, and foot.

molting The shedding and replacement of an outer covering such as an exoskeleton.

molting hormone A steroid hormone that stimulates growth and molting in insects. Also called *ecdysone.*

monoacylglycerol (mon″-o-as-il-glis′-er-ol) Lipid consisting of glycerol combined chemically with a single fatty acid. Also called *monoglyceride*. Compare with *diacylglycerol* and *triacylglycerol*.

monoclonal antibodies Identical antibody molecules produced by cells cloned from a single cell.

monocot (mon′-oh-kot) One of two classes of flowering plants; monocot seeds contain a single cotyledon, or seed leaf. Compare with *eudicot.*

monocyte (mon′-oh-site) A type of white blood cell; a large, phagocytic, nongranular leukocyte that enters the tissues and differentiates into a macrophage.

monoecious (mon-ee′-shus) Having male and female reproductive parts in separate flowers or cones on the same plant; compare with *dioecious.*

monogamy A mating system in which a male animal mates with a single female during a breeding season.

monoglyceride See *monoacylglycerol.*

monohybrid cross A genetic cross that takes into account the behavior of alleles of a single locus. Compare with *dihybrid cross.*

monokaryotic (mon″-o-kare-ee-ot′-ik) The condition of having a single *n* nucleus per cell, characteristic of certain fungal hyphae. Compare with *dikaryotic.*

monomer (mon′-oh-mer) A molecule that can link with other similar molecules; two monomers join to form a dimer, whereas many form a polymer. Monomers are small (e.g., sugars or amino acids) or large (e.g., tubulin or actin proteins).

monophyletic group (mon″-oh-fye-let′-ik) A group of organisms that includes a recent common ancestor and all its descendants; a clade. Compare with *polyphyletic group* and *paraphyletic group.*

monosaccharide (mon-oh-sak′-ah-ride) A sugar that cannot be degraded by hydrolysis to a simpler sugar (e.g., glucose or fructose).

monosomy A type of aneuploidy in which an individual lacks one member of a pair of chromosomes; designated $2n - 1$.

monotremes (mon′-oh-treemz) Egg-laying mammals such as the duck-billed platypus of Australia.

monounsaturated fatty acid See *fatty acid.*

monozygotic twins Genetically identical twins that arise from the division of a single fertilized egg; commonly known as *identical twins.* Compare with *dizygotic twins.*

Montreal Protocol International agreement designed to protect the ozone layer by gradually eliminating the production of ozone-depleting substances.

morphogen Any chemical agent thought to govern the processes of cell differentiation and pattern formation that lead to morphogenesis.

morphogenesis (mor-foh-jen′-eh-sis) The development of the form and structures of an organism and its parts; proceeds through a series of steps known as *pattern formation.*

mortality The rate at which individuals die; the average per capita death rate.

morula (mor′-yoo-lah) An early embryo consisting of a solid ball of cells.

mosaic development A rigid developmental pattern in which the fates of cells become restricted early in development. Compare with *regulative development.*

mosses A phylum of spore-producing nonvascular plants with an alternation of generations in which the dominant *n* gametophyte alternates with a *2n* sporophyte that remains attached to the gametophyte.

motor neuron An efferent neuron that transmits impulses away from the central nervous system to skeletal muscle.

motor program A coordinated sequence of muscle actions responsible for many behaviors we think of as automatic.

motor unit Functional unit consisting of a single motor neuron and the muscle fibers it innervates.

mRNA cap An unusual nucleotide, 7-methylguanylate, that is added to the 5′ end of a eukaryotic messenger RNA. Capping enables eukaryotic ribosomes to bind to mRNA.

mucosa (mew-koh′-suh) See *mucous membrane*.

mucous membrane A type of epithelial membrane that lines a body cavity that opens to the outside of the body, e.g., the digestive and respiratory tracts; also called *mucosa*.

mucus (mew′-cus) A sticky secretion composed of covalently linked protein and carbohydrate; serves to lubricate body parts and trap particles of dirt and other contaminants. (The adjectival form is spelled *mucous*.)

Müllerian mimicry (mul-ler′-ee-un mim′-ih-kree) The resemblance of dangerous, unpalatable, or poisonous species to one another so that potential predators recognize them more easily. Compare with *Batesian mimicry*.

multiple alleles (al-leelz′) Three or more alleles of a single locus (in a population), such as the alleles governing the ABO series of blood types.

multiple fruit A fruit that develops from many ovaries of many separate flowers, e.g., pineapple. Compare with *simple, aggregate,* and *accessory fruits*.

muscle (1) A tissue specialized for contraction. (2) An organ that produces movement by contraction.

muscle fibers Muscle cells; elongated cells that contain myofibrils, the contractile units.

muscle spindles Proprioceptors that detect muscle movement.

muscle tone The continuous, partial contraction of individual muscles and muscle groups.

mutagen (mew′-tah-jen) Any agent capable of entering the cell and producing mutations.

mutation Any change in DNA; may include a change in the nucleotide base pairs of a gene, a rearrangement of genes within the chromosomes so that their interactions produce different effects, or a change in the chromosomes themselves.

mutualism In ecology, a symbiotic relationship in which both partners benefit from the association. Compare with *parasitism* and *commensalism*.

mycelium (my-seel′-ee-um) (pl., *mycelia*) The vegetative body of most fungi and certain protists (water molds); consists of a branched network of hyphae.

mycology The study of fungi.

mycorrhizae (my″-kor-rye′-zee) Mutualistic associations of fungi and plant roots that aid in the plant's absorption of essential minerals from the soil. Hyphae of ectomycorrhizal fungi coat plant roots; those of endomycorrhizal fungi penetrate plant cell walls (see *arbuscules*).

mycotoxins Poisonous chemical compounds produced by fungi, e.g., aflatoxins that harm the liver and are known carcinogens.

myelencephalon Part of the vertebrate embryonic brain; gives rise to the medulla.

myelin sheath (my′-eh-lin) The white, fatty material that forms a sheath around the axons of certain nerve cells, which are then called *myelinated fibers*.

myocardial infarction (MI) Heart attack; serious consequence occurring when the heart muscle receives insufficient oxygen.

myofibrils (my-oh-fy′-brilz) Tiny threadlike structures in the cytoplasm of striated and cardiac muscle that are composed of myosin filaments and actin filaments; these filaments are responsible for muscle contraction; see *myosin filaments* and *actin filaments*.

myofilament See *filament*.

myoglobin (my′-oh-glo″-bin) A hemoglobin-like, oxygen-transferring protein found in muscle.

myosin (my′-oh-sin) A protein that together with actin is responsible for muscle contraction.

myosin filaments Thick filaments consisting mainly of the protein myosin; actin and myosin filaments make up the myofibrils of muscle fibers.

myxedema Hypothyroid condition in which there is almost no thyroid function, characterized by slowing down of physical and mental activity.

n The chromosome number of a gamete. The chromosome number of a zygote is $2n$. If an organism is not polyploid, the n gametes are haploid and the $2n$ zygotes are diploid.

NAD⁺/NADH Oxidized and reduced forms, respectively, of nicotinamide adenine dinucleotide, a coenzyme that transfers electrons (as hydrogen), particularly in catabolic pathways, including cellular respiration.

NADP⁺/NADPH Oxidized and reduced forms, respectively, of nicotinamide adenine dinucleotide phosphate, a coenzyme that acts as an electron (hydrogen) transfer agent, particularly in anabolic pathways, including photosynthesis.

nanoplankton Extremely minute ($< 10\ \mu m$ in length) algae that are major producers in the ocean because of their great abundance; part of phytoplankton.

natality The rate at which individuals produce offspring; the average per capita birth rate.

national conservation strategy Detailed plan for managing and preserving the biological diversity of a specific country.

natural killer cell (NK cell) A large, granular lymphocyte that functions in both nonspecific and specific immune responses; releases cytokines and proteolytic enzymes that target tumor cells and cells infected with viruses and other pathogens.

natural selection The mechanism of evolution proposed by Charles Darwin; the tendency of organisms that have favorable adaptations to their environment to survive and become the parents of the next generation. Evolution occurs when natural selection results in changes in allele frequencies in a population. Compare with *artificial selection*.

navigation Involves the use of cues to change direction when necessary in order to reach a specific destination; requires a sense of direction, called compass sense, and an awareness of location, called map sense.

Neandertals See *Homo neanderthalensis*.

necrosis Uncontrolled cell death that causes inflammation and damages other cells. Compare with *apoptosis*.

nectary (nek′-ter-ee) In plants, a gland or other structure that secretes nectar.

negative control A genetic control system in which a regulatory protein binds to DNA, turning off transcription of a gene. Compare with *positive control*.

negative feedback system A regulatory system in which a change in some steady state triggers a response that counteracts, or reverses, the change, restoring homeostasis, e.g., how mammals maintain body temperature. Compare with *positive feedback system*.

nekton (nek′-ton) Free-swimming aquatic organisms such as fish and turtles. Compare with *plankton*.

nematocyst (nem-at′-oh-sist) A stinging structure found within cnidocytes (stinging cells) in cnidarians; used for anchorage, defense, and capturing prey.

nematodes The phylum of animals commonly known as *roundworms*.

nemerteans The phylum of animals commonly known as *ribbon worms;* each has a proboscis (tubular feeding organ) for capturing prey.

Neogene period See *Cenozoic era*.

neonate Newborn individual.

neoplasm See *tumor*.

nephridial organ (neh-frid′-ee-al) The excretory organ of many invertebrates; consists of simple or branching tubes that usually open to the outside of the body through pores; also called *nephridium*.

nephron (nef′-ron) The functional, microscopic unit of the vertebrate kidney.

neritic province (ner-ih′-tik) Ocean water that extends from the shoreline to where the bottom reaches a depth of 200 m. Compare with *oceanic province*.

nerve A bundle of axons (or dendrites) wrapped in connective tissue that conveys impulses between the central nervous system and some other part of the body.

nerve cord A bundle of nerves that extends from a central ganglion or brain and gives rise to smaller nerves. In vertebrates the nerve cord is dorsal and tubular.

nerve net The network of neurons found in cnidarians and ctenophores.

nervous system In most invertebrates, consists of ganglia, sensory cells or sense organs, and networks of neurons. In vertebrates, consists of the brain, spinal cord, sense organs, and nerves; the body's main regulatory system.

nervous tissue A type of animal tissue specialized for transmitting electrical and chemical signals.

net primary productivity (NPP) The energy that remains in an ecosystem (as biomass) after cellular respiration has occurred; net primary productivity equals gross primary productivity minus respiration. Compare with *gross primary productivity (GPP)*.

neural circuit A functional group of neurons, typically consisting of one or more afferent neurons, one or more interneurons, and one or more efferent neurons.

neural crest cells (noor′-ul) A group of embryonic cells found only in vertebrates; develop along the neural tube and migrate to various parts of the embryo where they give rise to (or influence the development of) nerves, head muscles, cranium, jaws, and other structures.

neural plasticity The ability of the nervous system to change in response to experience.

neural plate See *neural tube*.

neural signaling The transmission of information by neurons (nerve cells).

neural transmission The conduction of a neural impulse, or action potential, along a neuron or from one neuron to another.

neural tube The hollow, longitudinal structure in the early vertebrate embryo that gives rise to the brain and spinal cord. The neural tube forms from the neural plate, a flattened, thickened region of the ectoderm that rolls up and sinks below the surface.

neuroendocrine cells Neurons that produce neurohormones.

neuroendocrine signaling Neuroendocrine cells produce neurohormones that are transported down axons and released into the interstitial fluid.

neurofibrillary tangles Abnormal fibrous deposits in the cytoplasm of neurons in the brains of individuals with Alzheimer's disease; interfere with neural signaling.

neurogenesis The production of new neurons.

neurohormones Hormones produced by neuroendocrine cells; transported down axons and released into interstitial fluid; common in invertebrates; in vertebrates, the hypothalamus produces neurohormones.

neuron (noor′-on) A nerve cell; a conducting cell of the nervous system that typically consists of a cell body, dendrites, and an axon.

neuropeptide One of a group of peptides produced in neural tissue that function as signaling molecules; many are neurotransmitters.

neuropeptide Y (NPY) A signaling molecule produced by the hypothalamus that increases appetite and slows metabolism; helps restore energy homeostasis when leptin levels and food intake are low.

neurotransmitters Chemical signals used by neurons to transmit impulses across a synapse.

neutral solution A solution of pH 7; there are equal concentrations of hydrogen ions [H^+] and hydroxide ions [OH^-]. Compare with *acidic solution* and *basic solution*.

neutral variation Variation that does not appear to confer any selective advantage or disadvantage to the organism.

neutron (noo′-tron) An electrically neutral particle with a mass of 1 atomic mass unit (amu) found in the atomic nucleus. Compare with *proton* and *electron*.

neutrophil (new′-truh-fil) A type of granular leukocyte important in immune responses; a type of phagocyte that engulfs and destroys bacteria and foreign matter.

niche (nich) The totality of an organism's adaptations, its use of resources, and the lifestyle to which it is fitted in its community; how an organism uses materials in its environment as well as how it interacts with other organisms; also called *ecological niche*. See *fundamental niche* and *realized niche*.

nicotinamide adenine dinucleotide See *NAD⁺/NADH*.

nicotinamide adenine dinucleotide phosphate See *NADP⁺/NADPH*.

nitric oxide (NO) A gaseous signaling molecule; a neurotransmitter.

nitrification (nie″-tra-fuh-kay′-shun) The conversion of ammonia (NH_3) to nitrate (NO_3^-) by certain bacteria (nitrifying bacteria) in the soil; part of the nitrogen cycle.

nitrogenase (nie-traa′-jen-ase) The enzyme responsible for nitrogen fixation under anaerobic conditions.

nitrogen cycle The worldwide circulation of nitrogen from the abiotic environment into living things and back into the abiotic environment.

nitrogen fixation The conversion of atmospheric nitrogen (N_2) to ammonia (NH_3) by certain bacteria; part of the nitrogen cycle.

nitrogen oxides Binary compounds of oxygen and nitrogen, produced by combustion, that are a necessary ingredient in photochemical smog.

nociceptors (no′-sih-sep-torz) Pain receptors; free endings of certain sensory neurons whose stimulation is perceived as pain.

nocturnal animals Animals that are most active at night. Compare with *crepuscular animals* and *diurnal animals*.

node The area on a stem where each leaf is attached. Compare with *internode*.

nodes of Ranvier (ron′-ve-a) Gaps in the myelin sheath of myelinated neurons where an action potential can be generated. In saltatory conduction, the action potential appears to "leap" along from one node of Ranvier to the next.

nodules Swellings on the roots of plants, such as legumes, in which symbiotic nitrogen-fixing bacteria (*rhizobia*) live.

noncompetitive inhibition The binding of a substance (the noncompetitive inhibitor) to a site other than the active site of an enzyme, thereby lowering the rate at which the enzyme catalyzes a reaction. Compare with *competitive inhibition*.

noncompetitive inhibitor See *noncompetitive inhibition*.

noncyclic electron transport In photosynthesis, the linear flow of electrons, produced by photolysis of water, through photosystems II and I; results in the formation of ATP (by chemiosmosis), NADPH, and O_2. Compare with *cyclic electron transport*.

nondisjunction Abnormal separation of sister chromatids or of homologous chromosomes caused by their failure to disjoin (move apart) properly during mitosis or meiosis.

nonpolar covalent bond Chemical bond formed by the equal sharing of electrons between atoms of approximately equal electronegativity. Compare with *polar covalent bond*.

nonpolar molecule Molecule that does not have a positively charged end and a negatively charged end; nonpolar molecules are generally insoluble in water. Compare with *polar molecule*.

nonsense mutation A base-pair substitution mutation that results in an amino acid–specifying codon being changed to a termination (stop) codon; when the abnormal mRNA is translated, the resulting protein is usually shortened and nonfunctional. Compare with *missense mutation*.

nonspecific immune responses See *innate immune responses*.

nonspecific immunity See *innate immune responses*.

norepinephrine (nor-ep-ih-nef′-rin) A neurotransmitter that is also a hormone secreted by the adrenal medulla.

norm of reaction The range of phenotypic possibilities that can develop from a single genotype under different environmental conditions.

Northern blot A technique in which RNA fragments, previously separated by gel electrophoresis, are transferred to a nitrocellulose membrane and detected by autoradiography or chemical luminescence. Compare with *Southern blot* and *Western blot*.

notochord (no′-toe-kord) The flexible, longitudinal rod in the anterior–posterior axis that serves as an internal skeleton in the embryos of all chordates and in the adults of some.

nuclear area Region of a prokaryotic cell that contains DNA; not enclosed by a membrane. Also called *nucleoid*.

nuclear envelope The double membrane system that encloses the cell nucleus of eukaryotes.

nuclear equivalence The concept that the nuclei of all differentiated cells of an adult organism are genetically identical to one another and to the nucleus of the zygote from which they were derived. Compare with *genomic rearrangement* and *gene amplification*.

nuclear pores Structures in the nuclear envelope that allow passage of certain materials between the cell nucleus and the cytoplasm.

nucleoid See *nuclear area.*

nucleolus (new-klee'-oh-lus) (pl., *nucleoli*) Specialized structure in the cell nucleus formed from regions of several chromosomes; site of assembly of the ribosomal subunits.

nucleoplasm The contents of the cell nucleus.

nucleoside triphosphate Molecule consisting of a nitrogenous base, a pentose sugar, and three phosphate groups, e.g., adenosine triphosphate (ATP).

nucleosomes (new'-klee-oh-sohmz) Repeating units of chromatin structure, each consisting of a length of DNA wound around a complex of eight histone molecules. Adjacent nucleosomes are connected by a DNA linker region associated with another histone protein.

nucleotide (noo'-klee-oh-tide) A molecule consisting of one or more phosphate groups, a five-carbon sugar (ribose or deoxyribose), and a nitrogenous base (purine or pyrimidine).

nucleotide excision repair A DNA repair mechanism commonly used to repair a damaged segment of DNA caused by the sun's ultraviolet radiation or by harmful chemicals.

nucleus (new'-klee-us) (pl., *nuclei*) (1) The central region of an atom that contains the protons and neutrons. (2) A cell organelle in eukaryotes that contains the DNA and serves as the control center of the cell. (3) A mass of nerve cell bodies in the central nervous system. Compare with *ganglion.*

nut A simple, dry fruit that contains a single seed and is surrounded by a hard fruit wall.

nutrients The chemical substances in food that are used as components for synthesizing needed materials and/or as energy sources.

nutrition The process of taking in and using food (nutrients).

obesity Excess accumulation of body fat; a person is considered obese if the body mass index (BMI) is 30 or higher.

obligate anaerobe An organism that grows only in the absence of oxygen. Compare with *facultative anaerobe.*

occipital lobes Posterior areas of the mammalian cerebrum; interpret visual stimuli from the retina of the eye.

ocean currents Mass movements of surface ocean water produced by winds blowing over the ocean.

oceanic province That part of the open ocean that overlies an ocean bottom deeper than 200 m. Compare with *neritic province.*

Okazaki fragment One of many short segments of DNA, each 100 to 1000 nucleotides long, that must be joined by DNA ligase to form the lagging strand in DNA replication.

olfactory bulbs Olfactory relay centers where axons from the olfactory nerves transmit information to neurons that signal higher centers.

olfactory epithelium Tissue containing odor-sensing neurons.

olfactory nerve The first cranial nerve; consists of the axons of the olfactory receptor cells and extends to the olfactory bulb in the brain.

oligodendrocyte A type of glial cell that forms myelin sheaths around neurons in the CNS.

omega-3 fatty acids Essential fatty acids found in salmon and other fatty fishes, walnuts, and certain vegetable oils (e.g., canola, soybean); studies suggest that omega-3 fatty acids help lower triglycerides and blood pressure, and have other health benefits.

ommatidium (om″-ah-tid′-ee-um) (pl., *ommatidia*) One of the light-detecting units of a compound eye, consisting of a lens and a crystalline cone that focus light onto photoreceptors called *retinular cells.*

omnivore (om′-nih-vore) An animal that eats a variety of plant and animal materials.

oncogene (on′-koh-jeen) An abnormally functioning gene implicated in causing cancer. Compare with *proto-oncogene* and *tumor suppressor gene.*

1000 Genomes Project An international collaborative initiative completed in 2012 to provide a detailed catalogue of human genetic variation by determining the genomic DNA sequences of over 1000 anonymous individuals from a number of different ethnic groups. Compare with *Human Genome Project.*

oocytes (oh′-oh-sites) Meiotic cells that give rise to egg cells (ova).

oogamy (oh-og′-uh-me) The fertilization of a large, nonmotile female gamete by a small, motile male gamete. Compare with *isogamy* and *anisogamy.*

oogenesis (oh″-oh-jen′-eh-sis) Production of female gametes (eggs) by meiosis. Compare with *spermatogenesis.*

oogonia Undifferentiated cells in the ovaries that give rise to primary oocytes.

oospore A thick-walled, resistant spore formed from a zygote during sexual reproduction in water molds.

open circulatory system A type of circulatory system in which the blood bathes the tissues directly; characteristic of arthropods and many mollusks. Compare with *closed circulatory system.*

open system An entity that exchanges energy with its surroundings. Compare with *closed system.*

operant conditioning A type of learning in which an animal is rewarded or punished for performing a behavior it discovers by chance.

operator site One of the control regions of an operon; the DNA segment to which a repressor binds, thereby inhibiting the transcription of the adjacent structural genes of the operon.

operculum In bony fishes, a protective flap of the body wall that covers the gills.

operon (op′-er-on) In prokaryotes, a group of structural genes that are coordinately controlled and transcribed as a single message, plus their adjacent regulatory elements.

opisthokonts Members of the unikont clade in which motile cells possess a single posterior flagellum; include fungi, choanoflagellates, and animals. Compare with *amoebozoa.*

opposable thumb The arrangement of the fingers so that they are positioned opposite the thumb, enabling the organism to grasp objects.

optic chiasm The X-shaped structure formed by the crossing of the optic nerves in the floor of the hypothalamus.

optic nerve The second cranial nerve; transmits visual information from the retina to the brain; composed of the axons of ganglion cells.

optimal foraging The process of obtaining food in a manner that maximizes benefits and/or minimizes costs.

orbital Region in which electrons occur in an atom or molecule.

orbital hybridization A rearrangement of the orbitals in the valence shell that may occur when an atom forms covalent bonds with other atoms.

order A taxonomic category made up of related families.

Ordovician period See *Paleozoic era.*

organ A specialized structure, such as the heart or liver, or a flower, made up of tissues and adapted to perform a specific function or group of functions.

organelle One of the specialized structures within the cell, such as the mitochondria, Golgi complex, ribosomes, or contractile vacuole; many organelles are membrane-enclosed.

organic compound A compound consisting of a backbone made up of carbon atoms. Compare with *inorganic compound.*

organism Any living system consisting of one or more cells.

organismic model Cooperative view of community, described by Clements, in which a community goes through certain stages of development (succession), like the embryonic stages of an organism, and eventually reaches an adult state (climax community). Compare with *individualistic model.*

organismic respiration See *respiration.*

organ of Corti The structure within the inner ear of vertebrates that contains receptor cells that sense sound vibrations.

organogenesis The process of organ formation.

organ system An organized group of tissues and organs that work together to perform a specialized set of functions, e.g., the digestive system or circulatory system.

orgasm (or′-gazm) The climax of sexual excitement.

origin of replication A specific site on the DNA where replication begins.

orthologous genes Homologous genes found in different species because they were inherited from a common ancestor.

osculum (os′kyuh-lum) In a sponge, the main opening between the spongocoel and the external environment.

osmoconformer An animal in which the salt concentration of body fluids varies along with changes in the surrounding sea water so that it stays in osmotic equilibrium with its surroundings. Compare with *osmoregulator*.

osmolarity The number of osmoles of solute per liter of solution. See *osmole*.

osmole The number of solute particles (molecules or ions) produced when a mole of solute dissolves. One mole of glucose is one osmol; one mole of sodium chloride (NaCl), which dissolves to give two types of particles, is two osmols.

osmoregulation (oz″-moh-reg-yoo-lay′-shun) The active regulation of the osmotic pressure of body fluids so that they do not become excessively dilute or excessively concentrated.

osmoregulator An animal that maintains an optimal salt concentration in its body fluids despite changes in salinity of its surroundings. Compare with *osmoconformer*.

osmosis (oz-moh′-sis) The net movement of water (the principal solvent in biological systems) by diffusion through a selectively permeable membrane from a region of higher concentration of water (a hypotonic solution) to a region of lower concentration of water (a hypertonic solution).

osmotic pressure The pressure that must be exerted on the hypertonic side of a selectively permeable membrane to prevent diffusion of water (by osmosis) from the side containing pure water.

osteichthyes (os″-tee-ick′-thees) Historically, the vertebrate class of bony fishes. Biologists now divide bony fishes into three classes: Actinopterygii, the ray-finned fishes; Actinistia, the lobe-finned fishes; and Dipnoi, the lungfishes.

osteoblast (os′-tee-oh-blast) A type of bone cell that secretes the protein matrix of bone. Also see *osteocyte*.

osteoclast (os′-tee-oh-clast) Large, multinucleate cell that helps sculpt and remodel bones by dissolving and removing part of the bony substance.

osteocyte (os′-tee-oh-site) A mature bone cell; an osteoblast that has become embedded within the bone matrix and occupies a lacuna.

osteon (os′-tee-on) The spindle-shaped unit of bone composed of concentric layers of osteocytes organized around a central Haversian canal containing blood vessels and nerves.

otoliths (oh′-toe-liths) Small calcium carbonate crystals in the saccule and utricle of the inner ear; sense gravity and are important in static equilibrium.

outbreeding The mating of individuals of unrelated strains, also called *outcrossing*. Compare with *inbreeding*.

outcrossing See *outbreeding*.

outgroup In cladistics, a taxon that represents an approximation of the ancestral condition; the outgroup is related to the *ingroup* (the members of the group under study) but separated from the ingroup lineage before they diversified.

ovary (oh′-var-ee) (1) In animals, one of the paired female gonads responsible for producing eggs and sex hormones. (2) In flowering plants, the base of the carpel that contains ovules; ovaries develop into fruits after fertilization.

oviduct (oh′-vih-dukt) The tube that carries ova from the ovary to the uterus, cloaca, or body exterior. Also called *fallopian tube* or *uterine tube*.

oviparous (oh-vip′-ur-us) Bearing young in the egg stage of development; egg laying. Compare with *viviparous* and *ovoviviparous*.

ovoviviparous (oh″-voh-vih-vip′-ur-us) A type of development in which the young hatch from eggs incubated inside the mother's body. Compare with *viviparous* and *oviparous*.

ovulation (ov-u-lay′-shun) The release of an egg from the ovary.

ovule (ov′-yool) The structure in the plant ovary that develops into the seed following fertilization; also called *megasporangium*.

ovum (pl., *ova*) Female gamete of an animal.

oxaloacetate Four-carbon compound; important intermediate in the citric acid cycle and in the C_4 and CAM pathways of carbon fixation in photosynthesis.

oxidants Highly reactive molecules such as free radicals, peroxides, and superoxides that are produced during normal cell processes that require oxygen; can damage DNA and other molecules by snatching electrons. Compare with *antioxidants*.

oxidation The loss of one or more electrons (or hydrogen atoms) by an atom, ion, or molecule. Compare with *reduction*.

oxidative phosphorylation (fos″-for-ih-lay′-shun) The production of ATP using energy derived from the transfer of electrons in the electron transport system of mitochondria; occurs by chemiosmosis.

oxygen-carrying capacity The maximum amount of oxygen transported by hemoglobin.

oxygen debt The oxygen necessary to metabolize the lactic acid produced during strenuous exercise.

oxygen–hemoglobin dissociation curve A curve depicting the percentage saturation of hemoglobin with oxygen, as a function of certain variables such as oxygen concentration, carbon dioxide concentration, or pH.

oxyhemoglobin Hemoglobin that has combined with oxygen.

oxytocin (ok″see-tow′-sin) Hormone secreted by the hypothalamus and released by the posterior lobe of the pituitary gland; stimulates contraction of the pregnant uterus and the ducts of mammary glands.

ozone (O_3) A blue gas with a distinctive odor that is a human-made pollutant near Earth's surface (in the troposphere) but a natural and essential component of the stratosphere.

P generation (parental generation) Members of two different true-breeding lines that are crossed to produce the F_1 generation.

P680 Chlorophyll *a* molecules that serve as the reaction center of photosystem II, transferring photoexcited electrons to a primary acceptor; named by their absorption peak at 680 nm.

P700 Chlorophyll *a* molecules that serve as the reaction center of photosystem I, transferring photoexcited electrons to a primary acceptor; named by their absorption peak at 700 nm.

pacemaker (of the heart) See *sinoatrial (SA) node*.

Pacinian corpuscle (pah-sin′-ee-an kor′-pus-el) A receptor located in the dermis of the skin that responds to pressure.

paedomorphosis Retention of juvenile or larval features in a sexually mature animal.

pair bond A stable relationship between animals of opposite sex that ensures cooperative behavior in mating and rearing the young.

paleoanthropology (pay″-lee-o-an-thro-pol′-uh-gee) The study of human evolution.

Paleogene period See *Cenozoic era*.

Paleozoic era That part of geologic time extending from roughly 541 million to 252 million years ago; divided into six periods: Cambrian (appearance of many new animal groups, the *Cambrian radiation* or *Cambrian explosion*); Ordovician (diversification of sea life); Silurian (appearance of jawed fishes, terrestrial plants, and air-breathing animals); Devonian (appearance of sharks and bony fishes); Carboniferous (great swamp forests formed coal deposits); Permian (ended with the greatest mass extinction of all time).

palindromic Reading the same forward and backward; DNA sequences are palindromic when the base sequence of one strand reads the same as its complement when both are read in the 5′ to 3′ direction.

palisade mesophyll (mez′-oh-fil) The vertically stacked, columnar mesophyll cells near the upper epidermis in certain leaves. Compare with *spongy mesophyll*.

pancreas (pan′-kree-us) Large gland located in the vertebrate abdominal cavity. The pancreas produces pancreatic juice containing digestive enzymes; also serves as an endocrine gland, secreting the hormones insulin and glucagon.

parabasilids Anaerobic, flagellated excavates that often live in animals; examples include trichonymphs and trichomonads.

parabronchi (sing., *parabronchus*) Thin-walled ducts in the lungs of birds; gases are exchanged across their walls.

paracrine regulation A type of regulation in which a signal molecule (e.g., certain hormones) diffuses through interstitial fluid and acts on nearby target cells. Compare with *autocrine regulation*.

paraphyletic group A group of organisms made up of a common ancestor and some, but not all, of its descendants. Compare with *monophyletic group* and *polyphyletic group*.

parapodia (par″-uh-poh′-dee-ah) (sing., *parapodium*) Paired, thickly bristled paddlelike appendages extending laterally from each segment of polychaete worms.

parasite A heterotrophic organism that obtains nourishment from the living tissue of another organism (the host).

parasitism (par′-uh-si-tiz″-m) A symbiotic relationship in which one member (the parasite) benefits and the other (the host) is adversely affected. Compare with *commensalism* and *mutualism*.

parasympathetic nervous system A division of the autonomic nervous system concerned with the control of the internal organs; functions to conserve or restore energy. Compare with *sympathetic nervous system*.

parathyroid glands Small, pea-sized glands closely adjacent to the thyroid gland; they secrete parathyroid hormone, which regulates calcium and phosphate metabolism.

parathyroid hormone (PTH) A hormone secreted by the parathyroid glands; regulates calcium and phosphate metabolism.

parenchyma (par-en′-kih-mah) Highly variable living plant cells that have thin primary walls; function in photosynthesis, the storage of nutrients, and/or secretion.

parental imprinting See *imprinting* (definition 1).

parental investment The contribution that each parent makes in producing and rearing offspring; increases the probability that their offspring will survive.

parietal lobes The region of the cerebrum between the frontal lobes and the occipital lobes; contains the general sensory association areas.

parsimony The principle based on the experience that the simplest explanation is most probably the correct one.

parthenogenesis (par″-theh-noh-jen′-eh-sis) The development of an unfertilized egg into an adult organism; common among honeybees, wasps, and certain other arthropods.

partial pressure (of a gas) The pressure exerted by a gas in a mixture, which is the same pressure it would exert if alone. For example, the partial pressure of atmospheric oxygen (P_{O_2}) is 160 mm Hg at sea level.

passive immunity Temporary immunity that depends on the presence of immunoglobulins produced by another organism. Compare with *active immunity*.

passive ion channel A channel in the plasma membrane that permits the passage of specific ions such as Na^+, K^+, or Cl^-.

patch clamp technique A method that allows researchers to study the ion channels of a tiny patch of membrane by tightly sealing a micropipette to the patch and measuring the flow of ions through the channels.

patchiness See *clumped dispersion*.

pathogen (path′-oh-gen) An organism, usually a microorganism, capable of producing disease.

pathogen-associated molecular patterns (PAMPs) Distinctive molecules on bacteria and other pathogens that are not found in animals; pattern recognition receptors bind them.

pattern formation See *morphogenesis*.

pattern recognition receptors Receptors on certain types of animal cells that bind pathogen-associated molecular patterns (PAMPs); binding activates innate immune responses.

pedigree A chart constructed to show an inheritance pattern within a family through multiple generations.

peduncle The stalk of a flower or inflorescence.

pellicle A flexible outer covering consisting of protein; characteristic of certain protists, e.g., ciliates and euglenoids.

penis The male sexual organ of copulation in reptiles, mammals, and a few birds.

pentose A sugar molecule containing five carbons.

people overpopulation A situation in which there are too many people in a given geographic area; results in pollution, environmental degradation, and resource depletion. Compare with *consumption overpopulation*.

PEP carboxylase Enzyme with an extremely high affinity for CO_2; responsible for initial fixation of CO_2 in C_4 plants and CAM plants.

pepsin (pep′-sin) An enzyme produced in the stomach that initiates digestion of protein.

pepsinogen The precursor of pepsin; secreted by chief cells in the gastric glands of the stomach.

peptide (pep′-tide) A compound consisting of a chain of amino acid groups linked by peptide bonds. A dipeptide consists of two amino acids, a polypeptide of many.

peptide bond A distinctive covalent carbon-to-nitrogen bond that links amino acids in peptides and proteins.

peptide hormones Water-soluble hormones composed of proteins, such as oxytocin and antidiuretic hormone (ADH).

peptidoglycan (pep″-tid-oh-gly′-kan) A modified protein or peptide having an attached carbohydrate; component of the bacterial cell wall.

peptidyl transferase The ribosomal enzyme (a ribozyme) that catalyzes the formation of a peptide bond.

perception Conscious awareness of our internal and external environments as a result of processing sensory input and comparing present sensory experience with memories of past experience.

perennial plant (purr-en′-ee-ul) A woody or herbaceous plant that grows year after year, i.e., lives more than two years. Compare with *annual plant* and *biennial plant*.

perfect flower A flower that has both stamens and carpels. Compare with *imperfect flower*.

pericentriolar material Fibrils surrounding the centrioles in the microtubule-organizing centers in cells of animals and other organisms having centrioles.

pericycle (pehr′-eh-sy″-kl) A layer of meristematic cells typically found between the endodermis and phloem in roots.

periderm (pehr′-ih-durm) The outer bark of woody stems and roots; composed of cork cells, cork cambium, and cork parenchyma, along with traces of primary tissues.

period An interval of geologic time that is a subdivision of an era; each period is divided into epochs.

periodic table A chart of the elements arranged in order by atomic number.

peripheral membrane protein A protein associated with one of the surfaces of a biological membrane. Compare with *integral membrane protein*.

peripheral nervous system (PNS) In vertebrates, the nerves and receptors that lie outside the central nervous system. Compare with *central nervous system (CNS)*.

peristalsis (pehr″-ih-stal′-sis) Rhythmic waves of muscular contraction and relaxation in the walls of hollow tubular organs, such as the ureter or parts of the digestive tract, that serve to move the contents through the tube.

peritubular capillaries In the mammalian kidney, a capillary network that surrounds each renal tubule; receives blood from the efferent arterioles.

permafrost Permanently frozen subsoil characteristic of frigid areas such as the tundra.

Permian period See *Paleozoic era*.

peroxisomes (pehr-ox′-ih-sohmz) In eukaryotic cells, membrane-enclosed organelles containing enzymes that produce or degrade hydrogen peroxide.

persistence A characteristic of certain chemicals that are extremely stable and may take many years to be broken down into simpler forms by natural processes.

petal One of the parts of the flower attached inside the whorl of sepals; petals are usually colored.

petiole (pet′-ee-ohl) The part of a leaf that attaches to a stem.

Pfr See *phytochrome*.

pH The negative logarithm of the hydrogen ion concentration of a solution (expressed as moles per liter). Neutral pH is 7, values less than 7 are acidic, and those greater than 7 are basic.

phage See *bacteriophage*.

phagocytosis (fag″-oh-sy-toh′-sis) Literally, "cell eating"; a type of endocytosis by which certain cells engulf food particles, microorganisms, foreign matter, or other cells. Compare with *pinocytosis* and *receptor-mediated endocytosis*.

pharmacogenetics A field of gene-based medicine in which drugs are personalized to match a patient's genetic makeup.

pharyngeal slits (fair-in′-jel) Openings that lead from the pharyngeal cavity to the outside; evolved as part of a filter-feeding system in chordates and later became modified for other functions, including gill slits in many aquatic vertebrates.

pharynx (fair'-inks) Part of the digestive tract. In complex vertebrates, it is bounded anteriorly by the mouth and nasal cavities and posteriorly by the esophagus and larynx; the throat region in humans.

phenetics (feh-neh'-tiks) An approach to classification based on measurable similarities in phenotypic characters without consideration of homology or other evolutionary relationships. Compare with *cladistics* and *evolutionary systematics*.

phenotype (fee'-noh-type) The physical or chemical expression of an organism's genes. Compare with *genotype*.

phenotype frequency The proportion of a particular phenotype in the population. Compare with *allele frequency* and *genotype frequency*.

phenylketonuria (PKU) (fee"-nl-kee'-toh-noor'-ee-ah) An inherited disease in which there is a deficiency of the enzyme that normally converts phenylalanine to tyrosine; results in intellectual disability if untreated.

pheromone (fer'-oh-mone) A substance secreted by an organism to the external environment that influences the development or behavior of other members of the same species.

phloem (flo'-em) The vascular tissue that conducts dissolved sugar and other organic compounds in plants.

phosphatases Enzymes that catalyze the removal of phosphate groups from proteins and other molecules. Compare with *kinases* and *protein kinases*.

phosphate group A weakly acidic functional group that can release one or two hydrogen ions.

phosphodiesterase Enzyme that breaks a phosphodiester bond; responsible for inactivating cyclic AMP by converting it to AMP.

phosphodiester linkage Covalent linkage between two nucleotides in a strand of DNA or RNA; includes a phosphate group bonded to the sugars of two adjacent nucleotides.

phosphoenolpyruvate (PEP) Three-carbon phosphorylated compound that is an important intermediate in glycolysis and is a reactant in the initial carbon fixation step in C_4 and CAM photosynthesis.

phosphoglycerate (PGA) Phosphorylated three-carbon compound that is an important metabolic intermediate.

phospholipids (fos"-foh-lip'-idz) Lipids in which two fatty acids and a phosphorus-containing group are attached to glycerol; major components of cell membranes.

phosphorus cycle The worldwide circulation of phosphorus from the abiotic environment into living things and back into the abiotic environment.

phosphorylation (fos"-for-ih-lay'-shun) The introduction of a phosphate group into an organic molecule. See *kinases*.

photoautotroph An organism that obtains energy from light and synthesizes organic compounds from inorganic raw materials; includes plants, algae, and some bacteria. Compare with *photoheterotroph, chemoautotroph,* and *chemoheterotroph.*

photochemical smog Mixture of several air pollutants that injure plant tissues, irritate eyes, and cause respiratory problems in humans.

photoheterotroph An organism that can carry out photosynthesis to obtain energy but cannot fix carbon dioxide and therefore requires organic compounds as a carbon source; includes some bacteria and archaea. Compare with *photoautotroph, chemoautotroph,* and *chemoheterotroph.*

photolysis (foh-tol'-uh-sis) The photochemical splitting of water in the light-dependent reactions of photosynthesis; a specific enzyme is needed to catalyze this reaction.

photon (foh'-ton) A particle of electromagnetic radiation; one quantum of radiant energy.

photoperiodism (foh"-teh-peer'-ee-o-dizm) The physiological response (such as flowering) of plants to variations in the length of daylight and darkness.

photophosphorylation (foh"-toh-fos-for-ih-lay'-shun) The production of ATP in photosynthesis.

photoreceptor (foh"-toh-ree-sep'-tor) (1) A sense organ specialized to detect light. (2) A pigment that absorbs light before triggering a physiological response.

photorespiration (foh"-toh-res-pur-ay'-shun) The process that reduces the efficiency of photosynthesis in C_3 plants during hot spells in summer; consumes oxygen and produces carbon dioxide through the degradation of Calvin cycle intermediates.

photosynthesis The biological process that captures light energy and transforms it into the chemical energy of organic molecules (e.g., carbohydrates), which are manufactured from carbon dioxide and water.

photosystem One of two photosynthetic units responsible for capturing light energy and transferring excited electrons; photosystem I strongly absorbs light of about 700 nm, whereas photosystem II strongly absorbs light of about 680 nm. See *antenna complex* and *reaction center.*

phototaxis Movement of a cell or organism in response to light.

phototroph (foh'-toh-trof) Organism that uses light as a source of energy. Compare with *chemotroph.* See *photoautotroph* and *photoheterotroph.*

phototropins (foh"-toh-troh'-pinz) Family of yellow pigments responsible for such blue light responses as the phototropic response and stomatal opening.

phototropism (foh"-toh-troh'-pizm) The growth of a plant in response to the direction of light.

phycocyanin (fy"-koh-sy-ah'-nin) A blue pigment found in cyanobacteria and red algae.

phycoerythrin (fy"-koh-ee-rih'-thrin) A red pigment found in cyanobacteria and red algae.

phyletic gradualism The idea that evolution occurs by a slow, steady accumulation of genetic changes over time; also called *gradualism.* Compare with *punctuated equilibrium.*

phylogenetic species concept An alternative to the biological species concept in which for a population to be declared a separate species, it must have undergone evolution long enough for statistically significant differences to emerge. Also called *evolutionary species concept.* Compare with *species.*

phylogenetic systematics See *cladistics.*

phylogenetic tree A branching diagram that shows lines of descent among a group of related species.

phylogeny (fy-loj'-en-ee) The complete evolutionary history of a group of organisms.

phylum (fy'-lum) (pl., *phyla*) A taxonomic grouping of related, similar classes; a category beneath the kingdom and above the class.

phytoalexins Antimicrobial compounds produced by plants that limit the spread of pathogens such as fungi.

phytochemicals Non-nutrient compounds found in plants that are biologically active in the body and may promote health.

phytochrome (fy'-toh-krome) A blue-green, proteinaceous pigment involved in a wide variety of physiological responses to light; occurs in two interconvertible forms, Pr (red-absorbing phytochrome) and Pfr (far-red-absorbing phytochrome).

phytoplankton (fy"-toh-plank'-tun) Microscopic floating algae and cyanobacteria that are the base of most aquatic food webs. Compare with *zooplankton.* See *plankton* and *nanoplankton.*

pia mater (pee'-a may'-ter) The inner membrane covering the brain and spinal cord; the innermost of the meninges; also see *dura mater* and *arachnoid.*

pigment A substance that selectively absorbs light of specific wavelengths.

pili (pie'-lie) (sing., *pilus*) Hairlike structures on the surface of many bacteria; function in conjugation or attachment. A sex pilus forms a cytoplasmic bridge with another bacterium and transfers DNA via this bridge.

pineal gland (pie-nee'-al) Endocrine gland located in the brain.

pinocytosis (pin"-oh-sy-toh'-sis) Cell drinking; a type of endocytosis by which cells engulf and absorb droplets of liquids. Compare with *phagocytosis* and *receptor-mediated endocytosis.*

pioneer The first organism to colonize an area and begin the first stage of succession.

pistil The female reproductive organ of a flower; consists of either a single carpel or two or more fused carpels. See *carpel.*

pith The innermost tissue in the stems and roots of many herbaceous plants; primarily a storage tissue.

pituitary gland (pi-too'-ih-tehr"-ee) An endocrine gland located below the hypothalamus; secretes several hormones that influence a wide range of physiological processes.

piwi-associated RNA (piRNA) Small RNAs (26–31 bases) involved in gene silencing of *retrotransposons* and regulating gene activity in animal germ line cells.

placenta (plah-sen′-tah) The partly fetal and partly maternal organ whereby materials are exchanged between fetus and mother in the uterus of placental mammals.

placoderms (plak′-oh-durmz) A group of extinct jawed fishes.

placoid scales (pla′-koid) The toothlike scales found in sharks and other cartilaginous fishes.

plankton Free-floating, mainly microscopic aquatic organisms found in the upper layers of the water; consisting of phytoplankton and zooplankton. Compare with *nekton.*

plants Members of the archaeplastid supergroup, distinguished by development of sporophytes from multicellular embryos enclosed in maternal tissues; also called *land plants.*

planula larva (plan′-yoo-lah) A ciliated larval form found in cnidarians.

plasma The fluid portion of blood in which red blood cells, white blood cells, and platelets are suspended.

plasma cell Cell that secretes antibodies; a differentiated B lymphocyte (B cell).

plasma membrane The selectively permeable surface membrane that encloses the cell contents and through which all materials entering or leaving the cell must pass.

plasma proteins Proteins such as albumins, globulins, and fibrinogen that circulate in the blood plasma.

plasmid (plaz′-mid) Small, circular, double-stranded DNA molecule that carries genes separate from those in the main DNA of a cell.

plasmodesmata (sing., *plasmodesma*) Cytoplasmic channels connecting adjacent plant cells and allowing for the movement of molecules and ions between cells.

plasmodial slime mold (plaz-moh′-dee-uhl) A funguslike amoebozoan protist whose feeding stage consists of a plasmodium; compare with *cellular slime mold.*

plasmodium (plaz-moh′-dee-um) A multinucleate mass of living matter that moves and feeds in an amoeboid fashion.

plasmogamy (1) Fusion of the cytoplasm of two cells without fusion of nuclei. (2) A stage in the asexual reproduction of some fungi; hyphae of two compatible mating types come together, and their cytoplasm fuses.

plasmolysis (plaz-mol′-ih-sis) The shrinkage of cytoplasm and the pulling away of the plasma membrane from the cell wall when a plant cell (or other walled cell) loses water, usually in a hypertonic environment.

plastids (plas′-tidz) A family of membrane-enclosed organelles occurring in photosynthetic eukaryotic cells; include chloroplasts, chromoplasts, and amyloplasts and other leukoplasts.

platelets (playt′-lets) Cell fragments in vertebrate blood that function in clotting; also called *thrombocytes.*

platyhelminths The phylum of acoelomate animals commonly known as *flatworms.*

pleiotropy The ability of a single gene to have multiple effects.

pleural membrane (ploor′-ul) The membrane that lines the thoracic cavity and envelops each lung.

ploidy The number of chromosome sets in a nucleus or cell. See *haploid, diploid,* and *polyploid.*

plumule (ploom′-yool) The embryonic shoot apex, or terminal bud, located above the point of attachment of the cotyledon(s).

pluripotent (ploor-i-poh′-tent) A term describing a stem cell that can divide to give rise to many, but not all, types of cells in an organism. Compare with *totipotent.*

pneumatophore (noo-mat′-uh-for″) Roots that extend up out of the water in swampy areas and are thought to provide aeration between the atmosphere and submerged roots.

polar body A small *n* cell produced during oogenesis in female animals that does not develop into a functional ovum.

polar covalent bond Chemical bond formed by the sharing of electrons between atoms that differ in electronegativity; the end of the bond near the more electronegative atom has a partial negative charge, and the other end has a partial positive charge. Compare with *nonpolar covalent bond.*

polar molecule Molecule that has one end with a partial positive charge and the other with a partial negative charge; polar molecules are generally soluble in water. Compare with *nonpolar molecule.*

polar nucleus In flowering plants, one of two *n* nuclei in the embryo sac that fuse with a sperm during double fertilization to form the 3*n* endosperm.

pollen grain The immature male gametophyte of seed plants (gymnosperms and angiosperms) that produces sperm capable of fertilization.

pollen tube In gymnosperms and flowering plants, a tube or extension that forms after germination of the pollen grain and through which male gametes (sperm cells) pass into the ovule.

pollination (pol″-uh-nay′-shen) In seed plants, the transfer of pollen from the male to the female part of the plant.

polyadenylation (pol″-ee-a-den-uh-lay′-shun) That part of eukaryotic mRNA processing in which multiple adenine-containing nucleotides (a poly-A tail) are added to the 3′ end of the molecule.

polyandry A mating system in which a female mates with several males during a breeding season. Compare with *polygyny.*

poly-A tail See *polyadenylation.*

polydnaviruses Virus particles that consist of multiple circles of dsDNA surrounded by capsid proteins and an envelope; they lack DNA coding for proteins needed for viral replication, but this DNA is provided by ovary cells of the wasps they inhabit.

polygenic inheritance (pol″-ee-jen′-ik) Inheritance in which several independently assorting or loosely linked nonallelic genes modify the intensity of a trait or contribute to the phenotype in additive fashion.

polygyny A mating system in which a male animal mates with many females during a breeding season. Compare with *polyandry.*

polymer (pol′-ih-mer) A molecule built up from repeating subunits of the same general type (monomers); examples include proteins, nucleic acids, or polysaccharides.

polymerase chain reaction (PCR) A method by which a targeted DNA fragment is amplified in vitro to produce millions of copies.

polymorphism (pol″-ee-mor′-fizm) (1) The existence of two or more phenotypically different individuals within a population. (2) The presence of detectable variation in the genomes of different individuals in a population.

polyp (pol′-ip) A hydralike animal; the sessile stage of the life cycle of certain cnidarians. Compare with *medusa.*

polypeptide See *peptide.*

polyphyletic group (pol″-ee-fye-let′-ik) A group made up of organisms that evolved from two or more different ancestors. Compare with *monophyletic group* and *paraphyletic group.*

polyploid (pol′-ee-ployd) The condition of having more than two sets of chromosomes per nucleus. Compare with *diploid* and *haploid.*

polyribosome A complex consisting of a number of ribosomes attached to an mRNA during translation; also known as a *polysome.*

polysaccharide (pol-ee-sak′-ah-ride) A carbohydrate consisting of many monosaccharide subunits (e.g., starch, glycogen, and cellulose).

polysome See *polyribosome.*

polyspermy The fertilization of an egg by more than one sperm.

polytene A term describing a giant chromosome consisting of many parallel DNA double helices. Polytene chromosomes are typically found in cells of the salivary glands and some other tissues of certain insects, such as the fruit fly, *Drosophila.*

polyunsaturated fatty acid See *fatty acid.*

pons (ponz) The white bulge that is the part of the brain stem between the medulla and the midbrain; connects various parts of the brain.

population A group of organisms of the same species that live in a defined geographic area at the same time.

population bottleneck See *bottleneck.*

population crash An abrupt decline in the size of a population.

population density The number of individuals of a species per unit of area or volume at a given time.

population dynamics The study of changes in populations, such as how and why population numbers change over time.

population ecology That branch of biology that deals with the numbers of a particular species that are found in an area and how and why those numbers change (or remain fixed) over time.

population genetics The study of genetic variability in a population and of the forces that act on it.

population growth momentum The continued growth of a population after fertility rates have declined, as a result of a population's young age structure.

positional information The exposure of cells to different concentrations of signaling molecules that specify where the cell is located relative to the body's axes; this information affects cell differentiation and tissue formation.

positive control A genetic control system in which a regulatory protein binds to DNA, turning on transcription of a gene. Compare with *negative control*.

positive feedback system A system in which a change in some steady state triggers a response that intensifies the changing condition. Compare with *negative feedback system*.

posterior Toward the tail end of a bilaterally symmetrical animal. Compare with *anterior*.

posterior pituitary The posterior, neuroendocrine lobe of the pituitary gland; secretes oxytocin and antidiuretic hormone (ADH). Compare with *anterior pituitary*.

postsynaptic neuron A neuron that transmits an impulse away from a synapse. Compare with *presynaptic neuron*.

posttranslational control Regulation of gene expression that controls activity or functions of proteins, usually by phosphorylation or other chemical modifications of the protein. Compare with *transcriptional-level control, translational-level control,* and *posttranscriptional control*.

posttranscriptional control Regulation of gene expression that occurs after the transcription of an mRNA, usually referring to pre-mRNA processing, mRNA export, or mRNA stability. Compare with *transcriptional-level control, translational-level control,* and *posttranslational control*.

postzygotic barrier One of several reproductive isolating mechanisms that prevent gene flow between species after fertilization has taken place, e.g., *hybrid inviability, hybrid sterility,* and *hybrid breakdown*. Compare with *prezygotic barrier*.

potential energy Stored energy; energy that can do work as a consequence of its position or state. Compare with *kinetic energy*.

potentiation A form of synaptic enhancement (increase in neurotransmitter release) that can last for several minutes; occurs when a presynaptic neuron continues to transmit action potentials at a high rate for a minute or longer.

Pr See *phytochrome*.

preadaptation A novel evolutionary change in a pre-existing biological structure that enables it to have a different function; feathers, which evolved from reptilian scales, represent a preadaptation for flight.

prebiotic soup hypothesis The hypothesis that simple organic molecules that are the precursors of life originated and accumulated at Earth's surface, in shallow seas or on rock or clay surfaces. Compare with *iron–sulfur world hypothesis*.

predation Relationship in which one organism (the predator, a secondary or higher level consumer) devours another organism (the prey).

predator See *predation*.

prefrontal cortex Region of the frontal lobes anterior to the motor areas; important in intellect, memory, judgment, language, emotion; and in interpreting incoming sensory information.

prehensile tail Tail adapted for grasping.

preimplantion genetic diagnosis (PGD) Technique by which single cells of embryos conceived by in vitro fertilization are tested for certain genetic diseases prior to the implantation of the embryo in the uterus.

premolars In mammals, teeth positioned between the canines and molars; adapted for crushing and grinding; compare with *incisors, canines,* and *molars*.

pre-mRNA RNA precursor to mRNA in eukaryotes; contains both introns and exons.

prenatal Pertaining to the time before birth.

preprophase band In plant cells, a dense array of microtubules just inside of the plasma membrane that appears just prior to mitosis and determines the plane in which the cell will divide.

pressure–flow model The mechanism by which dissolved sugar is thought to be transported in phloem; caused by a pressure gradient between the source (where sugar is loaded into the phloem) and the sink (where sugar is removed from phloem).

presynaptic neuron A neuron that transmits an impulse to a synapse. Compare with *postsynaptic neuron*.

prezygotic barrier One of several reproductive isolating mechanisms that interfere with fertilization between male and female gametes of different species, e.g., *temporal isolation, habitat isolation, behavioral isolation, mechanical isolation,* and *gametic isolation*. Compare with *postzygotic barrier*.

primary cilium Single nonmotile cilium on the cell surface of animal cells, especially those of vertebrates; binds specific molecules and serves as a "cellular antenna" in many signaling pathways.

primary consumer An animal that eats producers, e.g., plants or algae.

primary growth An increase in the length of a plant that occurs at the tips of the shoots and roots due to the activity of apical meristems. Compare with *secondary growth*.

primary immune response The response of the immune system to first exposure to an antigen. Compare with *secondary immune response*.

primary mycelium A mycelium in which the cells are monokaryotic and haploid; a mycelium that grows from either an ascospore or a basidiospore. Compare with *secondary mycelium*.

primary oocytes Diploid cells that develop from oogonia; undergo a first meiotic division, giving rise to haploid secondary oocytes.

primary producer See *autotroph*.

primary productivity The amount of light energy converted to organic compounds by autotrophs in an ecosystem over a given period. Compare with *secondary productivity*. See *gross primary productivity (GPP)* and *net primary productivity (NPP)*.

primary spermatocytes Diploid cells that develop from spermatogonia; undergo a first meiotic division, giving rise to haploid secondary spermatocytes.

primary structure (of a protein) The complete sequence of amino acids in a polypeptide chain, beginning at the amino end and ending at the carboxyl end. Compare with *secondary, tertiary,* and *quaternary protein structure*.

primary succession An ecological succession that occurs on land that has not previously been inhabited by plants; no soil is present initially. See *succession*. Compare with *secondary succession*.

primates Mammals that share such traits as flexible hands and feet with five digits; a strong social organization; and front-facing eyes; includes lemurs, tarsiers, monkeys, apes, and humans.

primer See *RNA primer*.

primitive groove See *primitive streak*.

primitive streak Dynamic, constantly changing structure that forms at the midline of the blastodisc in birds, mammals, and some other vertebrates. It is active in gastrulation as cells migrate to a narrow furrow at its center, the primitive groove, and sink into the interior of the embryo. The anterior end of the primitive streak is Hensen's node.

primosome A complex of proteins responsible for synthesizing the RNA primers required in DNA synthesis.

principle In science, a statement of a rule that explains how something works. A scientific principle has withstood repeated testing.

prion (priʹ-on) An infectious agent that consists only of protein.

producer See *autotroph*.

product Substance formed by a chemical reaction. Compare with *reactant*.

product rule The rule for combining the probabilities of independent events by multiplying their individual probabilities. Compare with *sum rule*.

profundal zone (pro-funʹ-dl) The deepest zone of a large lake, located below the level of penetration by sunlight. Compare with *littoral zone* and *limnetic zone*.

progesterone (pro-jesʹ-ter-own) A steroid hormone secreted by the ovary (mainly by the corpus luteum) and placenta; stimulates the uterus (to prepare the endometrium for implantation) and breasts (for milk secretion).

progymnosperm (pro-jimʹ-noh-sperm) An extinct group of plants that may have been the ancestors of gymnosperms.

prokaryote (pro-kar'-ee-ote) A cell that lacks a nucleus and other membrane-enclosed organelles; includes the bacteria and archaea (kingdoms Bacteria and Archaea). Compare with *eukaryote*.

prokaryotic cell See *prokaryote*.

prolactin Hormone secreted by pituitary gland that stimulates cells of the mammary glands to produce milk in nursing mother. Helps maintain water and electrolyte balance in fishes and amphibians. Inhibits metamorphosis in amphibians and stimulates molting in reptiles. Has role in immune function and in formation of new blood vessels.

prometaphase Stage of mitosis during which spindle microtubules attach to kinetochores of chromosomes, which begin to move toward the cell's midplane; occurs after prophase and before metaphase.

promoter The nucleotide sequence in DNA to which RNA polymerase attaches to begin transcription.

prop root An adventitious root that arises from the stem and provides additional support for a plant such as corn.

prophage (pro'-faj) Bacteriophage nucleic acid inserted into the bacterial DNA.

prophase The first stage of mitosis. During prophase the chromosomes become visible as distinct structures, the nuclear envelope breaks down, and a spindle forms.

prophase I See *meiosis* and *meiosis I*.

prophase II See *meiosis* and *meiosis II*.

proplastids Organelles that are plastid precursors; may mature into various specialized plastids, including chloroplasts, chromoplasts, or leukoplasts.

proprioceptors (pro''-pree-oh-sep'-torz) Receptors in muscles, tendons, and joints that respond to changes in movement, tension, and position; enable an animal to perceive the position of its body.

prostaglandins (pros''-tah-glan'-dinz) A group of local regulators derived from fatty acids; synthesized by most cells of the body and produce a wide variety of effects; sometimes called *local hormones*.

prostate gland A gland in male animals that produces an alkaline secretion that is part of the semen.

protease An enzyme that breaks down proteins by cleaving peptide bonds.

proteasome A large multiprotein structure that recognizes and degrades protein molecules tagged with ubiquitin into short, nonfunctional peptide fragments.

protein A large, complex organic compound composed of covalently linked amino acid subunits; contains carbon, hydrogen, oxygen, nitrogen, and sulfur.

protein domain See *domain* (definition 1).

protein kinases Enzymes that activate or inactivate other proteins by phosphorylating (adding phosphate groups to) them.

proteomics The study of all the proteins expressed by a cell at a given time.

Proterozoic eon The period of Earth's history that began approximately 2.5 billion years ago and ended 541 million years ago; marked by the accumulation of oxygen and the appearance of the first multicellular eukaryotic life-forms.

prothallus (pro-thal'-us) (pl., *prothalli*) The free-living, *n* gametophyte in ferns and other seedless vascular plants.

protists (pro'-tists) Eukaryotic organisms that may be unicellular, colonial, or simple multicellular; for example, algae, amoebas, ciliates, and slime molds.

protobionts (pro''-toh-by'-ontz) Assemblages of organic polymers that spontaneously form under certain conditions. Protobionts may have been involved in chemical evolution.

proton A particle present in the nuclei of all atoms that has one unit of positive charge and a mass of 1 atomic mass unit (amu). Compare with *electron* and *neutron*.

protonema (pro''-toh-nee'-mah) (pl., *protonemata*) In mosses, a filament of *n* cells that grows from a spore and develops into leafy moss gametophytes.

protonephridia (pro''-toh-nef-rid'-ee-ah) (sing., *protonephridium*) The flame-cell excretory organs of flatworms and some other simple invertebrates.

proto-oncogene A gene that normally promotes cell division in response to the presence of certain growth factors; when mutated, it may become an oncogene, possibly leading to the formation of a cancer cell. Compare with *oncogene*.

protostomes (pro'-toh-stomes) Animals that belong to the Protostomia, one of the major animal clades. Include the annelids, arthropods, and mollusks. Compare with *deuterostomes*.

protozoa (proh''-toh-zoh'-a) (sing., *protozoon*) An informal group of unicellular, animal-like protists, including amoebas, foraminiferans, actinopods, ciliates, flagellates, and apicomplexans. (The adjectival form is *protozoan*.)

provirus (pro-vy'-rus) A part of a virus, consisting of nucleic acid only, that was inserted into a host genome. See *DNA provirus*.

proximal Closer to the point of reference. Compare with *distal*.

proximal convoluted tubule The part of the renal tubule that extends from Bowman's capsule to the loop of Henle. Compare with *distal convoluted tubule*.

proximate causes (of behavior) The immediate causes of behavior, such as genetic, developmental, and physiological processes that permit the animal to carry out a specific behavior. Compare with *ultimate causes of behavior*.

pseudocoelom (sue''-doh-see'-lom) A body cavity between the mesoderm and endoderm; derived from the blastocoel. Compare with *coelom*.

pseudocoelomate (sue''-doh-seel'-oh-mate) An animal having a pseudocoelom. Compare with *coelomate* and *acoelomate*.

pseudoplasmodium (sue''-doe-plaz-moh'-dee-um) In cellular slime molds, an aggregation of amoeboid cells that forms a spore-producing fruiting body during reproduction.

pseudopodium (sue''-doe-poe'-dee-um) (pl., *pseudopodia*) A temporary extension of an amoeboid cell that is used for feeding and locomotion.

pterosaurs (ter'-uh-sawrs) Flying reptiles of the Mesozoic era.

puberty The period of sexual maturation during which secondary sex characteristics begin to develop and the individual becomes capable of reproducing.

puff In a polytene chromosome, a decondensed region that is a site of intense RNA synthesis.

pulmonary circulation The part of the circulatory system that delivers blood to and from the lungs for oxygenation. Compare with *systemic circulation*.

pulse, arterial The alternate expansion and recoil of an artery.

punctuated equilibrium The idea that evolution proceeds with periods of little or no genetic change, followed by very active phases, so that major adaptations or clusters of adaptations appear suddenly in the fossil record. Compare with *phyletic gradualism*.

Punnett square The grid structure, first developed by Reginald Punnett, that allows direct calculation of the probabilities of occurrence of all possible offspring of a genetic cross.

pupa (pew'-pah) (pl., *pupae*) A stage in the development of an insect, between the larva and the imago (adult); a form that neither moves nor feeds and may be in a cocoon.

purines (pure'-eenz) Nitrogenous bases with carbon and nitrogen atoms in two attached rings, e.g., adenine and guanine; components of nucleic acids, ATP, GTP, NAD⁺, and certain other biologically active substances. Compare with *pyrimidines*.

pyramid of biomass Ecological pyramid that illustrates the total biomass, as, for example, the total dry weight, of all organisms at each trophic level in an ecosystem. Compare with *pyramid of energy* and *pyramid of numbers*.

pyramid of energy Ecological pyramid that shows the energy flow through each trophic level of an ecosystem. Compare with *pyramid of biomass* and *pyramid of numbers*.

pyramid of numbers Ecological pyramid that shows the number of organisms at each trophic level in a given ecosystem. Compare with *pyramid of biomass* and *pyramid of energy*.

pyrimidines (pyr-im'-ih-deenz) Nitrogenous bases, each composed of a single ring of carbon and nitrogen atoms, e.g., thymine, cytosine, and uracil; components of nucleic acids. Compare with *purines*.

pyruvate (pyruvic acid) A three-carbon compound; the end product of glycolysis.

quadrupedal (kwad'-roo-ped''-ul) Walking on all fours. Compare with *bipedal*.

quantitative trait A trait that shows continuous variation in a population (e.g., human height) and typically has a polygenic inheritance pattern.

Quaternary period See *Cenozoic era.*

quaternary structure (of a protein) The overall conformation of a protein produced by the interaction of two or more polypeptide chains. Compare with *primary, secondary,* and *tertiary protein structure.*

r selection A reproductive strategy recognized by some ecologists, in which a species typically has a small body size, rapid development, and short lifespan and devotes a large proportion of its metabolic energy to the production of offspring. Compare with *K selection.*

r strategist See *r selection.*

radial cleavage The pattern of blastomere production in which the cells are located directly above or below one another; characteristic of early deuterostome embryos. Compare with *spiral cleavage.*

radial symmetry A body plan in which any section through the mouth and down the length of the body divides the body into similar halves. Jellyfish and other cnidarians have radial symmetry. Compare with *bilateral symmetry.*

radicle (rad'-ih-kl) The embryonic root of a seed plant.

radioactive decay The process in which a radioactive element emits radiation, and as a result, its nucleus changes into the nucleus of a different element.

radioisotopes Unstable isotopes that spontaneously emit radiation; also called *radioactive isotopes.*

radiolarians Those actinopods that secrete elaborate shells of silica (glass).

radula (rad'-yoo-lah) A rasplike structure in the digestive tract of chitons, snails, squids, and certain other mollusks.

rain shadow An area that has very little precipitation, found on the downwind side of a mountain range. Deserts often occur in rain shadows.

random dispersion The spatial distribution pattern of a population in which the presence of one individual has no effect on the distribution of other individuals. Compare with *clumped dispersion* and *uniform dispersion.*

range The area where a particular species occurs. Compare with *home range.*

Ras proteins A group of small G proteins, named by their discovery in **ra**t **s**arcoma cancer cells; important in many signaling pathways.

ratite (rat'-it) A flightless bird, such as an ostrich or kiwi.

ray A chain of parenchyma cells (one to many cells thick) that functions for lateral transport in stems and roots of woody plants.

ray-finned fishes A class (Actinopterygii) of modern bony fishes; contains about 95% of living fish species.

reabsorption The selective removal of certain substances from the glomerular filtrate by the renal tubules and collecting ducts of the kidney, and their return into the blood.

reactant Substance that participates in a chemical reaction. Compare with *product.*

reaction center The portion of a photosystem that includes chlorophyll *a* molecules capable of transferring electrons to a primary electron acceptor, which is the first of several electron acceptors in a series. See *antenna complex* and *photosystem.*

realized niche The lifestyle that an organism actually pursues, including the resources that it actually uses. An organism's realized niche is narrower than its fundamental niche because of interspecific competition. Compare with *fundamental niche.*

Recent Africa Origin model (RAO) See *(recent) out-of-Africa model.*

(recent) out-of-Africa model (also called *Recent Africa Origin* or *RAO*) Hypothesis that modern humans (*Homo sapiens*) originated in Africa and subsequently migrated to other parts of the world.

receptacle The end of a flower stalk where the flower parts (sepals, petals, stamens, and carpels) are attached.

reception Process of detecting a stimulus.

receptor (1) In cell biology, a molecule on the surface of a cell, or inside a cell, that serves as a recognition or binding site for signaling molecules such as hormones, antibodies, or neurotransmitters. (2) A sensory receptor. See *sensory receptor.*

receptor down-regulation The process by which some hormone receptors decrease in number, thereby suppressing the sensitivity of target cells to a hormone. Compare with *receptor up-regulation.*

receptor-mediated endocytosis A type of endocytosis in which extracellular molecules become bound to specific receptors on the cell surface and then enter the cytoplasm enclosed in vesicles. Compare with *phagocytosis* and *pinocytosis.*

receptor potential The change in membrane potential by a sensory receptor in response to a stimulus.

receptor up-regulation The process by which some hormone receptors increase in number, thereby increasing the sensitivity of the target cells to a hormone. Compare with *receptor down-regulation.*

recessive allele (al-leel') An allele that is not expressed in the heterozygous state. Compare with *dominant allele.*

reciprocal altruism A type of altruistic behavior in which an animal helps nonrelatives if they are likely to repay the debt in the future.

recombinant DNA Any DNA molecule made by combining genes from different organisms.

recombination, genetic The appearance of new allele combinations. Recombination in eukaryotes generally results from meiotic events, either crossing-over or shuffling of chromosomes.

rectum The last region of the large intestine.

red alga A member of a diverse group of archaeplastid algae that contain the pigments chlorophyll *a*, carotenoids, phycocyanin, and phycoerythrin.

red blood cell (RBC) See *erythrocyte.*

redox reaction (ree'-dox) The chemical reaction in which one or more electrons are transferred from one substance (the substance that becomes oxidized) to another (the substance that becomes reduced). See *oxidation* and *reduction.*

red tide A red or brown coloration of ocean water caused by a population explosion, or bloom, of dinoflagellates.

reduction The gain of one or more electrons (or hydrogen atoms) by an atom, ion, or molecule. Compare with *oxidation.*

reductionism Learning about a structure or process by studying its simplest components.

re-emerging diseases Diseases that have been almost eradicated and then suddenly recur, causing an epidemic. Compare with *emerging diseases.*

reflex action An automatic, involuntary response to a given stimulus that generally functions to restore homeostasis.

refractory period The brief period that elapses after the response of a neuron or muscle fiber, during which it cannot respond to another stimulus.

regulative development The very plastic developmental pattern in which each individual cell of an early embryo retains totipotency. Compare with *mosaic development.*

regulatory gene Gene that turns the transcription of other genes on or off.

regulatory T cells (T$_{regs}$) A population of T cells that help regulate immune responses.

reinforcement The increase in reproductive isolation that often occurs over time in a hybrid zone because natural selection strengthens and increases the number of prezygotic barriers between the two species.

releasing hormone A hormone secreted by the hypothalamus that stimulates secretion of a specific hormone by the anterior lobe of the pituitary gland.

renal (ree'-nl) Pertaining to the kidney.

renal artery An artery that branches from the aorta and delivers blood to the kidneys.

renal cortex The outer region of the mammalian kidney; surrounds the renal medulla. Compare with *renal medulla.*

renal medulla The inner region of the mammalian kidney. Compare with *renal cortex.*

renal pelvis The funnel-shaped chamber of the kidney that receives urine from the collecting ducts; urine then moves into the ureters.

renin (reh'-nin) An enzyme released by the kidney in response to a decrease in blood pressure; activates a pathway leading to production of angiotensin II, a hormone that increases aldosterone release; aldosterone increases blood pressure.

replacement-level fertility The number of children a couple must produce to "replace" themselves. The average number is greater than two, because some children die before reaching reproductive age.

replication See *DNA replication*.

replication fork Y-shaped structure produced during the semiconservative replication of DNA.

repolarization The process of returning membrane potential to its resting level.

repressible operon An operon that is normally active, but can be controlled by a repressor protein, which becomes active when it binds to a corepressor; the active repressor binds to the operator, making the operon transcriptionally inactive. Compare with *inducible operon*.

repressor protein A negative regulatory protein that inhibits transcription when bound to DNA; some repressors require a corepressor to be active; some other repressors become inactive when bound to an inducer molecule. Compare with *activator protein*.

reproduction The process by which new individuals are produced. See *asexual reproduction* and *sexual reproduction*.

reproductive isolating mechanisms The reproductive barriers that prevent a species from interbreeding with another species; as a result, each species' gene pool is isolated from those of other species. See *prezygotic barrier* and *postzygotic barrier*.

reptiles Vertebrates characterized by dry skin with horny scales and adaptations for terrestrial reproduction; include turtles, snakes, and alligators; reptiles are a paraphyletic group unless birds are included.

residual volume The volume of air that remains in the lungs at the end of a normal exhalation.

resin A viscous organic material that certain plants produce and secrete into specialized ducts; may play a role in deterring disease organisms or plant-eating insects.

resolution See *resolving power*.

resolving power The ability of a microscope to show fine detail, defined as the minimum distance between two points at which they are seen as separate images; also called *resolution*.

resource partitioning The reduction of competition for environmental resources such as food that occurs among coexisting species as a result of each species' niche differing from the others in one or more ways.

respiration (1) Cellular respiration is the process by which cells generate ATP through a series of redox reactions. In aerobic cellular respiration the terminal electron acceptor is molecular oxygen; in anaerobic cellular respiration the terminal acceptor is an inorganic molecule other than oxygen. (2) Organismic respiration is the process of gas exchange between a complex animal and its environment, generally through a specialized respiratory surface, such as a lung or gill.

respiratory centers Centers in the medulla and pons that regulate breathing.

respiratory system The body system that carries on gas exchange; in vertebrates, consists of the lungs and airways.

response The action of effectors in response to a stimulus.

resting potential The membrane potential (difference in electric charge between the two sides of the plasma membrane) of a neuron in which no action potential is occurring. The typical resting potential is about −70 millivolts. Compare with *action potential*.

restoration ecology The scientific field that uses the principles of ecology to help return a degraded environment as closely as possible to its former undisturbed state.

restriction enzyme One of a class of enzymes that cleave DNA at specific base sequences; produced by bacteria to degrade foreign DNA; used in recombinant DNA technology.

restriction fragment length polymorphism (RFLP) A difference, or variation, in the genomic DNA of a population caused by the presence or absence of a restriction enzyme site.

restriction map A physical map of DNA in which sites cut by specific restriction enzymes serve as landmarks.

reticular activating system (RAS) (reh-tik'-yoo-lur) A diffuse network of neurons in the brain stem; responsible for maintaining consciousness.

retina (ret'-ih-nah) The innermost of the three layers (retina, choroid layer, and sclera) of the eyeball, which is continuous with the optic nerve and contains the light-sensitive rod and cone cells.

retinal Visual pigment derived from vitamin A; present in eyes of insects, mollusks, and vertebrates.

retinular cells See *ommatidium*.

retrotransposon A chromosomal DNA segment that can move to a different site within the genome by forming an RNA intermediate that is converted to a DNA fragment using reverse transcriptase; also called a *mobile genetic element*.

retrovirus (ret'-roh-vy"-rus) An RNA virus that uses reverse transcriptase to produce a DNA intermediate, known as a *DNA provirus*, in the host cell. See *DNA provirus*.

reverse transcriptase An enzyme produced by retroviruses that catalyzes the production of DNA using RNA as a template.

reversible inhibitor A substance that forms weak bonds with an enzyme, temporarily interfering with its function; a reversible inhibitor is either competitive or noncompetitive. Compare with *irreversible inhibitor*.

Rh factors Red blood cell antigens, known as *D antigens,* first identified in *Rhesus* monkeys. People who have these antigens are Rh[+]; people lacking them are Rh[−]. See *erythroblastosis fetalis*.

rhizarians A diverse supergroup of amoeboid cells that often have hard outer shells, called tests, through which cytoplasmic projections extend; include forams, actinopods, and certain shell-less amoebas.

rhizobia See *nodules*.

rhizome (ry'-zome) A horizontal underground stem that bears leaves and buds and often serves as a storage organ and a means of asexual reproduction, e.g., iris.

rhodopsin (rho-dop'-sin) Visual purple; a light-sensitive pigment found in the rod cells of the vertebrate eye; a similar molecule is employed by certain bacteria in the capture of light energy to make ATP.

ribonucleic acid (RNA) A family of single-stranded nucleic acids that function mainly in protein synthesis

ribose The five-carbon sugar present in RNA and in important nucleoside triphosphates such as ATP.

ribosomal RNA (rRNA) See *ribosomes*.

ribosomes (ry'-boh-sohmz) Organelles that are part of the protein synthesis machinery of both prokaryotic and eukaryotic cells; consist of a larger and smaller subunit, each composed of ribosomal RNA (rRNA) and ribosomal proteins.

ribozyme (ry'-boh-zime) A molecule of RNA that has catalytic properties.

ribulose bisphosphate (RuBP) A five-carbon phosphorylated compound with a high energy potential that reacts with carbon dioxide in the initial step of the Calvin cycle.

ribulose bisphosphate carboxylase/oxygenase See *rubisco*.

RNA interference (RNAi) Phenomenon in which certain small RNA molecules interfere with the expression of genes or their RNA transcripts; RNA interference involves small interfering RNAs (siRNAs), microRNAs (miRNAs), piwi-associated RNAs (piRNAs), and other kinds of short RNA molecules.

RNA polymerase An enzyme that catalyzes the synthesis of RNA from a DNA template.

RNA primer The sequence of about five RNA nucleotides that are synthesized during DNA replication to provide a 3′ end to which DNA polymerase adds nucleotides. The RNA primer is later degraded and replaced with DNA.

RNA world A model that proposes that during the evolution of cells, RNA was the first informational molecule to evolve, followed at a later time by proteins and DNA.

rod One of the rod-shaped, light-sensitive cells of the retina that are particularly sensitive to dim light and mediate black-and-white vision. Compare with *cone*.

root cap A covering of cells over the root tip that protects the delicate meristematic tissue directly behind it.

root graft The process of roots from two different plants growing together and becoming permanently attached to each other.

root hair An extension, or outgrowth, of a root epidermal cell. Root hairs increase the absorptive capacity of roots.

root pressure The pressure in xylem sap that occurs as a result of the active absorption of mineral ions followed by the osmotic uptake of water into roots from the soil.

root system The underground portion of a plant that anchors it in the soil and absorbs water and dissolved minerals. Compare with *shoot system*.

rough ER See *endoplasmic reticulum*.

r-selected species See *r selection*.

rubisco The common name of ribulose bisphosphate carboxylase/oxygenase, the enzyme that catalyzes the fixation of carbon dioxide in the Calvin cycle.

rugae (roo'-jee) Folds, such as those in the lining of the stomach.

runner See *stolon*.

runoff Movement of excess surface water over land toward bodies of water.

S phase Stage in interphase of the cell cycle during which DNA and other chromosomal constituents are synthesized. Compare with G_1 *phase* and G_2 *phase*.

saccule The structure within the vestibule of the inner vertebrate ear that along with the utricle houses the receptors of static equilibrium.

salicylic acid A signaling molecule that helps plants defend against insect pests and pathogens such as viruses by helping activate systemic acquired resistance.

salinity The concentration of dissolved salts (e.g., sodium chloride) in a body of water.

salivary amylase An enzyme in saliva that hydrolyzes starch to the disaccharide maltose.

salivary glands Accessory digestive glands found in vertebrates and some invertebrates; in humans there are three pairs.

salt An ionic compound consisting of an anion other than a hydroxide ion and a cation other than a hydrogen ion. A salt is formed by the reaction between an acid and a base.

saltatory conduction The transmission of a neural impulse along a myelinated neuron; ion activity at one node depolarizes the next node along the axon.

salt marsh A wetland dominated by grasses in which the salinity fluctuates between that of sea water and fresh water; salt marshes are usually located in estuaries.

saprobe See *decomposer*.

saprotroph (sap'-roh-trof) See *decomposer*.

sarcolemma (sar"-koh-lem'-mah) The muscle cell plasma membrane.

sarcomere (sar'-koh-meer) A segment of a striated muscle cell located between adjacent Z lines that serves as a unit of contraction.

sarcoplasmic reticulum The system of vesicles in a muscle cell that surrounds the myofibrils and releases calcium in muscle contraction; a modified endoplasmic reticulum.

satellites Subviral agents that require a helper virus to reproduce.

saturated fatty acid See *fatty acid*.

savanna (suh-van'-uh) A tropical grassland containing scattered trees; found in areas of low rainfall or seasonal rainfall with prolonged dry periods.

scaffolding proteins Nonhistone proteins that help maintain the structure of a chromosome.

scaffold proteins Proteins that organize groups of intracellular signaling molecules into signaling complexes.

scanning electron microscope (SEM) See *electron microscope*.

schizocoely (skiz'-oh-seely) The process of coelom formation in which the mesoderm splits into two layers, forming a cavity between them; characteristic of protostomes. Compare with *enterocoely*.

Schwann cells Supporting cells found in nervous tissue outside the central nervous system; produce the myelin sheath around peripheral neurons.

scientific method The process that scientists use to investigate the natural world; includes observing, recognizing a problem or stating a critical question, developing a hypothesis, making a prediction that can be tested, making further observations, performing experiments, interpreting results, and drawing conclusions that support or falsify the hypothesis.

scientific theory In science, a widely accepted explanation supported by a large body of observations and experiments. A scientific theory relates facts that appear unrelated; it predicts new facts and suggests new relationships. Compare with *hypothesis*.

sclera (skler'-ah) The outer coat of the eyeball; a tough, opaque sheet of connective tissue that protects the inner structures and helps maintain the rigidity of the eyeball.

sclereid (skler'-id) In plants, a sclerenchyma cell that is variable in shape but typically not long and tapered. Compare with *fiber*.

sclerenchyma (skler-en'-kim-uh) Cells that provide strength and support in the plant body, are often dead at maturity, and have extremely thick walls; includes fibers and sclereids.

scramble competition See *exploitation competition*.

scrotum (skroh' tum) The external sac of skin found in most male mammals that contains the testes and their accessory organs.

sea grasses Flowering plants that have adapted to complete submersion in ocean water.

secondary consumer An animal that eats herbivores (primary consumers).

secondary growth An increase in the girth of a plant due to the activity of the vascular cambium and cork cambium; secondary growth results in the production of secondary tissues, i.e., wood and bark. Compare with *primary growth*.

secondary immune response The rapid production of antibodies induced by a second exposure to an antigen several days, weeks, or even months after the initial exposure. Compare with *primary immune response*.

secondary mycelium A dikaryotic mycelium formed by the fusion of two primary hyphae. Compare with *primary mycelium*.

secondary oocytes Haploid cells that undergo a second meiotic division, giving rise to haploid ootids.

secondary productivity The amount of food molecules converted to biomass by consumers in an ecosystem over a given period. Compare with *primary productivity*.

secondary sex characteristics Changes that develop during puberty; in males, include growth of facial and body hair, muscle development, and the increase in vocal cord length and thickness that causes the voice to deepen; in females, include development of the breasts, broadening of the pelvis, and the development and distribution of muscle and fat responsible for the female body shape.

secondary spermatocytes Haploid cells that undergo a second meiotic division, giving rise to haploid spermatids.

secondary structure (of a protein) A regular geometric shape produced by hydrogen bonding between the atoms of the uniform polypeptide backbone; includes the alpha helix and the beta-pleated sheet. Compare with *primary, tertiary,* and *quaternary protein structure*.

secondary succession An ecological succession that takes place after some disturbance destroys the existing vegetation; soil is already present. See *succession*. Compare with *primary succession*.

second law of thermodynamics The physical law stating that the total amount of entropy in the universe continually increases. Compare with *first law of thermodynamics*.

second messenger A substance, e.g., cyclic AMP or calcium ions, that relays a message from a signaling molecule (the *first messenger*) bound to a cell-surface receptor; leads to some change in the cell.

secretory vesicles Small cytoplasmic vesicles that move substances from an internal membrane system to the plasma membrane.

seed A plant reproductive body consisting of a young, multicellular plant and nutritive tissue (food reserves), enclosed by a seed coat.

seed coat The outer protective covering of a seed.

seed fern An extinct group of seed-bearing woody plants with fernlike leaves; seed ferns probably descended from progymnosperms and gave rise to cycads and possibly ginkgoes.

segmentation A body plan in which the body is divided into a series of compartments (segments).

segmentation genes In *Drosophila*, genes transcribed in the embryo that are responsible for generating a repeating pattern of body segments within the embryo and adult fly.

segregation, principle of The genetic principle, first noted by Gregor Mendel, that states that two alleles of a locus become separated into different gametes.

selectively permeable membrane A membrane that allows some substances to cross it more easily than others. Biological membranes are generally permeable to water but restrict the passage of many solutes.

self-incompatibility A genetic condition in which the pollen cannot fertilize the same flower or flowers on the same plant.

semelparous Having a single reproductive effort in a lifetime. Compare with *iteroparous*.

semen The fluid consisting of sperm suspended in various glandular secretions that is ejaculated from the penis during orgasm.

semicircular canals The passages in the vertebrate inner ear containing structures that control the sense of equilibrium (balance).

semiconservative replication See *DNA replication*.

semilunar valves Valves between the ventricles of the heart and the arteries that carry blood away from the heart; aortic and pulmonary valves.

seminal vesicles (1) In mammals, glandular sacs that secrete a component of semen (seminal fluid). (2) In some invertebrates, structures that store sperm.

seminiferous tubules (sem-ih-nif'-er-ous) Coiled tubules in the testes in which spermatogenesis takes place in male vertebrates.

senescence (se-nes'-cents) The aging process.

sense organ Sensory receptors along with other types of cells make up sense organs, e.g., eyes, ears, taste buds.

sensor In homeostasis, a receptor that detects a change, i.e., a deviation from the homeostatic state.

sensory adaptation The condition in which the response to a stimulus is reduced even though the stimulus continues at the same intensity.

sensory neuron A neuron that transmits an impulse from a receptor to the central nervous system.

sensory receptor The ending of an afferent neuron that is specialized to detect specific energy stimuli in its environment.

sepal (see'-pul) One of the outermost parts of a flower, usually leaflike in appearance, that protect the flower as a bud.

septum (pl., *septa*) A cross wall or partition. (1) In fungi, the walls that divide a hypha into cells. (2) In annelids, the partitions that separate the segments. (3) In birds and mammals, the wall that separates the two ventricles (and the two atria) of the heart.

sequencing See *DNA sequencing*.

serial endosymbiosis The hypothesis that certain organelles such as mitochondria and chloroplasts originated as symbiotic prokaryotes that lived inside other, free-living prokaryotic cells.

serotonin A neurotransmitter of the biogenic amine group; important in mood and helps regulate the sleep–wake cycle.

serous membrane (sir'-us) An epithelial membrane that lines a body cavity that does not open to the outside of the body.

Sertoli cells (sur-tole'-ee) Supporting cells of the tubules of the testis.

serum Plasma minus fibrinogen and other clotting agents.

sessile (ses'-sile) Permanently attached to one location, e.g., coral animals.

setae (sing., *seta*) Bristlelike structures that aid in annelid locomotion.

set point A normal condition maintained by homeostatic mechanisms.

sex chromosome Chromosome that plays a role in sex determination.

sex pili See *pili*.

sex-influenced trait A genetic trait that is expressed differently in males and females.

sex-linked gene A gene carried on a sex chromosome. In mammals almost all sex-linked genes are borne on the X chromosome, i.e., are X-linked.

sexual dimorphism Marked phenotypic differences between the two sexes of the same species.

sexual isolation See *behavioral isolation*.

sexual reproduction A type of reproduction in which two gametes (usually, but not necessarily, contributed by two different parents) fuse to form a zygote. Compare with *asexual reproduction*.

sexual selection A type of natural selection that occurs when individuals of a species vary in their ability to compete for mates; individuals with reproductive advantages are selected over others of the same sex.

shade avoidance The tendency of plants that are adapted to high light intensities to grow taller when they are closely surrounded by other plants.

shared ancestral characters Traits that were present in an ancestral species that have remained essentially unchanged; suggest a distant common ancestor. Also called *plesiomorphic characters*. Compare with *shared derived characters*.

shared derived characters Homologous traits found in two or more taxa that are present in their most recent common ancestor but not in earlier common ancestors. Also called *synapomorphic characters*. Compare with *shared ancestral characters*.

shoot system The aboveground portion of a plant, such as the stem and leaves. Compare with *root system*.

short-day plant A plant that flowers in response to lengthening nights; also called *long-night plant*. Compare with *long-day, intermediate-day,* and *day-neutral plants*.

short-night plant See *long-day plant*.

short tandem repeats (STRs) Molecular markers that are short sequences of repetitive DNA; because STRs vary in length from one individual to another, they are useful in identifying individuals with a high degree of certainty.

short-term memory Memory that stores only about seven chunks of information and allows us to recall that information only for seconds or for a few minutes. Compare with *long-term memory*.

sickle cell anemia An inherited form of anemia in which there is an abnormality in the hemoglobin beta chains; the inheritance pattern is autosomal recessive.

sieve tube Structure consisting of sieve tube elements joined end to end.

sieve tube elements Cells that conduct dissolved sugar in the phloem of flowering plants.

signal amplification The process by which a few signaling molecules can elicit major responses in the cell; the strength of each signaling molecule is magnified.

signaling molecule A molecule such as a hormone, local regulator, or neurotransmitter that transmits information when it binds to a receptor on the cell surface or within the cell.

signal-recognition particle (SRP) A protein–RNA complex that directs the ribosome–mRNA–polypeptide complex to the surface of the endoplasmic reticulum.

signal-recognition particle RNA See *signal-recognition particle (SRP)*.

signal transduction A process in which a cell converts and amplifies an extracellular signal into an intracellular signal that affects some function in the cell. Also see *cell signaling*.

sign stimulus Any stimulus that elicits a fixed action pattern in an animal.

silencer A regulatory element that associates with a eukaryotic gene and can decrease its transcription.

Silurian period See *Paleozoic era*.

simple diffusion See *diffusion*.

simple fruit A fruit that develops from a single ovary. Compare with *aggregate, accessory,* and *multiple fruits*.

simplest formula A type of chemical formula that gives the smallest whole-number ratio of the component atoms. Compare with *molecular formula* and *structural formula*.

single nucleotide polymorphisms (SNPs) Genetic variation among individuals in a population as measured by alleles of specific loci that differ by as little as a single nucleotide. The abbreviation is usually pronounced "snips."

single-strand binding proteins (SSBs) Proteins involved in DNA replication that bind to single DNA strands and prevent the double helix from re-forming until the strands are copied.

sink habitat A lower-quality habitat in which local reproductive success is less than local mortality. Compare with *source habitat*.

sinoatrial (SA) node The mass of specialized cardiac muscle in which the impulse triggering the heartbeat originates; the pacemaker of the heart.

sister chromatids See *chromatid*.

sister taxa Groups of organisms that share a more recent common ancestor with one another than either taxon does with any other group shown on a cladogram.

skeletal muscle The voluntary striated muscle of vertebrates, so called because it usually is directly or indirectly attached to some part of the skeleton. Compare with *cardiac muscle* and *smooth muscle*.

slash-and-burn agriculture A type of agriculture in which tropical rain forest is cut down, allowed to dry, and burned. The crops that are planted immediately afterward thrive because the ashes provide nutrients; in a few years, however, the soil is depleted and the land must be abandoned.

slime layer A protective layer surrounding the cell wall of many prokaryotic species; more loosely attached to the cell wall than a capsule. See *capsule*, definition 3.

slow block to polyspermy See *cortical reaction*.

slow-oxidative fibers Muscle fibers specialized for endurance activities; they contract slowly, fatigue slowly, and obtain most of their ATP from aerobic respiration. Compare with *fast-oxidative fibers* and *fast-glycolytic fibers*.

small interfering RNAs (siRNAs) Double-stranded RNA molecules about 23 nucleotides in length that silence genes at the posttranscriptional level by selectively cleaving mRNA molecules with base sequences complementary to the siRNA. See also *microRNA (miRNA)*, *RNA interference (RNAi)*, and *piwi-associated RNA (piRNA)*.

small intestine Portion of the vertebrate digestive tract that extends from the stomach to the large intestine.

small nuclear ribonucleoprotein complexes (snRNPs) Aggregations of protein and small nuclear RNA (snRNA) that associate to form a spliceosome that binds to pre-mRNA in eukaryotes and catalyzes the excision of introns and splicing of exons. The abbreviation is usually pronounced "snurps."

small nuclear RNA (snRNA) See *small ribonucleoprotein complexes (snRNPs)*.

small nucleolar RNA (snoRNA) RNA molecules involved in the processing of pre-ribosomal RNA during the formation of ribosome subunits in the nucleolus.

smooth ER See *endoplasmic reticulum*.

smooth muscle Involuntary muscle tissue that lacks transverse striations; found mainly in sheets surrounding hollow organs, such as the intestine. Compare with *cardiac muscle* and *skeletal muscle*.

SNP See *single nucleotide polymorphism*.

social behavior Interaction of two or more animals, usually of the same species.

social learning Learning through observing others and imitating them.

society A group of individuals belonging to the same species and often closely related; an organized society is an actively cooperating group.

sociobiology The branch of biology that focuses on the evolution of social behavior through natural selection.

sodium–potassium pump ATP-binding cassette transporter in the plasma membrane of all animal cells; uses ATP energy to transport Na$^+$ out of the cell and K$^+$ into the cell.

soil erosion The wearing away or removal of soil from the land; although soil erosion occurs naturally from precipitation and runoff, human activities (such as clearing the land) accelerate it.

solute A dissolved substance. Compare with *solvent*.

solvent Substance capable of dissolving other substances. Compare with *solute*.

somatic cell In animals, a cell of the body not involved in formation of gametes. Compare with *germ line cell*.

somatic division (of the PNS) That part of the vertebrate peripheral nervous system that keeps the body in adjustment with the external environment; includes sensory receptors on the body surface and within the muscles, and the nerves that link them with the central nervous system. Compare with *autonomic division* of the PNS.

somatomedins See *insulin-like growth factors*.

somatotropin See *growth hormone*.

somites A series of paired blocks of mesoderm that develop on each side of the notochord in cephalochordates and vertebrates. Somites define the segmentation of the embryo, and in vertebrates, they give rise to the vertebrae, ribs, and certain skeletal muscles.

sonogram See *ultrasound imaging*.

soredium (sor-id′e-um) (pl., *soredia*) In lichens, a type of asexual reproductive structure that consists of a cluster of algal cells surrounded by fungal hyphae.

sorus (soh′rus) (pl., *sori*) In ferns, a cluster of spore-producing sporangia.

source habitat A good habitat in which local reproductive success is greater than local mortality. Surplus individuals in a source habitat may disperse to other habitats. Compare with *sink habitat*.

Southern blot A technique in which DNA fragments, previously separated by gel electrophoresis, are transferred to a nitrocellulose or nylon membrane and detected by autoradiography or chemical luminescence. Compare with *Northern blot* and *Western blot*.

spatial summation The summing of several postsynaptic potentials resulting when several presynaptic neurons release neurotransmitter simultaneously. Compare with *temporal summation*.

speciation Evolution of a new species.

species According to the biological species concept, one or more populations whose members are capable of interbreeding in nature to produce fertile offspring and do not interbreed with members of other species. Compare with *phylogenetic species concept*.

species diversity A measure of the relative importance of each species within a community; represents a combination of species richness and species evenness.

species evenness Relative abundance of one species compared to other species in a community.

species richness The number of species in a community.

specific epithet The second part of the name of a species; designates a specific species belonging to that genus.

specific heat The amount of heat energy that must be supplied to raise the temperature of 1 g of a substance 1°C.

specific immune responses See *adaptive immune responses*.

specific immunity See *adaptive immune responses*.

sperm The motile male gamete of animals and some plants and protists; also called a *spermatozoan*.

spermatid (spur′-ma-tid) An immature sperm cell.

spermatocyte (spur-mah′-toh-site) A meiotic cell that gives rise to spermatids and ultimately to mature sperm cells.

spermatogenesis (spur″-mah-toh-jen′-eh-sis) The production of male gametes (sperm) by meiosis and subsequent cell differentiation. Compare with *oogenesis*.

spermatogonia Undifferentiated cells in the testes that give rise to primary spermatocytes.

spermatozoan (spur-mah-toh-zoh′-un) See *sperm*.

sphincter (sfink′-tur) A group of circularly arranged muscle fibers, the contractions of which close an opening, e.g., the pyloric sphincter at the exit of the stomach.

spicules (spik′-yuls) Slender skeletal spikes made of calcium carbonate or silica; found in sponges and some other animals.

spinal cord In vertebrates, the dorsal, tubular nerve cord.

spinal nerves In vertebrates, the nerves that emerge from the spinal cord; there are 31 pairs in humans.

spindle See *mitotic spindle*.

spine A leaf that is modified for protection, such as a cactus spine.

spiracle (speer′-ih-kl) An opening for gas exchange, such as the opening of a trachea on the body surface of an insect.

spiral cleavage A distinctive spiral pattern of blastomere production in an early protostome embryo. Compare with *radial cleavage*.

spirillum (pl., *spirilla*) A long, rigid, helical bacterium. Compare with *spirochete, vibrio, bacillus,* and *coccus*.

spirochete A long, flexible, helical bacterium. Compare with *spirillum, vibrio, bacillus,* and *coccus*.

spleen An abdominal organ located just below the diaphragm that removes worn-out blood cells and bacteria from the blood and plays a role in immunity.

spliceosome A large ribonucleoprotein particle that catalyzes the reactions that remove introns from pre-mRNA.

spongocoel (spon′-jo-seel) The central cavity of a sponge.

spongy bone Consists of a network of thin strands of bone; provides mechanical strength.

spongy mesophyll (mez'-oh-fil) The loosely arranged mesophyll cells near the lower epidermis in certain leaves. Compare with *palisade mesophyll*.

spontaneous reaction See *exergonic reaction*.

sporangium (spor-an'-jee-um) (pl., *sporangia*) A spore case, found in plants, certain protists, and fungi.

spore A reproductive cell that gives rise to individual offspring in plants, fungi, and certain algae and protozoa.

sporophyll (spor'-oh-fil) A leaflike structure that bears spores.

sporophyte generation (spor'-oh-fite) The 2*n*, spore-producing stage in the life cycle of a plant. Compare with *gametophyte generation*.

sporozoite The infective sporelike state in apicomplexans.

spring turnover Mixing of temperate lake waters in spring, caused by rising temperatures, in which surface water sinks to the bottom and bottom water rises to the surface. Compare with *fall turnover*.

stabilizing selection Natural selection that acts against extreme phenotypes and favors intermediate variants; associated with a population well adapted to its environment. Compare with *directional selection* and *disruptive selection*.

stamen (stay'-men) The male part of a flower; consists of a filament and anther.

standing-water ecosystem A lake or pond ecosystem.

starch A polysaccharide composed of alpha glucose subunits; made by plants for energy storage.

start codon The codon AUG, which signals the beginning of translation of messenger RNA. Compare with *stop codon*.

stasis Long periods in the fossil record in which there is little or no evolutionary change.

statocyst (stat'-oh-sist) An invertebrate sense organ containing one or more granules (statoliths); senses gravity and motion.

statoliths (stat'-uh-liths) Granules of loose sand or calcium carbonate found in statocysts.

stele The cylinder in the center of roots and stems that contains the vascular tissue; also called *vascular cylinder*.

stem cell A relatively undifferentiated cell capable of repeated cell division. At each division at least one of the daughter cells usually remains a stem cell, whereas the other may differentiate as a specific cell type. Compare with *embryonic stem cell (ES cell)* and *induced pluripotent stem cell (iPSC)*.

stereocilia Hairlike projections of hair cells; microvilli that contain actin filaments.

sterilization A procedure that renders an individual incapable of producing offspring; the most common surgical procedures are vasectomy in the male and tubal ligation in the female.

steroid hormones Hormones, such as insect molting hormone, cortisol, and male/female sex hormones, that are derived from cholesterol.

steroids (steer'-oids) Complex molecules containing carbon atoms arranged in four attached rings, three of which contain six carbon atoms each and the fourth of which contains five, e.g., cholesterol and certain hormones, including the male and female sex hormones of vertebrates.

stigma The portion of the carpel where pollen grains land during pollination (and before fertilization).

stipe A short stalk or stemlike structure that is a part of the body of certain multicellular algae.

stipule (stip'-yule) One of a pair of scalelike or leaflike structures found at the base of certain leaves.

stolon (stow'-lon) An aboveground, horizontal stem with long internodes; stolons often form buds that develop into separate plants, e.g., strawberry; also called a *runner*.

stomach Muscular region of the vertebrate digestive tract, extending from the esophagus to the small intestine.

stomata (sing., *stoma*) Small pores located in the epidermis of plants that provide for gas exchange for photosynthesis; each stoma is flanked by two guard cells, which are responsible for its opening and closing.

stop codon Any of the three codons in mRNA that do not code for an amino acid (UAA, UAG, or UGA) but signal the termination of translation. Compare with *start codon*.

stramenopiles Protists that have motile cells with two flagella, one of which has tiny hairlike projections off the shaft; include water molds, diatoms, golden algae, and brown algae. See *chromalveolates*; compare with *alveolates*.

stratosphere The layer of the atmosphere between the troposphere and the mesosphere. It contains a thin ozone layer that protects life by filtering out much of the sun's ultraviolet radiation.

stratum basale (strat'-um bah-say'-lee) The deepest sublayer of the human epidermis, consisting of cells that continuously divide. Compare with *stratum corneum*.

stratum corneum The most superficial sublayer of the human epidermis. Compare with *stratum basale*.

strobilus (stroh'-bil-us) (pl., *strobili*) In certain plants, a conelike structure that bears spore-producing sporangia.

stroke volume The volume of blood pumped by one ventricle during one contraction.

stroma A fluid space of the chloroplast, enclosed by the chloroplast inner membrane and surrounding the thylakoids; site of the reactions of the Calvin cycle.

stromatolite (stroh-mat'-oh-lite) A columnlike rock that consists of many minute layers of prokaryotic cells, usually cyanobacteria.

structural formula A type of chemical formula that shows the spatial arrangement of the atoms in a molecule. Compare with *simplest formula* and *molecular formula*.

structural isomer One of two or more chemical compounds having the same chemical formula but differing in the covalent arrangement of their atoms, e.g., glucose and fructose.

style The neck connecting the stigma to the ovary of a carpel.

subsidiary cell In plants, a structurally distinct epidermal cell associated with a guard cell.

subsistence agriculture Farming practice in which crops are grown only to meet the needs of the farm family.

substance P A peptide neurotransmitter released by certain sensory neurons in pain pathways; signals the CNS regarding pain; also stimulates other structures, including smooth muscle in the digestive tract.

substrate A substance on which an enzyme acts; a reactant in an enzymatically catalyzed reaction.

substrate-level phosphorylation The formation of ATP by the transfer of a phosphate to ADP from a phosphorylated intermediate.

subviral agents Infective agents that are smaller and simpler than viruses; include satellites, viroids, and prions.

succession The sequence of changes in the species composition of a community over time. See *primary succession* and *secondary succession*.

sucker A shoot that develops adventitiously from a root; a type of asexual reproduction.

sulcus (sul'-kus) (pl., *sulci*) A groove, trench, or depression, especially one occurring on the surface of the brain, separating the convolutions.

sulfhydryl group Functional group abbreviated —SH; found in organic compounds called thiols.

summation The process of adding together excitatory postsynaptic potentials (EPSPs).

sum rule The rule for combining the probabilities of mutually exclusive events by adding their individual probabilities. Compare with *product rule*.

superior vena cava In humans, a very large vein that delivers blood from the upper part of the body to the right atrium. Compare with *inferior vena cava*.

suppressor T cell T lymphocyte that suppresses the immune response.

suprachiasmate nucleus Main biological clock; located in the hypothalamus. Important in setting circadian rhythms.

supraorbital ridge (soop"-rah-or'-bit-ul) The prominent bony ridge above the eye socket; ape skulls have prominent supraorbital ridges.

surface tension The attraction that the molecules at the surface of a liquid may have for one another.

survivorship The probability that a given individual in a population or cohort will survive to a particular age; usually presented as a survivorship curve.

survivorship curve A graph of the number of surviving individuals of a cohort, from birth to the maximum age attained by any individual.

suspensor (suh-spen'-sur) In plant embryo development, a multicellular structure that anchors the embryo and aids in nutrient absorption from the endosperm.

sustainability See *environmental sustainability*.

swim bladder The hydrostatic organ in bony fishes that permits the fish to hover at a given depth.

symbionts The partners in a symbiotic relationship.

symbiosis (sim-bee-oh'-sis) An intimate relationship between two or more organisms of different species. See *commensalism, mutualism,* and *parasitism*.

sympathetic nervous system A division of the autonomic nervous system; its general effect is to mobilize energy, especially during stress situations; prepares the body for fight-or-flight response. Compare with *parasympathetic nervous system*.

sympatric speciation (sim-pa'-trik) The evolution of a new species within the same geographic region as the parental species. Compare with *allopatric speciation*.

symplast A continuum consisting of the cytoplasm of many plant cells, connected from one cell to the next by plasmodesmata. Compare with *apoplast*.

symporter Membrane carrier protein that transports two types of substances in one direction. Compare with *uniporter* and *antiporter*.

synapomorphic characters See *shared derived characters*.

synapse (sin'-aps) The junction between two neurons or between a neuron and an effector (muscle or gland).

synapsids (sin-ap'-sids) Members of a clade of amniotes in which the skull has one pair of temporal openings; include the extinct therapsid reptiles and mammals. Compare with *diapsids*.

synapsis (sin-ap'-sis) The process of physical association of homologous chromosomes during prophase I of meiosis.

synaptic enhancement An increase in neurotransmitter release thought to occur as a result of calcium ion accumulation inside the presynaptic neuron.

synaptic plasticity The ability of synapses to change in response to certain types of stimuli. Synaptic changes occur during learning and memory storage.

synaptonemal complex The structure, visible with the electron microscope, produced when homologous chromosomes undergo synapsis.

synthesis phase See *S phase*.

systematics The scientific study of the diversity of organisms and their evolutionary relationships. Taxonomy is an aspect of systematics. See *taxonomy*.

systemic acquired resistance (SAR) A defensive response in infected plants that helps fight infection and promote wound healing.

systemic anaphylaxis A rapid, widespread allergic reaction that can lead to death.

systemic circulation The part of the circulatory system that delivers blood to and from the tissues and organs of the body. Compare with *pulmonary circulation*.

systems biology A field of biology that synthesizes knowledge of many small parts to understand the whole. Also referred to as *integrative biology* or *integrative systems biology*.

systole (sis'-tuh-lee) The phase of the cardiac cycle when the heart is contracting. Compare with *diastole*.

T cell (T lymphocyte) The type of white blood cell responsible for a wide variety of immune functions, particularly cell-mediated immunity. T cells are processed in the thymus. Compare with *B cell*.

T cytotoxic cells (T_C) T cells that recognize and destroy cells infected with viruses or other intracellular pathogens; also destroy cancer cells and other pathogenic cells. Also known as *CD8 T cells* and *killer T cells*.

T helper cells (T_H) T cells that activate B cells (B lymphocytes) and stimulate T cytotoxic cell production. Also known as *CD4 T cells*.

T tubules Transverse tubules; system of inward extensions of the muscle fiber plasma membrane.

taiga (tie'-gah) See *boreal forest*.

taproot system A root system consisting of a prominent main root with smaller lateral roots branching off it; a taproot develops directly from the embryonic radicle. Compare with *fibrous root system*.

target cell or tissue A cell or tissue with receptors that bind a hormone.

TATA box A component of a eukaryotic promoter region; consists of a sequence of bases located about 30 base pairs upstream from the transcription initiation site.

taxon A formal taxonomic group at any level, e.g., phylum or genus.

taxonomy (tax-on'-ah-mee) The science of naming, describing, and classifying organisms; see *systematics*.

Tay-Sachs disease A serious genetic disease in which abnormal lipid metabolism in the brain causes mental deterioration in affected infants and young children; inheritance pattern is autosomal recessive.

T-cell receptors (TCR) The receptors on T cells that recognize specific antigens.

tectorial membrane (tek-tor'-ee-ul) The roof membrane of the organ of Corti in the cochlea of the ear.

telencephalon See *forebrain*.

telolecithal egg An egg with a large amount of yolk, concentrated at the vegetal pole. Compare with *isolecithal egg*.

telomerase A special DNA replication enzyme that can lengthen telomeric DNA by adding repetitive nucleotide sequences to the ends of eukaryotic chromosomes; typically present in cells that divide an unlimited number of times.

telomeres The protective end caps of chromosomes that consist of short, simple, noncoding DNA sequences that repeat many times.

telophase (teel'-oh-faze or tel'-oh-faze) The last stage of mitosis and of meiosis I and II when, having reached the poles, chromosomes become decondensed, and a nuclear envelope forms around each group.

telophase I See *meiosis* and *meiosis I*.

telophase II See *meiosis* and *meiosis II*.

temperate deciduous forest A forest biome that occurs in temperate areas where annual precipitation ranges from about 75 cm to 125 cm.

temperate grassland A grassland characterized by hot summers, cold winters, and less rainfall than is found in a temperate deciduous forest biome.

temperate phage See *temperate virus*.

temperate rain forest A coniferous biome characterized by cool weather, dense fog, and high precipitation, e.g., the north Pacific coast of North America.

temperate virus A virus that integrates into the host DNA as a prophage.

temperature The average kinetic energy of the particles in a sample of a substance.

template A pattern or guide; e.g., one strand of DNA functions as a template for the synthesis of a complementary DNA or RNA strand.

temporal isolation A prezygotic reproductive isolating mechanism in which genetic exchange is prevented between similar species because they reproduce at different times of the day, season, or year.

temporal lobes Region of the cerebrum that contains the auditory areas.

temporal summation The summing of several postsynaptic potentials produced when a single presynaptic neuron fires multiple times in rapid succession. Compare with *spatial summation*.

tendon A connective tissue structure that joins a muscle to another muscle, or a muscle to a bone. Tendons transmit the force generated by a muscle.

tendril A leaf or stem that is modified for holding or attaching onto objects.

tension–cohesion model The mechanism by which water and dissolved inorganic minerals are thought to be transported in xylem; water is pulled upward under tension because of transpiration while maintaining an unbroken column in xylem because of cohesion; also called *transpiration–cohesion model*.

teratogen Any agent capable of interfering with normal morphogenesis in an embryo, thereby causing malformations; examples include radiation, certain chemicals, and certain infectious agents.

terminal bud A bud at the tip of a stem. Compare with *axillary bud*.

termination (of protein synthesis) The final stage of protein synthesis, which occurs when a termination (stop) codon is reached, causing the completed polypeptide chain to be released from the ribosome. See *initiation* and *elongation*.

termination codon See *stop codon*.

territoriality Behavior pattern in which one organism (usually a male) stakes out a territory of its own and defends it against intrusion by other members of the same species and sex.

tertiary consumer See *carnivore*.

tertiary structure (of a protein) (tur'-she-air"-ee) The overall three-dimensional shape of a polypeptide that is determined by interactions involving the amino acid side chains. Compare with *primary, secondary,* and *quaternary protein structure*.

test A shell.

test cross The genetic cross in which either an F_1 individual, or an individual of unknown genotype, is mated to a homozygous recessive individual.

testis (tes'-tis) (pl., *testes*) The male gonad that produces sperm and the male hormone testosterone; in humans and certain other mammals; the testes are located in the scrotum.

testosterone (tes-tos'-ter-own) The principal male sex hormone (androgen); a steroid hormone produced by the interstitial cells of the testes; stimulates spermatogenesis and is responsible for primary and secondary sex characteristics in the male.

tetrad The chromosome complex formed by the synapsis of a pair of homologous chromosomes (i.e., four chromatids) during meiotic prophase I.

tetrapods (tet'-rah-podz) Four-limbed vertebrates: the amphibians, reptiles, birds, and mammals.

thalamus (thal'-uh-mus) The part of the vertebrate brain that serves as a main relay center, transmitting information between the spinal cord and the cerebrum.

thallus (thal'-us) (pl., *thalli*) The simple body of an alga, fungus, or nonvascular plant that lacks root, stems, or leaves, e.g., a liverwort thallus or a lichen thallus.

theca cells The layer of connective tissue cells that surrounds the granulosa cells in an ovarian follicle; stimulated by luteinizing hormone (LH) to produce androgens, which are converted to estrogen in the granulosa cells.

theory See *scientific theory*.

therapods Bipedal, saurischian dinosaurs that were predators; included *Tyrannosaurus*.

therapsids (ther-ap'-sidz) A group of mammal-like reptiles of the Permian period; gave rise to the mammals.

thermal stratification The marked layering (separation into warm and cold layers) of temperate lakes during the summer. See *thermocline*.

thermocline (thur'-moh-kline) A marked and abrupt temperature transition in temperate lakes between warm surface water and cold deeper water. See *thermal stratification*.

thermodynamics Principles governing energy transfer (often expressed in terms of heat transfer). See *first law of thermodynamics* and *second law of thermodynamics*.

thermoreceptor A sensory receptor that responds to heat.

thermoregulation The process of maintaining body temperature within certain limits despite changes in the surrounding temperature.

thigmomorphogenesis (thig"-moh-mor-foh-jen'-uh-sis) An alteration of plant growth in response to mechanical stimuli, such as wind, rain, hail, and contact with passing animals.

thigmotropism (thig"-moh-troh'-pizm) Plant growth in response to contact with a solid object, such as the twining of plant tendrils.

threatened species A species in which the population is small enough for it to be at risk of becoming extinct throughout all or part of its range but not so small that it is in imminent danger of extinction. Compare with *endangered species*.

threshold level The potential that a neuron or other excitable cell must reach for an action potential to be initiated.

thrombocytes Small, nucleated cells that function in blood clotting; found in most vertebrates other than mammals. Also see *platelets*.

thylakoid lumen See *thylakoids*.

thylakoids (thy'-lah-koidz) An interconnected system of flattened, saclike, membranous structures inside the chloroplast; the thylakoid membranes contain chlorophyll and enclose an internal space, the thylakoid lumen.

thymine (thy'-meen) A nitrogenous pyrimidine base found in DNA.

thymosin Hormone produced by the thymus gland that plays a role in immune responses.

thymus gland (thy'-mus) An endocrine gland that functions as part of the lymphatic system; processes T cells; important in cell-mediated immunity.

thyroid gland An endocrine gland that lies anterior to the trachea and releases hormones that regulate the rate of metabolism.

thyroid hormones Hormones, including thyroxin (T_4) and triiodothyronine (T_3), secreted by the thyroid gland; stimulate rate of metabolism.

thyroid-releasing hormone (TRH) Hormone secreted by the hypothalamus to increase thyroid hormone secretion when mammals are exposed to extreme cold. Compare with *thyroid-stimulating hormone (TSH)*.

thyroid-stimulating hormone (TSH) Hormone secreted by the anterior pituitary gland to regulate thyroid hormone secretion. Compare with *thyroid-releasing hormone (TRH)*.

thyroxine (T_4) See *thyroid hormones*.

tidal volume The volume of air moved into and out of the lungs with each normal resting breath.

tight junctions Specialized structures that form between some animal cells, producing a tight seal that prevents materials from passing through the spaces between the cells.

tissue A group of closely associated, similar cells that work together to carry out specific functions.

tissue culture The growth of tissue or cells in a synthetic growth medium under sterile conditions.

tissue engineering A developing technology that is striving to grow human tissues and organs (for transplantation) in cell cultures.

tissue fluid See *interstitial fluid*.

tolerance A decreased response to a drug over time.

Toll-like receptors A type of pattern recognition receptor. Cell-surface receptors on several cell types that recognize pathogen-associated molecular patterns (certain common features of classes of pathogens). See also *pathogen-associated molecular patterns (PAMPs)*.

tonoplast The membrane surrounding a vacuole.

top-down processes Control of ecosystem function by trophic interactions, particularly from the highest trophic level. Compare with *bottom-up processes*.

topoisomerases (toe-poe-eye-sahm'-er-ases) Enzymes that relieve twists and kinks in a DNA molecule by breaking and rejoining the strands.

torpor An energy-conserving state of low metabolic rate and inactivity. See *estivation* and *hibernation*.

torsion The twisting of the visceral mass characteristic of gastropod mollusks.

total fertility rate The average number of children born to a woman during her lifetime.

totipotent (toh-ti-poh'-tent) A term describing a cell or nucleus that contains the complete set of genetic instructions required to direct the normal development of an entire organism. Compare with *pluripotent*.

trace element An element required by an organism in very small amounts.

trachea (tray'-kee-uh) (pl., *tracheae*) (1) Principal thoracic air duct of terrestrial vertebrates; windpipe. (2) One of the microscopic air ducts (or tracheal tubes) branching throughout the body of most terrestrial arthropods and some terrestrial mollusks.

tracheal tubes See *trachea*.

tracheid (tray'-kee-id) A type of water-conducting and supporting cell in the xylem of vascular plants.

tract A bundle of nerve fibers within the central nervous system.

trait A heritable difference.

transcription The synthesis of RNA from a DNA template.

transcriptional-level control Regulation of gene expression by controlling RNA synthesis. Compare with *translational-level control, posttranslational control,* and *posttranscriptional control.*

transcription factors DNA-binding proteins that regulate transcription in eukaryotes; include positively acting activators and negatively acting repressors.

transduction (1) The transfer of a genetic fragment from one cell to another, e.g., from one bacterium to another, by a virus. (2) In the nervous system, the conversion of energy of a stimulus to electrical signals.

transfer RNA (tRNA) RNA molecules that bind to specific amino acids and serve as adapter molecules in protein synthesis. The tRNA anticodons bind to complementary mRNA codons.

transformation (1) The incorporation of genetic material into a cell, thereby changing its phenotype. (2) The conversion of a normal cell to a cancer cell (called a malignant transformation).

transgenic organism A plant or animal that has foreign DNA incorporated into its genome.

translation The conversion of information provided by mRNA into a specific sequence of amino acids in a polypeptide chain; process also requires transfer RNA and ribosomes.

translational control See *translational-level control.*

translational-level control Regulation of gene expression by controlling the translation of mRNA into protein. Compare with *transcriptional-level control, posttranscriptional control,* and *posttranslational control.*

translocation (1) The movement of organic materials (dissolved food) in the phloem of a plant. (2) Chromosome abnormality in which part of one chromosome has become attached to another. (3) Part of the elongation cycle of protein synthesis in which a transfer RNA attached to the growing polypeptide chain is transferred from the A site to the P site.

transmembrane protein An integral membrane protein that spans the lipid bilayer.

transmission electron microscope (TEM) See *electron microscope.*

transpiration The loss of water vapor from the aerial surfaces of a plant (i.e., leaves and stems).

transpiration–cohesion model See *tension–cohesion model.*

transport vesicles Small cytoplasmic vesicles that move substances from one membrane system to another.

transposon (tranz-poze′-on) A DNA segment that is capable of moving from one chromosome to another or to different sites within the same chromosome; also called a *mobile genetic element.*

transverse tubules See *T tubules.*

tree line Zone at high altitudes or high latitudes beyond which trees are unable to grow.

triacylglycerol (try-ace″-il-glis′-er-ol) The main storage lipid of organisms, consisting of a glycerol combined chemically with three fatty acids; also called *triglyceride.* Compare with *monoacylglycerol* and *diacylglycerol.*

Triassic period See *Mesozoic era.*

tricarboxylic acid (TCA) cycle See *citric acid cycle.*

trichome (try′-kohm) A hair or other appendage growing out from the epidermis of a plant.

tricuspid valve See *atrioventricular valve.*

triglyceride See *triacylglycerol.*

triiodothyronine (T₃) See *thyroid hormones.*

triose A sugar molecule containing three carbons.

triple-gene fusion The fusion of three separate genes into a single unit early in the course of eukaryote evolution; provides evidence of a bifurcation; characteristic of unikonts.

triplet A sequence of three nucleotides that serves as the basic unit of genetic information.

triplet code The sequences of three nucleotides that compose the codons, the units of genetic information in mRNA that specify the order of amino acids in a polypeptide chain.

triplobastic (trip-lo-blas′-tik) An animal body plan in which there are three embryonic tissue layers, the ectoderm, mesoderm, and endoderm. Compare with *diploblastic.*

trisomy (try′-sohm-ee) A type of aneuploidy in which an individual has two copies of each chromosome except for one, which has three copies; designated $2n + 1$. Compare with *monosomy* and *disomy.*

trisomy 21 See *Down syndrome.*

trochophore larva (troh′-koh-for) A larval form found in mollusks and many polychaetes.

trophic level (troh′-fik) Each sequential step of matter and energy in a food web, from producers to primary, secondary, or tertiary consumers; each organism is assigned to a trophic level based on its primary source of nourishment.

trophoblast (troh′-foh-blast) The outer cell layer of a late blastocyst, which in placental mammals gives rise to the chorion and to the fetal contribution to the placenta.

tropical dry forest A tropical forest where enough precipitation falls to support trees but not enough to support the lush vegetation of a tropical rain forest; often occurs in areas with pronounced rainy and dry seasons.

tropical rain forest A lush, species-rich forest biome that occurs in tropical areas where the climate is very moist throughout the year. Tropical rain forests are also characterized by old, infertile soils.

tropic hormone (trow′-pic) A hormone that regulates the secretion of another hormone.

tropism (troh′-pizm) In plants, a directional growth response that is elicited by an environmental stimulus.

tropomyosin (troh-poh-my′-oh-sin) A muscle protein involved in regulation of contraction.

troponin (tro-po′-nun) A regulatory protein in the actin filaments of muscle fibers.

true-breeding Refers to a genetic strain of an organism in which all individuals are homozygous at the loci under consideration.

trypsin (trip′-sin) A pancreatic enzyme that digests polypeptides to short peptides.

tube feet Structures characteristic of echinoderms; function in locomotion and feeding.

tuber A thickened end of a rhizome that is fleshy and enlarged for food storage, e.g., white potato.

tubular reabsorption The process by which epithelial cells lining the renal tubules selectively reabsorb about 99% of the glomerular filtrate and return it to the blood; an essential step in adjusting the chemical composition of the blood.

tubular secretion The selective transfer of substances from the blood in the peritubular capillaries into the renal tubule.

tubulin See *microtubules.*

tubular transport maximum (Tm) The maximum rate at which a substance is reabsorbed from the renal tubules of the kidney.

tumor A mass of tissue that grows in an uncontrolled manner; a neoplasm.

tumor necrosis factors (TNFs) Cytokines that kill tumor cells and stimulate immune cells to initiate an inflammatory response.

tumor suppressor gene A gene (also known as an *anti-oncogene*) whose normal role is to block cell division in response to certain growth-inhibiting factors; when mutated, may contribute to the formation of a cancer cell. Compare with *oncogene.*

tundra (tun′-dra) A treeless biome between the boreal forest in the south and the polar ice cap in the north that consists of boggy plains covered by lichens and small plants. Also called *arctic tundra.* Compare with *alpine tundra.*

tunicates Chordates belonging to subphylum Urochordata; sea squirts.

turgor pressure (tur′-gor) Hydrostatic pressure that develops within a walled cell and presses outward against the plasma membrane.

Turner syndrome An inherited condition in which only one sex chromosome (an X chromosome) is present in cells; karyotype is designated X0; affected individuals are sterile females.

two-point test cross A genetic cross used to test for linkage; individuals heterozygous at two loci are crossed with individuals who are homozygous recessive at those loci.

tyrosine kinase An enzyme that phosphorylates the tyrosine part of proteins.

tyrosine kinase receptor A plasma membrane receptor that phosphorylates the tyrosine part of proteins; when a ligand binds to the receptor, the conformation of the receptor changes and it may phosphorylate itself as well as other molecules; important in immune function and serves as a receptor for insulin.

ubiquitin A small eukaryotic regulatory polypeptide that can be covalently bonded to proteins, targeting the protein for destruction and recycling. Also used to regulate protein activities.

ultimate causes (of behavior) Evolutionary explanations for why a certain behavior occurs. Compare with *proximate causes of behavior.*

ultrasound imaging A technique in which high-frequency sound waves (ultrasound) are used to provide an image (sonogram) of an internal structure.

ultrastructure The fine detail of a cell, generally only observable by use of an electron microscope.

umbilical cord In placental mammals, the organ that connects the embryo to the placenta.

uniform dispersion The spatial distribution pattern of a population in which individuals are regularly spaced. Compare with *random dispersion* and *clumped dispersion.*

unikonts One of two main clades of all eukaryotes; had a common ancestor with a single posterior flagellum. See *opisthokonts* and *amoebozoa.* Compare with *bikonts.*

uniporter Membrane carrier protein that transports one type of substance in one direction. Compare with *symporter* and *antiporter.*

uniramous appendages Unbranched appendages. Compare with *biramous appendages.*

unsaturated fatty acid See *fatty acid.*

upwelling An upward movement of water that brings nutrients from the ocean depths to the surface. Where upwelling occurs, the ocean is very productive.

uracil (yur'-ah-sil) A nitrogenous pyrimidine base found in RNA.

urea (yur-ee'-ah) The principal nitrogenous excretory product of mammals; one of the water-soluble end products of protein metabolism.

ureter (yur'-ih-tur) One of the paired tubular structures that conducts urine from the kidney to the bladder.

urethra (yoo-ree'-thruh) The tube that conducts urine from the bladder to the outside of the body.

uric acid (yoor'-ik) The principal nitrogenous excretory product of insects, birds, and reptiles; a relatively insoluble end product of protein metabolism; also occurs in mammals as an end product of purine metabolism.

urinary bladder An organ that receives urine from the ureters and temporarily stores it.

urinary system The body system in vertebrates that consists of the kidneys, urinary bladder, and associated ducts.

urochordates A subphylum of chordates; includes the tunicates.

uterine tube (yoo'-tur-in) See *oviduct.*

uterus (yoo'-tur-us) The hollow, muscular organ of the female reproductive tract in which the fetus undergoes development.

utricle The structure within the vestibule of the vertebrate inner ear that, along with the saccule, houses the receptors of static equilibrium.

vaccine (vak-seen') A commercially produced, weakened or killed antigen associated with a particular disease that stimulates the body to make antibodies.

vacuole (vak'-yoo-ole) A fluid-filled, membrane-enclosed sac found within the cytoplasm; may function in storage, digestion, or water elimination.

vagina The elastic, muscular tube, extending from the cervix to its external opening, that receives the penis during sexual intercourse and serves as the birth canal.

valence electrons The electrons in the outer electron shell, known as the *valence shell,* of an atom; in the formation of a chemical bond, an atom can accept electrons into its valence shell or donate or share valence electrons.

van der Waals interactions Weak attractive forces between atoms; caused by interactions among fluctuating charges.

vascular cambium A lateral meristem that produces secondary xylem (wood) and secondary phloem (inner bark). Compare with *cork cambium.*

vascular cylinder See *stele.*

vascular tissue system The tissues specialized for translocation of materials throughout the plant body, i.e., the xylem and phloem.

vas deferens (vas def'-ur-enz) (pl., *vasa deferentia*) One of the paired sperm ducts that connects the epididymis of the testis to the ejaculatory duct.

vasoconstriction Narrowing of the diameter of blood vessels.

vasodilation Expansion of the diameter of blood vessels.

vector (1) Any carrier or means of transfer. (2) Agent, e.g., a plasmid or virus, that transfers genetic information. (3) Agent that transfers a parasite from one host to another.

vegetal pole The yolky pole of a vertebrate or echinoderm egg. Compare with *animal pole.*

vein (1) A blood vessel that carries blood from the tissues toward a chamber of the heart (compare with *artery*). (2) A strand of vascular tissue that is part of the network of conducting tissue in a leaf; also called a *vascular bundle.*

veliger larva The larval stage of many marine gastropods (snails) and bivalves (e.g., clams); often is a second larval stage that develops after the trochophore larva.

ventilation The process of actively moving air or water over a respiratory surface.

ventral Toward the lowermost surface or belly of an animal. Compare with *dorsal.*

ventricle (1) One of four interconnected chambers in the brain through which cerebrospinal fluid flows. (2) One of the chambers of the heart that receives blood from an atrium and pumps blood into arteries.

vertebrae (vert'teh-bray) (sing., *vertebra*) The bones that make up the spine.

vertebral column The spine, the rigid, bony structure in the midline of the back; composed of vertebrae.

vertebrates A subphylum of chordates that includes fishes, amphibians, reptiles, birds, and mammals; possess a bony vertebral column.

vertical gene transfer The transfer of genetic material from parent to offspring. Compare with *horizontal gene transfer.*

vesicle (ves'-ih-kl) Any small sac, especially a small, spherical, membrane-enclosed compartment, within the cytoplasm.

vessel In plants, a stack of vessel elements.

vessel element A type of water-conducting cell in the xylem of vascular plants; a stack of vessel elements is a vessel.

vestibular apparatus Collectively, the saccule, utricle, and semicircular canals of the inner ear.

vestigial (ves-tij'-ee-ul) Rudimentary; an evolutionary remnant of a formerly functional structure.

vestigial structure See *vestigial.*

vibrio A spirillum (spiral-shaped bacterium) that is shaped like a comma. Compare with *spirillum, spirochete, bacillus,* and *coccus.*

villus (pl., *villi*) A multicellular, minute, elongated projection from the surface of an epithelial membrane, e.g., villi of the mucosa of the small intestine.

virion A complete virus particle that is outside a cell.

viroid (vy'-roid) A tiny, naked, infectious particle consisting only of nucleic acid.

virulence Properties that render an infectious agent pathogenic (and often lethal) to its host. Compare with *avirulence.*

virus A tiny pathogen consisting of a core of nucleic acid usually encased in protein and capable of infecting living cells; a virus is characterized by total dependence on a living host.

viscera (vis'-ur-uh) The internal body organs, especially those located in the abdominal or thoracic cavities.

visceral mass The concentration of body organs (viscera) located above the foot in mollusks.

vital capacity The maximum volume of air a person exhales after filling the lungs to the maximum extent.

vitamin A complex organic molecule required in very small amounts for normal metabolic functioning.

vitelline envelope An acellular covering of the eggs of certain animals (e.g., echinoderms), located just outside the plasma membrane.

viviparous (vih-vip'-er-us) Bearing living young that develop within the body of the mother. Compare with *oviparous* and *ovoviviparous.*

voltage-activated ion channels Ion channels in the plasma membrane of neurons that are regulated by changes in voltage. Also called *voltage-gated channels*.

vomeronasal organ In mammals, an organ in the epithelium of the nose, made up of specialized chemoreceptor cells that detect pheromones.

vulva The external genital structures of female mammals.

warning coloration See *aposematic coloration*.

water mold A funguslike stramenopile protist with a body consisting of a coenocytic mycelium that reproduces asexually by forming motile zoospores and sexually by forming oospores.

water potential Free energy of water; the water potential of pure water is zero and that of solutions is a negative value. Differences in water potential are used to predict the direction of water movement (always from a region of less negative water potential to a region of more negative water potential).

watershed Area of land where all the water that drains off of it (runoff) goes into the same body of water.

water vascular system Unique hydraulic system of echinoderms; functions in locomotion and feeding.

wavelength The distance from one wave peak to the next; the energy of electromagnetic radiation is inversely proportional to its wavelength.

weathering processes Chemical or physical processes that help form soil from rock; during weathering processes, the rock is gradually broken into smaller and smaller pieces.

Wernicke's area Located in the left temporal lobe; center for language and comprehension.

Western blot A technique in which proteins, previously separated by gel electrophoresis, are transferred to paper. A specific labeled antibody is generally used to mark the location of a particular protein. Compare with *Southern blot* and *Northern blot*.

whisk ferns Fern relatives lacking true roots and leaves; characterized by dichotomous branching.

white blood cells (WBC) See *leukocytes*.

white matter Nervous tissue in the brain and spinal cord that contains myelinated axons. Compare with *gray matter*.

wild type The phenotypically normal (naturally occurring) form of a gene or organism.

winds Complex horizontal atmospheric movements caused in part by differences in atmospheric temperature and pressure changes, Earth's rotation, and uneven heating of the oceans and continents.

wobble hypothesis. Describes the ability of some tRNA anticodons to associate with more than one mRNA codon; in these cases the 5′ base of the anticodon is capable of forming hydrogen bonds with more than one kind of base in the 3′ position of the codon.

work Any change in the state or motion of matter.

X chromosome One of the two sex chromosomes of mammals and some other organisms; normal human females are XX, normal males are XY. Compare with *Y chromosome*.

X-linked gene A gene carried on an X chromosome.

X-ray diffraction A technique for determining the spatial arrangement of the components of a crystal.

xylem (zy′-lem) The vascular tissue that conducts water and dissolved minerals in plants.

XYY karyotype Chromosome constitution that causes affected individuals (who are fertile males) to be unusually tall, with severe acne.

Y chromosome One of the two sex chromosomes of mammals and some other organisms; the Y chromosome determines male gender in humans; normal females are XX, normal males are XY. Compare with *X chromosome*.

yeast A unicellular fungus (ascomycete) that reproduces asexually by budding or fission, and sexually by ascospores.

yolk In many animal eggs, a mixture of nutrients (mostly proteins and lipids) that nourish the developing embryo.

yolk sac One of the extraembryonic membranes; a pouchlike outgrowth of the digestive tract of embryos of certain vertebrates (e.g., birds) that grows around the yolk and digests it. Embryonic blood cells are formed in the mammalian yolk sac, which lacks yolk.

zero population growth Point at which the birth rate equals the death rate. A population with zero population growth does not change in size.

zona pellucida (pel-loo′-sih-duh) The thick, transparent covering that surrounds the plasma membrane of a mammalian ovum.

zoonotic disease An animal disease that crosses the species barrier and infects humans.

zooplankton (zoh″-oh-plank′-tun) The nonphotosynthetic organisms present in plankton, e.g., protozoa, tiny crustaceans, and the larval stages of many animals. See *plankton*. Compare with *phytoplankton*.

zoosporangium Structure in which zoospores form.

zoospore (zoh′-oh-spore) A flagellated motile spore produced asexually by chytrids, certain algae, water molds, and other protists.

zooxanthellae (zoh″-oh-zan-thel′-ee) (sing., *zooxanthella*) Endosymbiotic, photosynthetic dinoflagellates found in certain marine invertebrates; their mutualistic relationship with corals enhances the corals' reef-building ability.

zygomycetes (zy″-gah-my′-seats) Fungi characterized by the production of nonmotile asexual spores and sexual zygospores.

zygosporangium (zy″-gah-spor-an′-gee-um) A thick-walled sporangium containing a zygospore.

zygospore (zy′-gah-spor) A sexual spore produced by a zygomycete.

zygote The 2n cell that results from the union of n gametes in sexual reproduction. Species that are not polyploid have haploid gametes and diploid zygotes.

zygotic genes Genes that are transcribed after fertilization, either in the zygote or in the embryo. Compare with *maternal effect genes*.

Index

cutinase, 618
cuttlefish, tentacles of, 650
Cyanea, 640
cyanobacteria, **444**, 518, 522, 523, 607, 1218
Cycadophyta, 580, 583
cycads, **583**
cyclic adenosine monophosphase (cyclic AMP) (cAMP), **67**, 67i, **130**, 138, 138i, 139i, 161, **300**, 552, **870**, 894, **1050**–1051
cyclic electron transport, **193**
cyclic guanosine monophosphate (cGMP), **67**
cyclic response element binding protein (CREB), 894
cyclins, **215**
cyclin-dependent kinases (Cdks), **215**
cylinder
  stele, 760
  vascular, 760
cysteine, 61i, 62
cystic fibrosis, 348–349, 349i
cytochrome oxidase, 174
cytochromes, 174
cytokines, 959, **960**
  natural killer cells, release of, 959
cytokinesis, **212**
cytokinin, **216, 767, 804**
  for cells, division of, 804–805
cytoplasm, **81**, 1077
cytoplasmic extensions, 856
  types of, 824
cytoplasmic organelles, 3, 7i, 72, 81, 86–95, 88–89t
  chloroplasts, 81, 82i, 86, 89t, 93i, 93–95, 94i
  endoplasmic reticulum, 86–87, 87i, 88t, 89–90, 91i
  Golgi complex, 82i, 83i, 87, 88t, 89–90, 90i
  lysosomes, 83i, 88t, 90, 91, 92i
  mitochondria, 82i, 83i, 87i, 89t, 93–95, 94i
  peroxisomes, 82i, 83i, 86, 89t, 92–93, 93i
  plastids, 89t, 95
  of prokaryotic cells, 80–81, 81i
  ribosomes, 80, 81, 81i, 82i, 83, 83i, 84, 85, 88t, 91i
  vacuoles, 81, 88t, 91–92, 92i
  See also organelles
cytosine (C), **66**, 67i, **255**, 257
cytoskeleton, 89t, 95–100, **96**, 96i
  centrioles, 89t
  cilia, 89t
  flagella, 89t

intermediate filaments, 71i, 89t
microfilaments, 71i, 89t, 99i, 99–100
microtubules, 89t, 96i, 96–99
cytosol, **81**, 101i, 121–122, 123i, 124i

daddy longlegs, 660
daffodils, bulbs on, 793
dalton, **27**
Dalton, John, 27
dams, 1205
  humans, adverse effects of, 1219
dark adaptation, 925
dark current, 924
dark-field microscopy, 75i, 75–76
Darwin, Charles, 381, 381i, 383–387, 475, 801, 1228
  Beagle voyage, 383i, 383–384
  influences on, 384–385
  modern synthesis and, 386
  mutation and variation and, 386
  natural selection and, 384–385
  observations in Galápagos/Cape Verde Islands, 383–384, 385–386, 386i, 391, 1170–1171
  On the Origin of Species, 14, 385i
  theory of evolution, 14–15
Darwin, Francis, 801
data, in scientific method, 15–16
date seed (*Phoenix dactylifera*), 786
day-neutral plants, **808**
DDT pesticide, 1192–1193, 1193i
Dead Sea, 522
deafness, 917–918
deamination, **180,** 1027
death
  from atherosclerosis, 951
  from cardiovascular disease, 930, 951
Death Valley, 769
decapods, **662**
decarboxylations, **168**
deciduous, **705, 1211**
decline phase, 973
decomposers, **10,** 10i, **519, 1189**
decompression sickness, 998
deductive reasoning, 16
defecation, 1015
defibrillation, 952
deforestation, **1205, 1244**
  biodiversity, contribution to loss of, 1244
  carbon dioxide, increasing amount of, 1247
  economic growth, impact on, 1245
  tropical, 1245

dehydration, 1028
dehydrogenations, **168**
Deinonychus, 693
deletion, 344i, **344**–345
demographics, human, **1158**
demosponges, 637
denaturation, 66
dendrites, **824, 856,** 918, 959
dendritic cells, **935, 959**–960
dendritic spines, 895
dendrochronology, **746**
dengue fever, 1250
Denisovans, 469
denitrification, **1196**
dense connective tissue, 820t, **822**
density-dependent factors, **1149, 1152**–1153
density gradient centrifugation, **78,** 79, 79i, **259**–260
dental plaque, 523, 523i
dentin, 1009
deoxyribonucleic acid. *See* DNA (deoxyribonucleic acid)
deoxyribose, 49, 50i, **66, 255,** 255i
dependence on drugs
  physical, 898
  psychological, 898
dephosphorylation, 137
depolarization, **847, 861**–864
  wave of, 864, 866
Depo-Provera, 1091
deposit feeders, **1005**
depression, long-term, 893
derivatives
  amino acid, 1046
  fatty acid, 1046
derived character, 483
derived vertebrate character, 678–680
dermal tissue system, **705,** 712–714, 713–714, 713t
dermis, **837**
descending limb, 1034
desert-adapted amphibians, 1214–1215
desert-dwelling tamarisk (*Tamarix*), 756
desertification, **1215**
desert reptiles, 1214
deserts, **1214**
  amphibians in, 1215
  animals in, 1214–1215
  carnivores in, 1215
  groundwater in, 1215
  insects in, 1215
  irrigation in, 1215
  leaves in, 1214
  mammals in, 1215

in North America, 1214–1215
  precipitation in, 1214
  reptiles in, 1215
  rodents in, 1215
  vegitation in, 1214
desiccation, 786
desire, 1088
desmosomes, **125,** 125i
desmotubule, 126
"destroying angel," 616
determinate cleavage, **629**
determinate growth, **715**
determination, cell, 719, 1099
detritivores, **1189**
detritus, 661, **1189**
detritus feeders, **1189**
deuteromycetes, 601
deuterostomes (Deuterostomia), **629,** 670i, **671,** 670–701
  amniotes as, 688–701 (*See also* terrestrial vertebrates)
  basal, 671
  chordates as, 670–671, 675–678
  echinoderms as, 670–675
  groups of, 670
  jawless fish as, 680–688
  overview of, 701t
  shared derived characters of, 671
  tetrapods as, 685–688
  types of, 671
  vertebrates as, 678–680, 688–701
developing countries, 1159
  infectious diseases in, 501
development, 3–4, **359, 421,** 421, **716**
  Arabidopsis, pathways of, 777
  of atherosclerosis, 951–952
  of embryo, 583, 784, 1098, 1104
  of endosperm, 784
  experience, effects of, 894–895
  mosaic, 1103
  prenatal, 1113
  regulative, 1103
developmental genetics, **358**–380
  Arabidopsis and, 375–376, 376i
  Caenorhabditis elegans and, 371–372, 373i
  cancer and cell development, 376–378, 377i, 378i
  differential gene expression, 359, 360
  first cloned mammal, 362, 363i
  fruit fly and, 367i, 367–371
  model organisms, 365, 366i
  mouse and, 373–375, 374i, 375i
  stem cells, 364i, 364–365
  totipotency, 360–361, 361i, 362i
Devonian period, 448t, **449,** 560, 591, 664, 687

Scientific Measurement

Some Common Prefixes

kilo	1000	
centi	0.01	
milli	0.001	
micro (μ)	one-millionth	
nano (n)	one-billionth	
pico (p)	one-trillionth	

Examples
a kilogram is 1000 grams
a centimeter is 0.01 meter
a milliliter is 0.001 liter
a micrometer is 10^{-6} (one-millionth) of a meter
a nanogram is 10^{-9} (one-billionth) of a gram
a picogram is 10^{-12} (one-trillionth) of a gram

The relationship between mass and volume of water (at 20°C):
$1\,g = 1\,cm^3 = 1\,mL$

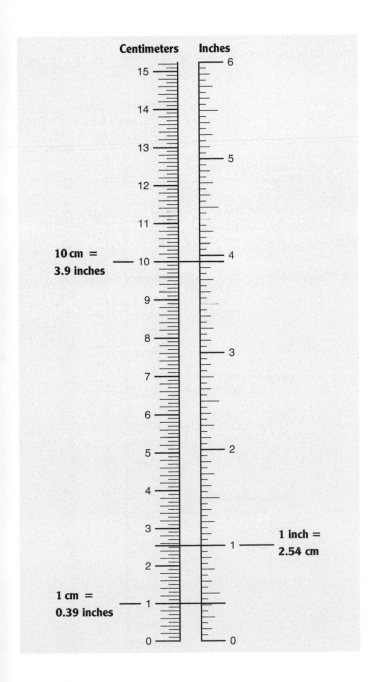

Centimeters   Inches

10 cm = 3.9 inches

1 inch = 2.54 cm

1 cm = 0.39 inches

Some Common Units of Length

Unit	Abbreviation	Equivalent
meter	m	approximately 39 in.
centimeter	cm	10^{-2} m
millimeter	mm	10^{-3} m
micrometer	μm	10^{-6} m
nanometer	nm	10^{-9} m

Length Conversions

1 in. = 2.5 cm	1 mm = 0.039 in.
1 ft = 30.48 cm	1 cm = 0.39 in.
1 yd = 0.9 m	1 m = 39 in.
1 mi = 1.6 km	1 m = 1.094 yd
	1 km = 0.6 mi

To convert	Multiply by	To obtain
inches	2.54	centimeters
feet	30.48	centimeters
centimeters	0.39	inches
millimeters	0.039	inches

Standard Metric Units

		Abbreviation
Standard unit of mass	gram	g
Standard unit of length	meter	m
Standard unit of volume	liter	L

Some Common Units of Volume

Unit	Abbreviation	Equivalent
liter	L	approximately 1.06 quarts
milliliter	mL	10^{-3} L (1 mL = 1 cm^3 = 1 cc)
microliter	μL	10^{-6} L

Volume Conversions

1 tsp = 5 mL	1 mL = 0.03 fluid ounce
1 tbsp = 15 mL	1 L = 2.1 pints
1 fl oz = 30 mL	1 L = 1.06 quarts
1 cup = 0.24 L	1 L = 0.26 gallon
1 pt = 0.47 L	
1 qt = 0.95 L	
1 gal = 3.79 L	

To convert	Multiply by	To obtain
fluid ounces	30	milliliters
quart	0.95	liters
milliliters	0.03	fluid ounces
liters	1.06	quarts

Some Common Units of Mass

Unit	Abbreviation	Equivalent
kilogram	kg	10^3 g (approximately 2.2 lb)
gram	g	approximately 0.035 oz
milligram	mg	10^{-3} g
microgram	μg	10^{-6} g
nanogram	ng	10^{-9} g
picogram	pg	10^{-12} g

Mass Conversions

1 oz = 28.3 g
1 lb = 453.6 g
1 lb = 0.45 kg

To convert	Multiply by	To obtain
ounces	28.3	grams
pounds	453.6	grams
pounds	0.45	kilograms
grams	0.035	ounces
kilograms	2.2	pounds

atomic mass unit (amu) or **Dalton** — the approximate mass of a proton or neutron

mole — the formula weight of a substance expressed in grams

Avogadro's number (N) = 6.02×10^{23} — the number of particles in one mole of any substance

Energy Conversions

calorie (cal) = energy required to raise the temperature of 1 g of water (at 16°C) by 1°C

1 calorie = 4.184 joules
1 kilocalorie (kcal) = 1000 cal
1 joule = 0.24 cal
1 kilocalorie = 4.184 kJ

Temperature Scales / Temperature Conversions

Temperature Scales	Temperature Conversions
Celsius (Centigrade) = °C	$°C = \dfrac{(°F - 32) \times 5}{9}$
Fahrenheit = °F	$°F = \dfrac{°C \times 9}{5} + 32$
Kelvin = K	$K = °C + 273$

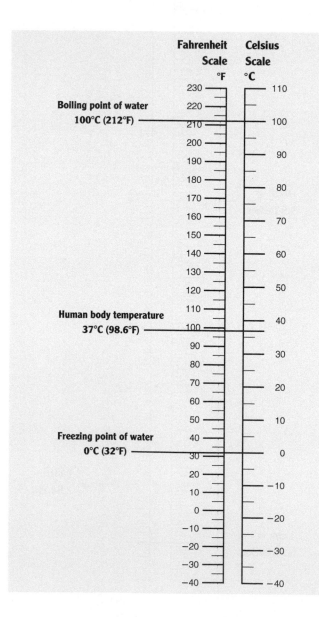